COINS

OF THE WORLD

1750-1850

by

WILLIAM D. CRAIG

Edited by Holland Wallace

WESTERN PUBLISHING COMPANY, INC.

WHITMAN COIN SUPPLY DIVISION
RACINE, WISCONSIN, U. S. A.

No. 9363   Printed in U.S.A.

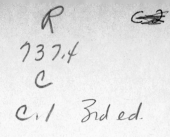

R
737.4
C
C.1 3rd ed.

ISBN: 0-307-09363-8
Library of Congress Catalog Card Number: 76-8365

Copyright © 1976, 1971, 1966
WESTERN PUBLISHING COMPANY, INC.
RACINE, WISCONSIN, U.S.A.

ACKNOWLEDGMENTS

Third Edition

I am again much indebted to Richard S. Yeoman, Neil Shafer, Holland Wallace, Richard Thompsen and Kenneth E. Bressett of Whitman for further valuable assistance in connection with preparation and publication of the third edition of this catalog.

Helpful contributions from the following persons and firms for their help in this and previous editions are gratefully acknowledged:

Stephen Album

American Numismatic Society

J. M. Attrell

John E. Barrett

Stanwood K. Bolton, Jr.

Richard K. Bright

Colin R. Bruce II

Werner Burger

Ray Byrne

Amon G. Carter, Jr.

Pavel Cerny

Fernando Chao Alduncin

Henry Christensen

William B. Christensen

Scott E. Cordry

Michael A. Cotta

Freeman L. Craig, Jr.

Monte Craviss

Norman C. Davis, Jr.

P. F. L. de Groot

Dr. Pablo I. de Jesus

John S. Deyell

Robert Doyle

Thomas Faistauer

Marvin L. Fraley

Russell Gallagher

Lawrence S. Goldberg

J. C. F. Gray

Frank N. Hall

Thomas B. Hamilton

Lee E. Harvey

Peter Hauser

R. N. P. Hawkins

Dr. J. A. Haxby

Helmut Heinz

Patrick D. Hogan

William D. Holberton

Louis D. Hudson

John Humphris

Charles H. Jackson

Prof. Dr. Hans-Dietrich Kahl

G. B. Kelemen

M. Howard Kramer

Delbert R. Krause

Samuel Lachman

William Laing

Robert Leonard, Jr.

Jack E. Lewis

James M. McWilliams

Richard Margolis

Robert W. Medeiros

Robert Mish

R. P. and Betty Mitchell

Münzen und Medaillen, A. G.

Richard A. Nelson

John A. Novak

Charles K. Panish

Pierre M. Pariat

Manfried W. Parijs

Theodore V. Peck

D. H. Pentland

William A. Pettit

Richard A. Phelps

Capt. N. W. Rehder

Jerome H. Remick

Bill Rightmire

G. N. Robbins

Capt. Albert J. Ruh

R. W. Scott

Scott Semans

Leonard Shafer

Milton Shapiro

Robert Shaw

James C. Shipley

Ladislav Sin

C. R. Singhal

Bruce W. Smith

R. C. Soxman

Dana Svobodova

Dr. M. L. Tarizzo

V. K. Thacker

Neil B. Todd

Carlo Valdettaro

Leonard Vezirian

Dr. Igor V. Victorov

Dr. Austin C. Wagenknecht

J. B. Westergaard

Robert E. Westfall

C. S. Yowell

Randolph Zander

Jeffrey S. Zarit

A number of illustrations have again been made available through courtesy of the American Numismatic Society.

INTRODUCTION
To The Third Edition

Contents

This catalog is designed to extend Richard S. Yeoman's *A Catalog of Modern World Coins* backward another century. The period covered is approximately 1750-1850, but listings for each state commence at a logical date (usually the beginning of a new reign) close to 1750, and end at Mr. Yeoman's point of beginning. Thus, for example, under Prussia coins from 1740 to 1873 are listed, while under Great Britain this catalog stops at 1837. It was thought that by thus keying the two catalogs together, identification and an indication of the retail value of most available non-ancient coins could be achieved at least expense to the collector.

My intent has been to include all official metal coins intended for circulation, struck by every state in the world during the period covered by the catalog. Minor die varieties, of which a multitude exist from this era owing to crude facilities, are not mentioned separately. As with any large undertaking, despite a great deal of work by a great many people since the first edition appeared, omissions still exist and errors are still to be expected. Comments, corrections and additional information (particularly with respect to details italicized) are therefore solicited, and should be sent to the author so that subsequent editions may be even more useful.

In compiling this catalog, medals, private tokens, patterns, essays, mis-struck coins, presentation pieces in off-metals, and the like, have been omitted intentionally. The existence of omitted material is often mentioned in supplementary notes to eliminate confusion. In many instances the question of inclusion or omission was a close one. Authoritative comments with respect to any of these matters will, of course, be welcomed by the author.

Valuations

The evaluation of a coin's worth is still a special problem. Substantial increases in the number of active collectors have kept the coin market in flux for several years. The "correct" price for any piece is supposed to be what an informed buyer will pay an informed seller when neither is under any compulsion. As there are variables which enter into the establishment of such a price, *it must be emphasized here that all values as shown in this book are to be considered only as estimates and not offers to buy or sell, as the publishers do not buy or sell coins of any kind.*

This third edition incorporates the feature of a specific condition heading for each column of prices, and sometimes for single coins, in an effort to aid in arriving at a true market value for the listed coins. There has also been dealer participation in the evaluating so that the resultant figures are, in the main, averages based on a broad and varied opinion survey of the market. In every case the value is given for the most common variety, date or mint of each type listed; prices are average retail in U.S. dollars.

Condition

The condition grade chosen to be priced is intended to be the "top average" grade in which the commonest variety of each listed type is found today. Interpretation of the meaning of "top average" is subject to the experience of each observer; therefore, comments on this method of cataloging are welcome from dealers and specialists with extensive experience. Coins in better condition should bring substantially more, and coins in poorer condition substantially less than the values given.

Following is a list of definitions of the condition headings as used in this book:

Uncirculated — Some mint lustre. Minor cabinet wear permissible, but otherwise the coin should be as it left the mint.

EF — Insignificant wear and no readily noticeable dents, gouges or scratches.

VF — Circulated, but all details clear, no unattractive dents, gouges or scratches.

Fine — Some wear and some dents, gouges, scratches, but still a desirable coin with all major details clear.

VG — Worn, but all inscriptions legible and the outlines of all major and minor details visible.

Good — As VG, but the outlines of certain minor details worn away.

Fair — Badly worn, but not mutilated. Sufficient visible detail to identify the coin fully.

Poor — Mutilated or so worn that some detail essential to complete attribution is not visible.

Cut and countermarked coins present special difficulty. Prices for these are for legible and complete countermarks on coins in identifiable condition.

Pierced Turkish coins are in a class by themselves. See TURKEY.

How to Find Coin Listings in this Book

All countries are listed in this catalog in alphabetic sequence. This is a change from the first edition, which was divided into the Western countries followed by the African and Asian.

Unless one knows Chinese, Arabic, or several other non-European alphabets and tongues, coins with legends in those languages may be harder to locate in this volume. In order to assist the collector in the location of such pieces, the following listing of country groupings is given:

Moslem or Arabic	Tunis
Afghanistan	Turkestan
Algiers	Turkey
Arabia	
Armenia (Caucasia)	
Bukhara (Turkestan)	**Oriental**
Caucasia	Annam
Egypt	China
India (and some State coinages)	Japan
Krim (Crimea)	Korea
Malay Peninsula	Turkestan (Chinese)
Mesopotamia (now Iraq)	
Morocco	**Slavic**
Netherlands East Indies	
Persia (now Iran)	Balkans
Syria	Russia
Tripoli	Russian Provinces

The section entitled "Arabic Mint Names" found just before the main catalog section of this book should also be quite useful in the identification of Arabic-legend pieces.

Other foreign coins, with European language legends, may nearly all be located by resort to the Index and Finding List at the rear. This is an index of states represented in the catalog, with which has been integrated an alphabetical list of key words, abbreviations and state names in other languages appearing on the coins themselves. To use the Index, examine your coin carefully, and disregarding such matters as the ruler's name, D(ei) G(ratia) and V.G.G. (also, "by God's Grace"), note words and abbreviations which might stand for the name of the state and its form of government. More probably than not, one or more of these words or abbreviations appear in the Index and Finding List. Inspection of the coins of the state to which the Index directs you should do the rest.

Countermarked coins may be identified in the list of Counterstamps on page 7.

Coins showing rulers' monograms may be located through use of the chart and list of monograms beginning a few pages farther into these introductory sections.

Abbreviations, Symbols and Conventions

In order to produce a really useful catalog at a price which most collectors can afford, certain abbreviations, symbols and conventions have been employed. These are:

1. The denomination is shown as it actually appears on the coin.

2. Coin legends, where reproduced, are shown in small capitals.

3. Essential information, such as the denomination or parts of it, not shown on the coin, is given in parentheses in the catalog.

4. Descriptive information concerning which there is some uncertainty is given in italics.

5. Where first and last dates are given for a coin, coins were not necessarily struck in each of the intervening years.

6. Coins taken into this catalog from R. S. Yeoman's *A Catalog of Modern World Coins* have been renumbered, but the Yeoman number is also shown in boldface parentheses, thus: (Y–).

7. Catalog numbers are in sequence by states, but some numbers have been omitted to permit ready inclusion of specialized material in subsequent editions.

8. Cross-references to other countries show the name of the other country fully capitalized. Cross-references to other states within the same country show the name of the other state with initial caps only. Example: Under Prussia (GERMAN STATE), cross-references are made to "POLAND" and "Hohenzollern" (another GERMAN STATE).

9. Abbreviations and symbols used:

/ — Legend divider. Shows beginning of new line.
. . . — Part of legend omitted.
★ — Coin illustrated.
—. — Same as above, except.
AD — Anno Domini (Western Christian date).
AH — Anno Hegira (Mohammedan date).
ca — Circa; about.
cmkd. — Countermarked; counterstamped.
Conv. — Convention.
cwn., cwnd. — Crown; crowned.
EF — Extremely Fine (condition).
etc. — Et cetera; means additional legend has been omitted.
F — Fine (condition).
G — Good (condition).
gr. — Grams (coin weight).
l. — Observer's left.
mm — Millimeters (coin diameter).
MM, mmk — Mint mark (or mintmaster's and/or warden's initials).
mon. — Monogram.
ND — No date; undated.
No. — Number (in this catalog).
Obv. — Obverse; face of coin.
r. — Observer's right.

Rev. — Reverse; back side of coin.
R.N. — Roman numerals (date in).
RR — Very Rare.
RRR — Extremely Rare.
SE — Samvat era
Sim. — Similar to coin described next above.
std. — Seated.
stdg. — Standing.
Unc. — Uncirculated (condition, =FDC).
var. — Varieties.
VF — Very Fine (condition).
VG — Very Good (condition).
w/out — Without.
yr. — Year (of reign, pontificate, or of the Republic, etc.).

Sample Listings

1 4 (kreuzer). IOSEPHUS etc.
Bust. Rev. Hope stdg. 20mm.
2.0 gr. 1765 R.N. 4.00

2 6 K(reuzer). Sim. but rev.
Charity std. N.D. (1772).... 6.00

No. 1 is a 4 kreuzer piece but the word kreuzer is omitted on the coin. It is 20 millimeters in diameter and weighs 2.0 grams. The obverse legend begins IOSEPHUS. His bust is on the obverse. A full length representation of Hope, standing, is on the reverse. The date, 1765 is in Roman numerals.

No. 2 is similar to No. 1 but has a different reverse, namely Charity, seated. The denomination is shown as 6 K. No. 2 is undated but was struck in 1772. No. 2 will probably be larger and heavier than No. 1. It is certainly not of the same size.

Unverified Data

Note: Throughout this catalog, any uncertain, indefinite or unconfirmed information is shown in *italic type*. Such material may be, for example, coin descriptions, dates and prices, names of rulers, or supplementary notes. Further information to confirm or correct *material in italics* should be sent to the author at the following address:

William D. Craig
c/o Whitman Coin Supply Division
1220 Mound Avenue
Racine, Wisconsin 53404, U.S.A.

COUNTERMARKS (=COUNTERSTAMPS)
APPLIED CIRCA 1750-1850

Since this section is intended primarily as a finding list, countermarks of a particular country or state on its own earlier coinage are excluded here. These are listed under their respective countries of issue.

Similarly, countermarks which include the complete state name are omitted. State names are all included in INDEX AND FINDING LIST (end of book).

I. LETTERS.

AR – MARTINIQUE.
B – LOW COUNTRIES (Belgium) on Netherlands cents.
C – CURAÇAO.
C and anchor – SANTO DOMINGO (Le Cap).
C cwnd. – FRENCH COLONIES.
CC – ST. MARTIN.
D (script) – DOMINICA.
E.D or E & D – BRITISH GUIANA.
FA – MARTINIQUE
F7O cwnd. – PHILIPPINE ISLANDS.
FIDELIDAD – ARGENTINA (Mendoza)
FR VII mon. – DANISH WEST INDIES.
G – GRENADA.
   – GUADELOUPE.
G cwnd. – GUADELOUPE.
GH (on plugged gold) – ST. VINCENT.
G.L.D. – GUADELOUPE (Isle Desirade).
GR (floriate in round indent) – JAMAICA.
GR (script cwnd. in relief) in rectangular or oval indent – BRITISH HONDURAS.
GR (script cwnd. incuse) – *fabrication*.
GR (cwnd. in octagonal indent) – fabrication.
GS – GRENADA.
G.T. or GT – GUADELOUPE (Grande Terre).
HABILITADA POR EL GOBIERNO, lion – COSTA RICA.
I-lis-D – GUADELOUPE (Isle Desirade).
I.G. – GUADELOUPE (Les Saintes).
IH – *GRENADA*.
I.S. (on plugged gold) – ST. VINCENT.
IW (script) – GRENADA.
JR (script) – *GRENADA*.
L – LOW COUNTRIES (Belgium) on Netherlands cents.
L.C. – SANTO DOMINGO (Le Cap).
L.S. – GUADELOUPE (Les Saintes).
M – ST. BARTHOLOMEW.
   – MOZAMBIQUE.
   – ST. MARTIN.
MG mon. – Maria Galiente, Colombian Penal Colony, after 1821.
N cwnd. – SANTO DOMINGO.
O/TB – TOBAGO (concoction).
P – ST. EUSTATIUS.
PATRIA mon. – ARGENTINA (Salta)
RF – GUADELOUPE.
S (incuse) – ST. KITTS.
S (retrograde) – ST. VINCENT.
SD or S:D – SANTO DOMINGO.
SE – ST. EUSTATIUS.
SER. under 3 mountains – CHILE.
S/Rom. Num. – ST. VINCENT.
S.K. – ST. KITTS.
SL mon. – ST. LUCIA.

S:Lucie – ST. LUCIA.
S-Mountain-S – SALVADOR.
St. M – ST. MARTIN.
sv mon. – ST. VINCENT.
T (incuse) – TORTOLA.
   – TRINIDAD.
T (script) – TOBAGO.
TR or TB/O – TOBAGO.
TIRTILA – TORTOLA.
TR – GRENADA.
V – VIEQUE.
VALD. or VALP. under 3 mountains – CHILE.
WR cwnd. – SIERRA LEONE.
WS (script) – GRENADA.
YII cwnd. – PHILIPPINE ISLANDS.

II. NUMERALS.

2.6 – DOMINICA.
3 (in circular indent) – CURAÇAO.
3 cwnd. – DOMINICA.
4 cwnd. – DOMINICA.
5 (in circular indent) – CURAÇAO.
6 cwnd. – DOMINICA.
12 cwnd. – DOMINICA.
16 cwnd. – DOMINICA.
20 and man's head – *GUADELOUPE*.
20/eagle – MARTINIQUE.
21 and rosace – CURAÇAO.
22 and man's head – *GUADELOUPE*.
22/eagle – MARTINIQUE.
25 under head – BALKANS (Ionian Islands).
30 under head – Same.
42/BZ – SWITZERLAND (Bern).
50 under head – BALKANS (Ionian Islands).
60 under head – Same.
82IO – GUADELOUPE.

III. OBJECTS.

Arrows (bundle) – ST. MARTIN.
Bear shield – SWITZERLAND (Bern).
Cross (pointed) – MONTSERRAT.
Crown – ST. BARTHOLOMEW.
Cwnd. numerals – DOMINICA.
Cwnd. numerals/M – ST. BARTHOLOMEW.
Eagle under 20 or 22 – MARTINIQUE.
Fleur de lis – GUADELOUPE.
   – PUERTO RICO (1884-85).
   – ST. MARTIN.
Head – of George III/numerals. BALKANS (Ionian Islands).
   – of George III. GREAT BRITAIN.
   – to right of 20 or 22 (on gold). *GUADELOUPE*.
Lattice – *Trinidad, Cuba, after 1811.*
Lion in oval (on cut gold and silver) – ITALY (Malta).
Pineapple – *BARBADOS*.
Portuguese arms – BRAZIL or PORTUGAL.
Ring – ST. LUCIA.
Rosace of 5 petals – CURAÇAO.
Star (5 pts.)/1794 – LOW COUNTRIES (Maestricht).
Star or sun (12 rays) – VIEQUE.

IV. ARABIC CMKS. ON WESTERN COINS.

See MALAY PENINSULA and
NETHERLANDS EAST INDIES.

DESCRIPTIONS OF CENTRAL HOLES AND PLUGS

1. Heart-shaped – DOMINICA.
2. Hexagonal – TRINIDAD.
3. Octagonal – GUADELOUPE, TOBAGO.
4. Round.
   (a) Smooth.
      3mm – PUERTO RICO.
      17mm – DOMINICA.
      23mm – DOMINICA – ST. VINCENT.

(b) Scalloped.
   14-15 crenelles – TRINIDAD.
   15 crenelles – DOMINICA.
   18 crenelles – BRITISH GUIANA.
5. Square (4 x 3 crenelles) – GUADELOUPE.

Beware Counterfeits of
Cut and Counterstamped Coins

Pridmore estimates that there may be twenty forgeries and concoctions for every genuine piece in the West Indian series. Before investing in this material, examine Pridmore, "The Coins of the British Commonwealth of Nations, Part 3 — West Indies" (Spink 1965).

DATES ON COINS

NUMERALS

WESTERN	1	2	3	4	5	6	7	8	9	0	10	100	1000
ARABIC	١	٢	٣	٤	٥	٦	٧	٨	٩	٠	١٠	١٠٠	١٠٠٠
ARABIC VARIANTS (Persia, etc.)	١	٢	٣	٣	۵	۶	٧	٨	٩	٠			
CHINESE, JAPANESE, KOREAN (Ordinary)	一	二	三	四	五	六	七	八	九		十	百	千
CHINESE, JAPANESE, KOREAN (Official)	壹	貳	叄	肆	伍	陸	柒	捌	玖		拾	(半=½)	
DEVANAGARI (India, Nepal)	१	२	३	४	५	६	७	८	९	०			

This chart of numerals will enable the collector to determine the dates found on most coins of the world. Many countries using Arabic or Persian numerals give the year in the Mohammedan Era (AH). This began July 16, 622 AD. The years of the Hegira are lunar years of 354 days. The Hegira date is rectified by multiplying it by 0.97 and adding 622, for example: AH 1255.

$$1255 \times 0.97 = 1217.$$
$$1217 + 622 = 1839 \text{ AD}.$$

In India several different eras have been used. Among these were the Samvat of Vikramaditya beginning in B.C. 57, the Saka of Salivanhn beginning AD 78, and the Nepalese Samvat Era beginning AD 880. These, and other eras, are mentioned as they occur in the catalog.

Many countries, both Occidental and Oriental, dated coins by reference to the regnal year of the current ruler, or to the number of years since some recent special date, such as the founding of the French Republic. These instances, too, are mentioned in the text as they occur.

Millimeter Scale

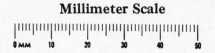

COATS OF ARMS

Since the attribution of many coins before 1850 is dependent upon proper identification of coats of arms, some knowledge of heraldry is necessary to any numismatist. There are, however, many excellent treatises on the subject, and a full coverage is not warranted here. This section is merely designed to review, with a numismatic slant, certain of the most basic heraldic precepts.

Coats of arms, sometimes identified as the offspring of early barbarian totem symbols, became a fixed part of life in Western Europe in the 12th century. As the families possessing different devices died out, married, and inherited the property of others, the combination of their symbols presented a problem. To resolve this problem certain basic rules were laid down, therms were invented, and heraldry was born.

Animals are *rampant* when walking on their hind legs and *passant* when on all fours.

Beasts are *guardant* when looking toward the viewer.

Eagles, which are always supposed to face the viewer with wings outspread, are said to be *displayed*. Other birds, such as falcons, are generally shown with folded wings.

Crests are helmets surmounting a shield of arms, generally decorated with a device from the shield. For example, if the shield contained a lion rampant, the crest was likely to be a lion's head atop a jousting helmet. Toward the middle 17th century crests were supplanted by crowns or coronets on most coins.

Crowns (worn by royalty) and coronets (worn by lesser nobility) differ according to centuries-old tradition. A due regard for these differences, as shown in the following sketches, frequently helps speed attribution.

Definition of Terms

Arms parted per pale	DEXTER / SINISTER	Arms parted per fesse	CHIEF / FOOT
Arms quartered		Six-fold arms	
Pale		Two pales	
Fesse		Two bars	
Bend		Two bends	
Quarterly		Nine pieces	
Billety		Bend sinister	
Arms parted bendwise		Checkered	(More than nine pieces)
Center shield or inescutcheon		Vair (conventionalized squirrel fur)	
Paly of six		Barry of four	

Cities and all nobles beneath the rank of prince (free barons, counts, etc.). Used occasionally by princes through 18th century.

Cities (Masonry Crown)

Princes (landgraves same, but no lining) — **Electors** — **Dukes**

Grand dukes and kings — **Crown of Charlemagne** (Holy Roman Empire)

Austrian Crown (Later Empire) — **Archdukes**

Another convention of considerable utility to the numismatist is that regarding tinctures (colors), adopted about 1600. The two heraldic metals and five heraldic colors were thenceforward shown on coins in the following fashion.

Gold (or Yellow) — **Silver** (Argent, White) — **Red** (Gules) — **Blue** (Azure)

Black (Sable) — **Green** (Vert) — **Purple**

Order of Combining Devices

When the arms of two states or houses were combined through conquest, marriage or inheritance, the device of the stronger or surviving state was given the place of honor on the new shield of arms. These places of honor are shown in black in the following sketches.

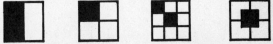

			A A 1	**AADS** 2	**AD** 3	**AEF** 4	**AF** 5	MONOGRAMS FOUND ON COINS 1750-1850	NOT EXHAUSTIVE~ INTENDED ONLY AS A FINDING LIST.	
AF 6	AFC 7	AFF 8	AFR 9	AL 10	AR 11	A3R 12	AU 13	BAG 14	C 15	CC 16
C7 17	DOUBLE C7 18	CVII 19	CA 20	CAC 21	CAMB 22	DOUBLE CE 23	DOUBLE CE 24	CF 25	CFCA 26	CFZL 27
CG 28	CJ 29	CXIVJ 30	CL 31	CP 32	CP 33	CRVII 34	CRVIII 35	CT 36	CWC 37	CWF 38
DAC 39	E 40	EAC 41	EAR 42	EFC 43	EJ 44	EJ 45	EP 46	DOUBLE EP 47	F 48	F5 49
F5 50	DOUBLE F5 51	FVII 52	FA 53 (PFA SIMILAR)	FA 54	FA 55	FA 56	FA 57	FA 58	FB 59	FC 60
FC 61	FDS 62	FF 63	FFAW 64	FFLL 65	FGC 66	DOUBLE FGC 67	FJ 68	FJDS 69	FL 70	FMBC 71
FR 72	FR 73	FR 74	F5R 75	FVIR 76	FV 77	FW 78	FW 79	FWR 80	FWR 81	G 82
GIII 83	GAIV 84	GFC 85	GH 86	GR 87	GR 88	GIVR 89	GVR 90	GRXII 91	GW 92	GW 93
H3 94	HEF 95	HN 96	J 97	JAEC 98	JEII 99	JF 100	JFC 101	JLA 102	JLVGZL 103	JPC 104
L 105	L 106	LFC 107	LG 108	LHA 109	DOUBLE L 110	DOUBLE L 111	LLX 112	LN 113	L.N. 114	LW 115
MC 116	MF 117	M DOUBLE F 118	MJ 119	M DOUBLE J 120	ML 121	MLH 122	M DOUBLE Y 123	N 124	NFP 125	DOUBLE N O 126
PAC 127	PF 128	PFA 129	SA 130	SAR 131	SGVA 132	SM 133	TVS (ORTDS) 134	VA 135	VF 136	VNZ 137
VOC 138	W 139	W 140	W 141	WA 142	WK 143	WL 144	W DOUBLE L 145	WLZH 146	WLZH 147	W DOUBLE R 148

Identification of Monograms 1750-1850

1. **A** — Anna Amalie of Saxe-Weimar-Eisenach 1758-75
2. **AADS** — Anna Amalie of Saxe-Weimar-Eisenach 1758-75
3. **AD** — James Murray, Duke of Athol 1736-64 (Isle of Man)
4. **AEF** — Adalbert II, Bishop of Fulda 1757-59
5. **AF** — Adolf Friedrich IV of Mecklenburg-Strelitz 1752-94
6. **AF** — Adolf Friedrich IV of Mecklenburg-Strelitz 1752-94
7. **AFC** — Alexius Friedrich Christian of Anhalt-Bernburg 1796-1834
8. **A Double F** — Adam Friedrich, Bishop of Wurzburg 1755-79
9. **AFR** — Adolph Friedrich of Sweden 1751-71 (Pomerania)
10. **AL** — August Ludwig of Anhalt-Cothen 1728-55
11. **AR** — Friedrich August II of Saxony 1733-63
12. **A3R** — Same, as August III of Poland
13. **AU** — Anton Ulrich of Saxe-Meiningen 1746-63
14. **BAG** — Beda Anghern, Abbot of St. Gall 1767-96
15. **C** — Carl of Brunswick-Wolfenbuttel 1735-80
    — Constantin of Löwenstein 1789-1806
16. **Double C** — Carl August Friedrich of Waldeck 1728-63
    — Carl Eugen of Württemberg 1744-93
17. **C7** — Christian VII of Denmark 1766-1808
18. **Double C7** — Christian VII of Denmark 1766-1808
19. **C VII** — Christian VII of Denmark 1766-1808
20. **CA** — Clemens August, Bishop of Münster 1719-61, Archbishop of Cologne 1723-61
    — Carl August of Nassau-Weilburg 1737-53
    — Christian August of Solms-Laubach 1738-84
21. **CAC** — Clemens August of Münster 1719-61, of Cologne 1723-61
22. **CAMB** — Alexander of Brandenburg-Ansbach 1757-91
23. **Double CE** — Carl Eugen of Württemberg 1744-93
24. **Double CE** — Carlo Emanuele IV of Sardinia 1796-1802
25. **CF** — Carl Friedrich of Baden 1738-1811
26. **CFCA** — Christian Friedrich Carl Alexander of Brandenburg-Ansbach 1757-91
27. **CFZL** — Carl of Löwenstein 1735-89
28. **CG** — Christian Günther III of Schwarzburg-Sondershausen 1758-94
29. **CJ** — Carl Joachim of Fürstenberg 1796-1804
30. **C XIV J** — Carl XIV Johann of Sweden and Norway 1818-44
31. **CL** — Christian Ludwig II of Mecklenburg-Schwerin 1747-56
    — Christoph Ludwig II of Stolberg-Stolberg 1738-61
    — Carl of Saxe-Meiningen (marriage with Louise of Stolberg 1780)
    CMAB — See CAMB No. 22
32. **CP** — Carl Philipp, Bishop of Würzburg 1749-54
33. **CP** — Christian IV of Pfalz-Zweibrücken 1735-75
34. **CR VII** — Christian VII of Denmark 1766-1808
35. **CR VIII** — Christian VII of Denmark 1840-48
36. **CT** — Carl Theodor of Pfalz 1742-99 (Jülich-Berg)
37. **CWC** — Clemens Wenzel, Archbishop of Trier 1768-94
38. **CWF** — Carl Wilhelm Ferdinand of Brunswick-Wolfenbuttel 1780-1806
39. **DAC** — Danish Asiatic Company (Tranquebar)
40. **E** — Ernst I of Saxe-Coburg 1806-44
41. **EAC** — Ernst August II Constantin of Saxe-Weimar 1756-58
42. **EAR** — Ernst August of Hannover 1837-51
43. **EFC** — Ernst Friedrich II Carl of Saxe-Hildburghausen 1745-80
44. **EJ** — Emerich Joseph, Archbishop of Mainz 1763-74
45. **EJ** — Ernst Johann of Curland 1762-69
46. **EP** — Elizabeth of Russia 1741-61
47. **Double EP** — Elizabeth of Russia 1741-61
48. **F** — Friedrich III of Saxe-Gotha 1732-72
    — Friedrich II of Brandenburg-Bayreuth 1735-63
    — Friedrich II of Mecklenburg-Schwerin 1756-85
    — Friedrich II of Hesse-Cassel 1760-85
    — Friedrich I of Saxe-Hildburghausen 1780-1826
49. **F5** — Frederik V of Denmark 1746-66
50. **F5** — Frederik V of Denmark 1746-66
51. **Double F5** — Frederik V of Denmark 1746-66
52. **F VII** — Frederik VII of Denmark 1848-63
53. **FA** — Friedrich August, Bishop of Lubeck 1750-85
54. **FA** — Friedrich Alexander of Wied-Neuwied 1737-91
55. **FA** — Friedrich August of Anhalt-Zerbst 1747-93
56. **FA** — Friedrich August III of Saxony 1763-1806
57. **FA** — Friedrich Albrecht of Anhalt-Bernburg 1765-96
58. **FA** — Friedrich Albrecht of Anhalt-Bernburg 1765-96
59. **FB** — Friedrich Botho of Stolberg-Rossla 1739-68
60. **FC** — Friedrich Christian of Brandenburg-Bayreuth 1763-69
    — Carl and Friederike of Württemberg (wedding 1749)
61. **FC** — Friedrich Carl of Schwarzburg-Rudolstadt 1790-93
62. **FDS** — Friedrich III of Saxe-Gotha (Saxe-Eisenach 1748-56)
63. **FF** — Friedrich Franz I of Mecklenburg-Schwerin 1785-1837
    — Friedrich Franz II of Mecklenburg-Schwerin 1842-83
64. **FFAW** — Friedrich Alexander of Wied-Neuwied 1737-91
65. **FFLL** — Friedrich II of Hesse-Cassel 1760-85
66. **FGC** — Franz Georg, Archbishop of Trier 1729-56
67. **Double FGC** — Franz Georg, Archbishop of Trier 1729-56
68. **FJ** — Franz Josias of Saxe-Coburg 1745-64
69. **FJDS** — Same, as regent of Saxe-Eisenach 1748-56

70. **FL** — Friedrich II of Hesse-Cassel 1760-85
71. **FMBC** — Friedrich II of Brandenburg-Culmbach 1735-63
72. **FR** — Friedrich II of Prussia 1740-86
73. **FR** — Friedrich II of Prussia 1740-86
74. **FR** — Friedrich II of Prussia 1740-86
    — Friedrich II of Württemberg 1797-1816
75. **F5R** — Frederik V of Denmark 1746-66
76. **F VI R** — Frederik VI of Denmark 1808-39
77. **F V** — Frederik V of Denmark 1746-66
78. **FW** — Friedrich Wilhelm II of Prussia 1786-97
    — Friedrich Wilhelm of Brunswick-Wolfenbuttel 1806-15
79. **FW** — Friedrich Wilhelm of Mecklenburg-Strelitz 1860-1904
80. **FWR** — Friedrich Wilhelm II of Prussia 1786-97
81. **FWR** — Friedrich Wilhelm II of Prussia 1786-97
    — Friedrich Wilhelm III of Prussia 1797-1840
82. **G** — Georg of Mecklenburg-Strelitz 1816-60
83. **G III** — Gustav III of Sweden 1771-92
84. **GA IV** — Gustav IV Adolf of Sweden 1792-1809
85. **GFC** — Günther Friedrich Carl I of Schwarzburg-Sondershausen 1794-1835
86. **GH** — Georg Heinrich of Waldeck 1813-52
87. **GR** — George II 1727-60 and III 1760-1820 of England (see Brunswick-Luneburg and Hannover)
88. **GR** — George II 1727-60 and III 1760-1820 of England (see Brunswick-Luneburg and Hannover)
89. **G IV R** — Georg IV of Hannover 1820-30
90. **G V R** — Georg V of Hannover 1851-66
91. **GR XII** — Heinrich XII of Reuss-Schleiz 1744-84
92. **GW** — Johann Ludwig Adolf of Wied-Runkel 1706-62
93. **GW** — Georg Wilhelm of Schaumburg-Lippe 1807-60
94. **H3** — Heinrich III of Reuss Unter-Greiz 1733-68
95. **HEF** — Heinrich VIII, Bishop of Fulda 1759-88
96. **HN** — Hieronymus Napoleon of Westphalia 1807-13
97. **J** — Joachim Murat of Berg 1806-08
98. **JAEC** — Johann Anton, Bishop of Chur 1755-77
99. **JE II** — Catherine II of Russia 1762-96
100. **JF** — Johann Friedrich of Schwarzburg-Rudolstadt 1744-67
101. **JFC** — Johann Friedrich Carl, Archbishop of Mainz 1743-63
102. **JLA** — Johann Ludwig Adolf of Wied-Runkel 1706-62
103. **JLVGzL(W)** — Johann Ludwig Vollrath of Löwenstein 1721-90
104. **JPC** — Johann Philipp, Archbishop of Trier 1756-68
105. **L** — Louis XVIII of France 1814-24
106. **L** — Leopold I of Belgium 1831-65
107. **LFC** — Ludwig Friedrich Carl of Hohenlohe-Neuenstein 1765-1805
108. **LG** — Ludwig Günther IV of Schwarzburg-Rudolstadt 1767-90
109. **LHA** — Ludwig Heinrich Adolf of Lippe-Detmold 1782-89
110. **Double L** — Ludwig VIII of Hesse-Darmstadt 1739-68
    — Ludwig IX of Hesse-Darmstadt (Hesse-Hanau-Lichtenberg 1736-90)
111. **Double L** — Ludwig VIII of Hesse-Darmstadt 1739-68
112. **LL X** — Ludwig X of Hesse-Darmstadt 1790-1806
113. **LN** — Louis Napoleon (Netherlands East Indies 1806-11)
114. **LN** — Louis Napoleon (Netherlands East Indies 1806-11)
115. **LW** — Ludwig of Gimborn 1782-1806
116. **MC** — Moritz Casimir I of Bentheim 1710-68
117. **MF** — Max Friedrich, Archbishop of Cologne 1761-84
118. **M Double F** — Max Friedrich, Archbishop of Cologne 1761-84
119. **MJ** — Max Joseph of Bavaria (Jülich-Berg 1799-1806)
120. **M Double J** — Max Joseph of Bavaria (Jülich-Berg 1799-1806)
121. **ML** — Maria Louise of Parma 1815-47
122. **MLH** — Mary of Hesse-Hanau-Münzenberg 1760-64
123. **M Double T** — Maria Theresia of Austria (Luxemburg 1740-80)
124. **N** — Napoleon I 1806-15 (see France, Kingdom of Italy, and Cattaro)
125. **NFP** — Nikolaus Friedrich Peter of Oldenburg 1853-1900
126. **Double NO** — Wilhelm V of Nassau-Dietz (Orange) 1751-1806
127. **PAC** — Philipp, Abbot of Corvey 1758-76
128. **PF** — Paul Friedrich of Mecklenburg-Schwerin 1837-42
129. **PFA** — Paul Friedrich August of Oldenburg 1829-53
130. **SA** — Simon August of Lippe-Detmold 1734-82
131. **SAR** — Stanislaus August of Poland 1764-95
132. **SGVA** — Friedrich III of Saxe-Gotha-Altenburg 1732-72
133. **SM** — City of Münster
134. **TVS (or TDS)** — Thomas III of Haldenstein 1747-70
135. **VA** — Vittorio Amadeo III of Sardinia 1773-96
136. **VF** — Victor Friedrich of Anhalt-Bernburg 1721-65
137. **VNZ** — Venezuela, circa 1821
138. **VOC** — Netherlands East India Company
139. **W** — Willem I of Netherlands 1815-40
140. **W** — Willem I 1815-40 and Willem II 1840-49 of Netherlands
141. **W** — Wilhelm I of Württemberg 1816-64
142. **WA** — Wenzel Anton of Rietberg 1746-94
143. **WK** — Wilhelm I or II of Hesse-Cassel 1803-47
144. **WL** — Wilhelm VIII or IX of Hesse-Cassel 1751-60, 1785-1803
145. **W Double L** — Wilhelm VIII or IX of Hesse-Cassel 1751-60, 1785-1803
146. **WLZH** — Wilhelm VIII of Hesse-Cassel 1751-60
147. **WLZH** — Same, in Hesse-Hanau-Münzenberg 1736-60
148. **W Double R** — Wilhelm IV of Hannover 1830-37

ARABIC MINT NAMES

Arabic is read from right to left. Certain other Arabic words found on Muhammadan coins are on the following page.

ابوشهر Abu Shahr (= Abu Shehr, Bushire), PERSIA.

ادرنة Adrana (= Adrianople), TURKEY.

احمد شاهى Ahmadshahy, AFGHANISTAN.

اقصو Aksu, TURKESTAN (Chinese).

المعبرة Al Suirah (= Mogador), MOROCCO.

امد Amid (= Diarbekr), ARMENIA (Turkish).

ارد بيل Ardebil, PERSIA.

ارض.اقدس Arz-i-akdas, PERSIA.

اسرا باو Astarabad, PERSIA.

اياثلق Ayasuluk, TURKEY.

باغجه سراى. Baghcheserai, KRIM (= CRIMEA).

بغداد Baghdad, MESOPOTAMIA.

بلخ Balkh, AFGHANISTAN.

بندرعباس Bandar Abbas, PERSIA.

بندر ابوشهر Bandar Abu Shahr, PERSIA.

البصره Basrah, PERSIA.

بهبهان Behbehan, PERSIA.

بهكر Bhukkur, PERSIA.

بروجرد Borujird, PERSIA.

بروسة Brusah, TURKEY.

بخارا. Bukhara, TURKESTAN.

د ماوند Demawand, PERSIA.

ديره فتح خان Dera Fath Khan.

د مشق Dimesk (= Damascus), SYRIA.

ام البلاد بصره El Basrah (= Basrah), PERSIA.

اروان Erivan, ARMENIA.

فرغانة Farghana (= Khokand), TURKESTAN.

فاس Fas (= Fez), MOROCCO.

گنجة Ganjah (= Elizabetpol).

حلب Halep (= Aleppo), SYRIA.

همدان Hamadan, PERSIA.

هرات Herat, AFGHANISTAN.

ايران IRAN (= PERSIA).

اصفهان Isfahan, PERSIA.

جزاپر Jazair (= ALGIERS).

كابل Kabul, AFGHANISTAN.

كفة Kaffa, KRIM (= CRIMEA).

قندهار Kandahar, AFGHANISTAN.

كاشان Kashan, PERSIA.

كاشغر Kashgar, TURKESTAN (Chinese).

قزوين Kazwin (= Kazbin), PERSIA.

كرمانشاهان Kirmanshahan, PERSIA.

خوى Khui (= Khoi), PERSIA.

خوقند Khokand, TURKESTAN.

كوجا Kuja (= Kuchar), TURKESTAN (Chinese).

خوارزم Kwarezm (= Khiva), TURKESTAN.

قسطنطنية Kustantinayah (= Constantinople), TURKEY.

لاهيجان Lahijan, PERSIA.

لمو Lamu, EAST AFRICA.

ممباسا Mombasa, EAST AFRICA.

سراكش Marakesh (= Morocco).

مزندران Mazandaran, PERSIA.

مكة Mecca, ARABIA.

مكناسة Meknas (= Miknasah = Mequinas), MOROCCO.

مشهد Meshed, PERSIA.

مصر MISR (= EGYPT).

نخجوان Nakhchuwan, ARMENIA (under PERSIA).

نوابرده Nuwa Bardeh (= Novaberdah = Novi Bazar), TURKEY (in Europe).

نخوى Nukha, CAUCASIA.

بناه اباد Panahabad (= Shusha), **Karabagh**, CAUCASIA, PERSIA.

راباط الفتح Rabat al Fath, MOROCCO.

رعمانش Ranash, PERSIA.

رشنت Resht, PERSIA.

رها Ruha (= Roha, ancient Edessa), **MESOPOTAMIA** (under TURKEY).

سرخس Sarakhs, PERSIA.

سارى Sari, PERSIA.

ساوج بلاغ Sauj-bulagh, PERSIA.

سراى Serai (capital of Bosnia), TURKEY.

شماخى Shamakha, CAUCASIA, PERSIA.

شيراز Shiraz, PERSIA.

طبرستان Tabaristan, PERSIA.

تبريز Tabriz, PERSIA.

تاقدمت Takidemt, ALGIERS.

طرابلس Tarabelus (=TRIPOLI).

طهرات Teheran, PERSIA.

تطوان Tetuan, MOROCCO.

تفليس Tiflis, Georgia, CAUCASIA.

تيرة Tireh, TURKEY.

نوى Tui, PERSIA.

تونس TUNIS.

اروى Urumi, PERSIA.

اوش Ush (=Ushi), TURKESTAN (Chinese).

وان Van, ARMENIA, CAUCASIA.

يارقند Yarkand, TURKESTAN (Chinese).

يزد Yazd, PERSIA.

رنجان Zanjan, PERSIA.

ضرب duriba, zuriba (=struck, minted, coined)

في or ﻓﻲ fi (=in, at)

سنة or سنه sanat, sanah (=year)

خان khan (=prince, chieftain, lord)

خاقان khaqan (=emperor)

سلطان sultan (=king, emperor)

السلطان al-sultan, as-sultan (=the sultan)

شاه shah (=king)

پاره para

غروش (b) غرش (a) (a) ghirsh   (b) ghurush (plural) } (=piastre)
قروش (b) قرش (a) (a) qirsh   (b) qurush (plural) }

فلوس fulus, falus (=copper coin)

روفيه rupiyah (=rupee)

A detailed glossary of Arabic and Persian words and phrases frequently encountered in numismatics may be found in Richard Plant, *Arabic Coins and How to Read Them* (1973); a more abbreviated list appears in W. H. Valentine, *The Copper Coins of India* (1914, reprinted 1971).

AFGHANISTAN
Kingdom (Emirate)

Mountainous inland country N.W. of India, bordering also on Persia (Iran) and Russian Central Asia. Achieved independence from Persia 1747 at the assassination of Nadir Shah. Expanded into India and Eastern Persia 1752-62 under Ahmed Shah. These conquests were thereafter lost piecemeal (Punjab circa 1793-99, Kashmir 1819, Peshawar 1834). The British occupied Afghanistan on several occasions during the 19th century.

Monetary System: Initially like that of Persia (q.v.), and suffering from the same confusion, tended to absorb more characteristics of the coinage of India with the passage of time.

Mints:

احمدشاهی	Ahmadshahi
احمدنگر فرخاباد	Ahmadnagar-Farrukhabad
احمدپور	Ahmadpur
انولة	Anwala, Anulah
اتک	Atak
بهاولپور	Bahawalpur
بلخ	Balkh
بریلی	Barili
بهكهر	Bhakhar
دیره	Derah
دیرجات	Derajat (=Multan)
غزنة	Ghazni
هرات، هراة	Herat
كابل	Kabul
كشمير	Kashmir
خان اباد	Khanabad
لاهور	Lahore
میرتة	Merat
ملتان	Multan (=Derajat)
مرادآباد	Muradabad
نجيب اباد	Najibabad
پشاور	Peshawar
قندهار	Qandahar
ركاب مبارك	Rikab-i-Mubarak
سهرند، سرهند	Sahrind, Sarhind
سرپل	Sar-i-Pul
شاة جهان اباد	Shahjahanabad (=Delhi)
سند	Sind
تاشقورغان	Tashqurghan
تتة	Tattah

Copper Coinage

The Afghan copper denominations of the period here covered defy classification and are referred to only as falus (="copper"). Nearly all are anonymous and are frequently called "autonomous" coppers, although many could be attributed to a particular ruler by analysis of the date and mint place.

1 The "autonomous" coppers shown above are mostly like the Persian, with Obv. some object (flower, lion, horse*, camel*, stag*, peacock*, star, fishes*, sword*, leaves, sunface, etc.), and Rev. legend, giving the mint place and often the A.H. date. Copper issued during the British invasions often shows the imperial crown. Mints: Ahmadshahi, Balkh, Dera, Derajat, *Ghazni*, Herat, Kabul, Khanabad, Qandahar, Sar-i-Pul, Tashqurghan.

Each..................2.00–10.00

Silver Coinage

Most, if not all, of the Afghan rulers struck rupees (11.5 gr.) with Arabic or Persian legends on each side, setting out the ruler's name and the mint place. Fractions of a rupee are also known, but are more scarce. Naturally, coinage of early rulers with short reigns is less common than that of rulers who governed for longer periods more recently. Silver mints included the copper mint places, Peshawar and Kashmir under Afghan occupation, and others as shown below.

Each...................3.00–200.00

Gold Coinage

Same general types as silver, but apparently not struck by all rulers. Denominations were the mohur (11-11.3 gr.), occasional 2 and 3 mohurs, and the dinar (=tilla or Ashrafi) (3.5-4.5 gr.).

Each...............100.00–2000.00

I. Durrani Dynasty, AH 1160-1258 (=AD1747-1842).

Ahmad Shah Durrani
1160-86AH (=AD1747-72)

Founded Durrani Dynasty. Ruled present-day Afghanistan and Northern India.

Mints: Atak, Ahmadshahi (new capital built adjoining Qandahar), Ahmadnagar-Farrukhabad, Anwala, Bhakhar, Peshawar, Dera, Derajat, Lahore, Rikab i Mubarak, Sahrind, Kabul, Multan, Shahjahanabad (Delhi), Kashmir, Najibabad, Herat, Bareli, Tatta, Balkh, Muradabad.

Copper

201 (falus). 1161-87AH.......

Silver

221 (⅛ rupee). 1.1 gr. 1167-70AH...............

231 *(ashrafi in silver)*. 4 gr. Yr. 14...................

241 (rupee). 1161-86AH.......

Gold

261 (ashrafi). 1171AH.........

Ahmadnagar-Farrukhabad mint illustrated

*271 (mohur). 1161-86AH......

AFGHANISTAN

Taimur (Timur) Shah

=Ahmad's son, Nizam (=Governor) in North India 1170-86AH (=1757-72AD).

Mints: Dera, Lahore, Multan, Sind and Bhakhar.

Copper
291 (falus). 1172AH.........

Silver
301 (rupee). 1170-86AH.......

Gold
321 (mohur). 1170-82AH......

Sulaiman Shah

Pretender 1186AH (=1772AD) at the death of Ahmad Shad. Captured and blinded by Taimur Shah.

Mints: Kabul, Ahmadshahi, Peshawar, Dera and Kashmir.

Silver
341 (rupee). 1186AH.........

Gold
351 (mohur). 1186AH.........

Taimur Shah (as sole ruler)
1186-1207AH (=1772-93AD)

Mints: Atak, Ahmadshahi, Bhakhar, Peshawar, Dera, Rikab, Kabul, Kashmir, Multan, Merat, Balkh, Tatta, Haidarabad, Sind, Derajat, Multan, Mashhad.

Copper
361 (falus). 1186-1206AH......

Silver

Ahmadshahi mint illustrated

*381 (rupee). 1186-1208, and (posthumous at Herat) 1240-57AH...............

Gold
401 (mohur). 1186-1209AH....

Humayun Shah
1207AH (=1793AD)

One of Taimur's 23 sons. Defeated and killed by his half brother Zaman Shah.

Mint: Ahmadshahi.

Silver
421 (rupee). 1207AH.........

Gold
425 (mohur). 1207AH........

Zaman Shah
1207-16AH (=1793-1801AD)

Ruled all Afghanistan except for the Province of Herat (which was held by Mahmud, full brother of Humayun Shah). Defeated and executed by Mahmud 1216AH.

Mints: Ahmadshahi, Bhakhar, Dera, Derajat, Qandahar, Kabul, Lahore, Multan, Herat, Peshawar, Kashmir, Mashhad.

Copper
431 (falus). 1208-15AH.......

Silver
441 (¼ rupee). N.D. ....
451 (½ rupee). 1212AH.......

Kabul mint illustrated

*461 (rupee). 1207-15, and (posthumous at Kabul) 1258AH.................
475 (2 rupee). 1212-14AH.....

Gold
481 (mohur). 1208-15AH......

Mahmud Shah

(Full brother of Humayun Shah). Ruler at Herat 1207-45AH (=1793-1829AH). Conquered and ruled most of Afghanistan twice, 1216-18AH and 1224-33AH.

Mints:

(a) Continuous. Herat.

(b) First Reign. 1216-18AH (=1801-03AD). Ahmadshahi, Bahawalpur, Bhakhar, Peshawar, Dera, Derajat, Kabul, Kashmir, Multan, Mashhad.

(c) Second Reign. 1224-33AH (= 1809-18AD). Same except including Ahmadpur and excluding Dera.

(d) Struck by others in Mahmud's name. 1241-67AH. Bhakhar, Bahawalpur, Derajat, Multan.

Copper
501 (falus). 1216-17, 24-35, and (Multan) 53-64AH........

Silver
521 (¼ rupee). 1217, 42AH....
531 (½ rupee). 1235-43AH....

Herat mint illustrated

*541 (rupee). 1216-45, and (at Bhakhar, Bahawalpur and Derajat) 41-64AH........
561 (2 rupee). 1217AH.......

Gold
571 (¼ mohur). 2.27 gr. 1224AH...............
575 (ashrafi). 1218AH........

Kabul mint illustrated

*581 (mohur). 1217-18, 24-25AH.................
591 (2 mohur). 1217-18AH.....

Shuja al Mulk Shah

(Full brother of Zaman Shah) also known as Shah Shuja or Shodja. Between times when not in control of most of Afghanistan, Shuja retired to Peshawar and Kashmir.

First Reign. 1216AH (=1801AD).
Second Reign. 1218-24AH (=1803-09AD).
Third Reign. 1255-58AH (=1839-42AD)

Mints:
Second Reign. Ahmadshahi, Bahawalpur, Rikab i Mubarak, Kabul, Multan, Peshawar, Dera, Derajat, Kashmir, Bhakhar.
Third Reign. Kabul, Ahmadshahi.

Copper
601 (falus). 1218-24, and (at Peshawar and Kashmir) 28AH..................

Silver
613 (⅛ rupee). 1 gr. 1227AH (Peshawar).............
615 (¼ rupee). 1218AH, N.D.

Kabul mint illustrated

*621 (rupee). 1218-24, 27, N.D. (Peshawar), 55-56, 59 (Kabul =posthumous) AH.
635 (2 rupee). 1218AH........

AFGHANISTAN

Gold
641 (ashrafi). 1222AH........

Kabul mint illustrated

*645 (mohur). 1218-24,
55-58AH.................

Qaisar Shah, Pretender
1218, 21-23AH (=1803-08AD)
Mints: Kabul, Kashmir, Ahmadshahi.

Silver
670 (rupee). 1218 (Ahmadshahi)
21-23 (Kabul, Kashmir)
AH.....................

Gold
680 (mohur). 1218 (Ahmadshahi)
AH.....................

Ata Muhammad Khan Bamizai
Autonomous ruler in Kashmir, who
coined in the name of Nur al-Din Shah,
a local saint, 1223-28AH (=1808-13
AD).

Copper
690 (falus). 1225AH..........

Silver
695 (rupee). 1223-28AH.......
701 (2 rupee). 1223AH........

Gold

*705 (2 mohur). 1225AH.......

Ali Shah (=Sultan Ali)
Pretender installed briefly in Kabul
1233AH (=1818AD). No coins known.

Ayyub Shah
Ruler installed by Azim Khan Barakzai
of Kashmir 1233-45AH (=1818-29AD).
Mints: Peshawar, Ahmadshahi, Kabul, Kashmir, Multan.

Copper
801 (falus). 1236-40AH........

Silver

*811 (rupee). 1233-45AH
(Peshawar illustrated).....

Gold
821 (mohur). Yrs. 6-7........

Sultan Muhammad
At Peshawar 1247-49AH (=1831-33
AD).

Silver   *Fine*
830 (rupee). In the name of
Sultan al-Zaman. Peshawar.
1247-49AH...............12.50

Kamran Shah
(Son of Mahmud Shah) at Herat 1245-
58AH (=1829-42AD).

Silver
831 (¼ rupee). 1248AH...... 7.50
837 (½ rupee). 125XAH...... 7.50
839 (½ rupee). Anonymous,
with Kalimah. Herat. 1261,
65AH................... 6.00
845 (rupee). 1252AH..........12.00

Fath Jang Shah
At Ahmadshahi and Kabul 1258AH
(=1842AD).

Silver
861 (rupee). 1258AH..........

Shahpur Shah
At Kabul 1258AH (=1842AD).

Silver
871 (rupee). 1258AH..........

II. Barakzai Dynasty, AH1239-
1393 (=1823-1973).

Dost Muhammad
(Younger brother of Azim Khan Barakzai, ruler of Kashmir). 1st reign, at
Kabul and Qandahar, 1239-55AH (=
1823-39AD).

Silver
824 (rupee). In the name of Sultan
al-Zaman. Kabul. 1239AH.10.00

*824a —. In the name of Sahib al-
Zaman. Kabul. 1240-45AH. 7.50

Fine

*825 (rupee). In the name of Dost
Muhammad's father, Payinda
Khan. Kabul. 1245-50AH.. 7.00
826 (rupee). Like No. 879 but
Ahmadshahi. 1246-54AH ...8.00

*827 (rupee). Amir Dost Mu-
hammad. Kabul. N.D. and
1250-55AH............... 7.50
828 (rupee). Peshawar.
1246AH.................15.00

Kohandil
1st reign, at Qandahar, 1256-67AH (=
1840-51AD).

Silver

*850 (½ rupee). Ahmadshahi.
1261-62AH............... 5.00
851 (rupee). Ahmadshahi.
1259AH.................17.50

Dost Muhammad
2nd reign, at Kabul, Qandahar, Herat
and Balkh, 1258-80AH (=1842-63AD).

Silver

*879 (rupee). Anonymous, with
the Kalimah. Kabul.
AH1258.................10.00
880 (½ rupee). In the name of
Dost Muhammad and his
son Akbar. Qandahar.
1272-78AH............... 5.00
882 (rupee). Sim. Kabul.
1265-79AH............... 6.00
882a —. Peshawar. N.D........12.50
882b —. Ahmadshahi. 1272-
73AH.................10.00

· 16 ·

AFGHANISTAN

Gold

887 (tilla). Like No. 827.
Kabul. 1269AH..........110.00

Kohandil

2nd reign, at Qandahar, 1273-78AH
(=1856-61AD).

Silver

891 (½ rupee). Ahmadshahi.
1270-72AH!.......... 5.00
893 (½ rupee). Qandahar.
1273-79AH............. 5.00

Sher Ali

1st reign, at Kabul and Qandahar, 1280-
83AH (=1863-66AD).

Silver

901 (½ rupee). Title Amir of
all Amirs. Qandahar.
1280-82AH............. 5.00

★903 (rupee). With couplet beginning "Z'aini marhamat."
Kabul. 1280-82AH....... 7.00

Muhammad Afzal, Rebel

At Kabul and Balkh, 1283-84AH (=
1866-67AD).

Silver

911 (½ rupee). Ahmadshahi.
1283AH............... 10.00

★913 (rupee). Kabul. 1283
(2 vars.), 84AH..........12.00

Muhammad A'zam

At Kabul, Balkh and Qandahar, 1283-
84AH (=1866-67AD).

Silver

917 (½ rupee). Qandahar.
1283-84AH............. 8.00

★919 (rupee). Kabul. 1284-85...14.00

Sher Ali

2nd reign, at Kabul, Kandahar, Herat
and Balkh, 1285-96AH (=1868-78AD).

Silver

Fine

921 (½ rupee). Like No. 901.
Qandahar. 1285-95AH..... 5.00

★922 (½ rupee). Toughra.
Qandahar. 1288AH....... 6.00
924 (½ rupee). Amir Sher Ali.
Kabul. 1288-94AH....... 4.50
924a —. Herat. 1295AH....... 4.00

★925 (½ rupee). Kalimah. Kabul.
AH1292, 95 (var.)........ 5.00
927 (rupee). With couplet beginning "Ziltifati." Kabul.
1285AH............... 8.50
928 (rupee). Toughra. Kabul.
1285-87AH............. 6.50
929 (rupee). Amir Sher Ali.
Kabul. 1287-95AH....... 5.00
930 (rupee). Like No. 925
Kabul. 1292-95AH.........7.50

Gold

932 (tilla). Amir of all Amirs.
Qandahar. 1283-85AH!...135.00

★933 (mohur). Amir Sher Ali.
Kabul. 1288AH..........175.00
935 (tilla). Kalimah. Kabul.
1294-95AH.............125.00

Muhammad Yaqub

In all Afghanistan, 1296-98AH (=
1879-81AD).

Silver

941 (⅓ rupee). Kabul. 1296AH. 6.00
943 (½ rupee). Qandahar.
1296-97AH............. 6.50

★943a —. Herat. 1296-98AH.... 4.00

Fine

945 (rupee). Kabul. 1296-
97AH.................. 7.50
945a —. Qandahar. 1298AH....10.00

Wali Muhammad

At Kabul, 1297AH (=1880AD).

Silver

★951 (rupee). Kabul. 1297AH...10.00

Wali Sher Ali

At Qandahar, 1297-98AH (=1879-80
AD).

Silver

★957 (½ rupee). Qandahar.
1297AH.................10.00
959 (rupee). Qandahar.
1297AH.................12.50

Gold

★965 (tilla). Qandahar.
1297AH.................175.00

Muhammad Ishak

At Balkh 1306AH (=1889AD).

Silver

968 (rupee). "Kabul." 1305-
06AH (var.).............17.50

'Abd al-Rahman

In all Afghanistan, 1297-1319AH (=
1880-1901AD). For machine-struck
coins of this ruler, see Yeoman, *Modern
World Coins.*

Silver

971 (⅛ rupee). Herat.
1307AH................. 7.00
973 (⅛ rupee). Kabul.
1298AH................. 7.50
975 (½ rupee). Herat.
1297-1307AH............. 3.00

AFGHANISTAN

*977 (rupee). Kabul. 1297-
1308AH................ *Fine* 4.00

977a —. Qandahar. 1298-
1307AH................ 7.00

Gold

*981 (tilla). Ahmadshahi.
1298AH............... 100.00

ALGIERS
(Jazair, Cezayir)

North African territory nominally subject to Turkey but actually ruled by a
local potentate called the *dey*. The dey's
writ ran among the coast dwellers, who
tended toward piracy, while inland,
semi-nomadic tribes held sway. Seacoast conquered by France 1830, and
the hinterland was absorbed between
1840 and 1847.

Except where otherwise indicated, all
coins struck at Algiers in the name of
a Turkish Sultan bear the Sultan's
name on the obverse and the mint
name on the reverse.

Monetary System:

232 asper(akcheh*)*=1, pataka(batlaka);
48 kharub =24 muzuna =3 pataka =
  1 budju (riyal budju);
2 budju =1 zudj budju (piastre);
108 muzuna =1 sultani (gold altun =
  fondukly =sequin =ducat).

After 1830 a gradual transition to 100
centimes =1 franc took place.

Mints:

جزاير Jaza'ir (=Algiers)

قسنطينة Qusantinah } (=Con-

قسنطينية Qusantiniah } stantine)

تاقدمت Taqidamt

**Copies (and fantasies) of Algerian
coins:** Many silver and gold coins of

Algeria (and Turkey) prior to the introduction of machine-struck coinage were
holed and used as ornaments on clothing. Brass copies or fantasy coins, usually with silver or gold plating, were
made for persons who could not afford
the real thing. An example was former
No. 114 (Pere 801); others resemble
Nos. 100 to 120. These jewelry "coins"
are generally not deceptive when actually seen because plating is generally
worn off the high spots and legends are
altered or blundered.

I. Deys of Algiers.

Coinage struck at city of Algiers in the
name of the Ottoman (Turkish) Sultans.

Sultan Mahmud I
1143-68AH (=1730-54AD)

Gold
Fine

10 (¼ Sultani). 2 lines each side.
.8 gr. 12mm. 1143-68.......*50.00*

11 (½ Sultani). 3 lines each side.
1.7 gr. 17mm. 1143-66......*75.00*

12 (Sultani). 4 lines each side.
3.2 gr. 25mm. 1143-66.....*100.00*

Sultan Osman III
1168-71AH (=1754-57AD)

Gold

20 (¼ Sultani). 2 lines each side.
.8-.9 gr. 12-13 mm. 1168-
71.......................*65.00*

21 (½ Sultani). 3 lines each side.
1.7 gr. 17mm. 1168-71......*90.00*

22 (Sultani). 4 lines each side.
3.4 gr. 23-24mm. 1168-69..*125.00*

Sultan Mustafa III
1171-87AH (=1757-74AD)

Silver

30 *(3 muzuna)*. 2 lines. Rev. 2 lines
in octagram. 16mm. 1173-
79....................... 7.50

30a —. No octagram. 17mm.
1.7 gr. 1180-86AH......... 7.50

*34 (¼ Budju). 1172AH......*12.50*

Fine

*34a —. Rev. no octagram. 20-22mm.
3.3 gr. 1174-87AH.......10.00

Gold
V.F.

38 (¼ Sultani). 2 lines each side.
.8 gr. 13mm. 1172-77......*50.00*

39 (½ Sultani). 3 lines each side.
1.7 gr. 17-18mm. 1172-
75 (var.).................*85.00*

40 (Sultani). 4 lines each side.
3.4 gr. 23mm. 1183........*120.00*

Sultan Abdul Hamid I
1187-1203AH (=1774-89AD)

Silver
Fine

45 *(3 muzuna)*. Like No. 49.
1.7 gr. 17mm. AH1188-96... 7.50

*49 (¼ *budju*). SULTAN/ABDUL
HAMID/KHAN. Rev. JAZAIR
etc./date. 3.3 gr. 20mm.
1188-1203.................10.00

Gold
V.F.

54 (¼ Sultani). 3 lines.
Rev. JAZAIR etc./date. .85 gr.
14mm. 1194-95AH.........*50.00*

57 (Sultani). 4 lines each side.
3.4 gr. 24-25mm. 1190-
96AH...................*100.00*

Sultan Selim III
1203-22AH (=1789-1807AD)

Silver
Fine

60 (3 muzuna). 3 lines.
Rev. JAZAIR etc./date. 16-17mm.
1.65 gr. 1204-21AH........ 7.50

64 (¼ *Budju*). 19-24mm. 3.4 gr.
1206-22AH................10.00

ALGIERS

Fine

*67 (½ *Budju*). 23-27mm. 5.8-
6.8 gr. 1213-20, *22* *17.50*

Gold

V.F.

68 (¼ Sultani). 2 lines.
Rev. JAZAIR étc./1213.
.85 gr. 16mm. *60.00*

68a —. Rev. JAZAIR etc. in
octagon. 1221AH *60.00*

69 (½ Sultani). 3 lines. Rev. like
No. 68. 1.5-1.7 gr. 18-19mm.
1217AH *85.00*

*70 (Sultani). 3.4 gr. 1214-
21AH *100.00*

Sultan Mustafa IV
1222-23AH (=1807-08AD)

Silver

Fine

75 (¼ *Budju*). 20mm. 3.4 gr.
AH1222-23...............*25.00*

Gold

V.F.

80 (¼ Sultani). 2 lines. Rev.
JAZAIR etc./1222 in octagram.
.8 gr. 15mm. *75.00*

81 (½ Sultani). 3 lines.
Rev. like No. 80. 1.6 gr.
19mm. 1222-23..........*110.00*

82 (Sultani). 4 lines.
Rev. JAZAIR etc./date.
3.4 gr. 24mm. 1222-23.....*140.00*

Sultan Mahmud II, in Algiers
AH1223-46 (=1808-30)

Copper

Fine

*85 (2 asper). SULTAN/MAHMUD.
Rev. JAZAIR etc./date. 12-14mm.
AH1237-44 ....5.00

90 (5 asper). Sim. but obv.
SULTAN/MAHMUD/KHAN.
15-18mm. 1237-44 .... 5.00

Billon

Fine

95 (kharub). Like No. 85. 0.7 gr.
14-15mm. AH1237-42 ...... 6.50

Silver

1. Budju =ca. 12.8-13.6 gr., AH1223-35.

100 (*3 muzuna*). Like No. 110.
1.5-1.7 gr. 18-20mm.
AH1225-33.............. 7.50

103 (¼ *budju*). Sim. but rev.
legend in octagram. 3.2 gr.
20mm. 1223..............*20.00*

108 —. Like No. 110. 3.2-3.4 gr.
19-21mm. 1226-34, *38* 9.00

Note: After the devaluation of AH
1236, the old 3 muzuna and ¼ budju
continued in use as 4 and 8 muzuna,
respectively.

2. Budju =ca. 10 gr., AH1236-46.

109 (ex 102) (*3 muzuna*). Like
No. 110. 1.1-1.4 gr. 16-17mm.
1237-45.................. 5.50

*110 (¼ *budju*). 3-line legend.
Rev. JAZAIR etc./date.
2.3-2.5 gr. 21mm. 1236-46. 5.00

113 (½ *budju*). Toughra.
Rev. Yr. 13/JAZAIR etc./
1223. Double ornate border
both sides. 5.35 gr.
25mm................*pattern*

113a —. 4.9 gr. 21mm. ......*pattern*

*115 (budju). 9.8-10.7 gr. 28-30mm.
AH1236-45..............11.00

120 (zudj budju). Sim. 19-20 gr.
37-40mm. 1237-43 ....*45.00*

The 1½ Budju AH1237 (33mm) is a
pattern.

---

3. In style of Turkish types, AH1245.

Fine

*105 (4 muzuna). Crude copy of
Turkey No. 197, but rev.
JAZAIR etc./date. 1.5 gr.
17-18mm. AH1245........8.00

112 (⅓ budju). Sim. 3.1 gr.
23-24mm. 1245..........15.00

117 (budju). *Sim.* 10 gr.
28mm. 1245.............*30.00*

Gold

V.F.

125 (¼ Sultani). 2 lines each side.
.80 gr. 15-16mm. 1228-
43AH.................*40.00*

128 (½ Sultani). 3 lines each side.
1.6 gr. 16-18mm. 1231-
40AH.................*65.00*

132 (Sultani). 4 lines each side.
3.2 gr. 22-25 mm. 1223-
43AH.................*90.00*

II. Algerian resistance forces.

A. Constantine (Qusantinah).

Seaport and resistance center east of Algiers; held out for seven years against
the French.

Sultan Mahmud II,
in Constantine
AH1246-53 (=1830-37)

Copper

Fine

*138 (*2 asper*). Like No. 85 but
rev. QUSANTINAH etc./date.
13-15mm. AH1247.........*RR*

Billon

145 (kharub). *Like No. 150.*
0.7-1.0 gr. 18-19mm.
1246-52.................*12.50*

Silver

150 (*4 muzuna*). Toughra.
Rev. like No. 138. 1.2-1.5 gr.
18mm. 1247-52 ....*12.50*

155 (budju). Sim. 7.0-9.2 gr.
30-31mm. 1248-53 ....*20.00*

Gold

160 (zeri mahbub). Like Egypt
No. 7 but toughra/QUSANTINAH/
date. 2.4 gr. 24mm. 1246...*RRR*

ALGIERS

B. Abd-el-Kader ('Abd al-Qadir), AH1250-64 (=1834-47).

Muslim tribal leader, organized resistance to French occupation in north-western Algeria. Defeated and exiled in 1847. He had no permanent capital.

Mint:
Taqidamt (Takidemt, Takidempt).

Copper

Fine

★**170** *(5 asper).* Religious legend. Rev. Mint name. 15-17mm. 1254-56AH 6.50

Billon

175 (kharub). Religious legend. Rev. Mint name. 24mm. .7 gr. 1258AH *10.00*

178 (3 muzuna). Legends both sides. N.D. 16mm. 1 gr. . . . *10.00*

180 (½ *budju*). Religious legend. Rev. Mint name. 24mm. 5.5 gr. *20.00*

ANGOLA
(Lower Guinea, Africa Portugueza)

Portuguese possession in West Africa

Monetary System:
50 réis = 1 macuta.

José I 1750-77
Copper

VG-F

1 V (réis). Like No. 2. 1752-57 . . . . 6.00

★**2** X (réis). Obv. legend ends GUINEÆ. 1752-57 . . . . 6.00

3 XX (réis). Sim. 1752-57 . . . . 8.00

4 XL (réis). Sim. 1753, 57 . . . . . 10.00

Note: Nos. 1-4 were also used in Guinea and in Brazil, and are of Brazilian type except for the legend ending in GUINEÆ instead of BRASILIÆ. They were previously listed as Guinea Nos. 1-4, but would have been used most extensively in the larger colony of Angola.

VG-F

★**4.5** V (réis). 1770-71 . . . . 4.00

5 MACU/TA/¼. Sim. 1762-71 . . . . 6.00

6 MACU/TA/½. Sim. 1762-70 . . . . 6.00

7 MACU/TA/1. Sim. 1762-70 . . . . 8.00

Note: A number of Angolan copper coins were cmkd. with Portuguese arms in Brazil in 1814 to double their face value. These are generally more common than the same coins without cmk.

Silver

F-VF

8 MACU/TAS/2. Sim. 1762-63 . . . . 30.00

9 MACU/TAS/4. Sim. 1762-70 . . . . 50.00

10 MACU/TAS/6. Sim. 1762-70 . . . . 100.00

11 MACU/TAS/8. Sim. 1762-70 . . . . 150.00

12 MACU/TAS/10. Sim. 1762-70 . . . . 300.00

13 MACU/TAS/12. Sim. 1762-70 . . . . 350.00

Maria I and Pedro III 1777-86
Copper

VG-F

14 MACU/TA/¼. Sim. but MARIA I E. PETRUS III etc. 1785 . . . . 5.00

15 MACU/TA/½. Sim. 1785-86 . . . . 5.00

★**16** MACU/TA/1. Sim. 1783-86. 6.00

Silver

F-VF

18 MACU/TAS/2. Sim. 1783 . . . 30.00

19 MACU/TAS/4. Sim. 1783-84 . . . . 45.00

20 MACU/TAS/6. Sim. 1784 . . 60.00

21 MACU/TAS/8. Sim. 1783 . 120.00

22 MACU/TAS/10. Sim. 1783 . . . . 175.00

23 MACU/TAS/12. Sim. 1783 . . . . 300.00

Maria I, Alone 1786-99
Copper

VG-F

23.5 MACU/TA/¼. Sim. but MARIA I D.G. etc. 1789 . . . . . 6.00

24 MACU/TA/½. Sim. 1789 . . . . 6.00

25 MACU/TA/1. Sim. 1789 . . . . 7.50

Silver

F-VF

★**27** MACU/TAS/2. 1796 . . . . 20.00

28 MACU/TAS/4. Sim. 1789, 96 . . . . 45.00

29 MACU/TAS/6. Sim. 1789, 96 . . . . 60.00

30 MACU/TAS/8. Sim. 1789, 96 . . . . 120.00

31 MACU/TAS/10. Sim. 1796 . . . . 175.00

32 MACU/TAS/12. Sim. 1796 . . . . 275.00

João (Joannes), Prince Regent 1799-1816
Copper

VG-F

33 MACU/TA/¼. Like No. 35. 2.5 gr. 1814 . . . . 25.00

33a —. 3.8-4.2 gr. Struck over older coins. 1814 . . . . 25.00

34 MACU/TA/½. Sim. 4.5 gr. 1814 . . . . 15.00

34a —. 7.4-8.2 gr. Struck over older coins. 1815 . . . . 15.00

ANGOLA

VG-F

★35 MACU/TA/1. 13.3-13.5 gr.
1814.................10.00

35a —. 18.5-19.0 gr. Struck
over older coins. 1814, 16..10.00

36 MACU/TAS/2. Sim.
1815-16.................40.00

Miguel (Michael) I 1828-34

The copper ¼, ½, 1 and 2 macutas of
1831 (former Nos. 71-74) are patterns.

Maria II 1834-53

Copper

75 MACUTA/½. Like No. 76
but MARIA II etc. 1848-53... 6.00

Pedro V 1853-61

Copper

★76 MACUTA/½. 1858, 60..... 5.00

77 MACUTA/1. Sim. 1860.... 7.50

ANNAM, Empire

Originally equivalent to present-day
North Vietnam but also included South
Vietnam from 1802 onward. Persecu-
tion of Christians in the 19th century
led to French absorption of Cochin
China 1862-67, and the rest of Annam
in 1883-84.

Modern research indicates that all
Annamese gold and virtually all Annamese silver pieces were not coins in
the true sense, but were produced for
some other purpose. The rectangular
silver were issued as bullion and passed
by weight. Nearly all of the round silver
were intended as medallions, charms,
bullion or presentation pieces. The gold
served similar ends. Accordingly, most
of these pieces have been deleted from
the listing which follows. Perhaps this
is convenient because much of this material in the market today is counterfeit.

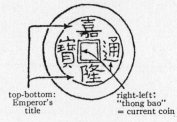

top-bottom: right-left:
Emperor's   "thong bao"
title   = current coin

Typical Obverse

Characters at top and bottom on the
obverse of Annamese coins are the ruler's reign title. The characters at right
and left are usually "thong bao" (=
current coin), but others sometimes occur (e.g., nearly 20 different characters
may appear at right or left on No. 2).

Reverses of zinc and copper-alloy
coins are often blank, but up to 4 characters may appear. These can be mint
marks, weights, denominations or (rarely) cyclical dates. When numerals appear, those with "phan" (Nos. 60, 62,
63) express weights, while numerals
with "van" (Nos. 202-207, 282) are denominations.

Note: For other cast copper-alloy coins
of the general style listed here, see
CHINA, JAPAN and KOREA.

Monetary System:

Zinc and copper: 600 dong (sapeque,
van, cash) = 10 mach = 1 quan (string
of cash). Originally (ca. 1813) 6 zinc
dong = 5 copper dong, but zinc depre-
ciated through the 19th century until
6 to 10 zinc dong = 1 copper dong.

Silver and gold: exchanged as bullion
by fineness and weight, with no fixed
relationship to copper or zinc.

Weights: 1000 li = 100 phan (fen, can-
dareens) = 10 tien (mace) = 1 lang (tael,
ounce) = 37.5-39 gr.; silver piastre = 26-
27.5 gr.

I. Le Empire in present North Vietnam.

Canh-Hung, Emperor 1740-87

Copper-alloy

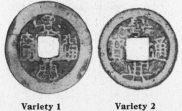

Variety 1   Variety 2

V.G.

★★1 (dong). "Canh-Hung thong bao."
Rev. blank............. 2.50

Two styles of script are shown for No. 1
(var. 2 is more common). Intermediate
varieties exist.

2 —. Different characters at right
or left (var.) 3.50

3 —. No. 1 or 2 with 1 or 2
characters on rev. 4.00

Chieu-Thong, Emperor 1787-89
Driven out by Nguyen Hue.

Copper-alloy

30 (dong). Obv. like No. 31.
Rev. blank............. 3.50

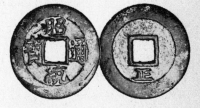

★31 —. "Chieu-Thong thong bao."
Rev. with 1 or 2 characters
(var.)................. 4.00

Chinese Invasion 1789
Kien Long =
Chinese Emperor Ch'ien-Lung

Copper-alloy

★34 (dong). Obv. like China No. 1-1.
Rev. 2 characters for
Annam.................40.00

II. Dong-Nai = Nguyen Kingdom in present South Vietnam.

Thien-Minh, King 1739-66

Zinc

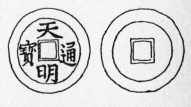

★36 (dong). "Thien-Minh thong
bao." Rev. blank.......... 7.00

ANNAM

III. Tayson Rebellion Period.

Three merchant-class brothers led a successful rebellion against the Nguyen ruler of South Vietnam, caused the death of the entire royal family except Nguyen-Anh, nephew of the last ruler, and after dividing the kingdom in three parts, each one set himself up as ruler of one of the divisions.

Nguyen Nhac 1778-93

One of the Tayson brothers, ruled as **Emperor Thai Duc** over central ruler of South Vietnam, caused the South Vietnam.

Copper-alloy

V.G.

38 (dong). Obv. like No. 39. Rev. blank.............. 5.00

★39 —. "Thai-Duc thong bao." Rev. 2 characters......... 6.50

Nguyen Hue 1777-92

Another Tayson brother. Initially ruled over northern South Vietnam. Conquered Le Empire of North Vietnam 1789 and was thereafter known as —

Emperor Quang Trung 1788-92

Copper-alloy

★41 (dong). "Quang Trung thong bao." Rev. blank.......... 2.50
42 —. Different characters at right and/or left (var.)..... 5.00
44 —. No. 41 with 1 or 2 characters on rev. (var.).... 4.00

Canh-Thinh, Emperor

Title adopted during minority 1792-1801 by Quang Trung's successor in North Vietnam.

Copper-alloy

★51 (dong). "Canh-Thinh thong bao." Rev. blank......... 3.00
52 —. Different characters at right and left.............. 5.00

★53 *(mach = 60 dong)*. Obv. like No. 51. Rev. dragon/2 fish. 43-46mm................. ——

Bao-Hung, Emperor

Title adopted 1801-02 by Canh-Thinh after reaching majority.

Copper-alloy

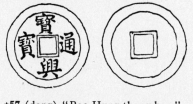

★57 (dong). "Bao-Hung thong bao." Rev. blank................RR

IV. United Vietnam.

Nguyen-Anh, surviving nephew of the last Nguyen king of South Vietnam commencing in the Mekong Delta, first reconquered his uncle's kingdom and then took the northern empire, entering Hanoi victoriously in 1802 where he adopted the title of —

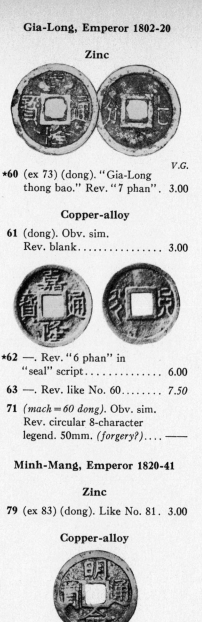

Gia-Long, Emperor 1802-20

Zinc

V.G.

★60 (ex 73) (dong). "Gia-Long thong bao." Rev. "7 phan". 3.00

Copper-alloy

61 (dong). Obv. sim. Rev. blank............... 3.00

★62 —. Rev. "6 phan" in "seal" script.............. 6.00
63 —. Rev. like No. 60........ 7.50
71 *(mach = 60 dong)*. Obv. sim. Rev. circular 8-character legend. 50mm. *(forgery?)*.... ——

Minh-Mang, Emperor 1820-41

Zinc

79 (ex 83) (dong). Like No. 81. 3.00

Copper-alloy

★81 (dong). "Minh-Mang thong bao." Rev. blank.......... 2.00
V.F.
84 *(mach = 60 dong)*. Obv. sim. Rev. circular 8-character legend (var.). 49-54mm..... ——
86 —. Rev. 4-character legend (var.). 49-54mm.......... ——

Round Silver

91 (½ piastre = 13.8 gr.). Legend like No. 81, sun. Rev. Dragon. N.D. 150.00
95 (½ ounce). Like No. 91. N.D.....................150.00
100 (piastre). Like No. 91. N.D. 150.00

ANNAM

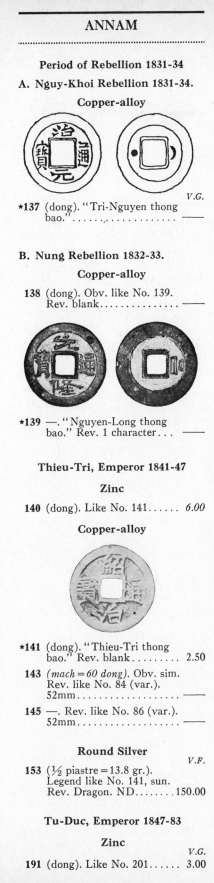

Period of Rebellion 1831-34

A. Nguy-Khoi Rebellion 1831-34.

Copper-alloy

*137 (dong). "Tri-Nguyen thong
bao." . . . . *V.G.* ——

B. Nung Rebellion 1832-33.

Copper-alloy

138 (dong). Obv. like No. 139.
Rev. blank. . . . . ——

*139 —. "Nguyen-Long thong
bao." Rev. 1 character. . . ——

Thieu-Tri, Emperor 1841-47

Zinc

140 (dong). Like No. 141. . . . . . *6.00*

Copper-alloy

*141 (dong). "Thieu-Tri thong
bao." Rev. blank. 2.50

143 *(mach = 60 dong).* Obv. sim.
Rev. like No. 84 (var.).
52mm. . . . . ——

145 —. Rev. like No. 86 (var.).
52mm. . . . . ——

Round Silver
V.F.

153 (½ piastre = 13.8 gr.).
Legend like No. 141, sun.
Rev. Dragon. ND. 150.00

Tu-Duc, Emperor 1847-83

Zinc
V.G.

191 (dong). Like No. 201. . . . . . 3.00

192 —. Rev. 2 characters
(var.). . . . .*Rare*

Copper-alloy

201 (dong). Obv. like No. 202.
Rev. blank. 25.00

*202 6 van (= copper dong
valued at 6 zinc dong).
"Tu-Duc thong bao." Rev.
value in 2 characters. 4.00

203 8 van. "Tu-Duc trung bao."
Rev. value top-bottom,
"Annam" at sides. . . . . ——

*204 10 van (= valued at 10
copper dong). "Tu-Duc bao
sau." Rev. vaue in 3
characters. . . . .*RR*

204a —. Rev. value in 4
characters. . . . .*RR*

205 20 van. Sim. 30mm. . . . .*RR*

205.5 30 van. Sim. 35mm. . . . .*RR*

206 40 van. Sim. 38mm. . . . .*RR*

206.5 50 van. Sim. 39-42mm. . . . . .*RR*

207 60 van. Sim. 39-45mm. . . . . .*RR*

213 *(mach = 60 dong).* Obv. like
No. 202. Rev. like No. 84
(var.). 47-51mm. . . . . ——

215 —. Rev. like No. 86 (var.).
47-51mm. . . . . ——

Round Silver
V.F.

234 (½ piastre). Legend like
No. 201, sun. Rev. Dragon.
ND. (13.4 gr.). 60.00

Hiep Hoa, Emperor 1883

No coins.

Kien Phuc, Emperor 1884

Zinc

V.G.

*271 (dong). "Kien-Phuc thong
bao." Rev. blank. . . . . .RR

Copper-alloy

272 (dong). Sim. . . . . .RR

Ham-Nghi, Emperor 1884-85

Copper-alloy

*281 (dong). "Ham-Nghi thong
bao." Rev. blank. . . . . .RRR

282 6 van. Obv. sim.
Rev. like No. 202. . . . . ——

Dong Khanh, Emperor 1885-89

Copper-alloy

*301 (dong). "Dong-Khanh thong
bao." Rev. blank. 4.00

ANTIGUA. See CARIBBEAN
ISLANDS AND TERRITORIES.

ARABIA

The Arabian Peninsula. Turkey had certain footholds in this area and was nominally sovereign over much more, but most of Arabia was actually governed by various local potentates.

MECCA

The Muhammedan Holy City, inland from the Red Sea. Mecca and Medina were conquered and held by the Wahabis of Nejd 1803-18.

Monetary System:

20 qaz = 1 mahmudi. This statement appears in the 1878 Fonrobert sale catalog, p. 305. Lachman suggests that the Wahabis were unlikely to have used the name mahmudi as a coin denomination. The Edinburgh Encyclopaedia (vol. XIV, 1830) under *Money* does not list "Mahmudi" as a coin then in use at Medina, Mecca or Mocha. Nevertheless, one notes that the founder of the Wahabi sect was Muhammad ibn 'Abd al-Wahhab.

Perhaps these were "comashees," of which the Edinburgh Encyclopaedia said 60 = 1 piastre?

Saud, Sultan
1218-30AH (=1803-14AD)

Copper

		G-VG
51	(½ mahmudi). Arabic: etc. MECCA. Rev. date etc. 22-23mm. 1219-21AH	*10.00*

★**53**	(½ mahmudi). Dove. Rev. 1223/fish/AH1223. 20-25mm	*7.50*

YEMEN, Imamate

In southwest Arabia. Independent of Turkey AD1630-1872. Capital and mint at San'a, which name appears on all coins unless otherwise shown.

Monetary System:
40 diwani = 1 girsh (piastre).

El Mehdi *III*
1162-71 AH (=1748-58 AD)

Silver
		G-VG
21	(2 diwani). .75 gr. 1162, 71AH	*7.50*
28	(5 diwani). 1.1 gr. 1168AH	*10.00*

Ahmed el-Mutawakel

Silver
81	(diwani). .4 gr. 1226AH	*7.50*
87	(5 diwani). 1.2 gr. 1226AH	*10.00*

ARGENTINA

Large republic in southeastern South America. Comprised of part of the former Spanish Viceroyalty of Rio de la Plata, together with part of Patagonia. Achieved independence in the period 1810-16. Conflicts between Federalists and Centralists persisted until 1880, resulting in much provincial coinage.

Monetary System:
8 reales = 8 soles = 1 peso;
2 pesos = 1 scudo.

I. National Coinage.

A. Provincias del Rio de la Plata.

Potosí (Bolivia) Mint – PTS mon.

Silver
		F-VF
11	(½ real). Like No. 12. 1813, 15	*10.00*

★**12**	1 R(eal). 1813, 15	*15.00*
13	2 R(eales). Sim. 1813, 15	*17.50*
14	4 R(eales). Sim. 1813, 15	*50.00*

		F-VF
★**15**	8 R(eales). Sim. 1813, 15	*60.00*
16	(½ sol). Sim. 1815 FL	*12.50*
17	1 S(ol). Sim. 1815	*17.50*
18	2 S(oles). Sim. 1815	*17.50*
19	4 S(oles). Sim. 1815	*65.00*
20	8 S(oles). Sim. 1815	*65.00*

Gold
		V.F.
21	1 S(cudo). Sim. 1813	——
21.5	*2 S(cudos). Like No. 22.* 1813	——
21.6	*4 S(cudos). Sim. 1813*	——
22	8 S(cudos). Sim. but trophies under arms (like No. 28). 1813	*3500.00*

Rioja (Argentina) Mint – RA.

Silver
		F-VF
23	1 R(eal). Like No. 12. 1824-25	*17.50*
23.5	2 R(eales). Sim. but crude. 1821R	*Unique*

★**24**	2 S(oles). 1824-26	*8.00*
25	4 S(oles). Sim. 1828, 32	*35.00*
26	8 R(eales). Sim. 1826-37	*70.00*

Gold
		V.F.
27	2 S(cudos). Sim. but trophies under arms. 1824-26	*350.00*

ARGENTINA

V.F.

★28 8 S(cudos). Sim. 1826-35..1600.00

B. Confederación Argentina.
Copper

Fine

★31 UN (=1)/CENTAVO.
1854..................... 2.50

32 DOS (=2)/CENTAVOS.
Sim. 1854................. 2.50

33 CUATRO (=4)/CENTAVOS.
Sim. 1854................. 2.50

II. Provincial Coinages.
A. Buenos Aires, Province.
Copper
10 décimos = 1 real.

VG-F

★41 UN (=1) DECIMO. 1822-
23..................... 1.75

42 ¼ (real). Like No. 43.
1827.................... 15.00

★43 5/10 (real). 1827-31....... 2.00

★45 10/DECIM(os). 1827-30.... 5.00

VG-F

47 20/DECIM(os). Sim. 1827-
31..................... 5.00

48 5/10 (real). Like No. 49.
1840.................... 9.50

Fine

★49 UN (=1)/REAL. 1840..... 2.00

50 DOS (=2)/REALES. Sim.
1840, 44................. 3.50

51 UN(=1) REAL. Like No. 52.
1854.................... 12.50

★52 DOS(=2) REALES.
1853-56................. 2.00

★53 DOS/REALES. BANCO etc.
Rev. value. 1860-61....... 2.00

B. Córdoba (Córdova), Province.

Silver

F (crude)

60 (¼ real). Castle. Rev. Sun.
No legends. 10.5mm.
N.D. *(1815-17)*..........100.00

★61 (¼ real). 1833, 38........20.00

★62 (¼ real). 1839-41.......... 4.25

F (crude)

64 (½ real). Sun. Rev. Argentine
arms. (See No. 12.) Obv.
PROVINCIA DE etc. Rev.
EN UNION etc. 16-17mm.
1839-40.................RRR

64a —. Obv. CONFEDERADA.
1839....................RRR

64b —. Rev. CONFEDERADA.
1840....................RRR

64c —. Rev. PROVINCIA etc.
1841....................RRR

64.5 (½ real). Like No. 70.
16-17mm. 1840...........RRR

64.5a —. Obv. CONFEDERADA.
Rev. PROVINCIA etc.
1841....................17.50

66 (real). Sun. Rev. Argentine
arms. (See No. 12.) Obv.
CONFEDERADA. Rev. PROVINCIA
DE etc. 19-22mm. 1840-44... 3.50

66a —. Obv. EN UNION etc.
1840-41.................. 9.00

66b —. Different combinations of
above 3 legends. (e.g. obv.
legend on rev., etc). 1840
(6 vars.)..................RRR

66c —. Obv. LIBRE etc. 1843.....RR

67 1 R(eal). Like No. 70. 1840-
41...................... 4.50

★63 ¼ (real). N.D. (1853-54)... 5.00

65 ½ (real). Like No. 68.
1850-54.................. 4.50

★68 1/REAL. 1848............. 5.00

F-VF

69 2 R(eales). Like No. 70.
1844-54.................. 7.50

★70 4 R(eales). 1844-52........18.00

71 8 R(eale)S. Sim. 1852......55.00

ARGENTINA

C. Entre Rios, Province (Colonia San José).

Silver

81 UN MEDIO (= ½ real). *Fine*
PROVINCIA DE ENTRE RIOS etc.
Arms. Rev. MONEDA etc.
1867....................65.00

D. La Rioja (Rioxa), Province.

Silver

91 1 R(eal). Sun, arms.
Rev. SVR AMERICA/RIOXA.
ND (1823) .... ——

Unique 1 real (silver) and 1 escudo (gold) *patterns* exist, dated 1823 with SUD AMERICA RIOXA, somewhat similar to No. 91.

93 2 (reales). Arms of Castile (castles) and Leon (lions) in corners of cross. Rev. 2 pillars, 2/R–IOX–A/date. Cob. (1)821-22....................125.00

94 4 (reales). Sim. but 4/S–RIOXA–R/M–date. Cob. (1)821.....450.00

Note: Other coins like Nos. 93-94 exist, namely (½ real) (1)822, 1 (real) (1)822, 2 (reales) (1)823 and 4 (reales) (1)822, but these appear to be virtually unique patterns. Cunietti-Ferrando also lists 4 (reales) (1)823 without RIOXA as having been struck here (worth *200.00-300.00*).

95 ½ R(eal). Like No. 100. *VG-F*
1844....................8.00

96 ½/REAL. REPUB. etc. Rev. *V.F.*
PROV.DE etc. 1854.......... 4.00

96a —. Sim. but rev. like No. 97a
1854...,................ 6.00

97 ½/REAL. CONFEDERACION etc.
Rev. like No. 96. 1854...... 4.00

97a —. 1854, 60............. 4.00

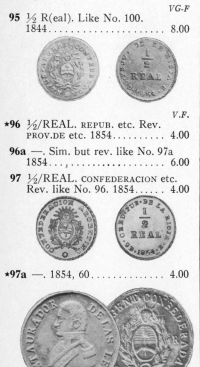

★98 2 R(eales). 1842.......... *F-VF* 35.00

★99 2 R(eales). 1843.......... 22.50

★100 2 R(eales). 1843-44......25.00

101 2/REALES. Like No. 97a.
1859-60................12.50

102 4 R(eales). Like No. 99.
1846-50................15.00

103 4 R(eales). Sim. but Rev.
PROV. DE LA RIOJA. Mountain.
1852 ....125.00

★104 8 R(eales). 1838-40.....100.00 *V.F.*

105 8 R(eales). Sim. but REPUBLICA ARGENTINA. Rev. EN UNION etc. Struck by rebels.
1840 .... *(Fine)* 300.00

Gold

106 2 E(scudos). Like No. 98 but arms on trophies. 1842 ...300.00

---

107 2 E(scudos). Like No. 100, *V.F.*
but arms on trophies.
1843.................300.00

The 1836 8 S(cudos), Gen. Rosas. Rev. Mountain, is a rare pattern.

109 8 S(cudos). Like No. 104 but arms on trophies.
1838, 40...........2000.00

110 8 S(cudos). Sim., but legends like No. 105.
Rebel issue. 1840......2500.00

111 8 E(scudos). Like No. 106.
1842.................... ——

★112 8 E(scudos). 1845......... ——

E. Mendoza, Province.

Copper

115 ⅛ (*real*). Provincial arms. *VG-F*
1835...................

Silver

119 (¼ *real*). Provincial arms.
1836.................... ——

120 (½ real). Arms like No. 123.
Rev. PLUS ULTRA mon./
1824.................300.00

121 I (real). Like No. 123.
Cob, usually partly off planchet. (1823)..........75.00

122 2 (reales). Sim.
(1)823-24................75.00

123 4 (reales). 4/cross, arms of Castile (Castles) and Leon (lions) in corners, P–V at sides. Rev. 2 pillars, P–4–M/LV–SVL–TR/P–date–V. Cob. (18)23-24...275.00

Cob coinage circulating in the province was validated in 1823-24 with a 12.5mm circular cmk. bearing the legend FIDEL-IDAD (= fidelity) around a balance scale (*RRR*).

See VENEZUELA for similar late 1 and 2 real cobs before 1822 or with blundered dates.

ARGENTINA

F. Salta, Province.

For about six months in 1817-18 cob coinage circulating in Salta, whether genuine or counterfeit, was officially cmkd. with an 8mm circular counterstamp bearing PATRIA (=fatherland) monogram in a crude laurel wreath. By directive of 24 May 1818 these coins were to be destroyed.

Silver

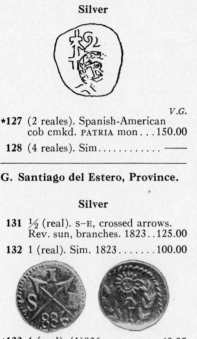

V.G.

★127 (2 reales). Spanish-American cob cmkd. PATRIA mon . . . 150.00

128 (4 reales). Sim . . . . —

G. Santiago del Estero, Province.

Silver

131 ½ (real). S–E, crossed arrows. Rev. sun, branches. 1823 . . 125.00

132 1 (real). Sim. 1823 . . . . . . 100.00

★133 1 (real). (1)836 . . . . 60.00

Note: Coins of this province in better condition than listed are often counterfeit.

H. Tucumán, Province.

Silver

VG-F

★152 2 (reales). Copy of Spanish-American cob from Potosí mint. Rev. mmk. TN at lower right. (1)752 (struck 1820-21) 75.00

Note: Cunietti-Ferrando lists similar type cob 2 reales without the TN mmk. and bearing fictitious dates 257, 577, 752 or 758 as having been struck officially or privately in Tucumán. If true, there appears to be no way of distinguishing these coins from those traditionally attributed to Venezuela.

AUSTRALIA

Island continent occupied first by British penal settlements which grew into colonies and thereafter became the states of the present commonwealth. Many private tokens were issued during the 19th century but there was little coinage.

Monetary System:
20 shillings = 1 pound (sovereign).

A. New South Wales.

Silver

Fine

★1 FIFTEEN/PENCE. 1813 . 150.00

★2 FIVE SHILLINGS. "Holey" dollar from which No. 1 was removed. 1813 . . . . 1500.00

Many forgeries of Nos. 1 and 2 exist.

B. Sydney Mint Gold.

V.F.

3 HALF SOVEREIGN. Like No. 4. 1855-56 . . . . 225.00

3a —. Like No. 4a. 1857-66 . . . . 75.00

4 ONE SOVEREIGN. Like No. 4a but larger head. 1855-56 . . . . 500.00

V.F.

★4a —. 1857-70 . . . . 90.00

C. South Australia.

Adelaide Assay Office Gold

★5 ONE/POUND. 1852 . . . . . 1400.00

UNVERIFIED DATA

Note: Throughout this catalog, any uncertain, indefinite or unconfirmed information is shown in *italic type*. Such material may be, for example, coin descriptions, dates and prices, names of rulers, or supplementary notes. Further information to confirm or correct *material in italics* should be sent to the author at the following address:

William D. Craig
c/o Whitman Coin Supply Division
1220 Mound Avenue
Racine, Wisconsin 53404, U.S.A.

AUSTRIA
(HAPSBURG LANDS)

Under this general heading are grouped the coins of the Hapsburg Empire in Central European denominations, excluding local issues for ITALY (Gorizia, Lombardy, Mantua, Milan and Venice), LOW COUNTRIES (Austrian Netherlands and Luxemburg), and POLAND (Galicia).

HAPSBURG MINT AND MINTMASTER/MINTWARDEN MARKS

A – Vienna. 1765-1872.
AH-AG – Carlsburg (Transylvania). 1765-76.
AH-GS – Carlsburg. 1776-80.
A-S – Hall (Tyrol). 1765-74.
AS-IE – Vienna. 1745.
AW – Vienna. 1764, 68.
B – Kremnitz (Hungary). 1765-1857.
B-L – Nagybanya (Hungary). 1765-71.
B-V – Nagybanya. 1772-80.
C – Carlsburg. 1762-64.
C – Prague (Bohemia). 1766-1857.
C-A – Carlsburg. 1746-66.
C-A – Vienna. 1774-80.
CG-AK – Graz (Styria). 1767-72.
CG-AR – Graz. 1767.
C-K – Vienna. 1765-73.
CM – Kremnitz. 1779.
CVG-AK – Gratz. 1767-72.
CVG-AR – Gratz. 1767.
D – Graz. 1765-72.
D – Salzburg. 1800-09.
E – Carlsburg. 1765-1867.
EC-SK – Vienna. 1766.
EvM-D – Kremnitz. 1765-74.
Ev S-AS – Prague. 1765-73.
Ev S-IK – Prague. 1774-80.
F – Hall. 1765-1807.
G – Graz. 1761-63.
G – Gunzburg (Burgau). 1764-79.
G – Nagybanya. 1766-1851. (On coins of Joseph II only until 1780.)
G-K – Graz. 1767-72.
GM – Governo Militare, Garnison Mantua or Gorzkowski Mantua (siege of Mantua 1848).
G-R – Graz. 1746-67.
GTK – Vienna. 1761.
H – Hall. (On coins of Maria Ther. and Franz I) 1760-80.
H – Gunzburg. (On coins of Joseph II only until 1780) 1765-1805.
H-A – Hall. 1746-65.
H-G – Carlsburg. 1765-77.
H-S – Carlsburg. 1777-80.
IB-FL – Nagybanya. 1765-71.
IB-IV – Nagybanya. 1772-80.
IC-FA – Vienna. 1774-80.

IC-IA – Vienna. 1780.
IC-SK – Vienna. 1765-73.
I-K – Graz. 1765-67.
I-K – Vienna. (Franz I posthumous year B = 1767.)
IZV – Vienna. 1763-65.
K – Kremnitz. 1760-63.
K-B – Kremnitz. 1619-1765.
K-D – Kremnitz. 1765.
K-M – Kremnitz. 1763-65.
M – Milan (Lombardy). 1780-1859.
N – Nagybanya. 1780.
N-B – Nagybanya. 1630-1777, 1849.
O – Oravicza (Hungary). 1783-1816. (Copper only.)
P – Prague. 1760-63.
P-R – Prague. 1746-67.
PS-IK – Prague. 1780.
S – Hall. 1765-80. (No copper.)
S – Schmöllnitz (Hungary). 1763-1816. (Copper only.)
S-C – Gunzburg. 1765-74.
SC-G – Gunzburg. 1765.
S-F – Gunzburg. 1775-80.
S-G – Gunzburg. 1764-65.
S-IE – Vienna. 1745.
SK-PD – Kremnitz. 1774-80.
TS – Gunzburg. 1762-88.
V – Venice (Venetia). 1805-66.
VC-S – Hall. 1774-80.
VS-K – Prague. 1774-80.
VS-S – Prague. 1765-73.
W – Vienna. 1748-63.
W-I – Vienna. 1746-71.

General Hapsburg Central European Monetary Scheme Until 1857

8 heller = 4 pfennig = 1 kreuzer; 120 kreuzer = 2 gulden (florins) = 1 Species or Conventions thaler; 2 Sp. or Conv. thaler = 1 ducat (approximately). Until 1750 the Hapsburg thaler (called "Species thaler" in this catalog) had a gross weight of 28.82 gr. (25.22 gr. fine silver). In 1750 it was reduced to 28.14 gr. gross (23.41 gr. fine silver). In 1753 it was further reduced to 28.06 gr. gross (23.39 gr. fine silver), and under the name "Conventions thaler" was coined from 1753 through 1857.

During the period approximately 1750-65, while the Central European pre-1750 heavier silver coinage of the Hapsburg Empire was being retired from circulation, the largest of these earlier coins were given values in excess of their face values: old 6 kreuzer (= 7 kr.); old 15 kr. (= 17 kr.); old ¼ Sp. thaler (= 34 kr.); old ½ Sp. th. (= 68 kr.); old Sp. th. (= 134 kr.). These arrangements explain the appearance at this time of the 7 and 17 kreuzer "bridge" coins.

Silver coins struck on the 1753 Convention standard (Convention thaler = 1/10 mark of fine silver by weight) were called "Conventionsmünze."

AUSTRIA (OESTERREICH)
Archduchy until 1804, Empire thereafter

Established as the Bavarian East Mark (Ostmark) about 800 A.D. Acquired by the Hapsburgs 1276/82. Rulers adopted title of archduke 1360. The office of Holy Roman Emperor became, in effect, hereditary in the Hapsburg family 1438.

Arms of Austria: Red, a white fesse.
Under Austria itself are listed all Hapsburg coins of standard Austrian types. Here, therefore, are included coins struck at mints in other Hapsburg lands where the only indication of such striking is a letter mint mark or initials. For coins with local designs, coats of arms and legends, see Bohemia, Hungary, etc. which follow the Austrian listing.

Maria Theresia, Archduchess and Queen 1740-80, Empress 1745-80

Copper

VG-F

3 1. H(eller). Austrian arms. Rev. I.H/1761-*63* 3.00

5 1/HEL/LER. Like No. 3. 1765, 68 .... 2.00

5a 1/HELLER. 1777-79 ...... 2.00

6 EIN (=1)/PFENING. Bust. Rev. value/date/w. 1748-50 .... 5.00

7 ¼ (kreuzer). Young bust. ND (1759) .... *Rare*

Note: Former No. 1 has been deleted. *It appears identical with No. 7.*

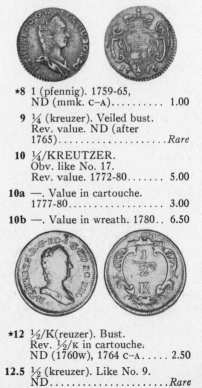

*8 1 (pfennig). 1759-65, ND (mmk. C–A) 1.00

9 ¼ (kreuzer). Veiled bust. Rev. value. ND (after 1765) .... *Rare*

10 ¼/KREUTZER. Obv. like No. 17. Rev. value. 1772-80 ...... 5.00

10a —. Value in cartouche. 1777-80 .... 3.00

10b —. Value in wreath. 1780 .. 6.50

*12 ½/K(reuzer). Bust. Rev. ½/K in cartouche. ND (1760w), 1764 C–A 2.50

12.5 ½ (kreuzer). Like No. 9. ND .... *Rare*

AUSTRIA
(HAPSBURG LANDS)

AUSTRIA (OESTERREICH) Cont.

Billon
VG-F

113 3 (kreuzer). Bust. Rev. Imp. eagle, 3 on breast. 1766-80.. 5.00

114 VII (kreuzer). Sim. but arms of Austria-Lorraine on eagle's breast. 1766-80.......... 9.50

Silver
F-VF

115 10 (kreuzer). Like No. 116. 1765-80................. 8.00

★116 20 (kreuzer). 1765-80...... 5.00

117 30 (kreuzer). Sim. but bust and eagle each in rhombus. 1767-69.....................40.00

118 (½ Convention thaler). Like No. 114. 14.07 gr. 1768A...95.00

119 (Conv. thaler). Sim. 1765-80.....................140.00

119a —. "Ordensthaler." Order ribbon on Emp's breast. 1768-69.................200.00

Gold (ducat = 3.49 gr.)
V.F.

120 ¼ (ducat). Like No. 124. 1765, 77...............180.00

★121 (ducat). Bust. Rev. arms supported. Royal title only. 1764.................450.00

122 (ducat). IOSEPHVS II D.G. ROM REX etc. Bust. Rev. HUNG etc. Cwnd. arms supported. 1765.................450.00

123 (ducat). Like No. 124. 1765-80.................400.00

124 2 (ducats). Bust. Rev. VIRTUTE etc. Imp. eagle, Aust. arms on breast. 1768-80.................500.00

125 3 (ducats). Sim. 1773-78.3000.00

B. Joseph II, Alone 1780-90.

Copper
VG-F

126 ¼/KREUTZER. Head. Rev. value. 1781-90 .... 3.00

VG-F

★127 ½/KREUTZER. 1780-90.. 5.00

128 EIN (=1) /KREUTZER. Sim. 1780-90............ 3.00

Billon

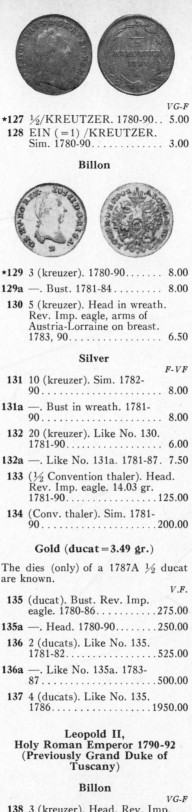

★129 3 (kreuzer). 1780-90...... 8.00

129a —. Bust. 1781-84........ 8.00

130 5 (kreuzer). Head in wreath. Rev. Imp. eagle, arms of Austria-Lorraine on breast. 1783, 90............ 6.50

Silver
F-VF

131 10 (kreuzer). Sim. 1782-90.................... 8.00

131a —. Bust in wreath. 1781-90.................... 8.00

132 20 (kreuzer). Like No. 130. 1781-90................. 6.00

132a —. Like No. 131a. 1781-87. 7.50

133 (½ Convention thaler). Head. Rev. Imp. eagle. 14.03 gr. 1781-90...............125.00

134 (Conv. thaler). Sim. 1781-90....................200.00

Gold (ducat = 3.49 gr.)

The dies (only) of a 1787A ½ ducat are known.
V.F.

135 (ducat). Bust. Rev. Imp. eagle. 1780-86..........275.00

135a —. Head. 1780-90.......250.00

136 2 (ducats). Like No. 135. 1781-82...............525.00

136a —. Like No. 135a. 1783-87.....................500.00

137 4 (ducats). Like No. 135. 1786.................1950.00

Leopold II,
Holy Roman Emperor 1790-92
(Previously Grand Duke of Tuscany)

Billon
VG-F

138 3 (kreuzer). Head. Rev. Imp. eagle, 3 on breast. 1790-92..25.00

Silver
F-VF

139 10 (kreuzer). Like No. 140. 1790-92.................17.50

F-VF

★140 20 (kreuzer). 1790-92......15.00

141 (½ Convention thaler). Head. Rev. Imp. eagle. 14.03 gr. 1790, 92...............225.00

142 (Conv. thaler). "Koenigsthaler." Issued before his election as emp. Head. Rev. arms supported. 1790.............375.00

143 (Conv. thaler). Like No. 141. 1790-92................275.00

Gold
VF-EF

144 (ducat) "Koenigsdukaten." Head. Rev. arms. 1790 .... Rare

145 (ducat). Like No. 141. 1790-92...............Rare

The dies (only) for a 2 ducats 1790A are known.

146 4 (ducats). Bust. Rev. Imp. eagle. 1790...............RR

Franz II (I) 1792-1835
A. As Franz II, Holy Roman Emperor 1792-1804.

Copper
VG-F

147 ¼ (kreuzer). FRANC. II etc. Imp. eagle. Rev. ¼. 1800.. 5.00

148 ½ (kreuzer). Like No. 149. 1800.................. 1.50

★149 1 (kreuzer). 1800.......... 1.00

150 3 (kreuzer). Sim. 17 gr. 1799 .... 9.00

150a —. 8-9 gr. 1800-03....... 2.50

★151 6/SECHS KREUTZER. Sim. but German legends. 1800, 03................ 6.50

Silver (or Billon)

152 3 (kreuzer). Head. Rev. Imp. eagle, 3 on breast. 1792-1801..................25.00

153 6/KREUTZER. Imp. eagle. Rev. Value. 1795 .... 8.00

• 31 •

AUSTRIA
(HAPSBURG LANDS)

....

AUSTRIA (OESTERREICH) Cont.

VG-F

154 7 (kreuzer). 1802......... 6.00
155 10 (kreuzer). Head in wreath. Rev. Imp. eagle. 1792-97...10.00
156 12/KREUTZER. Like No. 153. 1795..............10.00
157 20 (kreuzer). Like No. 155. 1792-1804.............. 5.00
158 24/KREUTZER. FRANZ II etc. Imp. eagle. Rev. value/ ERBLAENDISCH/1800......85.00

Silver
F-VF

159 (½ Convention thaler). Head. Rev. Imp. eagle. 1793-1804............160.00
160 (Conv. thaler) "Koenigsthaler." Head. Rev. arms supported. 1792A................600.00
161 (Conv. thaler). Like No. 159. 1792-1804..............160.00

Gold

The ½ ducat 1796E is a pattern.
VF-EF

162 (ducat) "Koenigsdukaten." Head. Rev. arms. 1792A .1100.00
163 (ducat). Head. Rev. Imp. eagle. 1792-1804........250.00
164 2 (ducats). Sim. 1799....2000.00
165 4 (ducats). Bust. Rev. Imp. eagle. 1793-1804.......1000.00

B. As Franz II, Holy Roman and Hereditary Austrian Emperor, 1804-06.

Silver

F-VF

166 20 (kreuzer). 1804-06...... 6.00
167 (½ Convention thaler). Head. Rev. Imp. eagle. 14.03 gr. 1804-06.................85.00
168 (Conv. thaler). Sim. 1804-06..................120.00

Gold
VF-EF

169 (ducat). Sim. 1804-06.....135.00
170 4 (ducats). Bust. Rev. Imp. eagle. 1804-06..........600.00

C. As Franz I, Emperor of Austria, 1806-35.

Copper
VG-F

171 ¼ (kreuzer). Obv. like No. 173. Rev. ¼. 1812....... 5.00

172 ½/KREUZER. 1812...... 3.00

173 1/KREUTZER. 1812..... 2.50
174 3/KREUTZER. Sim. 1812. 3.00

175 ¼/KREUTZER. 1816...... 2.50
176 ½/KREUTZER. Sim. 1816.. 1.50
177 EIN (=1) /KREUZER. Sim. 1816.................1.50
178 15 KREUTZER. Head in pearl border. Rev. Imp. eagle in same. 1807............. 5.00
179 30 KREUTZER. Head in pearl rhombus. Rev. Imp. eagle in same. 1807........ 6.50

Silver (or Billon)
F-VF

180 3 (kreuzer). Head. Rev. Imp. eagle, 3 on breast. 1814-15 .10.00
180a —. Rev. legend ends REX AA. 1817-24...............10.00
180b —. Short hair. 1825-30..... 5.00
180c —. Struck in collar. 1831-35.................. 9.50
181 5 (kreuzer). Like No. 181a but Rev. leg. ends FR:D. 1815..10.00

181a —. 1817-24..............10.00
181b —. Short hair. 1825-30.....10.00
181c —. Like No. 183d (var.). 1832-35..................14.00
182 10 (kreuzer). Like No. 183. 1809-10.................. 8.00
182a —. Like No. 181. 1814-15..10.00
182b —. Like No. 181a. 1817-24.12.00
182c —. Short hair. 1825-30....12.00

F-VF
182d —. Like No. 183d (var.). 1831-35.................14.00

183 20 (kreuzer). 1806-10, 14... 6.00
183a —. Like No. 181. 1811-16.. 5.00
183b —. Like No. 181a. 1817-24. 3.00
183c —. Short hair. 1825-30.... 3.00

183d —. 1831-35............. 3.00

Note: The Austrian type M(ilan) and V(enice) mint coinage of this period was current in Austrian Italy at 20 kreuzer = 20 soldi = 1 lira.

Silver

184 (½ Convention thaler). Head. Rev. Imp. eagle, leg. ends WIRC. 14.03 gr. 1807-10...160.00
184a —. Rev. leg. ends FR:DVX. 1811-15.................80.00
184b —. Rev. leg. ends REX AA. 1817-24.................90.00
184c —. Short hair. 1825-30.....90.00
184d —. Like No. 183d. 1831-35.................90.00
185 (Conv. thaler). Like No. 184. 1806-10.................160.00
185a —. Like No. 184a. 1811-15.55.00
185b —. Like No. 184b. 1817-24..................70.00
185c —. Like No. 184c. 1824-30.90.00
185d —. Like No. 184d. 1831-35.90.00

See ITALY (Lombardy-Venetia) for similar coins from A, M and V mints with arms of L-V on eagle's breast.

Gold
VF-EF

186 (ducat). Like No. 184. 1806-10..................400.00
186a —. Like No. 184a. 1811-15.225.00
186b —. Like No. 184b. 1816-24.225.00
186c —. Like No. 184c. 1825-30.225.00
186d —. Like No. 184d. 1831-35.225.00
187 4 (ducats). Bust. Rev. Imp. eagle, leg. ends WIRC. 1807-10..................1200.00
187a —. Rev. leg. ends FR:D: 1811-15.................1200.00

AUSTRIA
(HAPSBURG LANDS)

AUSTRIA (OESTERREICH) Cont.

VF-EF

187b —. Rev. leg. ends REX AA.
1816-30..............1200.00

See Burgau and Hungary (following AUSTRIA), and ITALY, LOW COUNTRIES (Austrian Netherlands) and POLAND, for other coins of this reign.

Ferdinand 1835-48

A. Obv. legend ends IMPERATOR.

Silver (or Billon)

F-VF

188 3 (kreuzer). Like No. 189a but 3 on eagle's breast.
1835-36.................16.50

189 5 (kreuzer). Like No. 189a.
1835-36.................16.50

190 10 (kreuzer). Sim.
1835-36.................14.00

191 20 (kreuzer). Sim.
1835-36................. 8.75

Silver

192 (½ Convention thaler).
Sim. 14.03 gr. 1835-36....160.00

193 (Conv. thaler). Sim.
1835-36................550.00

Gold

VF-EF

194 (ducat). Sim. 1835-36....190.00

B. Obv. legend ends H.N.V.

Silver (or Billon)

F-VF

188a 3 (kreuzer). Like No. 188.
1837-48................. 6.00

★189a 5 (kreuzer). 1837-48...... 8.50

190a 10 (kreuzer). Sim.
1837-48...............11.00

191a 20 (kreuzer). Sim.
1837-48................ 6.00

Silver

192a (½ Convention thaler). Sim.
14.03 gr. 1837-48.......40.00

193a (Conv. thaler). Sim.
1837-48................75.00

Gold

VF-EF

194a (ducat). Sim. 1837-48...135.00

VF-EF

★195 4 (ducats). Bust ★.
Rev. sim. 1837-48......1000.00

C. With mint mark GM. Struck by Austrian garrison during siege of Mantua.

Silver (or Billon)

F-VF

188b (ex 188a) 3 (kreuzer). Like No. 188a. 1848 GM.....Rare

191b (ex 191a) 20 (kreuzer). Like No. 189a. 1848 GM.....125.00

Silver

192b (ex 192a) (½ Conv. thaler).
Sim. 1848 GM.........300.00

For other coins of this reign see Hungary (following AUSTRIA) and ITALY (Lombardy-Venetia).

Franz Joseph 1848-1916

Period prior to the German Monetary Agreement of 1857.

Copper

Fine

196 2/KREUZER. Like No. 175.
1848...................12.50

197 ¼/KREUZER. Like No. 198.
1851................... 2.00

★198 ½/KREUZER. 1851...... 2.00

199 1/KREUZER. Sim. 1851.. 2.00

200 2/KREUZER. Sim. 1851.. 8.00

201 3/KREUZER. Sim. 1851..15.00

Billon

202 6/KREUZER. Like No. 175.
1848...................3.00

★202a —. 1849.............. 3.00

Silver

VF-EF

203 20 (kreuzer). Like No. 207 but head l. 1852.............60.00

204 (½ Convention thaler). Sim.
14.03 gr. 1848-51........900.00

205 (Conv. thaler). Sim. 1848-51.....................1000.00

205a —. 1852.............1200.00

206 10 (kreuzer). Like No. 207.
1852-55................20.00

★207 20 (kreuzer). 1852-56.....13.50

208 (½ Convention thaler).
Sim. 14.03 gr. 1852-56....120.00

209 (Conv. thaler). Sim. 1852-56.....................140.00

210 EIN (=1) GULDEN (on edge). Busts of Franz Joseph and Elizabeth. Rev. their wedding. 1854 R.N.......55.00

211 ZWEI (=2) GULDEN (on edge). Sim. 1854 R.N.....120.00

Gold

212 (ducat). Like No. 207.
3.49 gr. 1852-59.........95.00

213 4 (ducats). Sim. but robed bust r. 1854-59.....850.00

BOHEMIA (CECHY), Kingdom

Now the dominant portion of Czechoslovakia. First coins 10th century. Kingdom acquired by the Hapsburgs in 1526 and ruled by them from that date until 1918 (except for the periods 1619-20 and 1741-42).

Arms: Red, 2 tailed silver lion, rampant.

Monetary System:

Generally as Austria, except for local names and the greschl. 12 haler (pfennig) = 4 gresle (greschl) = 3 krejcaru (kreuzer) = 1 gros (groschen); 60 krejcaru = 1 zlaty (florin or gulden).

A temporary by-product in Bohemia of the 7 and 17 kreuzer bridge coin transition phase mentioned under Austria (Monetary Scheme) appears to have been the following system (circa 1765): 112 krejcaru = 2 zlaty = 1 tolar (Conventions thaler).

Maria Theresia 1740-80

Copper

VG-F

1 1 P(fennig). Lion l., no legend.
Rev. I. P./1758............ 8.00

2 EIN (=1) /GRESCHL. Arms cwnd., lion and 2 eagles, each in oval. Rev. value. 17.5mm.
1759...................10.00

2a —. 23-24mm. 1760-68..... 5.00

AUSTRIA
(HAPSBURG LANDS)

....

BOHEMIA, Kingdom, (Cont.)

Billon
VG-F

3 (½ kreuzer). M.T.D.R.H.B., lion shield. Rev. blank. 14mm. 1743-46.................. 6.50

4 ½ (kreuzer). Sim. but w/out legend. 1745-59............... 6.50

5 1 (kreuzer). Bust. Rev. 4 fold arms, lion centershield. 1744 . 10.00

★5a —. Rev. Imp. eagle, lion shield on breast. 1755-63.......... 6.50

5b —. 1757 **in pewter. Struck by Austrian defenders during siege of Prague**...........35.00

6 3 (kreuzer). Like No. 5. 1743, 45.................. 6.50

6a —. Like No. 5a. 1746-65.... 6.50

6b —. 1757 **in pewter. Siege of Prague**.................35.00

6c —. Like No. 5a but veiled bust. 1776-79.................. 8.00

7 VI (kreuzer). Like No. 5. 1743-44.................12.00

7a —. Like No. 5a. 1746-47....12.00

8 VII (kreuzer). Like No. 5a. 1754.................12.00

Silver

Fine
★9 10 (kreuzer). 1758-65....... 5.00

9a —. 1757 **in pewter**........25.00

9b —. Like No. 9 but bust veiled. 1777-80.................. 4.50

10 XV (kreuzer). Like No. 5. 1743-45.................17.50

10a —. Like No. 5a. 1747-52....17.50

11 XVII (kreuzer). Sim. 1751-55, 61-63.................20.00

12 20 (kreuzer). Like No. 9. 1754-65.................. 5.00

12a —. 1757 **in pewter**.......20.00

★12b —. 1768-80.............. 5.00

F-VF
13 (¼ Species thaler). Like No. 5. 1744...................110.00

14 (¼ Convention thaler). Like No. 5a. 1754, 59..........85.00

15 30 (kreuzer). Like No. 5a but bust and eagle each in rhombus. 1758-65.................40.00

15a —. 1765 w/out "30"......50.00

16 (½ Species thaler). Like No. 5. 14.4 gr. 1743-45...........65.00

17 (½ Convention thaler). Like No. 5a. 14 gr. 1751-65.....40.00

17a —. 1754 **in pewter** (struck 1757).............75.00

18 (Species thaler). Like No. 5a but manifold arms. 1746-50.................140.00

19 (Conv. thaler). Sim. 1751-61.................80.00

20 (Conv. Mining thaler). Bust. Rev. S. IOACHIMSTHALER etc. Imp. eagle, St. Joachim and Boh. lion on breast. 1758-59.................250.00

21 (Conv. thaler). Veiled bust. Rev. Imp. eagle. (Like AUSTRIA No. 50 but arms on eagle's breast include Moravia and Silesia.) *1769*-73 EvS-AS and 74-75 EvS-IK.............65.00

Gold

V.F.
★22 (ducat). Queen stdg. Rev. 4 fold arms, lion centershield. 1743-45.................425.00

23 (ducat). Like No. 5a. 1747-65.................400.00

23a —. Bust veiled. 1769-80...350.00

See Austria for regular Austrian type coins struck at Prague Mint during this and all succeeding reigns through 1857.

Joseph II, Emperor 1765-90, Alone 1780-90

Copper

VG-F
★25 EIN (=1) /GROESCHL. 1781-82A.................10.00

So ends the distinctive local coinage of Bohemia.

BURGAU, County
(Later Margraviate)

Near Ulm, Germany, on the Bavarian-Württemberg border. To Austria 1618-1805, then to Bavaria. Mint: Günzburg.

Monetary System:
20 Conv. kreuzer =
24 kreuzer Landmünze.

Maria Theresia 1740-80
I. Special Issue for Burgau.

Copper
VG-F

1 1/HELLER. Arms of Austria-Burgau. Rev. Value. 1768, 72-80.................. 5.00

2 ¼/KREUTZER. Sim. but with obv. legend. 1772-78... 5.00

3 ½/KREUTZER. Sim. Value in cartouche. 1772.......... 3.00

★4 EIN (=1) /KREUTZER. Sim. 1772-74, 79.......... 3.00

Silver (or Billon)

F-VF
★5 48/EIN (=1/48) CONVEN./ THALER (=2½ kreuzer). 1772-74.................35.00

6 (Conv. thaler.) Arms. Rev. ARCHID ... MARGGR. BURGAVIAE. AD/NORMAM etc. in wreath. 1766-67.................40.00

II. Austrian Type Coins with Burgau Arms.

Silver
Fine

8 5 (Conv. kreuzer). *Like No. 12. 1750-75*.................17.50

10 10 (Conv. kreuzer). *Sim. 1772-77*.................12.50

12 20 (Conv. kreuzer). Like Austria No. 39b but Burgau arms on eagle's breast. *1772, 73, 74-80*.................12.50

14 (Conv. thaler). Like Austria No. 50 but Burgau arms in lower right on eagle's breast. 1765-80.................70.00

See AUSTRIA for regular Austrian issues struck at Günzburg.

AUSTRIA
(HAPSBURG LANDS)

FURTHER AUSTRIA (VORDEROESTERREICH)

Name given to the combined Hapsburg provinces in South Swabia (Burgau, Freiburg im Breisgau, Breisach, etc.) Divided between Bavaria and Baden 1805.

Mints: Günzburg – H; Hall – F.

Joseph II, Alone 1780-90

Copper

VG-F

1 1/HELLER. Like Burgau No. 1. 1783-90............ 5.00
2 ¼/KREUTZER. Like Burgau No. 2 but IOS II etc. 1783-90............ 3.00
3 ½/KREUTZER. Like Burgau No. 3 but IOS. II etc. 1784, 89................. 6.00
4 EIN (=1) /KREUTZER. Like Burgau No. 4 but IOS. II etc. 1783-89................. 5.00

Billon

5 III/KREUTZER. 3 shields. Rev. VORD–OEST. etc. Value. 1786-87................. 8.00
6 VI/KREUTZER. Sim. 1786-87................. 12.00

Leopold II 1790-92

Copper

7 1/HELLER. Like No. 1. 1791-92................. 6.50
8 ½/KREUTZER. Like No. 3 but LEOP. II. 1791-92....... 8.00
9 EIN (=1) /KREUTZER. Like No. 4 but LEOP. II. 1791-92................. 10.00

Billon

10 III/KREUTZER. Like No. 5. 1791-92................. 10.00
11 VI/KREUTZER. Sim. 1792................. 14.00

Franz II, in Further Austria 1792-1805

Copper

12 1/HELLER. Like No. 1. 1793-1803................. 5.00
13 ¼/KREUTZER. Like No. 15 but w/out cartouche. 1792-1803................. 5.00
14 ½/KREUTZER. Like No. 15. 1792-1804................. 6.50
14a —. 1805................. 9.00

*15 EIN (=1) /KREUTZER. 1792-1804................. 5.00
15a —. FRANC. II D.G. ROM. etc. 1804-05................. 6.50

Billon

VG-F

16 III/KREUTZER. Like No. 5. 1793-1804................. 8.00
17 VI/KREUTZER. Sim. 1793-1805................. 10.00

GALICIA. See POLAND.

GÖRZ. See ITALY (Gorizia).

HUNGARY, Kingdom

During the years covered by this catalog, Hungary was much larger than it is now. It included Slovakia and parts of present-day Yugoslavia and Rumania. Except for several brief revolutionary periods, Hungary was ruled by the Hapsburgs 1527-1918.

Arms: Barry of 8, red and gold or red and silver.

Monetary System:
5 denare = 3 krajcar (kreuzer) = 2 poltura;
60 krajcar = 1 forint (gulden);
2 forint = 1 Species or Convention thaler.

Maria Theresia 1740-80

Copper

VG-F

1 (½ denar). Hung. arms. Rev. Madonna. 20mm. 1763-67... 5.00

*2 (denar). Sim. 22mm. 1760-67................. 2.50
3 POLTURA. Bust. Rev. Madonna. 1759, 61.........Rare

*4 POLTURA. Bust. Rev. Madonna. 1763, 65........... 8.00
4a —. Veiled bust. 1775....... 14.00

Billon

6 ½ (krajcar). N.D......... ——
8 (denar). Like No. 1. 1746-47, 50-60................. 5.00

VG-F

*9 1 (krajczar). Bust. Rev. Madonna. 1740-60............ 6.50

*11 POLTURA. (var.). 1747-61................. 6.00
13 3 (krajczar). Like No. 9. 1747-65................. 5.00
13a —. Veiled bust. 1766-79..... 5.00
15 10 (denare). Bust. Rev. Madonna. 1741-45...........25.00
17 VI (krajczar). Like No. 20. 1747................10.00
18 VII (krajczar). Sim. 1751-65................12.00

Silver

F-VF

*19 10 (krajczar). Unveiled bust in wreath. Rev. Madonna. 1755-65................. 6.50
19a —. Bust veiled. 1769....... 6.50

*20 XV (krajczar). 1742-50..... 8.50
21 XVII (krajczar). Sim. 1751-65................10.00
22 20 (krajczar). Like No. 19. 1755-65................. 5.50
22a —. Like No. 19a. 1766-80... 5.50
23 30 (krajczar). Bust. Rev. Madonna. 1742..............30.00

*24 30 (krajczar). Bust in rhombus. Rev. Madonna in rhombus. 1748-65.................22.50
24a —. Bust veiled. 1767-76....22.50

AUSTRIA
(HAPSBURG LANDS)

HUNGARY (Cont.)

F-VF

25 (½ Species thaler). Bust. Rev. stdg. Madonna. 14.4 gr. 1741-51 . . . . .37.50

26 (½ Convention thaler). Sim. 14 gr. 1753-65 . . . . .37.50

27 (½ Conv. thaler). Arms. Rev. Madonna. 1767-80 . . . . .37.50

28 (Species thaler). Like No. 25. 1741-52 . . . . .55.00

29 (Conv. thaler). Sim. but X after date. 1751-65 (var.) . . .55.00

30 (Conv. thaler). Like No. 27. 1767-80 . . . . .45.00

Gold (ducat = 3.49 gr.)

V.F.

31 ⅛ (ducat). Bust. Rev. Imp. eagle. 1761 N-B 120.00

32 ⅙ (ducat). Sim. 1752 N-B .140.00

33 (¼ ducat). Bust. Rev. Madonna. 1752, 55 . . . . .175.00

★34 (ducat). Queen stdg. Rev. Madonna. 1741-65 . . . . .350.00

35 (ducat). Bust. Rev. Madonna. 1743-65 . . . . .300.00

35a —. Veiled bust. 1766-80 . . . .275.00

36 2 (ducats). Like No. 34. 1763-65 . . . . .600.00

Franz I, Holy Roman Emperor 1745-65

Billon
Fine

42 POLTURA. Bust. Rev. Imp. eagle, arms of Lorraine-Tuscany on breast. 1748 K-B 8.50

Joseph II, Alone 1780-90

Note: *Two varieties of copper denars dated 1788A are patterns.*

Silver
F-VF

45 (½ Convention thaler). Arms. Rev. Madonna. 14 gr. var. 1782-90 . . . . .17.50

46 (Conv. thaler). Sim. var. 1781-89 . . . . .32.50

Gold
V.F.

47 (ducat). Emp. stdg. Rev. Madonna. 1781-85 . . . . .225.00

48 2 (ducats). Sim. 1781-85 . . .650.00

Leopold II 1790-92

Silver
F-VF

50 (½ Convention thaler). LEOP. II D. G.R.I. etc. Rev. Madonna. 14 gr. 1790-92 . . . . .175.00

51 (Conv. thaler). Sim. but LEOP. II D.G.HV. etc. 1790 . . . . . . .350.00

51a —. Like No. 50. 1790-91 . . .275.00

Gold
VF-EF

52 (ducat). King stdg. Rev. Madonna. 1790 . . . . .550.00

52a —. 1791-92 . . . . .375.00

Franz II 1792-1835

A. As Holy Roman Emperor 1792-1806.

Silver
F-VF

53 (½ Conv. thaler). Like No. 50 but FRANC. II etc. 1792-94 . .220.00

54 (Conv. thaler). Sim. but FRANC. II D.G.HV. etc. 1792 . . .700.00

54a —. Sim. but FRANC. II D.G.R. IMP. etc. 1792 . . . . .900.00

Gold
VF-EF

55 (ducat). FRANC II. etc. King stdg. Rev. Madonna. 1792-99 . . . . .210.00

B. As Austrian Emperor 1804-35.

Silver
Fine

56 20 (krajczar). Head. Rev. Madonna. 1830 . . . . . . .30.00

56a —. Struck in collar. 1833-35 . . . . 6.50

V.F.

57 (½ Conv. thaler). Sim. 14 gr. 1830 . . . . .135.00

57a —. Struck in collar. 1831-35 . . . . .135.00

58 (Conv. thaler). Sim. 1830 .240.00

★58a —. Struck in collar. *V.F.* 1830-33 . . . . .425.00

Gold
VF-EF

59 (ducat). Emp. stdg. Rev. Madonna. 1830-35 . . . .200.00

Ferdinand, King 1830-48, Emperor 1835-48

Silver
V.F.

60 10 (krajczar). Like No. 61. 1837-48 . . . . 9.00

★61 20 (krajczar). 1837-48 . . . . . . 7.00

62 (½ Conv. thaler). Sim. 14 gr. 1837, 39 . . . . .240.00

63 (Conv. thaler). Sim. 1837, 39 .450.00

Gold

VF-EF

★64 (ducat). Emp. stdg. Rev. Madonna. 1837-48 . . . . . . .190.00

Hungarian Revolution 1848-49

Copper
VG-F

65 EGY (=1)/KRAJCZAR. Like No. 67. 1848-49 . . . . . . 2.50

66 HAROM (=3)/KRAJCZAR. Sim. 1849 . . . . 4.50

Billon

V.G.

★67 HAT (=6)/KRAJCZAR. 1849 . . . . 5.00

Silver
F-VF

68 10 (krajczar). Like No. 69. 1848 . . . . .12.50

AUSTRIA
(HAPSBURG LANDS)

HUNGARY (Cont.)

F-VF

*69 20 (krajczar). 1848........ 8.00

Gold
VF-EF

70 (ducat). Like No. 64 but
Magyar legends. 1848.....225.00

LOMBARDY-VENETIA and
MILAN. See ITALY.

STYRIA (STEYERMARK),
Duchy

In south central Austria. Ruled by
members of the Austrian ruling family
from 1186 onward.

Arms: Green, silver panther rampant.

Mint: Graz, closed 1772.

Maria Theresia 1740-80

Silver (or Billon)
VG-F

1 (½ kreuzer) M(aria) T(heresia).
Panther shield. Rev. Blank.
14mm. 1741-42........... 8.00

2 ½ (kreuzer). 1744-45....... 8.00

3 ½ (kreuzer). 3 oval shields including Imp. eagle and panther.
Rev. Blank. 1740, 47-49....12.00

4 1 (kreuzer). Bust. Rev. 4 fold
arms, panther centershield.
1743-45.................. 8.00

*4a —. Rev. Imp. eagle, panther
shield on breast. 1747-58,
63...................... 6.50

5 3 (kreuzer). Like No. 4.
1742-45.................. 8.00

5a —. Like No. 4a. 1749-55.... 6.50

6 VI (kreuzer). Like No. 4.
1743-45.................12.00

6a —. Like No. 4a. 1747......10.00

7 VII (kreuzer). Like No. 4a.
1751...................10.00

VG-F

*8 10 (kreuzer). 1754-65....... 6.50

Silver
F-VF

9 XV (kreuzer). Like No. 4.
1742.....................22.50

9a —. Like No. 4a. 1748-50....16.50

10 XVII (kreuzer). Like No. 4a.
1752-65.................20.00

11 20 (kreuzer). Like No. 8.
1754-65.................. 7.50

11a —. Bust veiled. 1767-72.... 7.50

12 30 (kreuzer). Like No. 4 but
bust and arms each in rhombus.
1744-45.................35.00

12a —. Like No. 4a but each side
in rhombus. 1746-48.......32.50

13 (½ Species thaler). Like No. 4a.
14.4 gr. 1749-50...........85.00

14 (½ Conv. thaler). Sim. 14 gr.
1751-54.................85.00

15 (Species thaler). Sim. 1749-
50.....................225.00

16 (Conv. thaler). Sim. 1751-
54.....................180.00

16a —. 1765.................135.00

Gold
V.F.

17 (ducat). Like No. 4. 1743-
45.....................375.00

18 (ducat). Like No. 4a but 4 fold
arms, panther centershield on
eagle's breast. 1747-65.....300.00

18a —. Bust veiled. 1768-69....300.00

TRANSYLVANIA
(SIEBENBÜRGEN), Principality

In N.W. Rumania. Subordinate to Hungary 1003-1526, independent 1526-1699,
1704-11. To Austria 1699-1918.

Arms: 7 towers on gold field.

Monetary System:
3 pfennig = 1 greschl;
2 greschl = 1½ kreuzer = 1 poltura;
otherwise same as Hungary.

Maria Theresia 1740-80

Copper

Note: Former Nos. 1 and 2 are identical to Austria No. 8.

VG-F

*3 EIN (=1) /GRESCHL.
1763-65................ 8.00

Billon

*4 1 (kreuzer). 1762..........12.00

*5 POLTURA. 1747..........17.50

6 3 (kreuzer). Young bust.
Rev. 5 fold arms w/Transylvanian
arms in center shield. 1745...17.50

7 3 (kreuzer). Like No. 4.
1762, 65.................14.00

*8 (ex 7a) 3 (kreuzer). 1774-80..14.00

9 VII (kreuzer). Like No. 4.
1762-65.................22.00

Silver
Fine

11 10 (kreuzer). Like No. 15.
1765-66.................12.50

12 (ex 11a) 10 (kreuzer). Like
No. 16. 1776, 80..........11.50

*13 XV (kreuzer). 1748-50.....27.50

14 XVII (kreuzer). Like No. 4.
30mm. 1751, 63..........32.50

14a —. 27mm. 1763-65.......27.50

AUSTRIA
(HAPSBURG LANDS)

TRANSYLVANIA (Cont.)

Fine

★15 (ex 16) 20 (kreuzer).
1755, 65 . . . . 25.00

15a —. Legends changed.
1764 . . . . 27.50

★16 (ex 16a) 20 (kreuzer).
1767-80 . . . . 25.00

F-VF

★17 30 (kreuzer). 1744 . . . . 65.00

★18 (ex 17a, b) 30 (kreuzer).
1754, 65 . . . . 50.00

19 (ex 20) (½ Speciesthaler).
Like No. 6. 14.4 gr.
1742-44 . . . . 135.00

20 (ex 19a) (½ Speciesthaler).
Like No. 13. 1748-49 . . . . . . 150.00

20a (ex 19) —. 1740. Mule 175.00

F-VF

★21 (½ Convention thaler).
14 gr. 1752-65 . . . . 120.00

22 (Species thaler). Like No. 19.
1742-45 (var.) 225.00

23 (Species thaler). Like No. 21.
1747-50 . . . . 180.00

24 (Conv. thaler). Sim.
1751-65 . . . . 180.00

Gold (ducat = 3.49 gr.)

A. Young bust 1741-45.

V.F.

★29 ¼ (ducat). Bust.
Rev. Trans. arms. ND 175.00

32 (ducat). Like No. 6.
1741-42 . . . . 450.00

32a —. Smaller bust. 1743-45 . . 450.00

B. Mature bust 1746-65.

27 ⅛ *(ducat). Like No. 4.*
1749 . . . . *Rare*

30 ¼ (ducat). Like No. 4.
1749 . . . . 190.00

31 ½ (ducat). Sim. 1756-65.
The 1762 has the ⚒ lying
down 275.00

33 (ducat). Sim. 1746-65 . . . . . 400.00

34 2 (ducats). Sim.
1754, 64-65 . . . . 750.00

35 (4 ducats). Sim. 1764-65 . . 1950.00

36 (5 ducats). Sim. 1765 . . . . . 2500.00

C. Arms/Value.

★26 1/16 (ducat). 1778 . . . . 180.00

28 ⅛ (ducat). Sim. 1778 . . . . . 190.00

D. Veiled bust 1765-80.

30a ¼ (ducat). Like No. 33a.
1768-80 . . . . 175.00

31a ½ (ducat). Sim. 1770-80 . . 250.00

V.F.

★33a (ducat). 1765-80 . . . . 375.00

34a 2 (ducats). Sim. 1767-80 . . 750.00

35a 4 (ducats). Sim. 1778-79 . 1950.00

Special Series of Multiple Ducats

Struck with dies of silver coins. Thickness varies to provide proper weight.

(ducat = 3.49 gr.)

A. No. 19 in gold.

38 (ex 42) (5 ducats). 1742 . . . . . . RR

B. No. 22 in gold.

40 (ex 47) (6 ducats).
1743, 45 . . . . RR

41 (ex 54) (10 ducats).
1742-43 . . . . RR

C. No. 23 in gold.

43 (5 ducats). 1750 . . . . RR

44 (ex 49) (6 ducats). 1747 . . . . . RR

45 (ex 55) (10 ducats). 1750 . . . . RR

D. No. 21 in gold.

47 (ex 37) (3 ducats).
1754-61 . . . . RR

48 (ex 39) (4 ducats). 1760 . . . . . RR

49 (ex 44) (5 ducats).
1754-60 . . . . RR

50 *(6 ducats). 1750* . . . . RR

E. No. 24 in gold.

52 (ex 40) (4 ducats).
1759-62 . . . . RR

53 (ex 45) (5 ducats). 1765 . . . . . RR

54 (ex 51) (6 ducats). 1759 . . . . . RR

55 (ex 52) (7 ducats). 1759 . . . . . RR

56 (10 ducats). 1754-61 . . . . RR

Franz I, Holy Roman Emperor 1745-65

Note: The Transylvanian copper coinage struck in the name of Emperor Franz I (former Nos. 57 and 58) is identical with Austria Nos. 73 and 76. Austria continued to strike coins of regular Austrian types at Carlsburg (E) 1765-1867.

AUSTRIA
(HAPSBURG LANDS)

TYROL (TIROL),
Princely County

In Austria between Germany and Italy. Acquired by the Hapsburgs 1363. Frequently ruled by younger members of the family until 1665. The world's first dollar sized silver coin was struck at Hall, Tyrol, in 1484.

The Tyrol was occupied by Bavaria 1805-14.

Arms: Silver, a cwnd. red eagle with head in wreath.

Maria Theresia 1740-80

Billon

VG-F

1 QUADRANS/NOVVS/TIROLIS (= ¼ kreuzer). Eagle. Rev. value. 1742-47 .... 6.50

2 ¼ (kreuzer). Imp. eagle, Tyrol eagle on breast. Rev. blank. 1748-49 .... 12.00

4 ¼ (kreuzer). Tyrol eagle. Rev. ¼. *1750-59* 14.00

*6 1 (kreuzer). Bust. Rev. Tyrol eagle in cartouche. 1742-46 .. 20.00

8 1 (kreuzer). Bust. Rev. Imp. eagle, Tyrol eagle on breast. *1746-60* 12.00

10 3 (kreuzer). Bust. Rev. 4 fold arms, eagle centershield. 1745 .... 8.00

11 3 (kreuzer). Like No. 8. 1748-55 .... 6.50

11a —. Bust veiled. 1774 ...... 6.50

12 5 (kreuzer). Like No. 20a. 1778 .... 8.00

13 VI (kreuzer)Like No. 10. 1742-45 .... 13.50

14 *VI (kreuzer). Like No. 8. 1746-50* 13.50

16 VII (kreuzer). Like No. 8. 1751-54, 60-63 .... 14.00

Silver

F-VF

18 *1/12 (thaler). Bust. Rev. Arms.* 1741 .... 35.00

20 10 (kreuzer). Like No. 20a but unveiled bust. 1754-65 ...... 9.00

*20a —. 1770-80 .... 7.00

F-VF

22 XV (kreuzer). Like No. 10. 1744 .... 16.00

23 XV (kreuzer). Like No. 8. 1748-50 .... 14.50

24 XVII (kreuzer). Sim. 1751-63 .... 20.00

26 20 (kreuzer). Like No. 20. 1754-65 .... 6.00

26a —. Like No. 20a. 1768-80 ... 6.00

27 ¼ (thaler). Like No. 10. 1742-45 .... 35.00

29 30 (kreuzer). Like No. 36 but each side in rhombus. 1748-52, 60 .... 32.50

30 (½ Convention thaler). Bust. Rev. Imp. eagle, 20 fold arms with Tyrol centershield on breast. 14 gr. 1756-65 ...... 60.00

31 (½ Conv. thaler). Veiled bust. Rev. Imp. eagle, 4 fold arms (eagle lower right) on breast. 1767-73 A-S, 74-77 VC-S 55.00

32 (Species thaler). Like No. 30. 28.8 gr. 1746 .... 225.00

32a —. 28.1 gr. 1749-50 ...... 125.00

33 (Convention thaler). Sim. 1751-65. (var.) 125.00

34 (Conv. thaler). Like No. 31. 1765F, 65-74 A-S, 68S, 74-76 VC-S 115.00

Gold

V.F.

35 (ducat). Like No. 10. 1741-44 .... 300.00

*36 (ducat). 1746-64 .... 275.00

37 (ducat). Veiled bust. Rev. Imp. eagle, Tyrol arms on breast. 1768-79 .... 275.00

38 *2 (ducats). Like No. 10.* 1746 .... RR

Note: Austria continued to strike coins of regular Austrian types at Hall (F) until 1807.

Rebellion against Bavaria 1809.
Andreas Hofer

Copper

Fine

41 EIN (=1) /KREUZER. Like No. 42. 1809 .... 14.00

Silver

Fine

*42 20/KREUZER. 1809......30.00

AUSTRIA-HUNGARY
(STATES IN)

AUERSPERG, Princes

Estates in Austrian Carniola, Silesia and Swabia. Raised to princely rank 1653, made dukes of Münsterberg (Silesia) 1654. Sold Münsterberg to Prussia 1791.

Heinrich 1713-83

Silver

VF-EF

1 (Convention thaler). HENRICVS S.R.I. PRINCEPS AVRSPERG etc. Bust. Rev. Arms. 1762.....350.00

Gold

E.F.

2 (ducat). Sim. 1762.......800.00

Wilhelm 1800-22

Silver

VF-EF

*3 (Convention thaler). WILHELMVS S.R.I. PR. AVERSPERG etc. Head. Rev. Arms. 1805.........275.00

AUSTRIA-HUNGARY
(STATES IN)

BATTHYANI, Princes

A noble Hungarian family elevated to princely rank in 1764 (given the mint right 1763). Lands in Austria, Styria and Bohemia.

Carl 1764-72

Silver
VF-EF

1 (½ Convention thaler). CAROL S.R.I. PRINC. DE BATTYAN etc. Bust. Rev. arms. 14 gr. 1764-65.....................100.00

1a —. 1770................100.00

2 (Conv. thaler). Sim. 1764..250.00

2a —. 1768.................300.00

Gold (ducat = 3.49 gr.)
E.F.

3 (ducat). Sim. 1764-65, 70..225.00

4 V (ducats). Sim. 1764.....900.00

5 (10 ducat). Sim. 1764.......*Rare*

Ludwig 1788-1806

Silver
VF-EF

6 20 (kreuzer). LVDOVICVS S.R.I. PRINCEPS DE BATTYAN. etc. Bust. Rev. arms. 1790.....37.50

★7 (½ Conv. thaler). Sim. 1789....................100.00

8 (Conv. thaler). Sim. 1788..325.00

Gold
E.F.

9 (ducat). Sim. 1791/90.....275.00

9.5 *(5 ducats). No. 7 in gold.* 1789...................1000.00

10 (10 ducats). No. 8 in gold. 1788.....................*Rare*

BRIXEN, Bishopric

In South Tyrol. Bishops given the mint right in 1179. Secularized 1802, given to Austria.

Leopold, Graf v. Spaur, 1747-78

Gold

E.F.
★1 (ducat). 1768............600.00

Sede Vacante 1778-79

Silver
VF-EF

2 V EINE etc. (=2 Convention thaler). CAPITVLVM/BRIXINENSE/ etc. in circle of shields. Rev. eagle. 1779.............375.00

COLLOREDO-MANSFELD,
Princes

The Colloredos were a German-Italian family raised to the rank of count of the Empire 1724 and to the rank of prince in 1763. In 1780 Prince Franz Gundacker acquired the Mansfeld (GERMANY) titles by marriage.

Franz Gundacker 1788-1807

Silver
EF-AU

1 (Convention thaler). Like No. 2. 1794 (restrike)......400.00

Gold

E.F.
★2 (ducat). 1792.............325.00

2a —. Restrike 1792 (with half moon shaped die break)....200.00

ESZTERHAZY, Princes
Old, rich, famous Hungarian family.
Nikolas Joseph 1762-90

Silver
VF-EF

1 (½ Conv. thaler). Like No. 2. 1770....................100.00

2 (Conv. thaler). NICOL. S.R.I. PRINC. ESZTERHAZY etc. Bust. Rev. arms. 28 gr. 1770 ....350.00

Gold
E.F.

3 (ducat). Sim. 1770.......500.00

GURK, Bishopric

In Carinthia. Founded circa 1071. Mediatized and assigned to Austria 1806.

Franz Xavier, Count
(Later Prince)
v. Salm-Reifferscheid, 1783-1822

Silver
VF-EF

1 20 (kreuzer). Like No. 3. 1806.....................40.00

2 (Convention thaler). FRANC. D.G. EP. PRINC. GVRC. etc. Sim. 1801.....................275.00

Gold

E.F.
★3 (ducat). 1806............900.00

KHEVENHÜLLER,
Counts and Princes

A German family with lands in Carinthia. The Hohen-Osterwitz branch became counts of the Empire in 1673.

Johann Joseph,
Count 1742-63, Prince 1763-76

Silver
VF-EF

1 (Convention thaler). IO. IOS. S.R.I. COM. A. KEVENHVLLER etc. Bust. Rev. helmeted arms. 1761....................400.00

★2 (Conv. thaler). 1771.......375.00

Gold
E.F.

3 (ducat). Like No. 1 but cwnd. arms. 1761..............750.00

AUSTRIA-HUNGARY
(STATES IN)

LIECHTENSTEIN, Princes

An Austrian family which acquired estates in Moravia in the 13th century. Count Carl (1585-1627), an Imperialist leader in Bohemia-Moravia, was created duke of Troppau 1614, prince in 1618, and in 1623 he obtained the duchy of Jägerndorf in Silesia for his services. Between 1699 and 1712 the family acquired present-day Liechtenstein located between Austria and Switzerland.

Joseph Wenzel 1748-72

Silver
VF-EF

1 (½ Convention thaler). IOS. WENC. D.G.S.R.I. PR. & GUB. DOM. DE LIECHTENSTEIN. Bust. Rev. arms. 14 gr. 1758 . . . . 110.00

2 (Conv. thaler). Sim. 1758 . . 375.00

Gold
E.F.

3 (ducat). Sim. 1758 . . . . . . 1800.00

3a —. Restrike . . . . *(Unc.)* 65.00

Franz Joseph I 1772-81

Silver
VF-EF

4 20 (kreuzer). FRANC. IOS. . . . LIECHTENSTEIN. Bust. Rev. arms. 1778 . . . . 65.00

★5 (½ Conv. thaler). 14 gr. Sim. 1778 . . . . 100.00

6 (Conv. thaler). Sim. 1778 . . 375.00

Gold
E.F.

7 (ducat). Sim. 1778 . . . . . . 1500.00

7a —. Restrike . . . . *(Unc.)* 65.00

LOBKOWITZ, Princes

Bohemian family with members in high imperial office, especially in the 17th century.

Franz Joseph Maximilian, 1784-1816, Under Regency of His Mother, Maria Gabriele of Savoy-Carignan, and His Cousin, August, Until 1794

Silver

VF-EF

★1 20 (kreuzer). FR. IOS. MAX. PR. DE LOBK. etc. Bust. Rev. arms. 1794 . . . . 90.00

2 (Convention thaler). Sim. 1794 . . . . 400.00

Gold
E.F.

3 (ducat). Sim. 1794 . . . . . . 1500.00

MONTFORT, Counts

Line of noblemen in the Austrian Vorarlberg and the neighborhood of Lake Constance, stemming from the 12th century marriage of Hugo von Tübingen with the heiress of Bregenz. First coins 13th century. Montfort was sold to Austria in 1780.

Arms: Silver, red church banner.

Ernst 1734-58

Billon
G-VG

2 ½ (kreuzer). 2 shields. Rev. ½. 1733-37 . . . . 7.50

5 1 (kreuzer). Bust. Rev. helmeted arms. 1736 . . . . 15.00

7 KREUZER. Arms. Rev. MONTF/ RENT/KREUZER/1737 . . . . 35.00

★9 1 (kreuzer). ERN. COM. IN MONTF. Bust. Rev. Imp. eagle and church banner in 2 shields. 1741-57 (var.) 7.50

G-VG

12 3/KREV/ZER. Obv. like No. 9. Rev. value. 1744 . . . . 20.00

13 3 KR(euzer). Bust. Rev. Imp. eagle. 1744 . . . . 20.00

16 3 K(reuzer). ERN. C.I. MONTF. Bust. Rev. helmeted arms. 1749 . . . . 20.00

19 4 (kreuzer). Helmeted arms. Rev. Imp. eagle. 1735 . . . . . . 25.00

Silver

V.F.

★22 VI/EINEN (=⅙) /REICHS/ THALER. 1758 . . . . 50.00

24 30 (kreuzer). ERNEST COM IN MONTFORT. Bust. Rev. SPES etc. Helmeted arms. 1734 . . . . 75.00

26 *30 (kreuzer). 1735* 80.00

28 (½ thaler). Bust. Rev. PRO DEO etc., helmeted arms. 1736 . . . . . 1000.00

30 (thaler). Bust. Rev. AVITA etc. Arms. 1738 . . . . 2000.00

31 (thaler). Bust. Rev. PRO DEO etc. Arms. 1749, 52 . . . . 1750.00

32 (2 thaler). Like No. 30. 1738 . . . . ——

33 (2 thaler). Like No. 31. 1752 . . . . ——

Gold (Carolin = 9.7 gr.)

34 ¼ (Carolin). ERNEST: COM: IN MONTFORT. Bust. Rev. PRO DEO etc. Cwnd. double Es and Fs cruciform. 1736 . . . . 1500.00

35 (ducat). Bust. Rev. PRO DEO etc. Arms. 1745 . . . . 3000.00

36 *(½ Carolin). Sim. 1734-35* 1500.00

37 (Carolin). Like No. 34. 1735 . . . . 3500.00

38 (Carolin). Like No. 35. 1735-36 . . . . 2500.00

Franz Xaver 1758-80

Billon
F-VF

40 *1 (kreuzer). Bust. Rev. Arms. 1758-59* 12.50

42 I (kreuzer). F:X:C:I:M:. Bust. Rev. 1500 EIN etc. Imp. eagle with I on breast. 1763 . . . . . . 17.50

AUSTRIA-HUNGARY
(STATES IN)

MONTFORT (Cont.)

F-VF

*47 6 (kreuzer). 1759..........10.00

Silver
VF-EF

50 10 (kreuzer). Bust. Rev. 120
etc. Imp. eagle, arms. 1761..15.00

56 20 (kreuzer). Like No. 50 but
SECHZIG etc. 1761-62.......20.00

60 (thaler). Bust. Rev. arms.
1759. (var.)............125.00

61 X EIN etc. (= Conv. thaler).
Sim. 1761..............125.00

Gold
E.F.

62 (ducat). Sim. 1758......1950.00

OLMÜTZ
(OLOMOUC, OLOMUCENSIS),
Bishopric and (1777) Archbishopric

In Moravia. Wandering see affixed to
Olmütz 1063. Mint right obtained 1141,
but little coinage struck until the 17th
century.

Ferdinand Julius, Graf
Troyer v. Giessbach, 1745-58

Silver
V.F.

1 30 (kreuzer). Bust.
Rev. arms. 1750..........65.00

2 (½ Conv. thaler). Like No. 3.
1752..................175.00

3 (Conv. thaler). FERD. IUL.
D.G.S.R.E. CARDIN DE TROYER.
Bust. Rev. EPISC. OLOM. etc.
Arms. 1752, 56..........400.00

Gold
E.F.

4 (ducat). Sim. 1747.......600.00

Anton Theodor, Graf
v. Colloredo-Waldsee 1777-1811

Silver

VF-EF

*5 10 (kreuzer). Like No. 8.
1779...................45.00

VF-EF

6 20 (kreuzer). Sim. 1779.....60.00

7 (½ Convention thaler). Sim.
14 gr. 1779..............160.00

8 (Conv. thaler). ANT. THEODOR
D.G. PRIM A. EP. OLOMU.DUX.
Bust. Rev. arms. 1779.....400.00

Gold
E.F.

9 (ducat). Sim. 1779.......550.00

Rudolph Johann,
Archduke of Austria, 1819-31

Silver

10 20 (kreuzer) Like No. 12.
1820..................55.00

11 (½ Convention thaler). Sim.
1820..................140.00

12 (Convention thaler). RUDOLPH
JOAN. D.G. CAES. etc. Bust.
Rev. . . . ARCHIEP. OLOM. Arms.
28 gr. 1820..............350.00

Gold

13 (ducat). Sim. 1820.......750.00

ORSINI-ROSENBERG, Princes

Carinthian family given rank as counts
of the Empire in 1648. Count Wolfgang
Franz Xaver was made a prince in
1790.

(Wolfgang) Franz (Xaver) 1739-96

Silver
E.F.

1 (Convention thaler).
FRANCISCVS VRSIN. S.R.I.
PRINCEPS ROSENBERG. Head.
Rev. arms. 1793 (1853 restrike
from unused original dies)..600.00

PAAR, Princes

Italian family which held office as the
hereditary Austrian postmaster general
for almost 300 years. Given rank as
counts 1629, as princes (with the mint
right) 1769.

Johann Wenzel,
Count 1741-69, Prince 1769-92

Silver
VF-EF

1 (½ Convention thaler). IOH.
WEN. S.R. IMP. PRINCEPS A.
PAAR. Bust. Rev. arms. 14 gr.
1771..................165.00

2 (Conv. thaler). Sim. 1771..375.00

Gold
E.F.

3 (ducat). Sim. 1771......1100.00

3a —. 1781..............950.00

Wenzel 1792-1812

Silver
VF-EF

4 (½ Conv. thaler). WENCESLAUS.
S. ROM. IMP. PRINCEPS. A PAAR.
Bust. Rev. arms. 1794....190.00

*5 (Conv. thaler). Sim. 1794..475.00

Gold (ducat = 3.49 gr.)
E.F.

6 (ducat). Sim. 1794.......850.00

7 (5 ducats). No. 4 in gold.
1794.....................RR

8 (10 ducats). No. 5 in gold.
1794.....................RR

SALZBURG (SALISBURGENSIS),
Archbishopric

On the Austro-Bavarian frontier. Bishopric raised to the rank of archbishopric 798, first coins about 200 years later.
In 1803 Salzburg was secularized and
given as an electorate to the Archduke
Ferdinand, erstwhile ruler of Tuscany
(ITALY). In 1805 the electorate of
Salzburg was annexed to Austria. From
1809 to 1813 the district was part of
Bavaria, but in the latter year reverted
to Austria.

Arms: Parted per pale. Gold, a black
lion rampant in dexter. Red, a silver
fesse (Austria) in sinister.

Andreas, Graf v. Dietrichstein,
1747-53

Billon
Fine

3 (pfennig). Date/2 shields/
A(ndreas). Rev. blank.
1748-52..................7.50

4 ½ (kreuzer). Da–½–te/2
shields/A. Rev. blank.
1748, 52.................7.50

5 2 (kreuzer). Like No. 7.
1745 (!), 47..............6.50

AUSTRIA-HUNGARY
(STATES IN)

SALZBURG (Cont.)

Fine

★7 4 (kreuzer). Arms of Salzburg
and Dietrichstein. 1747, 50.. 9.00

Silver
V.F.

9 (½ thaler). Like No. 12.
34mm. 1752............110.00

11 (thaler). Like No. 18.
42mm. 1748, 50.........250.00

12 (thaler). Madonna. Rev.
S. RUPERTUS etc. St. R. std.
1752..................275.00

Gold (ducat = 3.49 gr.)
VF-EF

13 ¼ (ducat). Like No. 17.
1749.................450.00

14 ¼ (ducat). Like No. 18.
1751.................575.00

15 ½ (ducat). Like No. 17.
1749.................950.00

16 ½ (ducat). Like No. 18.
1751.................800.00

★17 (ducat). 1747-52.........900.00

★18 (ducat). 1748-51........1000.00

19 (2 ducats). Sim. 26mm.
1750................3000.00

20 (2 ducats). Like No. 17.
1752................2500.00

Sigismund III,
Graf v. Schrattenbach 1753-71

Billon
VG-F

24 (pfennig). Date/2 shields/
S(igismund). Rev. blank.
1753-71................4.50

VG-F

25 ½ (kreuzer). Da–½–te/
2 shields/S. Rev. blank.
1753, 58, 60............. 7.50

★27 1 (kreuzer). Arms of Schr.
Rev. arms of Salz. 1754-59 .. 4.75

F-VF

★29 1 (kreuzer). SIGISMUND D.G.
ARCHIEP. etc. 1759-64....... 6.00

31 2 (kreuzer). Like No. 7 but
arms of Salzburg and Schrat-
tenbach. 1753............15.00

32 2 K(reuzer). Arms. Rev. date/
SALZ(B)/LAND/MINZ/2K.
1754-56................ 6.00

34 2 (kreuzer). Arms. Rev.
SALZBURGER etc. 2 in ring.
1758-60................ 6.00

35 3 (kreuzer). Arms.
Rev. St. Rupert. 1754......15.00

36 3 (kreuzer). Bust. Rev. arms.
1755...................15.00

37 4 (kreuzer). Like No. 31.
1753...................15.00

38 CCXL/EIN(E) etc. (=5 kr.).
Arms. Rev. value. 1766-71 .. 8.00

Silver

★40 10 (kreuzer). 1754-61.......16.00

44 10 (kreuzer). Bust. Rev.
arms/date. 1765-71 ....17.50

44a —. Rev. Date/arms.
1765-67.................17.50

45 XVII (kreuzer). Arms.
Rev. St. Rupert. 1754......32.50

46 20 (kreuzer). Bust on pedestal
with 20. Rev. arms.
1754-56.................19.50

46a —. Bust. Rev. arms on pedestal
with 20. 1757-64..........19.50

46b —. Bust. Rev. arms/20.
1765-71.................19.50

48 30 (kreuzer). Bust in rhombus.
Rev. arms in rhombus.
1754, 60................30.00

50 ¼ (Conv. thaler). Bust.
Rev. arms. 1766..........50.00

F-VF

51 ¼ (Conv. thaler). Like No. 48
but arms cwnd. 1767......50.00

55 (½ Conv. thaler). Bust.
Rev. arms under hat.
34mm. 1757, 60...........65.00

56 (½ Conv. thaler). Bust.
Rev. cwnd. arms. 1766-69 ..67.50

56a —. 1770-71.............60.00

*The St. Sigismund's Gate $½ size
1767 R.N. is a medal.*

V.F.

60 (Conv. thaler). Bust. Rev.
oval arms. 1753-61........135.00

61 (Conv. thaler). Madonna.
Rev. St. Rupert std. 1754..150.00

61a —. Rev. St. Rupert stdg.
1758...................160.00

62 (Conv. thaler). Bust. Rev.
St. R. std. 1757..........175.00

62a —. Rev. St. Rup. on cloud.
1759...................160.00

63 (Conv. thaler). Double arms.
Rev. St. R. on cloud. 1759.160.00

64 (Conv. thaler). Bust. Rev. St. R.
with Madonna statue. 1759-
62. (var.)...............150.00

65 (Conv. thaler). Bust. Rev.
double arms. 1761. (var.) ..160.00

66 (Conv. thaler). Bust. Rev.
Angel over 2 arms. 1762-64 .190.00

67 (Conv. thaler). Bust. Rev.
cwnd. draped elaborate arms.
1761, 65-71. (var.)........150.00

Gold (ducat = 3.49 gr.)
VF-EF

69 ¼ (ducat). Arms.
Rev. St. Rupert. 1753.....375.00

70 (¼ ducat). Bust. Rev. arms
under cardinal's hat. 1755..450.00

70.2 ¼ (ducat). Sim. 1770.....450.00

71 ½ (ducat). Sim. 1755, 61..550.00

72 (ducat). Like No. 69. 1753.750.00

73 (ducat). Like No. 70.
1754-63.................800.00

74 (ducat). Like No. 66.
1762-63.................800.00

74a —. 1764...............800.00

75 (ducat). Arms. Rev. St. Rup.
with Madonna. 1763......750.00

76 (ducat). Like No. 79 but
bust/1763...............800.00

76a —. Rev. arms/date.
1764-71.................800.00

76b —. Rev. 1765/arms......800.00

76c —. N.D. 800.00

77 (2 ducats). Like No. 70.
24mm. 1755............1450.00

78 2 (ducats). Like No. 66.
1764................1800.00

AUSTRIA-HUNGARY
(STATES IN)

SALZBURG (Cont.)

VF-EF

★79 2 (ducats). 1765-71......1800.00

80 (3 ducats). Bust. Rev. ARTIS
MONETARIAE, Mint. 1766..3000.00

81 V DUCA(TS). Bust. Rev.
St. Rupert std. 1759........RR

82 VI DUCA(TS). Like No. 64.
1760......................RR

Sede Vacante 1771-72

Gold

E.F.

84 (ducat). CAPITULUM SALISBUR
etc. Arms. Rev. St. Rupert.
1772...................750.00

Hieronymus (Jerome),
Graf v. Colloredo-Wallsee
1772-1803

Copper

VG-F

86 1/PFEN/NING. Salzb. arms
divide S-B. Rev. value.
1775-81.................. 3.50

86a —. Rev. value in wreath.
1783-84.................. 4.00

★87 I/PFEN/NING. 1786-90... 3.00

87a —. Irregular shield. 1792.... 5.50

87b —. Irregular shield.
Rev. value over sprays.
1792-1802................. 3.00

88 I/PFEN/NING. SALZBURG.
Heart-shaped shield.
Rev. value. 1802.......... 4.75

89 II/PFEN-/NING. Like No. 86.
1777-82...................3.50

90 II/PFEN/NING. Like No. 87.
1786, 91................. 3.75

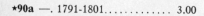

★90a —. 1791-1801............. 3.00

VG-F

91 2/PFEN/NING. Like No. 88.
1802..................... 3.75

92 I/KREU/TZER. Like No. 86.
1782-84.................. 3.75

93 I/KREU/TZER. Like No. 87.
1786, 90................. 3.50

93a —. Like No. 87b.
1790-1802................ 3.50

93b —. Rev. w/out sprays.
1802..................... 6.00

Billon

96 5 (Conv. kreuzer). Oval arms.
Rev. date/CCXL/EINE/–/–/5.
1773-84.................. 6.00

96a —. 1786, 88.............. 7.00

96b —. Squarish arms. 1792.... 7.00

96c —. 1793-1802............. 6.00

Silver

99 10 (Conv. kreuzer). Bust.
Rev. oval arms. 1772-86.... 7.50

★99a —. Rev. squarish arms.
1788-1802............... 7.50

103 20 (Conv. kreuzer). Like
No. 99. 1772-86 (var.)..... 9.00

103a —. Like No. 99a.
1787-1803............... 8.50

V.F.

104 (½ Conv. thaler). Like No. 99.
34mm. 1772-82...........55.00

104a —. Like No. 99a.
1787-1802...............60.00

106 (Convention thaler). Like
No. 99. 1772-86..........120.00

107 (Conv. thaler). Like No. 99a.
1787-1802...............130.00

107a —. 1803................475.00

108 (Conv. thaler). Bust. Rev.
arms supported by 2 lions.
1790.................... ——

Gold (ducat = 3.49 gr.)

VF-EF

109 (¼ ducat). Like No. 99.
1776-82.................190.00

110 (½ ducat). Sim. 1776....350.00

111 (ducat). Sim. 1772-86....400.00

★111a Like No. 99a. 1787-1802..400.00

VF-EF

111b —. 1803.................RR

112 (ducat). Bust. Rev. PRINCEPS
etc. Temple. 1782. (1200th
anniversary of See)......750.00

113 2 (ducats). Like No. 99.
1773.................1650.00

114 (2 ducats). Like No. 112.
1782.................1950.00

Ferdinand, Elector of Salzburg
1803-05
(Grand Duke of Würzburg,
Germany, 1806-14)

Copper

VG-F

115 I/PFENNING. Like No. 117.
1804..................... 4.00

115a EIN (=1)/PFENNING.
Sim. 1804-05............. 5.75

116 II/PFENNING. Sim.
1804..................... 6.50

116a ZWEI (=2)/PFENNING.
Sim. 1805-06............. 6.00

★117 EIN (=1) /KREUTZER.
1804-06................. 5.00

Billon

119 III/KREUZER. Obv. like
No. 117. Rev. KURF. SAL. etc.
Value. 1803-04.......... 9.00

119a —. Date in lozenge. 1805.. 9.00

121 VI/KREUZER. Like No.
119. (var.) 1803-05....... 12.00

121a —. Like No. 119a.
1805-06................. 12.00

Silver

V.F.

123 20 (kreuzer). FERDINANDUS
D.G. ... D.SAL. Bust. Rev. arms
on cwnd. mantle. 1804.....22.50

123a —. Rev. cwnd. arms.
1805-06.................22.50

125 (Convention thaler). Like
No. 123. 1803..........225.00

125a —. Like No. 123a. 1805,
06....................175.00

Gold

VF-EF

126 (ducat). Like No. 123. 1803-
04....................900.00

AUSTRIA-HUNGARY
(STATES IN)

SALZBURG (Cont.)

VF-EF

★126a —. Like No. 123a. 1805-
06.................750.00

See ITALY (Tuscany) and GERMA-
NY (Würzburg) for other coins of
Ferdinand.

SCHLICK, Counts

Imperial Chancellor Caspar von Schlick
was given the rank of count in 1436.
His great nephews, counts in the early
16th century, struck Joachimsthalers
(the first "dollars") from silver produced at their mines in that place. The
Schlicks represented in this catalog
were imperial office holders in Bohemia.

Franz Heinrich 1740-66

Silver

VF-EF

★1 (Convention thaler). FRANC: HEN
SCHLIK etc. Holy family over arms.
Rev. Imp. eagle. 1759.....400.00

Gold

E.F.

2 (ducat). Sim. but St. Anna
over the arms. 1759......1200.00

Leopold Heinrich 1766-70

Silver

VF-EF

3 (Conv. thaler). LEOPOL: HEN:
SCHLIK etc. Like No. 1.
1767...................400.00

Gold

E.F.

4 (ducat). LEOP:HE:S:R:I:C:D:
PASSAHH etc. Sim. 1767....850.00

TRENT (TRIDENT). See ITALY.

VIENNA (WIEN),
Archbishopric

Bishopric established at the Austrian
capital 1471. Bishops given the rank
of prince in 1631. See advanced to archbishopric 1722.

Christoph Anton,
Graf v. Migazzi 1757-1803

Silver

V.F.

★1 (Convention thaler). CHRIS
TOPHORVS D.M etc. Bust. Rev.
ARCHIEP. VIEN. etc. Arms.
1781...................250.00

Gold

E.F.

2 (ducat). Sim. 1781.......850.00

WINDISCHGRÄTZ, Counts

An old family with possessions in Styria as early as the 15th century. Elevated to the rank of count in the 17th
century and given the mint right in
1730.

Joseph Nicolaus 1744-1802

Silver

E.F.

1 20 (kreuzer). IOS NIC. S.R.I.
etc. . . . WINDISCHGRATZ. Bust.
Rev. arms. 1777.........100.00

★2 (½ Convention thaler). Sim.
1777...................175.00

Gold (ducat = 3.49 gr.)

3 (ducat). Sim. 1777.......850.00
4 (5 ducats). No. 2 in gold.
1777......................RR

UNVERIFIED DATA

Note: Throughout this catalog, any
uncertain, indefinite or unconfirmed information is shown in *italic type*. Such
material may be, for example, coin descriptions, dates and prices, names of
rulers, or supplementary notes. Further
information to confirm or correct *material in italics* should be sent to the
author at the following address:

William D. Craig
c/o Whitman Coin Supply Division
1220 Mound Avenue
Racine, Wisconsin 53404, U.S.A.

BALKANS

BAHAMAS. See CARIBBEAN ISLANDS AND TERRITORIES.

Area of southeastern Europe, which only fully emerged from Turkish control in the late 19th century. The coins which follow were struck by non-Turkish governments.

BULGARIA

Pazvantoglu, a feudal lord at Vidin, revolted against the Turks 1794 and made himself independent circa 1794-1807. It is said that he had a separate coinage, but such coins have not been identified.

CATTARO

Port and fortress in Dalmatia. Occupied by France 1805-13. Emergency cast coinage of besieged French defenders.

Silver

                                F-VF

*1 I F(ranc). 1813............85.00

2 5 F(rancs). DIEU PROTEGE etc. Cwnd. N(apoleon). Rev. CATTARO etc. Crossed arms. 1813...................600.00

3 10 F(rancs). Sim. 1813...1600.00

CORFU, CEPHALONIA and ZANTE

Three of the Ionian Islands in the Adriatic Sea, which, until 1797, belonged to the Republic of Venice.

Monetary System:
2 soldi = 1 gazetta.

Under Venice

Copper

                                    VG-F

1 I (soldo). S. CORFU/CEFA/ZAN. Rev. Lion of St. Mark. N.D. (17th-18th centuries).......9.00

2 II (soldi). Sim. N.D. (17th-18th centuries)...........9.00

DALMATIA and ALBANIA

Strip along the Adriatic which belonged to Venice from the 14th century through 1797. To Austria 1797-1805, to France 1805-13, back to Austria 1813-1918.

Under Venice
Copper

                                    V.G.

1 I (soldo). Like No. 2. N.D. (1626-1797).............4.50

                                    Fine

*2 II (soldi = gazetta). N.D. (Under 6.5 gr. = 1710-97. Older coins are heavier.)..........6.00

DUBROVNIK.
See Ragusa.

GREECE

Mother of western civilization. Ruled by Turkey from mid 15th century until the early 19th. Achieved its freedom 1828.

I. Republic 1828-31.
Count Capo D'Istria, President

Monetary System:
100 lepta = 1 phoenix.

Copper

                                    Fine

1 1 lepton. Phoenix. Rev. Value. 1828, 30, 31............22.50

2 5 lepta. Sim. 1828, 30, 31...20.00

*3 10 lepta. Sim. 1828, 30, 31...17.50

                                    Fine

4 20 lepta. Sim. 1831.........20.00

Each year of Nos. 1-4 is a distinct variety.

Silver

                                    F-VF

*5 1 phoenix. 1828..........125.00

II. Kingdom

Othon (Otto of Bavaria) 1831-62

Monetary System:
100 lepta = 1 drachma.

Copper

A. Legend ΒΑΣΙΛΕΙΑ etc.

6 1 lepton. Like No. 8. 1832-43...................7.50

7 2 lepta. Sim. 1832-42......10.00

*8 5 lepta. 1833-42...........4.00

9 10 lepta. Sim. 1833-44......8.50

B. Legend ΒΑΣΙΛΕΙΟΝ etc.

6a 1 lepton. Sim. 16.5mm. 1844-49...................12.50

6b —. 15mm. 1851, 57.......12.50

7a 2 lepta. Sim. 18.5mm. 1844-49..................7.50

7b —. 17mm. 1851, 57.......7.50

8a 5 lepta. Sim. 25mm. 1844-49..................5.00

8b —. 23mm. 1851, 57........6.00

9a 10 lepta. Sim. 1844-57......8.50

Silver

10 ¼ drachma. Like No. 12. 1833-46..................13.50

11 ½ drachma. Sim. 1833-47...20.00

*12 1 drachma. 1832-47........20.00

13 5 drachmai. Sim. 1833-45...40.00

BALKANS

GREECE (Cont.)

V.F.

14 ¼ drachma. Like No. 15. 1855 . . . . .120.00

★15 ½ drachma. 1851, 55 . . . . .120.00

15.5 1 drachma. Sim. 1851 . . . . .150.00

15.7 5 drachmai. Sim. 38.2mm. 1846 . . . .*Pattern*

16 5 drachmai. Sim. 36.2mm. 1851 . . . . .350.00

Gold

17 20 drachmai. Like No. 13 but head l. 1833 . . . . .1200.00

Note: The RRR 20 and 40 drachmai 1852 were never circulated and are considered patterns.

IONIAN ISLANDS
(ΙΟΝΙΚΟΝ ΚΡΑΤΟΣ)

Group of seven large and various smaller islands in the Adriatic Sea, including Corfu, Cephalonia and Zante. To Venice until 1797 (see Corfu, etc). To France 1797-99. Under Russian-Turkish protection 1799-1807. Back to France 1807-14. Britain acquired the islands piecemeal 1809-14. Under British protection 1814-63. To Greece 1863 onward.

I. Under Russia/Turkey 1799-1807.

Monetary System:
2 soldi = 1 gazetta.

Copper

VG-F

★1 J/ΓΑΖΕΤΑ (= 1 gazetta). Lion of St. Mark. Rev. value. 1801 . . . . .500.00

2 5/ΓΑΖΕΤΑΙΣ (= 5 gazette) Sim. 1801 . . . . .500.00

2a 5/GAZZETE 500.00

II. Under Great Britain 1809-63.

A. Turkish System 1809-21:

40 paras = 1 piastre;
220 paras = 1 dollar.

Cmkd. Silver

Crude

10 25 (paras). 25 in square cmkd. on Spanish and Sicilian coins. (1813) . . . . ——

11 30 (paras). Sim. (1813) . . . . . ——

Crude

12 50 (paras). Sim. (1813) . . . . . ——

13 60 (paras). Sim. (1813) . . . . . ——

Note: Nos. 10-13 are unknown except with the No. 16-19 cmk. added. Nos. 16-19 are rare.

★16 25 (paras). Head of George III/ 25 in oval, cmkd. on Spanish and Sicilian silver, including Nos. 10-11. (1813) 500.00

17 30 (paras). Sim. (1813) 600.00

18 50 (paras). Sim. (1813) 500.00

19 60 (paras). Sim. (1813) . . . . . ——

B. First Decimal System 1821-35:
400 lepta = 100 oboli = 1 dollar.

Copper

Fine

20 4 (= ¼ obol) (lepton). Like No. 22 but crude local issue. 19mm. 1821 . . . . .75.00

21 (½ obol). Like No. 22. 21.8mm. 1819-20 . . . . .4.50

★22 (obol). 1819 . . . . .12.50

23 (2 oboli). Sim. 35mm. 1819 . .22.50

C. Second Decimal System 1835-63:

500 lepta = 100 oboli = 1 dollar.

Copper

F-VF

★24 (lepton). 16mm. 1834-62 . . . . .5.00

Silver

25 30 (lepta). Value. Rev. Britannia. 1834-62 . . . . .17.50

ISOLE and ARMATA

Coinage for the Venetian military, island and coastal holdings along the Greek and Albanian Adriatic shorelines after the loss of Morea in 1718.

Copper

VG-F

1 I (soldo). ISOLE/ET/ARMATA. Rev. Lion of St. Mark. N.D. (ca 1718-97) 12.50

2 II (soldi). Sim. N.D. (ca 1718-97) 12.50

Note: Similar coins for ARM .TA/ET/ MOREA were struck before the period covered by this catalog.

MOLDAVIA and WALLACHIA
Principalities

Nucleus of present-day Romania. Dominated by Turkey for almost 400 years until 1858. Russia frequently intervened in the affairs of the two principalities from the 18th century onward.

Russian Occupation 1768-74
Catherine II of Russia

Bronze
(from captured Turkish guns)

VG-F

★1 3 DENGI. Imp. eagle with arms of M & W on breast. Rev. value, cwnd. E II mon. 1771. (var.) 85.00

★2 PARA/(=)3/DENGI. 1772-73 . . . . .35.00

3 2/PARA/(=)3/KOPECK. Sim. 1772-74 . . . . .20.00

Note: The 3 dengi 1771 with value on obverse and the 5 kopeck 1771 are patterns.

RAGUSA (DUBROVNIK), City

Aristocratic republic in Dalmatia. Under Turkish protection 1526-1806. Suppressed by Napoleon 1808. Now part of Yugoslavia.

Monetary System:
6 soldi = 1 grosetto;
12 grosetti = 1 perpero;
40 grosetti = 1 ducato (silver);
60 grosetti = 1 tallero.

BALKANS

RAGUSA (Cont.)

Copper

VG-F

★1 (soldo). CIVITAS RACVSII (or abbreviation). St. Blaze over city wall. Rev. Christ. (var.) 1689-1797................. 7.50

2 (3 soldi). PROT. REIP. RHACVSINE. St. Blaze. Rev. DEVS etc. Christ. 1795-99........... 9.00

Silver (or Billon)

V.G.

3 (grosetto). S. BLASIVS RHAGUSII. St. Blaze. Rev. TVTA SALVS. Christ. (var.). 1612-1757.... 9.00

4 GROS/SETTI/VI (=6 g). PROT. REIPU. RHACUSI. St. Blaze. Rev. value. 1801.....15.00

5 (perpero). Like No. 3. 1801-03....................20.00

Silver

F-VF

6 DUCAT(o). DUCAT. REIP. RHACUSIN. Arms. Rev. TUIS etc. St. Blaze. 1797........30.00

★9 DUCAT ET SEM (=tallero). RECTOR REIP RHACVSIN. Bust of rector. Rev. Arms. 1751-79....................47.50

10 (2 ducati). RHACVS. RESPVBL. Liberty, bust r. Rev. Arms. 1791....................85.00

11 (2 ducati). Obv. sim. Rev. LI/BER/TAS in shield. 1792-95....................75.00

ZARA

Port and fortress in Dalmatia. To France 1805-13. Emergency coinage of French defenders 1813.

Silver

V.F.

1 1.0 (ounce)/4 F(rancs) 60 C(entimes). Imp. eagle. Rev. value. 1813.............150.00

★2 2.0 (ounces)/9 F(rancs) 20 C(entimes). Sim. Rev. value. 1813....................600.00

3 4.0 (ounces)/18 F(rancs) 40 C(entimes). Sim. 1813....1250.00

BARBADOS. See CARIBBEAN ISLANDS AND TERRITORIES.

BELGIUM. See LOW COUNTRIES.

BERBICE. See CARIBBEAN ISLANDS AND TERRITORIES.

BERMUDA

British island possessions in the Atlantic about 700 miles distant from the U.S.

Money of Account: See GREAT BRITAIN.

George III 1760-1820

Copper

Fine

★1 (penny). 1793.............15.00

Uncirculated specimens are mostly unofficial restrikes or concoctions, and are moderately scarce .... (Unc.) 75.00

BOHEMIA. See AUSTRIA.

BOLIVIA

Inland republic in South America established by Bolivar and Sucre in 1825-26. Under Spain this area formed the northern part of the Viceroyalty of Rio de la Plata after being separated from the Viceroyalty of Peru. Bolivia contained rich mines. The initial coinage of newly independent Argentina was struck in Potosi 1813-15. Potosi mint mark PTS monogram.

Monetary System:
16 reales = 1 escudo (scudo).

I. Under Spain.

Cob silver was struck at Potosi probably no later than 1773.

For other similar Spanish and Spanish-American coins, see Spain, Argentina, Chile, Colombia, Guatemala, Mexico, Peru and Venezuela.

Carlos III 1759-88

Milled Silver

A. Pillar Type.

F-VF

9 (½ real). Like No. 11. 1767-70..................20.00

10 R(eal) I. Sim. 1767-70......20.00

★11 R(eales) 2. CAR. III etc. Rev. mmk. PTS mon. at left of date. 1767-70..........17.50

12 4 (reales). Sim. but CAROLUS III etc. Rev. mmk. each side of date. 1767-70..........75.00

13 8 (reales). Sim. 1767-70.............(V.F.) 75.00

BOLIVIA

B. Bust Type.

Fine

14 (½ real). Like No. 16.
1773-89 . . . . 2.50

15 1 R(eal). Sim. 1773-89 . . . . . . 3.50

★16 2 R(eales). Rev. mmk. PTS
mon. follows REX. 1773-89 . . . 4.00

17 4 R(eales). Sim. 1773-89 . . . . 20.00

V.F.

18 8 R(eales). Sim. 1773-89 . . . . 30.00

Gold

19 1 S(cudo). Bust, CAROL. III
etc. Rev. arms, IN UTROQ.
etc. 1778-87 . . . . 150.00

20 2 S(cudos). Sim. 1778-88 . . . *500.00*

21 4 S(cudos). Sim. 1778-88 . . *1250.00*

22 8 S(cudos). Sim. 1778-88 . . . 500.00

Carlos IV 1788-1808
Silver

A. Bust of Carlos III.

F-VF

23 (½ real). CAROLUS IV etc.
Like No. 16. 1789-90 . . . . 5.00

★24 1 R(eal). Sim. 1789-90 . . . . . . 7.50

25 2 R(eales). Sim. 1789-90 . . . . 6.50

26 4 R(eales). Sim. 1789-90 . . . . 65.00

27 8 R(eales). Sim.
1789-91 . . . . (V.F.) 40.00

B. Castle/Lion.

★32 ¼ (real). PTS mon. – castle
– ¼. Rev. lion. 1796-1808 . . 12.50

C. Bust of Carlos IV.

Fine

33 (½ real). Like No. 16
but CAROLUS IIII etc.
His own bust. 1791-1809 . . . . 2.50

34 1 R(eal). Sim. 1791-1809 . . . . 3.00

35 2 R(eales). Sim. 1791-1808 . . 3.50

Fine

36 4 R(eales). Sim. 1791-1809 . . 15.00

V.F.

37 8 R(eales). Sim. 1791-1808 . . 17.50

Gold

A. Bust of Carlos III,
legend CAROL. IV.

28 1 S(cudo). Like No. 19 but
CAROL. IV. 1789-90 . . . . 250.00

29 2 S(cudos). Sim. 1789-90 . . . *650.00*

30 4 S(cudos). Sim. 1789-90 . . . . . RR

31 8 S(cudos). Sim. 1790 . . . . . 600.00

B. Bust of Carlos III,
legend CAROL. IIII.

28a 1 S(cudo). Like No. 19 but
CAROL. IIII. 1791 . . . . 300.00

29a 2 S(cudos). Sim. 1791 . . . . . *650.00*

30a 4 S(cudos). Sim. 1791 . . . . *1250.00*

31a 8 S(cudos). Sim. 1791 . . . . . 600.00

C. Bust of Carlos IV.

38 1 S(cudo). Like No. 19
but CAROL IIII, his own bust.
1793-1808 . . . . 125.00

39 2 S(cudos). Sim.
1793-1808 . . . . *350.00*

40 4 S(cudos). Sim.
1792-1808 . . . . *900.00*

41 8 S(cudos). Sim.
1791-1808 . . . . 500.00

Fernando VII 1808-33,
In Bolivia 1808-25

Silver

F-VF

42 ¼ (real). Like No. 32.
1809 . . . . 25.00

★43 (½ real). FERDIN VII etc.
His draped bust. Rev. like
rev. No. 16. 1816-25 . . . . 2.50

44 1 R(eal). Sim. 1816-25 . . . . . . 3.50

45 2 R(eales). Sim. 1808-25 . . . . 3.50

46 4 R(eales). Sim. 1808-25 . . . . 17.50

V.F.

47 8 R(eales). Sim. 1808-25 . . . . 17.50

Gold

48 1 S(cudo). Like No. 19 but
FERDIN VII etc., his head.
1822-24 . . . . 140.00

49 8 S(cudos). Uniformed bust.
Rev. sim. 1809 . . . . Unique

50 8 S(cudos). Like No. 48.
1822-24 . . . . 600.00

II. Republic, 1825 on.

Monetary System:
8 sueldos (soles) = 1 peso;
2 pesos = 1 scudo.

Silver

F-VF

51 (½ sueldo). Bust of Bolivar.
Rev. Tree, llamas. 1827-30 . . 3.00

★52 1 S(ueldo). Sim. 1827-30 . . . . 3.00

53 2 S(ueldos). Sim. 1827-30 . . . 4.50

54 4 S(ueldos). Sim. 1827-30 . . . 4.00

55 8 S(ueldos). Sim. 1827-40 . . . 12.50

Gold

V.F.

56 ½ (scudo). Bust of Bolivar.
Rev. Mountain, llama, etc.
1838-40 . . . . 90.00

57 1 S(cudo). Sim. 1831-39 . . . 100.00

★58 2 S(cudos). Sim. 1834-39 . . . 225.00

59 4 S(cudos). Sim. 1834 . . . . 1200.00

60 8 S(cudos). 1831-40 . . . . . . 375.00

Silver

★61 8 S(ueldos). Laureate
head of Bolivar. 1841-48 . . . . 17.50

BOLIVIA

V.F.

*62 (8 sueldos). Bare head to left.
1848-51...................17.50

Gold

63 ½ (scudo). Obv. like No. 61.
Rev. like No. 56. 1841-47...75.00
64 *1 S(cudo)*. Sim. *1841-47*...125.00
65 *2 S(cudos)*. Sim. 1841......750.00
66 4 S(cudos). Sim. 1841....1800.00
67 8 S(cudos). Sim. 1841-*47*...375.00
69 8 E(scudos). Obv. like
No. 62. 1851.............800.00

BRAZIL (BRASIL)

Largest country in South America. Portuguese colony until 1822. The Portuguese court emigrated here in 1807 to escape Napoleon. Brazil became an independent empire in 1822 under its then Portuguese prince-regent.

Monetary Systems:

Until 1833 — 6400 reis = 1 peça (dobra, Joe) = 4 escudos.
After 1833 — 1000 reis = 1 milreis.

Mints: Lisbon (until 1807) – No mmk; Bahia – B; Cuiabá (Mato Grosso) – C; Goiás – G; Minas Gerais – M; Rio de Janeiro – R (occasionally no mmk, as indicated hereafter); São Paulo – SP.

Forgeries: Prober says that excellent forgeries exist of virtually all rare Brazilian gold and silver coins.

José (Joseph) I 1750-77

Copper

VG-F

1 V (reis). Like No. 2. (Lisbon).
1752 (rare), 53 .... 3.50
1a —. Cmkd. shield.......... 3.75

*2 V (reis). 1762-77.......... 2.00

VG-F

2a —. Cmkd. shield.......... 2.50
3 X (reis). Sim. Globe has 2
meridians. No MM (Rio).
1751...................22.50
3a —. Cmkd. shield..........27.50
4 X (reis). Like No. 1 (Lisbon).
1752-53................. 3.50
4a —. Cmkd. shield.......... 2.50
5 X (reis). Like No. 2. 1762B,
73-76................... 1.75

*5a —. Cmkd. shield............1.25
6 XX (reis). Like No. 3 (Rio).
1751-52.................15.00
6a —. Cmkd. shield..........12.50
7 XX (reis). Like No. 1 (Lisbon).
1752-57................. 3.50
7a —. Cmkd. shield.......... 1.75
8 XX (reis). Like No. 2. 1761B,
73-76................... 1.75
8a —. Cmkd. shield............1.25
9 XL (reis). Like No. 1 (Lisbon).
1752 (unique), 53-60 .... 2.00
9a —. Cmkd. shield.......... 1.50
10 XL (reis). Like No. 2. 1762B,
74..................... 2.00
10a —. Cmkd. shield......... 1.50

Note: For similar coins 1752-57 with obverse legend ending GUIN(EÆ), see ANGOLA. Many of these actually circulated in Brazil as well as a result of trade between the colonies.

Silver

Fine

11 80 (reis). Like No. 14.
1751R...................25.00
11a —. 1768-71...............10.00
12 160 (reis). Sim. 1751R......25.00
12a —. 1752-76...............10.00
13 320 (reis). Sim. 1751-55R...10.00
13a —. 1752-76...............10.00
14 640 (reis). IOSEPHUS I D G
P(ORT) REX E. BRAS. D. Cwnd.
Portuguese arms. Rev. SUBQ.-
SIGN-etc. Globe. 1751-55R ..25.00
14a —. 1752-56. No MM.......60.00
14b —. 1757-71...............25.00

Issues for Minas Gerais

Silver

Fine

21 75 (reis). Cwnd. "J." Rev.
Globe. 1752-54B..........50.00
21a —. Cmkd. shield..........60.00

*22 75 (reis). Sim. 1754-60R....40.00
22a —. Cmkd. shield..........50.00
23 150 (reis). Sim. 1752-68B...50.00
23a —. Cmkd. shield..........60.00
24 150 (reis). Sim. 1754-60R...30.00
24a —. Cmkd. shield..........30.00
24b —. 1771R................60.00
24c —. 24b cmkd.............60.00
25 300 (reis). Sim. 1752-68B...60.00
25a —. Cmkd. shield..........60.00
26 300 (reis). Sim. 1754-71R...30.00
26a —. Cmkd. shield..........30.00
27 600 (reis). Sim. 1752-68B...60.00
27a —. Cmkd. shield..........60.00
28 600 (reis). Sim. 1754-74R...40.00
28a —. Cmkd. shield..........40.00

Gold

Common coinage with Portugal. R and B mints. For the same coins with no mmk, see Portugal.

F-VF

31 (800 reis). Like No. 34.
16mm. 1752-77..........200.00
31a —. Mule. 1751B..........RRR
32 (1600 reis). Sim. 20mm.
1752B (RRR), 77B (RRR).
1754-74.................250.00
33 (3200 reis). Sim. 24mm.
1752B (unique), 54B (unique),
1756-73 B or R..........300.00

*34 (6400 reis). 14.3 gr.
1751-77.................500.00

BRAZIL

Provincial Gold Coinage

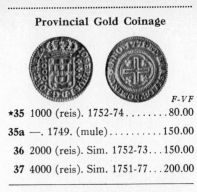

		F-VF
★35	1000 (reis). 1752-74	80.00
35a	—. 1749. (mule)	150.00
36	2000 (reis). Sim. 1752-73	150.00
37	4000 (reis). Sim. 1751-77	200.00

Maria I and Pedro III 1777-86

Copper

		VG-F
★41	V (reis). 1778-84	2.00
41a	—. Cmkd. shield	3.50
42	X (reis). Sim. 1778-85	2.00
42a	—. Cmkd. shield	.50
43	XX (reis). Sim. 1778-84	2.00
43a	—. Cmkd. shield	.75
44	XL (reis). Sim. 1778-84	2.00
44a	—. Cmkd. shield	.75

Silver

		Fine
★45	80 (reis). MARIA I ET PETRUS III etc. 1778-86	10.00
46	160 (reis). Sim. 1778-86	10.00
47	320 (reis). Sim. 1778-86	10.00
48	640 (reis). Sim. 1778-86	20.00

Gold

Common coinage with Portugal. R and B mints only. See note preceding No. 31.

		F-VF
50	(800 reis). Like No. 53. 16mm. 1782, 86	400.00
51	(1600 reis). Sim. 20mm. 1780-84	400.00
52	(3200 reis). Sim. 24mm. 1780-86	600.00

		F-VF
★53	(6400 reis). 14.3 gr. 1777-86	500.00

Provincial Gold Coinage

54	1000 (reis). Like No. 35 but MARIA etc. 1778-82	100.00
55	2000 (reis). Sim. 1778-83	175.00
56	4000 (reis). Sim. 1778-86	225.00

Maria I, as Widow, 1786-1805 (Under Regency 1799 Onward)

Copper

		VG-F
60	V (reis). Like No. 41 but MARIA I.D.G. etc. 1786-97	2.50
60a	—. Cmkd. shield	3.00
61	X (reis). Sim. 1786-96	3.00
61a	—. Cmkd. shield	.50
62	XX (reis). Sim. 1786-99	3.00
62a	—. Cmkd. shield	.50
63	XL (reis). Sim. 1786-96	7.50
63a	—. Cmkd. shield	.75

Same types. Coin weights reduced.

★64	V (reis). 1799 (=1881-82!)	100.00
65	X (reis). Sim. 1799	1.25
65a	—. Cmkd. shield	2.00
66	XX (reis). Sim. 28.5mm. 1799	2.00
66a	—. Cmkd. shield	3.00
66b	—. Cmkd. 10 (reis)	2.00
67	XL (reis). Sim. 1799	1.50
67a	—. Cmkd. shield	2.00
67b	—. Cmkd. 20 (reis)	1.50

Silver

		Fine
70	80 (reis). Like No. 72. 1787-96	10.00
71	160 (reis). Sim. 1787-97	10.00

		Fine
★72	320 (reis). 1787-1802	12.50
73	640 (reis). Sim. 1787-1805	20.00

Gold

Common coinage with Portugal. See note preceding No. 31. R and B mints only.

		F-VF
74	(6400 reis). Like No. 53 but MARIA I D G. Her veiled bust. 1786-90	500.00
75	(6400 reis). Sim. but bust with elaborate hairdress. 1789-1805	500.00

Provincial Gold Coinage

76	1000 (reis). Like No. 35 but MARIA I D.G. etc. 1787	100.00
77	2000 (reis). Sim. 1787-93	175.00
78	4000 (reis). Sim. 1787-1805	225.00

João (John), Prince Regent 1799-1816

Copper

		VG-F
80	X (reis). Like No. 65 but JOANNES D. G. P(ORT) E. BRASILIA P. REGENS. 1802-16 (18B = counterfeit)	1.00
80a	—. Cmkd. shield	3.00
81	XX (reis). Sim. 1802-18	1.75
81a	—. Cmkd. shield	2.00
81b	—. Cmkd. 10 (reis)	1.50
82	XX (reis). Sim. but JOANNES D.G. PORT. BRAS. ET ALG. etc. 1816	20.00
82a	—. Cmkd. 10 (reis)	8.50
83	XL (reis). Like No. 80. 1802-17 (1818B =counterfeit)	1.00
83a	—. Cmkd. shield	2.00
83b	—. Cmkd. 20 (reis)	2.00

BRASIL

84 XL (reis). Like No. 82.
1816 .... 4.00
84a —. Cmkd. 20 (reis) 6.50
85 LXXX (reis). Like No. 80.
1811-12 .... 12.50
85a —. Cmkd. 40 (reis) 17.50

VG-F

Note: For similar 20, 40 and 80 reis coins (Arabic numerals of value), see MOZAMBIQUE.

Regional Copper for Goiás and Mato Grosso R and B Mints

86 XX (reis). Like No. 81 but size further reduced. 25mm.
1818 .... 3.50
87 XL (reis). Sim. 30mm. 1818 . 20.00
87a —. Cmkd. 10 (reis) 15.00

★88 LXXX (reis). Sim. 35mm.
1818 .... 8.50
88a —. Cmkd. shield 7.50

Silver
R, B and M (rare) mints.

F-VF

90 80 (reis). Like No. 72 but
JOANNES etc. 1810-16 ...... 35.00
91 160 (reis). Sim. 1810-15 .... 20.00
92 320 (reis). Sim. 1809-17 .... 20.00
93 640 (reis). Sim. 1806-16 .... 20.00

V.F.

94 960 (reis). Sim. 1809-18 .... 17.50
94a —. ... BRAS. ET ALG. etc.
1816 .... 65.00

Countermarks on Foreign Dollars 1808-21

(Prices are for countermarked Spanish-American issues. Others are scarcer.)

A. Minas Gerais.

F-VF

★96 960 (reis). Cwnd. arms of Portugal/960. Rev. globe. Round. 18mm. (1808) 45.00

B. Mato Grosso.

★97 (960 reis). Oval Port. arms/
MATO GROSSO. Rev. globe.
(1818) 850.00
No. 97 with crown entirely of pearls is counterfeit.

C. Cuiabá.

98 (960 reis). CUYABA cmk.
(1820) .... RRR

F-VF

★99 960 (reis). Cwn./value/c.
Rev. Port. arms on globe
(1821) 450.00
No. 99 with crosses instead of five nails in the five small shields in the Portuguese arms is counterfeit.

Gold

100 (6400 reis). JOANNES D.G.
PORT. ET ALG. P. REGENS. Bust.
Rev. Arms. 14.3 gr. 1805-
17R 600.00
100a —. ... PORT. BRAS. ET ALG.
1816R 1000.00

For similar gold without mint mark (Lisbon), see PORTUGAL.

Provincial Gold Coinage

101 4000 (reis). Like No. 35 but
JOANNES etc. 1805-17 ..... 275.00
101a —. ... PORT. BRAS. ET ALG.
1816 .... 400.00

João (John), as João VI, King of the United Kingdom of Brazil and Portugal 1816-22

Copper

Fine

105 X (reis). Like No. 106.
1818-23 .... .75

★106 XX (reis). 1818-22 .... 1.00

BRAZIL

106a —. Cmkd. 10 (reis)........ 1.00

107 XL (reis). Sim. 1818-23.... 1.00

107a —. Cmkd. 20 (reis)....... 1.25

108 LXXX (reis). Sim. 1820-
23..................... 1.50

108a —. Cmkd. 40 (reis)....... 1.00

Local Coinage for Minas Gerais

★109 37½ (reis). 1818-21...... 10.00

109a —. Cmkd. 10 (reis)........ 10.00

110 75 (reis). Sim. 1818-21..... 10.00

110a —. Cmkd. 20 (reis)....... 10.00

Local Coinage for Goiás and Mato Grosso

111 XL (reis). Like No. 107 but
reduced size. 30mm. 1820..15.00

111a —. Cmkd. 10 (reis)........ 15.00

112 LXXX (reis). Sim. 35mm.
1820.................. 10.00

112a —. Cmkd. 20 (reis)........ 10.00

Note: See Mozambique for similar 20, 40 and 80 reis coins (with Arabic numerals).

Silver

F-VF

★113 80 (reis). 1818, 21........ 50.00

114 160 (reis). Sim. 1818-21.... 25.00

115 320 (reis). Sim. 1818-21.... 20.00

115a —. 1818M 400.00

116 640 (reis). Sim. 1818-22.... 25.00

116a —. 1818M 500.00

---

117 960 (reis). Sim. 1818-22.... 20.00

Gold

118 (6400 reis). JOANNES VI D.G.
PORT. BRAS etc. Bust. Rev.
Arms. 14.3 gr. 1818-22R ..850.00

For similar gold w/out mmk, see PORTUGAL.

Provincial Gold Coinage

119 4000 (reis). Arms. Rev. JOANNES
VI etc. Cross. Date btwn.
flowers. (Rio). 1818-22....300.00

119a —. Date btwn. crosses.
(Bahia). 1819-20.........500.00

Independent Empire Pedro I 1822-31

Countermarked Copper

120 20 (reis). Round 18mm.
cmk. on earlier X reis coins:
"20" in cwnd. wreath. Rev.
globe on cross in circle of
stars (Imp. arms). N.D.
(1822)................. RRR

121 40 (reis) on XX reis. Sim.
(1822)................375.00

122 80 (reis) on XL reis. Sim.
(1822)................500.00

Regular Issue Copper

R, B and SP mints.

125 10 (reis). Like No. 126.
1824-28................. 2.00

★126 20 (reis). 1823-30 (22R,
31R=counterfeits)....... 1.50

126a —. Cmkd. 10 (reis)....... 1.00

127 40 (reis). Sim. 1823-31..... 1.50

127a —. Cmkd. 20 (reis)....... 1.00

128 80 (reis). Sim. 1823-31..... 1.50

128a —. Cmkd. 40 (reis)....... 1.00

128b —. 1825-29 SP.......... 4.00

128c —. No. 128b. Cmkd.
40 (reis)............... 5.00

Regional Copper

Size reduced. G, C and M mints.

129 20 (reis). Like No. 126.
1825C (29G=counterfeit)..12.50

129a —. Cmkd. 10 (reis)...... ——

130 37½ (reis). Sim. 1823-28M. 7.50

130a —. Cmkd. 10 (reis)...... 7.50

131 40 (reis). Sim. 1823-31..... 2.50

131a —. Cmkd. 10 (reis)....... 1.50

132 75 (reis). Sim. 1823G.....25.00

132a —. Cmkd. 20 (reis).....12.50

133 80 (reis). Sim. 1826-31..... 2.50

133a —. Cmkd. 20 (reis)...... 1.00

Silver

134 80 (reis). Like No. 135.
1824, 26...............600.00

★135 160 (reis). 1824, 26.......225.00

136 320 (reis). Sim. 1824-30....25.00

137 640 (reis). Sim. 1824-27....20.00

★138 960 (reis). Sim. 1823-27....25.00

Gold

139 (6400 reis). Head. Rev. Arms.
1822. Coronation........6000.00

140 4000 (reis). Bust in uniform.
Rev. IN HOC etc. Arms.
1823-28................600.00

141 6400 (reis). Sim.
1823-30................1800.00

Pedro II 1831-89

Copper

Types of last reign. R and SP mints.

145 20 (reis). Like No. 126 but
PETRUS II etc. 1832R.....125.00

145a —. Cmkd. 10 (reis)......150.00

146 40 (reis). Sim. 1823R
(31R=counterfeit, 33R=
pattern)................. 5.00

146a —. Cmkd. 20 (reis)....... 2.00

BRAZIL

INDEPENDENT EMPIRE (Cont.)

Fine

147 80 (reis). 1831-32R....... 1.50
147a —. Cmkd. 40 (reis)....... .75
147b —. 1832 SP.......Counterfeit!

Regional Copper

Size reduced. G and C mints.
148 40 (reis). Sim. 1832G (var.),
   33C.................... 5.00
148a —. Cmkd. 10 (reis)....... 1.00
148b —. 1833C. Cmkd. 20 (reis). 2.00
149 80 (reis). Sim. 1832-33G... 4.00
149a —. Cmkd. 20 (reis)....... 1.50
149b —. 1833G. PETRUS I.......30.00
149c —. No. 149b. Cmkd.
   20 (reis)............. 5.00

Local Countermarks

Applied about 1829-35 to Imperial coins, reducing their value. Prices are for clear cmks. on appropriate coins. These, as well as other Brazilian cmks., have been much counterfeited.

A. Ceará (1834).

Cmk. 5 pointed star with C-E-A-R-A in points.

Copper

150 (★=10 reis) on 20 reis.....10.00
151 (★=20 reis) on 40 reis.....10.00
152 (★=40 reis) on 80 reis.....10.00

Some authorities claim that the CEARA cmk. is not genuine on any silver coins.

B. Maranhão (1834).

Cmk. M/roman numerals, in rectangle

Copper

154 V (reis) on 20 reis........30.00

★155 X (reis) on 40 reis........11.00
156 XX (reis) on 80 reis......11.00

C. Maranhão (1835).
Cmk. "M."

Copper

157 (M=10 reis) on 20 reis....30.00
158 (M=20 reis) on 40 reis....11.00
159 (M=40 reis) on 80 reis....11.00

D. Pará (1835).

Cmkd. crude numerals of value in indent.

Copper

Fine

160 10 (reis) on XX reis...... 1.75

★161 10 (reis) on 40 reis. G or C
   mints................. 2.25
162 20 (reis) on XL reis...... 1.35
163 20 (reis) on 80 reis. G or C.. 2.25
164 20 (reis) on 40 reis. R or B.. 1.35
165 40 (reis) on LXXX reis.... 1.75

E. The ICO, YCO, IGO, and JGO cmks. are false.

Regular Imperial Minor Coinage Resumed

Bronze

F-VF

169 10 R(ei)s. Like No. 170.
   1868-70.................. .75

★170 20 R(ei)s. 1868-70........1.00
171 40 R(ei)s. Sim. 1873-80.....1.00

Copper-Nickel

The 50 reis 1871 like No. 174 did not circulate. RRR.

173 100 REIS. Like No. 174.
   1871-85..................1.00

★174 200 REIS. 1871-84........1.00

F-VF

★175 50 REIS. 1886-88.......... .85
176 100 REIS. Sim. 1886-89... .65
177 200 REIS. Sim. 1886-89....1.00

Silver
First Issue

VF-EF

178 80 (reis). Like No. 179.
   1833..................400.00

★179 160 (reis). 1833..........450.00
180 320 (reis). Sim. 1833.......RR
181 640 (reis). Sim. 1832-33..2000.00
182 960 (reis). Sim. 1832-34..1500.00

Second Issue

183 100 (reis). Like No. 185.
   1834-48..................30.00
184 200 (reis). Sim. 1835-48....35.00

★185 400 (reis). 1834-48........65.00
186 800 (reis). Sim. 1835-46...400.00
187 1200 (reis). Sim. 1834-47..150.00

Dates of second issue not shown above are counterfeit.

Third Issue

V.F.

188 500 (reis). Like No. 185.
   1849-52..................10.00
189 1000 (reis). Sim. 1849-52...12.50
190 2000 (reis). Sim. 1851-52...15.00

Dates of third issue not shown above are either counterfeits or essays.

BRAZIL

INDEPENDENT EMPIRE (Cont.)

Fourth Issue

V.F.

191 200 (reis). Like No. 193.
1854-67.................. 4.00

192 500 (reis). Sim. 1853-67.... 4.50

★193 1000 (reis). 1853-66...... 6.50

194 2000 (reis). Sim. 1853-67...15.00

Fifth Issue

195 200 REIS. Like No. 196.
1867-69................. 5.00

★196 500 REIS. 1867-68........ 6.00

197 1000 REIS. Sim. 1869..... 9.00

198 2000 REIS. Sim. 1868-69,
75-76...................18.50

Sixth Issue

★199 500 REIS. 1876-89........ 5.00

200 1000 REIS. Sim. 1876-89..10.00

201 2000 REIS. Sim. 1886-89..13.50

Gold
First Issue

V F-EF

202 4000 (reis). Child head.
Rev. IN HOC etc. Arms. 1832-
33....................1200.00

203 6400 (reis). Sim. 1832-33..800.00

Second Issue

★204 (10,000 reis). 1833-40.....600.00

Third Issue

VF-EF

205 (10,000 reis). Uniformed bust.
Rev. Arms. 1841-48......950.00

Fourth Issue

206 (10,000 reis). Bust in court
dress. Rev. Arms. 1849-51.350.00

207 (20,000 reis). Sim. 29mm.
1849-51.................350.00

Fifth Issue

208 (20,000 reis). Head. Rev.
Arms. 1851-52..........275.00

Sixth Issue

209 (5,000 reis). Sim. 18mm.
1854-59................110.00

210 (10,000 reis). Sim. 22mm.
1853-89................150.00

211 (20,000 reis). Sim. 28.5mm.
1853-89................275.00

Republic of Piratini
(Republica Rio Grandense)
1835-45

Brazilian coins and other coins cmkd.
two hands grasping curved sword with
Liberty cap on its point, all in oval
indent, no legend (1835).......RRR

**All other Piratini cmks. are coun-
terfeit.**

BRITISH GUIANA

Former British possession on the northeast coast of South America. Taken
from the Batavian Republic (Netherlands) 1796, returned 1802, retaken
1803. Comprised of Berbice and Essequibo and Demerara, all united in
1831 to form British Guiana.

Monetary Systems:

Until 1839 — 20 stiver = 1 guilder
(gulden); 3 guilders =
12 bits = 5 shillings =
1 dollar.

After 1839 — 3⅛ guilders = 50 pence
= 100 cents = 1 dollar.

I. Essequibo and Demerara.

George III of England,
in E & D 1796-1802, 03-20

Countermarked Coins

Silver

V.F.

★1 3 B(i)TS. Disk cut from No. 2.
(1808)...................500.00

V.F.

★2 3 G(ui)l(ders). 8 reales from
which No. 1 removed.
(1808).................2500.00

Modern counterfeits of Nos. 1 and 2
are common. See III Pridmore 36.

Gold

3 (22 guilders) Brazilian Joe
(= 6400 reis). Cmkd. E.D. in
square. (Essequibo 1798-
99..............Unknown today

3a —. Cmkd. E.D. in oval.
(1798-99). Supposed to have
been for Demerara alone, but
apparently for both
colonies.................. *Rare*

Regular Coinage

Copper

Fine

4 HALF/STIVER. Like No. 5.
1813.................... 2.50

★5 ONE/STIVER. 1813....... 4.50

Silver

F-VF

6 ¼ (guilder). Like No. 9.
1809.................... 7.50

7 ½ (guilder). Sim. 1809.....12.50

8 1 (guilder). Sim. 1809......22.50

BRITISH GUIANA

		F-VF
*9	2 (guilders). 1809	85.00
10	3 (guilders). Sim. 1809	400.00

		V.F.
11	¼ (guilder). Like No. 13. 1816	10.00
12	½ (guilder). Sim. 1816	12.00

*13	1 (guilder). 1816	17.50
14	2 (guilders). Sim. 1816	80.00
15	3 (guilders). Sim. 1816	350.00

William IV 1830-37

Silver

16	⅛ (guilder). Like No. 18. 1832, 35	7.50
17	¼ (guilder). Sim. 1832-35	7.50

*18	½ (guilder). 1832, 35	11.00
19	1 (guilder). Sim. 1832-35	16.50
20	2 (guilders). Sim. 1832	100.00
21	3 (guilders). Sim. 1832	550.00

II. British Guiana.

Silver

22	⅛/GUILDER. Like No. 18 but legend BRITISH GUIANA. 1836	7.50

		V.F.
23	¼/GUILDER. Sim. 1836	7.50
24	½/GUILDER. Sim. 1836	10.00
25	ONE/GUILDER. Sim. 1836	17.50

*26	FOUR PENCE. 1836-37	6.00

Note: The above 4d circulated in more than one colony.

BRITISH HONDURAS
(MOSQUITO COAST)

Colony in Central America. First settled by shipwrecked sailors 1638. Promoted from "settlement" to "colony" in 1864. Subservient to Jamaica until 1884.

George III 1760-1820

Monetary System:

6s.8d. (Jamaican) = 8 reales.

Cmkd. Silver

		Fine
1	(8 reales). Cwnd. GR script (relief) in rectangular or oval indent, cmkd. on Spanish-American dollars dated 1806-1818 (applied circa 1810-18)	200.00

Notes: The cwnd. script GR incuse cmk. is probably a modern concoction. The cmk. cwnd. GR in an octagonal indent is a 20th century fabrication. See III Pridmore 59, 282-283.

BRITISH WEST INDIES.
See CARIBBEAN ISLANDS AND TERRITORIES.

BUKHARA.
See TURKESTAN (Bukhara).

CAMBODIA, Kingdom

Khmer state in South Indo-China. Powerful Hindu kingdom 5th-14th centuries AD, thereafter declined and was intermittently subject to Annam or Siam. Submitted to French protectorate 1863.

Monetary System:

64 att = 32 pe = 8 fuang = 4 salong (sleng) = 1 baht (tical).

I. North Cambodia.

Under Siam 1794-1907. Anonymous coinage issued in Battambang and Siem Reap provinces to ca. 1902. These were originally (16th cent.) issued in good silver, valued at 1 salong. As they were gradually debased, they were later revalued at 1 fuang; finally at 1 pe as they approached pure copper. Coins were hand-struck to 1880, machine-struck thereafter.

Billon

V.F.

*★13 *(fuang)*. Hamza bird. Rev. blank. 11-16mm. ND (ca. 17th-mid-19th cent.)...... 5.00

Copper (Plain or Silver-washed)

*★10 *(pe)*. Hamza bird, Chinese "chi" (luck) in square above. Rev. blank. 11-15mm. ND (ca. 1860-80).......... 4.00

*★14 (pe). Garuda bird. Rev. mint name. 14mm. ND (ca. 1880-1902)............... 4.50

II. Khmer Kingdom.

Coins struck at Udong in 1847 for the investiture of Ang Duong. Nos. 20, 22 and 22a are unique among world coinage in bearing dates in four different calendar systems (all equivalent to AD 1847).

Ang Duong, AD1841-59

Copper

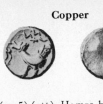

V.F.

*★16 (ex 5) (att). Hamza bird, date above. Rev. blank. 13-14mm. Rev. blank............... 6.00

17 (pe). Sim. 15-16mm.......15.00

Silver

19 (fuang). Hamza bird, no legend. Rev. single-towered pagoda. 1.75 gr. 9-14mm. ND.......................RR

*★20 (salong). Sim. but obv. dates around bird. 3.2 gr. 20-22mm...................RR

22 (baht). Sim. but rev. 3-towered pagoda. 15.2 gr. 35mm....................75.00

*★22a —. 15.2 gr. 30mm.......65.00

The sim. 3 baht (44mm) is a pattern. The "gold fuang" (former No. 40) is a private fantasy.

CANADA

Under France until 1763. To England thereafter. The regular 1 and 2 sol billon coins of France circulated here, as well as in the French West Indies. A number of regal and non-regal tokens were struck for the Canadian Provinces before adoption of the decimal system in 1858. The authorized bank and regal tokens, which have most of the characteristics of coins, are listed below.

Monetary System:

120 sous = 60 pence = 6 livres = 5 shillings = 1 dollar.

I. French Canada (Nouvelle France).

No coinage was struck by France specifically for Canada. For some of the general colonial issues used in this region, see FRENCH COLONIES Nos. 1, 2, 3, 5, 6.

II. Lower (Bas) Canada (Quebec Province).

Copper

VG-F

*★1 UN(=1)/SOUS. N.D. (1835).................... 1.75

2 UN/SOUS. Sim. but BANK OF MONTREAL. N.D. (1836).................... 1.75

*★3 UN/SOU. BANQUE DU PEUPLE. Star and Liberty cap at 9 and 3 o'clock on rev. N.D. (1837).................... 3.50

4 UN/SOU. Sim. but no star or cap. N.D. (1838).......... 1.50

Note: Many other "bouquet" sous, varieties of the foregoing, all inscribed TOKEN/MONTREAL, but without the name of the issuing bank, were privately struck during the period 1837-38.

*★5 UN (=1) SOU. Rev. CITY BANK on ribbon. 1837...... 2.00

5a —. QUEBEC BANK. 1837..... 2.00

5b —. BANQUE DU PEUPLE. 1837.................... 2.75

5c —. BANK OF MONTREAL. 1837.................... 2.25

CANADA

LOWER CANADA (Cont.)

VG-F

6 DEUX (=2) SOUS (=1 penny). Sim. CITY BANK. 1837...... 2.50

6a —. QUEBEC BANK. 1837..... 2.50

6b —. BANQUE DU PEUPLE. 1837.................... 3.50

6c —. BANK OF MONTREAL. 1837.................. 2.25

V.F.

★7 HALF PENNY. 1838-39 . .150.00

8 ONE PENNY. Sim. 1838-39................300.00

Nos. 7 and 8 were rejected because of poor quality.

III. Province of Canada.

Copper

VG-F

★13 HALF PENNY. 1842, 44... 1.25

14 ONE PENNY. Sim. 1842 .. 3.00

★15 HALF PENNY. 1852...... 1.75

16 ONE PENNY. Sim. 1852... 2.50

★17 ONE HALF-PENNY. 1850-57.................. 1.00

18 ONE PENNY. Sim. 1850-57................. 1.50

IV. New Brunswick.

See Yeoman, *Modern World Coins*, for half penny and penny tokens dated 1843 and 1854.

V. Nova Scotia.

Copper

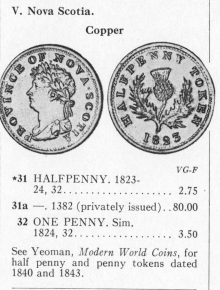

VG-F

★31 HALFPENNY. 1823-24, 32.................. 2.75

31a —. 1382 (privately issued). .80.00

32 ONE PENNY. Sim. 1824, 32.................. 3.50

See Yeoman, *Modern World Coins*, for half penny and penny tokens dated 1840 and 1843.

VI. Prince Edward Island.

Silver

★41 (shilling). 17mm. disk from No. 42, cmkd. rayed sun. ND (1813)...............800.00

★42 (5 shillings). Spanish-American 8 reales from which No. 41 removed. Cmkd. rayed sun. ND (1813)...............600.00

All Canadian tokens of this period not listed above are deemed unofficial.

CARIBBEAN ISLANDS AND TERRITORIES

Nearly all of the cut and counterstamped coins listed in this catalog were produced in the islands in or adjacent to the Caribbean Sea. Convenience has dictated that these coins be listed in one place for easy reference. Similarities between the crude coins of this area far outweigh differences arising from the identity of the nation then controlling a given piece of Caribbean real property.

ANTIGUA

British possession in the Leeward Islands, West Indies. The farthing token dated 1836 was privately issued by Hannay and Coltart, merchants, probably about 1850.

William IV 1830-37

Copper

Fine

★1 ONE/FARTHING. Palm. Rev. value. 1836.........27.50

BAHAMAS

British island possession in the Atlantic southeast of Florida.

George III 1760-1820

Copper

V.F.

★1 (penny). Engrailed edge. 1806....................35.00

Proof restrikes exist dated 1806-07 with reverses struck from rusty dies. The 1806 restrikes have plain edges.

CARIBBEAN ISLANDS AND TERRITORIES

BARBADOS

Erstwhile British colony in the West Indies.

Monetary System:

12 pence = 1 shilling; 75 pence = 10 bits = 5 pistareens = 8 reales.

Cut Silver

Cut Spanish American circulated in Barbados 1704-1838 w/out cmk. A pineapple cmk. on a center plug inserted into 2 and 8 reales coins is attributed by Pridmore to Barbados ca. 1791-99.

George III 1760-1820

Copper

		F-VF
★1	PENNY. Obv. like No. 3. Rev. ★. 1788	12.00
1a	—. Restrike......(Unc.)	50.00
2	HALF PENNY. Like No. 3. 1792	22.50
2a	—. Restrike......(Unc.)	85.00

★3	PENNY. 1792	15.00
3a	—. Restrike......(Unc.)	40.00

NOTE: Restrikes of Nos. 1-3 were struck in a collar. Originals were not.

BERBICE

The Brazilian and other gold coins cmkd. with a script "B," previously attributed to Berbice, are said at III Pridmore, page 30, not to be attributable on present knowledge to any locality.

BRITISH WEST INDIES

General coinage for all British colonies using the Spanish-American "dollar" (8 reales). Coins of the same type dated 1820 were struck for MAURITIUS. Part of the 1822 series was also struck for that place, but when Mauritius turned to sterling in 1826, dollar series coins on hand were shipped to B.W.I.

George IV 1820-30

Silver

		Fine
1	XVI (=1/16 dollar). Like No. 3. 1822	6.00
2	VIII (=⅛ dollar). Sim. 1822	7.00

★3	IV (=¼ dollar). 1822	8.00
4	II (=½ dollar). Sim. 1822	100.00

CURAÇAO

Netherlands West Indian island possession off the coast of Venezuela. Taken from Spain by Dutch West India Company 1634. Handed over by the Company to the States General 1787. Occupied twice by British during the Napoleonic Wars, the latest being the period 1807-16. Returned to Netherlands 1816.

Monetary Systems:

Until 1826, 6 stuivers = 1 reaal (schelling). Originally 8 reaals = 1 peso. This became 10 reaals = 1 peso in the late 18th century. 12 reaals = 1 peso (1801-26).

After 1827 — 100 cents = 40 stuivers = 4 reaals = 1 gulden.

During the early 19th century the Curaçao reaal sank to 1/18 peso.

A. Batavian Republic in Curaçao 1799-1803.

Cut and Cmkd. Silver

		Fine
1	(3 reaals = 18 stuivers). Cut ¼ of peso cmkd. 5 leafed rosace in circle. N.D. (1801)	400.00

Gold

1.5 (8 pesos). Portuguese "Joe" cmkd. GI, L, MH and B at 12, 3, 6 and 9 o'clock, GH in middle. Rev. cmk. W(illemstad). (1799)......RRR

B. British Occupation 1807-16.

Cut and Cmkd. Silver

		Fine
2	21 (stuiver = 3½ reaals). No. 1 with additional cmk: 21 in oval. (1814) 6.73 gr.	RR

★3	(3 reaals). 1/5 of peso cmkd. like No. 1. (1814) 5.39 gr.	60.00

Gold

4 22 (gulden). Portuguese "Joe" cmkd. 22 in square. (See III Pridmore 31)...... ——

Beware: The cut and cmkd. coins of Curaçao have been extensively counterfeited.

C. Netherlands Restored 1816.

(Willem I 1813-40) Cut and Cmkd. Silver

5	3 (reaals). 1/5 of peso cmkd. like No. 5a but 3 in plain circle. (1818)	60.00

★5a	—. 1/5 of peso cmkd. 3 in dentilated circle. (Privately made 1819-25)	60.00
6	5 (reaals). 1/3 of peso cmkd. 5 in plain circle. (1818)	RRR

Note: The various foreign silver coins cmkd. 3, 5, 7, 9, 14 and 18, often with "C" in addition, are not attributable to Curaçao (see III Pridmore 286).

7 (25 cents). ¼ of Netherlands gulden cmkd. C. (1838)....*400.00*

Struck Silver

★8	1/stuiver. 1822 (mostly struck 1840-41)	45.00

★8.5	¼ (reaal). CURA/CAO. Rev. value/1821	*Unique?*

CURAÇAO (Cont.)

V.F.

★9 1/REAAL. 1821.........120.00

DANISH WEST INDIES (DANSK VESTINDIEN)

Islands in the Lesser Antilles acquired by the Danish West Indies Company in 1671. Bought by the United States in 1917 and now known as the U.S. Virgin Islands.

Monetary Systems

Until 1849 – 96 skilling = 1 daler; 1849-1904 – 100 cents = 1 daler.

Christian VI of Denmark 1730-46

Copper

V.G.

1 I/SKILLING. Like No. 2. 1740...................150.00

★2 II/SKILLING. Double C6 mon. Rev. value. 1740.........150.00

Silver

VG-F

★3 XII SKIL(ling). Double C6 mon. Rev. Ship. 1740.......30.00

Frederik V of Denmark 1746-66

Silver

VG-F

★4 XII SKIL(ling). Bust. Rev. Ship. 1748...........30.00

5 XII SKILL(ing). Like No. 6 but FOR DE DANSK AMERIC. INSULER. 1748.................25.00

5a —. Like No. 6. 1757-65.....12.50

★6 XXIIII SKILL(ing). Double F5 mon. Rev. Ship. 1763-65....12.50

Gold

E.F.

★7 (ducat). King on horseback. Rev. Arms with DWC. 3.5 gr. 1749...................1500.00

8 (2 ducats). Sim. 7 gr. 1749....RR

Christian VII of Denmark 1766-1808

Silver

VG-F

9 VI SKILL(ing). Like No. 11 but C7 mon. 1767.........30.00

10 XII SKILL(ing). Like No. 11. 1767.............10.00

★11 XXIIII SKILL(ing). CVII mon. Rev. ship. 1766-67...................17.50

Frederik VI of Denmark 1808-39

Silver

Fine

★12 II/SKILLING. Arms. Rev. value. 1816, 37...........12.50
13 X/SKILLING. Sim. 1816...17.50
14 XX/SKILLING. Sim. 1816.25.00

Christian VIII of Denmark 1839-48

Silver

15 II/SKILLING. Like No. 12. 1847.................12.50

★16 X/SKILLING. 1840-47...................15.00
17 XX/SKILLING. Sim. 1840-47...................20.00

Frederik VII of Denmark 1848-63

A. Skilling System Silver.

18 II/SKILLING. Like No. 12. 1848.................10.00
19 X/SKILLING. Sim. 1848...15.00
20 XX/SKILLING. Sim. 1848.20.00

B. Coins Countermarked 1849-59.

Copper

21 ½ cent. FR VII mon. cmkd. on foreign ½ cent..........75.00
22 1 cent. Sim...............75.00

Silver

23 10 cents. Sim............100.00
24 ¼ dollar. Sim.........150.00
25 ½ dollar. Sim.........350.00

★26 dollar. Sim...............750.00

Nos. 21-26 have been extensively counterfeited. See Byrne, "The Nobles and the Rogues," May 1967 *Numismatist.*

DANISH WEST INDIES (Cont.)

Coinage Resumed

Bronze

		Fine
★27	1/CENT. Arms. Rev. value. 1859-60	3.00

Silver

★28 3/CENTS. 1859 . . . . 5.00

★29 5 CENTS. 1859 . . . . 4.00

30 10 CENTS. Head. Rev. sugar cane. 1859, 62 . . . . 7.00

31 20 CENTS. Like No. 29. 1859, 62 . . . . 10.00

DOMINICA

A British island possession in the West Indies.

Monetary System (circa 1761-1862): Until 1798: 10 bits = 7s.6d. = 1 dollar
1798-1813: 11 bits = 8s.3d. = 1 dollar
1813 onward: 12 bits = 10 shillings = 1 dollar

Cut and Cmkd. Silver

(List very substantially revised in light of Pridmore's findings.)

Type I 1761-64

Spanish and Spanish-American coins center-punched with crude heart shape.

		Fine
1	(½ bit) from ½ real	Rare
2	(1 bit) from real	Rare
3	(2 bits) from 2 reales	100.00
4	(5 bits) from 4 reales	RRR
5	(10 bits) from 8 reales	750.00

Type II 1764

Spanish and Spanish-American coins center-punched with more true heart shape.

		Fine
6	(½ bit) from ½ real	Rare
7	(1 bit) from real	Rare
8	(2 bits) from 2 reales	100.00
9	(5 bits) from 4 reales	RRR
10	(10 bits) from 8 reales	750.00

Type III 1765

Spanish and Spanish-American coins center-punched with true heart, patterned borders.

11	(½ bit) from ½ real	Rare
12	(1 bit) from 1 real	Rare
13	(2 bits) from 2 reales	100.00
14	(5 bits) from 4 reales	RRR
15	(10 bits) from 8 reales	750.00

Type IV 1770-72

Spanish and Spanish-American coins center-punched with blunt heart, patterned borders.

16	(½ bit) from ½ real	100.00
17	(1 bit) from 1 real	100.00

★18	(2 bits) from 2 reales	100.00
19	(5 bits) from 4 reales	RR
20	(10 bits) from 8 reales	400.00

Various Mutilations 1798-1818

21 (1½ bits = "moco"). 14mm disk with 15 crenelles on edge, cut from No. 22, cmkd. script D ringed by droplets. ND (1798) 35.00

22 (11 bits). Spanish-American 8 reales from which No. 21 removed. ND (1798) 225.00

23 16 (bits). No. 22 cmkd. cwnd. 16. (1813) 300.00

24 (2 bits). Spanish pistareen (debased 2 reales) with 17mm disk removed. N.D. (1816) . . 50.00

25 3 (bits). Cwnd. 3 on ½ of 23mm disk cut from pillar dollar. N.D. (1813) 200.00

26 2 (shillings) 6 (pence). Cut ¼ of 8 reales cmkd. 2.6. N.D. (1816-18) 160.00

27 4 (bits). Cwnd. 4 on 23mm ring cut from No. 22 after No. 21 removed. N.D. (1813) 300.00

Fine

★28 6 (bits). 23mm disk from No. 29, cmkd. cwnd. 6. ND (1813) 50.00

29 12 (bits). Spanish-American 8 reales from which No. 28 (or 21 and 27) removed, cmkd. cwnd. 12 four times. ND (1813) 500.00

Beware of numerous modern counterfeits of Nos. 1-29. See III Pridmore.

DUTCH WEST INDIES.
See Netherlands West Indies.

GRENADA

One of the Windward Islands in the Caribbean. British colony.

Monetary System: 1 bit = 9 pence.
1787-98: 11 bits = 8 shillings, 3 pence = 1 dollar.
1798-*1840:* 12 bits = 9 shillings = 1 dollar.

George III 1760-1820

Silver

Fine (cmk.)

1 (bit). Wedge-shaped. 1/11 of Spanish-American dollar cmkd. G (1787) 60.00

1.5 1 (bit). GS G 1 or TR G 1 cmkd. on cut ⅓ of 2 reales. *(1818)* 90.00

2 2 (bits). Cut ⅙ of 8 reales with sim. cmks. (1814) 90.00

3 4 (bits). Cut ⅓ of 8 reales with sim. cmks. (1814) 175.00

4 6 (bits). Cut ½ of 8 reales with sim. cmks. (1814) 275.00

Gold

★10 (66 shillings). Light Portuguese or Brazilian 6400 reis. IW (or *WS* or *JR*) script plug to bring up weight. Cmkd. 3 Gs near edge. (1798) . . . . Rare

CARIBBEAN ISLANDS AND TERRITORIES

GRENADA (Cont.)

Fine (cmk.)

10.5 (66 shillings). Heavier 6400 reis cmkd. 3 Gs near edge. (1798).................Rare

11 (72 shillings). Full weight 6400 reis. Cmkd. G in middle.........Unknown today

The coins of Grenada have been extensively counterfeited.

GUADELOUPE

French colony in the Caribbean, consisting of 2 large and 5 small islands.

Monetary System:

12 deniers = 1 sou; 15 sous = 1 escalin; 20 sous = 1 livre; 82 livres 10 sous = 4 gold escudos or 6400 reis.

I. French Administration prior to 1810.

Copper

Fine (cmk.)

★2 (3 sous, 9 deniers). RF in oval cmkd. on FRENCH COLONIES No. 4. (1793).............40.00

Note: All other coins with this RF cmk. are modern concoctions.

Silver

14 (escalin). ⅛ of the ring from No. 16, cmkd. RF. (1802)..100.00

★16 4 E(scalins)/R(epublique) F(rancais) on 21mm octagonal plug cut from silver dollar. (1802)...................... ——

Gold

21 (4 escudos). Cmkd. G in 15 pointed circular indent. (1803)....................RR

Note: Copper and silver coins bearing No. 21 cmk. are modern concoctions.

Fine (cmk.)

22 20# and small human head in rectangular indent cmkd. on low quality 4 escudos. With or w/out additional cmk. 20 in rectangle. (1804)....... RR

24 Similar cmks. except 22# and 22 in lieu of 20# and 20 on good quality 4 escudos. (1804)..................... RR

Note: Nos. 22 and 24 were formerly listed under ST. MARTIN.

For Isle Desirade

31 Cmkd. G(uadeloupe) L(a) D(esirade)................ ——

33 Cmkd. I–lis–D........... ——

For Grande Terre

41 Cmkd. GT in dentilated rectangle................ ——

43 Cmkd. GT punched........ ——

45 Cmkd. GT monogram...... ——

For Les Saintes

51 Cmkd. I G in heart-shaped depression. Rev. Cmk. L S.. ——

Pridmore omits Nos. 31-51.

II. British Occupation 1810-16.

Silver

61 (10 sous). Spanish ½ real, English 3 pence or French 6 sol cmkd. cwnd. G. (1811)....................75.00

62 (20 sous). Sim. Cmkd. on real, 6 pence or 12 sol. (1811)....60.00

64 (20 sous). G radiate on 12mm square with 12 crenations cut from Spanish-American dollar. 3 gr. (1811).............100.00

★66 These are modern concoctions.

68 (40 sous). English shilling or French 24 sol cmkd. as No. 61. (1811)............50.00

70 (2 livres 5 sous). Cut ¼ dollar cmkd. cwnd. G in each corner. (1813)....................65.00

72 (9 livres). Dollar from which No. 64 removed. Cmkd. cwnd. G. 23.97 gr. (1811).......400.00

Note: The foregoing coins have been extensively counterfeited. Concoctions of No. 72 appear on French, U.S. and British dollars.

Gold

75 (82 livres, 10 sous). 4 escudo cmkd. (a) 82.10 in rectangular indent, and (b) cwnd. G. Known on 1759-99 R(io). (1811)..................... RR

HAITI (HAYTI)

A negro republic occupying the western third of the Island of Hispaniola in the West Indies. Originally the whole island was Spanish but France acquired present day Haiti in the 17th century, calling it St. Domingue (see SANTO DOMINGO for coins). In the late 18th century the French were ousted by a slave revolt led by Toussaint l'Ouverture. Full independence was achieved in 1804 (first year of the Republic = AN 1 = 1803). Spain reoccupied the eastern end of the island 1806-22. In 1807 Haiti, on the western end, split into warring northern and southern governments. General Boyer became master of the whole island in 1822. In 1844 the Spanish speaking people on the east end broke away to form the Dominican Republic (see Modern World Coins).

Monetary System:

Until about 1809 —
  12 deniers = 1 sol; 20 sols = 1 livre.
  Circa 1804-10: 100 centimes = 1 franc.
About 1810 on —
  100 centimes = 1 gourde.

There are numerous die varieties of most Haitian coins through 1850.

Henri Christophe, in North Haiti, President 1806-10, King 1810-20

Note: Former No. 11 and all coins of Henri Christophe after 1809 are patterns.

Silver

Fine

15 7 (sols) 6 (deniers). Like No. 17. 1807-09...............70.00

★17 15 S(ols). 1807-08..........60.00

Alexandre Petion, in South Haiti, President 1807-18

Silver

21 6 C(entimes). Like No. 23. An 10....................75.00

22 12 C(entimes). Sim. An 10-12, XI..............15.00

★23 25 C(entimes). An 10-13, XI........................ 6.00

CARIBBEAN ISLANDS AND TERRITORIES

....

HAITI (Cont.)

Fine

24 6 C(entimes). Like No. 25.
An 15 . . . . Rare

*25 12 C(entimes). An 14 . . . . . . 6.00

26 25 C(entimes). Sim. An 14 . . 4.00

General Jean Pierre Boyer,
In South Haiti 1818-22,
In the whole Island 1822-43

Copper

VG-F

31 UN (=1)/CENTIME. Like
No. 32. 1828-42 . . . . 3.00

*32 DEUX (=2)/CENTIMES.
1828-42 . . . . 3.00

Silver

Fine

33 6 C(entimes). Like No. 35.
An 15 . . . . 22.50

34 12 C(entimes). Sim.
An 24-26 . . . . 7.00

*35 25 C(entimes). An 15-31 . . . . 4.00

36 50 C(entimes). Sim.
An 24-30 . . . . 6.00

37 100 C(entimes). Sim.
An 26-30 . . . . 15.00

Louis Pierrot,
President in West,
April 16, 1845 to March 1, 1846
Jean Baptiste Riche,
President in West,
March 1, 1846 to February 27, 1847

Copper

The division of Nos. 41-43 and 51-53
between Presidents Pierrot and Riche
as shown in the first two editions of this
work apparently was first advocated by
Fonrobert. Recent study has cast doubt
on this division. The series actually
consists of three major groups with
many die varieties. Until further research clarifies the murk, the Fonrobert
division must be abandoned and the
whole series assigned to both presidents
without distinction.

Group I

Small Phrygian cap folds left.

Fine

*41 UN (=1)/CENTIME.
22mm. 1846 . . . . 2.50

42 DEUX (=2)/CENTIMES.
Sim. 26mm. 1846 . . . . 2.00

43 6 C(entimes and) ¼. Sim.
1846 . . . . 10.00

Group II

Larger Phrygian cap droops both sides.
Leaves on inside of wreath only.

*51 UN (=1)/CENTIME.
21mm. 1846 . . . . 2.00

52 DEUX (=2)/CENTIMES.
Sim. 24mm. 1846 . . . . 4.00

Group III

Large Phrygian cap droops right.

*51a UN (=1)/CENTIME.
21mm. 1846 . . . . 2.00

52a DEUX (=2)/CENTIMES.
Sim. 24mm. 1846 . . . . 2.00

53 SIX CENTIMES. Sim.
1846 . . . . 5.00

Faustin Soloque Robespierre
Napoleon, President in NW
February 27, 1847 to
August 26, 1849, Emperor as
Faustin I 1849-58

I. As President.

Copper

F-VF

61 DEUX (=2)/CENTIMES.
Like No. 62. 1849 . . . . 50.00

Fine

*62 SIX CENTIMES. 1849 . . . . 30.00

II. As Emperor.

F-VF

66 UN (=1)/CENTIME. Like
No. 67. 1850 . . . . 75.00

*67 DEUX (=2)/CENTIMES.
1850 . . . . 55.00

68 SIX CENTIMES. Sim.
1850 . . . . *Rare*

69 UN (=1) CENTIME. Like
No. 70. 1850 . . . . 2.50

*70 DEUX (=2)/CENTIMES.
1850 . . . . 2.50

CARIBBEAN ISLANDS AND TERRITORIES

HAITI (Cont.)

F-VF

★71 SIX CENTIMES UN QUART (=6¼ c). 1850.... 6.00

Coins of Faustin not listed are patterns.

ISLES DU VENT (WINDWARD ISLANDS)

Certain French possessions in the Lesser Antilles.

Monetary System:
20 sols = 1 livre.

Louis XV of France, 1715-74

Silver

Fine

1 (6 sols). Like No. 2. 17mm. 1731-32...........35.00

★2 (12 sols). 1731-32.........20.00

JAMAICA

A former British colony in the West Indies.

Monetary System:
8 reales = 6 shillings, 8 pence.

George II 1727-60
Cmkd. Silver (1758)

Fine

★1 ½ real. Cmkd. GR in circular indent...................150.00

2 1 real. Sim. 250.00

3 2 reales. Sim. 750.00

Fine

4 4 reales. Sim. 1250.00

5 8 reales. Sim. 400.00

The indent increases in diameter on the larger coins.

Cmkd. Gold (1758)

★10 2 escudos. Cmkd. like No. 1. RRR

12 8 escudos. Sim. ....RRR

The ½, 1 and 4 escudos with this cmk. have not been seen.

Note: The cwnd. GR in octagonal indent cmk. often assigned to Jamaica is a 20th century fabrication (see III Pridmore 282-283). See BRITISH HONDURAS for cmk. cwnd. script GR in indent.

William IV 1830-37

Silver

V.F.

★21 1½ (pence). 1834-37....... 4.00

No. 21 corresponded to ¼ real. Also used elsewhere in the British West Indies, and in Ceylon, Mauritius, and Sierra Leone.

MARTINIQUE

French possession in the West Indies. Held by the British on several occasions in the late 18th and early 19th centuries.

Monetary System:
12 deniers = 1 sol; 15 sols = 1 escalin; 20 sols = 1 livre; 66 livres = 4 escudos or 6400 reis.

A. British Occupation 1793-1801.

Silver

Fine

11 (escalin). Cut ⅓ of 2 reales, crenated edges. (1797)......35.00

13 (3 escalins). Cut ¼ of 8 reales, crenated edges. (1797)......45.00

Beware forgeries of Nos. 11 and 13.

Gold

Fine

21 (66 livres). Portuguese 4 escudos plugged to restore them to 11.67 gr. AR or FA cmkd. on plug. (1798)..... Rare

B. French Restored 1802-09.

Gold

31 Light Portuguese and Brazilian 6400 reis cmkd. 20 (livres per gros)/eagle in indent. (1805)............. Rare

32 Good weight 6400 reis cmkd. 22 (livres per gros)/eagle in indent (1805) ....Rare

Nos. 31 and 32 have been extensively forged.

Pridmore omits all countermarked copper and billon coins commonly attributed to Martinique. He states that most are modern concoctions and that there is presently no evidence that any of the rest were officially struck.

MONTSERRAT

A British island possession in the West Indies.

Monetary System:

6 black dogs (see FRENCH COLONIES No. 6) = 9 pence = 1 bit;
1740-87: 10 bits = 1 dollar
1787-98: 11 bits = 1 dollar
1798 on: 12 bits = 1 dollar

George III 1760-1820

Billon

Good

1 (black dog). 2 sous of Cayenne cmkd. M (in relief) in circular indent. (ca 1785-1801)......12.50

Silver circa 1785-1801

5 (½ bit). Cut ¼ of Spanish 2 reales cmkd. M (in relief) in square.................RRR

6 (bit). Cut ½ of 2 reales cmkd. as No. 5...........85.00

8 (⅛ dollar). Cut ⅛ of 8 reales cmkd. as No. 5.....RRR

10 (¼ dollar). Cut ¼ of 8 reales. Obv. cmkd. pointed cross. Rev. cmkd. M (as No. 5) in each corner...........150.00

11 (¼ dollar). Spanish-American 2 reales cmkd. pointed cross...................150.00

13 (dollar). Spanish-American 8 reales cmkd. 3 pointed crosses.................RRR

Notes:
1. The cwn/numeral/M cmk. frequently assigned to Montserrat has now been attributed to St. Bartholomew.
2. The coins of Montserrat have been extensively counterfeited. See III Pridmore.

CARIBBEAN ISLANDS AND TERRITORIES

NETHERLANDS WEST INDIES

General coinage for all West Indian possessions of the United Netherlands.

Monetary System:
20 stuiver = 1 gulden.

Silver

V.F.

*1 (2 stuiver). Cwnd. arms of the United Netherlands (lion with sword and bundle of arrows). Rev. W/1794............125.00

*2 ¼ G(u)L(den). 1794.......75.00
3 I G(u)L(den). Sim. 1794...175.00
4 3 G(u)L(den). Sim. 1794..3000.00

VF-EF

NEVIS

A British island possession in the West Indies.

Monetary System:
72 black dogs (see FRENCH COLONIES No. 6) = 9 shillings = 8 reales = 1 dollar.

Circa 1801

Billon
G-VG
1 Black dog cmkd. NEVIS.....65.00

Silver

5 Various worn silver coins cmkd. NEVIS and numeral 4, 6, 7 or 9 (= value in black dogs)....150.00

The coins of Nevis have been extensively counterfeited. See III Pridmore.

ST. BARTHOLOMEW

Island in the West Indies, located between St. Martin and St. Eustatius. To France 1639-1784, 1878 to date. To Sweden 1784-1878.

Monetary System:
6 stivers = 1 real; 11 reals = 1 dollar.

Under Sweden
Minor Metals

Fine (cmk.)

*1 Cwn. cmkd. on U.S. cents (scarcer), Cayenne sous★, Swedish and Polish billon, etc. (1797-1808, 1834).....125.00

Silver

11 Spanish and other silver cmkd. as No. 1. (1797-1808, 1834)....................100.00
23 3 (stivers). Light ½ real size cmkd. like No. 26. (1808)...................200.00
24 4 (stivers). Same on heavy ½ real size. (1808).......200.00
25 7 (stivers). Same on light ½ real size. (1808).......200.00

*26 9 (stivers). Cwnd. 9/M in oval indent cmkd. on heavy real. (1808).............200.00
27 14 (stivers). Same on light 2 real size. (1808)........200.00
28 18 (stivers). Same on heavy 2 real size. (1808)........200.00

Notes:

1. Nos. 23-28, often assigned to MONTSERRAT are attributed to St. Bartholomew pursuant to Byrne, "St. Bart's Revisited" (Dec. 1967 *Numismatist).*
2. The cwnd. O cmk. has been omitted on the same authority.
3. The coins of St. Bartholomew have been extensively counterfeited.

SAINT-DOMINGUE.
See Santo Domingo.
ST. CHRISTOPHER.
See St. Kitts.

SAINT EUSTATIUS

Netherlands possession in the West Indies. Captured by the French or English on several occasions.

Monetary System:
6 stuivers = 1 reaal.

A. French Occupation 1781-1801.

Billon
Fine (cmk.)
1 (stuiver). Cayenne sous (or other similar coins). Cmkd. SE incuse. (1797)..........65.00
1a —. Cmkd. SE (relief) in circular indent. *(1797 – may be contemporary forgery)*.................25.00

B. Netherlands Restored 1801-10.

Billon

8 (stuiver). Nos. 1 and 1a cmkd. P(ierre dit Flamand, diesinker) in relief (in circular indent). (1809)...................25.00

C. British Occupation 1810-14.

Billon

9 (ex 21) (stuiver). Cayenne sous etc. cmkd. as No. 8. (1810-12)................25.00

Silver

11 Worn silver coins cmkd. with P in beaded circle. (1810-12)................——

ST. KITTS (ST. CHRISTOPHER)

English possession in the Leeward Islands, West Indies.

Monetary System:
108 pence = 9 shillings = 12 bits = 1 dollar.

George III 1760-1820

Billon
Fine (cmk.)
1 (1½ pence). Black dog (see FRENCH COLONIES No. 6). Cmkd. S incuse. (1801).....35.00

*2 (1½ pence). Same, cmkd. S.K. incuse *(1809-12)*......30.00

Silver

4 (⅛ dollar). Cut ⅛ of 8 reales cmkd. S (incuse) three times (in corners). (1801).......200.00
5 (¼ dollar). Cut ¼ of 8 reales cmkd. same. (1801).......200.00
6 (½ dollar). Cut ½ of 8 reales cmkd. same. (1801).......300.00

The coins of St. Kitts have been extensively counterfeited. See III Pridmore.

CARIBBEAN ISLANDS AND TERRITORIES

ST. LUCIA (ST. LUCIE)

One of the principal Windward Islands, West Indies. Claimed by both France and England for two centuries. Definitively ceded to England 1814.

Monetary System:
12 deniers = 1 sou;
15 sous = 1 escalin;
20 sous = 1 livre;
6 black dogs = 4stampees =
1 bit = 9 pence.

Circa 1798-1817:
9 livres = 9 shillings = 12 bits = 1 dollar.
1817 onward:
10 livres = 10 shillings = 1 uncut dollar.

Under Great Britain
George III 1760-1820

Cut Silver (Circa 1798)

11 (2 escalins). 1/6 of 8 reales cmkd. with 2 SL mons.....RRR

Fine (cmk.)

★13 (3 escalins). 1/4 of 8 reales with 3 SL mons.................100.00
14 (4 escalins). 1/3 of 8 reales cmkd. 3 SL mons..........150.00
15 (6 escalins). 1/2 of 8 reales cmkd. 2 SL mons..........150.00

Cut Silver (Circa 1811)

31 (3 stampees). 1/4 of 2 reales, edges crenated.............50.00
34 (escalin). 1/3 of 2 reales cmkd. 4.5 mm ring...............50.00
36 (1½ escalins). 1/4 of 4 reales cmkd. 2 rings..............50.00
38 (2 escalins). 1/3 of 4 reales cmkd. 3 rings..............50.00

Cut Silver (1813)

Various Spanish-American coins cut into 3 parallel strips. The two outer moon-shaped pieces are hereinafter called Part A. The center rectangle with curved ends is called Part B. **All cmkd. like No. 46.**

41 (11 sous, 3 deniers). Part A of 2 reales............... —

Fine (cmk.)

42 (1 livre, 6 deniers). Part A of 4 reales................ —
43 (1 livre, 13 sous, 9 deniers). Part B of 2 reales.......... —
44 (2 livres, 5 sous). Part A of 8 reales................75.00
45 (3 livres, 7 sous, 6 deniers). Part B of 4 reales.......... —

★46 (6 livres, 15 sous). Part B of 8 reales...............160.00

Note: Apparently all existing examples of Nos. 41-43, 45 are counterfeits. In addition, many modern concoctions have been falsely attributed to St. Lucia. The coins of St. Lucia have been extensively counterfeited. See III Pridmore.

ST. MARTIN

Island in West Indies. Abandoned by Spain 1648. Divided between France and Netherlands. Occupied by Great Britain during the Napoleonic period until 1816, when it was again divided between France and Netherlands.

Monetary System:
6 stuivers = 1 reaal;
20 stuivers = 1 gulden;
12 (later 15) reaals = 1 dollar.

Billon

Fine (cmk.)

1b (stuiver). Cayenne sous (and other similar coins). Cmkd. St. M in beaded circle. (1798, 1805)................RR
1d —. Cmkd. M incuse. (1820)...................75.00
1e —. No. 1b cmkd. fleur-de-lys (for circulation in French St. Martin).................RR

Note: The cmks. (i) bundle of arrows, (ii) St. M in square, and (iii) SM, are said in III Pridmore to be nonexistent.

Silver

8 Various small silver coins cmkd. as No. 1b. *(1798-1805)*.................... —

★11 *(3 reaals).* 1/5 or 1/6 of 8 reales cmkd. St. MARTIN and circular bundle of arrows. (1809)...................250.00

Fine (cmk.)

12 18 (stuivers). 1/4 of 8 reales cmkd. CC and 18. (1797).....RR
13 18 (stuivers). No. 12 with additional cmk. circular bundle of arrows. (1797-98)...RR

Pridmore says the cmks. 20 and 22 often assigned to St. Martin belong to GUADELOUPE.

BEWARE counterfeits of St. Martin coins, especially of No. 11.

ST. VINCENT

A British possession in the Windward Islands, West Indies.

Monetary System:
6 black dogs = 4 stampees = 1 bit =
9 pence;

1797:
8 shillings, 3 pence = 11 bits = 1 dollar;

1811:
9 shillings = 12 bits = 1 dollar.

George III 1760-1820

Billon (1797)

Fine (cmk.)

3 (black dog). FRENCH COLONIES No. 6. Cmkd. SV mon............50.00
4 (stampee). FRENCH COLONIES No. 7, 7a or 7b. Cmkd. SV mon............50.00

Silver (1797)

9 (1/4 dollar). 1/4 of 8 reales. Cmkd. SV mon. in corners..................100.00
10 (1/2 dollar). 1/2 of 8 reales. Cmkd. SV mon. 3 times....100.00
10a —. Weight increased by insertion of silver plug.....100.00

Billon (1814)

12 (black dog). Like No. 3 but cmkd. S retrograde.........40.00
13 (stampee). Like No. 4 but cmkd. as No. 12...........40.00

Silver (1811-14)

15 IV 1/2 B(its). 2 reales cmkd. S/IV 1/2/B in cruciform indent. 250.00
16 VI (bits). 23mm. disk from No. 17. Cmkd. S/VI.......200.00
16.5 IX (bits). 4 reales cmkd. S/IX....................800.00

CARIBBEAN ISLANDS AND TERRITORIES

ST. VINCENT (Cont.)

Fine (cmk.)

★17 XII (bits)..............800.00

Gold (1798)

21 (66 shillings). Brazilian 6400 reis. Cmkd. S in square indent 3 to 4 times, mostly at edge of design, plugged in center with IS or GH cmkd. on plug.....................Rare

The coins of St. Vincent have been extensively counterfeited.

SANTO-DOMINGO (SAINT-DOMINGUE)

Hispaniola, the West Indian island on which Haiti and the Dominican Republic are situated, was originally a Spanish colony. In the 17th century France acquired the western third of the island (present-day Haiti). The Spanish part is frequently called Hispaniola or Española, the French part Saint-Domingue.

A slave revolt erupted in the French part in 1791. The Spanish portion was ceded to France in 1795. A British occupation force was ousted in 1798 by Toussaint l'Ouverture, who remained in control of the island until his capture by the French in 1802.

After the French evacuation in 1803, Haiti became independent. The Spanish reoccupied the eastern two-thirds of the island, thereafter known as Santo Domingo, 1806-22.

See HAITI for coins of the French part after 1803. See DOMINICAN REPUBLIC (Modern World Coins) for later coins of that place.

I. French Government.

Monetary System:
15 sols (sous) = 1 escalin (= 1 real).

A. Town of Le Cap.
(Old Cap François).

Bronze

V.G.

3 L.C. and *cape* btwn. 2 stars (cmk.) on various bronze coins.....................25.00

3a —. L.C. in rectangle cmk...25.00

Silver

Fine (cmk.)

8 Various silver coins and fractions cmkd. C enlaced with cwnd. anchor. (1781).50.00-100.00

8a —. Ring substituted for cwn. over anchor. (1792)...50.00-100.00

B. Crude Copies of French Coins. Period 1791-1801.

Copper or Bronze

Various French bronze coins of the revolutionary era were copied in St. Domingue during this period. Genuine copies are very scarce, but being essentially nothing more than bad counterfeits, which could have been made anywhere, unless of known provenance, copies are worth only 50¢ to $1.00 as contemporary counterfeits.

C. Coinage of Toussaint l'Ouverture, 1798-1802.

Silver

VG-F

31 DEMY (= ½)/ESCALIN. Like No. 32. (1802)......150.00

★32 UN (=1) /ESCALIN. (1802)..................125.00

33 DEUX (=2)/ESCALIN(s). Sim. (1802)..............125.00

D. Countermarks of the Napoleonic Occupation 1802-03.

Bronze

VG-F

41 French (and other) bronze coins cmkd. S:D in rectangular indent..................50.00

42 —. Cmkd. N(apoleon)/SD incuse...................50.00

43 —. Cmkd. SD incuse......50.00

44 —. Cmkd. cwnd. N incuse..50.00

II. Spanish Portion.

Monetary System:
16 reales = 1 escudo.

Ferdinand (Fernando) VII, In Santo Domingo 1808-22

Copper

V.G.

48 ¼ (real). Lion, no legend. Rev. value. 16-17mm. ND.100.00

49 ²/4 (real). Cwnd. Spanish arms. Rev. value. 19-22mm. ND.100.00

Nos. 48-49, formerly listed as Mexico Nos. 92 and 94, are tentatively reassigned to Santo Domingo on the basis of style.

★51 ¼ (real). N.D............15.00

Silver

55 1 R(eal). Crude bust of Ferdinand VII btwn. F–7. Rev. cwnd. arms btwn. I–R. N.D.....................75.00

56 2 R(eales). Sim. N.D......*100.00*

TOBAGO

Small island in the West Indies, lying N.E. of Trinidad. Acquired by Great Britain several times, most lately in 1793 (permanent 1814).

Monetary System Until 1811:

6 black dogs = 4 stampees = 9 pence = 1 bit;
11 bits = 8s3d = 8 reales.

George III of England 1760-1820

Billon

Fine (cmk.)

5 (black dog). Various French (No. 12) and French Colonial (No. 6) coins cmkd. TB incuse. (1798)............12.50

CARIBBEAN ISLANDS AND TERRITORIES

TOBAGO (Cont.)

Fine (cmk.)

*6 (stampee). French Colonial coins (Nos. 7, 7a, 7b cmkd. cwnd. C) cmkd. TB/o incuse. (1798).................40.00

Note: Many Tobago No. 5 (possibly including the coin illustrated above) were fraudulently raised in value to No. 6 by addition of an "O" beneath the TB. Many forgeries of both No. 5 and 6 exist. Forged and fantasy cmks. O/TB, T and IT on billon and TB on copper have been wrongly attributed to Tobago. See III Pridmore.

Silver

*11 (1½ bits). Plug cut from 8 reales. 14 crenations. 3.1 gr. Cmkd. script J. (1798).....200.00

12 (11 bits). 8 real piece from which No. 11 removed. 23.8 gr. (1798).................450.00

Note: Nos. 11 and 12 were listed under TRINIDAD in the first edition. Beware: forgeries of these coins exist. No gold coins were officially cmkd. in, or for, Tobago.

TORTOLA

Island in the British Virgin Islands, West Indies.

Monetary System:
8 shillings, 3 pence = 11 bits = 8 reales.

Billon Coins

The H in a square or lozenge cmk. on black dogs was privately issued.

Fine (cmk.)

3 (1½ pence). Black dog cmkd. incuse T. (1801)..........30.00

Silver
I. Cmkd. Tortola in shaped indent (1801).

Fine (cmk.)

5 On cut ½ of 2 reales......125.00
6 On cut ⅛ of 8 reales......150.00
7 On cut ¼ of 8 reales.......70.00
8 On cut ½ of 8 reales......100.00

II. Cmkd. Tortola in rectangular indent (1801-05).

10 On cut ⅛ of 8 reales......35.00

*11 On cut ¼ of 8 reales......30.00
12 On cut ½ of 8 reales......30.00

III. Cmkd. Tirtila in shaped indent. (1805-24).

13 On cut ½ of 2 reales......40.00
17 On cut ⅛ of 8 reales......35.00
19 On cut ¼ of 8 reales......30.00
20 On cut ½ of 8 reales......30.00

The foregoing silver pieces are the commonest of West Indian cut and countermarked coins, in use until 1889. All coins of Tortola have been extensively counterfeited.

Tortola cmks. often appear on coins already cut and cmkd. elsewhere. Many of the cut pieces are substantially underweight.

TRINIDAD

West Indian island lying off the N.E. coast of South America. Acquired by Great Britain from Spain in 1797.

Monetary System:

9 bits = 9 shillings = 8 reales.

George III of England
1760-1820

Silver

In 1804 many 1 real coins were cut into halves and quarters to pass for 6 and 3 pence, respectively. These were not cmkd. and are not identifiable today.

Fine (cmk.)

15 (shilling). 1/9 of 8 reales cmkd. incuse T. 3.0 gr. (ca. 1798-1801)........... ——

25 (shilling). 11mm octagonal plug cut from 8 reales. Cmkd. T incuse. 2.98 gr. (1811)...100.00

26 (9 shillings). 8 reales from which No. 25 removed.....250.00

Notes:

1. Nos. 25-26 are perhaps the most extensively counterfeited of all cut and countermarked coins. Pridmore estimates the ratio of copies to originals at 25 to 1.

2. See BRITISH HONDURAS for cwnd. script GR in indent cmk.

3. The cwnd. script GR incuse cmk. found on 8 reales of 1806-18 formerly assigned to Trinidad is believed to be a modern concoction.

4. The lattice countermark on 2 reales is listed by Pridmore as unattributed. Some others are now attributing it to Trinidad, Cuba, apparently w/out authority.

5. The IH cmk. on plugged gold is possibly from GRENADA.

VIEQUE (Crab Island)

Off Puerto Rico.

Fine (cmk.)

1 Danish West Indian coins. Cmkd. 12 rayed circle...... ——

2 Spanish-American coins. Cmkd. V................ ——

UNVERIFIED DATA

Note: Throughout this catalog, any uncertain, indefinite or unconfirmed information is shown in *italic type*. Such material may be, for example, coin descriptions, dates and prices, names of rulers, or supplementary notes. Further information to confirm or correct *material in italics* should be sent to the author at the following address:

William D. Craig
c/o Whitman Coin Supply Division
1220 Mound Avenue
Racine, Wisconsin 53404, U.S.A.

CAUCASIA

Mountainous area between the Black and Caspian Seas, scene of almost continual warfare between Persia, Turkey, and eventually Russia. Most of Caucasia proper was annexed to Russia in the early 19th century.

Monetary System:
200 dinar = 40 kazbegi = 20 nim bisti = 10 bisti = 1 abbasi. Other denominations identified in the text.

ARMENIA

I. Erivan (Irwan, Yerevan).
Capital of present-day Russian Armenia. Under Persia to 1724, occupied by Ottomans 1724-35, then again Persian until annexed by Russia in 1828.

Copper Under Persia

Coin Sizes: kazbeg 19-21mm;
nim bisti 22mm;
bisti 27-29mm.

1 Horse, lion and sun★, lion and cub, fish, goose, rabbit, ram, elephant, ape★, dromedary★, etc. Rev. legend (including ERIVAN) in Persian. 1057-1241AH.
Many varieties.......2.50–10.00

Silver Under Persia
Types of PERSIA (q.v.).

II. Turkish Armenia.
Monetary System:
40 para = 1 piastre.

A. Kars (Qars).
City in present-day eastern Turkey.

Mahmud I
AH1143-68 (=1730-54)

Silver *Fine*
51 (10 para). Toughra. Rev. Arabic DURIBA/FI/KARS/ 1143. 22mm..............10.00

B. Van (Wan).
City in present-day eastern Turkey.

Mustafa III
1171-87AH (=1757-74AD)

Copper *G-VG*
101 (para). Arabic: SULTAN/ MUSTAFA/1177AH. Rev. VAN. 15mm.......... 7.50

Abdul Hamid I
1187-1203AH (=1774-89 AD)

Copper
151 (para). Toughra. Rev. VAN. 1201 AH. 15mm..........10.00

Mahmud II
1223-55AH (=1808-39AD)

Copper

★175 (asper). Toughra. Rev. DURIBA/FI/VAN/1231...... 7.50

GANJAH
(KHANDSCHAH, KENDSCHEN, GENCE, ELIZABETPOL)

City in Russian Caucasia. Under Persia to 1804, except occupied by Ottoman Turks 1723-35. Annexed by Russia in 1804. Now Kirovabad, capital of Azerbaijan.
Coin Sizes: Same as Armenia (Erivan) except kazbeg 17-20mm.

I. Under Persia.

Copper

1 Deer, lion and sun, horse★, lion and cub, goose★, 2 bladed sword★, etc. Rev. legend (including GANJAH) in Persian. 1123-1215AH.
Many varieties........3.50–7.50

Silver
Types of PERSIA (q.v.).

II. Turkish Occupation 1723-35.

Mahmud I, in Ganjah
AH1143-48 (=1730-35)

Silver *Fine*
21 (5 para). Toughra. Rev. Arabic DURIBA/FI/GANJAH/ 1143. 2.7 gr. 18mm........10.00
22 (10 para). Sim. 24mm. 5.2 gr....................10.00

Nos. 21-22 were struck over ½ and 1 abbasi coins.

GEORGIA, Kingdom
Christian state in Caucasia. Had its own coinage off and on for 2000 years. Subject to Persia or Turkey for centuries prior to 1783 when King Heracles II became a vassal of Russia. Georgia was annexed piecemeal to Russia 1799-1838. Capital and mint: Tiflis (name appears on all coins).

Monetary System:
200 dinar = 40 puli (kazbegi) = 10 bisti = 1 abazi (abbasi); 5 abazi = 1 rouble.

I. Turkish Occupation 1723-35.

Mahmud I, in Tiflis
AH1143-48 (=1730-35)

Silver *Fine*
3 (10 para). Toughra. Rev. Arabic DURIBA/FI/TIFLIS/ 1143. 5.3 gr. 21mm........10.00

II. Local Kings 1744-1801.

T'eimuraz II
AH1157-76 (=1744-62)

A. Alone AH1157-66.

Copper

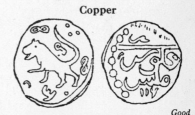

Good
★5 (puli). Tiger, Georgian TMRZ around. Rev. Persian DURIBA/FULUS/TIFLIS/date. Ca. 5 gr. AH1160-63....... 5.00

Silver *Fine*
10 (abazi). Persian legends: LOVE GOD etc. Rev. 1166AH/ TIFLIS. 3 gr...............10.00

B. With Erekle II, AH1166-76.

Copper

CAUCASIA

GEORGIA (Cont.)

Good

★**15** *(2 puli).* Falcon striking heron. Rev. TIFLIS etc. 20-24mm. AH1165-69...... 5.00

Silver

Fine

20 (abazi). *Like No. 10.* 3.1 gr. AH1168............*10.00*

Erekle (Heracles) II
AH1176-1213 (=1762-98)

Copper

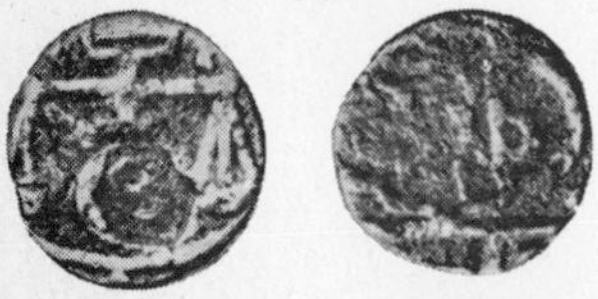

Good

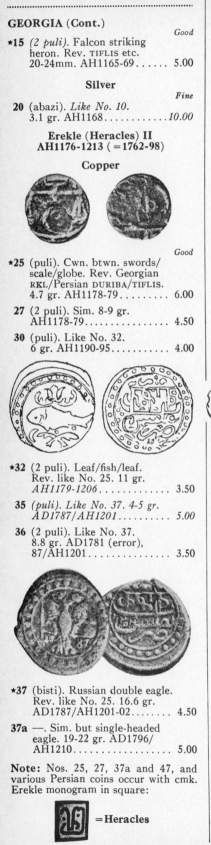

★**25** (puli). Cwn. btwn. swords/scale/globe. Rev. Georgian RKL/Persian DURIBA/TIFLIS. 4.7 gr. AH1178-79......... 6.00

27 (2 puli). Sim. 8-9 gr. AH1178-79................ 4.50

30 (puli). Like No. 32. 6 gr. AH1190-95........... 4.00

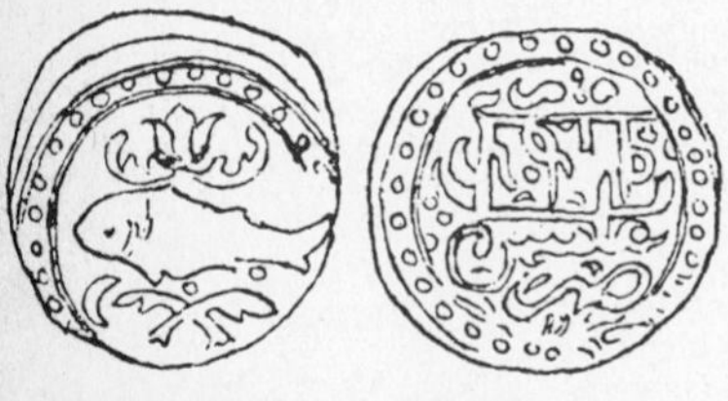

★**32** (2 puli). Leaf/fish/leaf. Rev. like No. 25. 11 gr. *AH1179-1206*............. 3.50

35 *(puli). Like No. 37. 4-5 gr. AD1787/AH1201*.......... *5.00*

36 (2 puli). Like No. 37. 8.8 gr. AD1781 (error), 87/AH1201.............. 3.50

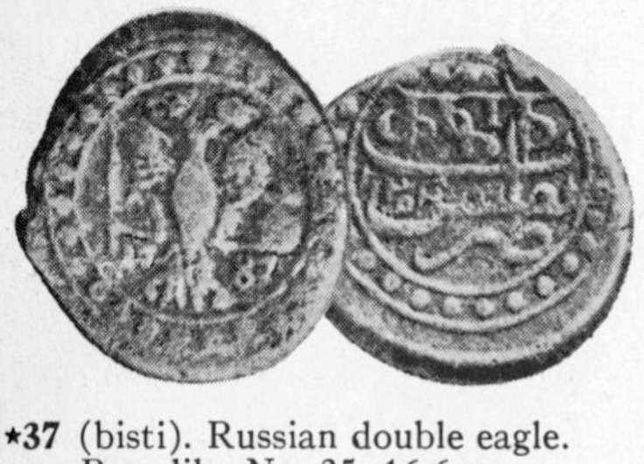

★**37** (bisti). Russian double eagle. Rev. like No. 25. 16.6 gr. AD1787/AH1201-02........ 4.50

37a —. Sim. but single-headed eagle. 19-22 gr. AD1796/AH1210.................. 5.00

Note: Nos. 25, 27, 37a and 47, and various Persian coins occur with cmk. Erekle monogram in square:

 =**Heracles**

Silver

Fine

45 (½ abazi). Persian YA KERIM. Rev. TIFLIS/DURIBA/date. 1.5 gr. 15-17mm. AH1183-1211...................... 8.00

47 (abazi). Like No. 10 but rev. YA KERIM added at top. 3.1 gr. 18-22mm. AH1179-1211...................... 7.50

54 *(3 abazi).* Sim. 8.9 gr. AH1182..................*15.00*

Giorgi XII
AH1213-15 (=1798-1800)

Copper

Good

60 (puli). Like No. 32 but rev. GIORGI at top. 4.4 gr. AH1213.................. 4.00

61 (2 puli). Sim. 9-10 gr. 21-26mm. AH1213-15...... 4.00

Silver

Fine

64 (½ abazi). Like No. 45. AH1213-15...............*10.00*

65 (abazi). Like No. 47. AH1213..................*10.00*

David, Regent
AH1215-16 (=1801)

Copper

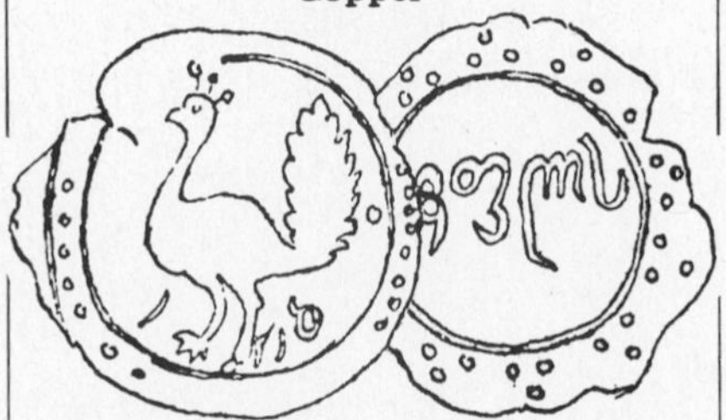

★**75** *(bisti).* Peacock. Rev. Georgian TPLS *(=Tiflis).* AH1215......*RR*

III. Under Russia.

Alexander I 1801-25
Nicholas I 1825-55

Dates and denominations in Georgian numerals (style can vary slightly):

1	2	3	4	5	6	7	8	9	10
ა	ბ ბ	გ	დ დ	ე	ვ ვ	ზ	ჱ	თ	ი

11	20	30	100	200	400	800	1000
ია	კ	ლ	რ	ს	უ	ყ	ჩ

Copper

V.G.

81 5 (dinar). Like No. 82. 21mm. 1805-10............10.00

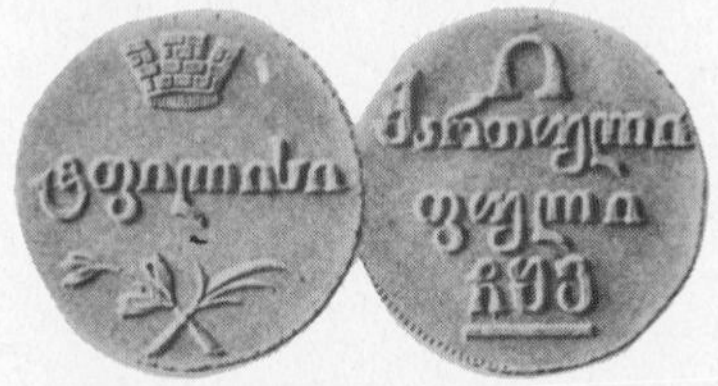

★**82** 10 (dinar). 25mm. 1805-10..10.00

83 20 (dinar). Sim. 31mm. 1805-10................... 7.50

Silver

Fine

84 100 (dinar). Like No. 85. 1.58 gr. 16mm. 1804-33.....10.00

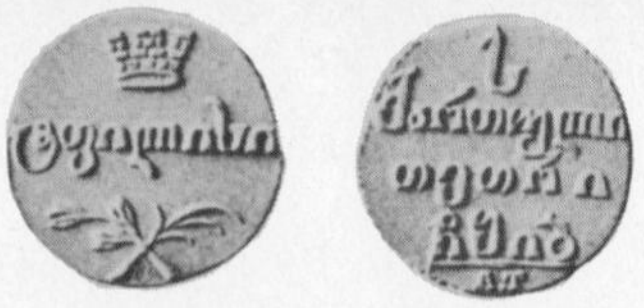

★**85** 200 (dinar). 3.16 gr. 19-20mm. 1804-33......... 8.00

86 400 (dinar). Sim. 6.31 gr. 22-25mm. 1804-33.........10.00

KARABAGH (QARABAGH, PANAHABAD, SHUSHA), Khanate

Panahabad (=Shusha) was the capital of the Khanate of Karabagh, lying southeast of Georgia in Russian Caucasia. Russian Protectorate 1805, annexed 1822.

Ibrahim Khalil
AH1177-1221 (=1763-1806)

Copper

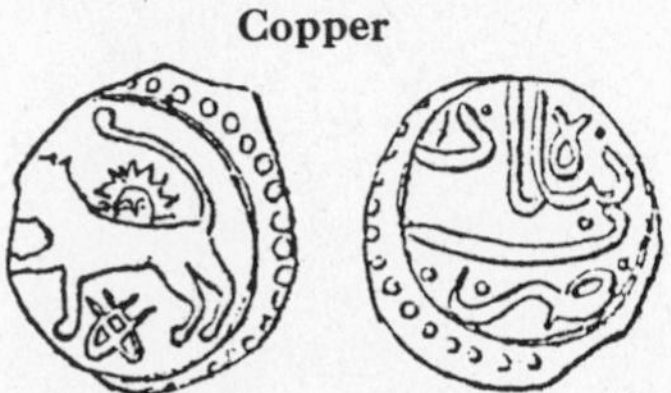

Good

★**21** (½ bisti). Lion r. or l., sun. Rev. Persian DURIBA/PANAHABAD. AH1198, ND.. 3.00

Mahdi Quli Khan
AH1221-35 (=1806-20)

Silver

G-VG

41 (abbasi). 4.3 gr. 1222-37AH.................... *6.00*

SCHAMAKHI (SHARMAKHI, SCHEMACHA), Khanate

In Azerbaijan, Russian Caucasia. Under Persian suzerainty until the late 18th century, during which period Persian coins were struck at Schamakhi. Russian pressure loosed Schamakhi from Persia but the Russians thereafter annexed the Khanate in 1813.

Anonymous Khans

Copper

Good

21 (kazbeg). Sword btwn. tendrils. Rev. Persian legend. 22x13mm. 1212-13AH................ 4.00

23 *(½ bisti).* Lion. Rev. Persian legend. 22mm. 1212AH..... 5.00

Silver

G-VG

31 (abbasi). Persian legends both sides. 2-3 gr. 1199-1215AH.. *7.50*

CAUCASIA

SHAMAKHI (Cont.)

Nassr Qan

Silver

V.G.

51 (abbasi). 1.6-2.3 gr. 1227-
35AH.................... *7.50*

SHEKI
(SCHEKI, NUKHUI, NUKHA,)
Khanate

In Russian Caucasia. Nukhui was the
residence of the Khans of Sheki from
the mid 18th century. Occupied by
Russia 1807, annexed 1819.

Copper

Good

5 (bisti). Turreted crown/1221AH.
Rev. Legend............. 5.00

7 (bisti). 31-34mm. 1226AH... 4.00

*10 (bisti). Crude Russian Imperial
Crown/date. Rev. Legend.
1228-33AH............... 4.00

Silver

G-VG

21 (½ abbasi). 1.2 gr. 1231,
32AH.................... *7.50*

23 (abbasi). 2.1 gr. 1232AH.... *10.00*

CAYENNE.
See FRENCH GUIANA.

CENTRAL AMERICAN
REPUBLIC.
See COSTA RICA, GUATE-
MALA and HONDURAS.

CEYLON

Island off the south tip of India. Coastal region conquered by the Netherlands
United East India Company from Portugal 1602-58. Island lost to British
1795-96, cession permanent 1802.

Monetary Systems:

Under Netherlands:
4 duits = 1 stuiver; 4 stuivers =
1 fanam; 9½ stuivers = 1 larin;
12 fanams = 1 Rixdollar.

Under British:
192 pies = 48 stivers = 1 Rixdollar =
1 rupee = 1½ shillings.

Countermarks:
Many Portuguese Indian, Indian and
Persian coins were countermarked by
the Netherlands Company in Ceylon
during the last half of the 17th century:
GALL mon. = Galle;
C/VOC mon. = Colombo;
I/VOC mon. = Jaffna.

I. Under Netherlands Company.

Base Metals

V.G.

1 (⅛ duit). 17/47. Rev. 4
Sinhalese characters. 1.3 gr.
Tin..................... RRR

2 I D(uit). c(olombo)/voc mon.,
date. Rev. Dove on mango
tree divides value. 15-16 gr.
Tin 1782............... *35.00*

2a —. 9-11 gr. 1785-86....... *30.00*

3 ¼/ST(uiver). c(olombo)/
voc mon. Rev. value. N.D.
(1783). Copper........... 15.00

4 I/D(ui)^T. c(olombo)/voc mon.
Rev. value/date. 1789-91.
Lead................... *20.00*

4a I/DUIT. 1792-93......... *25.00*

5 I/STUIVER. c(olombo)/voc
mon. Rev. value/date.
1783-95. Copper.......... 6.00

6 I S(tuiver). I(affna). Like No. 9.
1783-92. Copper.......... Rare

*7 I S(tuiver). G(alle)/voc mon.
Rev. Date/value in Sinhalese.
1783-93. Copper.......... 17.50

8 I/S^T(uiver). T(rincomalee)/
voc mon. Rev. value/date.
1789-93. Copper.......... 17.50

*9 2 S(tuiver). I(affna)/voc
mon/value. Rev. Date/value in
Tamil. 1783-93. Copper..... 30.00

9a —. 1783. Tin............. RRR

*10 2 S(tuiver). G(alle). Rev.
value in Sinhalese. 1783-92.
Copper.................. 15.00

Fine

14 4¾/ST(uiver). Copper bonk
(bar) 58-105mm. long, stamped
at ends: 1.C(olombo)/voc mon.
and 2. Value. (1785)..... 225.00

Silver

18 (rupee). Degenerate Malay-
Arabic legends both sides.
European dates 1784-*89*.
12 gr. Colombo and Tuti-
corin Mints............. *100.00*

II. Under Great Britain.

George III, In Ceylon
1796-1820

Copper

The "48 TO ONE RUPEE" pieces (Bale
mark, rev. elephant) dated 1794 and
1797 are patterns or fantasies.

Fine

22 48(th rupee). Like No. 25 but
dump (crude, thick flan).
1801-15................. 10.00

23 24(th rupee). Sim.
1801-15................. 12.00

23a —. Elephant r. 1803...... 35.00

24 12(th rupee). Like No. 22.
1801-15................. 15.00

24a —. Elephant r. 1803...... 35.00

*25 192(nd rupee). Machine-
struck. 1802.............. 4.00

CEYLON

BRITISH (Cont.)

Fine

25a —. 1804 proof............80.00
26 96 (th rupee). Sim. 1802.... 5.00
27 48 (th rupee). Sim. 1802.... 6.00
27a —. 1803-04. Proof.......100.00

★27.5 ¼ PICE. C(eylon)
G(overnment)/1813.
Rev. PI ¼ CE................. ──────

No. 27.5, formerly listed as British India No. 70, has been attributed to Ceylon by Pridmore.

★28 ONE/HALF STIVER.
1815................... 2.50
29 ONE STIVER. Sim. 1815.. 3.50
30 TWO STIVERS. Sim.
1815................... 4.50

Silver

31 24/ST(ivers). Dump issue like
No. 33. 1803-09...........30.00
32 48/ST(ivers). Sim. 1803-09..40.00
32a —. Elephant r. 1803........RR

★33 96/ST(ivers). 1803-09......55.00

The Rix Dollars of 1812, 15 and the Two Rix Dollar of 1812 are extremely **rare** patterns. The gold 4 Rix dollars of 1812 is thought to be a modern fantasy.

34 FANAM. Circular legends.
FANAM. Rev. TOKEN. N.D.
(1814-15)................. 7.50

George IV 1820-30
Copper

Fine

★37 (½ farthing). 1827-30.....10.00

Silver

V.F.

37.5 (4 fanams). Madras Arcot
¼ rupee cmkd. crown incuse.
(1823)..................*45.00*
37.6 (16 fanams). Rupee cmkd.
sim. (1823).............*95.00*

Fine

★38 ONE/RIX DOLLAR.
1821...................12.50

William IV 1830-37
Copper

39 (½ farthing). Head.
Rev. Britannia. 1837.......14.00

Silver

F-VF

★40 1½ (pence). 1834-37....... 4.00

No. 40 was also used in Jamaica where it passed as a substitute for the ¼ real.

CHILE

Republic extending along the southwestern coast of South America. Constituted the Spanish Presidency of Chile prior to 1818, independent thereafter.

Mint: Santiago – Ŝ, established 1743.

Monetary System:
8 reales = 1 duro (peso);
16 duros = 8 escudos (scudos) = 1 onza.

Fernando VI 1746-59
Milled Silver

V.F.

1 (½ real). FRD. VI D.G. HISP.
ET IND. R. Arms. Rev. VTRA
QUE VNUM. Hemispheres between
2 pillars of Hercules. 1756.1000.00
3 2 (reales). Sim. 1758........RRR
5 8 (reales). Sim. but
FERDINANDUS VI etc.
1751-58.................4000.00

Gold (escudo = 3.38 gr.)

7 (escudo). *Like* No. 8.
1754, 58.....................RR
8 (2 escudos). FERDINANDUS VI
etc., bust of Felipe V.
Rev. NOMINA etc., 4 fold arms.
1758.....................RRR
9 (4 escudos). Sim. but proper
bust (like No. 10). 1749-
56......................675.00

★10 (8 escudos). Sim. but rev.
manifold arms in order chain.
1750-59..................900.00
11 (escudo). Like No. 9 but
FERDIND VI etc. 1759......500.00
13 (4 escudos). Sim. 1757...*Pattern?*
14 (8 escudos). Sim. but rev.
like No. 10. 1759-60......1000.00

Carlos III 1759-88
Silver

A. Pillar type.

15 (½ real). Like No. 1 but
CRL III D.G. etc. 1760.....1000.00
18 4 (reales). Sim. but CAROLUS
III etc. 1760............6000.00
19 8 (reales). Sim. 1760-68...3500.00

B. Bust type.

F-VF

20 (½ real). Like No. 22.
1773-89................. 15.00
21 1 R(eal). Sim. 1773-89......17.50

CHILE

F-VF

*22	2 R(eales). 1773-89	20.00
23	4 R(eales). Sim. 1775-89	350.00
24	8 R(eales). Sim. 1773-89	600.00

Gold (escudo = 3.38 gr.)

A. Bust of Fernando VI.

V.F.

25	(escudo). CAROLUS III etc., bust as No. 10. Rev. NOMINA etc., 4 fold arms. 1760-62	450.00
26	(4 escudos). Sim. 1762-63	1000.00
27	(8 escudos). Sim. but rev. like No. 10. 1760-63	750.00

B. Young Standard Bust.

28	(escudo). CAR. III etc. Rev. IN UTROQ. FELIX, 4 fold arms. 1763-66	500.00
29	(2 escudos). Sim. but CAROLUS III etc., rev. IN UTROQ...DEO. 1764	1500.00
30	(4 escudos). Sim. 1763-65	1400.00
31	(8 escudos). Sim. but rev. manifold arms in order chain. 1764-71	750.00

C. Older Standard Bust.

32	1 S(cudo). Like No. 35. 1772-88	175.00
33	2 S(cudos). Sim. 1773-88	275.00
34	4 S(cudos). Sim. 1773-89	800.00

V.F.

*35	8 S(cudos). 1772-88	650.00

Carlos IV 1788-1808

A. Bust of Carlos III, legend on silver (except ¼ real) CAROLUS IV, on gold CAROL IV.

Silver

F-VF

*36	(¼ real). CAROL IV. 1790-91	30.00
37	(½ real). Bust. Rev. Arms between two pillars. 1789-91	15.00
38	1 R(eal). Sim. 1789-91	15.00
39	2 R(eales). Sim. 1789-90	20.00
40	4 R(eales). Sim. 1789-91	200.00

V.F.

41	8 R(eales). Sim. 1789-91	450.00

Gold

42	1 S(cudo). Bust. Rev. AUSPICE etc. Arms. 1790	200.00
43	2 S(cudos). Sim. 1790	400.00
44	4 S(cudos). Sim. 1789-90	800.00
45	8 S(cudos). Sim. 1789-90	600.00

B. Bust of Carlos III, legend on silver (except ¼ real) CAROLUS IIII, on gold CAROL IIII.

Silver

F-VF

46	(¼ real). Like No. 36 but CAROL IIII. 1791-92	30.00
47	(½ real). Like No. 37 but CAROLUS IIII. 1791	25.00
48	1 R(eal). Sim. 1791	20.00
49	2 R(eales). Sim. 1791-92	15.00
50	4 R(eales). Sim. 1791-92	—
51	8 R(eales). Sim. 1791	—

Gold

V.F.

52	1 S(cudo). Like No. 42 but CAROL IIII. 1791	200.00
53	2 S(cudos). Sim. 1791-1808	300.00
54	8 S(cudos). Sim. 1791-1808	600.00

C. Bust of Carlos IV, legend CAROL or CAROLUS IIII.

Silver

F-VF

55	(¼ real). Like No. 36 but CAROL IIII, his own bust. 1792	35.00

*56	¼ (real). 1796-1808	17.50

F-VF

57	(½ real). Like No. 59. 1792-1808	7.50
58	1 R(eal). Sim. 1792-1808	10.00

*59	2 R(eales). Sim. 1792-1808	12.50
60	4 R(eales). Sim. 1792-1808	60.00

V.F.

61	8 R(eales). Sim. 1791-1808	200.00

Gold

62	1 S(cudo). Like No. 42 but CAROL IIII, his own bust. 1791-1808	150.00
63	4 S(cudos). Sim. 1791-1808	500.00

Fernando VII 1808-17

Silver

F-VF

64	¼ (real). Like No. 56. 1809-18	15.00

(Lack of Republican dies necessitated the striking of the 1818 pieces.)

Bust of Carlos IV

65	(½ real). Like No. 66. 1808-17	8.00

*66	1 R(eal). 1808-17	10.00
67	2 R(eales). Sim. 1808-09	20.00
68	4 R(eales). Sim. 1808-15	75.00

Gold

V.F.

69	1 S(cudo). Like No. 72. 1811-17	250.00
70	2 S(cudos). Sim. 1814-17	350.00
71	4 S(cudos). Sim. 1810-17	750.00

CHILE

*72 8 S(cudos). 1811-17 . . . . . . .500.00

Non-Laureate Local or Military Bust
Silver

*73 8 R(eales). Obv. *. Rev. like
No. 66. 1808-09 . . . . .200.00

Gold

74 1 S(cudo). Obv. sim. to No. 73.
Rev. like No. 42. 1808-
09 .V. Rare

75 2 S(cudos). Sim. 1808-
09 . . . . .Ex. Rare

76 4 S(cudos). Sim. 1808-
09 . . . . .Ex. Rare

77 8 S(cudos). Sim. 1808-11 . . .500.00

Laureate Local or Military Bust
Silver

78 2 R(eales). Bust. Rev. like
No. 66. 1810-11 . . . . .20.00

79 8 R(eales). Sim. 1810-11 . . .200.00

General Draped Bust
Silver

V.F.

80 2 R(eales). Bust. Rev. like
No. 66. 1812-17 . . . . .10.00

81 8 R(eales). Sim. 1812-17 . . .110.00

Republic, 1817 to Date
I. First Issue, 1817-34.
Silver
A. Santiago mint.

F-VF

82 UN CUART (= ¼ real),
both sides. 1832-34 . . . . .22.50

83 (½ real). Like No. 85.
1833-34 . . . . .17.50

84 UN (=1) R(eal). Sim.
1834 . . . . .17.50

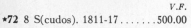

*85 DOS (=2) R(eales). 1834 . . .22.50

V.F.

86 UN (=1) PESO. Sim.
1817-34 . . . . .75.00

B. Coquimbo mint.

87 ½ R(eal). Sim. Coquimbo
mint. 1828 . . . . .exist?

*88 UN (=1) PESO.
Like No. 87. 1828 . . . . .4000.00

Gold

89 1 E(scudo). Like No. 90.
1824-34 . . . . .90.00

*90 2 E(scudos). 1818-34 . . . . . .150.00

V.F.

91 4 E(scudos). Sim. 1824-34 . .400.00

92 8 E(scudos). Sim. 1818-34 . .375.00

II. Second Issue, 1835-51.

Copper

Fine

*93 (Y-7) MEDIO (= ½)/
CENTAVO. 1835 . . . . 1.75

94 (Y-8) UN (=1)/CENTAVO.
Sim. 1835 . . . . 1.75

Silver

96 (Y-19) ½ R(eal). Like No.
98a. 17mm. 1838-42 . . . . . . .12.50

96a (Y-19a) —. 15.5mm.
1844-51 . . . . 6.00

97 (Y-20) 1 R(eal). Sim.
21.5mm. 1838-42 . . . . 8.00

97a (Y-20a) —. 19mm. 1843-50 . . 3.50

98 (Y-21) 2 R(eales). Sim.
24.5mm. 1839 . . . . .exist?

*98a (Y-21a) —. 23mm.
1843-52 . . . . 3.00

100 (Y-22) 8 R(eales). Sim.
39mm. 1839 . . . . .40.00

100a (Y-22a) —. 38mm.
1848-49 . . . . .40.00

Gold

V.F.

101 (Y-23) 1 E(scudo).
Like No. 103. 1838 . . . . .60.00

102 (Y-24) 2 E(scudos). Sim.
1837-38 . . . . .75.00

*103 (Y-25) 4 E(scudos).
1836-37 . . . . .300.00

CHILE

104 (Y-26) 8 E(scudos). Sim.
1835-38 . . . . 200.00

105 (Y-27) 1 E(scudo).
Generally like No. 108b.
1839-45 . . . . 50.00

105a (Y-31) —. Modified dies.
1847-51 . . . . 50.00

106 (Y-28) 2 E(scudos). Like
No. 105. 1839-45 . . . . 75.00

106a (Y-32) —. Like No. 105a.
1846-51 . . . . 75.00

107 (Y-29) 4 E(scudos). Like
No. 105. 1839-41 . . . . 550.00

108 (Y-30) 8 E(scudos). Sim.
Reeded edge. 1839-43 . . . . 200.00

108a (Y-30a) —. Lettered edge.
1844-45 . . . . 200.00

★108b (Y-33) —. Modified dies.
1846-51 . . . . 200.00

NECESSITY COINAGE

Chiloé

Archipelago under Spanish rule until
1826.
Royalist leader Antonio Quintanilla

Silver

N1 8 R(eales). Cast copy of Potosi
8 reales 1822 with "chi-loe"
beside Fernando VII's
head 750.00

Copiapó

Revolution of 1859

Coinage of Don Pedro Leon Gallo.

Uniface Silver
V.F.

N11 50 C(entavos). Raised 5
pointed star in incuse shield,
value below. N.D 35.00

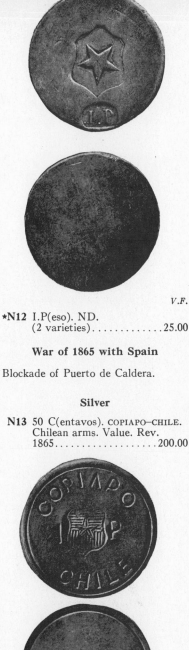

V.F.

★N12 I.P(eso). ND.
(2 varieties) 25.00

War of 1865 with Spain

Blockade of Puerto de Caldera.

Silver

N13 50 C(entavos). COPIAPO–CHILE.
Chilean arms. Value. Rev.
1865 . . . . 200.00

★N14 1 P(eso). Sim. 1865 . . . . 27.50

San Bernardo de Maypo

Copper

N21 ¼ (real). 1821. Struck to
pay canal workers 200.00

Valdivia

Emergency coinage of Don Antonio
Adriazola by order of the Governor.

Base Silver
V.F.

N31 1 R(eal). Column, 3 stars.
Rev. I.R./V.A./1822 . . . . . . 85.00

★N32 2 R(eales). Sim. 1822 . . . . 100.00

N34 8 R(eales). Sim. 1822 . . . . 650.00

CHILEAN VALIDATIONS

Latin American (mostly Argentine
coins struck at Potosi) silver coins of
the era 1813-22 were validated (countermarked) by Chilean authorities at
Valparaiso, Valdivia and Serena in the
first years of the Republic. Cmk. 8mm.
diameter: 3 mountains with VALP., SER.
or VALD. below. **All are extremely
rare, and all have been counterfeited.**

CHINA, Empire

In East Asia. The most populous country in the world.

Monetary System:
1000 cash = 1 Tael of silver (37.1 gram)

Cash Coinage of the
Ch'ing (Manchu) Dynasty
(1644-1911)

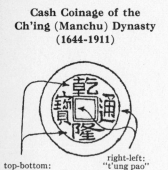

top-bottom:
Emperor's
title

right-left:
"t'ung pao"
= current
coin

*For examples of "chung pao" and "yuan pao" see Nos. 1-6 and 1-11.

Typical Obverse

An ordinary Chinese square-hole type coin has on its obverse four characters: the top and bottom character are the ruler's reign title. The characters on the right and left are "t'ung-pao" (current coin). During the reign of Hsienfeng multiple value cash was introduced as an emergency measure, because of the war against the Taiping Rebels. Usually those coins have "chung-pao" (heavy coin) for the values up to 50, and "yuan-pao" (large coin) for the values up to 1000.

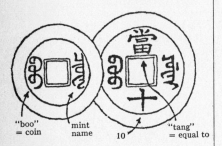

"boo"
= coin

mint
name

10

"tang"
= equal to

Typical Reverses

All cash coins (of the period in question) show on their reverse two words in Manchu: on the left "boo" (coin) and on the right the mint's name. Multiple value cash have on the top the Chinese character "tang" (equal to) and on the bottom a Chinese numeral.

There can also be additional characters or signs on the reverse or in the field of the obverse. These indicate the date or the branch of a mint, or serve as marks against fraud. Usually the price for such a coin is about five times that of the ordinary pieces. Contemporary forgeries of cash are very numerous and are nearly always smaller and thinner than the originals. Most such forgeries were made in Annam and ad-

joining Chinese provinces. Often their Manchu is incorrect or imaginary. Modern numismatic counterfeits of many of the rarer pieces, both copper and silver, are now said to exist.

Chinese cash of the Ch'ing dynasty are usually brass, sometimes copper or bronze. There are also some very rare iron cash from Kwangtung and Szechuan. But during the Taiping war (Hsien-feng period) all kinds of other metals were used: iron, lead, tin, zinc and various alloys. Due to ready oxidation, some of these coins in other metals are now quite rare.

Note: For other cast coins with square center hole, of the general style listed here, see ANNAM, JAPAN, KOREA.

Illustrations: See page 83.

A. CENTRAL MINTS (Peking)

Cast Brass or Copper

1. Board of Revenue (Hu Poo)
(Manchu: "boo ciowan" on rev.)

                                        Fine

*1-1   Ch'ien-lung t'ung-pao
(1736-95)............... .25

*1-2   Chia-ching t'ung-pao
(1796-1820)............. .30

*1-3   Tao-kuang t'ung-pao
(1821-50)............... .30

*1-4   Hsien-feng t'ung-pao
(1851-61)............... .75

1-4a —. Iron................25.00

                                       Fine

1-5   Hsien-feng chung-pao,
5 cash.................100.00

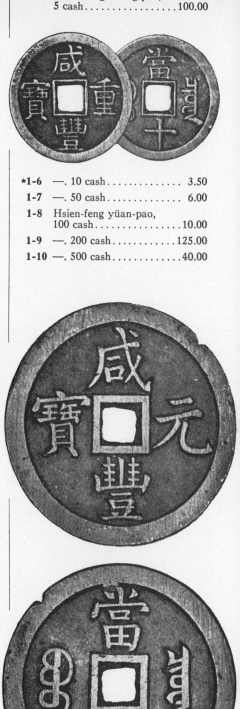

*1-6 —. 10 cash............. 3.50

1-7   —. 50 cash............. 6.00

1-8   Hsien-feng yüan-pao,
100 cash................10.00

1-9   —. 200 cash...........125.00

1-10 —. 500 cash...........40.00

*1-11 —. 1000 cash..........175.00

CHINA

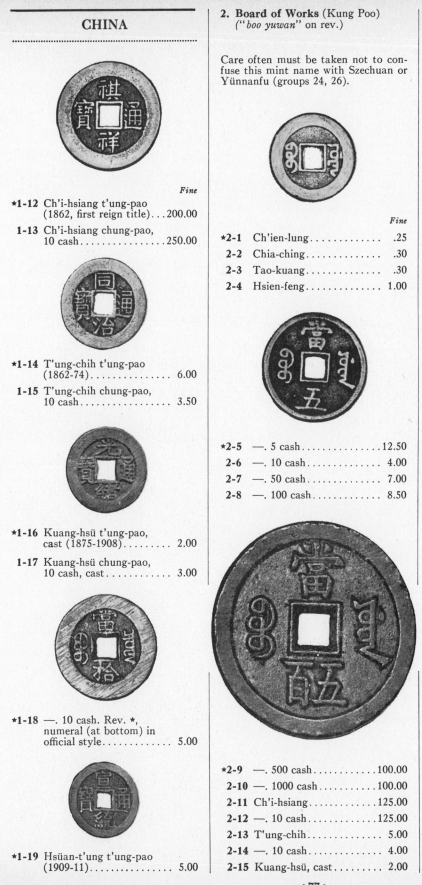

Fine

★1-12 Ch'i-hsiang t'ung-pao
(1862, first reign title)...200.00

1-13 Ch'i-hsiang chung-pao,
10 cash...............250.00

★1-14 T'ung-chih t'ung-pao
(1862-74)............. 6.00

1-15 T'ung-chih chung-pao,
10 cash............... 3.50

★1-16 Kuang-hsü t'ung-pao,
cast (1875-1908)........ 2.00

1-17 Kuang-hsü chung-pao,
10 cash, cast........... 3.00

★1-18 —. 10 cash. Rev. ★,
numeral (at bottom) in
official style............. 5.00

★1-19 Hsüan-t'ung t'ung-pao
(1909-11).............. 5.00

2. Board of Works (Kung Poo)
(*"boo yuwan"* on rev.)

Care often must be taken not to confuse this mint name with Szechuan or Yünnanfu (groups 24, 26).

Fine

★2-1 Ch'ien-lung............. .25
2-2 Chia-ching............. .30
2-3 Tao-kuang............. .30
2-4 Hsien-feng............. 1.00

★2-5 —. 5 cash.............12.50
2-6 —. 10 cash............ 4.00
2-7 —. 50 cash............ 7.00
2-8 —. 100 cash............ 8.50

★2-9 —. 500 cash...........100.00
2-10 —. 1000 cash..........100.00
2-11 Ch'i-hsiang.............125.00
2-12 —. 10 cash.............125.00
2-13 T'ung-chih.............. 5.00
2-14 —. 10 cash............ 4.00
2-15 Kuang-hsü, cast........ 2.00

Fine

2-16 —. 5 cash..............
2-17 —. 10 cash............. 3.50
2-18 —. 10 cash, numeral in
official style (see No.
1-18)..................10.00

B. PROVINCIAL MINTS

3. Anhwei (Rev. "boo *hui*").

Attribution of these coins to this mint is in dispute.

★3-1 Kuang-hsü, cast.........25.00
3-2 —. struck...............100.00

4. Chekiang (Rev. "boo je").

★4-1 Ch'ien-lung............. .30
4-2 Chia-ching............. .35
4-3 Tao-kuang............. .35
4-3.5 Hsien Feng............. 2.00
4-4 —. 10 cash............ 4.00
4-5 —. 20 cash............90.00
4-6 —. 30 cash............125.00
4-7 —. 40 cash............125.00
4-8 —. 50 cash............90.00
4-9 —. 10 cash, on top
only small "10"..........90.00
4-10 —. 100 cash, on top
only small "100"........185.00
4-11 —. 10 cash, left Manchu,
right Chinese...........140.00
4-12 —. 20 cash, Sim. 140.00
4-13 —. 30 cash, Sim. ....R

★4-14 —. 40 cash, Sim. 1000.00
4-15 —. 50 cash, Sim. ....RRR
4-16 —. 100 cash, Sim. ....RRR
4-17 T'ung-chih.............. 1.25
4-18 —. 10 cash.............. ——
4-19 Kuang-hsü, cast........ 1.50
4-20 —. 10 cash, cast........ ——

CHINA

5. Chihli (now Hopei)

I. Mint in Paoting (Rev. "boo j'i").

		Fine
★5-1	Ch'ien-lung	.35
5-2	Chia-ching	.60
5-3	Tao-kuang	1.00
5-4	Hsien-feng	12.50
5-4a	—. Iron	10.00
5-5	—. 10 cash	17.50
5-6	—. 50 cash	20.00
5-7	—. 100 cash	25.00
5-8	T'ung-chih	10.00
5-9	—. 10 cash	—
5-10	Kuang-hsü	5.00
5-11	—. 10 cash	—

II. Mint in Chengte (Rev. "boo de").

6-1	Hsien-feng	100.00

★6-2	—. 5 cash	40.00
6-3	—. 10 cash	40.00
6-4	—. 50 cash	45.00
6-5	—. 100 cash	50.00

III. Mint in Chichow (Manchu "boo gi," same as group 17, Kirin).

7-1	Hsien-feng, 5 cash	50.00
7-2	—. 10 cash	50.00
7-3	—. 50 cash	100.00
7-4	—. 100 cash	150.00

IV. Mint in Tientsin (Rev. "boo jiyen").

★8-1	Kuang-hsü, cast	3.00

9. Fengtien (Rev. "boo fung").

9-1	Kuang-hsü, cast	—

10. Fukien (Rev. "boo fu").

		Fine
★10-1	Ch'ien-lung	.30
10-2	Chia-ching	1.00
10-3	Tao-kuang	3.50
10-4	Hsien-feng, 1 cash	1.50
10-5	—. 5 cash, on rim "2 Mace and 5 Candreens"	75.00
10-6	—. t'ung-pao, 10 cash, on top "1" on bottom "10"	4.00
10-7	—. chung-pao, 10 cash, on top "1" on bottom "10"	10.00

★10-8	—. chung-pao, 10 cash, + on rim: "Weighing 5 Mace"	15.00
10-9	—. chung-pao, 10 cash, + in field: "Weighing 5 Mace"	75.00
10-10	—. t'ung-pao, 20 cash, on top "2" on bottom "10"	7.00
10-11	chung-pao, 20 cash, on top "2" on bottom "10"	8.00
10-12	—. chung-pao, 20 cash, + on rim: "Weighing 1 Tael"	20.00
10-13	—. chung-pao, 20 cash, + in field: "Weighing 1 Tael"	75.00
10-14	—. t'ung-pao, 50 cash, on top "5" on bottom "10"	8.00
10-15	—. chung-pao, 50 cash, on top "5" on bottom "10"	10.00
10-16	—. chung-pao, 50 cash, + on rim: "2 Tael and 5 Mace"	100.00
10-17	—. chung-pao, 50 cash, + in field: "2 Tael and 5 Mace"	150.00
10-18	—. t'ung-pao, 100 cash, on top "1" on bottom "100"	10.00
10-19	—. chung-pao, 100 cash, on top "1" on bottom "100"	12.50
10-20	—. chung-pao, 100 cash, + on rim: "Weighing 5 Tael"	75.00

		Fine
10-21	—. chung-pao, 100 cash, + in field: "Weighing 5 Tael"	150.00

★10-22	T'ung-chih, 1 cash	3.50
10-23	—. 10 cash	—

Silver

★10-24	(dollar). "Fukien Ration" dollar. Var.	1000.00

Many counterfeits of No. 10-24 exist.

Brass or Copper

10-25	Kuang-hsü, cast	1.00
10-26	—. 10 cash	—

11. Honan (Rev. "boo ho").

★11-1	Hsien-feng, 1 cash	300.00
11-2	—. 10 cash	30.00
11-3	—. 20 cash	—
11-4	—. 30 cash	—
11-5	—. 50 cash	30.00
11-6	—. 100 cash	37.50
11-7	—. 500 cash	90.00
11-8	—. 1000 cash	125.00

CHINA

*11-9 Kuang-hsü, 1 cash......15.00

12. Hunan (Rev. "boo nan").

Var. 1   Var. 2

**12-1 Ch'ien-lung............ .40

*12-2 Chia-ching............ .60
12-3 Tao-kuang............ 4.50
12-4 Hsien-feng............ 2.00
12-5 T'ung-chih............ 3.00
12-6 —. 10 cash............ ——
12-7 Kuang-hsü............ 5.00
12-8 —. 10 cash............ ——

13. Hupeh (Rev. "boo u").

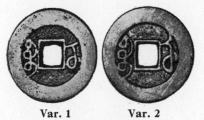

Var. 1   Var. 2

**13-1 Ch'ien-lung........... .35

*13-2 Chia-ching............ 1.25
13-3 Tao-kuang............ 2.00

Fine

*13-4 Hsien-feng............ 1.50
13-5 —. 5 cash............75.00
13-6 —. 10 cash............ 5.00
13-7 —. 50 cash............10.00
13-8 —. 100 cash............15.00
13-9 T'ung-chih............12.50
13-10 —. 10 cash............ ——
13-11 Kuang-hsü, cast....... 9.00
13-12 —. 10 cash............ ——

14. Kansu (Rev. "boo gung").

*14-1 Hsien-feng............12.50
14-2 —. 5 cash............50.00

*14-3 —. 10 cash............20.00
14-4 —. 50 cash............27.50
14-5 —. 100 cash............27.50
14-6 —. 500 cash............75.00
14-7 —. 1000 cash............75.00
14-8 T'ung-chih............17.50
14-9 —. 5 cash............75.00
14-10 —. 10 cash............40.00

15. Kiangsi (Rev. "boo cang").

*15-1 Ch'ien-lung............ .35
15-2 Chia-ching............ .75
15-3 Tao-kuang............ .50
15-4 Hsien-feng............ 1.00
15-5 —. 10 cash............ 6.00
15-6 —. 50 cash............10.00
15-7 T'ung-chih............ 2.00
15-8 —. 10 cash............ ——

15-9 Kuang-hsü............ 9.00
15-10 —. 10 cash............ ——

16. Kiangsu

Mint in Soochow (Rev. "boo su").

*16-1 Ch'ien-lung............ .25
16-2 Chia-ching............ .50
16-3 Tao-kuang............ .50
16-4 Hsien-feng............ 1.50
16-5 —. 5 cash............25.00
16-6 —. 10 cash............ 5.00
16-7 —. 20 cash............30.00

*16-8 —. 30 cash............RRR
16-9 —. 50 cash............R
16-10 —. 100 cash ....R
16-11 T'ung-chih............ 2.00
16-12 Kuang-hsü, cast....... 1.75
16-13 —. 5 cash............10.00
16-14 —. 10 cash............ ——

17. Kirin (Manchu "boo gi," same as group 7, Chichow).

17-1 Kuang-hsü, cast........10.00

*17-2 —. 10 cash. Rev. Chinese "chi" for Kirin at top......RR

CHINA

18. Kwangsi (Rev. "boo gui").

		Fine
*18-1	Ch'ien-lung	.25
18-2	Chia-ching	.50
18-3	Tao-kuang	.50
18-4	Hsien-feng	1.00
18-5	—. 10 cash	3.50
18-6	—. 50 cash	15.00
18-7	T'ung-chih	2.00
18-8	—. 10 cash	——
18-9	Kuang-hsü	9.00
18-10	—. 10 cash	——

19. Kwangtung (Rev. "boo guwang").

19-1	Ch'ien-lung	.30

*19-2	Chia-ching	.40
19-3	Tao-kuang	.30
19-4	Hsien-feng	3.00
19-5	T'ung-chih	4.00
19-6	—. 10 cash	——
19-7	Kuang-hsü, cast	12.50
19-8	—. 10 cash, cast	——

20. Kweichow (Rev. "boo giyan").

*20-1	Ch'ien-lung	.30

*20-2	Chia-ching	.60

		Fine
20-3	Tao-kuang	.60
20-4	Hsien-feng	3.00
20-5	—. 10 cash	10.00
20-6	—. 50 cash	75.00
20-7	T'ung-chih	——
20-8	—. 10 cash	——
20-9	Kuang-hsü	15.00
20-10	—. 10 cash	——

21. Shansi (Rev. "boo jin").

*21-1	Ch'ien-lung	.35
21-2	Chia-ching	2.50
21-3	Tao-kuang	10.00
21-4	Hsien-feng	27.50
21-5	—. 10 cash	25.00
21-6	T'ung-chih	18.00
21-7	—. 10 cash	——
21-8	Kuang-hsü	12.50
21-9	—. 10 cash	——

22. Shantung (Rev. "boo ji").

*22-1	Ch'ien-lung	2.00
22-2	Hsien-feng	100.00
22-3	—. 50 cash	100.00
22-4	—. 100 cash	100.00

There are many Hsien-feng, T'ung-chih and Kuang-hsü 1 cash thick forgeries.

23. Shensi (Rev. "boo san").

*23-1	Ch'ien-lung	.50

*23-2	Chia-ching	1.50

		Fine
23-3	Tao-kuang	4.00
23-4	Hsien-feng	4.00
23-5	—. 10 cash	15.00
23-6	—. 10 cash, on top "shen" for Shansi	60.00
23-7	—. 50 cash	17.50
23-8	—. 100 cash	35.00
23-9	—. 500 cash	50.00
23-10	—. 1000 cash	60.00
23-11	T'ung-chih	——
23-12	—. 10 cash	——
23-13	Kuang-hsü	——
23-14	—. 10 cash	——

24. Szechuan (Rev. "boo cuwan").
Care often must be taken not to confuse this mint name with the Boards of Revenue or Works (groups 1, 2).

*24-1	Ch'ien-lung	.25
24-2	Chia-ching	.60
24-3	Tao-kuang	.75
24-4	Hsien-feng	3.00
24-5	—. 10 cash	5.00
24-6	—. 50 cash	15.00
24-7	—. 100 cash	22.50
24-8	T'ung-chih	4.50
24-9	Kuang-hsü	10.00
24-10	—. 10 cash	——

25. Taiwan (Rev. "boo tai").

*25-1	Ch'ien-lung	10.00

Silver

CHINA

Fine

★25-3 Tao-kuang (1837
"Old Man Dollar")
Var............200.00-300.00

Many counterfeits of No. 25-3 exist.

★25-4 Hsien-feng (1853
dollar).........225.00-300.00

Fine

★25-5 —. (1862 dollar)..200.00-250.00

Copper or Brass

Fine

★25-6 Hsien-feng.............10.00
25-7 T'ung-chih *(forgery?)*..... ——

26. Yunnan

I. Mint in Yünnanfu (now Kunming)
(Rev. "boo yôn").

Care often must be taken not to confuse this mint name with the Board of Works (group 2).

★26-1 Ch'ien-lung............ .25
26-2 Chia-ching............. .30
26-3 Tao-kuang............. .35
26-4 Hsien-feng............. .50
26-5 —. 10 cash............. 6.00
26-6 —. 50 cash............35.00
26-7 T'ung-chih............. 2.50
26-8 —. 10 cash............20.00
26-9 Kuang-hsü............. 1.50
26-10 —. 10 cash............. ——

II. Mint in Tungchwan
(Rev. "boo dong").

Var. 1   Var. 2

★★27-1 Chia-ching............. 3.00
27-2 Tao-kuang............. .85
27-3 Hsien-feng............. 1.50
27-4 —. 10 cash............17.50
27-5 T'ung-chih............. 2.00
27-6 Kuang-hsü, cast........ 9.00
27-7 Hsüan-t'ung, cast......25.00

C. SINKIANG
(Chinese Turkestan)

Emperor Ch'ien-lung added this vast area to his empire about 1758 and called it Sinkiang ("New Frontiers"). A great part of it, however, was annexed by Russia in the latter half of the 19th century.

The obverses of the coins are identical to those from the rest of China, but on their reverse they show the mint's name in Manchu on the left and in Turki on the right. Many "Ch'ien-lung" and "Tao-kuang" coins were actually cast during the T'ung-chih and Kuang-hsü period, especially when they have additional characters. With the exception of the Ili and Tihua Mint all other Sinkiang mints used T'ung-pao for their 5 cash, and 10 cash coins and not Chung-pao.

Nearly all coins are red copper.

28. Mint in Ili (Rev. "boo i").

Fine

★28-1 Ch'ien-lung............35.00
28-2 Chia-ching.............20.00
28-3 Tao-kuang.............20.00
28-4 Hsien-feng............35.00

★28-5 —. 4 cash................R
28-6 —. 10 cash...............R
28-7 —. 50 cash...............R
28-8 —. 100 cash..............R
28-9 T'ung-chih, 4 cash........R
28-10 Kuang-hsü, 10 cash..... ——

29. Mint in Tihua (Urumtsi)
(Rev. "boo di").

★29-1 Hsien-feng, 8 cash.........R
29-2 —. 10 cash.................R

C. SINKIANG (Cont.)

30. Mint in Aksu

		Fine
30-1	Ch'ien-lung	20.00
30-2	—. 10 cash (later cast)	25.00
30-3	—. 10 cash, on top "A" for Aksu, (later cast)	20.00
30-4	—. 10 cash, on top "9" for Kuang-hsü 9th year (1883)	25.00
30-5	Chia-ching	30.00
30-6	Tao-kuang	20.00
30-7	—. 5 cash, on top "8th year" (1828)	20.00

★30-8	—. 10 cash, on top "8th year" (1828)	45.00
30-9	Hsien-feng	25.00
30-10	—. 5 cash	22.50
30-11	—. 10 cash	15.00
30-12	—. 50 cash	40.00
30-13	—. 100 cash	40.00
30-14	T'ung-chih	35.00
30-15	—. 10 cash	25.00
30-16	Kuang-hsü	35.00

★30-17	—. chung-pao, 10 cash	120.00
30-18	—. 10 cash, on top "A" for Aksu	25.00
30-19	—. 10 cash, on top "K'a" for Kashghar	30.00

31. Mint in Hotien (Khoten)

		Fine
★31-1	Ch'ien-lung	——
31-2	Hsien-feng, 1000 cash	——

32. Mint in Kashghar
(Also see group 37).

32-1	Ch'ien-lung	——
32-2	Hsien-feng, 10 cash	35.00
32-3	—. 50 cash	75.00

★32-4	—. 100 cash	RR
32-5	—. 1000 cash	——
32-6	Kuang-hsü, 10 cash, on top "K'a" for Kashghar	——

33. Mint in K'u-ch'e (Kuche, Kuldja, Kuja). Also see group 36.

33-1	Ch'ien-lung (later cast)	40.00
33-2	—. 10 cash, (later cast)	40.00
33-3	—. 10 cash, Rev. r. and l. Manchu "boo kuce," on top "K'u" for Kuche (later cast)	40.00
33-4	—. 10 cash, "boo kuce," on top "K'a" for Kashghar (later cast)	40.00
33-5	—. (10 cash), "boo kuce," on top "K'u," on bottom "Chü" for Kuche Office, (later cast)	40.00
33-6	Tao-kuang, 10 cash, on top "K'u," (later cast)	40.00
33-7	—. 10 cash, on top "Hsin" for Sinkiang (later cast)	40.00
33-8	Hsien-feng, 5 cash	40.00
33-9	—. 10 cash	40.00
33-10	—. 50 cash	50.00
33-11	—. 100 cash	75.00
33-12	—. 1000 cash	——

		Fine
★33-13	T'ung-chih, 10 cash, on top "K'u"	40.00
33-14	—. 10 cash, "boo kuce," on top "K'u"	40.00
33-15	—. 10 cash, "boo kuce," on top "Hsin"	40.00
33-16	Kuang-hsü, 10 cash	40.00
33-17	—. 10 cash, on top "9th year," (1883)	40.00
33-18	—. 10 cash, "boo kuce," on top "K'u"	40.00
33-19	—. 10 cash, "boo kuce," on top "A"	40.00
33-20	—. 10 cash, "boo kuce," on top "Hsin," cast	40.00
33-21	—. 10 cash, "boo kuce," on top "Hsin," struck	40.00
33-22	Kuang-hsü Ting-wu (cyclical characters for 1907), Rev. as above	——
33-23	Kuang-hsü Mou-shen (cyclical characters for 1908), Rev. as above	75.00

★33-24	Kuang-hsü, 10 cash, "boo sin," on top "Hsin"	40.00
33-25	—. 10 cash, "boo sin," on top "K'a"	40.00
33-26	Hsüan-tung, 10 cash	——

34. Mint in Ushi (Wushi)

★34-1	Ch'ien-lung	35.00

35. Mint in Yarkand

★35-1	Ch'ien-lung, Manchu reads "Yerkim" (before 1761)	40.00

CHINA

C. SINKIANG (Cont.)

		Fine
★35-2	—. Manchu reads "Yerkiyang"	20.00
35-3	Hsien-feng, 10 cash	25.00
35-4	—. 50 cash	55.00
35-5	—. 100 cash	75.00
35-6	—. 1000 cash	——
35-7	—. T'ung-chih, 10 cash	40.00

D. MUSLIM UPRISINGS

Monetary System:
26 cash = 1 tanga; 20 tanga = 1 tilla.

36. K'u-ch'e (Kuja).
Also see group 33.

Under Ghazi Rashid

Declared himself Khan of Turkestan in 1862, murdered 1867.

Copper

★36-1 (cash). Turki: GHAZI RASHID KHAN, SANAT (yr.) 2. Rev. DURIBA DAR AL-SULTANAT KUJA. AH1280 (=1864). 2 var.........60.00

37. Kashghar (Also see group 32).

Under Amir Yakub Beg
AH1282-94 (=AD1865-77)

Conquered Kashghar 1865, murdered Rashid in 1867. Was killed 1877 during the Chinese reconquest of the territory. Struck coins in name of Sultan of Turkey.

Copper

V.G.

★37-0.5 (falus). Turki: ʿABD AL-ʿAZIZ KHAN. Rev. DURIBA KASHGHAR. AH1292-93 (=1875-76)...........5.00

Silver

Fine

★37-1 (tanga). Obv. sim. Rev. DURIBA KASHGHAR LATIF. 1.45 gr. AH1291-94 (=1874-77)............15.00

Gold

★37-2 (tilla). Turki: SULTAN ʿABD AL-ʿAZIZ KHAN. Rev. DURIBA DAR AL-SULTANAT KASHGHAR. 3.7 gr. AH1290-95 (=1873-78)..300.00

E. TAIPING UPRISING (1851-64)

The chief of the rebellion Hung Hsiu-ch'uan, inspired by Christian missionaries, declared himself "Heavenly King" and took residence in Nanking after he had conquered most of South China. The Taiping Uprising, one of the most devastating civil wars in history, was finally crushed by Imperial troops in 1864.

There are other very rare cash coins issued by sympathizing societies and Taiping generals.

Copper or Brass

38-1	T'ai-p'ing t'ien-kuo (Heavenly Kingdom of Great Peace) (top-bottom-right-left), Rev: Sheng-pao (Holy Money) (top-bottom), 77mm	——
38-2	—. 54mm	*40.00*
38-3	—. ca 42mm (var.)	*30.00*
38-4	—. ca 31mm (var.)	*20.00*
★38-5	—. ordinary cash size (var.)	6.00

Fine

38-6	—. Rev. right-left, ca 42mm (var.)	*17.50*
38-7	—. 31mm (var.)	*15.00*
★38-8	—. ordinary cash size (var.)	4.00
38-9	—. Obv. (right-left-top-bottom)	*10.00*

★38-10	Obv. "T'ien-kuo" (top-bottom). Rev. "Sheng-pao" (top-bottom), ca 38mm	*20.00*
38-11	ordinary cash size	*25.00*
38-12	—. Obv. T'ai-p'ing Sheng-pao. Rev. T'ien-kuo (right-left)	8.00
38-13	—. Obv. T'ien-kuo Sheng-pao. Rev. T'ai-p'ing (right-left)	*20.00*

Illustrations:
Some of the illustrations in this section have been retouched to aid in identifying details or to show style, size and position of characters. These are meant only as a guide and are not necessarily from actual coins.

NOTES

COLOMBIA
(NUEVA GRANADA)

Presently a republic at the northwest corner of South America. Formerly the chief province of the Spanish Viceroyalty of Nueva (New) Granada. Achieved independence under Simon Bolivar 1811-23. At first Colombia was part of the Republic of Gran Colombia (including Venezuela and Ecuador), but this splintered in 1829-31.

Mints:

Santa Fe de Bogotá – NR, NR or Ň–Ř (=Nuevo Reino or New Kingdom of Granada); Popayán – P, PN or Pᴺ.

Monetary Systems:

Until 1847 —
8 reales=1 peso; 16 pesos=8 escudos (scudos)=1 onza.

Circa 1847-86 —
10 décimos (tenths)=10 reales=1 peso.

For other similar Spanish and Spanish-American coins, see Spain, Argentina, Bolivia, Chile, Guatemala, Mexico, Peru and Venezuela.

I. Bogotá Mint.

Fernando VI 1746-59

Mint marks: Ň-date-Ř on silver
NR on gold

Milled Silver

V.F.

*5 8 (Reales). FERDND VI D.G. HISPAN ET IND. REX, arms. Rev. VTRA etc, 2 hemispheres btwn. pillars. 1759..............7500.00

Gold (escudo =3.38 gr.)

V.F.

7 (escudo). Like No. 8. 1756-59..............150.00

*8 (2 escudos). 1756-61......225.00

9 (4 escudos). Sim. 1757-58..600.00

10 (8 escudos). Sim. but with order chain around arms. 1756-60..................700.00

Carlos III 1759-88

Mint marks: N-date-R on No. 11
Ň-date-Ř on No. 13
NR on Nos. 14-28
NR on Nos. 29-32

Silver

A. Pillar type.

F-VF

*11 I (real). CRS. III etc. 1760. 2000.00

13 8 (reales). Sim. but CAROLUS III etc. 1762.......RRR

B. Bust type.

14 (½ real). Like Popayán No. 15a. 1773-84..........125.00

15 1 R(eal). Sim. 1772-84......75.00

16 2 R(eales). Sim. 1772-84...150.00

Gold (escudo =3.38 gr.)

A. Bust of Fernando VI.

22 (2 escudos). Like No. 8 but CAROLS. III etc. 1760-62.................250.00

23 (4 escudos). Sim. 1760.....850.00

24 (8 escudos). Sim. but with order chain. 1759-62.......750.00

B. Young Standard Bust.

V.F.

25 (escudo). CAR. III etc., bust. Rev. IN UTROQ. FELIX, arms. 1767.....................175.00

26 (2 escudos). Sim. but CAROLUS III etc., rev. IN UTROQ...DEO. 1762-71.................150.00

V.F.

27 (4 escudos). Sim., with order chain. 1769-71......600.00

28 (8 escudos). Sim. 1763-71..600.00

C. Older Standard Bust.

29 1 S(cudo). CAROL. III etc., bust. Rev. IN UTROQ...A.D., arms in order chain. 1772-89......100.00

30 2 S(cudos). Sim. but rev. IN UTROQ...DEO. 1772-89...125.00

31 4 S(cudos). Sim. 1775-86...500.00

32 8 S(cudos). Sim. 1772-89...450.00

Carlos IV 1788-1808

Mint marks: NR on Nos. 41, 51-58
NR on Nos. 42-44

Silver

Fine

*41 ¼ (real). NR–Castle–¼. Rev. Lion. 1796-1808.......15.00

42 (½ real). Bust of Charles IV. Rev. Arms btwn. pillars. 1792-1801.................60.00

43 1 R(eal). Sim. 1792-1804....30.00

44 2 R(eales). Sim. 1792-1800..90.00

Gold

A. Bust of Carlos III.

V.F.

51 1 S(cudo). Like No. 29 but CAROL IV etc. 1790........150.00

52 2 S(cudos). Sim. but rev. like No. 30. 1789-91.......150.00

53 4 S(cudos). Sim. 1789-90...500.00

54 8 S(cudos). Sim. 1789-91...450.00

B. Bust of Carlos IV.

55 1 S(cudo). CAROL IIII etc., bust. Rev. like No. 29. 1791-1809.................90.00

56 2 S(cudos). Sim. but rev. like No. 30. 1790-1806.....125.00

57 4 S(cudos). Sim. 1792-1808.450.00

58 8 S(cudos). Sim. 1791-1808.400.00

Fernando VII, in Colombia 1808-23

All Bust-Type Coins Have Portrait of Carlos IV

Silver

F-VF

61 ¼ (real). Like No. 41. 1810-19..................14.00

62 (½ real). Like Popayán No. 66. 1810-19......45.00

63 1 R(eal). Sim. 1810-19......20.00

64 2 R(eales). Sim. 1816-19....20.00

COLOMBIA

Gold
V.F.

81 1 S(cudo). Like No. 55 (bust
of Carlos IV) but FERDND. VII
etc. 1808-20..............100.00
82 2 S(cudos). Sim. but rev.
like No. 30. 1808-11......125.00
83 4 S(cudos). Sim. 1818-19...475.00
84 8 S(cudos). Sim. 1808-20...375.00

II. Popayán Mint

Fernando VI 1746-59

Mint mark: PN.

Gold (escudo = 3.38 gr.)

7a (escudo). Like No. 8 but
mmk. PN. 1758-59.......150.00
8a (2 escudos). Sim. 1758-61..225.00
9a (4 escudos). Sim. 1758-60..600.00
10a (8 escudos). Sim., with
order chain around arms.
1758-60.................700.00

Carlos III 1759-88

Silver
F-VF

14a (½ real). Like No. 15a.
1774 P................200.00

★15a 1 R(eal). 1772 P........250.00

Gold (escudo = 3.38 gr.)
A. Bust of Fernando VI (mmk. PN).

V.F.

★21a (escudo). Like No. 8 but
CAROLS III etc. 1760-69...125.00
22a (2 escudos). Sim. 1760-71.200.00
23a (4 escudos). Sim. 1760-69.600.00
24a (8 escudos). Sim., with
order chain. 1760-71.....600.00

B. Older Standard Bust (mmk. P).

29a 1 S(cudo). Like No. 29.
1772-89................100.00
30a 2 S(cudos). Like No. 30.
1772-89................125.00
31a 4 S(cudos). Sim. 1773-88..500.00
32a 8 S(cudos). Sim. 1772-89..450.00

Carlos IV 1788-1808

Gold
A. Bust of Carlos III (mmk. P).
V.F.

51a 1 S(cudo). Like No. 51.
1789-90................125.00
52a 2 S(cudos). Like No. 52.
1789-91................150.00
53a 4 S(cudos). Sim. 1790....500.00
54a 8 S(cudos). Sim. 1789-91..450.00

B. Bust of Carlos IV (mmk. P).

★55a 1 S(cudo). Like No. 55.
1792-1808...............90.00
56a 2 S(cudos). Like No. 56.
1791-1804..............125.00
57a 4 S(cudos). Sim. 1792-
1808...................450.00
58a 8 S(cudos). Sim. 1791-
1808...................400.00

Fernando VII,
in Colombia 1808-23

All Bust-Type Coins Have
Portrait of Carlos IV

Mint mark: P or PN

Silver
F-VF

61a ¼ (real). Like No. 41 but
PN at left of castle. 1816...14.00
62a (½ real). Like No. 64a.
1810...................40.00
63a 1 R(eal). Sim. 1810-22.....25.00

★64a 2 R(eales). 1810-20.......20.00

F-VF

★65 2 R(eales). Sim. but FERDND.
7 D.G.ET CONST. 1822.......30.00
V.F.

66 8 R(eales). Like No. 64a.
1810-20.................550.00

Gold

81a 1 S(cudo). Like No. 81.
1808-19................100.00
82a 2 S(cudos). Like No. 82.
1817-19................125.00
84a 8 S(cudos). Sim. 1808-20..375.00

III. Popayán Provisional Coinage.

Copper
VF-EF

74 MEDIO (= ½)/REAL.
P/AÑO/1813. Rev. value ...500.00
76 2/REALES. Like No. 77.
1813...................75.00

★77 8/REALES. 1813........250.00

IV. Santa Marta, Province.

Copper

Fine(crude)

★71 (¼ real). 1813............50.00

★72 ¼ (real). 1820-21.........12.50

COLOMBIA

Silver

		F-VF
★73	2 R(eales). 1820.........300.00

REPUBLICAN ISSUES

Colombian silver coins of the first half of the 19th century are often weakly struck and subject to uneven wear.

I. Cartagena, State.

Copper
VG-F (crude)

91 ½ (real). Like No. 93.
N.D., 1811-14............17.50

92 *UN (=1) REAL. 1816.....* ——

★93 DOS (=2) REALES. 1811-
14......................20.00

II. Cundinamarca, State.

Silver

Fine

★101 1-4 (= ¼ real). Liberty cap.
Rev. Pomegranate (Granada).
1814-15.................60.00

102 ½ R(eal). Like No. 104.
1814..................125.00

103 1 R(eal). Sim. 1813-16.....35.00

★104 2 R(eales). 1815-16.......35.00

III. Nueva Granada Provisional Issues.

Silver
Fine

105 1-4 (=¼ real). Like No. 101.
1820-21................50.00

105a ¼ (real). Like No. 105
with Bᴬ at left. 1821......60.00

106 1 R(eal). Like No. 107.
1819.................50.00

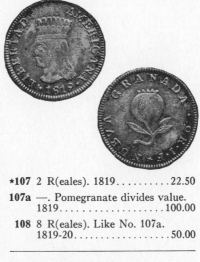

★107 2 R(eales). 1819.........22.50

107a —. Pomegranate divides value.
1819..................100.00

108 8 R(eales). Like No. 107a.
1819-20................50.00

IV. Republic of Colombia Province of Cundinamarca.

Bᴬ – Bogotá Mint.

Silver
Fine

111 ½ R(eal). Like No. 112.
1821..................35.00

★112 1 R(eal). 1821...........17.50

113 2 R(eales). Sim. 1820-21...12.50

115 8 R(eales). Sim. 1820-21...35.00

115a —. Obv. sim. Rev. like
No. 108 (mule). 1820.....200.00

V. Republic of Colombia.

Bogotá – B, Bᴬ; Popayán – P, Pᴺ.

Copper

118 UN QUARTO DE (=¼)
REAL. Liberty head. Rev.
value. 1825............*Pattern?*

Silver

Fine

★121 ¼ (real). *1824-36*........ 7.50

Fine

122 ½ REAL. Like No. 123.
1834-36................15.00

★123 1 REAL. 1827-36........ 5.00

V.F.

★126 OCHO (=8)/REALES.
Like No. 123. 1834-36....100.00

Gold

131 1 (peso). Like No. 133. 1825-
36. Bogotá.............45.00

132 1 S(cudo). Sim. 1822-37.
Bogotá.................50.00

132a 1 E(scudo). Sim. 1823-36.
Popayán................60.00

★133 2 S(cudos). 1822-37.
Bogotá.................100.00

134 4 S(cudos). Sim. *1823*, 26.
Bogotá.................750.00

135 8 S(cudos). Sim. 1822-37.
Bogotá.................350.00

136 8 E(scudos). Sim. 1822-36.
Popayán................375.00

COLOMBIA

REPUBLICAN ISSUES (Cont.)

VI. Republica de Nueva Granada.

A. 8 reales = 1 peso.

Silver

		V.F.
★141	¼/DE/REAL. Cornucopia. Rev. value. 1837-47	7.50
142	½/REAL. Like No. 143. 1838-47	6.00

		Fine
★143	1/REAL. 1837-46	4.50

★144	DOS (=2)/REALES. 1839-46	7.50
145	8/REALES. Pointed shield. Rev. like No. 143. 1837 (E.F.)	300.00

		V.F.
147	OCHO (=8) REALES. Like No. 144. 1839-46	35.00

Gold

Bogotá or Popayán.

148	(ex 166) UN(=1) PESO. Like No. 168. 1837-49	35.00
149	(ex 167) DOS(=2) PESOS. Sim. 1837-49	50.00

		V.F.
★150	(ex 168) DIEZ I SEIS (=16) PESOS. 1837-49	250.00

B. 10 reales = 1 peso.

Copper

★151	½/DECIMO/DE (=1/20) REAL. 1847-48	6.00
152	1/DECIMO/DE (=1/10) REAL. Sim. 1847-48	6.00

Silver

★153	¼ (real). Pomegranate. Rev. value. 1849-55	6.00
154	MEDIO (=½)/REAL. Like No. 162. 1850-53	5.00

★154a	—. 1862. Popayán	15.00

★155	UN (=1)/REAL. 1847	10.00
155a	—. Like No. 162. 1851-53	4.00
156	DOS (=2)/REALES. Like No. 156a but date above shield. 1847	75.00

★156a	—. 1847-49	5.00
156b	—. Rev. Like No. 162. 1849-53	6.00
158	OCHO (=8)/REALES. Like No. 156a. 1847	45.00
159	DIEZ (=10)/REALES. Sim. but arms on trophies and condor above. 1847-49	50.00

		V.F.
160	DIEZ/REALES. Sim. but spreadwing condor. 1850-51	50.00

Gold

170	3.2258 G(rams = 2 pesos). REPUBLICA DE LA NUEVA GRANADA. Liberty head. Rev. Arms. 1849-51	135.00
172	25.8064 G(rams = 16 pesos). Sim. 1849-53	500.00

C. 10 décimos = 1 peso.

Silver

161	MEDIO (=½)/DECIMO. Like No. 162. 1854-58	5.00

		V.F.
★162	UN (=1)/DECIMO. 1853-58	4.50
163	DOS (=2)/DECIMOS. Like No. 156b. 1855-57	10.00
165	UN (=1)/PESO. Like No. 160. 1855-58	25.00

Gold

171	16.400 G(rams = 10 pesos). Like No. 170. 1853-57	375.00
173	1/PESO. NUEVA GRANADA. Liberty head. Rev. value. 1856, 58	175.00
174	2/PESOS. Sim. 1856-58	125.00
175	5/PESOS. Sim. 1856-58	250.00
176	DIEZ (=10) PESOS. Like No. 170. 1856-58	375.00

VII. Confederación Granadina.

Silver

		Fine
180	¼ (real). Like No. 153 1859-62. Popayán	7.50

★181	¼ (decimo). Sim. Rev. Caducei. 1860. Bogotá	20.00
181a	—. Sim. Rev. 9 stars. 1861. Bogotá	12.50

COLOMBIA

REPUBLICAN ISSUES (Cont.)

Fine

182 MEDIO (=½)/DECIMO.
Like No. 183. 1860-61.....10.00

★183 UN (=1)/DECIMO.
1859-60.................. 7.50

★184 DOS (=2)/REALES.
1862. Popayán........... 7.00

186 UN (=1)/PESO. Like No.
165 but CONFEDERACION
GRANADINA. 1859-60.......20.00

Gold

V.F.

187 1/PESO. Like No. 173 but
CONFEDERACION etc. 1862.200.00

188 2/PESOS. Sim. 1859-60...175.00

189 5/PESOS. Sim. 1862....1500.00

190 *CINCO (=5) PESOS.* Like
No. 176 but CONFEDERACION
etc. 1859..............1500.00

191 DIEZ (=10) PESOS. Sim.
1858-62................700.00

192 VEINTE (=20) PESOS. Sim.
1859................1500.00

VIII. Estados Unidos de Nueva Granada.

Silver

Fine

★195 UN (=1)/DECIMO. Like
No. 183 but ESTADOS UNIDOS
DE NUEVA GRANADA.
1861....................35.00

197 UN (=1)/PESO. Like No. 165
but ESTADOS etc. 1861....140.00

COSTA RICA

A small state in Central America. Part of the Spanish Captaincy - General of Guatemala until 1821. To Mexico 1822-23. From 1824 to 1840 Costa Rica was a state in the Republic of Central America. About 1846 it became obvious that Central America was not to be reunited and Costa Rica first adopted the style Republica de Costa Rica on its coins.

Monetary System:
8 reales =1 peso; 16 pesos =8 escudos =1 onza.

I. Central American Types.

Mint mark: CR.

For similar coins with other mint marks see Guatemala (NG or G) and Honduras (T).

Silver

F-VF

★1 ¼ (real). Mountains. Rev.
Tree. 1845...............75.00

2 ½ R(eal). Like No. 3.
1831-49..................15.00

★3 1 R(eal). 1831-49.........22.50
4 2 R(eales). Sim. 1849..... ——

V.F.

5 8 R(eales). Sim. 1831.....500.00

Gold

5.1 ½ E(scudo). Like No. 9 but
rev. palm tree. 1825.......RRR

6 ½ E(scudo). Like No. 9.
1828-48..................65.00

7 1 E(scudo). Sim. 1828-49..125.00

8 2 E(scudos). Sim. 1828-50..225.00

★9 4 E(scudos). 1828-49.....1000.00

10 8 E(scudos). Sim. 1828,
33, 37.................2000.00

II. State of Costa Rica.

Cmk. radiate 6-pointed star in circle (sim. to obverse of No. 11). Silver coins have 4 to 9mm perforation.

Silver

F-VF (cmk.)

10.1 (½ real). Cmk. on Spanish-
American ½ real.
(1841-42)..............RRR

10.2 (1 real). Sim. 100.00

★10.3 (2 reales). Sim...........75.00

10.4 (4 reales). Sim.........250.00

10.5 (8 reales). Sim.........150.00

Gold

10.6 (4 escudos). Cmk. on No. 9
(without perforation)......RR

Silver

F-VF

★11 ½ R(eal). 1842...........45.00

No. 11 often found with hole (worth $20.00 to $25.00).

Gold

★16 1 E(scudo). Like No. 11.
1842..................350.00

III. Provisional Issues.

Silver

V.G.

★14 (2 reales). Cmk: COSTA RICA.
Female head. Rev. Tree. On
(Spanish) 2 reales. (1845)...15.00

12 1 R(eal). Like No. 13. Struck
over cob 1 real. 1846.......15.00

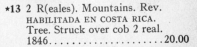

★13 2 R(eales). Mountains. Rev.
HABILITADA EN COSTA RICA.
Tree. Struck over cob 2 real.
1846....................20.00

COSTA RICA

V.G.

13.5 (4 reales). Die of No. 12 used
on cob 4 real with additional
cmk: 4 in square. 1846 . . . . 350.00

15 (8 reales). Die of No. 13 used
on cob dollar with additional
cmk: 8 in circle. 1846 . . . . . . 500.00

IV. Republica de Costa Rica Countermarked Issues.

About the middle of the 19th century,
many early Costa Rican and foreign
silver coins were cmkd: HABILITADA POR
EL GOBIERNO, lion.

This stamp on 8 real (dollar) size
coins is thought to be a modern fabrication.

Silver

Fine

17 (½ real). Cmkd. on No. 2 . . . 6.50

17a —. Cmkd. on No. 11 . . . . . . 25.00

18 (1 real). Cmkd. on No. 3 . . . . 20.00

★18a —. Cmkd. on Great Britain
6 pence 15.00

Fine

★19 (2 reales). Cmkd. on No. 4 . . 10.00

19a —. Cmkd. on Great Britain
shilling 17.50

Gold

F-VF

20 ½ E(scudo). No. 6 cmkd.
like Nos. 17-19 . . . . 50.00

21 1 E(scudo). No. 7 cmkd. like
Nos. 17-19 . . . . 85.00

21a —. No. 16 cmkd. like
Nos. 17-19 . . . . ——

V. First Regular Issues.

22 1 R(eal). Like No. 23 but
A LA CONSTIT^ON DE . . . 1847.
Female. Rev. REFORMAS
etc. 1846. Coffee tree 15.00

★23 (Y-4) 1 R(eal). 1849-50 . . . . 6.50

CURAÇAO. See CARIBBEAN ISLANDS AND TERRITORIES.

UNVERIFIED DATA

Note: Throughout this catalog, any
uncertain, indefinite or unconfirmed information is shown in *italic type*. Such
material may be, for example, coin descriptions, dates and prices, names of
rulers, or supplementary notes. Further
information to confirm or correct *material in italics* should be sent to the
author at the following address:

William D. Craig
c/o Whitman Coin Supply Division
1220 Mound Avenue
Racine, Wisconsin 53404, U.S.A.

DANISH WEST INDIES.
See CARIBBEAN ISLANDS AND TERRITORIES.

DEMERARA AND ESSEQUIBO.
See BRITISH GUIANA.

DENKARK, KINGDOM

A monarchy occupying the Jutland peninsula and adjacent islands, between the North and Baltic Seas.

Norway was united to the crown of Denmark until 1814. Denmark also ruled portions of Germany (Oldenburg until 1773, Schleswig and Holstein until 1864, Lauenburg 1816-64). See these states for local coins. **Danish type coins with crossed hammer mint mark (Kongsberg) are listed under Norway. Coins of the same types from Copenhagen and Altona Mints are listed below.**

Monetary Systems:

Until 1813 — 64 skilling danske = 4 mark = 1 krone (corona danica); 96 skilling danske = 6 mark = 1 Speciedaler (Rigsspeciedaler after 1775); 12 marks = 1 courant ducat.

During the inflation of 1794-1813, the Rigsdaler courant (paper, copper, billon) sank from ⅘ to ⅙ Rigsspeciedaler in value. By 1813 the Danish State was bankrupt and a new monetary system was established: 96 rigsbank skilling = 1 rigs(bank)daler = ½ Speciedaler = 30 schillinge (Schleswig-Holstein).

Arms:

Denmark —
 Gold, 3 blue lions flanked by 9 red hearts.

Norway —
 Through 1844: Red, a gold lion on a curved silver axe.

Sweden —
 Blue, 3 gold crowns.

Frederik V 1746-66

Copper
Fine

1 ½/SKILLING. Cwnd. double F5 mon. Rev. value. 1751-62 . . . . 4.00

Billon

V.G.

*2 I/SKILLING. Arms. Rev. value. 1751-64 . . . . 2.00

4 II/SKILLING. Like No. 1. 1750-61 . . . . 3.00

V.G.

*6 IIII/SKILLING. Cwnd. double FV mon. Rev. value. 1764 . . . 3.50

Silver
Fine

8 VIII/SKILLING. Like No. 1. 1763 . . . . 12.50

8a —. Single F5 mon. 1763 . . . . 20.00

8b —. Single FV mon. 1763 . . . . 17.50

10 24 SKILLING. Head. Rev. Arms. 1750-51 . . . . 42.50

10a —. Bust. 1751 . . . . 42.50

11 24 SKILLING. Cwnd. double F5 mon. Rev. Arms. 1750-64 . . . . 12.50

V.F.

*12 (krone). 1747 . . . . 75.00

13 (krone). Head. Rev. Arms. 1748 . . . . 75.00

14 (Speciedaler). King stdg. under canopy. Rev. Arms supported by Wildmen. 1747 . . . . 200.00

Note: The 1749 piece of dollar size with bust, rev. Oldenburg arms, is a scarce medal.

16 (Speciedaler). Head. Rev. Arms of Denmark, Norway and Sweden in oval shield. 1764-65 . . . . 175.00

17 (2 kroner). No. 12 double thick. 1747 . . . . 175.00

18 (thick 3 kroner). FRIDERICVS V etc. His head. Rev. CHRISTIANVS VI etc. His head. On death of Christian and accession of Frederik. 45.4 gr. (1746) . . . 300.00

V.F.

19 (2 Speciedaler). No. 14 double thick. 57.8 gr. 1747 . . . . 450.00

Gold (ducat = 3.49 gr.)

A. General Issues.
VF-EF

20 (ducat). Like No. 18 but busts both sides. (1746) 450.00

22 (ducat). Bust. Rev. Arms. 1747 . . . . 600.00

23 (ducat). King stdg. Rev. Arms. 1747. (var.) 350.00

24 (thick ducat). King galloping. Rev. cwnd. double F5 mon. 1748 . . . . 300.00

25 (ducat). Head. Rev. Ship. 1753-56 . . . . 450.00

26 (ducat). Bust. Rev. Arms/ EBENEZER. 1758 . . . . 650.00

27 XII M(arks). Helmeted bust. Rev. Cwn. 1757-58 . . . . 275.00

28 XII M(arks). Cwnd. FFVs around triangle. Rev. cwn. 1757, 63 . . . . 250.00

29 XII M(arks). Head. Rev. Cwn. 1757-65 . . . . 125.00

30 (2 ducats). Like No. 20. (1746) 1250.00

30a —. Head of FV . . . . Unique

31 (2 ducats). Like No. 22. 1747 . . . . 1500.00

32 (2 ducats). Head. Rev. Arms. 1747 . . . . 1000.00

33 (2 ducats). Like No. 23. 1747 . . . . 1500.00

34 (2 ducats). Like No. 24. 1748 . . . . RR

35 (2 ducats). Like No. 25. 1753 . . . . Unique

B. Struck from Chinese gold obtained by the Danish-Asiatic Trading Co.

(All with EX AURO SINICO and dated 1746.)

36 (ducat). Bust. Rev. Arms . . 600.00

36a —. Rev. Galley 450.00

37 (ducat). Head. Rev. Arms . . 500.00

37a —. Rev. Galley 750.00

38 (2 ducats). No. 36 double thick . . . . RR

38a —. Like No. 36a 500.00

39 (2 ducats). Like No. 37 . . . Unique

C. Struck from Guinea gold.

40 (ducat). Head. Rev. ship and Christiansborg Fort. 1746 . . 600.00

41 (ducat). King stdg. Rev. Christiansborg Fort. 1747 . . 600.00

42 (2 ducats). Like No. 40. 1746 . . . . RR

43 (2 ducats). Like No. 41. 1747 . . . . 1500.00

DENKMARK

Christian VII 1766-1808

Copper

Fine

46 ½/SKILLING. Cwnd. C7 mon. Rev. Value/DANSKE/K.M/ 1771 .... 1.50

47 1/SKILLING. Cwnd. double C7 mon. Rev. as last. 1771, 79 (RRR) .... .75

47a —. DANAKE, DNASKE or DANKSE 25.00

Billon

V.G.

*49 1/SKILLING. Cwnd. C7 mon. Rev. value. 1779, 82 .... 1.25

51 2 SKILLING. Cwnd. C7 mon. Rev. Arms. 1778-85 .... 1.00

*53 2/SKILLING. 1801, 05 ..... .75

55 IIII/SKILLING. Cwnd. C VII mon. Rev. value. 1783 ...... 2.00

56 4 SKILLING. Like No. 53. 1807 .... 1.75

Silver

F-VF

57 VIII/SKILLING. Like No. 49. 1773, 83 .... 5.00

58 8 SKILLING. Cwnd C7 mon. Rev. Arms. 1782 .... 40.00

*59 12/STYKKER/1.(=1/12) RIGSDALER/COURANT. Obv. *. Rev. value. 1796-99 M.F. (Altona) 6.00

62 24 SKILLING. Cwnd. CVII mon. Rev. 17/3 fold arms/ 67 .... 75.00

62a —. Rev. Arms/1782 .... 60.00

*64 (¼ Speciedaler). Cwnd. double C7 mon. Rev. Arms in ribbon. 7.2 gr. 1769 .... 60.00

F-VF

66 24 SKILLING. Like No. 58. 1778-83 .... 40.00

68 (½ krone). Bust. Rev. DEN/ 29/JANUA/RII in wreath. King's birthday 1771. 8.9 gr 115.00

70 32 SKILLING. Bust. Rev. Arms. 1775 .... 150.00

V.F.

74 (½ Speciedaler). Like No. 64. 14.5 gr. 1769 .... 75.00

74a ½ SP(eciedaler). Sim. 1769 .... 125.00

74b ½ SP(eciedaler). Rev. Arms in wreath. 1777 (unique), 86 .... 65.00

76 (krone). Like No. 68. 1771 . 175.00

Silver

This coin was struck for the Danish Asiatic Company for trade with the Orient (inscribed ISLAN(D), GRÖNLAND, FERÖ, often erroneously called "Greenland Trade Dollar").

E.F.

*78 (piastre). 1771, 77 ...... 3750.00

V.F.

*80 (Speciedaler). 1769 .... 750.00

81 (Speciedaler). Like No. 64. 1769 .... 75.00

81a —. Like No. 74a. 1771-80 ... 50.00

81b —. Sim. but Rev. longer legend. 1777 .... 60.00

82 1 RIGSDALER SPECIES. Head. Rev. 3 fold oval arms. 1795-1801 .... 60.00

82a —. Smaller head. 1799 ...... 65.00

Note: No. 82 struck at Altona and Copenhagen, and similar coins struck at Kongsberg 1791-1801, were circulated chiefly in Norway. Very similar coins with values in schillings were struck for Schleswig-Holstein.

Gold (ducat=3.49 gr.)

VF-EF

83 (ducat). Like No. 68. 1771 . 500.00

84 XII M(arks). Bust. Rev. Cwn. 1781-85 .... 175.00

85 I SPECIES/DUCAT. Wildman stdg. Rev. value in square. 1791-1802 .... 450.00

86 (Christian d'or). Bust. Rev. cwnd. double C7 monograms around triangle. 1775, ND . 600.00

Frederik VI 1808-39
Inflationary Copper

Fine

87 I/SKILLING. Cwnd. FR VI mon. Rev. value/DANSK/ 1812 .... 1.25

88 2 S(killing). Like No. 90. 1809-11 .... 1.50

89 3 S(killing). Sim. 1812 ...... 1.25

*90 12 SK(illing). Struck over No. 47. 1812 .... 7.50

The 1 sk. 1809, 3 sk. 1811, 4 sk. 1812 and 6 sk. 1812 are patterns.

DENmark

New Copper Token Coinage

Fine

93 1/RIGSBANK/SKILLING. Bust. Rev. value. 1813 ..... 1.50

94 2 SKILLING. RIGSBANKTEGN (=National Bank Token). Like No. 98. 1815 .... 1.50

95 3 SKILLING. Sim. 1815 ... 2.00

96 4 SKILLING. Sim. 1815 ... 3.00

97 6 SKILLING. Sim. 1813 ... 4.00

★98 12 SKILLING. 1813 .... 3.00

99 16 SKILLING. Sim. but squarish shield. 1814 .... 5.00

Regular Copper Coinage

★100 ½ R(igs)B(ank)SK(illing). 1838 .... 1.75

101 1/RIGSBANK/SKILLING. Like No. 102. 1818 .... 2.00

★102 2/RIGSBANK/SKILLING. 1818 .... 5.00

The 2 RBS 1818 with head, rev. value, is a rare pattern.

Inflationary Silver

F-VF

104 I/SKILLING. Cwnd. FR VI mon. Rev. value/DANSK/M.F. (Altona) 1808-09 .... 2.50

F-VF

★105 ⅙ RIGSDALER COURANT. Cwnd. FR VI mon. Rev. FRIVILLIGT etc. 1808. Offering for Fatherland 12.50

New Regular Silver

106 2/RIGSBANK/SKILLING. Cwnd. FR VI mon. Rev. value. 1836 .... 4.00

107 3/RIGSBANK/SKILLING. Sim. 1836 .... 6.00

108 4/RIGSBANK/SKILLING. Sim. 1836 .... 10.00

For 8 and 16 Reichsbankschilling see GERMANY (Schleswig-Holstein).

109 32/RIGSBANK/SKILLING. Sim. 1818, 20 .... 22.00

110 EN (=1) RIGSBANKDALER. Head. Rev. Arms. 1813-19 .. 30.00

110a —. Smaller head. 1826-39 .. 37.50

111 EN (=1) RIGSDALER SPECIES. Head. Rev. oval arms. 1819 .... 225.00

★112 EN (=1) RIGSDALER SPECIES. 1820-39 .... 55.00

Gold

VF-EF

113 1/FREDERIKS/D'OR (=5 Speciedaler). Head. Rev. value. 1827 .... 1000.00

VF-EF

114 1 FR. D'OR. Head l. Rev. Arms. 1828 .... 1000.00

114a —. 1829-38 .... 625.00

115 2/FR./D'OR. Like No. 113. 1826-27 .... 1000.00

116 2 FR. D'OR. Like No. 114. 1828-36 .... 750.00

117 2 FR. D'OR. Head r. Rev. Arms supported. 1836-39 .... 750.00

Christian VIII 1839-48

Mint Marks:
Copenhagen – Crown or heart.
Altona – Orb.

Copper

Fine

118 1/5/RIGSBANKSKILLING. Like No. 120. 1842 .... 2.50

118a —. Abbreviated 1/5 R.B.S. 1842 .... 1.00

119 ½/R.B.S. Sim.1842 .... 1.50

★120 1/R.B.S. 1842 .... 2.50

121 2/R.B.S. Sim. 1842 .... 20.00

Silver

F-VF

122 3 RIGSBANKSKILLING. Sim. 1842 .... 3.00

★122a 3 R.B.S. Sim. 1842 .... 3.00

123 4 RIGSBANKSKILLING or 1¼ SCH(illing in Schleswig-Holstein). Sim. 1841-42 .... 4.00

124 8 RIGSBANKSKILLING or 2½ SCHILL(ing). Like No. 127. 1843 .... 15.00

125 16 RIGSBANKSKILLING or 5 SCHILLING. Sim. 1842, 44 (RRR) 20.00

126 32 RIGSBANKSKILLING or 10 SCHILL(ing). Sim. 1842-43 .... 17.50

DENMARK

F-VF

★127 1 RIGSBANKDALER or
30 SCHILL(ing). 1842-48..37.50

128 1 SPECIES(daler). Head.
Rev. Arms supported. 1840-
48.....................75.00

Gold
VF-EF

129 1 CHR(istian) D'OR (=5
Sp. daler). Sim. 1843-47 .. 750.00

130 2 CHR. D'OR. Sim. 1841-
47.....................750.00

Frederik VII 1848-63

Copper

F-VF

★131 ½ R(igs)B(ank)SK(illing).
1852.............. 4.00

132 1/R.B.S. Large head.
Rev. like No. 120. 1852.... 7.50

132a —. Small head. 1853...... 2.50

The 1854 ½, 1 and 16 SKILLING are
rare patterns.

Bronze

134 ½/SKILLING. Like No. 135.
1857.....................1.50

★135 1/SKILLING. 1856-63.....1.00

Silver
F-VF

136 4/SKILLING R(igs) M(ont).
Like No. 138. 1854, 56..... 3.00

137 16/SKILLING. Sim. 1856-
58.................... 6.00

★138 ½ RIGSDALER. 1854-
55....................12.50

139 1 RIGSBANKDALER.
Head. Rev. Arms. 1849,
51....................50.00

140 1 RIGSDALER. Like No.
137. 1854-55.............22.50

V.F.

★141 1 SPECIES(daler). On death
of Ch. VIII and accession of
Fr. VII. 1848............150.00

142 1 SPECIES(daler). Head.
Rev. Arms. 1849-54......100.00

143 2/RIGSDALER. Like No.
138. 1854-63............75.00

Gold
VF-EF

144 1 FR(ederik) D'OR. Head.
Rev. Arms, supporters.
1853.................1500.00

145 2 FR. D'OR. Sim. 1850-
63...................1100.00

**DOMINICA. See CARIBBEAN
ISLANDS AND TERRITORIES.**

**DUTCH WEST INDIES. See
CARIBBEAN ISLANDS
AND TERRITORIES,**
Netherlands West Indies.

EAST AFRICA

Arab settlements along the coast. Denominations of the coins are unknown.

I. Lamu Mint.

Tin

★1 (—). Arabic: LAMU.
Rev. STRUCK AT. 13mm.
ND (19th cent.)........... —

II. Mombasa Mint.

Salim 1826-35

Tin

★21 (—). Arabic: MOMBASA.
Rev. STRUCK AT. 18mm.
ND..................... —

ECUADOR

Small republic in Northwest South America. Constituted the Spanish Presidency of Quito until 1822. United with Colombia and Venezuela in the Republic of Gran Colombia 1822-30. Independent 1830 onward.

Mint: Quito.

Monetary System:
8 reales = 1 peso; 2 pesos = 1 escudo.

I. As Ecuador in Colombia.

Silver

Fine

1 M(edio = ½)R(eal). Like
No. 2. 1833, 35.............20.00

★2 1 R(eal). EL ECUADOR EN
COLOMBIA. 1833-35......... 9.00
3 2 R(eales). Sim. 1833-35..... 9.00

Gold

V.F.

4 1 E(scudo). Like No. 5.
1833-35, 45..............200.00

The existence of No. 4 dated 1845 is unexplained.

V.F.

★5 1 D (= Double escudo).
Sim. 1833, 35...........225.00

II. República del Ecuador.

Billon

Fine

★6 (Y1) UN/CUARTO
(= ¼ real). 1842-43.......60.00

Silver

7 (Y2) M(edio = ½) R(eal).
REPUBLICA DEL ECUADOR.
Rev. EL PODER etc. 1838,
40.....................20.00
8 (Y3) 1 R(eal). Sim. 1836-41. 6.00
8a —. Like No. 9a. 1837-38....75.00
9 (Y4) 2 R(eales). Like No. 7.
1836-41..................6.00

★9a —. Obv. and rev. legends
transposed. 1837-38.......15.00
10 (Y5) 4 R(eales). Like
No. 7. 1841-43............12.50

★11 (Y6, 7) 4 R(eales).
Head of Bolívar. 1844-45
(var.)...................75.00

Gold

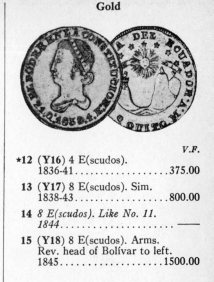

V.F.

★12 (Y16) 4 E(scudos).
1836-41.................375.00
13 (Y17) 8 E(scudos). Sim.
1838-43.................800.00
14 8 E(scudos). Like No. 11.
1844.................... —
15 (Y18) 8 E(scudos). Arms.
Rev. head of Bolívar to left.
1845.................1500.00

EGYPT (MISR)

Northeast African country which formed part of the Turkish Empire during the period covered by this catalog.

Egyptian coins are similar to those of Turkey, but show the mint place, MISR, usually just above the accession year.

MISR =

Monetary System:
Silver: 3 akcheh (akçe, aspers) = 1 para (medino); 40 para = 8 beshlik = 4 onluk = 2 yirmilik = 1 piastre (ghirsh, guerche, grusch).
Gold: 2 nisfiye (nessfijeh) = 1 zeri mahbub (2.6 gr.); 1 altun = 3.4 gr. (initially).

By reason of gross inflation, the number of para required to equal a silver dollar increased during this period from about 60 to 800.

Dating:
Coins of Egypt, like those of Turkey, usually bear the accession year of the reigning Sultan, together with his regnal year for the date of issue. Their combination indicates the A.H. date.

Mahmud I, Sultan
AH1143-68 (= AD1730-54)

All with date 1143, no regnal year.

Copper

G-VG

1 (asper). Like No. 2. 17mm... —

EGYPT

Billon

*2 (para). Toughra. Rev. MISR *Fine* etc./1143. .5 gr. 16mm..... 3.25

Gold

V.F.

6 (½ zeri mahbub). Like No. 7. 1.2 gr. 10mm.

*7 (zeri mahbub). Toughra/ MISR/1143. Rev. 4-line legend. 2.3-2.5 gr. 19-21mm.......*50.00*

8 (2 zeri mahbub). Sim. 5.0 gr. 27mm.............. ——

9 (3 zeri mahbub). Sim. 7.6 gr. 36mm.............. ——

10 (½ altun). Like No. 11. 1.7 gr. 15mm.............. ——

*11 (altun). Toughra. Rev. MISR etc./1143. 3.4 gr. 19-20mm................. ——

11a —. 26mm................. ——

Osman III, Sultan
AH1168-71 (=AD1754-57)

All with date 1168, no regnal year.

Copper

G-VG

12 (asper). Like No. 13. 15mm. ——

Billon

*13 (para). Toughra. Rev. *Fine* MISR etc./1168. 0.5 gr. 16mm.................. 6.00

Gold

V.F.

18 (½ zeri mahbub). Like No. 19. 1.2 gr. 20mm.

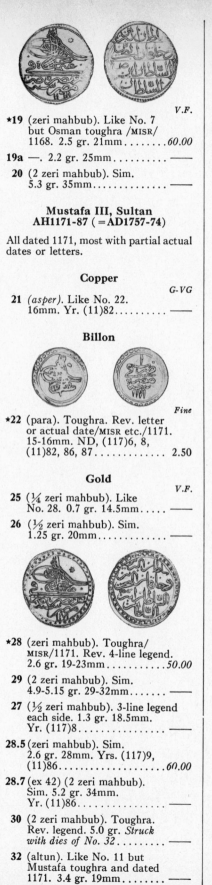

V.F.

*19 (zeri mahbub). Like No. 7 but Osman toughra /MISR/ 1168. 2.5 gr. 21mm.......*60.00*

19a —. 2.2 gr. 25mm.......... ——

20 (2 zeri mahbub). Sim. 5.3 gr. 35mm.............. ——

Mustafa III, Sultan
AH1171-87 (=AD1757-74)

All dated 1171, most with partial actual dates or letters.

Copper

G-VG

21 (asper). Like No. 22. 16mm. Yr. (11)82.......... ——

Billon

Fine

*22 (para). Toughra. Rev. letter or actual date/MISR etc./1171. 15-16mm. ND, (117)6, 8, (11)82, 86, 87............. 2.50

Gold

V.F.

25 (¼ zeri mahbub). Like No. 28. 0.7 gr. 14.5mm..... ——

26 (½ zeri mahbub). Sim. 1.25 gr. 20mm............. ——

*28 (zeri mahbub). Toughra/ MISR/1171. Rev. 4-line legend. 2.6 gr. 19-23mm..........*50.00*

29 (2 zeri mahbub). Sim. 4.9-5.15 gr. 29-32mm...... ——

27 (½ zeri mahbub). 3-line legend each side. 1.3 gr. 18.5mm. Yr. (117)8............... ——

28.5 (zeri mahbub). Sim. 2.6 gr. 28mm. Yrs. (117)9, (11)86.................*60.00*

28.7 (ex 42) (2 zeri mahbub). Sim. 5.2 gr. 34mm. Yr. (11)86............... ——

30 (2 zeri mahbub). Toughra. Rev. legend. 5.0 gr. *Struck with dies of No. 32*........ ——

32 (altun). Like No. 11 but Mustafa toughra and dated 1171. 3.4 gr. 19mm........ ——

Government of 'Ali Bey in Egypt
AH1183-86 (=AD1769-72)

This series has been revised in accordance with Samuel Lachman, "The Coins Struck by Ali Bey in Egypt," *The Numismatic Circular*, May and September 1975.

Note: Nos. 34-35 and 40-41 have Mustafa's accession date 1171; Nos. 36-38 have Ali's accession date 1183. All coins have toughra or name of Mustafa III, and all but No. 34 also have Ali's initial.

Copper

34 (asper). Like No. 22. *G-VG* 18-19mm. Yr. (11)85....... ——

Billon

Fine

*35 (para). Like No. 22 but rev. 'A(li)/MISR etc./1171..... 7.50

Silver

36 (5 para). Sim. but accession date 1183. 1.6-2.1 gr. 18-20mm. No regnal yr. .... ——

36.5 (10 para). Sim. 4.15 gr. 24mm. No regnal yr. ...... ——

37 (20 para). Sim. 6.8-7.8 gr. 29-30mm. No yr. and (11)85................. ——

38 (piastre). Sim. 11.5-16.5 gr. 35.5-37mm. No yr. and (11)85................. ——

Gold

40 (½ zeri mahbub). Like *V.F.* No. 27 but obv. A(li) at top. 1.1-1.3 gr. 17mm. Yr. (11)83. ——

41 (zeri mahbub). Sim. 2.2-2.6 gr. 19-22mm. Yr. (11)83............. ——

Abdul Hamid I, Sultan
AH1187-1203 (=AD1774-89)

All dated 1187, most with partial actual dates.

Billon

Fine

*44 (para). Toughra. Rev. MISR etc./1187. .30-.40 gr. 15-16mm. ND, (118)8, (119)0-3, (1)200, 201............. 2.50

46 (5 para). 1.45 gr. Yr. 1..... ——

Gold

V.F.

52 (½ zeri mahbub). 4-line legend each side. 1.3 gr. 17-18mm. Yrs. (118)8, (119)2................. ——

EGYPT

V.F.

53 (zeri mahbub). Sim. 2.6 gr.
18mm. Yr. (119)2........*60.00*

58 (2 zeri mahbub). Sim.
4.9 gr. 39mm............ ——

53.5 (½ zeri mahbub). Like No. 7
but Abdul Hamid toughra/
MISR/1187. 1.25 gr. 19.5mm. ——

54 (zeri mahbub). Sim. 2.3-
2.6 gr. 21-23mm........*60.00*

55 (ex 59) (2 zeri mahbub).
Sim. 4.9-5.1 gr. 35mm.
Yr. (119)2.............. ——

56 (ex 55) (¼ altun). Like No. 44.
.85 gr. 14mm............ ——

57 (altun). Sim. 3.5 gr.
19-20mm. Yr. (117)9...... ——

Selim III, Sultan
AH1203-22 (=AD1789-1807)

All dated 1203, plus regnal years.

Billon

Fine

★61 (asper). Uniface. Yr. 16..... 2.50

★63 (para). Toughra. Rev.
regnal yr./legend/1203.
14-16mm. Yrs. 1-22........ 1.50

64 (5 para). Sim. 20mm.......12.50

66 (20 para). Sim. 28-29mm.
Yr. 13.................... 15.00

★68 (piastre). Sim. 34-37mm.
Yr. 16..................40.00

68a —. Yr. 13. French
occupation...............40.00

Gold

V.F.

76 (¼ zeri mahbub). Like No. 68.
.65-.9 gr. 16mm..........*25.00*

78 (½ zeri mahbub). Like No. 7
but Selim toughra/MISR/1203,
wider rims. 1.3 gr. 20mm...*35.00*

80 (zeri mahbub). Sim. 2.5 gr.
27mm....................65.00

81 (2 zeri mahbub). Sim. 4.8-
5.0 gr. 31-39mm. Yr. 21.... ——

V.F.

82 (3 zeri mahbub). Sim. 7.7 gr.
36mm. Yr. 14............ ——

*Nos. 76-80 dated yr. 13 were struck dur-
ing the French occupation of Egypt.
They are said to show an Arabic B(ona-
parte), but no examples of this were
known to Lane-Poole.*

Mustafa IV, Sulatn
AH1222-23 (=AD1807-08)

Billon

Fine

84 (asper). Like No. 111 but
dated 1222. 0.2 gr. 13mm.
Yr. 1....................15.00

85 (para). Sim. 0.4 gr. 15mm.
Yr. 1....................10.00

Gold

95 (zeri mahbub). Toughra/
MISR/1222. Rev. 4-line legend.
2.3-2.5 gr. Yr. 1.........*90.00*

96 (2 zeri mahbub). Sim.
4.66 gr. 30mm............ ——

Mahmud II, Sultan
AH1223-55 (=AD1808-39)

I. First Issue.

Billon

Fine

110 (asper). Like No. 111.
.10-.13 gr. 11-13mm.
Yrs. 2-21................ 3.00

★111 (para). Toughra. Rev. date/
MISR/1223. .15-.28 gr.
12-13mm. Yrs. 1-20....... 1.00

112 (5 para). Sim. .55-.71 gr.
15-17mm. Yrs. 9-21......*12.50*

113 (10 para). Sim. 0.8-1.5 gr.
17-19mm. ND, Yrs. 8-20...*12.50*

114 (20 para). Sim. 2.4-3.8 gr.
22-24mm. Yrs. 5-11......*15.00*

★116 (piastre). Sim. 6.8-7.7 gr.
27-31mm. Yrs. 3-8........*25.00*

115 (20 para). Like No. 119.
3.5 gr. 24mm. Yr. 5.......*20.00*

117 (piastre). Sim. 6.9 gr.
31mm. Yr. 5.............*30.00*

Gold

F-VF

118 (¼ zeri mahbub). Like
No. 111 but rev. 2-line
legend/MISR/1223. .55 gr.
15mm..................*30.00*

118.3 —. Like No. 111. .56-
.60 gr. 14mm. Yrs. 8-14.....*RR*

118.5 (ex 128) —. Sim. .34-.39 gr.
12-13mm. Yrs. 15-21.....*20.00*

119 (½ zeri mahbub). Like
No. 7 but Mahmud toughra/
MISR/1223. 1.15 gr. 19-
20mm. Yrs. 1-8.........*35.00*

120 (zeri mahbub). Sim.
2.1-2.35 gr. 25-26mm.
Yrs. 1-14..............*50.00*

120a —. 2.35 gr. 23mm.
Yr. 15.................*Rare*

124 (zeri mahbub). Like No. 131
but vinelike borders. 2.35 gr.
23mm. Yr. 11............*RR*

126 *(altun).* Sim. but diff.
floral borders. 3.6 gr.
28mm. Yr. 5.............*RR*

II. Second Issue.

Billon

Fine

★130 (5 para). Toughra, flower.
Rev. regnal yr./MISR/1223.
14mm. Yrs. 21-26........ 7.50

★131 (10 para). Toughra in
wavy octagon. 17-18mm.
Yrs. 21-25.............. 6.00

132 (20 para). Sim. 21-23mm.
Yrs. 21-26.............. 6.00

133 (piastre). Sim. 26-28mm.
Yrs. 21-27.............. 7.00

Gold

V.F.

137 (¼ zeri mahbub). Like No. 131
but vinelike borders. .3-.4 gr.
13mm. Yrs. 21-27........*25.00*

★138 (½ zeri mahbub). Like
TURKEY No. 233a but
MISR. .7-.9 gr. 16-17mm.
Yrs. 21-28..............*Rare*

EGYPT

III. Third Issue.

Brass
Fine

140 (asper). (Yr.)28/legend/1223.
Rev. blank. 13mm........*10.00*

*Neumann says the year 28 asper was
struck uniface using either the obverse or
the reverse die. Thus this coin exists also
with toughra only and no legend.*

Copper

141 (para). Like No. 146.
17-18mm. Yrs. 28-29...... 5.00

142 (5 para). Sim. 22-24mm.
Yrs. 28-29.............. 3.50

Billon

144 (10 para). Like No. 146.
12-14mm. Yr. 29.........*10.00*

145 (20 para). Sim. 15-16mm.
Yrs. 28-29.............. 3.00

★146 (piastre). 19-20mm.
Yrs. 28-29. (var.)........ 7.50

Gold
V.F.

151 (5 piastres). Like No. 146
but pearl border. .3 gr.
12mm. Yr. 29.............*RR*

152 (10 piastres). Like No. 146.
.65-.80 gr. 14-15mm.
Yrs. 28-29.............*40.00*

IV. Fourth Issue.

Copper
Fine

161 (para). Like No. 162a but
no value below toughra.
15-17mm. Yrs. 28-29......*10.00*

161a 1 (para). Sim., value
added. Yrs. 29-32........ 7.50

162 (5 para). Sim., w/o value.
20-23mm. Yrs. 28-29...... 5.00

★162a 5 (para). Sim., value added.
Yrs. 29-32.............. 2.00

Silver
Fine

163 10 (para). Like No. 165.
14mm. Yrs. 29-32........*Rare*

164 20 (para). Sim. 15-16mm.
Yrs. 29-32.............*15.00*

★165 1 (piastre). 19-21mm.
Yrs. 29-32............. 7.50

166 5 (piastres). Sim. 24mm.
Yrs. 29-31.............*RR*

167 10 (piastres). Sim. 30mm.
Yr. 29.................*RRR*

168 20 (piastres). Sim. 36-37mm.
Yrs. 29-32.............*225.00*

Gold
V.F.

169 (5 piastres). *Like No. 165*
but no value below toughra.
12mm. Yr. 29............ ——

169a (ex 169) 5 (piastres).
Sim., value added.
Yrs. 30, 32.............*35.00*

170 10 (piastres). Sim. 15mm.
Yrs. 29-32.............*50.00*

171 20 (piastres). Sim. 18mm.
Yr. 31.................*70.00*

171a (ex 171) —. Roses around
border both sides. Yr. 32...*70.00*

172 100 (piastres). *Like No. 165.*
22mm. Yrs. 30-*31*.......*175.00*

Abdul Mejid, Sultan
AH1255-77 (=AD1839-61)

Copper

Fine

★191 5 (para). Toughra/value.
Rev. regnal yr./MISR etc./
1255. Yrs. 6-8............ 1.50

★193 1 (para). Like No. 191 but
w/o floral ornaments.
Yrs. 1-6................*10.00*

194 5 (para). Sim. 20mm.
Yrs. 1-6................ 1.25

195 10 (para). Sim............*RRR*

196 1 (para). Like No. 197.
Yrs. 8-15................*Rare*

Fine

★197 5 (para). Toughra/regnal yr.
Rev. value, circular legend
with MISR at 3-5 o'clock.
21-23mm. Yrs. 8-16...... 1.25

198 10 (para). Sim. 29mm.
Yrs. 8-16............... 2.25

Note: For coins sim. to Nos. 196-198
with Arabic "Constantinople" in rev.
legend see TURKEY Nos. 282-284b.

Silver

205 10 (para). Like No. 207.
14-15mm. .40 gr. Yrs.
1-22................... 7.50

206 20 (para). Sim. 16mm.
.70 gr. Yrs. 1-23.........*10.00*

★207 1 (piastre). 19mm.
1.4 gr. Yrs. 1-23......... 7.50

208 5 (piastres). Sim. 25-26mm.
7 gr. Yrs. 1-16..........*100.00*

209 10 (piastres). Sim.
Yrs. 1-5................*75.00*

210 20 (piastres). Sim. 28 gr.
Yrs. 2, 4...............*275.00*

Gold

V.F.

★211 5 (piastres). Sim. 13mm.
.40 gr. Yrs. 1-22.........*25.00*

213 20 (piastres). Sim. 19mm.
1.7 gr. Yr. 1............*50.00*

214 50 (piastres). Sim. 17mm.
4.2 gr. Yrs. 4, 15........*100.00*

215 100 (piastres). Sim. 21mm.
8.4 gr. Yrs. 1-18.........*85.00*

**ESSEQUIBO and DEMERARA.
See BRITISH GUIANA.**

ETHIOPIA. See HARAR.

FRANCE

Important country in Western Europe. Kingdom until 1793 (absolute monarchy until 1789, constitutional 1789-93). (First) Republic 1793-1804. New calendar adopted (year 1=1793). Republican Government headed by 5 man Directory 1795-99 (years 4-7), by Napoleon Bonaparte as First Consul 1799-1804 (years 8-12). In 1804 France became an empire with Napoleon as emperor 1804-14, and again for 100 days 1815. The Kingdom was restored 1814/15-48.

Monetary Systems:

Until 1794 —

12 deniers = 4 liards = 1 sol (sou); 20 sols = 1 livre; ecu (crown) = 5 livres (1715), 6 livres (1718), 9 livres (1724), 4 livres (1724), 5 livres (1737), 6 livres (1740 onward); gold Louis d'or = 24 livres.

After 1794 —

100 centimes = 10 décimes = 1 franc.

MINT MARKS:

A – Paris.
AA – Metz.
B – Rouen.
BB – Strasbourg.
C – Caen.
CC or CL – Genoa (Italian mint of Napoleon I).
D – Lyon.
G – Poitiers (pre 1789).
G – Geneva (Swiss mint of Napoleon I).
H – La Rochelle.
I – Limoges.
K – Bordeaux.
L – Bayonne.
M – Toulouse.
MA mon. – Marseille.
N – Montpellier.
O – Riom.
P – Dijon.
Q – Perpignan.
R – Orléans (pre 1789).
R cwnd. – Rome (Italian mint of Napoleon I).
S – Reims.
T – Nantes.
U – Turin (Italian mint of Napoleon I).
V – Troyes.
W – Lille.
X – Besançon.
X – Amiens.
Y – Bourges.
Z – Grenoble.
& – Aix.
a cow – Pau.
9 – Rennes.
mast with pennant – Utrecht (Netherlands mint of Napoleon I).

Louis XV 1715-74

Copper

Fine

1 (liard). LUDOVICUS XV DEI GRATIA. Infant head. Rev. FRANCIÆ . . . REX. Arms. 21mm. 1720-21 . . . . 6.00

2 (½ sol). Sim. 25mm. 1720-23 . . . . 8.00

3 (sol). Sim. 29mm. 1719-23 . . . 9.00

Fine

★4 (Mining sol). LUD. XV D.G. FR ET NAV. RE. Double LLs in trefoil. Rev. PRODUIT/DES MINES/DE FRANCE. 1723 (Bearn) 15.00

5 (liard). Like No. 9 but rev. shield differently shaped. Aix mint. 1767-68 . . . . 5.00

6 (½ sol). Sim. 1767-68 . . . . . . 7.50

7 (sol). Sim. 1767-68 . . . . 7.50

8 (liard). Like No. 9. 1768-74 . . . . 3.00

★9 (½ sol). 1768-74 . . . . 4.00

10 (sol). Sim. 1768-74 . . . . 6.00

Billon

11 (sol). Like No. 12. 18mm. 1740, 48 . . . . 60.00

★12 (2 sols). 1738-64 . . . . 20.00

Note: Nos. 11 and 12 were reduced to 9 and 18 deniers, respectively, in France and Canada in 1744. No. 12 was used extensively in the West Indies, where it was called "sol marqué" or (in English colonies) "black dog." Many of No. 12 in worn condition were cmkd. cwnd. C between 1763-79 for use in the French West Indies. These were called "sols tampés" or (in English colonies) "stampees." See FRENCH COLONIES.

Silver

F-VF

13 (¼ ecu). LUD XV D.G. FR. etc. Child bust. Rev. SIT NOMEN etc. 3 crowns in triangle. 28mm. 1715 . . . . 1500.00

14 (½ ecu). Sim. 34mm. 1715 . . . . 2500.00

15 (ecu). Sim. 42mm. 1715 . . . 5000.00

F-VF

16 (1/20 ecu). Obv. sim. Rev. 3 lis in round cwnd. shield. 20mm. 1716 . . . . 100.00

17 (1/10 ecu). Sim. 24mm. 1716-18 . . . . 20.00

18 (¼ ecu). Sim. 30.5mm. 1715-17 . . . . 35.00

19 (½ ecu). Sim. 35.5mm. 1716-18 . . . . 100.00

20 (ecu = 5 livres). Sim. 1716-18 . . . . 150.00

21 (ex Navarre No. 1) (1/10 ecu). LVD. XV D.G. FR. etc., laureate child bust. Rev. 4-fold arms of France and Navarre. 22mm. 1718 . . . . 50.00

22 (ex Navarre No. 2) (¼ ecu). Sim. 27mm. 1718 . . . . 40.00

23 (ex Navarre No. 3) (½ ecu). Sim. 34mm. 1718-19 . . . . 125.00

24 (ex Navarre No. 4) (ecu). Sim. 38mm. 1718-19 . . . . 175.00

25 (ex Navarre No. 5) X S(ols). Sim. 20mm. 1719 . . . . 25.00

26 (ex Navarre No. 6) XX S(ols). Sim. 23mm. 1719-20 . . . . 35.00

Note: The silver coinage of 1718-1720 bore the Bourbon lilies and the Navarre escarbuncle (=8 spoked shield strengthener). Although popularly styled "of Navarre," they were for general circulation throughout France. Former Navarre Nos. 1-6 have therefore been relisted as France Nos. 21-26.

27 (Petit Louis d'Argent). LUD XV D.G. FR. etc. Bust. Rev. CHRS. REGN etc. 4 double Ls cruciform. 8.2 gr. 1720 . . . . . . 60.00

28 (1/12 ecu). Older armored bust. Rev. 3 lis in cwnd. squared shield. 1720-21 . . . . 40.00

29 (⅙ ecu). Sim. 1719-23 . . . . . . 35.00

30 (⅓ ecu). Sim. 27-28.5mm. 1720-23 . . . . 45.00

31 (½ ecu). Sim. 1721 . . . . 300.00

32 (ecu = 9 livres). Sim. 38mm. 1720-24 . . . . 200.00

33 (1/16 ecu). Bust. Rev. 4 LLs cruciform. 18mm. 1725 . . . . . 60.00

34 (⅛ ecu). Sim. 21mm. 1725 . . 70.00

35 (¼ ecu). Sim. 27mm. 1725 . . . . 125.00

36 (½ ecu). Sim. 32mm. 1724-25 . . . . 150.00

37 (ecu = 4 livres). 38.5mm. 1724-25 . . . . 175.00

38 (1/20 ecu). Bust l. in court dress. Rev. 3 lis in oval shield. 18.5mm. 1727 . . . . 20.00

39 (1/10 ecu). Sim. 21.5mm. 1726-32 . . . . 15.00

FRANCE

40 (1/5 ecu). Sim. 27mm. 1726-
28.....................15.00

41 (½ ecu). Sim. 34mm. 1726-
38.....................35.00

42 (ecu = 5 livres). Sim. 40mm.
1726-41..................35.00

Final Silver Series

A. Mature Head.

43 (6 sols). LUD XV D.G. FR. ET
NAV. REX. Mature head.
Rev. SIT NOMEN etc. 3 lis in
oval shield. 17.5mm.
1743-70..................20.00

44 (12 sols). Sim. 21mm. 1743-
70......................15.00

45 (24 sols). Sim. 28.5mm.
1741-68..................20.00

46 (½ ecu). Sim. 34mm. 1741-
70......................30.00

47 (ecu = 6 livres). Sim. 42mm.
1740-71..................35.00

B. Old Head.

43a (6 sols). Like No. 43 but old
head, draped shoulder.
1771-73.................25.00

44a (12 sols). Sim. 1771-72.....17.50

45a (24 sols). Sim. 28.5mm.
1771....................35.00

46a (½ ecu). Sim. 1772-74.....125.00

47a (ecu = 6 livres). Sim. 42mm.
1770-74..................60.00

Gold

V.F.

48 (½ Louis d'or). LUD. XV D.G.
FR. etc. Child head. Rev. CHRS.
etc. 4 LLs cruciform. 4.05 gr.
1715...................*2000.00*

49 (Louis d'or). Sim. 8.1 gr.
1715...................*2500.00*

50 (½ Louis d'or). Child head.
Rev. 3 lis in oval shield.
3.04 gr. 1716...........*1400.00*

51 (Louis d'or). Sim. 8.2 gr.
1716....................*800.00*

52 (2 Louis d'or). Sim. 16.15 gr.
1716...................*3000.00*

53 (½ Louis d'or). Cwnd. head l.
Rev. Arms of France (2) and
Navarre (2), cruciform. 3.05 gr.
1717-18.................*900.00*

54 (Louis d'or). Sim. 6.1 gr.
1717-18.................*950.00*

55 (2 Louis d'or). Sim. 12.2 gr.
1717-18.................*650.00*

56 (½ Louis d'or). Young head r.
Rev. Maltese cross. 4.9 gr.
1718-19................*1000.00*

57 (Louis d'or). Sim. 9.75 gr.
1718-19.................*450.00*

58 (½ Louis d'or). Young head r.
Rev. 2 Ls cwnd. 4.9 gr. 1720,
22.....................*900.00*

59 (Louis d'or). Sim. 9.75 gr.
1720, 22................*450.00*

60 (2 Louis d'or). Sim. 1720,
22....................*1200.00*

61 (½ Louis d'or). Young head.
Rev. 2 script Ls intertwined,
cwnd. 3.2 gr. 1723-25......*900.00*

62 (Louis d'or). Sim. 6.4 gr.
1723-25.................*450.00*

63 (2 Louis d'or). Sim. 12.95 gr.
1723-25................*1200.00*

64 (½ Louis d'or). Draped bust l.
Rev. Arms of France and
Navarre in 2 ovals, cwnd.
4.07 gr. 1726-28..........*175.00*

65 (Louis d'or). Sim. 8.15 gr.
1726-28.................*200.00*

66 (½ Louis d'or). Mature head.
Rev. Arms of F. and N. in
2 ovals, cwnd. 4.05 gr.
1740-65.................150.00

67 (Louis d'or). Sim. 8.1 gr.
1740-65.................175.00

67a —. Old laureate head, draped
shoulder. 1765-74........300.00

68 (2 Louis d'or). Like No. 66.
16.25 gr. 1740-65.........450.00

68a —. Like No. 67a. 1765-74..650.00

Louis XVI 1774-93
Pre-Constitutional Issues

Bronze

★71 (liard). LUDOV. XVI. D. GRATIA.
Head. Rev. FRANC ET NAVARR.
REX. 3 lis in cwnd. shield.
22mm. 1774-91...........1.50

72 (½ sol). Sim. 26mm. 1774-
91......................5.00

73 (sol). Sim. 30mm. 1774-91..2.50

Silver

F-VF

74 (6 sols). Like No. 75 but
heavier bust. 18mm.
1782-83..................22.50

★75 (12 sols). 1774-90..........7.50

76 (24 sols). Sim. 26.5mm. 1774-
90.....................12.50

77 (½ ecu). Sim. 33mm. 1774-
92.....................30.00

78 (ecu = 6 livres). Sim. 41mm.
1774-92.................30.00

Gold

V.F.

79 (½ Louis d'or). Uniformed bust.
Rev. Arms of France and
Navarre in 2 ovals. 4.05 gr.
1775-84.................500.00

80 (Louis d'or). Uniformed bust.
Rev. Arms of France on
branches. 8.13 gr. 1774....750.00

81 (Louis d'or). Like No. 79.
7.65 gr. 1774-84..........200.00

82 (Louis d'or). Head. Rev. as
last. 1785..............1200.00

★83 (Louis d'or). 1785-92......150.00

84 (2 Louis d'or). Like No. 79.
16.2 gr. 1775-84..........750.00

85 (2 Louis d'or). Like No. 83.
15.3 gr. 1786-92..........250.00

Constitutional Period
Bronze or Brass

Fine

86 3 D(eniers). Like No. 88.
1791-93.................15.00

86a —. ROI DES FRANCAIS. 1792..22.50

87 6 D(eniers). Like No. 88.
1791-93.................15.00

87a —. Like No. 86a. 1792......25.00

★88 12 D(eniers). 1791-93.......3.00

88a —. Like No. 86a. 1792......5.00

89 2 S(ols). Like No. 88. 1791-
92......................5.00

89a —. Like No. 86a. 1792-93...8.00

FRANCE

Silver

F-VF

90 15 SOLS. Like No. 91.
1791-93 . . . . 10.00
90a —. FRANCAIS. 1791-92 . . . . . . 22.50

★91 30 SOLS. 1791-93 . . . . 15.00
91a —. FRANCAIS. *1791-93* 35.00
92 (3 livres). Sim. 33mm.
1792-93 . . . . 125.00
92a —. FRANCAIS. 1792 . . . . 200.00
93 (ecu = 6 livres). Sim. 39mm.
1792-93 . . . . 85.00
93a —. FRANCAIS. 1792-93 . . . . . 250.00

Gold

VF-EF

94 (Louis d'or = 24 livres). Sim.
1792-93 . . . . RR

Note: In addition to these official coins of the Central Government, many essays, trial pieces, and tokens, official, semi-official and private, exist dated 1790 and 1791-93 (years 3-5).

1793 Emergency Issues

Lyon. Royalist defenders, besieged by Republican army 1793.

Cast Bronze

VG-F

101 TROIS (= 3) SOLS. Liberty cap on sword. Rev. Lion. 28mm. N.D. 75.00
101a —. Rev. script JT and value. 40mm. ND 85.00
102 5 SOLS (sols). Crossed LL XIV. Rev. legend. 35mm. ND 100.00
103 SIX (= 6) SOLS. Script JT. Rev. value, crescent. 28, 39mm. N.D. 60.00
104 ∂ (= 6) SOL(s). Crossed cannon. Rev. Fasces, value. 44mm. 1793 . . . . 175.00
105 10 S(ols). Legend. Rev. Fasces. 1793 . . . . 150.00
106 VINGT (= 20) SOLS. Like No. 101. 30mm. N.D. 100.00

Nos. 102, 104 and 105 are apparently later concoctions, but are RRR.

Mayence. See GERMANY, Mainz.

Valenciennes. French, under General Ferrand, besieged by Duke of York.

Cast Bronze

V.G.

111 3 LIV(res). Liberty cap in triangle. Rev. 1793 in wreath 125.00

First Republic.

A. Old monetary system 1793-94 (year II).

Bronze

Fine

121 ½ S(ol). Like No. 122. 1793 L'An II 45.00

★122 1 S(ol). 1793 L'An II 8.00
122a —. (1794) L'An II 20.00
123 2 S(ols). Sim. 1793 L'An II 12.00
123a —. (1794) L'An II 25.00

Silver

F-VF

124 SIX (= 6)/LIVRES. Like No. 125. 1793 L'An II 100.00
124a —. (1794) L'An II 400.00

Gold

V.F.

★125 24/LIVRES. 1793 L'An II 3500.00

B. Directory, years 4-7 (1795-99), and years 8-11 of the Consulate (1799-1803).

Monetary System:
100 centimes = 10 décimes = 1 franc.

Bronze or Copper

Fine

131 5/CENTIMES. Like No. 134. L'An 4, 5 . . . . 2.50
132 DECIME. Like No. 135. L'An 4, 5 . . . . 12.50
133 2/DECIMES. Sim. L'An 4, 5 . . . . 10.00
133a —. 2/DECIME. L'An 5 . . . 40.00

Same. Coin Weights Increased

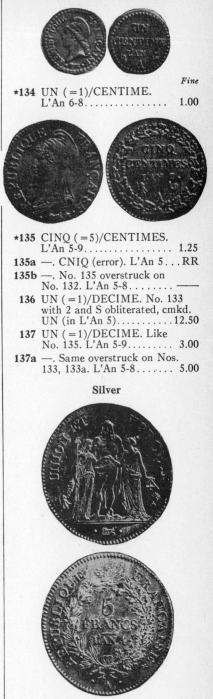

Fine

★134 UN (=1)/CENTIME. L'An 6-8 . . . . 1.00

★135 CINQ (=5)/CENTIMES. L'An 5-9 . . . . 1.25
135a —. CNIQ (error). L'An 5 . . . RR
135b —. No. 135 overstruck on No. 132. L'An 5-8 . . . . ——
136 UN (=1)/DECIME. No. 133 with 2 and S obliterated, cmkd. UN (in L'An 5) 12.50
137 UN (=1)/DECIME. Like No. 135. L'An 5-9 . . . . 3.00
137a —. Same overstruck on Nos. 133, 133a. L'An 5-8 . . . . . . 5.00

Silver

F-VF

★138 5/FRANCS. L'An 4-11 . . . . 30.00

C. Consulate, years 11-12 (1803-04).

(Napoleon) Bonaparte, First Consul 1799-1804

Silver

141 QUART (=¼ franc). Like No. 143. AN 12 . . . . 10.00
142 DEMI (=½)/FRANC. Sim. AN XI, 12 . . . . 12.50

FRANCE

FIRST REPUBLIC (Cont.)

F-VF

★143 1/FRANC. AN XI, 12....15.00
144 2/FRANCS. Sim. AN 12..60.00
145 5/FRANCS. Sim.
AN XI, 12.............30.00

Gold

146 20/FRANCS. Sim. but head l.
AN XI, 12.............100.00
147 40/FRANCS. Sim. AN XI,
12....................250.00

Napoleon I, Emperor
1804-14, 15

Bronze

VF-XF

149 5/CENT(imes). Like No. 150
but uncwnd. N. 1808......25.00

No. 149 is thought to be an essay which
saw circulation.

Billon

Fine

★150 10/CENT(imes). 1808-10...1.50

I. Reverse REPUBLIQUE
FRANÇAISE.

Silver

A. Young Head.

F-VF

151 QUART (= ¼ franc).
Like No. 152. An 12-14,
1806-07................. 8.00

★152 DEMI (= ½)/FRANC.
AN 12-14, 1806-07........10.00
153 1/FRANC. Sim.
AN 12-14, 1806-07........12.50
154 2/FRANCS. Sim.
AN 12-14, 1806-07........55.00
155 5/FRANCS. Sim. An 12...80.00

B. Older Bare Head.

F-VF

151a QUART (= ¼ franc).
Like No. 154a. 1807......30.00
152a DEMI (= ½)/FRANC.
Sim. 1807.............75.00
153a 1/FRANC. Sim. 1807...125.00

★154a 2/FRANCS. 1807.......175.00
155a 5/FRANCS. Sim.
An 13-14, 1806-07........50.00
155b —. Struck in collar.
1807A..................RR

C. Laureate Head.

151b QUART (= ¼ franc). Like
No. 154b. 1807-08.......45.00
152b DEMI (= ½)/FRANC.
Sim. 1807-08........... 8.00
153b 1/FRANC. Sim. 1807-08..15.00

★154b 2/FRANCS. 1807-08.....45.00
155c 5/FRANCS. Sim.
1807-08................40.00

Gold

156 20/FRANCS. Like No. 152
but head l. AN 12.......100.00
156a —. AN 13-14, 1806-07.....85.00
156b —. Head laureate. 1807-08.85.00
157 40/FRANCS. Like No. 156a.
AN 13-14, 1806-07.......200.00
157a —. Head laureate. 1807-08 225.00

II. Reverse EMPIRE FRANÇAISE.

Silver

161 QUART (= ¼ franc). Like No.
163 but EMP. FRA. 1809... 30.00
162 DEMI (= ½)/FRANC.
Like No. 163. 1809-14.....10.00

★163 1/FRANC. 1809-14.......10.00

F-VF

164 2/FRANCS. Sim. 1809-14..30.00
165 5/FRANCS. Sim. 1809-14..22.50

Gold

166 20/FRANCS. Sim. but head l.
1809-14................75.00
167 40/FRANCS. Sim.
1809-14................175.00

Louis XVIII, First
Restoration 1814-15

Silver

★168 5 FRANCS. 1814........17.50

Gold

170 20/FRANCS. Bust r.
Rev. Arms. 1814..........75.00

Napoleon I, Restored 1815
"The Hundred Days"

Silver

V.F.

★171 2/FRANCS. 1815........400.00
172 5/FRANCS. Sim. 1815...100.00

Gold

173 20/FRANCS. Sim. but head l.
1815..................100.00

FRANCE

Strasbourg Provisional Coinage 1814-15

Brass

For Napoleon I

174 UN (=1)/DECIME. 1814, 15 . . . . 6.00

VG-F (above entry)

For Louis XVIII

175 UN (=1)/DECIME. 1814, 15 . . . . 6.00

Louis XVIII, Second Restoration 1815-24

Silver

F-VF

176 5 FRANCS. Like No. 168. 1815 . . . . 17.50

177 ¼ F(ranc). Head l. Rev. Arms. 1817-24 . . . . 3.00

F-VF

178 ½ F(ranc). Sim. 1816-24 . . . 5.00

179 1 F(ranc). Sim. 1816-24 . . . . 7.50

180 2 F(rancs). Sim. 1816-24 . . . 20.00

181 5 F(rancs). Sim. 1816-24 . . . 12.00

Gold

182 20 FRANCS. Like No. 170. 1815 . . . . 70.00

183 20 F(rancs). Head r. Rev. Arms. 1816-24 . . . . 60.00

184 40 F(rancs). Sim. 1816-24 . . . . 125.00

Charles X 1824-30

Silver

185 ¼ F(ranc). Like No. 188. 1825-30 . . . . 2.50

186 ½ F(ranc). Sim. 1825-30 . . . 5.00

187 1 F(ranc). Sim. 1825-30 . . . . 7.50

188 2 F(rancs). 1825-30 . . . . . . 20.00

189 5 F(rancs). Sim. 1824-30 . . . 12.00

Gold

190 20 F(rancs). Sim. but head r. 1825-30 . . . . 60.00

191 40 F(rancs). Sim. 1824-30 . . . . 150.00

Louis-Philippe I 1830-48

Silver

196 ¼/FRANC. Like No. 202. 1831-45 . . . . 2.50

197 25/CENT(imes). Sim. 1845-48 . . . . 2.50

198 ½/FRANC. Sim. 1831-45 . . 4.00

199 50/CENT(imes). Sim. 1845-48 . . . . 4.00

200 1/FRANC. Sim. but head w/out laurel wreath. 1831 . . 17.00

201 1/FRANC. Like No. 202. 1832-48 . . . . 6.00

F-VF

202 2/FRANCS. 1831-48 . . . . . 17.50

203 5/FRANCS. Like No. 200. 1830-31 . . . . 20.00

203a —. w/out I after PHILIPPE. 1830 . . . . 35.00

204 5/FRANCS. Like No. 202. 1831-48 . . . . 9.00

Gold

205 20/FRANCS. Like No. 200 but head l. 1830-31 . . . . 60.00

206 20/FRANCS. Like No. 202 but head l. 1832-48 . . . . 45.00

207 40/FRANCS. Sim. 1831-39 . . . . 125.00

Note: Throughout most of the period covered by this catalog, the various French Governments struck quantities of patterns, essays, trial pieces and the like, not all of which are marked "ES-SAI." Coins not listed here fall into one of these categories, and were not for circulation. See V.G(uilloteau), *Monnaies Françaises* (Paris 1943).

Also omitted are propaganda medals in coin form of Pretenders Napoleon II, Henri V and Napoleon IV, none of whom actually reigned.

FRANCE (PROVINCES)

Navarre

A former kingdom on French-Spanish border.

Louis XV of France 1715-74

The French silver coinage of 1718-20 bore the Bourbon lilies and the Navarre escarbuncle. Although popularly styled "of Navarre," they were for general circulation throughout France. Former Navarre Nos. 1-6 have therefore been relisted as France Nos. 21-26.

Strasbourg (Strassburg)

Chief town of Alsace. Acquired by France 1681.

Silver

F-VF

1 (40 sols). LUD XV D.G. FR etc. Bust. Rev. MONETA NOVA ARGENTINENSIS. Arms. 1716 . 75.00

FRENCH COLONIES

Listed under this heading are colonial coins generally used in French Canada and the West Indies, not restricted to use in any particular colony.

Monetary System: Same as France.

Louis XV 1715-74

Bronze

Fine

★1 VI/DENIERS. LUD XV D.G. FR etc. Child bust. Rev. Value/COLONIES/1717.........1750.00

2 XII/DENIERS. Sim. 1717.................2000.00

V.G.

★3 (9 deniers). 1721-22.......20.00

V.F.

★4 (12 deniers). 1767.........65.00

For No. 4 cmkd. RF in oval, see CARIBBEAN ISLANDS (Guadeloupe).

Billon

Fine

★5 (12 deniers). 1740, 48......60.00

6 (24 deniers). Sim. 23mm. 1738-64.................20.00

Note: Nos. 5 and 6 were struck for Metropolitan France and are there listed as Nos. 11 and 12. In 1744 they were reduced to 9 and 18 deniers, respectively. Many were shipped to the Western Hemisphere. No. 6 was known as the "sol marqué" or "black dog" in the West Indies.

V.G.

7 (stampee = 18, 24 or 30 deniers, depending on the colony.) No. 6, badly worn, cmkd. cwnd. small C(olonies) in depressed outline. (1763-67)................10.00

7a —. Cmkd. cwnd. small (3mm) C, in relief. (1763-67).......8.00

7b —. Cmkd. cwnd. larger (5mm) C, in relief. (1763-67).......8.00

Silver

F-VF

8 (20 sols). Young bust. Rev. SIT NOMEN etc. Cwnd. double L. 21mm. 1720.............40.00

Louis XVI 1774-93

Billon

9 3/SOUS. 3 lis cwnd. Rev. Value/1781..............22.50

★10 (stampee). Cmk. cwnd. C in relief on 23mm blank planchet. (1779)..................6.00

Charles X 1824-30

Brass

Fine

11 5/CENT(imes). Like No. 12. 1825, 27-30...............3.00

★12 10/CENT(imes). 1825, 27-29...................3.50

Louis-Philippe I 1830-48

Bronze

Fine

★13 5/CENT(imes). 1839-44.... 2.50

14 10/CENT(imes). Sim. 1839-44...................3.00

FRENCH GUIANA

On the northeast coast of South America. Acquired by France 1626. Site of the famous penal colony, Devil's Island.

Monetary System:
Same as France.

A. As Colonie de Cayenne.

Louis XVI 1774-93

Billon

V.G.

★1 2/SOUS. LOUIS XVI R. DE FR. etc. 3 lis cwnd. Rev. COLONIE DE CAYENNE. Value. 1780-*90*.... 4.00

E.F.

2 3/SOUS. Sim. 1781.........*35.00*

Louis XVIII 1814-24

Billon

3 2/SOUS. Sim. 1816.........*35.00*

Nos. 2 and 3 were not placed in circulation.

FRENCH GUIANA

B. As Guyane Française.

Louis XVIII

Billon

Fine

*4 10/CENT(imes). 1818...... 5.00

Louis-Philippe 1830-48

Billon

Fine

*5 10/CENT(imes). 1846...... 5.00

NOTES

GERMAN STATES

Until 1871 Germany was divided into a number of independent states (several hundred before Napoleon, several dozen thereafter). Prior to 1806 these states all acknowledged to some extent the overlordship of the Holy Roman Emperor (see AUSTRIA). During the 19th century some or all of them belonged from time to time to various loose confederations, and to assorted customs and monetary unions. Real unification, however, came only after the defeat of France in the Franco-Prussian War 1870-71.

Here follow the coins of the States prior to the monetary reform of 1873:

MONETARY SYSTEMS GENERALLY:

North Germany before 1837-38:

2 Heller = 1 Pfennig;
8 Pfennige = 1 Mariengroschen;
12 Pfennige = 1 (gute) Groschen;
24 (gute) Groschen = 1 (Reichs) Thaler;
2 Gulden = 1⅓ Reichsthaler =
  1 Speciesthaler (before 1753) =
  1 Convention Thaler (after 1753).
All references to "thaler" mean Reichsthaler.

North Germany 1837-73:

12 (10 in Saxony and a few other states) Pfennige = 1 Groschen (or Silbergroschen or Neugroschen);
30 Groschen = 1 Thaler (Vereinsthaler after 1857).

South Germany before 1837-38:

8 Heller = 4 Pfennige = 1 Kreuzer;
24 Kreuzer Landmünze (local money) = 20 Kreuzer Convention Münze (convention money);
120 Convention Kreuzer = 2 Convention Gulden = 1 Convention Thaler.

South Germany 1837-73:

8 Heller = 4 Pfennige = 1 Kreuzer;
60 Kreuzer = 1 Gulden;
3½ Gulden = 2 North German Thaler.

Denominations on coins of the German States were expressed in terms of the number of coins required to make up a certain weight of fine silver (or gold). Until 1857 this weight was generally the Cologne Mark (Marck), containing 233.855 grams. After 1857 it was the Zollpfund (pound) weighing 500 grams.

Weights were shown on coins as follows:

X E(INE) F(EINE) MAR(C)K = ¹/₁₀ fine mark = 1 convention thaler.

LXXX EX MARCA PURA COLON. = ¹/₈₀ fine mark = ¹/₆ reichsthaler.

XIV FEINE MARK = ¹/₁₄ fine mark = 1 thaler (1837-57).

XXX EIN PFUND FEIN = ¹/₃₀ fine pound = 1 vereinsthaler.

Many silver coins, mostly before 1763, bore neither denomination nor indication of fine-silver weight. These are mostly Species or Convention Thalers (28-29 gr.) and their multiples and fractions (proportional by weight).

Also noteworthy are the symbols for Pfennig (₰) and Groschen (ℊℯ) which appear on some coins.

Other local monetary units and systems will be mentioned as they occur.

AACHEN (ACHEN, URBS AQUENSIS, AQUIS GRANI), Free City

In the Rhineland. City coinage 14th century until 1798.
In 1801 Aachen was incorporated into France. In 1815 it fell to Prussia.

Local Monetary System:
24 heller = 1 marck;
48 marck = 1 Reichsthaler.

Copper

		V.G.
1	IIII (heller). Like No. 2 but rev. REICHS/STAT. ACH/IIII. (16)70-1759	1.00
1a	—. Rev. IIII/REICHS/STAT. ACH. 1722-98	1.00

★2	XII/HELLER. 1757-97	1.00

Silver

		V.G-F
3	I/MARCK. Like No. 5 1753-54	3.00
4	II/MARCK. Sim. 1753	3.00

★5	III/MARCK. 1754	6.00
6	8 (marck). Like No. 7 1752-63	12.00

		VG-F
★7	16 (marck). VRBS AQVENSIS. etc. Eagle. Rev. Crown. 1752-56	12.00
8	32 (marck). Eagle with 32 on breast. Rev. LOCUS CORONATIONIS etc. Altar with imp. insignia. N.D. (1752-63)	25.00

Gold

		V.F.
9	DUCATUS (=ducat) Emp. Franz I stdg. Rev. DUCATUS/ NOVUS/REG. SED/URBIS/ AQVIS. GR. 1753	1000.00

ANHALT, Principality (Duchy after 1806-07)

In the central part of present-day East Germany, southwest of Berlin. First coinage 12th century. Divided into 5 branches 1603, later further subdivided.

Anhalt arms: Parted per pale. Dexter: Silver, a half red eagle. Sinister: Barry of 10, black and gold, upon which is superimposed the arc of a coronet.

ANHALT-BERNBURG

Bernburg arms: Bear on wall.

Victor II Friedrich 1721-65

Copper

		VG-F
★1	I/PFENNING. 1746-57	2.00
1a	—. I/PFENNIG. 1756-60	2.00
2	1½/PFENNIG. Obv. sim. Rev. value/F.A.B.L.M./1747	4.00
3	3/PFENNING. Like No. 2 but PERRVMPENDVM above bear. 1753	4.00
3a	—. 3/PFENNIG. 1760	2.00

Billon

4	1/PFENNING. VF mon. Rev. Value. 1744-55	2.00
5	2/PFENNING. Sim. 1744-45	2.50
6	3/PFENNING. Sim. 1744-45	3.00
7	3/PFENNING. Like No. 2 1749	4.00
8	4/PFENNING. Like No. 4 1744-45	3.00
9	4/PFENNING. Like No. 2 1747-49	3.00
9a	—. IIII/PFENNING. 1764	2.00
10	VI/PFENNING. Sim. 1744-58	3.00

GERMAN STATES

ANHALT-BERNBURG (Cont.)

VG-F

11 48/EINEN (=1/48)/THALER.
Sim. 1760-61 . . . . 3.00

12 1/MARIEN/GROS(chen).
Bear on wall. Rev. FURSTL.
ANHALT BERNB etc. Value.
1744-50, 61 . . . . 3.00

13 24/EINEN (=1/24)/REICHS/
THALER. Like No. 2 but
NACH DEM etc. 1744-57 . . . . . 3.00

14 24/EINEN (=1/24)/THALER.
Like No. 1. 1759-61 . . . . 3.00

15 12/EINEN (=1/12)/REICHS/
THALER. Obv. like No. 3.
Rev. like No. 13. 1750, 57 . . 5.00

16 12/EINEN (=1/12)/REICHS/
THALER. Like No. 2 but
w/out F.A.B. 1760 . . . . 6.00

Silver

Fine

17 1/6 (thaler). Like No. 22.
1727-52 . . . . 7.00

18 VI/EINEN (=1/6)/THALER.
Head. Rev. value 1754, 58 . . 7.00

19 VI/EINEN (=1/6)/REICHS/
THALER. Cwnd. VF mon.
Rev. value. 1758 . . . . 12.00

★20 VI/EINEN (=1/6)/REICHS/
THALER. 1758-60 . . . . 7.00

21 XII/MARIENGROS(chen
=1/3 T). Bear on wall.
Rev. value. 1727 . . . . 14.00

★22 1/3 (thaler). 1727-50 . . . . 12.00

23 1/3 (thaler). Bust.
Rev. Arms. 1744 . . . . 16.00

24 1/3 (thaler). Cwnd. VF mon.
Rev. Bear on wall. 1758 . . . . 14.00

25 3/EINEN (=1/3)/REICHS/
THALER. Like No. 18.
1758 . . . . 14.00

26 8/GUTE/GROSCHEN
(=1/3 T). Sim. 1758 . . . . 10.00

27 8/GUTE/GROSCHEN.
Like No. 24. 1760 . . . . 10.00

Fine

28 XXIIII/MARIENGROS(chen =
2/3 T). Like No. 21. 1727 . . . . 28.00

29 2/3 (thaler). Like No. 22.
1727-30 . . . . 22.00

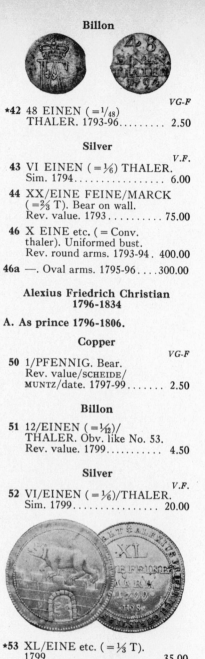

V.F.

★33 (thaler). 1744 . . . . 300.00

33a —. 1750 . . . . 200.00

34 (thaler). Like No. 22.
1746 . . . . 375.00

35 (Mining thaler). Bears hold
arms. Rev. EIN HIMMLISCH etc.
Mining scene. 1747 . . . . 450.00

Gold

36 (ducat). Like No. 22.
1730-61 . . . . 950.00

37 2½ THALER. Bust.
Rev. Arms. 1744 . . . . 1400.00

38 5 THALER. Sim. 1744 . . . 1500.00

Friedrich Albrecht 1765-96

Copper

★40 I/PFENNIG. 1776-95 (var.) 2.50

VG-F

★41 1½/PFENNIG.
Rev. value/F.A.B.S.M.
1776-77 . . . . 4.50

Billon

VG-F

★42 48 EINEN (=1/48)
THALER. 1793-96 . . . . 2.50

Silver

V.F.

43 VI EINEN (=1/6) THALER.
Sim. 1794 . . . . 6.00

44 XX/EINE FEINE/MARCK
(=2/3 T). Bear on wall.
Rev. value. 1793 . . . . 75.00

46 X EINE etc. (= Conv.
thaler). Uniformed bust.
Rev. round arms. 1793-94 . 400.00

46a —. Oval arms. 1795-96 . . . . 300.00

Alexius Friedrich Christian 1796-1834

A. As prince 1796-1806.

Copper

VG-F

50 1/PFENNIG. Bear.
Rev. value/SCHEIDE/
MUNTZ/date. 1797-99 . . . . 2.50

Billon

51 12/EINEN (=1/12)/
THALER. Obv. like No. 53.
Rev. value. 1799 . . . . 4.50

Silver

V.F.

52 VI/EINEN (=1/6)/THALER.
Sim. 1799 . . . . 20.00

★53 XL/EINE etc. (=1/8 T).
1799 . . . . 35.00

54 24/MARIENGROSCHEN.
(=2/3 T). Sim. 1796-97 . . . . . 60.00

54a —XXIV/MARIEN etc.
1796 . . . . 75.00

54b —XXIIII/MARIEN etc.
1796 . . . . 50.00

55 XX/EINE etc. (=2/3 T).
Sim. 1799 . . . . 50.00

Gold

GERMAN STATES

ANHALT-BERNBURG (Cont.)

V.F.

*56 5 THALER. FRID. CHRISTIAN
FURST ZU ANHALT, bust.
Rev. Arms. 1796........1000.00

B. As Duke 1806-34.

Copper

Fine

57 1/PFENNIG. Obv. like
No. 58. Rev. I/PFENNIG/
1807.................. 2.00
57a —. Rev. 5 lines. 1808....... 2.00

*58 1/PFENNIG. 1822-27...... 1.50
58a 1/PFENNING. Sim. 1831.. 2.25
59 4/PFENNIGE. Sim.
1822-23.................. 3.25
59a 4/PFENNINGE. Sim.
1831.................. 4.00

Billon

60 48/EINEN (=1/48)/
THALER (=6 pf.). Oval
Anhalt arms. Rev. value.
1807.................. 5.50
61 24/EINEN (=1/24)/THALER.
Obv. like No. 53.
Rev. value. 15.5mm. 1822-
23.................. 3.50
61a —. Larger. 1827 (17mm),
31 (19mm).............. 3.00

Silver

V.F.

62 XX/EINE etc. (=2/3 T).
Like No. 53 but HERZOG ZU
ANHALT 1806, 08-09....... 22.50
63 X/EINE etc. (=Conv. thaler).
Arms. Rev. like rev. No. 62.
1806, 09................ 500.00

Gold

*64 1/DUCATEN (=Harzgold
ducat). 1825 .... 1500.00

Alexander Carl 1834-63

A. Joint coinage with Anhalt-
Cöthen and Anhalt-Dessau.

Copper

Fine

65 1/PFENNIG. Like No. 120.
288 EINEN THALER. 1839-40. 2.00

Fine

*66 1/PFENNIG. 360
EINEN THALER. 1856, 62...... 2.00
67 3/PFENNIGE. Sim.
96 EINEN THALER. 1839-40.. 2.00
68 3/PFENNIGE. Sim.
120 EINEN THALER. 1861.... 4.00

Billon

69 6/PFENNIGE. Sim.
1840.................. 2.25
70 1/GROSCHEN. Sim.
1839-40................ 2.00
71 1/SILBER/GROSCHEN.
Sim. 1851-62............. 2.00

*72 2½/SILBER/GROSCHEN.
1856-62................ 3.00

B. Anhalt-Bernburg alone.

Silver

V.F.

73 6/EINEN (=1/6)/THALER.
Like No. 74 but LXXXIV etc.
1856.................. 6.50

*74 6/EINEN (=1/6)/THALER.
1861-62................ 6.00
75 EIN (=1 mining) THALER.
Arms. Rev. SEGEN/DES ANHALT/
etc. 1834...........35.00
76 EIN (=1 mining) THALER.
Bear on wall. Rev. like rev.
No. 75. 1846-55...........22.50
77 EIN (=1) VEREINSTHALER.
Head. Rev. Arms. 1859.....40.00
78 EIN (=1 mining) THALER.
Obv. like No. 74. Rev. like
rev. No. 75. 1861-62........20.00
79 2 THALER. Head.
Rev. Arms. 1840-55.......300.00

**Anhalt-Bernburg extinct 1863.
To Dessau.**

ANHALT-CÖTHEN

August Ludwig 1728-55

Billon

VG-F

100 3 (pfennig). F.A.C.L.M. Arms.
Rev. 3 in orb. 1751...... 5.00
101 IIII/PFENNINGE. Arms.
Rev. value. 1751 ..... 5.00
102 VI/PFENNINGE. Sim.
1751.................. 6.00
103 24/EINEN (=1/24)/REICHS-/
THALER. Cwnd. AL mon.
Rev. value. 1751 ...... 6.00
104 12/EINEN (=1/12)/REICHS-/
THALER. Sim. 1751...... 6.00

Silver

V.F.

105 ⅓ (thaler). Arms. Rev.
Bear on wall. 1750........15.00
106 ⅔ (thaler). Arms supported.
Rev. Bear holds shield.
1747, 50.................25.00
107 (Reichsthaler). D. G. AVGVSTVS
LVDOVICVS PRINCEPS ANHALT,
bust. Rev. Bear holds arms.
1751....................175.00
108 4/3 (Reichsthaler =Species
thaler). Like No. 106.
1747....................600.00
109 1⅛ (Reichsthaler =Species
thaler). Like No. 107.
1747....................750.00

Gold

111 (ducat). Like No. 106.
1747, 51.................550.00
112 (ducat). Head. Rev.
Bear with shield. 1751....650.00

Heinrich 1830-47

Silver

115 2 THALER. HEINRICH
HERZOG ZU ANHALT. Head.
Rev. Arms. 1840........500.00

**Anhalt-Cöthen extinct 1847.
To Dessau.**

ANHALT-DESSAU

Leopold Friedrich 1817-71,
Duke of all Anhalt 1863

Copper

V.F.

*120 1/PFENNIG. 1864, 67.....4.00
121 3/PFENNIGE. Sim.
1864, 67.................4.00

Billon

122 2½/SILBER/GROSCHEN.
Sim. 1864...............4.00

ANHALT-DESSAU (Cont.)

Silver

V.F.

★123 VI EINEN (= ⅙) THALER.
1865.................... 6.00
124 EIN (= 1) VEREINS-
THALER. Head. ZU ANHALT.
Rev. arms supported.
1858.................... 27.50
125 EIN (= 1 Vereins) THALER.
Head. Rev. GETHEILT 1603
etc., arms. Reunion of
duchies 1863............ 22.50
126 EIN VEREINSTHALER.
Like No. 124 but VON
ANHALT. 1866, 69........ 22.50
127 2 THALER Young head. Rev.
draped arms. 1839, 43, 46..450.00

ANHALT-SCHAUMBURG
Carl Ludwig 1772-1806

Silver

V.F.

130 (gulden). Legend. Rev.
Holzapfel mining scene.
14 gr. 1774............. 225.00
131 (Conv. thaler). Sim.
28 gr. 1774............. 260.00

ANHALT-ZERBST
Johanna Elisabeth von
Holstein-Gottorp,
Dowager Princess Regent
1747-52, died 1760

Billon

VG-F

135 IIII/PFENN(ige). Cwnd.
I(ohanna) E(lis.) F(ürstin)
A(nhalt) mon. Rev. value/
F.A.Z.L.M/1749........... 12.00
136 VI/PFENNING. Sim.
1749.................... 14.00
137 24/EINEN (= 1/24)/
REICHS/THALER. Sim.
but NACH DEM etc. added.
1749.................... 9.00

Silver

V.F.

★138 (gulden). On her death.
1760.................... 200.00

Friedrich August 1747-93

Copper

VG-F

145 1 HELLER. Like No. 146.
1766.................... 8.00

★146 1 PFENNING. 1766...... 5.00

Billon

147 IIII/PFENN(ig). AD NORMAM
etc. Arms. F.A.F.Z.A. Rev.
Value. F.A.Z.L.M. 1767..... 20.00
147.5 48/EINEN (= 1/48)/
THALER. Cwnd. FA mon.
Rev. value. 1758........ 20.00
148 16 P(fennige =) 5 K(reuzer)
D.G. FRID. AUGUST P. ANHALT,
bust. Rev. Arms. 1764.... 35.00
149 XVI/PFENN(ig). Like No.
147. 1767............... 35.00
150 32 P(fennige =) 10 K(reuzer).
Like No. 148. 1764....... 15.00

Silver

V.F.

151 *VI/EINEN (= ⅙)/THALER.*
Cwnd. mon. Rev. value.
1766.................... 27.50
152 IV/GROSCHEN. Value/
F.A.Z.L.M. etc. Rev. LXXX/
E.F. MARCK etc. 1767...... 12.00
153 8/GUTE/GROSCHEN.
Head. Rev. value. 1758.... 30.00
154 ⅔ (thaler). Armored bust.
Rev. Arms supported. 1763,
67...................... 90.00
155 X E.F.M. (= Conv. thaler).
Sim. 1767............... 1000.00

Gold

157 (ducat). Bust. Rev. Arms.
1767. (1764?).......... 1750.00

**Anhalt-Zerbst extinct 1793.
Divided between Bernburg,
Cöthen and Dessau.**

ARENBERG (AREMBERG),
Duchy

On the German-Belgian border. Lands
on the left bank of the Rhine taken
by France 1801, residue mediatized 1810.

Ludwig Engelbert 1778-1803

Silver

V.F.

1 X EINE MARCK F. (=
Conv. thaler). LVD. ENG. D.G.
DVX ARENBERGAE, gross head.
Rev. Arms. 1783......... 400.00
1a —. Refined head. 1785..... 225.00

Gold

2 (ducat). Head. Rev. Arms.
1783.................... 1800.00

ASCHAFFENBURG.
See Prince Primate.

AUERSPERG.
See AUSTRIA (STATES).

AUGSBURG
(AUGUSTA VINDELICORUM),
Bishopric

In Bavaria. First ecclesiastical coins
10th century. Mediatized to Bavaria
1803.

Joseph, Landgraf v. Hessen,
Bishop 1740-68

Silver

V.F.

1 ¼ (Species thaler).
JOSEPH D.G. EP. AUGUST etc.
Bust. Rev. URGET etc.
2 shields. 1744......... 50.00
2 (½ Species thaler). Sim. but
rev. NON FECIT etc. 1744...250.00
3 (Sp. thaler). Sim. but rev.
AUGUSTANO etc. 1744...... 500.00

Gold

4 (ducat). Sim. 1744 .... 2000.00

Clemens Wenzel,
Prince of Poland and Saxony,
Bishop 1768-1803, died 1812

(also archbishop-elector of Trier, administrator of Prüm, and Provost-
Coadjutor of Ellwangen).

Copper

VG-F

10 1/HELLER. Like No. 13 but
w/out obv. legend. 1773.... 3.00
11 ¼/KREUTZER. Like
No. 13. 1773............. 3.00
12 ½/KREUTZER. Sim.
1773.................... 3.00

GERMAN STATES

AUGSBURG, Bishopric (Cont.)

*13 EIN (=1)/KREUTZER.
1773-75................. 3.00 VG-F

Silver
Fine

14 48/EIN (=1/48)
CONVEN(tion)/THALER
(=2½ kreuzer). Sim. 1773.. 5.00
15 24/EIN CONVEN./
THALER (=5 K.). Sim.
1773.................. 5.00
16 10 (kreuzer). Bust. Rev.
Arms. 1773-75............ 6.00
17 20 (kreuzer). Sim. 1773.....12.00

AUGSBURG
(Augusta Vindelicorum),
Free City

Freed from episcopal control 1276. Obtained mint right 1521. Absorbed by Bavaria 1806.

Arms: Pinecone.

Copper

VG-F
*1 (heller). 1742-47.......... 4.00
1a —. Pinecone btwn branches.
1744-61................. 4.00
1b —. Pinecone in cartouche.
1763-75................. 4.00

Note: Hellers similar to No. 1 but with dates on Obv. issued 1621-1743.

*2 I/HELLER. 1780-1801......4.00
2a —. Oval shield 1801-05......4.00
3 I/PFENNING. Like No. 4
1758.................16.00
3a —. Pinecone in cartouche.
1759-80.................3.00

*3b —. Pinecone in shield.
1780-1800.................3.00

VG-F
3c —. w/out STADTMYNZ.
1764-69.................. 3.00
3d —. STADTMÜNZ. 1801-05.... 3.00

*4 II/PFENNING. 1758-59... 3.00
4a —. Like No. 3a. 1759-80... 3.00
4c —. Like No. 3c. 1764-69.... 3.00

Billon or Silver

7 1 KR(euzer). Arms.
Rev. value. 1766......... 12.00
9 2½ K(reuzer). Like No. 10.
1758.................. 4.00

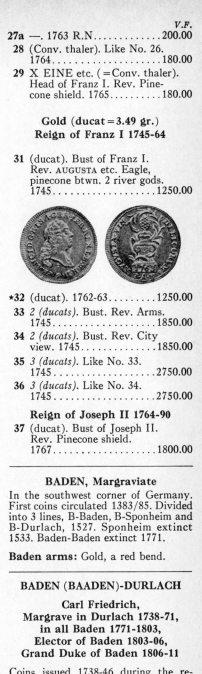

*10 5 K(reuzer Conv. money=)
VII K(reuzer city money).
1758-59.................. 4.00

*12 V K(reuzer Conv. money).
1766.................. 5.00
13 X K(reuzer). Like No. 16.
1760....................7.00
14 10 (kreuzer). Pinecone on
pedestal; CXX EINE etc. Rev.
FRANCISCUS I D.G. etc. Imp.
eagle. 1765, 67............ 7.00
16 XX K(reuzer). COLON. AUGUSTA
etc., pinecone. Rev. var. of
rev. No. 14. 1760.......... 10.00
18 20 (kreuzer). Like No. 14 but
LX EINE etc. 1764.........12.00

Silver
V.F.
20 (½ thaler). Pinecone shield.
Rev. Imp. eagle. 1745......17.50
22 XX E.F.M. (=½ Conv. thaler).
FRANCISCUS I etc. Head. Rev.
Pinecone shield. 1760......40.00
24 (thaler). FRANCISCUS I etc.
Bust. Rev. City deity with
pinecone and lance. 1745...250.00
26 (Conv. thaler). Bust of Franz I.
Rev. AUGUSTA etc. Imp. eagle.
1760.................180.00
27 (Conv. thaler). Bust of Franz I.
Rev. AUGUST VIND etc. Pinecone, 3 river gods. 1760
R.N....................200.00

V.F.
27a —. 1763 R.N.............200.00
28 (Conv. thaler). Like No. 26.
1764................180.00
29 X EINE etc. (=Conv. thaler).
Head of Franz I. Rev. Pinecone shield. 1765.........180.00

Gold (ducat = 3.49 gr.)
Reign of Franz I 1745-64

31 (ducat). Bust of Franz I.
Rev. AUGUSTA etc. Eagle,
pinecone btwn. 2 river gods.
1745.................1250.00

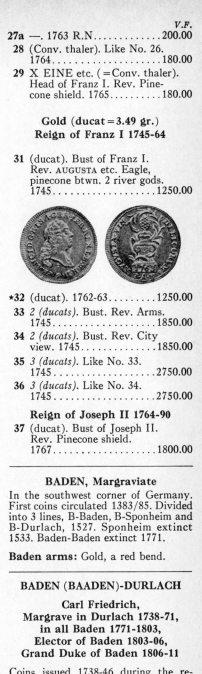

*32 (ducat). 1762-63........1250.00
33 2 (ducats). Bust. Rev. Arms.
1745.................1850.00
34 2 (ducats). Bust. Rev. City
view. 1745.............1850.00
35 3 (ducats). Like No. 33.
1745.................2750.00
36 3 (ducats). Like No. 34.
1745.................2750.00

Reign of Joseph II 1764-90

37 (ducat). Bust of Joseph II.
Rev. Pinecone shield.
1767.................1800.00

BADEN, Margraviate

In the southwest corner of Germany. First coins circulated 1383/85. Divided into 3 lines, B-Baden, B-Sponheim and B-Durlach, 1527. Sponheim extinct 1533. Baden-Baden extinct 1771.

Baden arms: Gold, a red bend.

BADEN (BAADEN)-DURLACH

Carl Friedrich,
Margrave in Durlach 1738-71,
in all Baden 1771-1803,
Elector of Baden 1803-06,
Grand Duke of Baden 1806-11

Coins issued 1738-46 during the regency of Carl Friedrich's grandmother and uncle are omitted.

A. Carl Friedrich, alone as Margrave, 1746-1803.

Copper
V.G.
1 ¼/KREUZ(er). Like No. 2.
1766.................. 2.25

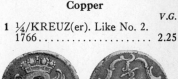

GERMAN STATES

BADEN-DURLACH (Cont.)

V.G.

*2 ½/KREUZ(er). 1766, 72.... 3.00
3 1/KREUZ(er). Sim.
1766, 72................. 3.00

Billon or Silver

VG-F

4 ½/KR(euzer). BAAD-DURL.,
value. Rev. blank. 1749-50..Scarce
5 I/KREV/ZER. CARL
FRID—MARG. ZU. B., arms.
Rev. value. 1749.........Scarce
6 1/KREUZ(er). Like No. 7.
1751.................... 4.00

*7 I/ALBUS (=2 kreuzer).
1749-51. For the county
of Sponheim............. 5.00
8 480 ST. E. FEINE etc.
(=2½ Conv. kreuzer). Arms.
Rev. BADEN/DURLACH/1768. 7.00
9 3/KREUZ(er Landmünz).
500 EINE etc. Arms. Rev.
value/B.D.L.M./1764....... 7.00
10 240 EINE etc. (=5 Conv.
kreuzer). Like No. 11a but
no armor. 1765-66........ 8.00
10a —. Like No. 11. 1767-75.... 8.00

Silver

V.F.

11 10 (Conv. kreuzer). No
armor. 1765-66...........10.00
*11a —. 1767-75-77...........10.00
12 XII KREUZ(er). CARL
FRIDER etc. 3 arms. Rev.
BAAD. DURL. etc., value.
1747....................14.00

*12a XII KR(euzer). 1748, 50..12.00
13 XII K(reuzer). 10 fold arms.
Rev. value/BAADEN etc.
1750....................12.00

V.F.

14 20 (Conv. kreuzer). Head.
Rev. Baden arms only.
1763-64.................15.00
14a —. Like No. 11a. 1771-74..15.00
14b —. Head. Rev. 3 fold arms.
1779....................15.00
16 (gulden). CAR. FRID. etc. Bust.
Rev. MONETA NOVA BAADA.
DURLACENSIS. Arms. 1747...50.00
17 XX EINE etc. (=½ Conv.
thaler). Armored bust. Rev.
oval arms supported by 2
stdg. griffins. 1766.........85.00
17a XX E. F. etc. Rev. different
shield. 1766-68...........85.00
18 XX EINE etc. (=Conv.
gulden). Head. Rev. oval
arms, unsupported. 1778-
79.....................140.00
19 X EINE etc. (=Conv. thaler).
Short armored bust. Rev. 3
shields. 1763............275.00
19a —. Head. Rev. Baden arms
only. 1763..............275.00
20 X EINE etc. (=Conv. thaler).
½ length armored bust. Rev.
arms supported by 2 griffins
(one reclining). 1764-66....180.00
20a —. Rev. arms supported by
2 stdg. griffins. 1766-72....160.00
21 X EINE etc. (=Conv. thaler).
Like No. 18. 1778-79......160.00

Gold (ducat=3.49 gr.)

*25 (¼) DUCAT. Arms.
Rev. BAADA/DURLA/1747...400.00
26 (½) DUCAT. Bust. Rev. 3
shields. 1747............900.00
27 (ducat). Bust. Rev. arms.
1747...................1200.00
28 (ducat). Bust. Rev. arms
divide date. 1751.........1000.00
29 (Rheingold ducat). Head.
Rev. EX SABULIS RHENI, arms.
1765-68.................2800.00
30 (ducat). AMAL(ie)
FRID(erika) PRINC(ess)
etc., her bust. Rev. 2 shields.
On birth of first children (twins)
to crown princess. 1776...1500.00
31 (ducat). CATH. AMAL. etc.,
heads of the twins. Rev.
MATRI/etc. 1776........1300.00
32 (ducat). CAR FRID. etc., his bust.
Rev. NATO EX FILIO etc. On
birth of Prince Carl. 1786.1400.00

B. Carl Friedrich as Elector of Baden 1803-06.

Copper

VG-F

40 ¼/KREUZ(er). Like No. 41.
1802.................... 5.00

VG-F

*41 ½/KREUZ(er). 1803-05.....3.50
42 I/KREUZER. Sim.
1803-05, 06..............12.00

Billon

43 III/KREUZER. KUR BADEN
etc. Arms as on No. 41.
Rev. value. 1803, 06....... 5.00
45 VI/KREUZER. Like No. 43.
1804.................... 9.50
46 VI/KREUZER. Sim. but
4 fold arms. 1804-05....... 7.50

Silver

V.F.

*48 (Conv. thaler). 1803......850.00

C. Carl Friedrich as Grand Duke of Baden 1806-11.

Copper

VG-F

50 ½/KREUZ(er). Like No. 52.
1809-10..................3.00

BADEN (Cont.)

VG-F

*51 I/KREUZER. Sim. but lion in shield faces left. 1807-08.. 3.00

*52 I/KREUZER. 1809-11..... 3.00

Billon

53 III/KREUZER. G(ros) H(erzogthum) BADEN etc. Arms like No. 55. Rev. value/ 1808.................. 3.50

54 III/KREUZER. Sim. but arms like No. 69. 1809-11........ 2.50

*55 VI/KREUZER. 1807-08.................. 3.00

56 VI/KREUZER. Like No. 54. 1809.................... 10.00

Silver

V.F.

57 10 (kreuzer). CARL FRIEDRICH GROSHERZOG VON BADEN. Head (long hair). Rev. arms as No. 52. 1808............. 15.00

58 10 (kreuzer). Sim. but short hair like No. 62. 1809...... 15.00

59 20 (kreuzer). Like No. 57 but arms as No. 51. 1807...... 22.50

60 20 (kreuzer). Like No. 57. 1808.................. 15.00

61 20 (kreuzer). Like No. 58. 1809-10.................. 12.50

V.F.

*62 ZEHN EINE etc. (= Conv. thaler). 1809-11.......... 240.00

Gold

E.F.

63 (Rheingold ducat). Head. Rev. AUS RHEINSAND, Rhine god. 1807.............. 2200.00

Carl, Grand Duke 1811-18

Copper

VG-F

64 ½/KREUZ(er). Like No. 50. 1812.................... 2.00

65 I/KREUZER. Like No. 52. 1812.................... 2.75

66 1/KREUZER. Sim. but G:HERZ:BADEN added to obv., LAND-MÜNZ to Rev. 1813.... 1.75

66a 1/KREUZ/ER. 1813........ 1.75

*66b 1/KREUT/ZER. 1813.... 1.75

*67 ½/KREUT/ZER. 1814-17.. 2.00

67a ½/KREU/ZER. 1817...... 2.00

68 1/KREU/ZER. Sim. 1813-14..................... 1.50

68a I/KREU/ZER. 1814-17.... 1.25

68b I/KREUT/ZER. 1813-17... 1.50

Billon

V.G.

*69 III/KREUZER. 1812-13.................. 2.00

70 VI/KREUZER. Like No. 56. 1812-13................. 2.50

71 3/KREUT/ZER. Like No. 72. 1813-16............... 2.00

71a 3/KREU/ZER. 1817-18.... 2.00

*72 6/KREUT/ZER. 1814-17... 1.75

72a 6/KREU/ZER. 1816-18.... 2.25

Silver

V.F.

73 I KRONENTHALER (=162 kreuzer). Sim. (var.) 1813-18...................... 80.00

Ludwig, Grand Duke 1818-30

Copper

VG-F

74 ½/KREUT/ZER. Like No. 67. 1821.................. 2.00

75 I/KREU/ZER. Sim. 1820... 1.50

*76 ¼/KREU/ZER. 1824...... 2.00

77 ½/KREUZER. Sim. 1822-26..................... 1.75

78 1/KREUZER. Sim. 1821-26..................... 2.00

*79 ½/KREUZER. 1828-30..... 1.50

80 EIN (=1)/KREUZER. Sim. 1827-30.................. 1.25

Billon

F-VF

81 3/KREU/ZER. Like No. 71a. 1819-20.............. 2.00

82 3/KREU/ZER. Like No. 76. 1820-25.................. 2.25

83 DREI (=3)/KREUZER. Like No. 79. 1829-30...... 1.75

84 6 K(reuzer). Small head. v. BADEN. Rev. arms on mantle. 1819............. 20.00

85 6 K(reuzer). Sim. but larger head. VON BADEN. 1820..... 20.00

86 6 K(reuzer). Head. Rev. arms in wreath. 1820-21........ 5.00

GERMAN STATES

BADEN (Cont.)

Silver

V.F.

*87 ZEHN (=10)/KREUZER.
1829-30.................10.00

88 1 G(ulden). Head. Rev. arms.
1821-25..................50.00

88a —. Curly hair. 1826......*200.00*

90 2 G(ulden). Sim. 1821-25...80.00

91 1 KRONENTHALER. Like
No. 73. 1819............100.00

92 KRONENTHALER. Like
No. 84. 1819-21..........100.00

93 EIN (=1) THALER (=100
kreuzer). Head. Rev. arms.
1829-30.................50.00

**Note: Nos. 79-80, 83, 87, 93 and 97
represent an abortive attempt to
introduce the decimal system.**

Gold

E.F.

94 5 G(ulden). Like No. 95.
1819-26................1300.00

94a —. Curly hair. 1827-28...1300.00

*95 10 G(ulden). 1819-25.....1750.00

97 FÜNF (=5) THALER (=500
kreuzer). Like No. 93.
1830..................1600.00

Leopold, Grand Duke 1830-52

Copper

F-VF

*100 ½/KREUZER. 1830-44....1.50

100a —. Larger head like
No. 102a. 1845-52.........1.50

102 1/KREUZER. Like No. 100.
1831-45..................1.00

*102a —. 1845-52.............1.00

F-VF

*103 (kreuzer). On recovery of
Grand Duchess Sophie.
1832..................25.00

*104 (kreuzer). On erection of
statue of Carl Friedrich.
1844..................15.00

E.F.

Billon

Fine

106 3/KREUZER. Like No. 100
but GRH. V. BAD. 1832-37... 1.75

*107 3/KREUZER. 1841-52.... 1.25

108 6/KREUZER. Like No. 100.
1831-37.................. 2.00

109 6/KREUZER. Like No. 107.
1839-50.................. 1.50

Silver

V.F.

110 ½/GULDEN. Like No. 100.
1838-46..................12.50

110a —. Larger head. 1845-52...15.00

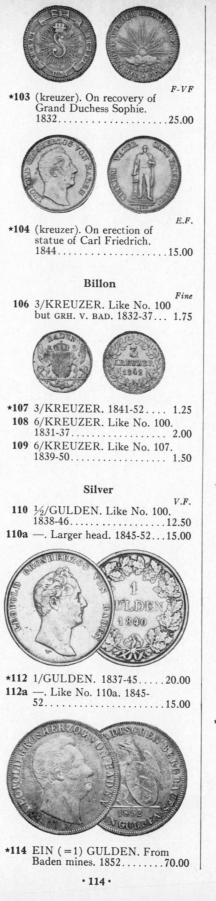

*112 1/GULDEN. 1837-45.....20.00

112a —. Like No. 110a. 1845-
52....................15.00

*114 EIN (=1) GULDEN. From
Baden mines. 1852.......70.00

V.F.

115 KRONENTHALER. Head.
Rev. arms. 1830-37......60.00

116 KRONENTHALER. Head.
Rev. ALEXANDRINE et al
BESUCHEN etc. 1832. Mint
visit...................600.00

117 KRONENTHALER. Head.
Rev. crossed hammers cwnd.
From Baden mines. 1834..150.00

118 KRONENTHALER. Like
No. 114. 1836..........135.00

119 KRONEN-THALER. Head.
Rev. ZU/IHRER/etc. in circle
of shields. Formation of
German customs union.
1836...................75.00

120 ZWEI (=2) GULDEN.
Head. Rev. Arms. 1846-
52....................32.50

121 3½ GULDEN (=2 thaler).
Head. Rev. value. 1841-
43....................135.00

122 VII E.F.M. (=3½ gulden).
Head. Rev. statue of Carl
Friedrich. 1844 R.N....175.00

123 3½ GULDEN. Head. Rev.
Arms. 1845-52..........150.00

Gold

E.F.

124 EIN (=1) DUCAT. Small
head. 1832-42.........1750.00

*124a —. Medium head. 1843-
46...................1750.00

124b —. Large head. 1847-52.1750.00

124c —. Star under head. Posthumous coinage. 1852.....2000.00

Friedrich, as Prince Regent 1852-56

Copper

V.F.

*130 1 KREUZER. 1856...... 4.00

Billon

131 3/KREUZER. Like No. 107.
1853-56................. 6.00

132 6/KREUZER. Sim. 1855-
56....................12.00

Silver

133 ½/GULDEN. Like No. 130.
1856...................30.00

GERMAN STATES

BADEN (Cont.)

V.F.

134 1/GULDEN. Sim. 1856...100.00

135 ZWEY (=2) GULDEN.
Head. Rev. Arms. 1856...225.00

136 3½ GULDEN (=2 th.).
Head. Rev. Arms. 1854...500.00

136a —. 1852, 55 ....RRR

Gold

VF-EF

137 EIN (=1) DUCAT. Head.
Rev. Arms. 1854.......1900.00

Friedrich, as Grand Duke 1856-1907

Copper

V.F.

138 ½/KREUZER. Like No. 139.
1856................. 4.00

★139 1/KREUZER. 1856...... 2.00

140 (kreuzer). Head. Rev.
CARLSRUHE/DER IUGEND
etc. 1857. Birth of heir....20.00

141 ½/KREUZER. Like
No. 150. 1859-71......... 2.00

★142 1/KREUZER. 1859-71.... 1.75

★143 (kreuzer). Head of Leopold.
Rev. DAS/LEOPOLDS/etc.
Erection of his statue.
1861...................12.00

144 1 KREUZER. Arms.
Rev. VERFASSUNG etc. 50th
anniversary of Constitution.
1868...................15.00

V.F.

★145 1 KREUZER. Victory
over France. 1871........ 3.00

145a —. SCHEIDE MÜNZE in lieu
of value (mule) 12.00

Copper Gedenk-Kreuzer (no denomination shown)

E.F.

146 Church at Seckenheim.
Rev. legend. 1869........25.00

147 Bühl city arms. Rev. legend.
1871. Victory celebration...35.00

148 Sim. but Karlsruhe. 1871...12.00

149 Sim. but Offenburg. 1871...25.00

Billon

V.F.

★150 3/KREUZER. 1866-71.... 2.00

Silver

V.F.

★151 ½/GULDEN. 1856-65....10.00

152 ½/GULDEN. Sim. but head
l. with beard. 1867-69.....16.50

153 1/GULDEN. Like No. 151.
1856-60.................20.00

154 1 GULDEN. Münzbesuch
(mint visit) Jan. 1857....125.00

155 1 GULDEN. Head. Rev.
Baden stdg. Mannheim
Landesschiessen (shooting
fest). 1863..............40.00

156 1 GULDEN. Head. Rev.
value. Karlsruhe Landes-
schiessen (shooting fest).
1867...................40.00

157 EIN (=1) VEREINS-
THALER. Obv. like No. 151.
Rev. arms. 1857-65......30.00

158 EIN VEREINSTHALER.
Sim. but obv. like No. 152.
1865-71.................30.00

BAMBERG, Bishopric

In northern Bavaria. Founded 1007,
first coinage immediately thereafter.
Secularized and given to Bavaria 1802.
Patron: St. Heinrich (Emperor).

Arms: Gold, a black double tailed lion
behind a silver diagonal (bend).

Johann Philip Anton, Freiherr von Frankenstein, Bishop 1746-53

Silver

V.F.

3 (death groschen). JOANN.
PHILIPP. ANTON. D.G. EP.
BAMB. etc. Arms. Rev. 10
lines: +NATUS/D. 27 MART
1695/etc. 1753............20.00

7 (thaler). IOANN etc. Bust. Rev.
INVIOLATA etc. Arms. 1750.350.00

Gold

8 (goldgulden). Arms. GRATVI
etc. Rev. Knight with flag
SENATVS etc. ... BAMBER-
GENSIS. Homage of Bamberg
city (dated 1746 in chronogram).................1250.00

9 (ducat). Like No. 7. 1750..1250.00

Franz Conrad, Graf von Stadion, Bishop 1753-57

Silver

12 (death groschen). FRANCISCUS
CONRADUS D.G. EP. BAMB. etc.
Arms. Rev. 10 lines: +NATUS
DIE 29 AUG. 1697 etc. 1757..30.00

Gold

14 (ducat). Bust. Rev. ASTRAEA
LONGOS etc. Arms. Homage of
Bamberg (date 1753 in chrono-
gram).................1250.00

Adam Friedrich, Graf v Seinsheim, Bishop of Würzburg 1755-79, of Bamberg 1757-79

Copper

VG-F

★15 1/GUTER (good)/HELLER.
Bamberg lion behind diagonal.
Rev. value. 1761 .... 4.00

16 1/HELLER. Sim. 1772..... 4.00

17 1/LEICHTER (light)/PFEN-
NING. Sim. 1761 .... 3.50

★18 ½/LEICHTER/KREUZER.
1762-63................. 4.00

GERMAN STATES

BAMBERG (Cont.)

Billon

VG-F

19 1 KR(euzer). Sim. but NACH DEM KRAIS SCHLVSS added to Rev. 1765-66 . . . . 4.00

20 2½ (kreuzer). Obv. like No. 25. Rev. value/BAMBERG/ LANDM./1766 . . . . 4.00

23 (death groschen). ADAM FRID-ERIC. D.G. EP. BAMB. ET HERB. etc. Arms under 5 helmets. Rev. 9 lines: +NATUS etc. 1779 . . . . (V.F.) 14.00

★25 V K(reuzer). 1766 . . . . 6.00

Silver

V.F.

31 ZEHEN EINE etc. (=Conv. thaler). Bust/OEXLEIN. Rev. mantled arms supported by 2 lions. G.N.—B.W. 1760 . . . . 400.00

See Würzburg for coins similar to Nos. 23, 31 (with mmk. G.N. (W.) P.B.) and others.

Gold

33 (ducat). ADAM FRID etc. bust/ ELECTVS etc. Rev. LONGAEVOS etc., stdg. knight. Homage of Bamberg. 1757 . . . . 1250.00

Franz Ludwig, Freiherr von Erthal, Bishop of Bamberg and Würzburg 1779-95

Copper

VG-F

36 1/HELLER. Like No. 16. 1780-86 . . . . 4.00

Billon

37 1 KR(euzer). Like No. 19. 1786 . . . . 4.00

Silver

V.F.

★39 (death groschen). 1795 . . . . . . 16.00

V.F.

47 ZEHN EINE etc. (=Conv. thaler). FRANZ LUDWIG B. ZU BAMBERG etc. Arms. Rev. ZUM BESTEN/ etc. 1795. Struck to pay episco-pal contribution to war against France 110.00

Gold

E.F.

50 (ducat). Bust. Rev. Pyramid and seated female. 1779. Homage of Bamberg 1500.00

Christoph Franz, Freiherr von Buseck, Bishop of Bamberg 1795-1802, Died 1805

Silver

V.F.

55 LX/EINE etc. (=20 Conv. kreuzer). CHRISTOPH FRANZ BISCHOF Z. BAMBERG etc. Arms. Rev. value. 1800 . . . . 25.00

56 XX/EINE etc. (=½ Conv. thaler). CHRISTOPH etc. Bust. Rev. Bamberg City view. 1800 . . . . 50.00

57 X/EINE etc. (=Conv. thaler). Arms. Rev. City view. 1800. (var.) 75.00

Gold

E.F.

★59 (ducat). Homage of Bamberg. 1795 . . . . 1000.00

Union of Bamberg With Bavaria 1802

Gold

60 (ducat). CONCORDIA etc. 2 fe-males (Bav. and Bamb.) stdg. by tree. Rev. 7 lines: SENATUS/ etc. . . . /BAVARIA. (1802) . . 1100.00

BAVARIA (BAIERN, BAYERN)

Important South German State, orig-inally (555-1805) a duchy. First ducal coins 10th century.

Bavaria ruled by the Wittelsbach family 1180-1918. Pfalz (Rhenish Pala-tinate) acquired 1214/15. After various temporary divisions, the Bavarian hold-ings were divided by the Treaty of Pavia (1329) between the elder line (Pfalz) and the younger line (Bavaria). In 1356 the Pfalz was given the elec-toral dignity to the exclusion of Ba-varia. This was reversed in 1623, dur-ing the 30 Years' War. Both the dukes of Bavaria and the counts palatine ranked as electors after 1648.

Through a series of fortuitous deaths all of the Wittelsbach possessions were reunited in 1799.

In 1805 Bavaria was given the rank of Kingdom by Napoleon.

Bavarian Arms: Alternate silver and blue lozenges.

Maximilian III Joseph, 1745-77

Bavarian coins of this and the follow-ing reign were struck at Münich (no mmk.) and Amberg ("A"). Coins with A.S. were struck at Mannheim for Pfalz (q.v.).

Copper

VG-F

0.5 1/H(eller). Value/17—lozenge shield–63. Rev. blank . . . . . . Scarce

1 1/HEL/LER. Da–lozenge shield–te in rhombus. Rev. value in rhombus. 1761, 65 . . . 3.00

1a —. 1765/c–lozenge shield–B. 6.00

1.5 1/HELLER. Obv. like No. 1a. Rev. value, no rhombus. 1765 . . . . 4.00

★2 1/PFEN/NING. Lozenge shield. Rev. value/date. 1761-77 . . . . 2.00

3 II/PFEN/NING. Lozenge shield divides C–B. Rev. value/date. 1766-67 . . . . 2.00

Billon

4 (pfennig). Da–C–te/lozenge shield. Rev. blank. 1745-65 . . 3.00

5 1/PFEN/NING. Obv. sim. Rev. value. 1759-61 . . . . 3.00

★6 ½ (kreuzer). Uniface. 1746-67 . . . . 3.00

6.5 1 (kreuzer). Head. Rev. Imp. eagle with lozenge shield on breast. Vicariat. 1745 . . . . . . Scarce

★7 1 (kreuzer). Head. Rev. lozenge shield/da–1–te. 1745-69 . . . . . 3.00

9 2 (kreuzer). M.I.U.B. ET. P. etc. Arms. Rev. SOLI DEO etc. 2 in orb. 1753-54 . . . . 3.00

10 (2½ kreuzer). Lozenge shield. Rev. LAND/MUNZ. 1754 . . . . . Scarce

12 3 K(reuzer). Like No. 16. Vicariat. 1745 . . . . Scarce

GERMAN STATES

BAVARIA (Cont.)

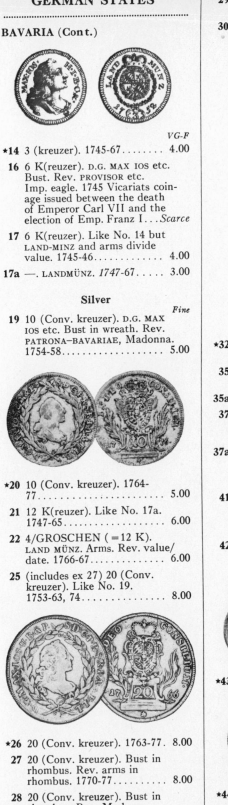

VG-F

★14 3 (kreuzer). 1745-67....... 4.00

16 6 K(reuzer). D.G. MAX IOS etc. Bust. Rev. PROVISOR etc. Imp. eagle. 1745 Vicariats coinage issued between the death of Emperor Carl VII and the election of Emp. Franz I...*Scarce*

17 6 K(reuzer). Like No. 14 but LAND-MINZ and arms divide value. 1745-46............ 4.00

17a —. LANDMÜNZ. *1747-67*..... 3.00

Silver

Fine

19 10 (Conv. kreuzer). D.G. MAX IOS etc. Bust in wreath. Rev. PATRONA—BAVARIAE, Madonna. 1754-58.................. 5.00

★20 10 (Conv. kreuzer). 1764-77.................. 5.00

21 12 K(reuzer). Like No. 17a. 1747-65.............. 6.00

22 4/GROSCHEN (=12 K). LAND MÜNZ. Arms. Rev. value/ date. 1766-67.............. 6.00

25 (includes ex 27) 20 (Conv. kreuzer). Like No. 19. 1753-63, 74.............. 8.00

★26 20 (Conv. kreuzer). 1763-77. 8.00

27 20 (Conv. kreuzer). Bust in rhombus. Rev. arms in rhombus. 1770-77......... 8.00

28 20 (Conv. kreuzer). Bust in rhombus. Rev. Madonna in rhombus. 1770-76........ 8.00

28.5 24 K(reuzer). Like No. 17a. 1747.................. *Scarce*

Fine

29 30 K(reuzer). Like No. 17. 1746..................*Scarce*

30 30 (Conv. kreuzer). D.G. MAX. etc. Bust/30. Rev. S. MARIA etc. Madonna. 1754, 56........*Scarce*

V.F.

★32 (½ Conv. thaler). Bust. Rev. Madonna. 1754-74....20.00

35 (Conv. thaler). Sim. 1753-59..................25.00

35a —. 1760-77..............25.00

37 (Conv. thaler). Bust. Rev. arms supported by 2 lions (like No. 44) 1753-59.....30.00

37a —. 1760-68.............30.00

Gold (ducat = 3.49 gr.)

E.F.

41 (ducat). Bust. Rev. IN PART RH etc. Imp. eagle with Bav. arms on breast. 1745. On the Vicariat................900.00

42 (ducat). Busts of Max. Jos. and Maria Anna of Poland-Saxony. Rev. landscape. On their marriage. 1747..........1200.00

★43 (ducat). Homage ceremony (1747 R.N.)............1200.00

★44 (ducat). 1755-75.........900.00

45 (Danube gold ducat). Obv. like No. 46. Rev. EX AURO DANUBII, river god/R.N. date 1756, 60, 62..............RRR

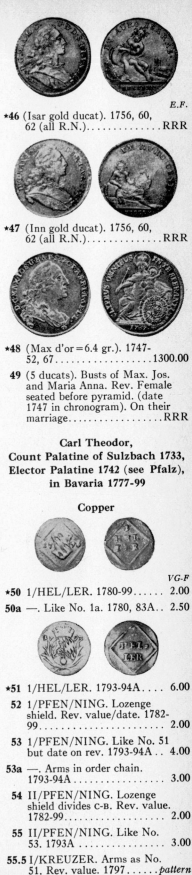

E.F.

★46 (Isar gold ducat). 1756, 60, 62 (all R.N.)..............RRR

★47 (Inn gold ducat). 1756, 60, 62 (all R.N.)..............RRR

★48 (Max d'or = 6.4 gr.). 1747-52, 67.................1300.00

49 (5 ducats). Busts of Max. Jos. and Maria Anna. Rev. Female seated before pyramid. (date 1747 in chronogram). On their marriage.................RRR

Carl Theodor, Count Palatine of Sulzbach 1733, Elector Palatine 1742 (see **Pfalz**), in Bavaria 1777-99

Copper

VG-F

★50 1/HEL/LER. 1780-99...... 2.00

50a —. Like No. 1a. 1780, 83A.. 2.50

★51 1/HEL/LER. 1793-94A.... 6.00

52 1/PFEN/NING. Lozenge shield. Rev. value/date. 1782-99...................... 2.00

53 1/PFEN/NING. Like No. 51 but date on rev. 1793-94A.. 4.00

53a —. Arms in order chain. 1793-94A................. 3.00

54 II/PFEN/NING. Lozenge shield divides C-B. Rev. value. 1782-99.................. 2.00

55 II/PFEN/NING. Like No. 53. 1793A 3.00

55.5 I/KREUZER. Arms as No. 51. Rev. value. 1797......*pattern*

GERMAN STATES

BAVARIA (Cont.)

Billon

VG-F

57 1 (kreuzer). Like No. 59 but rev. round arms/da-1-te. 1794-98 .... 3.00

57a —. (1 kreuzer). 1795-97 ..... 3.00

★59 3 K(reuzer). 1794-98 .... 4.00

61 6 K(reuzer). Like No. 59. 1794-98 .... 6.00

Silver

Note: Former Nos. 60, 63-67, 72-73, 77a, 78, 81a, 82, 85 and 86 struck at Mannheim for the Palatinate have been transferred to Pfalz.

V.F.

69 10 (Conv. kreuzer). Bare bust in wreath. Rev. Madonna. 1778-98 .... 8.00

71 20 (Conv. kreuzer). Sim. 1778-99 .... 10.00

74 20 (Conv. kreuzer). Obv. sim. Rev. 3 fold oval arms. 1793-94A 10.00

75 (½ Conv. thaler). Head. Rev. S.R.I. ARCHID. etc., 3 fold arms. 1778-98 .... 20.00

76 (½ Conv. thaler). Head. Rev. Madonna. 1779, 82 .... 20.00

80 (Conv. thaler). Bound hair. 1778-82 .... 20.00

★80a —. Unbound hair. 1778-94 .... 20.00

V.F.

80b —. Old bust. 1791-99 ..... 20.00

83 ZEHEN EINE etc. (=Conv. thaler). Bust/A. Rev. 3 fold arms. 1793-94 .... 300.00

Silver Münich Vicariats Coinage
A. 1790 Vicariat.

65a 10 (Conv. kreuzer). Clothed bust. Rev. I.C. & M etc., Imp. eagle with 3 fold arms in shield on breast. 1790 ..... 12.00

72a 20 (Conv. kreuzer). Sim. but armored bust. 1790 .... 16.00

77 (½ Conv. thaler). Obv. sim. Rev. IVL. CL. & etc., Imp. eagle with 3 fold oval arms on breast. 1790 .... 30.00

84 (Conv. thaler). Sim. 1790 .. 125.00

84a —. Draped bust. 1790 ..... 125.00

84b —. Clothed bust l. 1790 ... *pattern*

B. 1792 Vicariat.

67a 10 (Conv. kreuzer). Head. Rev. I.C. & M etc., Imp. eagle with 3 fold oval arms on breast. 1792 .... 12.00

72b 20 (Conv. kreuzer). Bust. Rev. eagle has manifold arms on breast. 1792 .... 16.00

78a (½ Conv. thaler). Obv. like No. 67a. Rev. like No. 72b. 1792 .... 30.00

87 (Conv. thaler). Sim. but IVL. CL. & etc. 1792 .... 125.00

Gold (ducat = 3.49 gr.)

90 (ducat). Like No. 83. 1778-93 .... 1400.00

90a —. Older head. 1794-98 ... 1400.00

91 (Danube gold ducat). Head. Rev. EX AURO DANUBII, river god/R.N. date. 1779, 80, 93 .... 2500.00

92 (Inn gold ducat). Sim. but Rev. EX AURO OENI, river god/R.N. date. 1779, 80, 93, 98 .... 2500.00

93 (Isar gold ducat). Sim. but Rev. EX AURO ISARAE, river god/R.N. date. 1779, 80, 93, 98 .... 3000.00

94 (ducat on the Vicariat). Head. Rev. Imp. eagle, 3 fold arms on breast. 1790, 92. 2 vars. each year (Munich, Mannheim) 1200.00

95 2 (ducats). Like No. 83. 1787 .... 3000.00

96 2 (ducats). Like No. 94. 1790, 92 .... 2500.00

97 3 (ducats). Like No. 83. 1787 .... RRR

98 3 (ducats). Like No. 94. 1790, 92 .... RRR

For other coins of Carl Theodor, see Pfalz (Chur Pfalz) and Julich-Berg.

Maximilian IV Joseph, Count Palatine of Pfalz-Birkenfeld-Zweibrücken 1795-99, Elector of Bavaria and Elector Palatine 1799-1805, King of Bavaria as Maximilian I Joseph 1806-25

A. As Elector 1799-1805.

Copper

VG-F

100 1/HEL/LER. Lozenge shield divides date. Rev. value. 1800-05 .... 2.00

101 1/PFEN/NING. Like No. 102. 1800-05 .... 2.00

★102 II/PFEN/NING. 1800-05 .... 2.00

Billon

103 1 (kreuzer). MAX. IOS. P.B. etc. Head. Rev. arms/ da-1-te. 1801 .... 4.00

103a —. Value not shown. 1799-1803 .... 4.00

103.1 1 (kreuzer). MAX. IOS. H.I. etc. Sim. 1804 .... 4.00

103.1a —. Value not shown. 1800-03 .... 4.00

103.2 1 K(reuzer). MAX. IOS. C.Z. etc. Sim. 1804-05 .... 4.00

104 3 K(reuzer). Like No. 104a but MAX. IOS. P.B. etc. 1799-1802 .... 4.00

★104a —. MAX. IOS. H.I. etc. 1803-04 .... 3.00

104b —. MAX. IOS. C.Z. etc. 1804-05 .... 4.00

105 6 K(reuzer). Like No. 104. 1799-1803 .... 6.00

105a —. Like No. 104a. 1801-04 .... 4.00

105b —. Like No. 104b. 1804-05 .... 5.00

Silver

V.F.

108 10 (Conv. kreuzer). Head in wreath. Rev. 3 fold arms. 1800-01 .... 10.00

112 20 (Conv. kreuzer). Sim. 1799-1803 .... 18.00

114 20 (Conv. kreuzer). Like No. 128. 1804-05 .... 15.00

GERMAN STATES

BAVARIA (Cont.)

V.F.

115 (½ Conv. thaler). Head. Rev. 3 fold arms. 1799-1802....*Scarce*

116 (½ Conv. thaler). Like No. 128. 1804-05.............40.00

118 (Conv. thaler). D.G. MAX. IOS. etc. Head. Rev. PRO DEO etc. Arms. 1799-1802.........85.00

118a —. D.G. MAXIM. IOSEPH etc. 1802.................130.00

118b —. MAXIMILIAN etc. 1802.130.00

118c —. D.G. MAX IOSEPH etc. 1802-03.............145.00

120 (Conv. thaler). Like No. 128 but obv.... IN BAIERN. Rev. GOTT UND DAS ... 1803.................85.00

121 ZEHEN etc. (on edge = Conv. thaler). Sim. but ZU PFALZ-BAIERN. 1803-05.......185.00

122 ZEHEN etc. (on edge = Conv. thaler). Like No. 128 1805.................80.00

School Prize Coin

E.F.

★123 (½ Conv. thaler). N.D. (1799-1805).............160.00

Gold

V.F.

124 (ducat). Like No. 118. 1799-1803.............1350.00

126 (goldgulden). Bust. Rev. palm tree, Würzburg arms, S.P.–Q.W. 1803.........2000.00

★128 (ducat). 1804-05.......1500.00

For other coins of Max Joseph during this era, see Berg and Pfalz.

B. As King Max I Joseph 1805-25.

I. Coins with first royal arms (orb and lion centershield).

Copper

V.G.

130 1/KREUZER. Arms. Rev. BAIERISCHE etc., value. For Tyrol. 1806.............3.00

Billon

F-VF

★131 6 K(reuzer). 1806........15.00

Silver

132 ZEHEN etc. (on edge = Conv. thaler). Like No. 133 but supporting lions face inward. 1806.................120.00

132a —. Like No. 133. 1806....200.00

Gold

V.F.

★133 (ducat). 1806..........1500.00

II. Coins with second royal arms (cwnd. crossed sword and sceptre centershield).

Copper

Fine

★134 1/HELLER. 1806-25...... 1.25

135 1/PFENNING. Like No. 157. 1806-25................ 1.00

136 2/PFENNING. Sim. 1806-25..................... 2.00

Billon

★137 1 K(reuzer). 1806-25...... 3.50

138 3 K(reuzer). Sim. 1807-25..................... 6.00

139 6 K(reuzer). Sim. 1806-25..................... 5.00

Silver

V.F.

140 20 (kreuzer). Bust. Rev. FUR GOTT etc. Arms. 1806-25.................15.00

140a —. Head. 1809.........

141 ZEHEN etc. (on edge = Conv. thaler). Like No. 133 but new arms. 1807.........100.00

142 ZEHEN etc. (on edge = Conv. thaler). Sim. but short hair instead of pigtail. 1807-21..50.00

143 KRONTHALER (on edge, = 162 kreuzer). Head. Rev. PRO DEO etc. Cwnd. sword and sceptre. 1809-25......40.00

143a —. Error. IOEPHUS. 1813..100.00

144 ZEHEN etc. (on edge, = Conv. thaler). Bust in armor. Rev. MAGNUS etc. Stone. 1818 R.N. Granting of constitution.....................85.00

145 ZEHEN etc. (on edge, = Conv. thaler). Like No. 142 but older bust. 1822-25....75.00

School Prize Coins

146 (½ Conv. thaler). N.D. Like No. 123 but legend KÖNIG instead of CHURFÜRST. (1806-08)..............180.00

147 (½ Conv. thaler). Sim. but head. N.D. (1807-08).....150.00

148 (½ Conv. thaler). Sim. but head; legends in block letters. N.D. (1807-37)......100.00

Gold

E.F.

★149 (ducat). 1807-22.........900.00

149a —. BAEIRN. 1821-22.....1000.00

149b —. Older head. 1823-25...900.00

★150 EIN (= 1) GOLD GULDEN. 1815. (2 var.)..........1200.00

150a —. Rev. S.P.–Q.W., Würzburg arms. 1817, N.D...1850.00

151 (Danube gold ducat). Head. Rev. EX AURO DANUBII, river god. 1821 R.N..........3000.00

152 (Inn gold ducat). Sim. but EX AURO OENI. 1821 RN.............3000.00

BAVARIA (Cont.)

E.F.

*153 (Isar gold ducat). 1821
R.N..................RRR

*154 (Rhinegold ducat). 1821
R.N.................2500.00

Ludwig I 1825-48

Copper

Fine

155 1/HELLER. Like No. 134.
1828-35..................1.25

156 1/PFENNING. Like No.
157. 1828-35.............1.00

*157 2/PFENNING. 1828-35... 1.00

158 1/HELLER. Like No. 160.
1839-48..................1.00

159 1/PFENNIG. Sim. 1839-
48.......................1.00

*160 2/PFENNIGE. 1839-48....1.00

Billon

*161 1 K(reuzer). 1827-29......2.00

161a —. LUDWIG I etc. 1830-35 .. 2.00

162 3 K(reuzer). Like No. 161.
1827-30.................3.00

162a —. Like No. 161a. 1830-
35......................2.00

Fine

*163 6 K(reuzer). 1827-29..... 6.00

163a —. Like No. 161a. 1830-
35....................... 5.00

Silver

V.F.

164 KRONTHALER (on edge, =
162 kreuzer). Obv. like No.
161. Rev. cwn. in wreath.
1826-29.................90.00

164a —. Obv. like No. 161a.
1830-37.................60.00

Series of Historical Convention Thalers.

Common Obverse: LUDWIG I etc., Head, ZEHN EINE etc.

Reverse Only is Described.

E.F.

165 1825. Rev. TRITT etc. King
stdg. Coronation.......250.00

165a —. BESCHWORT etc. (= Pattern)

166 1826. Rev. Heads of scientists
Reichenbach and Fraun-
hofer...................250.00

167 1826. Rev. VERLEGUNG etc.
Removal of University to
Münich.................250.00

168 1827. Rev. Cornucopias,
Caduceus. Customs Union
with Württemberg.......250.00

168a —. R.N. date (= Pattern).

169 1827. Rev. establishment of
Ludwigs Order.........250.00

169a —. c.v. beneath head.
(= Pattern).

170 1827. Rev. establishment of
Theresien Order........250.00

170a —. AM 12 DEC. 1827.
(= Pattern).

171 1828. Rev. Queen and 8
children. ("Blessings of
Heaven")...............225.00

171a —. R.N. date. (= Pattern).

172 1828. Rev. VERFASSUNGSSAEULE
Constitution Monument .. 250.00

172a —. Steps to monument marked.
(= Pattern).

173 1829. Rev. HANDELSVERTRAG
etc. Commercial treaty with
Prussia, etc............250.00

174 1830. Rev. BAYERNS TREUE.
Loyalty to Royal
Dynasty...............250.00

E.F.

175 1831. Rev. Lion and stone,
GERECHT etc. Opening of
Legislature.............350.00

176 1832. Rev. Greece, holding
shield in which is Greek cross,
offering Crown to Prince
Otto...................250.00

176a —. Varieties with blank shield,
Bavarian lozenges on cross,
or Phoenix, are patterns.

177 1833. Rev. ZOLLVEREIN with
Prussia, etc............250.00

178 1833. Rev. DENKMAHL etc.
Monument to Bavarians who
fell in Russia...........250.00

179 1834. Rev. LANDTAG. Honor-
ing the Legislature.......275.00

180 1834. Rev. DENKMAHL etc.
Monument to Wittelsbach
family.................275.00

181 1835. Rev. BEYTRITT etc.
Baden joins the Zollverein.350.00

182 1835. Rev. HYPOTHEKEN BANK.
Bavarian Mortgage Bank
established.............350.00

183 1835. Rev. DER TRENNUNG
etc. Monument to leave-
taking of King Otto of Greece
from his mother........250.00

184 1835. Rev. ERSTE EISENBAHN
etc. First German steam
railway................400.00

185 1835. Rev. DENKMAHL.
(Monument) to King Max
Joseph................250.00

185a —. Rev. sceptre does not
extend beyond shoulder...275.00

186 1835. Rev. School given to
Benedictine Order........300.00

187 1836. Rev. Chapel erected
on King Otto's departure
for Greece.............250.00

188 1837. Rev. St. Michael's
Order..................300.00

Under Convention of 1837

Billon

Fine

189 1/KREUZER. Like No. 190.
1839-48..................1.00

*190 3/KREUZER. 1839-48.....1.00

191 6/KREUZER. Sim. 1839-
48..................... 2.00

Silver

V.F.

*192 ½/GULDEN. 1838-48....18.00

GERMAN STATES

BAVARIA (Cont.)

		V.F.
193	1/GULDEN. Sim. 1837-48	30.00
194	ZWEY (=2) GULDEN. Head. Rev. Arms. 1845-48	40.00
195	3½/GULDEN (=2 thaler). Head. Rev. Value in wreath. 1839-41	120.00
196	3½ GULDEN. Head. Rev. Arms. 1842-48	120.00

Series of Commemorative Double Thalers.

Common Obverse:

LUDWIG I etc., head, value.
DREY-EIN HALB GULDEN
on edge.

		E.F.
197	1837. Rev. MUNZVEREINIGUNG etc. South German Mint Union	300.00
198	1838. Rev. redistribution of Bavaria on historical basis	300.00
199	1839. Rev. Equestrian Statue of Elector Max I	300.00
200	1840. Rev. Statue of Albrecht Durer	300.00
201	1841. Rev. Statue of J. P. F. Richter	350.00
202	1842. Rev. WALHALLA	300.00
203	1842. Rev. marriage of Crown Prince Max	300.00
203a	—. 1 OCTB. 1842	400.00
204	1843. Rev. centenary of foundation of Erlangen University	350.00
205	1844. Rev. FELDHERRN-HALLE	350.00
206	1845. Rev. Statue of Chancellor von Kreittmayr	375.00
207	1845. Rev. birth of 2 princes	350.00
208	1846. Rev. Ludwigs Canal	350.00
209	1847. Rev. Statue of Bishop von Mespelbrunn	400.00
210	1848. Rev. Ludwig gives crown to his son, Max	1000.00

Gold

		V.F.
★211	(ducat). 1826-28	950.00
★211a	—. LUDWIG I etc. 1828-34.	850.00
211b	—. Struck in collar. 1835	1000.00
211c	—. Head by Voigt. 1840-48	850.00
★212	(Danube gold ducat). 1830 R.N	2250.00
212a	—. Obv. legend in German. 1830 R.N	2250.00
★213	(Inn gold ducat). 1830 R.N	2250.00
214	(Isar gold ducat). Sim. but EX AURO ISARAE. 1830 R.N	2250.00
★215	(Rhine gold ducat). 1830 R.N	2250.00
215a	—. Obv. legend in German. 1830 R.N	2250.00
215b	—. New dies. EX AURO RHENI above Speyer city view. 1842, 46 R.N	1000.00
★216	(gold gulden) (1826)	1000.00
217	EIN (=1) GOLDGULDEN. Generally like No. 218 but head l. N.D. (1827-36)	1100.00
★218	EIN GOLDGULDEN. N.D. (1843)	1100.00

		V.F.
★219	EIN GOLDGULDEN. N.D. (1843)	1100.00

Maximilian II, 1848-64

Copper

220	1/HELLER. Like No. 223. 1849-56	2.00
★221	1/PFENNIG. 1849-56	2.00
222	2/PFENNIGE. Sim. 1849-50	2.00
★223	½/KREUZER. 1851-56	2.00
★224	1/PFENNING. 1858-63	2.00
225	2/PFENNING. Sim. 1858-63	2.00

Billon

226	1/KREUZER. Like No. 190. 1849-56	2.00
227	3/KREUZER. Sim. 1849-56	3.00
228	6/KREUZER. Sim. 1849-56	4.00
★229	1/KREUZER. 1858-63	1.00

Silver

★230	½/GULDEN. 1848-64	22.50

GERMAN STATES

BAVARIA (Cont.)

V.F.

231 1/GULDEN. Sim. 1848-64..................30.00

232 ZWEY (=2) GULDEN. Head. Rev. arms. 1848-56..37.50

★233 ZWEY GULDEN. Head. Rev. ★ statue of B.V.M. in Münich. 1855.....(E.F.) 45.00

★234 EIN (=1) VEREINS- THALER. Head. Rev. arms. 1857-64..................30.00

235 3½ GULDEN (=2 thaler). Head. Rev. arms. 1849- 56..................110.00

236 ZWEI (=2) VEREINS- THALER. Like No. 234. 1859-64..................160.00

Series of Commemorative Double Thalers

Common Obverse: Head.

No indication of value, Except on edge one of 3 Inscriptions:

(a) VEREINSMÜNZE, etc.
(b) CONVENTION★VOM, etc.
(c) DREY EIN HALB, etc.

E.F.

★237 1848. Rev. ★. Constitution of 1848. Edge (a).......375.00

237a —. Edge (b)...........450.00

237b —. Edge (c)...........450.00

238 1848. Rev. Statue of von Gluck. Edge (a).......1000.00

238a —. Edge (c)...........1150.00

239 1849. Rev. Statue of De Latre. Edge (a).....1200.00

239a —. Edge (c)...........1350.00

★240 1854. Rev. Glass Palace at Münich. Edge (a).......375.00

240a —. Edge (b)...........375.00

241 1856. Rev. Statue of Maxi- milian II. Edge (c).....550.00

Gold

VF-EF

242 EIN DUCATEN (=1 ducat). Like No. 243 but w/out AUS DEM etc. 1849-56........700.00

★243 EIN DUCATEN. Gold. Kronach Mine 1855.......RRR

★244 EIN (=1) GOLDGULDEN. N.D. (1850)...........1850.00

VF-EF

★245 EIN GOLDGULDEN. N.D. (1850)...........1850.00

★246 (Rhine gold ducat). 1850-56 R.N...........1850.00

246a —. 1863 R.N...........3000.00

247 EIN GOLDGULDEN. Mule. Obv. No. 246. Rev. No. 244. N.D. (1850-63) 1600.00

248 ½ KRONE. Head. Rev. value. 1857-64.....2500.00

249 1 KRONE. Sim. 1857-64.................RRR

Ludwig II 1864-86

Copper

V.F.

250 1/PFENNING. Like No. 224. 1864-71...........1.00

★251 2/PFENNING. 1864-71... 1.00

Billon

252 1/KREUZER. Like No. 229. 1864-71..............1.00

★253 3/KREUZER. 1865-68.... 2.00

254 6/KREUZER. Sim. 1866-67.................6.00

Silver

★255 ½/GULDEN. 1864-71....30.00

GERMAN STATES

BAVARIA (Cont.)

V.F.

256 1/GULDEN. Sim.
1864-71.................40.00

257 EIN (=1) VEREINS-
THALER. Head. Rev. arms.
1864-71.................45.00

258 (Vereinsthaler). Head. Rev.
Madonna. N.D. (=1865),
1866-71...............25.00

259 (Vereinsthaler). Head. Rev.
DURCH KAMPF etc., Victory
with wreath. 1871........25.00

260 ZWEI (=2) VEREINS-
THALER. Like No. 257.
1865-69...............3600.00

Gold

E.F.

★261 ½/KRONE. 1864-69....2000.00

262 1/KRONE. Sim.
1864-69...............3500.00

No. 263   No. 264

★263 EIN (=1) GOLDGULDEN.
Head. Rev. Würzburg city
view ★. N.D. (1864)....1200.00

★264 EIN GOLDGULDEN. Head.
Rev. Würzburg city arms ★.
N.D. (1864)...........1200.00

**The undated ducats with Rev.
Crown and Rev. ZUM 2OO JAEH-
RIG etc. *are medals*.**

BENTHEIM, County
Lands near Münster. First coins 13th
century.

TECKLENBURG-
RHEDA BRANCH
Tecklenburg to Prussia 1707.

Moritz Casimir I,
In Rheda 1710-68

Copper

VG-F

1 I/PFEN(ning). MC script mon.
Rev. G(rafschaft) B(entheim)
T(ecklenburg) RHEDA LANT
MUNTZ. Value in circle. 1760.12.00

2 III/PFENNING. Sim.
1760.................12.00

VG-F

3 VI/PFENNING. Sim.
1760-61...............12.00

**Rheda was mediatized in 1805. The
other 18th century Bentheim
branches, Bentheim and Steinfurt,
issued no coins after 1750.**

BERG
On the right bank of the Rhine in Westphalia. County from 1101, duchy from
1380. United to Jülich 1423-1801 (See
Jülich-Berg for coins). Jülich absorbed
by France 1801.
   Berg was taken from Bavaria in 1806,
joined with Cleve and erected into the
grand duchy of Berg for Joachim Murat, Napoleon's marshal. In 1808 when
Murat was made King of Naples, Berg
and Cleve became part of the Kingdom
of Westphalia. In 1814 both districts
fell to Prussia.

Monetary System:

   60 stüber = 1 Reichsthaler

Maximilian IV Joseph
of Bavaria,
In Berg 1799-1806

Copper

VG-F

★1 ½/STUBER. BERGISCHE etc.
1802-05................ 4.00

Billon

★2 III/STUBER. 1801-06...... 4.00

2a —. Royal crown. 1806...... 6.00

Silver

Fine

3 XXXII EINE FEINE MARK
(=½ Reichsthaler). D.G. MAX
IOS etc. Head. Rev. BERGISCHE
etc. Value. 1803-04.......125.00

4 XVI EINE etc. (=Reichs-
thaler). Sim. 1802-05......225.00

4a —. Larger head/T.S. 1805-
06...................250.00

Joachim Murat 1806-08

Billon

Fine

★5 III/STUBER. 1806-07...... 4.00

Silver

V.F.

★6 XVI/EINE etc. (=Reichs-
thaler). 1806............650.00

★7 1 CASSATHALER (=¹/₁₈
fine mark). 1807........1400.00

**Note: Nos. 2, 2a and 5 were officially
restruck by the Kingdom of Westphalia in 1808-09 for circulation.
(=10 centimes).**

GERMAN STATES

BIRKENFELD, Principality

District in S.W. Germany erected 1817 into a principality for the benefit of Oldenburg.

Paul Friedrich August of Oldenburg 1829-53

Copper

F-VF

*1 1/PFENNIG. 1848........ 7.00

2 2/PFENNIGE. Sim. 1848... 7.00

3 3/PFENNIGE. Sim. but GR. HZL. OLDENB./FURSTTM. BIRKENFELD. 1848........ 8.00

Billon

4 1/SILBER/GROSCHEN. Arms. Rev. value. 1848....10.00

5 2½/SILBER/GROSCHEN. Sim. 1848................12.00

Nikolaus Friedrich Peter of Oldenburg 1853-1900

Copper

6 1/PFENNIG. G.H. OLDENB. F(urstenthum) BIRKENF., NFP mon. Rev. value. 1859..10.00

7 2/PFENNIGE. Sim. 1858.. 7.00

8 3/PFENNIGE. Sim. 1858.. 7.00

Billon

9 ½/SILBER/GROSCHEN. Like No. 10. 1858........10.00

*10 1/SILBER/GROSCHEN. 1858................ 6.00

11 2½/SILBER/GROSCHEN. Sim. 1858................20.00

BOCHOLT, Town

Provincial town in bishopric of Münster near Netherlands border. Local copper coinage 1616-1762.

Bocholt fell to Salm-Salm in 1803 and later passed to Prussia.

Monetary system:

21 heller = 1 stüber; 60 stüber = 1 Reichsthaler

Copper

VG-F

0.5 X (=10½!) H(eller). Like No. 1. 1762............10.00

0.5a X (=10½ heller). Sim. 1762.................10.00

*1 XXI/HEL(ler). STADT BOCHOLT CVM PRIV(ilegio = with mint right). Uprooted beech tree with beam across its trunk. Rev. value. 1761-62.................10.00

BRANDENBURG IN FRANCONIA

North Bavarian ancestral lands of the Hohenzollern rulers of Prussia and Germany. Two branches of Ansbach and Bayreuth established 1603.

Brandenburg arms: Silver, a red eagle holding sword and sceptre.

Hohenzollern arms: Quarterly, silver and black.

BRANDENBURG-ANSBACH (ANSPACH, ONOLZBACH), Margraviate

Carl Wilhelm Friedrich, Ruling Alone 1729-57 (Inherited Sayn-Altenkirchen, which see, 1741).

Copper

V.G.

1 1/PFENNING. Eagle with Hohenz. Arms on breast, B(randenburg) o(nolzbach) above. Rev. value. 1752.... 6.00

2 1½/PFENNING. Sim. 1752.................... 9.00

3 2/PFENNING. Sim. but value and date in cartouche. 1752.................... 6.00

4 4/PFENNING. Sim. 1752..10.00

Billon

VG-F

5 1 ₰ (=pfennig). 1729-57... 5.00

5a —. Two shields. Rev. blank. 1731-49................ 5.00

Note: Similar coins from Brandenburg-Bayreuth.

7 1 (kreuzer). CAR. WILH. FR. D.G.M. BRAND., bust. Rev. Eagle, 1 on breast. 1732-57.. 5.00

9 (groschen). Bust. Rev. SIS/ FELIX in wreath. On his accession 1729 (var.) .. *(F-VF)* 10.00

VG-F

*11 1/GROSCHEN. BRANDENBURG A. SCHEIDE MUNZ/, arms. Rev. value/S(chwabach Mint.) 1757............. 5.00

Silver

Fine

13 (2 groschen). Bust. Rev. EURE TREU etc. On his accession. 1729.............18.00

14 12/EINEN (=1/12)/THALER. Bust. Rev. value. N.D 6.00

*16 6 (kreuzer). 1745-54........ 8.00

18 VI/EINEN (=1/6)/REICHS-/ THALER. C.W. FRIDERIC M.B.D. BORUS etc. Bust. Rev. value. N.D..........12.00

19 VI/EINEN/REICHS/THALER. Bust. Rev. value. 1756.....10.00

20 (1/6 thaler). Bust. Rev. 9 line legend. On his death 1757 R.N....................16.00

22 (1/4 thaler). Bust. Rev. Arms. His accession 1729........24.00

24 30 KREUTZER. Bust. Rev. Arms. 1735-36........16.00

26 (1/4 thaler). Bust. Rev. new Ansbach High School. IN-AUGURATO IN/ etc. 1736 R.N....................35.00

28 30 (kreuzer). Bust. Rev. Eagle in rhombus. 1754..........15.00

30 (1/2 thaler). Busts of Carl *V.F.* Wm. Friedr. and Frederika Louise facing. Rev. PERPETVO over altar. 1729 R.N........35.00

32 (1/2 thaler). Bust. Rev. Justice with sword and balance. Erection of Ansbach Justice College. 1730................55.00

34 (1/2 thaler). Bust. Rev. Arms on mantle. 1746........35.00

36 2/3 (Reichsthaler). Bust. Rev. Arms supported by eagles. 1753..............22.50

38 (thaler). Like No. 30. 1729 R.N...............275.00

39 (thaler). Bust. Rev. Arms. 1729....................275.00

40 (thaler). Bust of Carl Wm. Friedr. Rev. Bust of Georg. 2nd centenary of Augsburg Confession. 1730 R.N......250.00

GERMAN STATES

BRANDENBURG-ANSBACH
(Cont.)

V.F.

41 (thaler). Obv. Sim. Rev. Female with cross. 1730 R.N . 350.00

41a —. Mule. Reverses of Nos. 40 and 41 . . . . 500.00

42 (thaler). Bust. Rev. Arms. 1732 . . . . 200.00

43 (thaler). Bust. Rev. Arms. 1746 . . . . 175.00

44 EIN (= 1) REICHSTHALER. Bust. Rev. Arms. 1752 . . . . 150.00

45 ZEHEN EINE etc. (= Conv. thaler). Bust. Rev. Eagle. 1754 . . . . 105.00

46 (thaler). Bust. Rev. Arms supported. 1757 . . . . 130.00

47 (thaler). Like No. 20. On his death. 1757 R.N 255.00

Gold (ducat = 3.49 gr.)

48 (ducat). Bust. Rev. Eagle. 1729 . . . . 2000.00

49 (ducat). Bust. Rev. 2 shields. 1740, 47, 50 . . . . 1100.00

50 (ducat). Bust. Rev. Eagle with shield. 1744 . . . . 1100.00

51 (ducat). Bust. Rev. Eagle over arms. 1753 . . . . 1100.00

52 (ducat). OBLECTAMINA etc. Falconer riding. Rev. Falcon. N.D 1600.00

53 (2 ducats). Like No. 48. 1729 . . . . 1750.00

53a —. No. 48 double thick. 1729 . . . . 2200.00

54 (½ Carolin). Bust. Rev. Arms. 4.9 gr. 1734-35 . . . . 1500.00

55 (Carolin). Sim. 9.7 gr. 1734-35 . . . . 1800.00

See Sayn-Altenkirchen for other coins of the reign of Carl Wilhelm Friedrich.

(Christian Friedrich Carl) Alexander, in Ansbach 1757-91, Inherited Bayreuth 1769, Sold his lands to Prussia 1791, Died 1806

Copper

VG-F

60 EIN (= 1)/PFEN/NING. Like No. 61. 1757 . . . . 3.50

★61 II/PFEN/NING. 1757 . . . . . 3.50

VG-F

63 I/PFENNING. Arms over branches/S(chwabach Mint). Rev. value. 1766 . . . . 3.50

Billon

65 (*pfennig*). 1759-91, N.D 3.50

66 (pfennig). Brandenburg and Hohenzollern arms, date above. Rev. blank. 1763 . . . . 3.50

68 1 P(fennig). Hohenzollern arms. Rev. 1–Eagle–P. 1781 . 3.50

69 I (pfennig). Sim. but I on eagle's breast. 1791 . . . . 3.50

70 4 PFENNING. Eagle in shield with arms on breast. Rev. value. 1766-89 . . . . 3.00

72 1 (kreuzer) ABRN-DGME. Head r. Rev. cwnd. eagle divides date, 1 on breast. 1761 . . . . 4.00

72.5 1/KREUZER. BRAND. ONOLZB. CONV. MUNZ. Eagle in rhombus. Rev. value in rhombus. 1765S 3.00

72.7 1 (kreuzer). 1780, 84 . . . . 3.00

★73 1/KREUZ(er). BRAND. ANSP. 1785-90 . . . . 3.00

75 2 (kreuzer). BRANDENBURG ONOLZBACHISCHE, arms. Rev. Eagle. 1760 . . . . 5.00

★76 (2½ Conv. kreuzer = 3 kreuzer Landmünze). 1767-79 . . . . 2.00

77 (2½ Conv. kreuzer). ALEXANDER D.G. MARCH. BRAND., bust. Rev. CONVENTIONS LAND- MUNZ, eagle. 1779, 85 . . . . . . 4.00

78 (2½ Conv. kr.). Obv. like No. 77. Rev. NACH DEM CONVENTIONS FVS. Eagle. 1786S 5.00

79 IIII (kreuzer). Cwnd. C.F.C.A. mon. Rev. Eagle on arms. 1758 . . . . 5.50

81 4 (kreuzer). BRANDENBURG ONOLZBACH, eagle in shield. Rev. LANDMUNZ, Hohenzollern arms. 1760 . . . . 7.00

83 5 (Conv. kreuzer). BRAND. ONOLZB etc. Shield on pedestal. Rev. 240 EINE etc. 1766, 84 . 5.50

84 5 (Conv. kreuzer). Like No. 95a. 1781 . . . . 8.00

86 6 (kreuzer). ALEXANDER etc., bust. Rev. LANDMUNZ, eagle shield. 1758 . . . . 8.00

Silver

F-VF

88 VI/EINEN (=⅙)/REICHS-/ THALER. C.F. ALEXANDER D.G.M.B. etc., bust. Rev. value. 1757 . . . . 12.00

89 VI/EINEN/REICHS/THALER. Cwnd. C.F.C.A. mon. Rev. value. 1757 . . . . 14.00

89a —. Uncwnd. mon. 1758 . . . . . 16.00

★91 10 (Conv. kreuzer). 1759 . . . . 10.00

92 10 (*Conv. kreuzer*). 1765, 80. 10.00

94 20 (Conv. kreuzer). Like No. 91. *1759-60* 14.00

★95 20 (Conv. kreuzer). 1761- 87 (var.) 7.50

95a —. 20 beneath the pedestal. 1785 . . . . 7.50

96 20 (Conv. kreuzer). ALEXANDER MARCHIO BRAND. etc., bust in rhombus. Rev. 4 fold arms supported, in rhombus. 1779 . . . . 8.50

96a —. Rev. Eagle in rhombus. 1779 . . . . 8.50

98 (¼ Conv. thaler). 1760, 63 . . 18.00

100 (¼ Conv. thaler). Margrave mounted. Rev. SECURITATI etc., eagle with lion shield. 1765 R.N 50.00

101 (¼ Conv. thaler). Bust. Rev. BRUCKBERG PORCELLAIN FABRIQUE. The Factory. 1767 R.N 75.00

102 (¼ Conv. thaler). Head. Rev. Eagle holds ribbon uniting 2 shields. Acquisition of Bayreuth. 1769. R.N 65.00

103 (¼ Conv. thaler). 1775 . . . . 25.00

104 (¼ Conv. thaler). Like No. 137. Peace of Teschen. 1779 R.N 65.00

106 8/GUTE/GROSCHEN. 1758 . . . . 20.00

GERMAN STATES

BRANDENBURG-ANSBACH
(Cont.)

V.F.

108 ⅔ (Reichsthaler). Bust. Rev. Arms supported by eagles. 1757............40.00

110 (½ *Conv. thaler*).1759-61...35.00

111 XX EINE etc. (=½ Conv. thaler). 1760...........100.00

112 (½ *Conv. thaler*). 1764.....35.00

113 (½ Conv. thaler). Bust. Rev. NACH DEM etc. 3 shields. 1765................100.00

114 (½ *Conv. thaler*). Like No. 100. 1765 R.N..........120.00

115 (½ Conv. thaler). Like No. 101. 1767 R.N..........150.00

116 (½ *Conv. thaler*) Bust. Rev. Arms supported by eagles. 1775.............40.00

117 EIN (=1) REICHSTHALER. Bust. Rev. Arms. 1757....75.00

118 ZEHEN EINE etc. (=Conv. thaler). Like No. 118b but C.F.C. ALEXANDER etc. 1758................120.00

118a —. ALEXANDER D.G. etc. 1758-63................150.00

See Brandenburg-Bayreuth and Sayn-Altenkirchen for other coins of this reign.

*118b —. 1764..............120.00

119 ZEHEN EINE etc. (=Conv. thaler). Armored bust. Rev. 3 shields. 1765-66........125.00

120 (Conv. thaler). Like No. 100. 1765 R.N.............135.00

121 ZEHEN etc. (=Conv. thaler). Nude bust. Rev. 3 shields. 1767-68................120.00

V.F.

122 (Conv. thaler). Like No. 146. Acquisition of Bayreuth. 1769 R.N..............180.00

123 (Conv. thaler). Like No. 102. 1769 R.N..............225.00

124 ZEHEN etc. (=Conv. thaler). Head. Rev. Arms. 1769, 71..................120.00

125 ZEHEN etc. (=Conv. thaler). Head. Rev. Lion holds shield. 3 var. 1773-74..........120.00

125a —. Rev. Eagle holds shield. 1773.................135.00

126 (Conv. thaler). Bust. Rev. SYLVARUM etc. Trees. Prize for Foresters. 1774......300.00

127 (Conv. thaler). Bust. Rev. BELOHNVNG etc. Prize. 1775................ 550.00

128 ZEHEN etc. (=Conv. thaler). Armored bust. Rev. Arms. (5 var.) 1775-76........120.00

128a —. Head. 1775................120.00

129 ZEHEN etc. (=Conv. thaler). Bust. Rev. helmeted arms. 1777.................120.00

130 X.E–F.M (=Conv. thaler). Bust. Rev. Arms in 2 order chains. 1778.............135.00

131 X.E.F.M. (=Conv. thaler). Bust. Rev. Arms supported by 2 eagles. 1778........120.00

132 X E.F.M. (=Conv. thaler). Bust. Rev. Arms/trophies. 1778.................150.00

133 (Conv. thaler). Bust. Rev. Star of (revived) Order of Red Eagle. 1779........225.00

134 (Conv. thaler). Bust. Rev. Eagle in 2 circles of shields. 1779.................120.00

135 ZEHEN etc. (=Conv. thaler). Bust. Rev. Lion holds eagle shield/SCHWABACH. 1779..180.00

136 (Conv. thaler). 9 lines: DOM PRO etc. Rev. VIRTVTE etc. Germania discards weapons. Peace of Teschen. 1779 R.N...................135.00

137 (Conv. thaler). DEO CON-SERVATORI etc. Germania at altar. Rev. . . . ./PACIS/ TESCHINENSIS. Peace of Teschen. 1779 R.N......135.00

138 ZEHEN etc. (=Conv. thaler). Armored bust. Rev. Eagle in draped shield. 1780....120.00

138a —. Head (2 var.). 1784, 85.120.00

139 ZEHEN etc. (=Conv. thaler). Bust. Rev. 4 fold arms supported on mantle. 1786..120.00

Gold (ducat=3.49 gr.)

140 (ducat) Brandenburg eagle and Saxon arms in 2 shields. Rev. NUPTIARUM etc. His wedding. 1754 R.N.....1300.00

V.F.

141 (ducat). Bust. Rev. Eagle shield. 1757...........950.00

142 (*ducat*). Bust. Rev. Arms. 1762...................950.00

143 (ducat). Bust. Rev. 3 shields. 1763.................950.00

143a —. 1777.............1300.00

*144 (ducat). Like No. 100. 1765 R.N.............1500.00

145 (ducat). Like No. 102. 1769 R.N.............1500.00

*146 (ducat). Acquisition of Bayreuth. 1769 R.N.....1100.00

147 (ducat). Knight at altar. Rev. Legend SP.D.D./CHR. FRID etc. Homage. 1769 R.N..................1100.00

148 (ducat). Like No. 133. 1779.................1400.00

149 (2 ducats). Like No. 140. 1754.................1600.00

150 (*Carolin*). Bust. Rev. Arms in order chain. 9.7 gr. 1758, 66...................1800.00

BRANDENBURG-BAYREUTH
(CULMBACH)

Arms of Burgraviate of Nürnberg (a title of this branch of the family): Gold, a black lion in a border gobony (checkered) red and silver.

Friedrich II 1735-63

Copper

VG-F

*1 1/HEL/LER. Script F cwnd. Rev. value. 1738-45........4.00

*2 HELLER. Obv. sim. Rev. BAYREU/THER/HELLER. 1750-53..............4.00

GERMAN STATES

BRANDENBURG-BAYREUTH
(Cont.)

VG-F

4 ½/KREUZER. Obv. sim. Rev. value/FRAENCKISCH/ etc. 1752................ 9.00

5 1/KREUZER. sim. 1752... 9.00

Billon

*8 1 ₰ (=1 pfen'nig). Arms of Hohenzollern and Burgraviate of Nurnberg. 1736-50...... 4.00

8a —. Rev. blank. 1747-54.... 4.00

*9 GUTER (good) PFENNIG. 1751-53................. 4.00

*11 II/GUTE PF(ennig). Eagle divides C.L.–R(uckdeschel, MM at Bayreuth. 1742-65). Rev. value, BR: LAND MUNZ. 1751-52.......... 4.00

12 3 pf (=3 pfennig). 1736, 41, 49.............. 4.00

14 1 (kreuzer). 1741, 43....... 4.00

14a —. Arms. Rev. I in orb/ C.L.R. 1746.............. 4.00

*16 1 (kreuzer). 1745-53........ 4.00

F-VF

*17 6 ₰ (=6 pfennig). N.D..... 4.00

19 48 (=1/48 Reichsthaler =6 pf.). V.G.G. FRIEDRICH MARG. etc. Eagle. Rev. ST.P.C. etc. Hohenz. arms/48 (var.). 1736-46................ 4.00

20 48/EINEN (=1/48)/REICHS-/ THALER. Eagle with Hohenz. Arms on breast. Rev. value, C.L.R. 1748-51........... 4.00

21 24 (=1/24 thaler). FRIEDERICUS etc. Bust. Rev. IN MEMOR HOMAGII, arms. On his accession. 1735........ (F-VF)10.00

VG-F

22 24 (=1/24 thaler). V.G.G. FRIEDERICH MARGG Z. BRAND CULMB. 24 in orb. Rev. NACH etc. Eagle with Hohenz. Arms on breast. 1736-37. 6.00

23 24 (=1/24 thaler). 1738-40................. 5.00

24 24/EINEN (=1/24)/REICHS-/ THALER. Bust. Rev. value. 1752................ 7.00

*25 24 (=1/24 thaler). 1752-53................. 5.00

26 24 (=1/24 thaler). 1758-60, 63................. 7.00

28 IIII KREUZ(er). 1762-63................. 10.00

Silver

30 12/EINEN (=1/12)/REICHS-/ THALER. Eagle. Rev. value. 1746-47.............. 10.00

31 12/EINEN (=1/12)/REICHS/ THALER. FRIDERICUS D.G. M.B. etc. Bust. Rev. LAND MUNZ. value. 1747-58....... 10.00

33 VI/EINEN (=1/6)/REICHS-/ THALER. Bust. Rev. value. 1752, 57-59.............. 10.00

34 VI/EINEN (=1/6)/REICHS/ THALER. Mon. Rev. value. 1758................. 25.00

*35 20 (kreuzer). FRIDERICUS M.B. DUX BORUS etc. Bust in wreath. Rev. Eagle on pedestal. 1760-63................. 10.00

F-VF

36 LX EINE etc. (=20 Conv. kreuzer). FRIDERICVS etc. Bust. Rev. NATVS/etc. On his death. 1763 R.N................. 40.00

*37 30 kreuzer. 1735-37, N.D....20.00

V.F.

39 ZWANZIG EINE etc. (=½ Conv. thaler). Bust. Rev. Arms/ BAYREUTH. 1754-55........ 50.00

*40 ⅔ (Reichsthaler). Bust. Rev. Arms. 1758.......... 45.00

41 XX EINE etc. (=½ Conv. thaler). 1760............ ——

42 XX EINE etc. (=½ Conv. thaler). Gen. like No. 36. 1763 R.N............... 50.00

43 EIN (=1) REICHSTHALER. Bust. Rev. Eagle on shield and trophies. 1752, 57 (var.)............... 100.00

44 ZEHEN etc. (=Conv. thaler). Bust. Rev. Arms in branches, trophies below/BAYREUTH. 1754-55, 60............. 100.00

45 ZEHEN etc. (=Conv. thaler). Bust. Rev. Arms supported by lions. 1755, 60........ =150.00

46 X EINE etc. (=Conv. thaler). Bust. Rev. PRINCEPS etc. On his death. 1763 R.N....... 300.00

Gold

47 (ducat). Bust. Rev. Arms. 1735, 46............... 1000.00

48 (ducat). Friedrich mounted. Rev. Order. 1746........ 1000.00

49 5 THLR (thaler). Head. Rev. Arms, mon. 1746...1300.00

Friedrich Christian 1763-69

Copper

VG-F

50 1/HELLER. FC script mon. Rev. I/BAYR./HELLER/ 1767................ 4.00

50a —. w/out BAYR. 1767....... ——

BRANDENBURG-BAYREUTH (Cont.)

Billon

VG-F

51 (pfennig). Eagle and Hohenzollern arms in 2 shields.
Rev. blank. 1763-68 . . . . 4.00

52 GUTER (=good) PFENNIG.
Like No. 9. 1764 . . . . 4.00

53 1 (kreuzer). FRID. CHRIST.
M.B.D. etc. Bust. Rev. Eagle
with 1 on breast. 1764-68 . . . 4.00

55 2½ (Conv. kreuzer = 3 kreuzer
landmünze). BAYR. CONV.
LANDMUNZ, FC mon. Rev. Eagle
shield. *1765-68* 4.00

56 (groschen). Bust. Rev. legend.
On homage giving 1765 . . . . . 9.00

57 IIII/KREUZ(er). Eagle shield
on pedestal in which is 300.
Rev. value/B(ayreuth),
C.L.R. 1763 . . . . 6.00

58 5 *(Conv. kreuzer)*. 1763-68 . . . 9.00

Silver

F-VF

59 *12/EINEN (=1/12)/REICHS/
THALER* 1763 . . . . 10.00

60 10 (Conv. kreuzer). Like No.
63. *1763, 65* 9.00

60a —. Like No. 63a. *1766, 68* . . . 9.00

61 *VI/EINEN (=1/6)/REICHS-/
THALER*. Bust. Rev. value.
1763 . . . . 12.00

62 *XV (Conv. kreuzer)*. 1763 . . 15.00

★63 20 (Conv. kreuzer).
1763-65 . . . . 7.50

63a —. Rev. Eagle shield on
pedestal. *1766, 68* 7.50

64 *30 (Conv. kreuzer)*. 1767 . . . 15.00

V-VF

66 *XX EINE etc. (= ½ Conv.
thaler)*. 1763, 66, 67 . . . . . . 60.00

68 ZEHEN etc. (=Conv. thaler).
Bust. Rev. Arms/trophies/
BAYREUTH. 1763 . . . . 150.00

68a —. 1766 . . . . 100.00

69 ZEHEN etc. (=Conv. thaler).
Bust. Rev. Arms supported.
1766, 68 . . . . 100.00

V.F.

70 (Convention thaler). Bust.
Rev. PRINCEPS/PIVS etc.
On his death. 1769 . . . . 200.00

Gold

71 (ducat). Bust. Rev. Arms.
1763 . . . . 1000.00

72 (ducat). Bust. Rev. GLORIA
PRINCIPIVM, bible, cross and
sword. 1764 . . . . 1000.00

73 (ducat). Margrave galloping.
Rev. Star of Black Eagle
Order. 1767 . . . . 1000.00

Alexander of Brandenburg-Ansbach 1757-91, In Bayreuth 1769-91

Billon

VG-F

75 I/PFENNIG. Hohenz arms.
Rev. value/B(ayreuth).
1780-83 . . . . 4.00

78 *4/PFENNIG*. Eagle/B. Rev.
value. 1779 . . . . 6.00

80 *4/PFENNIG*. Like No. 75.
1780 . . . . 6.00

82 1/KREUZER. Like No. 75.
1785-86B 4.00

★83 1/KREUZ(er).
1789 s(chwabach Mint) 6.00

84 *(2½ Conv. kreuzer)*. Bust.
Rev. Eagle. 1779B 7.00

85 (2½ Conv. kreuzer). Arms.
Rev. BR./BAYREUTH/LAND.
M/date. 1780-86 . . . . 4.00

Silver

V.F.

90 10 (Conv. kreuzer). Bust.
Rev. Eagle shield on pedestal,
BAYREUTH. 1780 . . . . 8.00

92 20 (Conv. kreuzer). Like No.
90. 1780, 82 . . . . 9.00

92a —. 1785 . . . . 11.00

92b —. 20 beneath the pedestal.
1787 . . . . 14.00

95 ZEHEN etc. (=Conv. thaler).
Bust. Rev. Lion holds 4 fold
arms/BAYREUTH. 1779, 82,
83 (var.) 160.00

96 ZEHEN etc. (=Conv. thaler).
Bust. Rev. 4 fold arms supported by eagles/B(ayreuth).
1786 . . . . 160.00

BRANDENBURG-ANSBACH-BAYREUTH

Friedrich Wilhelm II of Prussia, In Ansbach-Bayreuth 1791-97

Billon

VG-F

1 (pfennig). Cwnd. FWR mon.
divides date/s(chwabach).
Rev. eagle with FWR on breast.
1792-96 . . . . 4.00

2 1/PFEN/NIG. Like No. 9.
1796-97B 10.00

★3 1/KREUZ(er). 1792-97S,
96B, also 1797B with ANSB . . 4.00

5 III/KREUZER. Eagle on
trophies. Rev. K. PR. ANSP.
BAYR. L.M., value. 1794-
97S 4.00

6 VI/KREUZER. Like No. 14.
1797 . . . . 9.00

Silver

V.F.

7 XXI EINE etc. (=gulden).
FRIEDR. WILHELM KOENIG VON
PREUSSEN, bust. Rev. Eagle
shield supported by wildmen.
1792, 94S 65.00

8 ZEHN EINE etc. (=Conv.
thaler). Sim. 1794-96 . . . . . . 200.00

Friedrich Wilhelm III of Prussia, In Ansbach-Bayreuth 1797-1805

Billon

Fine

9 1/PFEN/NIG. Cwnd. FWR
mon. Rev. value/B. 1798-
1803B 4.00

★11 1/KREUZ(er). 1798-1800B . 4.00

★12 1/KREU/ZER. 1802-04B . . . 4.00

13 III/KREUZER. Like No. 5.
1798-1802B 7.50

GERMAN STATES

BRANDENBURG-ANSBACH-BAYREUTH (Cont.)

	Fine
*14 VI/KREUZER. 1798-1802B	8.50

Gold

	VF-EF
*15 (ducat). Fürstenzeche Mine. 1803	RRR

See Prussia for similar coins of other provinces.

Ansbach and Bayreuth were ceded to Bavaria in 1805.

BRAUNSCHWEIG. See Brunswick.

BREMEN
(REIP. BREMENSIS, FREIE HANSESTADT BREMEN), Free City

Upriver seaport in N.W. Germany. Founded about 787. First coins about 1369. Became a free Imperial city 1646. Absorbed by France 1806, but regained its independence 1813.

Arms: Red, a silver key.
Monetary System: 5 schwaren = 1 grote; 72 grote = 1 Thaler Gold; 5 Thaler Gold = 1 Louis d'or.

Copper

	Fine
*1 1/SCHWA/REN. 1719-97, 1859 (var.)	3.00

*2 2½/SCHWA/REN. 1797-1866 (var.)	3.00

	Fine
*3 ½/GROTEN. 1841	8.00

Billon

5 (½ grote). Obv. like No. 6 but key divides 17-63. Rev. CRVX. CHR. NOST: SAL, quatrefoil	4.00
6 ½/GROT(e). MON. NOV. REIP. BREM. Cwnd. key. Rev. value, date. 1781, 87	4.00
6a —. Key divides date. Rev. value. 1789	4.00
*8 1 (grote). In name of Franz I. 1745-64	3.00
*11 1/GROTEN. 1840	3.00

Silver

*14 12 (=¹⁄₁₂ Rthlr. =6 grote). 1763	7.00

	V.F.
15 6/GROTE. Like No. 15b but fineness 11L. 15G. 1840	6.00
15a —. Like No. 19. 1857	6.00
*15b —. 1861	7.00

*19 12/GROTE. 1840-46	10.00

	V.F.
19a —. Legend begins at bottom. 1859-60	9.00
20 24 GROT(e). BREMER STATGELT, cwnd. arms. Rev. FRANCISCVS etc. Imp. eagle. 1748-49	18.00
21 36/GROTE. Oval arms. Rev. value. 1840-59	25.00

*22 36/GROTE. 1859, 64	35.00
23 (48 grote). MON. LIB. REIP. BREMENSIS, arms. Rev. Imp. eagle. *14 gr.* 1748	50.00
24 48 (grote). MONETA NOVA etc., arms. Rev. Imp. eagle. 1753	15.00
25 (thaler). No. 23 on thick planchet. 1743	100.00

	VF-EF
*26 EIN (=1)/THALER. Obv. like No. 28. Rev. ⋆. 50th anniv. German liberation. 1863	50.00

	E.F.
*27 GEDENKTHALER (=private medal). Opening of new Exchange. 1864	110.00

GERMAN STATES

BREMEN (Cont.)

*28 EIN (=1)/THALER. *E.F.*
2nd German shooting fest.
1865 . . . . .50.00

29 EIN (=1) THALER. Obv.
sim. Rev. . . . /FRIEDEN/etc.
Victory. 1871 . . . . .40.00

Gold (ducat = 3.49 gr.)

V.F.
*30 (ducat). 1745, 46 . . . . .1100.00

31 2 (ducats). Sim. 1746 . . . . .1600.00

BRESLAU (WRATISLAVA, VRATISLAVIENSIS), Bishopric

The bishops of Breslau in Silesia (now Poland) became princes of the Empire and obtained the mint right in 1290. Most of the bishopric (except certain portions in Austria) was secularized in 1810-11.

Philipp Gotthard, Prince of Schaffgotsch, Bishop 1747-95

Silver
V.F.

1 (½ Conv. thaler). PHIL. GOTT-HARD D.G. PR. DE SCHAFGOTSCH, clerical bust. Rev. Arms. 14 gr. 1754 . . . . .90.00

2 (Conv. thaler). Sim. 1753, 70, 73, 77 . . . . .150.00

Gold (ducat = 3.49 gr.)

3 (ducat). Sim. 1748-77 . . . . . .900.00

4 (5 ducats). Sim. 1748 . . . . . . .RRR

Joseph (Christian), Prince of Hohenlohe-Waldenburg, Bishop 1795-1823

Silver
V.F.

5 (½ Conv. thaler). IOSEPH D.G. PRIN AB HOHENLOHE etc., bust. Rev. EPISC. WRATISL. etc., arms. 1796 . . . . 400.00

Gold
VF-EF

6 (ducat). Sim. 1796 . . . . . .1400.00

BRETZENHEIM (BREZENHEIM), Principality

Created 1790 for the favorite natural son of Elector Carl Theodor of Pfalz-Bayern.
Mediatized to Hesse-Darmstadt 1803.

Carl August 1790-1803

Silver
V.F.

1 10 (Conv. kreuzer). CAR. AVG. D.G. S.R.I. PRINC. DE BREZEN HEIM, bust. Rev. 5 fold arms with pretzel middle shield. 1790 . . . . .60.00

2 20 (Conv. kreuzer). Sim. 1790 . . . . .30.00

3 (½ Conv. thaler). Sim. but arms supported by ostriches. 14 gr. 1790 . . . . .90.00

4 (Conv. thaler). Sim. 1790 . .275.00

Gold

VF-EF
*5 (ducat). 1790 . . . . .2200.00

BRUNSWICK (BRAUNSCHWEIG) -LÜNEBURG, Electorate

The first coinage of the north central German duchy of Brunswick appeared in the 12th century. Ernst August, of the Lüneburg-Celle line, was elevated to the rank of elector in 1692. His son, Georg Ludwig, became King of England through inheritance in 1714.

Arms: The most common Brunswick device was the leaping white Westphalian horse on a red field.

Monetary System: Usual North German denominations; and 2 thaler = 1 goldgulden.

Georg II, King of Great Britain and Elector of Brunswick-Lüneburg 1727-60

Copper

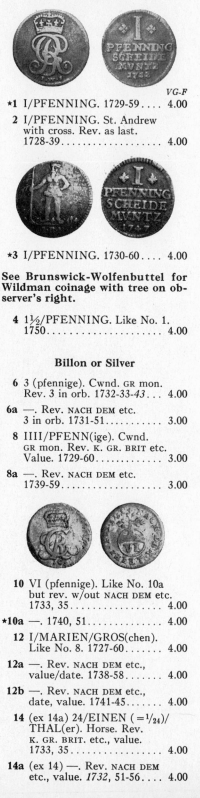

VG-F
*1 I/PFENNING. 1729-59 . . . . 4.00

2 I/PFENNING. St. Andrew with cross. Rev. as last. 1728-39 . . . . 4.00

*3 I/PFENNING. 1730-60 . . . . 4.00

See **Brunswick-Wolfenbuttel** for Wildman coinage with tree on observer's right.

4 1½/PFENNING. Like No. 1. 1750 . . . . 4.00

Billon or Silver

6 3 (pfennige). Cwnd. GR mon. Rev. 3 in orb. 1732-33-*43* . . . 4.00

6a —. Rev. NACH DEM etc. 3 in orb. 1731-51 . . . . 3.00

8 IIII/PFENN(ige). Cwnd. GR mon. Rev. K. GR. BRIT etc. Value. 1729-60 . . . . 3.00

8a —. Rev. NACH DEM etc. 1739-59 . . . . 3.00

10 VI (pfennige). Like No. 10a but rev. w/out NACH DEM etc. 1733, 35 . . . . 4.00

*10a —. 1740, 51 . . . . 4.00

12 I/MARIEN/GROS(chen). Like No. 8. 1727-60 . . . . . 4.00

12a —. Rev. NACH DEM etc., value/date. 1738-58 . . . . 4.00

12b —. Rev. NACH DEM etc., date, value. 1741-45 . . . . 4.00

14 (ex 14a) 24/EINEN (=1/24)/THAL(er). Horse. Rev. K. GR. BRIT. etc., value. 1733, 35 . . . . 4.00

14a (ex 14) —. Rev. NACH DEM etc., value. *1732,* 51-56 . . . . 4.00

BRUNSWICK-LÜNEBURG (Cont.)

VG-F

16 24/EINEN/THAL(er).
Like No. 8. 1735.......... 4.00

16a —. Rev. NACH DEM etc.,
value. 1741-48-*51*......... 4.00

Silver

Fine

18 II/MARIEN/GROS (chen).
Like No. 8. 1727-40-*42*..... 5.00

18a —. Like No. 12a. 1741-60... 5.00

18b —. Like No. 12b. 1740-53... 5.00

20 II/MARIEN/GROS(chen).
GEORGE II D.G.M. BR. etc.
value. Rev. Wildman. 1730-
60...................... 6.00

23 12/EINEN (=1/12) /THAL(er).
Like No. 14. 1732-35...... 6.00

23a —. Rev. value/N.D. LEIPZ/
FVS. 1738-40............. 6.00

23b —. Like No. 14a. 1741-52,
57..................... 6.00

V.F.

25 IIII/MARIEN/GROS (chen).
Arms. Rev. value. 1727-35... 7.00

25a —. Rev. value/N.D. LEIPZ./
FVS. 1738............... 8.00

★25b —. Rev. NACH DEM etc.,
value. *1745, 46, 52*........ 9.00

27 IIII/MARIEN/GROS(chen).
Cwnd. GR mon. Rev. value.
1727-29................Scarce

★28 IIII/MARIEN/GROSCH(en).
Like No. 20. 1730-60......9.00

30 R(1/8)T (=1/8 species thaler =
1/6 thaler). Bust. Rev. 4 shields
cruciform. 1728...........Rare

31 R(1/8)T. Arms. Rev. horse.
1730....................Rare

32 1/6 (thaler). Bust. Rev. 4
shields cruciform. 1727, *58*...24.00

32a —. Rev. arms. No mint
standard shown. 1730-36....14.00

32b —. Sim. but Leipziger fuss.
1739-40.................14.00

32c —. Sim. but Reichs fuss.
1746....................14.00

V.F.

33 1/6 *(thaler)*. Bust. Rev. horse.
1739....................Rare

★34 1/6 (thaler). 4 shields cruciform.
Rev. St. Andrew. 1729....16.00

34a —. Obv. arms. No mint
standard shown. 1730-32..14.00

34b —. Sim. but Reichs fuss.
1746-59.................14.00

36 1/6 (thaler). 4 shields cruciform.
Rev. horse. 1727-29......16.00

36a —. Obv. Arms. 1730-32...16.00

36.5 1/6 *(thaler)*. 4 shields cruciform.
Rev. Wildman. 1727......Rare

37 6 (mariengroschen). Arms.
Rev. Wildman. 1727-36... 9.00

★37a —. With FEIN (1/6) SILB
on obv. 1737-60......... 9.00

39 R(1/4)T (=1/4 Species thaler =
1/3 thaler). Like No. 32.
1728....................35.00

39a —. Rev. arms. 1732.....30.00

40 R(1/4)T. Arms. Rev. Wildman.
1730-54.................Scarce

40.5 R(1/4)T. Arms. Rev. horse.
1732, 39................Scarce

40.7 (1/4 Species thaler). WILHELMA
etc., her bust. Rev. DIVAE/
CAROLINAE etc. On death of
his wife. 1737 RN........Rare

41 1/8 (thaler). Like No. 32.
1727-29.................20.00

41a —. Like No. 32a.
1730-36-*46*.............20.00

42 1/8 *(thaler)*. Like No. 33.
1730, 36................Rare

43 1/8 (thaler). Like No. 36a.
1732-36.................20.00

43a —. With N.D. REICHS etc.
1754....................Scarce

43.5 1/8 *(thaler)*. 4 shields cruciform.
Rev. St. Andrew. 1729...Scarce

44 1/8 (thaler). Like No. 34a.
1731-34.................22.00

44a —. With N.D. LEIPZ. etc.
1740....................Scarce

44b (ex 44a) —. With N.D.
REICHS etc. 1740-51.......22.00

44c —. 1757-58 I.W.S. 22.00

V.F.

45 1/8 (thaler). Arms.
Rev. Wildman. 1730-36...16.00

45a —. (=) 12 (mariengroschen).
1737-60.................14.00

46 VIII/GUTE/GROSCH(en).
Bust. Rev. value. 1742....22.50

47 VIII/GUTE/GROSCH(en).
Value. Rev. Horse. 1742...22.50

48 R(1/2)T (=1/2 Species
thaler =2/3 thaler). Bust.
Rev. Arms. 1732.........Rare

48.5 R(1/2)T. Arms. Rev.
Wildman. 1731-35........Rare

48.7 R(1/2)T. Arms. Rev. horse.
1740....................Rare

49 2/3 (thaler). Like No. 32.
1727-29-*39*.............30.00

49a —. Like No. 32a. 1730-40..25.00

49b —. Like No. 32b. 1739....25.00

49c —. Like No. 32c. 1740-52..25.00

49d —. Diff. arms. 1752-54....25.00

50 2/3 (thaler). Like No. 36
(var.). 1727-29...........28.00

50a —. Obv. 4 fold arms in
single shield, value.
No mint standard shown.
1730-37 C.P.S. 28.00

50b —. Sim. but value on rev.
1730-49.................28.00

50c —. With N.D. LEIPZ. F.
1738-40.................28.00

50d —. With N.D. REICHS. F.
1740-60.................28.00

50e —. Baroque arms.
1744-60 I.B.H............28.00

52 2/3 (thaler =) 24 (mariengroschen). 4 shields
cruciform. Rev. Wildman.
1727-29, *31*.............Scarce

52a —. Obv. 4 fold arms in
single shield. 1730-43.....26.00

52b —. Obv. baroque arms.
1743-60 I.B.H. 26.00

54 (1/2 Species thaler). Like
No. 40.7. 1737 RN........Rare

56 XVI/GUTE/GROSCH(en).
Like No. 46. 1741-56.....85.00

57 XVI/GUTE/GROSCH(en).
Like No. 47. *1739*-40-56...60.00

58 XVI/GUTE/GROSCH(en).
Arms. Rev. value. 1741-42.Rare

59 XXIV/GUTE/GROSCH(en =
1 Reichsthaler, but says 2/3).
Value. Rev. horse. 1750....95.00

61 (thaler). Bust. Rev. Arms
in garter, supported.
1727-29................140.00

62 (thaler). Bust. Rev. 4 shields
cruciform. 1729.........200.00

63 (thaler). Bust. Rev. Arms,
no supporters. 1730-51....140.00

64 (thaler). 4 shields cruciform.
Rev. horse. 1727, 29 ....130.00

64a —. Date in RN. 1727, 29.130.00

BRUNSWICK-LÜNEBURG (Cont.)

V.F.

65 (thaler). Arms in garter, supported. Rev. Horse. 1727, 29 . . . . 160.00

66 (thaler). Arms, no supporters. Rev. Horse. 1730-60 . . . . . 135.00

66a —. Date in RN. 1730-53 . . 160.00

67 (thaler). Obv. like No. 65. Rev. St. Andrew. 1727, 29 . . . . 150.00

68 (thaler). Obv. like No. 66. Rev. St. Andrew. 1730-60 . 130.00

69 (thaler). Obv. like No. 65. Rev. Wildman. 1727-29 . . 130.00

70 (thaler). Obv. like No. 64. Rev. Wildman. 1727, 29 . . 130.00

71 (thaler). Obv. like No. 66. Rev. Wildman. 1730-55 . . 130.00

72 (Species thaler). Like No. 40.7 1737 RN . . . . *Rare*

E.F.

73 (Mining thaler). Arms. Rev. Swan. WEISSER SCHWAN Mine. 1744-56 . . . . 400.00

74 (Mining thaler). Arms. Rev. mining scene. CRONENBVRGS GLVCK Mine. 1745-52 . . . . 400.00

75 (Mining thaler). Arms. Rev. lute player. LAUTENTHALS GLVCK Mine. 1745-56 . . . . 400.00

76 (Mining thaler). Arms. Rev. mining scene. GVTE DES HERRN Mine. 1745-56 . . . . 400.00

77 (Mining thaler). Arms. Rev. Rainbow over mine. REGENBOGEN Mine. 1745-52 . . . . 400.00

78 (Mining thaler). Arms. Rev. cwnd. pillar in front of mine. BLEYFELD Mine. 1750, 52 . . . . 400.00

79 (Mining thaler). Arms. Rev. Pillars of Hercules, mining scene. KÖNIG CARL Mine. 1752 . . . . 400.00

Gold (ducat = 3.49 tr.)

V.F.

80 (¼ ducat). Cwnd. GR mon. Rev. Horse. 1730 . . . . 275.00

81 (¼ ducat). Head. Rev. Horse. 1737 . . . . 300.00

81a —. *Rev. arms. 1737* . . . . . . *Query*

82 (½ ducat). Bust. Rev. Arms. 1730-37 . . . . . 500.00

83 (ducat). Sim. 1730 . . . . . . 900.00

84 (ducat). Sim. but with AUR. HERC. (Harzgold). 1747 . 1200.00

85 (ducat). 4 shields cruciform. Rev. Horse. 1728, 30 . . . . 900.00

86 (ducat). Sim. but AUR HERC. 1727, 29 . . . . 1200.00

86.5 (ducat). Bust. Rev. 4 shields cruciform. EX/AUR. HERC. 1729 . . . . 1200.00

V.F.

86.5a —. W/out EX/AUR. etc. 1729 . . . . 1200.00

87 (ducat). Arms. Rev. Horse. 1730-38 . . . . 900.00

88 (ducat). Sim. but EX AUR HERCIN. 1730-56 . . . . . . 1200.00

89 1/DUCAT. Bust. Rev. value. 1751 . . . . . . 1000.00

90 1/DUCAT. Horse. Rev. value. 1751 . . . . . . 1200.00

90a —. EX AURO etc. 1751 . . . . . *Rare*

91 ¼/GOLDG(ulden) = ½ THAL(er). Head. Rev. value. 1754-57 . . . . . 275.00

92 ½/GOLD/GULDEN = 1 THAL(er). Sim. 1749-56 . . . . 500.00

93 I/GOLD/GULDEN = 2 THAL(er). Sim. 1749-54 . . . . 600.00

94 I/GOLD/GULDEN = 2 THAL(er). Arms. Rev. value. 1749-56 . . . . . 600.00

95 II/GOLD/GULDEN = 4 THALER. Like No. 91. 1749-54 . . . . 900.00

96 II/GOLD/GULDEN = 4 THALER. Like No. 94. 1749-55 . . . . 900.00

97 V THALER. Arms. Rev. value. 1758 . . . . . . 1200.00

98 IIII/GOLD/GULDEN = 8 THALER. Like No. 91. 1749-52 . . . . 1200.00

98a —. Head. 1750 . . . . *Rare*

Georg III, King of Great Britain 1760-1820,

Elector of Brunswick-Lüneburg 1760-1807,

Ousted from German possessions by Napoleon 1807-13.

See Westphalia.

In 1814 Brunswick-Lüneburg became the kingdom of Hannover. For Georg III's coinage 1813-20 see Hannover.

Copper

VG-F

★100 1/PFENN(ig). 1761-1806 . . 3.00

101 1½/PFENNING. Sim. 1792 . . . . 6.00

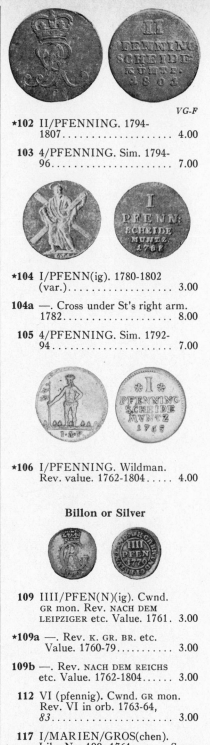

VG-F

★102 II/PFENNING. 1794-1807 . . . . 4.00

103 4/PFENNING. Sim. 1794-96 . . . . 7.00

★104 I/PFENN(ig). 1780-1802 (var.) 3.00

104a —. Cross under St's right arm. 1782 . . . . 8.00

105 4/PFENNING. Sim. 1792-94 . . . . 7.00

★106 I/PFENNING. Wildman. Rev. value. 1762-1804 . . . . . 4.00

Billon or Silver

109 IIII/PFEN(N)(ig). Cwnd. GR mon. Rev. NACH DEM LEIPZIGER etc. Value. 1761. 3.00

★109a —. Rev. K. GR. BR. etc. Value. 1760-79 . . . . 3.00

109b —. Rev. NACH DEM REICHS etc. Value. 1762-1804 . . . . . . 3.00

112 VI (pfennig). Cwnd. GR mon. Rev. VI in orb. 1763-64, 83 . . . . 3.00

117 I/MARIEN/GROS(chen). Like No. 109. 1761 . . . . . . *Scarce*

117a (ex117)—.Like No. 109a. 1760-71-77 . . . . 3.00

117b (ex 117a)—. Like No. 109b. 1762-1804 . . . . 3.00

121 24/EINEN (=1/24)/THAL(er). Horse. Rev. NACH DEM REICHS etc. Value. 1760-69 . . . . 3.00

121a —. Leipziger fuss. 1760 . . . . *Rare*

BRUNSWICK-LÜNEBURG (Cont.)

Silver

VG-F

123 II/MARIEN/GROSCH(en). Like No. 109. 1760, 62..... 4.00

124 II/MARIEN/GROSCH(en). Value. Rev. Wildman (var.). 1763-85............... 5.00

126 12/EINEN (=¹⁄₁₂)/THAL(er). Horse. Rev. NACH DEM LEIP-ZIGER etc. Value. 1760..... 6.00

★126a —. Like No. 121. 1760-1807................... 4.00

★128 IIII/MARIEN/GROSCH(en). *V.F.* 1762-88................. 8.00

130 ⅙ (thaler). Arms. Rev. St. Andrew. 1761-90......... 20.00

130a —. Sim. but arms and titles changed after abandonment of claim to France. 1804... 45.00

132 ⅙ (thaler =) 6 (marien-groschen). Date in outer legend. 1762-84......... 20.00

132a —. Arms divide date. 1785-91................. 20.00

★132b —. Date in outer legend. 1793-1800.............. 20.00

132c (ex 132a) —. Obv. like No. 130a. 1804......... 45.00

134 ⅙ (thaler). Bare bust. Rev. arms. 1773-82...... 20.00

134a —. Armored bust. 1776-79................. 18.00

★134b —. Bare bust. 1783-1800..30.00

V.F.

★137 ⅙ (thaler). 1786-89...... 20.00

138 ⅙ (thaler). Bust. Legend includes BRIT. FR. & HIB. REX. Rev. 4 fold arms with center shield. 1800-04........... 20.00

138a —. w/out French arms or titles. 1802-04........... 40.00

138b —. Rev. like No. 137. 1807................. 25.00

143 ⅓ (thaler). Like No. 130. 1764-93............... 20.00

★143a —. Like No. 130a. 1804... 50.00

145 ⅓ (thaler =) 12 (marien-groschen). Like No. 132. 1762-84................. 35.00

145a —. 1785-89............. 35.00

146 ⅓ (thaler). Arms. Rev. horse. 1767............. 30.00

147 ⅓ (thaler). Bare bust. Rev. arms w/out supporters. 1774-82................. 38.00

147a —. Rev. arms supported. 1778-79................. 38.00

147b —. Rev. date over cwnd. arms. 1785-88............. 38.00

147c —. Rev. cwn. over arms divides date. 1789-1800.... 38.00

147d —. Rev. 4 fold arms with center shield. 1803-04.... 38.00

150 ½/THALER/CASSENGELD. Bust. Rev. value. 1801... 125.00

152 24/MARIEN/GROSCH(en). Arms. Rev. value. 1761-1800................. 24.00

154 ⅔ (thaler =) 24 (marien-groschen). Arms. Rev. Wildman. 1762-84............. 26.00

154a —. 1785-89............. 26.00

156 ⅔ (thaler). Bust. Rev. Arms supported. 1776-81....... 30.00

V.F.

158 ⅔ (thaler). Head. Rev. arms w/out supporters. 1772-1800.............. 25.00

160 ⅔ (thaler). Head. Rev. ⅔. 1801-02.............30.00

162 ⅔ (thaler). Square arms. Rev. ⅔. 1801-05......... 30.00

★162a —. 1805-07............ 45.00

164 (thaler). Like No. 130. 1761-73.............125.00

165 (Mining thaler). Arms. Rev. lute player. LAVTEN THALS GLVCK Mine. 1763..250.00

166 (thaler). Like No. 132. 1763-84................ 275.00

167 (Mining thaler). Arms. Rev. mining scene. SEGEN GOTTS Mine. 1765. 200.00

168 (thaler). Bust. Rev. Arms, no supporters (var.). 1773-97................. 275.00

BRUNSWICK-LÜNEBURG (Cont.)

V.F.

*169 (Mining thaler). GUTE DES HERRN Mine. 1774......250.00

170 (thaler). Bust. Rev. Arms supported. 1777-78.........300.00

171 I/THALER/CASSENGELD. Like No. 150. 1801......400.00

Gold

*172 (ducat). Arms. Rev. Horse/ EX AURO HERC. (Harzgold). Mmk. on obv. 1767-97 ...900.00

172a —. Mmk. on rev. 1791-1800.............900.00

172b —. Obv. 4 fold arms with center shield. 1802-04....900.00

173 (2 ducat). Bust/c. Rev. arms. 1768............1200.00

173a —. 1783............1200.00

174 I/PISTOLE (=5 thaler). Horse. Rev. value. 1803.1000.00

During the period 1806-13, Brunswick-Lüneburg was part of the kingdom of Westphalia.

For Brunswick-Lüneburg coinage after the restoration in 1813 see Hannover.

BRUNSWICK-WOLFENBUTTEL, Duchy (HERZOGTHUM BRAUNSCHWEIG)

In north central Germany. Product of the same 1559 division which gave birth to the Lüneburg branch.

Monetary system: Same as Brunswick-Lüneburg; and 13 deniers = 1 mattier = 4 pfennig. (Struck to facilitate trade with French occupation troops in seven years' war.)

Carl I 1735-80

Copper

Fine

*1 I/DENIER. 1758........ 9.00

VG-F

*2 I/PFENNING. 1736-80 (var.).................. 2.00

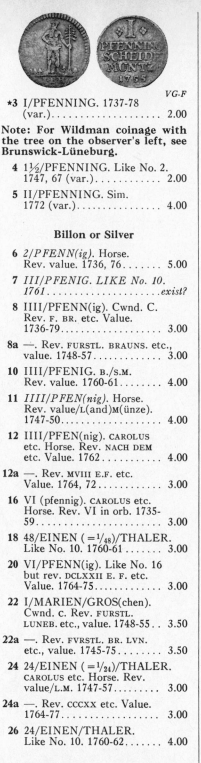

VG-F

*3 I/PFENNING. 1737-78 (var.)............... 2.00

Note: For Wildman coinage with the tree on the observer's left, see Brunswick-Lüneburg.

4 1½/PFENNING. Like No. 2. 1747, 67 (var.)........... 2.00

5 II/PFENNING. Sim. 1772 (var.)............... 4.00

Billon or Silver

6 2/PFENN(ig). Horse. Rev. value. 1736, 76...... 5.00

7 III/PFENIG. LIKE No. 10. 1761...................exist?

8 IIII/PFENN(ig). Cwnd. C. Rev. F. BR. etc. Value. 1736-79............... 3.00

8a —. Rev. FURSTL. BRAUNS. etc., value. 1748-57........... 3.00

10 IIII/PFENIG. B./S.M. Rev. value. 1760-61....... 4.00

11 IIII/PFEN(nig). Horse. Rev. value/L(and)M(ünze). 1747-50............... 4.00

12 IIII/PFEN(nig). CAROLUS etc. Horse. Rev. NACH DEM etc. Value. 1762.......... 4.00

12a —. Rev. MVIII E.F. etc. Value. 1764, 72........... 3.00

16 VI (pfennig). CAROLUS etc. Horse. Rev. VI in orb. 1735-59.................. 3.00

18 48/EINEN (=¹⁄₄₈)/THALER. Like No. 10. 1760-61....... 3.00

20 VI/PFENN(ig). Like No. 16 but rev. DCLXXII E. F. etc. Value. 1764-75............. 3.00

22 I/MARIEN/GROS(chen). Cwnd. C. Rev. FURSTL. LUNEB. etc., value. 1748-55.. 3.50

22a —. Rev. FVRSTL. BR. LVN. etc., value. 1745-75....... 3.50

24 24/EINEN (=¹⁄₂₄)/THALER. CAROLUS etc. Horse. Rev. value/L.M. 1747-57....... 3.00

24a —. Rev. CCCXX etc. Value. 1764-77............. 3.00

26 24/EINEN/THALER. Like No. 10. 1760-62....... 4.00

Silver

Fine

*30 2 M(arien) G(roschen). 1735-80................. 5.00

Fine

32 II/MARIEN/GROS(chen). Cwnd. C. Rev. value. 1747-59.................. 5.00

34 II/MARIEN/GROS(chen). Value. Rev. Wildman. 1735-80.................. 6.00

36 12/EINEN (=¹⁄₁₂)/THALER. CAROLUS etc. Horse. Rev. NACH DEM etc., value. 1737-64.............. 9.00

36a —. Rev. value. Landmünze. 1747-58.............. 6.00

36b —. Rev. CLX etc., value. 1764-80.............. 6.00

43 4 M(arien) G(roschen). Like No. 30. 1736-80....... 6.00

*45 IIII/MARIEN/GROSCH(en). 1735-80.............. 7.00

V.F.

*47 VI/EINEN (=¹⁄₆)/THALER. 1747-59..............10.00

51 VI/EINEN/THALER. Cwnd. C. Rev. value. 1759-62..............14.00

53 VI/MARIEN/GROSCH(en). Like No. 45. 1735-80.....11.00

55 VI/EINEN/THALER. CAROLUS etc. Horse. Rev. LXXX etc., value. 1764-80....... 9.00

56 ¼ (thaler). Arms. Rev. Wildman. 1736-50........20.00

57 ¼ (Albertus) THALER. Burgundian cross. Rev. Lion. 1748.................75.00

59 XII/MARIEN/GROSCH(en). Like No. 45. 1735-80.....12.00

61 VIII/GUTE (good)/GROS(chen). Arms. Rev. value. 1756-59.. 9.00

63 VIII/GUTE/GROS. Horse. Rev. value. 1758-59...... 8.00

65 VIII/GUTE/GROS. Cwnd c. Rev. value. 1759-62.....12.00

*67 ⅓ (thaler). 1764-70.......10.00

BRUNSWICK-WOLFENBUTTEL (Cont.)

V.F.

69 ⅓ (thaler). Head. Rev. Horse. 1771-79 ....10.00

70 ½ *(thaler)*. Arms. Rev. Wildman. 1736-37 ....*Rare*

71 ½ (Albertus) TH(aler). Like No. 57. 1747-48 ....35.00

73 24/MARIEN/GROSCH(en). Like No. 45. 1735-80 ....25.00

74 ⅔ *(thaler)*. Bust r. Rev. horse. 1737, 40 ....25.00

74a —. Bust l. 1736-40 ....25.00

75 ⅔ (thaler). Bust. Rev. Horse. 1764-79 ....25.00

77 24/MARIEN/GROSCH(en). Value. Rev. Horse. 1736-80..35.00

79 ⅔ (thaler). Head. Rev. Horse. 1775-79 ....25.00

81 (thaler). Arms. Rev. Wildman. 1735-63 ....120.00

82 (thaler). Arms. Rev. Horse. 1735-63 ....120.00

83 (thaler). Bust. Rev. Horse. 1742 ....150.00

84 1 (Albertus) THALER. Like No. 57. 1747 ....175.00

85 1 THALER. Bust. Rev. Horse. 1758-59 ....90.00

86 1/THALER. Cwnd. C. Rev. value/HZ. BR. L.L.M/ 1759 ....150.00

87 X EINE etc. (=Conv. thaler). Bust. Rev. Horse. 1763-65, 76 ....85.00

88 ZEHEN EINE etc. (=Conv. thaler). Bust. Rev. Arms. 1768-69 ....300.00

89 X EINE etc. (=Conv. thaler). Head. Rev. Horse. 1779 ...160.00

Series of mining thalers Nos. 90-97. The common obverse, arms supported by wildmen, comes in 2 types: Type I 1744-48; Type II 1750-61.

E.F.

90 (thaler). Type I. Rev. Swan. WEISSER SCHWAN Mine. 1744-48 ....300.00

90a —. Type II. 1750, 52 .....250.00

91 (thaler). Type I. Rev. CRONENBURGS GLVCK Mine. 1744-48 ....300.00

91a —. Type II. 1750, 52 .....200.00

92 (thaler). Type I. Rev. lute player. LAVTENTHALS GLVCK Mine. 1745, 48 ....300.00

92a —. Type II. 1752, 61 .....300.00

93 (thaler). Type I. Rev. mining scene. GVTE DES HERRN Mine. 1745-48 ....250.00

93a —. Type II. 1752 ....250.00

94 (thaler). Type I. Rev. Rainbow. REGEN BOGEN Mine. 1746-48 ....250.00

E.F.

94a —. Type II. 1750, 52.....275.00

95 (thaler). Type II. Rev. Shield on pillar. H. AVG FRIED: BLEYFELD Mine. 1750, 52......200.00

96 (thaler). Type II. Rev. Pillars of Hercules. KONIG CARL Mine. 1752 ....200.00

97 (thaler). Type II. Rev. mining scene. SEGEN GOTTES Mine. 1761.....................200.00

Gold

V.F.

100 (Lower-Harzgold ducat). CAROLUS D.G. DVX BR. ET. LVN. Bust l. Rev. horse/ EX AVR. HERC. INF. 1736 RN.............1500.00

101 (ducat). Sim. but w/out EX AVR etc. 1736.......950.00

102 (Lower-Harzgold ducat). Like No. 100 but bust r. 1739.................950.00

102.5 (Harzgold ducat). Bust r. Rev. horse. 1749........*Rare*

103 (ducat). Head r. Rev. horse. 1738-42....950.00

103.5 (ducat). Bust r. Rev. horse. 1742........*Rare*

103.7 1 DVCAT. Sim. 1742....*Rare*

★104 5 THALER. 1742 (2 var.)...............1200.00

105 10 THALER. Sim. 1742.1500.00

106 2½ THALER. Like No. 108. 1742-75.................350.00

107 5 THALER. Sim. 1742-75.....................450.00

★108 X THALER. 1742-64...1000.00

109 2½ THALER. Bare bust. Rev. horse. 1777.........300.00

110 5 THALER. Head. Rev. horse. 1776-78...........400.00

111 X THALER. Sim. 1777....*Rare*

Carl Wilhelm Ferdinand, Duke 1780-1806, Mortally wounded at Jena fighting Napoleon.

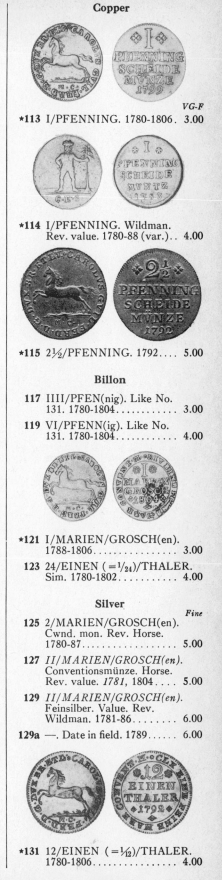

Copper

★113 I/PFENNING. 1780-1806. *VG-F* 3.00

★114 I/PFENNING. Wildman. Rev. value. 1780-88 (var.).. 4.00

★115 2½/PFENNING. 1792.... 5.00

Billon

117 IIII/PFEN(nig). Like No. 131. 1780-1804........... 3.00

119 VI/PFENN(ig). Like No. 131. 1780-1804........... 4.00

★121 I/MARIEN/GROSCH(en). 1788-1806............... 3.00

123 24/EINEN (=1/24)/THALER. Sim. 1780-1802........... 4.00

Silver

Fine

125 2/MARIEN/GROSCH(en). Cwnd. mon. Rev. Horse. 1780-87................. 5.00

127 II/MARIEN/GROSCH(en). Conventionsmünze. Horse. Rev. value. *1781*, 1804.... 5.00

129 II/MARIEN/GROSCH(en). Feinsilber. Value. Rev. Wildman. 1781-86........ 6.00

129a —. Date in field. 1789...... 6.00

★131 12/EINEN (=1/12)/THALER. 1780-1806............... 4.00

GERMAN STATES

BRUNSWICK-WOLFENBUTTEL (Cont.)

F-VF

133 4/MARIEN/GROSCH(en).
Like No. 125. 1781-84..... 6.00

135 IIII/MARIEN/GROSCH(en).
Like No. 127. 1784....... mule

137 IIII/MARIEN/GROSCH(en).
Like No. 129. 1781-86..... 6.00

137a —. Date in field. 1787-89.. 6.00

★139 VI/EINEN (=⅙)/THALER.
1780-1804............10.00

141 VI /MARIEN/GROSCH(en).
Like No. 129. 1781-88..... 8.00

143 XII/MARIEN/GROSCH(en).
Like No. 129. 1781-85....15.00

143a —. 1786..............15.00

143b —. 1787-89............15.00

145 VIII/GVTE (good)/
GROSCH(en). Arms. Rev.
value. 1783-1805 ....10.00

V.F.

147 24/MARIEN/GROSCH(en).
Like No. 129. Date in circular
legend. 1781-86..........40.00

147a —. Date in field. 1784-89..40.00

149 XVI/GVTE/GROSCH(en).
Like No. 145. 1780-1805...26.00

151 24 (mariengroschen). Arms.
Rev. Wildman. 1781-83....50.00

151a —. Different arms. 1784....Rare

152 24/MARIEN/GROSCH(en).
Value. Rev. horse. 1781....50.00

153 XXIIII/MARIEN/
GROSCH(en). Horse.
Rev. value. 1789-1800.....25.00

155 24/MARIEN/GROSCH(en).
Arms. Rev. value. 1789-
1806..................26.00

156 I/SPECIES/THALER.
Like No. 145. 1782-83....350.00

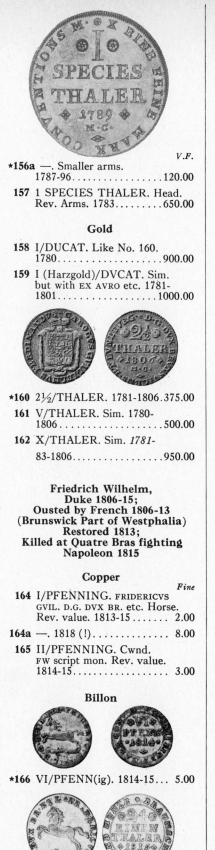

V.F.

★156a —. Smaller arms.
1787-96.................120.00

157 1 SPECIES THALER. Head.
Rev. Arms. 1783........650.00

Gold

158 I/DUCAT. Like No. 160.
1780..................900.00

159 I (Harzgold)/DVCAT. Sim.
but with EX AVRO etc. 1781-
1801.................1000.00

★160 2½/THALER. 1781-1806.375.00

161 V/THALER. Sim. 1780-
1806.................500.00

162 X/THALER. Sim. 1781-
83-1806.................950.00

Friedrich Wilhelm, Duke 1806-15; Ousted by French 1806-13 (Brunswick Part of Westphalia) Restored 1813; Killed at Quatre Bras fighting Napoleon 1815

Copper

Fine

164 I/PFENNING. FRIDERICVS
GVIL. D.G. DVX BR. etc. Horse.
Rev. value. 1813-15....... 2.00

164a —. 1818 (!)............. 8.00

165 II/PFENNING. Cwnd.
FW script mon. Rev. value.
1814-15................ 3.00

Billon

★166 VI/PFENN(ig). 1814-15... 5.00

Fine

★167 24/EINEN (=1/24)/THALER.
Sim. but LAND MÜNZE.
1814-15................ 5.00

168 12/EINEN (=1/12)/THALER.
Like No. 166. 1813-15.... 5.00

168a —. Mmk. F.R. on obv.
1815.................15.00

Silver

V.F.

169 VI/EINEN (=⅙)/THALER.
Sim. 1813...............40.00

169a —. 1814...............40.00

170 24/MARIEN/GROSCH(en).
Arms. Rev. value. 1814-
15...................25.00

Gold

VF-EF

★171 I (Harzgold)/DVCAT. 1814-
15.................1350.00

172 2½/THALER. Sim. but w/out
EX AVRO etc. 1815......1000.00

173 V/THALER. Sim. 1814-
15...................900.00

174 X/THALER. Sim. 1813-
14.................1000.00

Carl, Duke 1815-30
A. First period 1815-20.
Under Regency of George, Prince Regent of Great Britain

Copper

Fine

175 I/PFENNING. GEORG P.R.T.N.
CAROLI etc. Horse. Rev. value.
1816.................... 4.00

★175a —. GEORG T.N. etc. 1816-
20.................... 4.00

175b —. GEORG D.G.T.N. etc.
1818.................. 7.00

175c —. Like No. 175a but leg.
begins 8 o'clock. 1819..... 9.00

Billon

176 IIII/PFENN(ig). Like No.
179. 1820............... 5.00

177 VI/PFENN(ig). Sim. 1816,
19.................... 5.00

178 I/MARIEN/GROSCH(en).
Sim. 1819.............. 6.50

GERMAN STATES

BRUNSWICK-WOLFENBUTTEL (Cont.)

Fine

*179 12/EINEN (=½)/THALER.
1816-19 . . . . 8.50

Silver

V.F.

180 24/MARIEN/GROSCH(en).
Arms. Rev. value. 1815-
18 . . . . 60.00

Gold

VF-EF

181 2½/THALER. Like No.
182. 1816-19 . . . . 550.00

*182 V/THALER. 1816-19 . . . . 650.00
183 X/THALER. Sim. 1817-
19 . . . . 1000.00

B. Second period 1820-23.

Under Regency of George IV, King of Great Britain

Copper

Fine

184 I/PFENNING. Like No.
185. 1820, 22-23 . . . . 2.50

*185 II/PFENNING. 1820, 23 . . 2.50

Billon

186 IIII/PFENN(ig). Like No.
179 but GEORG IV etc.
1823 . . . . 4.00
187 VI/PFENN(ig). Sim.
1823 . . . . 6.00

Silver

188 24/EINEN (=1/24)/THALER.
Sim. 1820, 23 . . . . 10.00
189 12/EINEN (=½)/THALER.
Sim. 1820-23 . . . . 10.00

Fine

*190 24/MARIEN/GROSCH(en).
Arms. Rev. value. 1820-
22 . . . . 60.00
190.5 I/SPECIES/THALER.
Arms. Rev. value. 1821.
. . . . (E.F.) 1100.00

Gold

E.F.

191 2½/THALER. Like No. 182
but GEORG IV. 1822 . . . . . . 600.00
192 V/THALER. Sim. 1822 . . . 700.00
193 X/THALER. Sim.
1822 . . . . 1100.00

C. Third period 1823-30. Carl, alone.

Copper

Fine

194 I/PFENNING. Like No. 195
but BR. U. LUEN. 1823-30
(var.) 2.00

*195 II/PFENNING. 1824-30 . . 2.00

Billon

196 VI/PFENN(ig). Horse.
Rev. legend, value. 1828 . . . 5.00
197 24/EINEN (=1/24)/THALER.
Sim. 1825 . . . . 15.00
198 12/EINEN (=½)/THALER.
Sim. 1823-30 . . . . 4.00

Silver

F-VF

199 24/MARIEN/GROSCH(en).
Arms. Rev. value. 1823-
29 . . . . 25.00

The 1829 ½ Convention thaler (XX
EINE etc.) is a pattern.

Gold

VF-EF

200 I (Harzgold)/DUCAT. CARL etc.
Value. Rev. Arms. 1825 . . 1400.00
201 2½/THALER. Like No. 203.
1825, 28 . . . . 650.00
202 V/THALER. Sim. 1824-
30 . . . . 950.00

VF-EF

*203 X/THALER. 1824-30 . . . 1950.00
204 2½ THALER. Like No.
205. 1829 . . . . 1000.00

*205 ZEHN (=10) THALER.
1827-29 . . . . 1850.00

Wilhelm, Duke 1831-84

Copper

Fine

206 I/PFENNING. WILHELM
HERZOG ZU BR. etc. Horse.
Rev. value 1831-34 . . . . 2.00

*207 1/PFENNIG. 1851-56B . . . 2.00
207a —. 1854, 56 w/out B 10.00

*208 1/PFENNIG. 1859-60 . . . . . 2.00
209 II/PFENNING. Like No.
206. 1823-34 . . . . 3.00

*210 2/PFENNIGE. 1851-56 . . . . 1.50

*211 2/PFENNIGE. 1859-60 . . . 2.00

GERMAN STATES

BRUNSWICK-WOLFENBUTTEL (Cont.)

Billon

Fine

212 ½/GROSCHEN. Generally sim. to No. 208. 1858-60... 2.00

Note: A number of rare patterns not listed here were struck during this reign.

213 1/GROSCHEN. Sim. 1857-60............ 2.00

Silver

V.F.

214 4/GUTE/GROSCHEN. Head. Rev. value. 1840....17.50

*215 24/MARIEN/GROSCH(en). Arms. Rev. value. 1832-34..................25.00

216 EIN (=1) THALER. Like 219. FRITZ F. on neck. 1837-39....................60.00

216a — . w/out FRITZ. 1839-51...45.00

217a —. Leg. ends LUN. 1853-55.45.00

*219 EIN (=1) VEREINS-THALER. 1858-71.......35.00

220 2 THALER. Head. Rev. Arms on mantle. 1842-55...75.00

221 2 TH(aler). Head. Rev. ZUR FEIER etc. Arms in wreath. 25th Anniversary of Reign. 1856............(E.F.) 195.00

Gold

E.F.

*222 X/THALER. 1831.....1500.00

E.F.

223 2½/THALER. Like No. 225. 1832.................600.00

224 V/THALER. Sim. 1832...900.00

225 X/THALER. WILHELM HERZOG. Arms supported/ Z. BR. U.L. Rev. value. 1832-34................1400.00

226 2½/THALER. Head. Rev. value. 1851........650.00

227 ZEHN (=10) THALER. Like No. 219. 1850-57...1200.00

*228 1/KRONE. (var.). 1857-59...............900.00

BURGAU (BURGOVIA), County. See AUSTRIA (STATES).

CHUR (Electoral) BAYERN, COLLN, MAINZ, PFALZ, TRIER, etc.
See Bavaria, Cologne, Mainz, Pfalz, Trier.

CLEVE (CLEVES, CLIVIAE, KLEVE), Duchy

On the Rhine at the Netherlands border. First coins (as a county) 13th century. Obtained by Brandenburg-Prussia in the early 17th century at the extinction of the ruling house.

Monetary System: 8 duit=1 stüber; 60 stüber=1 Reichsthaler; 5 Reichsthaler=1 Friedrich d'or.

Arms: Red, a gold and silver escarbuncle (shield strengthener; looks like spokes).

For other Prussian stüber denominations see East Friesland.

Friedrich II (the Great) of Prussia, 1740-86

Copper

VG-F

*1 (duit). 1749-53............ 4.00

2 ¼/STÜBER. Obv. sim. Rev. value. 1753-55C........... 4.00

Billon

3 1/STÜBER. CLEVISCHE MUN(T)ZE. Cleve arms. Rev. value. 1751-52C...... 6.00

4 1/STÜBER. Cwnd. FR. Rev. value. 1764C........ 7.00

VG-F

*6 2 STÜBER. 1751-58C...... 6.00

Silver

Fine

9 5 STÜV(er). FRIDERICUS BORUSSORUM REX. Head. Rev. value. 1764-66C......12.00

11 10 STÜV(er). Like No. 9. 1764-65C.................16.00

13 60 STÜV(er). Head. Rev. EIN REICHSTHALER. Eagle on trophies. 60 etc. 1765C.....45.00

Gold (Fr. d'or=6.65 gr.)

VF-EF

15 (½ Friedrich d'or). Bust. Rev. Eagle, trophies. 1753C.................1000.00

16 (Fr. d'or). Sim. 1751-53C.1000.00

17 (Fr. d'or). Head. Rev. as last. 1754-55C..............2500.00

18 (2 Fr. d'or). Like No. 15. 1752-53C..............2500.00

Note: In addition to the foregoing, other Prussian coins of regular denominations from ½ groschen (48 EINEN THALER) through Reichsthaler, and three exotics (4 kreuzer 1755, 6 East Prussian groszy and an undated Emden Co. piastre), were struck at Cleve mint during this reign. Mintmarks: G.K 1741-50; A.G.P. 1742-43; C 1750 on; I.C.M. 1751. See Prussia and Poland for these coins.

COESFELD (COSVELDT, KOSFELD), Town

Belonged to the bishopric of Münster. Local copper coinage 1578-1763.

Copper

Fine

1 IIII (4 pfennig). STADT COSVELDT. Bull's head. Rev. value. 1763.........12.00

COLOGNE (CHUR CÖLN, CÖLLN; KUR KÖLN), Archbishopric/Electorate

Lands along the left bank of the Rhine between Coblenz and Crefeld, and in Westphalia. See founded 313, raised to the archiepiscopal dignity under Charlemagne.

First ecclesiastical coins 10th century. Became one of the three religious electorates of the Holy Roman Empire. Secularized 1801.

Arms: Silver, black cross.

COLOGNE, Archbishopric (Cont.)

Monetary System:
16 heller = 1 stüber;
60 stüber = 1 Reichsthaler;
10 Convention stüber = 12 stüber Landmünze;
78 albus = 1 Reichsthaler.

Clemens August v. Bayern, Archbishop of Cologne 1723-61

(also Bishop of Hildesheim, Münster, Osnabruck and Paderborn, and Master of the Teutonic Order, where he struck coins too).

Copper

VG-F

★1 1/4/STVBER. Cwnd. CCA mon. 1736-60 .... 4.00

Billon or Silver

3 *8 (heller)*. Bavarian lozenge shield. Rev. Cologne cross in shield. 1724 .... 5.00

5 I/STÜBER. Like No. 1 but cwnd. CA mon. 1741-49 ..... 4.00

6 2/STÜBER. Sim. 1749 ..... 6.00

8 *24/EINEN* (= 1/24)/*THALER*. Like No. 1. 1755 .... 7.00

★10 3/STÜBER. Arms. Rev. like No. 1 Rev. 1749-50 .... 6.00

11 4 ALB(us). CLEM. AUG. etc. 4 fold Bavarian arms. Rev. Cologne cross shield. 1726 .. 8.00

12 *4/ALBUS*. Arms. Rev. value. 1739 .... 6.00

14 *12/EINEN* (= 1/12)/*THALER*. Arms. Rev. value. 1739 ..... 6.00

16 10/KREUTZ(er). CLEM. AUG. D.G. AR. ET EL COL. etc. 7 shields. Rev. value/LAND/MUNTZ/ date/I.H. 1735-36 .... 6.00

17 20/KREUTZ(er). Sim. 1735 .... 10.00

Silver

V.F.

18 (1/8 Mining thaler). Cwnd. mon. Rev. crossed hammers. 1759. From Westphalian Mines ... 50.00

19 VI/MARIEN/GROS(chen). Like No. 20. 1754 .... 35.00

V.F.

★20 VI/EINEN (= 1/6)/REICHS/ THALER. Arms. Rev. value. 1754-55 .... 25.00

24 (1/4 Mining thaler). PIETATE etc. Arms. Rev. 2 mines. GLÜCK AUF/WESTF etc. 1759 .... 100.00

See Teutonic Order Nos. 5 and 9 for groschen and 1/4 conv. thaler 1761 on his death.

28 (1/2 Mining thaler). Bust. Rev. 2 mines. ARGENT. PUR. E.FOD/WESTP. Date (1759) in chronogram 150.00

30 (Mining thaler). Like No. 28. 41mm. (1759) 600.00

Gold (ducat = 3.49 gr.)

E.F.

32 (ducat). Bust. Rev. STI. 3. REGES . . . CIVIT. COLN. Adoration of the Magi. 1726, 42, 44 .... 900.00

33 (ducat). Bust. Rev. TUO PRAESIDIO. Madonna, arms. 1750 .... 1500.00

34 (ducat). Bust facing. Rev. NON MIHI/etc. in sun rays. 1750 .... 1000.00

34a —. Bust r. 1750 .... 1200.00

35 (1/2 Carolin = 4.85 gr.). Bust. Rev. Bavarian arms, 6 small shields. 1735-36 .... 1000.00

36 (Carolin). Sim. 1735 ..... 1950.00

36a —. Rev. Madonna, arms. 1735 .... RR

Sede Vacante 1761

Silver

V.F.

★38 80 EINE etc. (= 1/8 Conv. thaler). St. Peter with shield. Rev. legend. 1761 .... 75.00

39 40 EINE etc. (= 1/4 Conv. thaler). Like No. 40. 1761 .. 120.00

40 10 EINE etc. (= Conv. thaler). CAPIT. ECCLES. METROPOLIT. COLON. St. Peter with shield. Rev. Adoration of Magi. 1761 .... 600.00

Maximilian Friedrich, Graf v. Königsegg-Rothenfels, Archbishop of Cologne 1761-84

(also Bishop of Münster).

Copper

VG-F

★42 1/4/STÜBER. MFF mon. 1763-67 .... 4.00

Billon or Silver

44 1/4/STÜBER. MAX. FRID. D.G. etc. Bust. Rev. CHUR COLLN etc. Value. 1776 .... 7.00

46 I/STÜBER. Like No. 44. 1776-77 .... 4.00

48 320/EINE/etc. (= 2 1/2 stüber). MAX. FRID. D.G. AR. ET. EL. COL. Cologne cross, Königsegg middleshield. Rev. value. 1765 .... 8.00

50 160/EINE/etc. (= 5 stüber). Like No. 48. (var.). 1764-65 .... 10.00

★50a —. 1766 .... 12.00

Silver

Fine

52 80/EINE etc. (= 10 stüber). MAX. FRID. etc. 8 fold arms of Cologne, Königsegg middle-shield. Rev. value. 1764-66 .... 12.00

V.F.

54 40 EINE etc. (= 20 stüber). Bust. Rev. JUSTITIA etc., arms. 1766 .... 28.00

56 2/3 (Reichsthaler). Bust. Rev. 8 fold arms with Königsegg middleshield, supported. 1764 .... 42.00

See Münster for coin similar to No. 56.

58 *20 EINE* etc. (= 40 stüber). Bust. Rev. Arms. *Like No. 54*. 1765 .... 55.00

60 10 EINE etc. (= 80 stüber). Bust l. Rev. JUSTITIA etc., irregular arms supported. 1762 .... 160.00

61 10 EINE etc. (= 80 st.). Sim. but bust r. 1764-65 ... 150.00

62 X EINE etc. (= 80 st.). Like No. 61 but oval arms. 1766 .... 200.00

62a —. 1777 .... 130.00

GERMAN STATES

COLOGNE (STADT CÖLN, COLONIA), City

On the Rhine between Bonn and Düsseldorf. Received right of self government 1288, acquired the mint right 1474. Occupied by France 1794, absorbed by that country 1797-1813. To Prussia 1815.

City arms: Red, 3 gold crowns. Below: silver, 11 red flames.

Fine

★1 IIII/HELLER. 1750-92.... 2.00

★1a —. Rev. 17/BRODT/PENNING/ 89. Ration token.......... 6.00

1b —. Rev. BRODT/PENNING (1789)................... 4.00

2 8/HELLER. Sim. 1793..... 5.00

Gold
V.F.

3 DUCAT. FRANC. D.G. etc. Bust of Emp. Franz I. Rev. DUCAT CIVIT. COLON. Arms. N.D., 1750, 53....1200.00

4 DUCAT. Sim. but name and bust of Emp. Joseph II. 1767...................2250.00

CONSTANCE (COSTNITZ, KONSTANZ), Bishopric

On Lake Constance between Germany and Switzerland. Bishopric founded in 6th century. First coins struck early 10th century. Secularized in 1802-03.

Arms: Red, a silver cross.

Franz Conrad, Freiherr von Rodt, Bishop 1750-75

Copper
Fine

1 ½/KREUTZER. F.C.S.R.E.P.C. DE RODT. E. CONSTAN etc. Arms. Rev. value/G(unzburg). 1772.................. 9.00

2 EIN (=1)/KREUTZER. Sim. 1772................. 7.00

Silver (lower values billon)
V.F.

4 48/EIN (=¹⁄₄₈) CONVEN(tion) THALER (=3 kreuzer landmünze). Sim. 1772........ 7.00

5 24/EIN etc. (=6 kr. L.M.). Sim. 1772................12.00

6 (20 kr. Conv. münze = 24 kr. L.M.). Bust. Rev. PRO ECCLESIA ET PRO PATRIA. Arms. 1761...............22.00

7 (½ Conv. thaler). Sim. 14 gr. 1761.................65.00

8 (Conv. thaler). Sim. 1761..260.00

Gold

9 (ducat). Sim. 1761......1850.00

CORVEY (CORBEI, CORVEI), Abbey

In Westphalia. Founded 820 A.D. by Benedictine monks from Corbei, Picardy. First coins with Abbot's name 11th century. Abbey raised to bishopric 1793, secularized to Nassau-Dietz 1803.

Arms: Parted per fesse: red and gold.

Caspar von Böselager, Abbot 1737-58

Silver
V.F.

1 (24 mariengroschen =1 gulden). D.G. CASPARIUS PRINCEPS ET ABBAS CORBEIENSIS. Cwnd. arms. Rev. POSVIT etc. St. Vitus stdg. 1753..........65.00

1a —. Helmeted arms. N.D. (1753)...................60.00

2 24 M(arien) G(roschen). Obv. like No. 1a. Rev. DA PACEM etc. St. Vitus. N.D. (1753)...................60.00

3 (thaler). CASPARIUS etc. Arms. Rev. SANCTUS VITUS etc. St. V. stdg. 1739..........250.00

Gold

4 (ducat). Sim. 1743, 53....1200.00

Philipp, Freiherr Spiegel zum Desenberg, Abbot 1758-76

Billon or Silver
F-VF

6 III/PFENN(ig). Monogram. 1765..................... 7.00

8 12/EINEN (=¹⁄₁₂)/THALER. PHILIPPUS D.G.S.R.I. PRINCEPS ET ABB. CORBEI. Arms. Rev. value. 1765 ....16.00

10 VI/EINEN (=¹⁄₆)/THALER. Arms. Rev. value. 1765.....26.00
V.F.

12 (thaler). Arms. Rev. SANCTUS VITUS etc. St. V. stdg. 1758.................. 300.00

Gold
V.F.

13 (ducat). Sim. 1758-59....1200.00

Theodor, Freiherr von Brabeck, Abbot 1776-93, Bishop 1793-94

Copper

Fine

★14 II/PFEN(nig). 1787........12.00

★15 IIII/PFEN(nig). 1787......14.00

COSVELDT. See COESFELD.

COURLAND (CURLAND). See POLAND.

DANZIG. See POLAND.

DEUTSCHER ORDEN. See Teutonic Order.

DORTMUND (TREMONIA), Free City

In Westphalia. Site of an imperial mint prior to 1000 A.D. Dated city coinage circulated 1553-1760; older undated coins exist. Dortmund was annexed to Nassau-Dillenburg in 1803, whence it passed to Prussia in 1815.

Arms: Silver, a black eagle.

Copper
VG-F

1 ¼/STÜBER. Cwnd. eagle. Rev. DORTMUNDS SCHEIDE MUNTZ. Value. 1744-56...... 5.00

★1a —. Uncrowned eagle. 1758-60................. 3.00

GERMAN STATES

DORTMUND (Cont.)

Billon or Silver
VG-F

3 VI (pfennig = 1¼ stüber). Eagle, DORTMUND. Rev. VI in orb. 1755-56 . . . . 5.00

5 24/EINEN (=¹⁄₂₄)/REICHS/ THALER. Eagle, DORTMUND. Rev. value. 1752-58 . . . . 5.00

7 12/EINEN etc. (=¹⁄₁₂ R. thaler). Like No. 5. 1758-59 . . . . 7.00

9 VI/EINEN etc. (=⅙ R. thaler). FRANC. I.D.G. RO. etc. Bust of Emp. Franz I. Rev. MONETA NOVA. ARG. TREMONIENS. value. 1758 . . . . 250.00

EAST FRIESLAND (OSTFRIESLAND), Principality

Area on the North Sea coast between the Ems and the Weser. At the death of Prince Carl Edzard in 1744, East Friesland was absorbed by Prussia, to which it belonged until 1807. During the period 1815-66 East Friesland was part of Hannover.

Monetary System: 288 pfennige = 54 stüber = 36 mariengroschen = 1 Reichsthaler; 20 witten = 2 stüber = 1 schaf.

Prussian mint marks: A-Berlin; D-Aurich, East Fr.; B.I.D.-Dedekind, MM at Aurich; I.C.G.-Gitterman, MM at Esens, East Fr.

For other Prussian stüber denominations see Cleve.

Friedrich II (the Great) of Prussia, in East Friesland 1744-86

Copper

VG-F

★1 IIII/EINEN (=¼) /STÜBER. 1752-57D 4.00

2 ¼/STÜBER. Sim. 1764, 65, 67D, 74-84A 4.00

Billon

4 ¼/STÜBER. FR. mon. Rev. value. 1746-52 . . . . 8.00

5 ½/STÜBER. Sim. 1772, 81A 5.00

6 H(alber = ½) S(tüber). MO:NO: GRO: ALB:P:F:O. Cwnd. eagle. Rev. SU-UM-CUI-QUE. Flower cross, in angles O-F/H-S. 1781-82 . . . . . 15.00

VG-F

★7 I/STÜBER. 1771-81A 4.00

8 2/STÜBER. Sim. 1773, 75A 7.00

9 IIII/PFENN(ig). FWR mon. Rev. value. 1746 I.C.G. . . . . . ——

10 IIII/PFEN(nig). FR mon. Rev. value/date/B.I.D. 1747-48 . . . . 4.00

11 IIII/PFEN(nig). Sim. 1752-58D 5.00

12 IIII/GUTE/PFEN(nig). Sim. 1764D 2.50

13 I/MARIEN/GROS(chen). FR mon. Rev. value. 1746 I.C.G., 47 B.I.D. 30.00

★15 I/MARIEN/GROS(chen). 1752-68D 4.00

17 I/MARIEN/GROS(chen). FR mon. Rev. value. 1774-75A 6.00

18 24/EINEN (=¹⁄₂₄)/THALER. FR mon. Rev. value. 1746. I.C.G 12.00

19 24/EINEN/THALER. FR mon. in cwnd. cartouche. Rev. value/1748/B.I.D 7.00

20 II/MARIEN/GROSCH(en). FR mon. Rev. value. 1746 I.C.G. 7.00

21 II/MARIEN/GROS(chen). Like No. 15. 1752D, 64D 7.00

22 IX/EINEN (=¹⁄₉)/REICHS/ THALER. Head. Rev. value. 1755D 20.00

23 IIII/MARIEN/GROS(chen). Eagle. Rev. value. 1756-57D 12.00

Fine

25 VI/MARIEN/GROSCHEN. Head. Rev. value. 1758 . . . . 15.00

27 XII/MARIEN/GROSCHEN. Like No. 25. 1758 . . . . 21.00

Nos. 25 and 27 are said to have been struck at Dresden Mint during the Prussian occupation.

Other coins of regular Prussian denominations struck at Aurich (D) are listed under Prussia.

Gold
VF-EF

30 (Friedrich d'or = 5 thaler). Bust. Rev. Eagle, lion's head, trophies. 1752-53D . . . . RRR

Friedrich Wilhelm II, 1786-97

Copper
VG-F

32 ¼/STÜBER. FWR mon. Rev. value. 1787A 6.00

33 ¼/STÜBER. Like No. 35. 1792, 94A 5.00

Friedrich Wilhelm III of Prussia, in East Friesland 1797-1807

Copper

★35 ¼/STÜBER. 1799-1804A . . 4.00

Billon
Fine

37 1/STÜBER. FRIEDR. WILH. III etc. Bust. Rev. value/ OST/FRIESISCH. 1804A 10.00

38 2/STÜBER. Sim. 1804A 20.00

East Friesland under Hannover George IV of Great Britain 1820-30

Copper

★40 ¼/STÜBER. 1823-25 . . . . . . 6.00

Billon

41 1/STÜBER. Sim. 1823 . . . . . 10.00

42 2/STÜBER. Sim. 1823 . . . . . 10.00

EAST PRUSSIA. See POLAND.

EICHSTÄDT (EICHSTÄTT, EUSTETTENSIS, EYSTETTENSIS) Bishopric

In west-central Bavaria. Founded in 745 by St. Willibald. Willibald and his sister, St. Walburga, were the patron saints of Eichstädt. The bishops obtained the right to mint imperial coins in 908 A.D., but the regular episcopal coinage began in the 11th century. In 1803 Eichstädt was secularized and given to Ferdinand, elector of Salzburg.

Arms: Red, a silver crozier.

GERMAN STATES

EICHSTÄDT (Cont.)

Johann Anton II v Freiberg, Bishop 1736-57

Silver (lower values billon)
V.F.

3 1/KREUZER. Arms (see rev. of No. 14). Rev. value. 1755 . . . . 8.00

4 (2 kreuzer). Obv. sim. Rev. LAND/MUNZ. 1755 . . . . . 8.00

5 3 K(reuzer). Obv. sim. Rev. SANCTUS WILIBALD. St. W. std. N.D. (1755) 11.50

6 5 K(reuzer). Sim. N.D. (1755) 11.50

7 10 K(reuzer). Obv. sim. Rev. 120/EINE/etc. 1755 . . .16.00

8 20 K(reuzer). Sim. but 60/EINE/etc. 1755 . . . . .18.50

9 30 (kreuzer). Like No. 14 but bust and arms each in rhombus. 1755 . . . . .35.00

10 20 EINE etc. (=½ Conv. thaler). Like No. 14. 1755 . . .85.00

11 10 EINE etc. (=Conv. thaler). Sim. 1755 . . . .(E.F.) 275.00

Gold
VF-EF

12 (ducat). IOAN. ANT:II etc. Arms. Rev. St. Willibald. 1738 . .1000.00

13 (ducat). Obv. sim. Rev. St. Walburga. 1738 . . . . .1000.00

*14 (ducat). 1755 . . . . .1400.00

Sede Vacante 1757

Silver
E.F.

15 10 EINE etc. (= Conv. thaler). CAPITULUM REGNANS etc. 15 shields around arms. Rev. the 2 saints 225.00

Raimund Anton, Graf von Strasoldo, Bishop 1757-81

Silver (lower values billon)
V.F.

18 2½ KR(euzer). 2 shields, N-S.R. (Nürnberg Mint). Rev. 2½ KR. EYCHST. etc. 1764 . . . . 9.00

19 V K(reuzer). RAI. ANT. D.G. E. ET. P.E. Arms. Rev. CCXL etc. 1763 . . . . .10.00

20 X K(reuzer). Sim. but CXX etc. 1763, 65 . . . . .15.00

V.F.

21 XX K(reuzer). Sim. but LX etc. 1763, 65 . . . . .17.50

22 30 (kreuzer). Bust. Rev. Arms. 1764 . . . . .35.00

23 XX EINE etc. (=½ Conv. thaler). Sim. 1764 . . . . .75.00

24 X EINE etc. (= Conv. thaler). Sim. 1764 R.N 120.00

Sede Vacante 1781

Silver

25 10 EINE etc. (= Conv. thaler). CAPITULUM REGNANS etc. 13 shields around 3 shields. Rev. 2 saints above city. 1781 . . . .(E.F.) 175.00

Johann Anton III, Freiherr von Zehmen, Bishop 1781-90

Silver

26 20 EINE etc.(=½ Conv. thaler). IOANN. ANTON III D.G. EP. EYSTETTENSIS etc. Bust. Rev. Arms. 1783 . . . . .100.00

27 10 EINE etc. (= Conv. thaler). Sim. 1783 . . . . .250.00

Sede Vacante 1790

Silver
E.F.

28 V EINE etc. (= 2 Conv. thaler). CAPITULUM EYSTETTENSE etc. Saints over vacant throne. Rev. shields on tree. 1790 . .285.00

Joseph, Graf von Stubenberg, Bishop 1790-1803

Silver

29 XX EINE etc. (=½ Conv. thaler). IOSEPHVS D.G. EPISC. EVSTETTENSIS etc. Bust. Rev. VASCVLIS etc. (date 1796 in chronogram) 150.00

30 X EINE etc. (=Conv. thaler). Sim. (1796) 250.00

ELBING. See POLAND.

ELLWANGEN, Provostry

In Württemberg. Founded as an abbey 764 A.D. Converted into a college of secular canons in 1460. Ellwangen obtained the mint right about 1555. In 1803 it was mediatized under Württemberg.

Arms: Silver, a golden mitre.

Anton Ignaz von Fugger-Glot Provost 1756-87

Silver
E.F.

1 XX EINE etc. (=½ Conv. thaler). Like No. 2. 1765 . . .225.00

2 X EINE etc. (= Conv. thaler). ANT. IGN. D.G. S.R.I. PRINCEPS PRAEP. AC. DOM. ELVACENSIS. Bust. Rev. Arms. 1765 . . . .900.00

ERBACH, County

The so-called "kleethaler" 1793 R.N. of Franz of Erbach-Erbach 1775-1806 is a medal.

ERFURT, CITY

On the northern edge of Thuringia. Independent from 13th century until 1664 when it again became subject to the archbishop-electors of Mainz. The city first obtained the right to mint its own coins in 1351. In 1802 at the secularization of Mainz, Erfurt fell to Prussia.

Arms: Red, silver wheel (=Mainz).

Monetary System:
12 pfennig =1 groschen;
24 groschen =1 (Reichs)thaler

For similar coins on the kreuzer system, see Mainz.

Archbishop Emerich Joseph, Freiherr v. Breitbach 1763-74

Billon
VG-F

1 3/PFENNIG. E.I. over arms (wheel). Rev. value in cartouche. 1770-71 . . . . .6.00

*2 ¹/₄₈ (thaler =6 pf). 1770-73 . . . . .10.00

2a —. Like No. 1. 1770 . . . . . . .10.00

Archbishop Friedrich Carl Joseph, Frhr. von und zu Erthal, 1774-1802

Billon
Fine

3 ¹/₄₈ (thaler). Like No. 2 but w/out obv. legend. 1781 . . . . 6.00

*4 48/EINEN (=¹/₄₈)/THALER. 1784 . . . . 5.00

GERMAN STATES

ERFURT (Cont.)

Fine

4a —. Value in cartouche.
1788-94 .... 5.00

4b —. 1798 .... 5.00

6 48/EINEN (=1/48)/THALER.
Arms in long shield.
Rev. value. 1800 .... 5.00

7 6 PF(ennig). Like No. 9
1801 .... 5.00

8 24/EINEN (=1/24)/
THALER (=1 groschen).
Like No. 6. 1800 .... 5.00

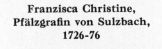

★9 Ein (=1)/groschen.
1801, 02 (oval arms) 8.00

ESSEN, Nunnery

Northeast of Düsseldorf in the Rhineland. Founded in 9th century. First coinage 11th century. Secularized to Prussia in 1802/03.

**Franzisca Christine,
Pfälzgrafin von Sulzbach,
1726-76**

Gold

V.F.

★1 (ducat). 1754 .... 2750.00

FRANCONIA (EASTERN), Dukes.
See Würzburg, Bishopric.

FRANKFURT AM MAIN
(REIPUB. FRANCOFURT,
FREIE STADT FRANKFURT),
Free City

In Hesse-Nassau. Established as a Roman settlement in 1st century A.D. Site of Royal Mint from early times. City obtained mint right in 1428. Frankfurt was given to Dalberg, the Prince Primate, by Napoleon 1806-14. Regained its independence 1814-66. Absorbed by Prussia 1866.

Arms: Red, crowned silver eagle.

Copper

VG-F

1 1/HELLER. Like No. 2 but
F on eagle's breast, not below.
1767-73 .... 2.00

VG-F

★2 1/HELLER. 1773-1804,
1814-37 (var.) 1.25

See Prince Primate for hellers of Grosherzogthum (Grand Duchy of) Frankfurt 1810, 12.

Fine

3 1/HELLER. F. STADT/eagle/
FRANKFURT. Rev. value.
1838 .... 2.50

3a —. Struck in collar.
1841-52 .... 1.00

3b —. Sim. but FREIE STADT.
1843 .... 4.50

★3c (ex 4) —. Diff. eagle, legend
at sides. 1853-58 .... 1.00

★5 1/HELLER. 1859-65 .... 1.00

★6 I/PFENNIG. 1786-1806
(var.) 1.00

8 II/PFENNIG. Sim. 1795
(var.) 2.50

Billon or Silver

10 ¼ (kreuzer). 1765 .... 4.00

13 I/KREUZER. FRANCKFURT.
Eagle. Rev. value. 1765 .... 3.00

13a —. FRANKFURT. 1780-89 .. 3.00

★15 1 K(reuzer). FRANCFURT.
Eagle. Rev. City view. 1773-
74 .... 3.00

17 1/KREU/ZER. ST./FRANK/
FURT. Rev. value. 1778 ..... 5.00

19 1/KREUZER. FRANKFURT.
Rev. value. 1778-*84* 4.00

Fine

★19a 1/KREU/ZER. FRANC/FURT.
1784, 87, *88* 5.00

21 1/CONVENT./KREUZER.
STADT/FRANKFURT/date.
Rev. value. 1803-06, *07* 5.00

★23 1 K(reuzer). FREIE STADT
FRANKFURT. Eagle. Rev.
City view. ND. (1839) 3.00

★24 1/KREUZER. Obv. sim.
Rev. value. 1838-57 .... 2.00

25 1/KREUZER. Obv. like
No. 5. Rev. value. 1859-66 .. 1.25

29 3/KREUZER. Like No. 24.
1838-46 .... 2.50

★29a —. Obv. legend at sides.
1846-56 .... 2.00

★30 3/KREUZER.
1866 .... 3.50

32 5 KR(euzer). Eagle in shield.
S.F., P.C.B. and G.N. (mint
officials). Rev. JUSTIRT –
120 EINE etc. 1765 ...... 10.00

34 5 (kreuzer). Eagle divides
S–F. Rev. 240 STUCK EINE
etc., 5 in wreath. 1778-85 ... 7.00

Former Nos. 28 and 36 (types of No. 23 on 3 and 6 kreuzer flans, without denominations shown) are scarce medallic mules.

Silver

V.F.

37 6/KREUZER. Like No. 24.
1838-46 .... 6.00

37a —. Like No. 29a. 1846-56 ... 4.50

FRANKFURT AM MAIN (Cont.)

V.F.

★38 6/KREUZER. 1852-56..... 5.50

39 6/KREUZER. Like No. 25.
1866.................... 8.00

42 10/KREUZER. Arms on
pedestal. Rev. FRANKFURTER/
value. 1762 .... 7.50

44 10 (kreuzer). AD NORMAM etc.
Eagle. Rev. 120 STUCK etc.
10 in wreath. 1778........ 7.50

46 10 (kreuzer). STADT FRANKFURT.
Eagle/10. Rev. CXX STUCK
etc. 1788................ 7.50

48 20/KREUZER. Like No. 42.
1762.................... 7.50

50 20 (kreuzer). Arms on pedestal. Rev. NOMEN etc. Flower
cross/20. 1763........... 7.50

52 20 (kreuzer). 60 EINE etc.
Arms on pedestal. Rev. AD
NORMAM etc. Flower cross.
1764.................... 10.00

52a —. FRANCOFURTI on rev.
1765-67................ 7.50

54 20 (kreuzer). 1771.......... 7.50

56 20 (kreuzer). Like no. 44.
1776................... 9.00

★58 20 (kreuzer). 1781-84...... 9.00

60 20 (kreuzer). Like No. 46 but
LX etc. 1790.............. 9.00

62 XL E.F. etc. (=30 kreuzer).
AD NORMAM etc. Eagle/I.O.T.
Rev. NOMEN etc. Flower cross.
1762.................... 20.00

64 ½/GULDEN. Like No. 24.
1838, 41 .... 14.00

64a —. 1842-49.............. 14.00

64b —. 1862................ 27.50

66 XX E.F. etc. (=½ Conv.
thaler). Like No. 62. 1762...25.00

66a —. FRANCOFURTI. 1764.... 18.00

68 XX STUCK etc. (=½ Conv.
thaler). Eagle/H ★ I.G.B. ★ H.
Rev. value. 1791......... 25.00

70 1/GULDEN. Like No. 24.
1838-41................ 18.00

V.F.

★70a —. 1842-55............. 20.00

70b —. 1859-63............. 17.50

72 X E.F. MARK (= Conv.
thaler). Like No. 62. 1762-
63..................... 60.00

72a —. Eagle in cartouche (var.).
1764................... 100.00

72b —. Like No. 66a. 1764-65...60.00

72c —. 1766-67............. 200.00

73 X ST. EINE etc. (= Conv.
thaler). MONETA REIPVBL.
FRANCOFURT etc. Eagle.
Rev. City view. 1772...... 90.00

74 X EINE etc. (= Conv. thaler).
A DEO etc. 3 figures/FRANKFURT.
Rev. AD NORMAM etc. in wreath.
Opening of bridge at Hausen.
1776................... 95.00

75 X EINE etc. (= Conv. thaler).
STADT FRANKFURT. Eagle.
Rev. value. 1793, 96 ..... 120.00

76 X EINE etc. (= Conv. thaler).
DER STADT etc. Rev. AUS DEN
etc., value. Contribution thaler.
1796.................. 125.00

77 EIN (=1) VEREINS-
THALER. Variety of No. 78.
1857-58............... 60.00

★78 EIN VEREINSTHALER.
(var.) 1859-65............ 18.00

VF-EF

79 EIN GEDENKTHALER.
Eagle. Rev. ZU/SCHILLER'S etc.
1859. Centenary of Schiller's
birth.................: 65.00

80 EIN GEDENKTHALER.
Eagle. Rev. stdg. female.
Shooting fest. 1862........ 48.00

81 EIN GEDENKTHALER.
Eagle. Rev. city square.
Fürstentag. 1863......... 70.00

82 2/GULDEN. Eagle.
Rev. value. 1845-56....... 40.00

E.F.

★83 ZWEY (=2) GULDEN (on
edge). Establishment of German
Parliament. 1848......... 100.00

84 ZWEY (=2) GULDEN (on
edge). Obv. sim. Rev. ERZ-
HERZOG/JOHANN/etc. Election
of Archduke Johann as Vicar
of Empire. 1848.......... 55.00

85 ZWEY (=2) GULDEN (on
edge). Obv. sim. Rev. FRIED-
RICH/WILHELM IV/etc. Election
of F. W. IV of Prussia as Emperor. 1849............. 2500.00

86 ZWEY (=2) GULDEN (on
edge). Eagle. Rev. ZU/GÖTHE'S/
etc. Centenary of Goethe's
birth. 1849............. 85.00

87 ZWEY (=2) GULDEN. Eagle.
Rev. ZUR/DRITTEN/etc. 3rd
Centenary Religious Peace.
1855.................. 65.00

88 2 THALER. ERÖFFNUNG/DER
etc. Rev. value etc. Opening
of new Mint. 1840....... 900.00

89 2/THALER. City view.
Rev. value. 1840-44..(V.F.) 125.00

90 2/THALER. Eagle. Rev. value.
1841-55............(V.F.) 90.00

91 ZWEI (=2) VEREINS-
THALER. Like No. 78.
1860-66................ 60.00

Gold

V.F.

93 DUCATUS (=ducat) NOME
etc. Eagle. Rev. flower cross.
1762................... 1850.00

94 (ducat). City view. Rev. AUS
DEN/ . . . /DER STADT/
FRANCKFURT/1796. Contri-
bution ducat............ 475.00

95 1/DUCAT. Eagle. Rev. value.
1853, 56............... 600.00

Note: Gold pieces commemorating the
imperial elections and coronations of
1764, 1790 and 1792 at Frankfurt are
essentially medals. Most of them also
exist in silver.

The 1817 reformation tercentenary
"ducat" is a medal.

GERMAN STATES

FRANKFURT AM MAIN (Cont.)

Copper Tokens

The following tokens, known as "Jew pfennigs," circulated during the Napoleonic era until 1823 when they were banned by the city of Frankfurt. Although privately issued, their anonymous nature and frequent appearance generates so much correspondence that it is undesirable to omit them. Many bear fictitious dates and denominations.

Fine

T1 I/THELER. Crossed staves in shield. Rev. value. 1703, 1740, 1807 . . . . 7.00

★T2 I/ATRIBUO. Hand holding branch, in shield. Rev. value. 1809 . . . . 4.00

T3 ¼/HALBAG. A + S over shield. Rev. value. 1818 . . . . 5.00

T4 I (pfennig). Heart shield per pale: silver and purple. Rev. I/1819 . . . . 3.00

★T4a I/PFENNIG/1819 . . . . 3.00

★T5 1/PFENNIG/1819 . . . . 3.00

T6 I/PFENNIG. Lion. Rev. value. 1819 . . . . 5.00

★T6a I/HELLER/1821 . . . . 2.00

T7 1/PFENNIG. Rose branch. Rev. value. 1819 . . . . .17.50

T8 1/HELLER. Griffin. Rev. value. 1819 . . . . .17.50

T9 I/HELLER. Wreath, no legend. Rev. value. 1820 . . 2.00

T10 1/PFENNING. Rooster. Rev. value. 1822 . . . . 5.00

FREISING (FRISING), Bishopric

In Bavaria. Founded 724. First coinage about 1150. Secularized 1802.

Arms: Crowned Moor's head.

Clemens Wenzel v. Sachsen, Bishop 1763-68

Gold

V.F.

★1 (ducat). 1765-66 . . . . .1500.00

Joseph Conrad, Freiherr von Schroffenberg, Bishop 1790-1803

Silver

VF-EF

2 X EINE etc. (= Conv. thaler). IOS. CONRAD. D.G. EP. FRISING etc. Bust. Rev. Arms. 1790, N.D 200.00

FRIEDBERG (BURG FRIEDBERG IN DER WETTERAU)

Town and imperial castle in Hesse-Darmstadt governed and garrisoned by an association of local nobles under an elected burgrave. Obtained the mint right 1541. Substantially absorbed into Hesse-Darmstadt in 1806.

Franz Heinrich, Freiherr von Dalberg, Burgrave 1755-76

Silver

E.F.

1 20 (kreuzer). MONETA NOVA CASTRI. FRIDBERG etc. Arms. Rev. IOSEPHUS II etc. Imp. eagle. 1766 . . . . .100.00

2 (½ Conv. thaler). MONETA CASTRI IMP. FRIDBERG. St. George stdg. Rev. Imp. eagle. 1766 . . . . .140.00

3 X EINE etc. (= Conv. thaler). St. George mtd. Rev. Imp. eagle. 1766 . . . . .600.00

Johann Maria Rudolph, Graf von Waldbott-Bassenheim, Burgrave 1777-1805

Silver

V.F.

4 X EINE etc. (= Conv. thaler). MON. NOV. CASTRI IMP. FRIEDBERG. St. George mtd. Rev. Imp. eagle. 1804 . . . . . 290.00

FÜRSTENBERG (FUERSTENBERG), Princes

Noble family with lands in present-day Baden and Württemberg. Assumed rank of count in 13th century. The Swabian branch, which struck all of the coins listed here except No. 21, was given the rank of prince in 1716. The Fürstenbergs were mediatized in 1806.

Joseph Wilhelm Ernst 1704-62, Prince 1716

Silver

V.F.

1 AVSBEUT (= mining) THALER. IOS. WILH ERN. S.R.I. PRINC. DE FURSTENBERG etc. Bust. Rev. mining scene. 1729 . . . . .400.00

2 AUSBEUT THALER. IOSEPH etc. Bust. Rev. Arms. 1762 . . . . .400.00

Gold

3 (ducat). D.G. IOSEPHUS S.R.I. PRINC. IN. FVRSTENBERG. Bust. Rev. Arms. 1750-51 . . . . . .1500.00

Joseph Wenzel 1762-83

Copper

Fine

★4 ½/KREUTZER. I.W.S.R.I.P. DE FURSTENBERG etc. 1772 . . 8.00

5 EIN (=1)/KREUTZER. Sim. 1772-73 . . . . 7.50

Billon

6 48/EIN (=¹⁄₄₈) CONVEN(tion)/ THALER (=2½ Conv. kreuzer =3 kreuzer landmünze). Sim. 1772 . . . . .12.50

7 24/EIN etc. (=6 kr. land-münze). Sim. 1772 . . . . .10.00

Silver

V.F.

8 (Mining thaler). IOSEPHUS WENCESLAUS S.R.I. PR. DE FURSTENBERG. Bust. Rev. St. Wenzel and mining scene. 28 gr. 1767 . . . . .1250.00

9 (3 Mining thaler). Sim. but 64 mm. 1767 . . . . .RRR

9a (4 Mining thaler). 1767 . . . .RRR

9b (9 Mining thaler). 1767 . . . .RRR

9c (10 Mining thaler). 1767 . . . . .RRR

GERMAN STATES

FÜRSTENBERG (Cont.)

Joseph Maria Benedict 1783-96

Silver

E.F.

11 X EINE etc. (= Mining Conv. thaler). IOS. M.B. FURST ZU FURSTENBERG. Bust. Rev. mining scene. 1790 ....375.00

Carl Joachim 1796-1804

Copper

F-VF

13 EIN (=1)/KREUZER. C. J. D.G. PRINC. IN FURSTENBERG. Arms. Rev. value. 1804 .... 7.50

Billon

Fine

14 III KR(euzer). FURST. FURSTENB. etc. CJF mon. Rev. Arms. 1804 ....17.50

*15 VI/KREUZER. Sim. 1804 ..20.00

*16 10 (kreuzer). CAROLUS IOACHIM D.G. PRINC. FURSTENBERG. Bust. Rev. CXX etc. Arms. 1804 ....30.00

17 20 (kreuzer). Sim. but LX etc. 1804 ....35.00

Silver

V.F.

18 (Conv. thaler). Sim. 1804 ..600.00

Younger Line in Bohemia Carl Egon I, Died 1787

Gold

E.F.

21 (ducat). CAROLUS EGON PRIN. IN FÙRSTENBERG. Bust. Rev. Arms. 1772 ....1300.00

FUGGER, Counts

Wealthy banking and commercial family of Augsburg. Given hereditary rank of counts of Kirchberg and Weissenhorn (in Swabia) with the mint right, 1534. Mediatized to Bavaria and Württemberg 1806.

Joint Coinage of Cajetan zu Zinnenberg 1751-91 (Elder Line) and Carl zu Norndorf 1710-84 (Younger Line)

Silver

V.F.

1 (thaler). CAI. & CAR. COM. DE FVGGER etc. Arms. Rev. IOSEPH II etc. Imp. eagle. 1781 ....295.00

FULDA, Abbey and Bishopric

About 70 miles N.E. of Frankfurt am Main. Abbey founded 744. First coins 11th century. Raised to bishopric 1752. Secularized 1802. To Nassau-Orange 1802-07; to Westphalia 1807-13 (part to Grand Duchy of Frankfurt 1810-13); finally to Hesse-Cassel 1813-66.

Arms: Silver, black cross.

Coinage of the Bishopric Adalbert II, Freiherr von Walderdorf, Bishop 1757-59

Copper

Fine

2 II/HELLER. A.E.F. Script mon. cwnd. Rev. F.F.L.M. value. 1759 .... 8.00

Silver (lower values billon)

4 4/KREUZER. FURST. FULD. 3 shields. Rev. LAND MUNZ. value. 1757 .... 8.00

6 VI/EINEN (= ⅙)/REICHS/THALER. Bust. Rev. value. 1757 ....14.00

*8 VI/EINEN/REICHS/THALER. Cwnd. AEF mon. 1758-59 ....16.00

10 20 (kreuzer). ADALBERTUS D.G. EP.ET AB. FULD etc., bust. Rev. NACH DEM etc. 60 EINE etc. 3 shields. 1758 ....15.00

12 20 STÜCK etc. (= ½ Conv. thaler). Bust. Rev. 3 shields. 1758 ....55.00

Gold (ducat =3.49 gr.)

E.F.

14 (2 ducats). Bust. Rev. RELIGIONE etc. Arms, supported. 1759 ....1900.00

Heinrich VIII, Freiherr von Bibra, Bishop 1759-88

Copper

Fine

16 1/PFENNING. H.E.F. mon. cwnd. Rev. F.F.L.M./value. 1769 .... 6.00

Billon

18 II/PFENNIGE. 1769 ...... 7.00

20 IIII/PFENNIGE. F.F.L.M. Cwnd. Rev. value. 1763 .... 7.00

22 1/KREUZER. Arms/MM. Rev. value. 1765 H.M., 1769 V.H 9.00

24 (groschen or "schilling"). F over arms. Rev. S. BONIFACI GERMA APOSTOL, St. Boniface. 1762 .... 8.00

*26 240/EINE etc. (= 5 Conv. kreuzer). Fulda and Bibra (beaver) arms. 1763 .... 8.00

28 240 EINE etc. (= 5 Conv. kreuzer). Arms divide F-F/H.M. Rev. IUSTIRT/240 etc. 1765 .... 8.00

30 240 EINE etc. (= 5 Conv. kreuzer). HEF mon. divides F-F. Rev. as No. 28. 1765 ...18.00

Silver

V.F.

32 10 (Conv. kreuzer). Arms. Rev. value. 1761 ....18.00

34 10 (kreuzer). AD NORMAM etc. Arms on pedestal. Rev. CXX EINE etc. 1765-66 ....14.00

38 CXX EINE etc. (= 10 Conv. kreuzer). Arms. Rev. legend. On his death. 1788 ....16.00

40 20 (Conv. kreuzer). HENRICUS D.G. EPIS. ET ABB. etc. Bust. Rev. Arms (var.). 1761-70 ...22.00

42 LX EINE etc. (= 20 Conv. kreuzer). Arms in 2 shields. Rev. value. 1763 ....18.00

*46 LX EINE etc. (= 20 Conv. kreuzer). On his death. 1788 ....22.00

48 XX E.F. etc. (½ Conv. thaler). Bust. Rev. Arms. 1762 .....55.00

GERMAN STATES

FULDA (Cont.)

50 X EINE etc. (= Conv. thaler).
Bust. Rev. CONSILIO etc. Arms.
1764 . . . . 400.00 *(V.F.)*

50a 10 EINE etc. 1765 (2 var.).110.00

Gold

*51 (ducat). 1779 . . . . 1800.00

51a —. Rev. legend. 1779 . . . . 2000.00

51b —. Obv. legend. 1779 . . . . 2000.00

Nos. 51a and 51b are mules commemorating Heinrich's 50th Jubilee as a priest and the 1000th anniversary of the death of St. Sturm, the first abbot.

Sede Vacante 1788

Silver
E.F.

52 X E.F.M. (= Conv. thaler).
MONETA CAPIT. CATHEDR.
FULD etc. St. Boniface. Rev.
15 shields encircle Fulda arms.
1788 . . . . 165.00

Adalbert III, Freiherr von Harstall, Bishop 1788-1802

Silver
V.F.

53 XX EINE etc. (= ½ Conv.
thaler). Like No. 55. 1796 . . . 45.00

54 XX EINE etc. (= ½ Conv.
thaler). Like No. 56 but arms
cwnd. 1796 . . . . 60.00

55 X EINE etc. (= Conv. thaler).
ADALBERTUS D.G. EPIS. etc.
Bust. Rev. PRO DEO etc. Arms.
1795-96 . . . . 150.00

56 X EINE etc. (= Conv. thaler).
ADALBERTUS etc. Arms under
3 helmets. Rev. PRO DEO etc.
in wreath. 1795 . . . . 350.00

57 X EINE etc. (= Conv. thaler).
Obv. like No. 55. Rev. like
No. 56. 1795 . . . . 175.00

FÜRSTENBERG.
Indexed as Fuerstenberg.

GIMBORN (WALLMODEN-GIMBORN), County

In the Rhineland. Bought by Field Marshal Count Johann Ludwig von Wallmoden in 1782. Mediatized to Berg in 1806.

(Johann) Ludwig 1782-1806

Billon
V.F.

1 24/EINEN (=¹/₂₄)/THALER.
MONETA GIMBORNENSIS, LW
mon. Rev. value. 1802 . . . . . 35.00

Silver

2 XX/EINE etc. (= ½ Conv.
thaler). LUDOV. S.R.I. COMES
A WALLMODEN GIMBORN. Arms.
Rev. value. 1802 . . . . 125.00

Gold

3 I/DUCAT. Obv. like No. 1.
Rev. value. 1802 . . . . RRR

GOSLAR, Free City

31 miles S.W. of Brunswick. Founded about 920. Had its own local coinage from the mid 14th century until 1764. Absorbed by Prussia 1802.

Copper

Fine

*1 I/LEICHTER (light)/
PFENNING. 1749-58 . . . . . . 4.00

1a —. 1763-64 . . . . 5.00

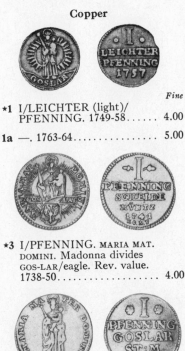

*3 I/PFENNING. MARIA MAT.
DOMINI. Madonna divides
GOS-LAR/eagle. Rev. value.
1738-50 . . . . 4.00

*4 I/PFENNING. MARIA
MATER etc. Madonna. Rev.
value/GOSLAR/ST. M. 1752-
60 . . . . 4.00

*5 I PFENN(ing). MARIA MA etc.
Madonna. Rev. value/
SCHEIDE/MUNTZ/1763-64 . . . . 4.00

Billon

F-VF

*7 VI (pfennig). 1764 . . . . 6.00

7a —. Obv. Eagle/GOSLAR.
1764 . . . . 5.00

9 I/MARIEN/GROS(chen).
1764 . . . . 10.00

11 24/EINEN (=¹/₂₄)/THALER.
MON. NOV. CIVIT. IMPERIAL
GOSL. Arms. Rev. value.
1764 . . . . 7.00

13 12/EINEN (=¹/₁₂)/THALER.
Like No. 11. 1764 . . . . 7.00

GÜLICH. See Jülich-Berg.

HALL (AM KOCHER) in SWABIA (REIPUBLICA HALAE SUEVICAE), Free City

Old city 35 miles N.E. of Stuttgart. Original mint place of the heller in the 12th century. Hall was annexed to Württemberg in 1803.

Arms: Imperial eagle, cross, hand.

Billon

F-VF

*3 (pfennig). Uniface. 1751-
74, N.D 7.50

Silver
VF-EF

5 (½ Conv. thaler). MONETA
NOVA REIPUBLICÆ HALÆ
SUEVICÆ. 3 shields. Rev.
IOSEPHVS II etc. Bust of Emp.
Joseph II. 14 gr. 1777 . . . . . 80.00

7 (Conv. thaler). Like No. 5.
1777 . . . . 225.00

Gold
V.F.

10 (ducat). Like No. 5.
1777, N.D 950.00

HAMBURG, Free City

North Sea port some 75 miles up the Elbe. Founding member of the Hanseatic League. City coinage 13th through 20th centuries.

Many die varieties of early Hamburg coins exist.

Arms: City wall with 3 towers, center of which is highest.

Monetary System:
12 pfennige = 4 dreilinge = 2 sechslinge = 1 schilling; 16 schillinge = 1 Mark.
1753-1815:
54-60 schillinge courant = 48 schillinge banco = 1 Conv. thaler.
1815-71:
48 schillinge courant = 1 Reichsthaler.

GERMAN STATES

HAMBURG (Cont.)

Billon or Silver

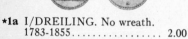

F-VF

*1 I/DREI/LING. 3 towers in
wreath. Rev. value. 1750-
66.................. 2.00

*1a I/DREILING. No wreath.
1783-1855.............. 2.00

3 I/SECHS/LING. HAMBURGER,
3 towers in wreath.
Rev. value. 1726-64 .... 4.00

*3a I/SECHSLING. 1778-1885.. 2.00

*5 I/SCHIL/LING. 1726-68 ... 2.00

*6 I/SCHILLING. 3 towers.
Rev. value/HAMBURGER/
COURANT. 1776-1819........ 2.00

*6a —. Rev. value/HAMB.COUR./
1823-55 .... 1.50

10 II SCHIL(ling). HAMBURGER
CURRENT. 3 towers in wreath.
Rev. FRANCISCVS D.G. etc.
Imp. eagle. 1762.......... 6.00

Silver

13 IIII SCHIL(ling). Like No.
10. 1749-65 .... 4.00

15 4 SCHILLING. Like No.
21. 1797................. 3.00

F-VF

17 6 SCHIL(ling). 1762...... 8.00

19 8 SCHILL(ing). HAMBURGER
CURRENT GELDT. Arms. Rev.
FRANCISCVS etc. Imp. eagle.
1761-64.................. 8.00

*21 8 SCHILLING. 1797...... 5.00

23 12 SCHIL(ling). 1762.....15.00

25 16 SCHIL(ing). Like No. 19.
1764.................... 15.00

27 16 SCHILLING. HAMBURGER
COURANT. Arms. Rev.
IOSEPHUS II etc. Imp. eagle.
1789.................... 15.00

30 32 SCHILL(ing). Like No. 19.
1748-64.................. 20.00

30a —. 1767 .... 20.00

33 32 SCHILLING. Like No. 27.
1788-89 .... 20.00

*35 32 SCHILLING.
FRANCISCVS II etc.
1794, 95, 96, 97........... 25.00

39 32/SCHILLINGE. Like No.
39a. 38mm. 1808.......... 30.00

F-VF

*39a 1809. Reduced size........30.00

40 48 SCHILL(ing). MONETA
NOVA HAMBURGENSIS. Arms.
Rev. FRANCISCVS etc. Imp.
eagle. 1761-64.......(V.F.) 65.00

Gold (ducat = 3.49 gr.)

V.F.

41 (ducat). Like No. 42.
1746-65 ....500.00

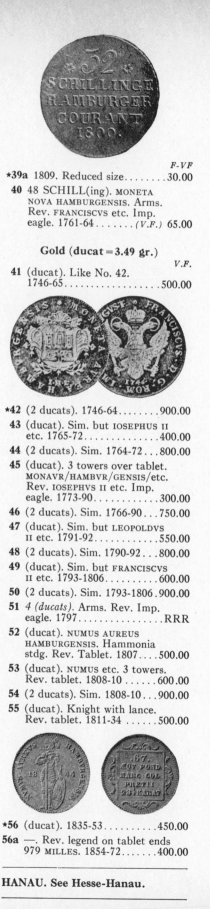

*42 (2 ducats). 1746-64.......900.00

43 (ducat). Sim. but IOSEPHUS II
etc. 1765-72.............400.00

44 (2 ducats). Sim. 1764-72...800.00

45 (ducat). 3 towers over tablet.
MONAVR/HAMBVR/GENSIS/etc.
Rev. IOSEPHVS II etc. Imp.
eagle. 1773-90...........300.00

46 (2 ducats). Sim. 1766-90...750.00

47 (ducat). Sim. but LEOPOLDVS
II etc. 1791-92..........550.00

48 (2 ducats). Sim. 1790-92...800.00

49 (ducat). Sim. but FRANCISCVS
II etc. 1793-1806.........600.00

50 (2 ducats). Sim. 1793-1806.900.00

51 4 (ducats). Arms. Rev. Imp.
eagle. 1797...............RRR

52 (ducat). NUMUS AUREUS
HAMBURGENSIS. Hammonia
stdg. Rev. Tablet. 1807....500.00

53 (ducat). NUMUS etc. 3 towers.
Rev. tablet. 1808-10 ......600.00

54 (2 ducats). Sim. 1808-10...900.00

55 (ducat). Knight with lance.
Rev. tablet. 1811-34 ......500.00

*56 (ducat). 1835-53.........450.00

56a —. Rev. legend on tablet ends
979 MILLES. 1854-72.......400.00

HANAU. See Hesse-Hanau.

GERMAN STATES

HANNOVER (KÖNIGREICH HANNOVER), Kingdom

In 1814 the Electorate of Brunswick-Lüneburg, which had been re-established after the downfall of Napoleon, became the Kingdom of Hannover. See B-L for coins of 1807 and prior.

Georg III,
King of Great Britain 1760-1820, Elector of Brunswick-Lüneburg 1760-1807, 13-14, King of Hannover 1814-20

Copper

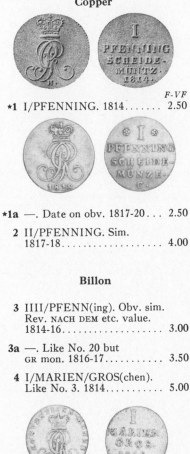

F-VF

*1 I/PFENNING. 1814 . . . . . . 2.50

*1a —. Date on obv. 1817-20 . . . 2.50

2 II/PFENNING. Sim. 1817-18 . . . . 4.00

Billon

3 IIII/PFENN(ing). Obv. sim. Rev. NACH DEM etc. value. 1814-16 . . . . 3.00

3a —. Like No. 20 but GR mon. 1816-17 . . . . 3.50

4 I/MARIEN/GROS(chen). Like No. 3. 1814 . . . . 5.00

*4a —. 1816-18 . . . . 4.50

5 24/EINEN (=1/24)/THALER. Horse/date. Rev. NACH etc. value/c. 1814 . . . . 4.00

6 24/EINEN/THALER. Like No. 3a. 1817-18 . . . . 4.00

7 12/EINEN (=1/12)/THALER. Like No. 5. 1814-16 . . . . 4.00

F-VF

*8 3/MARIEN/GROSCHEN. 1816-20 . . . . 6.00

Silver

V.F.

*9 ⅔ (thaler). 1813 . . . . pattern

*10 ⅔ (thaler). 1813-14 . . . . 35.00

11 16/GUTE (good)/GROSCHEN. horse. Rev. value. 1820 . . . . . 75.00

11a —. with BRITANNIARUM. 1820 . . . . 300.00

Gold

12 I/DUCAT. Horse. Rev. EX AURO HERCINIAE (=Harzgold). value. 1815, 18 . . . . 1200.00

13 2½/THALER. Horse. Rev. value. 1814 . . . . 750.00

*14 V/THALER. 1813-15 . . . . . 800.00

15 V/THALER. Like No. 13 but EX AURO etc. (=Harzgold). 1814 . . . . 2500.00

V.F.

16 X/THALER. Like No. 13. 1813 . . . . 1850.00

16a —. 1814 . . . . 1500.00

Georg IV,
King of Great Britain and Hannover 1820-30, Prince-Regent of Brunswick-Wolfenbuttel (q.v.) 1815-23

Copper

F-VF

17 I/PFENNING. GR mon. Rev. value. 1821 . . . . 1.50

17a I/PFENNIG. 1821-30 . . . . . . 1.50

18 II/PFENNING. Sim. 1821- 3.50

18a II/PFENNIGE. 1822-30 . . . 2.00

19 4/PFENNIGE. Sim. 1827 . . 15.00

Note: For coins of Georg IV in stüber denominations, see East Friesland.

Billon or Silver

*20 IIII/PFENN(ig). 1822-30 . . . 3.00

21 24/EINEN (=1/24)/THALER. Sim. 1826-28 . . . . 3.00

22 3/MARIEN/GROSCHEN. Horse. Rev. value. 1821 . . . . 3.00

23 12/EINEN (=1/12)/THALER. Sim. 1822-24 . . . . 3.00

Silver

24 6/EINEN (=⅙)/THALER. Sim. 1821 . . . . 8.50

*25 16/GUTE/GROSCHEN. 1820-21 (var.) 17.50

25a —. Rev. value/date. 1822-30 . . . . 17.50

HANNOVER (Cont.)

F-VF

26 ⅔ (thaler). Like No. 26a but larger head. Rev. BRUNVICENSIS etc. 1822-29C 40.00
★26a —. 1826-28B 55.00
27 X EINE etc. (= Conv. mining thaler). Head. Rev. DIE GRUBE/BERGWERKS/ WOHLFAHRT/etc. 1830 .....450.00

Gold

VF-EF

28 I/DUCAT. Horse. Rev. EX AURO etc. (=Harzgold), value. 1821, 24, 27 ....1450.00
29 2½/THALER. Head. Rev. value. 1821-30 ....600.00
30 V/THALER. Like No. 28. Harzgold. 1821 ....RRR
31 V/THALER. Like No. 29. 1821-30 ....800.00
32 X/THALER. Sim. 1821-30 ....1450.00

WILHELM IV,
King of Great Britain
and Hannover 1830-37

Copper

F-VF

★35 I/PFENNIG. 1831-34 ...... 1.50
35a —. w/out SCHEIDE/MUNZE. 1834 .... 4.00

★36 1/PFENNIG. 1835-37 ..... 3.00

F-VF

37 II/PFENNIGE. Like No. 35. 1831-34 .... 1.50
38 2/PFENNIGE. Like No. 36. 1835-37 .... 2.00
38a 2/PFENNIG. 1837 .... 10.00
39 4/PFENNIGE. Like No. 35. 1831 ....17.00

Billon

40 4/PFENN(ig). Like No. 36. 1835-37 .... 6.00
41 24/EINEN (=1/24)/THALER. Sim. 1834. (var.) 5.00
41a —. 1835-37 .... 2.00

★43 12/EINEN (=1/12)/THALER. Head. Rev. value. 1834-37 .. 4.00

Silver

V.F.

44 VI EINEN (=1/6) THALER. Head. Rev. Arms. 1834 .....12.50
45 16/GUTE/GROSCHEN. Horse. Rev. value. 1830-34 ....35.00

The 1834 struck in a collar is a pattern.

46 ⅔ (thaler). Arms. Rev. ⅔. 1832-33 ....35.00
46.5 ⅔ (Mining thaler). Legend: AUSBEUTE/etc. Rev. ⅔. 1833 ....80.00

★47 ⅔ (thaler). 1834 ....30.00
47a —. Struck in collar. 1834 ...60.00
47b —. ⅔ divides 18-34 ....90.00

VF-EF

★48 XVIII EINE etc. (=⅔ Mining thaler). Head. Rev. ★ 1834 ....300.00

V.F.

49 EIN (=1) THALER. Variety of No. 49a. 1834 .... 45.00
★49a —. 1835-37 .... 30.00
50 I/THALER. Head Rev. value. 1834-35 .... 40.00

Gold

VF-EF

★51 I/DUCAT. (Harzgold). 1831 ....1250.00
52 2½/THALER. Head. Rev. value. 1832-35 ....700.00
52a —. 1836-37 ....700.00
53 FÜNF (=5) THAL(er). Head. Rev. Arms. 1835 ....1450.00
54 ZEHN (=10) THALER. Head. Rev. Arms. 1832 ...1200.00
55 ZEHN THAL(er). Like No. 53. 1833-37 ....1100.00

Ernst August,
Duke of Cumberland,
King of Hannover 1837-51

Copper

F-VF

56 1/PFENNIG. EAR mon. Rev. value. 1837-46 .... 2.50
56a —. SCHEIDE MUNZE on rev. 1838 .... 8.00
58 (pfennig). EAR mon. Rev. GLÜCK/AUF! Royal mint visit (1839) 25.00

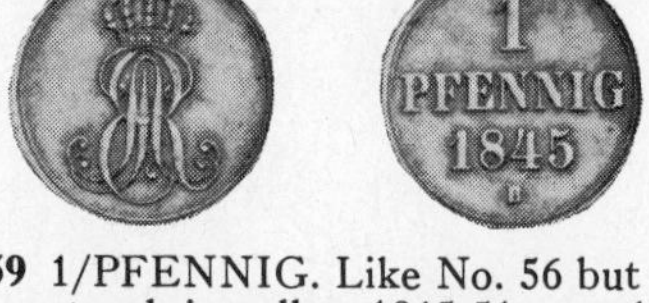

★59 1/PFENNIG. Like No. 56 but struck in collar. 1845-51 .... 1.00

HANNOVER (Cont.)

F-VF

60 2/PFENNIGE. Like No. 56.
1837-46 . . . . 2.00

61 2/PFENNIGE. Like No. 59.
1845-51 . . . . 1.50

Billon

62 4/PFENN(ig). Arms.
Rev. value. 1838-42 . . . . 2.50

***63** 6/PFENNIGE. 1843-45 . . . 2.50

***64** 6/PFENNIGE. 1846-51 . . . . 2.50

***65** 24/EINEN (=¹/₂₄)/THALER.
1838-46 . . . . 2.50

Silver

Fine

66 12/EINEN (=¹/₁₂)/THALER.
Head. Rev. value. 1838B,
39-40S 4.75

66a —. Larger head. 1841-44S . 3.75

66b —. Head changed.
1844-47B 3.75

66c —. Older head. 1848-51B . . 4.50

67 VI EINEN (=¹/₆) THALER.
Head. Rev. arms. 1840S 10.00

67a —. Different cwn. over arms.
1841S, 44B 8.00

67b —. Altered dies. 1845, 47B . . 8.00

V.F.

68 ⅔ (thaler). Head.
Rev. ⅔. 1838 . . . . 80.00

68a —. 1839 . . . . 15.00

69 EIN (=1) THALER. Small
head (21mm high). Rev. Arms
in order chain. 1838-39 . . . . . 35.00

69a —. Head 24mm. 1838-40 . . . 30.00

70 (thaler). Head. Rev. Glückauf!
etc. Royal mint visit.
1839 . . . . (E.F.) 200.00

V.F.

***71** EIN (=1) THALER.
1840 . . . . Rare

71a —. w/out FEINES-SILBER.
1840-49. (5 var.) 18.00

73 (thaler). Head. Rev. GEORG/
KRONPRINZ etc. Marriage of
Crown Prince. 1843
. . . . (E.F.) 325.00

74 EIN (=1 mining) THALER.
Like No. 71a but with HARZ-
SEGEN. 1849 . . . . 65.00

***74a** —. BERGSEGEN DES HARZES.
1850-51 . . . . 30.00

Gold

VF-EF

76 2½/THALER. Head.
Rev. value. 1839-48 . . . . . . 550.00

77 2½ THALER. Head.
Rev. Arms. 1850 . . . . 650.00

78 FUNF (=5) THAL(er). Head.
Rev. Arms. 1839-43 . . . . 600.00

79 FÜNF (=5) THAL(er). Head.
Rev. Arms. 1845-51 . . . . 650.00

80 5 THALER. Head. Rev. HARZ-
GOLD. Arms. 1849-50 . . . . . 1000.00

81 ZEHN (=10) THAL(er).
Like No. 78. 1837-39 . . . . . 1100.00

82 ZEHN (=10) THAL(er).
Like No. 79. 1844-51 . . . . . 1200.00

Georg V, King 1851-66
Ousted by Prussia, Which
Absorbed Hannover 1866

Monetary System: Prior to 1857 —
24 groschen = 1 thaler; 1857 on — 30
groschen = 1 Vereinsthaler.

Copper

F-VF

***83** 1/PFENNIG. Decorated
GvR mon. Rev. value.
1852 . . . . 20.00

***84** 1/PFENNIG. 1853-56 . . . . . . 1.00

85 1/PFENNIG. Like No. 87.
1858-64 . . . . 1.00

86 2/PFENNIGE. Like No. 84.
1852-56 . . . . 1.00

***87** 2/PFENNIGE. 1858-64 . . . . 1.00

Billon

Fine

***88** 6/PFENNIGE. Horse.
Rev. value. 1852-56 . . . . 1.50

***89** ½/GROSCHEN. 1858-65 . . . 1.50

90 24/EINEN (=¹/₂₄)/THALER.
Like No. 88. 1854-56 . . . . 2.00

***91** 1/GROSCHEN. 1858-66 . . . . 1.50

GERMAN STATES
....

HANNOVER (Cont.)

F-VF

92 12/EINEN (=1/12)/THALER.
Head. Rev. value. 1852-53 .. 3.00

93 12/EINEN (=1/12)/THALER.
Head. Rev. value. 1859-62.. 3.50

Silver

V.F.

*94 6 EINEN (=1/6) THALER.
1859-66................ 8.00

95 EIN (=1 mining) THALER.
Head. Rev. BERGSEGEN etc.
Arms. 1852-56...........35.00

96 (thaler). Head. Rev. ZUR
ERIN-NERUNG etc. Royal
mint visit. 1853.....(E.F.) 2400.00

*97 EIN (=1) VEREINS-
THALER. Head. Rev. Arms.
supported. 1857-66........20.00

98 (thaler). Head. Rev. DEN/
SIEGERN etc. Waterloo
anniversary. 1865.........75.00

99 EIN (=1) THALER. Head.
Rev. legend ZUR/50 etc.
50th anniv. union of East
Friesland with Hannover.
1865...................450.00

100 EIN (=1) THALER. Head.
Rev. Upstalboom Tree.
Same occasion. 1865.....325.00

101 (2 thaler). Head. Rev.
MARIE/GEORG etc. (names
of Royal family). Mint
visit. 1854........ (E.F.) 3000.00

102 2 THALER. Like No. 97.
1854-55................100.00

103 ZWEI (=2) VEREINS-
THALER. Sim. 1862, 66..100.00

Gold

Gold

VF-EF

104 2½ THALER. Head.
Rev. Arms. 1853, 55.....500.00

105 FÜNF (=5) TH(a)L(e)R.
Sim. 1853-56...........500.00

106 5 THALER. Head.
Rev. HARZ-GOLD. Arms.
1853..................1200.00

107 ZEHN (=10) THLR.
Like No. 104. 1853-56...1200.00

108 ½/KRONE. Like No. 109.
1857-66................800.00

*109 1/KRONE. 1857-66.....1000.00

HENNEBERG.

**See Saxe-Meiningen Nos. 3 and
8, and Saxony Nos. 96 and 99.**

HESSE-CASSEL
(HESSEN-CASSEL),
Landgraviate until 1803,
Electorate 1803-66

State in S.W. Germany ruled from the
13th century by landgraves descended
from the landgraves of Thuringia. In
1803 Landgraf Wilhelm IX was given
the title of Elector (Kurfürst) of the
Holy Roman Empire which he and his
successors retained despite the aboli-
tion of the Empire in 1806. Hesse-
Cassel was temporarily merged into the
kingdom of Westphalia 1807-13 and
was finally absorbed by Prussia in 1866.

Arms: Blue, single tailed lion. Body
covered by barry of 10, silver and red.

Monetary Systems: Until 1838 —
12 heller = 1 albus; 32 albus = 24 gute
groschen = 1 Reichsthaler.

1838-66 —
12 heller = 1 silbergroschen; 30 silbergroschen = 1 (Vereins)thaler.

Wilhelm VIII, Count of
Hesse-Hanau-Münzenberg (q.v.)
1736-60, in Hesse-Cassel 1751-60

Copper

VG-F

1 I/HELLER. Like No. 2.
1751-58................. 2.00

*2 II/HELLER. 1751-58...... 2.50

VG-F

3 III/HELLER. WILH. VIII D.G.
HASS. LANDG. Bust. Rev.
value. 1755 .... 3.50

*4 I/HELLER. 1758-59...... 2.00

5 III/HELLER. Sim. 1758... 5.00

Billon

7 IIII/HELLER. Cwnd. lion
shield, no legend. Rev. value.
1753-57.................. 4.00

9 6 HELLER. 1756.......... 5.00

11 (albus). WL cwnd. Rev. Hessian
lion. 1751-53.............. 4.00

Silver

V.F.

13 1/9 I. MARCK etc. (=Species
thaler). WILHELM VIII etc. Bust.
Rev. RECTUS etc. Arms supported. 1754 R.N........275.00

14 1/9 MARCK etc. (=Sp. th.).
Sim. but with AUS BIEBER
(=Bieber mining thaler).
1754, 59................175.00

Gold (ducat = 3.49 gr.)

16 ¼ (ducat) Mon. Rev. lion.
1752...................450.00

*17 (ducat). 1751, 54.........950.00

**See Hesse-Hanau-Münzenberg and
Schmalkalden for other coins of
Wilhelm VIII.**

Friedrich II, in Hesse-Cassel
1760-85

Copper

Fine

20 I/HELLER. Double FL mon.
Rev. value/SCHEIDE/MUNTZ.
1760-61................. 2.50

21 III/HELLER. Sim. 1760-
61...................... 2.50

22 IIII/HELLER. Sim. 1760-
62...................... 3.50

23 1/HELLER. Like No. 27.
1772.................... 2.00

24 2/HELLER. Sim. 1772..... 2.50

25 3/HELLER. Sim. 1772..... 3.00

26 4/HELLER. Sim. 1773..... 4.00

GERMAN STATES

HESSE-CASSEL (Cont.)

Fine

★**27** 6/HELLER. 1772 . . . . 6.00

28 8/HELLER. Sim. 1772 . . . . . 8.00

29 2/HELLER. FL mon. Rev. value/SCHEIDE/MUNTZ. 1765 . . . . 2.00

30 4/HELLER. Sim. 1765 . . . . . 3.00

31 3/HELLER. Sim. but w/out SCHEIDE/MUNTZ. 1774 . . . . . . 2.00

32 6/HELLER. Sim. 1775 . . . . . 5.00

★**33** I/HELLER. 1774-75 . . . . 2.00

34 2/HELLER. Like No. 36. 1774-77 . . . . 2.00

35 4/HELLER. Sim. 1774-82 . . 4.00

★**36** 8/HELLER. 1774-82 . . . . 7.00

Copper Coinage for Ober (Upper) Hessen

37 ¼/KREUZER. HESSEN CASSEL. Arms. Rev. value. 1783 . . . . . 4.00

38 ½/KREUZER. Sim. 1783 . . 4.00

39 1/KREUZER. Sim. 1783 . . . 4.00

Billon

41 *6 HELLER*. 1770 . . . . 4.00

43 8/HELLER. Lion. Rev. value. 1769 . . . . 5.00

★**45** I/ALBUS. Cwnd. FL mon. Rev. I/HESSEN/ALBUS. 1768-70 . . . . 4.00

Fine

47 24/EINEN (=1/24)/THAL(er). Type of No. 48 but mmk. B.R. under lion. 1780 . . . . 5.00

★**48** 24/EINEN (=1/24)/THALER. 1783-85 . . . . 5.00

50 II/ALBUS. Like No. 45. 1775-82 . . . . 5.00

Silver

F-VF

52 *12/EINEN* (=1/12)/*REICHS/THALER*. Arms. Rev. value. 1764 . . . . 6.00

★**54** XII/EINEN (=1/12)/REICHS/THAL(er). Lion holds shield. Rev. FURSTL. HESS etc., value. 1765-69 . . . . 5.00

56 4/ALBUS. Like No. 58. 1763-64 . . . . 6.00

★**58** VIII/EINEN (=1/8)/REICHS/THAL(er). *V.F.* 1766-69 . . . . 8.00

60 *VIII EINEN REICHS THALER*. 1776 . . . . 8.00

62 VI/EINEN (=1/6)/REICHS/THAL(er). Like No. 54. 1766-72 . . . . 9.00

66 6/EINEN etc. (=1/6 Reichs th.). Lion. Rev. value. 1773 . . . . . 9.00

68 IV/EINEN etc. (=¼ Reichs th.). Like No. 58. 1763-72 . . . 8.00

70 40 ST. EINE MARK etc. (=⅓ Reichs th.=¼ Conv. th.). FRIDER II D.G. HASS. LANDG. Bust. Rev. Arms. 1766 . . . . . 13.00

71 ⅓ (Reichs th.). Sim. but head. 1767-71 . . . . 13.00

★**73** EIN HALBER (=½ Reichs) THALER. 1776 . . . . 16.00

V.F.

75 XX ST. EINE etc. (=⅔ Reichs th.). Like No. 70. 1766 . . . . 28.00

76 ⅔ (Reichsthaler). Like No. 71. 1767 . . . . 26.00

78 ⅔ *(Reichsthaler)*. Bust. Rev. Arms. 1785 . . . . 28.00

80 1/10 MARCK etc. (= Conv. thaler). Bust l. Rev. Arms. 1763 . . . . 275.00

81 X EINE etc. (= Conv. thaler). Sim. but bust r. 1765 . . . . . . 180.00

82 X ST. EINE etc. (= Conv. thaler). Like No. 70. 1766 . . 160.00

83 X ST. EINE etc. (= Conv. thaler). Like No. 71. 1766 . . 140.00

84 EIN (=1 Reichs) THALER. Like No. 73. 1776-79 . . . . 90.00

Gold (pistole = 6.7 gr.)

85 (ducat). FRIDERICVS II etc. Bust. Rev. SIC. FVLG etc. (=Edder River gold). 1775 R.N 2500.00

86 (pistole = 5 thaler). Like No. 73. 1771-85 . . . . 1000.00

87 (2 pistoles). Sim. 1773-85 . 2000.00

See Schaumburg-Hessen for other coins of Friedrich II.

Wilhelm IX, Count of Hesse-Hanau-Münzenberg 1760-1821, Landgrave of Hesse-Cassel 1785-1803, Elector of H-C 1803-21, Ousted by French 1807-13

A. As Landgrave Wilhelm IX, 1785-1803.

Copper

Fine

88 I/HELLER. Like No. 33. 1790 . . . . 2.00

★**89** I/HELLER. 1791-1803 . . . . . 2.00

90 2/HELLER. Lion supports shield on which is WL mon. Rev. value. 1790-95 . . . . 2.00

91 3/HELLER. Like No. 89. 1791 . . . . 4.00

92 4/HELLER. Like No. 90. 1788-94 . . . . 5.00

Copper coinage for Ober (Upper) Hessen

93 ¼/KREUZER. Like No. 37 1801-02 . . . . 4.00

94 ½/KREUZER. Sim. 1801-03 . . . . 4.00

Billon

96 24/EINEN (=1/24)/THALER. Like No. 48. 1786-1802 . . . . . 3.00

GERMAN STATES

HESSE-CASSEL (Cont.)

Silver

V.F.

98 *VI/EINEN* (=1/6) */THALER.* Arms. Rev. value. 1790-96 .. 9.00

99 VI/EINEN/THALER. Lion shield. Rev. value/date/F. 1798-1802.......... 10.00

★101 EIN HALBER (=1/2 Reichs) THALER. 1789.......... 28.00

103 XX EINE etc. (=1/2 Conv. thaler). *Head. Rev. Arms.* From Bieber Mines. 1786 .. 40.00

105 EIN (=1 Reichs) THALER. Like No. 101. 1789....... 165.00

106 X EINE etc. (= Conv. thaler). Head. Rev. Arms/BIBERER (Mines)/SILBER. 1785 .... 200.00

106a —. BIEBER etc. above arms. 1787-1802............... 200.00

108 ZWEY (=2 Reichs) THALER. Like No. 101. 1789....... 600.00

Gold

VF-EF

109 (5 thaler). Head. Rev. Order star. 1786-90............ 900.00

110 5 THALER. Head. Rev. Arms, lion, etc. 1791-1801....... 850.00

B. As Elector Wilhelm I 1803-07, 13-21.

Copper

Fine

111 I/HELLER. Like No. 113. 1803-06, 14-20............ 2.00

112 2/HELLER. Sim. 1814-20...................... 3.00

★113 4/HELLER. 1815-21...... 4.00

Copper coinage for Ober-Hessen, etc.

114 1/2/KREUZER. KUR HESSEN. Arms. Rev. value. 1803-04..................... 4.00

Billon

Fine

115 24/EINEN (=1/24)/THALER. Like No. 48. 1803-07F, 07C, 14-21.................... 2.75

Silver

V.F.

116 VI/EINEN (=1/6)/THALER. Lion in scalloped shield. Rev. value. 1803F 14.00

116a —. Oval shield. 1803-07F, 07C..................... 9.00

117 EIN/HALBER (=1/2) / THALER. Head. Rev. value. 1819-20.................. 20.00

118 EIN (=1) THALER. Sim. 1819-20.................. 75.00

The 1813 Convention thaler is a pattern.

Gold

VF-EF

119 5 THALER. Like No. 110. 1803-06................. 850.00

★120 5 THALER. 1814-20. (var.).................. 950.00

See Hesse-Hanau-Münzenberg and Schaumburg-Hessen for additional coins of Wilhelm I (IX).

Wilhelm II, alone 1821-31

Copper

Fine

121 I/HELLER. Like No. 113. 1822-24................. 2.00

121a —. (var.). 1825-31........ 2.00

122 2/HELLER. Like No. 121a. 1831.................... 2.00

123 4/HELLER. Sim. 1821-31.. 4.00

Billon

124 24/EINEN (=1/24) /THALER. Like No. 48. 1822..... 4.00

Silver

V.F.

125 VI/EINEN (=1/6) /THALER. Lion in cwnd. oval. Rev. value. 1821-22 .... 17.50

126 6/EINEN (=1/6) THALER. Obv. like No. 129. Rev. value. 1823 .... 17.50

126a —. S.L.V.HESSEN. 1823-31 .. 10.00

126b —. THAELR. 1828........ *Rare*

127 3/EINEN (=1/3) /THALER. Like No. 126a. 1822-29.... 15.00

128 EIN (=1)/THALER. Like No. 126. 1821-22......... 125.00

Gold

VF-EF

★129 5 THALER. 1821, 23.... 750.00

129a —. S.L.V. HESSEN. 1823-29.................. 1000.00

Coinage for Ober Hessen, Hanau and Fulda

Copper

Fine

130 1/4/KREUZER. KURHESSEN. Arms. Rev. value. 1824-30..................... 3.00

131 1/2/KREUZER. Sim. 1824-30..................... 3.00

132 1/KREUZER. Sim. 1825-29..................... 3.00

Billon

133 6/KREUZER. Sim. 1826-28..................... 3.00

For additional coins of this reign, see Schaumburg-Hessen.

Wilhelm II 1821-47, Under Regency of Prince Friedrich Wilhelm 1831-47

Copper

F-VF

134 2/HELLER. Cwnd. WK mon. (var. No. 113). Rev. value. 1833.................. 3.00

135 1/HELLER. KURHESSEN. Arms. Rev. value. 1842 .... 4.50

136 2/HELLER. Sim. 1842.... Rare

137 3/HELLER. Sim. 1842.... Rare

138 1/HELLER. Like No. 140. 1843-47.................. 1.25

139 2/HELLER. Sim. 1843.... 3.00

★140 3/HELLER. Sim. 1843-46..................... 1.50

Billon

141 1/2/SILBER/GROSCHEN. KURFÜRSTENTHUM HESSEN. Arms. Rev. value. 1842.................... 4.00

142 1/SILBER/GROSCHEN. Sim. 1841-47............ 1.50

143 2/SILBER/GROSCHEN. Sim. 1842.............. 4.00

GERMAN STATES

HESSE-CASSEL (Cont.)

Silver

V.F.

144 6/EINEN (= ⅙) /THALER.
Obv. like No. 147.
Rev. value. 1833-46 . . . . 7.50

144a —. Obv. like No. 147a.
1846-47 . . . . .30.00

145 EIN (= 1)/THALER. Sim.
1832-42 . . . . .20.00

146 2/THALER. Draped arms.
Rev. value. 1840-45 . . . . . 125.00

146a —. 1847 . . . . .550.00

Gold

E.F.

147 V/THALER. Like No. 147a
but KURPR. U. etc. 1834-
45 .550.00

★147a —. 1847 . . . . .900.00

148 X/THALER. Like No. 147.
1838-41 . . . . .850.00

Coinage for Ober Hessen, Hanau and Fulda

Copper

Fine

149 ¼/KREUZER. Like No.
130. 1834-35 . . . . 4.00

150 ½/KREUZER. Sim. 1834.
(1835 = pattern) 4.00

151 1/KREUZER. Sim.
1832-35 . . . . 4.00

Billon

152 6/KREUZER. Sim. but improved dies. 1831-34 . . . . 5.00

**For additional coins see Schaum-
berg-Hessen.**

Friedrich Wilhelm I 1847-66, Deposed by Prussia 1866

Copper

V.F.

★153 1/HELLER. 1849-66 . . . . . . 1.00

154 3/HELLER. Sim. 1848-66 . . 1.25

Billon

V.F.

155 1/SILBER/GROSCHEN.
Like No. 142. 1851-66 . . . . . 2.00

★156 2½/SILBER/GROSCHEN.
1852-65 . . . . 4.75

Silver

157 VI EINEN (= ⅙) THALER.
Head. Rev. Arms. 1851-
56 .17.50

158 EIN (= 1) THALER. Sim.
1851-55 . . . . .40.00

159 EIN (= 1) VEREINS-
THALER. Head. Rev. arms.
1858-65 . . . . .35.00

160 2 THALER. Sim. 1851-
55 .110.00

Gold

E.F.

161 FÜNF (= 5) THAL(er).
Head. Rev. Arms. 1851 . .1500.00

HESSE-DARMSTADT (HESSEN-DARMSTADT, GROSHERZOGTHUM HESSEN)
Landgraviate until 1806, Grand Duchy 1806-1918

In S.W. Germany. Founded in 1567 by
Georg I, the Pious, a younger brother
of Wilhelm IV, the Wise, of Hesse-
Cassel.

Arms: Until 1806, same as Hesse-
Cassel, except that lion has 2 tails; after 1806 lion carries sword.

Ludwig VIII 1739-68

Billon

VG-F

2 I/KREU/TZER. Like No. 8.
1741-66 . . . . 2.00

4 1 KR(euzer). H.D. over lion
shield. Rev. value/A.K./AD
NORM. etc. in shield. 1763 . . . 3.00

★8 2/KREU/TZER. 1741-44 . . . 2.00

11 4/KREU/TZER. H.D. over
lion. Rev. LAND MUNZ. value.
1746-48 . . . . 4.00

Silver

F-VF

14 240 STÜCK etc. (=5 Conv.
kreuzer). Double L mon.
Rev. lion shield divides H-D.
1763 . . . . 5.00

16 V (Conv.)/KREUZER.
HESSEN DARMST. lion shield.
Rev. value in rhombus 5.00

18 10 (Conv. kreuzer). LUDOVICUS
VIII D.G. LANDG. HASS. Bust.
Rev. NACH etc., lion shield in
circle of 7 small shields (var.).
1763-65 . . . . 7.00

19 X/KREUZER. HESSEN DARMST.
Double L mon. Rev. value/
NACH etc. 1765 . . . . 7.00

21 XII/KREUTZER. LUDOVICUS
D.G. HASSIAE etc. Arms. Rev.
PRINCEPS etc., value. 1759 . . . 8.00

23 20 (Conv. kreuzer). 4 double
L mons. in cruciform, H.D. in
center. Rev. like No. 18.
1762 . . . . 8.00

25 20 (Conv. kreuzer). Like No.
18. 1766 . . . . 9.00

27 30 KR(euzer). Obv. like No.
23. Rev. Arms. 1759 . . . . . . .15.00

Notes:

**1. See Hesse-Hanau-Lichtenberg
for similar coins.**

**2. Various gulden-sized pieces of
this ruler (with no face value), N.D.
and 1740-50, are medals.**

V.F.

35 (Species thaler). ⅓ length bust r.
Rev. SINCERE etc. Arms, unsupported. 1751, 58 . . . . . . .280.00

36 X EINE etc. (= Conv. thaler).
Obv. sim. Rev. like No. 37.
1760, 63 . . . . .325.00

★37 X EINE etc. (= Conv. thaler).
1760 . . . . .600.00

GERMAN STATES

HESSE-DARMSTADT (Cont.)

V.F.

38 X EINE etc. (= Conv. thaler).
Sim. but bust l. 1764...... ——

39 X EINE etc. (= Conv. thaler).
⅓ length bust r. Rev. AD
NORMAM etc. Arms supported.
1764.................200.00

40 (Conv. thaler). Obv. sim.
Rev. like No. 18. 1764.....250.00

41 X EINE etc. (= Conv. thaler).
Obv. sim. Rev. cwnd. arms,
unsupported. 1765.......225.00

41a —. Bust l. 1765........... ——

42 X EINE etc. (= Conv. thaler).
Bust r. Rev. helmeted arms
supported. 1765..........225.00

42a —. Bust l. 1765........... ——

Gold (ducat = 3.49 gr.)

44 (ducat) Mon. Rev. lion
holds arms. 1740-41.......750.00

50 DUCATUS (=ducat). DUCATUS
HASS. DARMST. Double L mon.
Rev. lion holds arms. N.D.,
1742-53 R.N...........1200.00

51 (ducat). Bust. Rev. SINCERE
etc. Arms. N.D., 1746-55..1500.00

52 (ducat). Bust. Rev. lion holds
arms. 1746.............1200.00

53 (ducat). Like No. 23. 1760-
61.................1200.00

54 2 (ducats). Sim. 1760.....2000.00

Medallic Gold

VF-EF

56 (ducat). Mon. Rev. horse.
N.D.................1000.00

57 (ducat). Mon. Rev. lion holds
mon. shield. N.D.......1000.00

58 (ducat). Horse. Rev. as last.
1741.................1000.00

59 DUCATEN (=ducat). DURCH
DIE DUCATEN. 4 double L's
cruciform. Rev. stag. N.D..1200.00

60 DUCATEN. Obv. sim.
Rev. boar. N.D........1200.00

61 (2 ducats). Hunter and stag.
Rev. stag and 3 dogs.
N.D..................1950.00

Ludwig IX,
Count of Hesse-Hanau-
Lichtenberg 1736-68,
Landgrave of H-D 1768-90

Copper

VG-F

65 I/PFENNIG. H.D., lion in
cartouche, flags, cannons.
Rev. value. 1773........ 3.00

66 I/PFENNIG. Sim. but lion in
oval, only 1 cannon. 1774... 3.00

VG-F

★67 II/PFENNIG. 1776........ 3.00

★68 I/ZOLL (=toll)/PFENNIG.
HESSEN DARMST. lion in oval.
Rev. value. 1777.......... 4.00

69 I/PFENNIG. Sim. 1784-
90..................... 2.00

70 I/PFENNIG. Sim. but H.D.
only. 1789.............. 3.00

Billon

71 I/KREUZER. Obv. like No. 68.
Rev. value. 1771.......... 3.00

72 I KREUZER. 1772........ 3.00

74 1/KREUZ(er). H.D., lion in
oval. Rev. value. 1784..... 3.00

75 2 KREUZ(er). 1768........ 4.00

Silver

V.F.

78 20 (kreuzer). LUDOVICUS IX
D.G. LANDGRAVIUS HASS. Bust.
Rev. lion shield, trophies.
1772....................25.00

80 XX EINE etc. (=½ Conv.
thaler). Like No. 78. 1771...40.00

82 X EINE etc. (= Conv. thaler).
Like No. 78. 1770.........155.00

83 X EINE etc. (= Conv. thaler).
Bust. Rev. helmeted arms
supported. 1770, 72.......150.00

Gold

84 DUCAT. Like No. 83.
1758, 72...............1450.00

**For earlier coins of Ludwig IX see
Hesse-Hanau-Lichtenberg.**

Ludwig X, as Landgrave
1790-1806

Copper

Fine

85 I/PFENNIG. Like No. 69.
1791-97.............. 2.50

86 I/PFENNIG. Like No. 70.
1797-1806............. 1.00

Fine

★87 ¼/STÜBER. Cwnd. LLX mon.
Rev. value/1805/R.F. For
that part of Westphalia
acquired from Cologne..... 6.00

88 ½/STÜBER. Sim. 1805.... 3.00

Billon

★90 I/KREUZER. Lion on pedestal
in which is H.D. Rev. value.
1800................. 3.00

92 I/KREUZER. Lion divides
H-D. Rev. LANDMUNZ. value.
1801-05.............. 3.00

94 3/KREUZER. Sim. 1800-05. 3.00

Silver

V.F.

96 XX EINE etc. (=½ Conv.
thaler). Like No. 101. 1793..45.00

96a —. Rev. like No. 103.
1793...................60.00

100 X EINE etc. (= Conv. thaler).
Head. Rev. Arms supported.
1793...................185.00

101 X EINE etc. (= Conv. thaler).
Civilian bust. Rev. as last.
1793...................185.00

102 X EINE etc. (= Conv. thaler).
Armored bust. Rev. as last.
1793...................290.00

103 X EINE etc. (= Conv. thaler).
Armored bust. Rev. Arms, no
supporters. 1793.........180.00

Ludwig X, as Grand Duke
Ludwig I 1806-30

Copper

Fine

106 ¼/KREUZER. Like No. 107
but G. HESS etc. 1809, 16... 1.50

106a —. Like No. 107. 1809,
16-17.................. 1.00

★107 I/PFENNIG. 1811, 19.... 1.00

107a —. G.H.K.M. 1819......... 1.25

108 I/HELLER (=pfennig in
Darmstadt). Like No. 107a.
1824.................. 1.50

HESSE-DARMSTADT (Cont.)

Fine

*109 ½/KREUZER. 1809, 17... 1.50
109a —. Like No. 106a. 1817.... 1.50

Billon

110 I/KREUZER. Like No. 92.
1806................... 3.00
110a —. Lion with sword. 1806.. 3.50
111 I/KREUZER. H.D.L.M./
Lion with or w/out sword.
1806-07................. 2.25
111a I/KREUZEK. 1807...... 15.00
112 I/KREUZER. G.H.L.M./
Lion with sword. Rev. value.
1807-09................. 2.00
113 I/KREUZER. Sim. but
G.H.L.M./lion on shield.
1809-10, 17............. 3.00
114 1/KREUZER. Sim. but
G.H.S.M. 1819............. 3.00
115 III/KREUZER. Like No.
113. 1808-10............. 4.50
116 3/KREUZER. Sim. 1817.. 4.00
117 3/KREU/ZER. Like No.
120a but GR:HERZOGTH.
HESSEN. 1819, 22......... 3.00
118 5/KREUZER. GROSHERZOG
VON HESSEN. cwnd. L. Rev.
value. 1807.............. 10.00
119 240 EINE etc. (=5 Conv.
kreuzer). LUDEWIG GROSHERZOG
etc. Head. Rev. Arms.
1808................... 12.50
120 6/KREU/ZER. Like No.
117. 1819-20............. 4.50

*120a —. 1821-28............. 2.75

Silver

V.F.

121 10 (Conv. kreuzer). Like
No. 119. 1808........... 25.00
122 20 (Conv. kreuzer). Sim.
1807-09................. 12.50
123 ZEHN EINE etc. (= Conv.
thaler). Sim. 1809....... 190.00
124 EIN (=1) KRONENTHALER
(=162 kreuzer). Military bust.
Rev. Arms. 1819......... 200.00
125 EIN KRONENTHALER.
Head. Rev. Arms. 1825... 175.00

Gold

V.F.

*126 ZEHN (=10) GULDEN.
1826-27...............1800.00

Ludwig II 1830-48

1 heller = ¼ kreuzer in Darmstadt.

Copper

Fine

127 1/HELLER. Like No. 107a.
1837-47................. 2.50
128 I/HELLER. Sim. but rectangular shield. 1847....... 1.50

Billon

129 1/KREU/ZER. Like No.
120a. 1834-38............ 2.50

*130 1/KREUZER. Obv. sim.
Rev. value in wreath. 1837-
42.................... 2.00
131 1/KREUZER. Like No.
138. 1843-47............. 2.00
132 3/KREU/ZER. Like No.
117. 1833............... 3.75
132a —. Like No. 120a. 1833-
36.................... 3.00
134 3/KREUZER. Like No.
130. 1838-42............. 2.50
135 3/KREUZER. Like No.
138. 1843-47............. 2.25
136 6/KREU/ZER. Like No.
120a. 1833-37............ 3.50
137 6/KREUZER. Like No.
130. 1838-42............. 2.50

*138 6/KREUZER. 1843-47.... 2.00

Silver

V.F.

139 ½/GULDEN. Like No. 140.
1838-46................. 20.00

V.F.

*140 1/GULDEN. Head. Rev.
value. 1837-47........... 14.00

VF-EF

*141 ("Konzert gulden"). Head of
Prince Ludwig. 1843..... 275.00
142 (gulden). LUDWIG ERBGROSH.
U. MITREGENT etc. Head.
Rev. PRESSFREIHEIT/etc.
1848...................150.00

V.F.

143 EIN (=1) KRONEN-
THALER. Head. Rev. Arms.
1833-37.................125.00
144 ZWEY (=2) GULDEN.
Head. Rev. Arms. 1845-
47.....................45.00
145 2/THALER. Head. Rev.
value. 1839-42.......... 100.00
146 2 THALER. Head.
Rev. Arms. 1844........ 140.00

Gold

147 5 G(ulden). Head. Rev. AUS
HESS. RHEINGOLD etc. Arms.
1835................... *3500.00*
148 FÜNF (=5) GULDEN.
Like No. 149. 1835-41.... 700.00

*149 ZEHN (=10) GULDEN.
1840-42...............1350.00

Ludwig III 1848-77

Copper

F-VF

*150 I HELLER. 1848-55...... 1.20

GERMAN STATES

HESSE-DARMSTADT (Cont.)

		F-VF
*151	1/PFENNIG. 1857-72	1.50

Billon

		Fine
152	1/KREUZER. Like No. 138. 1848-56	1.75
153	1/KREUZER. Like No. 155. 1858-72	1.25
154	3/KREUZER. Like No. 138. 1848-56	2.50

*155	3/KREUZER. 1864-67	1.25
156	6/KREUZER. Like No. 138. 1848-56	2.50

*157	6/KREUZER. 1864-67	3.50

Silver

		V.F.
158	½ GULDEN. Head. Rev. value. 1855	30.00

*159	1 GULDEN. 1848, 54-56	18.00

		V.F.
*160	EIN (=1) VEREINS-THALER. 1857-71	30.00
161	ZWEY (=2) GULDEN. Sim. 1848-56	50.00
162	2 THALER. Head. Rev. Arms. 1854	375.00

HESSE-HANAU, County

The counts of Hanau, east of Frankfurt am Main, acquired the mint right in 1368. At the death of Johann Reinhard III, the last count of the male line, his lands were divided between Hesse-Cassel, Hesse-Darmstadt and Mainz.

Hanau arms: Gold, 3 red chevrons.

HESSE-HANAU-LICHTENBERG

Ludwig, Count 1736-90, Heir Apparent in Hesse-Darmstadt 1739-68, Landgrave as Ludwig IX 1768-90

Billon or Silver

		VG-F
2	1 KREUZER	8.00
4	2 KREUZER	8.00
6	II/ALBUS. H.D. over 3 shields, H.L. below. Rev. LAND MUNZ/value/C.H.S./1757	15.00
8	4/KREU/ZER. H.D. over lion, H.L. below. Rev. value/E.G.F./1759	15.00
10	5 KREUZER	14.00

*12	10 (Conv. kreuzer).1760	14.00
14	12 KREUZER	18.00

*16	VI/EINEN (=⅙)/THALER. Cwnd. LL mon. 1758	22.00

Gold

		V.F.
20	(ducat). Bust. Rev. Arms. 1758	1400.00

HESSE-HANAU-MÜNZENBERG

Wilhelm, Count 1736-60, Landgrave of Hesse-Cassel as Wilhelm VIII 1751-60

Copper

		VG-F
1	1/HELLER. WLL script mon. Rev. HELLER/HANAU/etc. 1739-46	5.00
2	II/HELLER. Sim. 1745	8.00
3	1/HELLER. WL mon., Z.H. above. Rev. value/SCHEIDE/MUNTZ/date. 1752-57	8.00

The WL monogram on No. 3 has an ornate L to right of the w. See Hesse-Cassel No. 1 for somewhat similar coin with L over the w.

Mary of England, Regent 1760-64 for her minor son, Wilhelm, Heir apparent of Hesse-Cassel

Silver

		V.F.
10	10 (kreuzer). MARIA D.G. LAND. HASS etc. MLH mon. Rev. 2 shields, pillar. 1763	18.00
12	20 (kreuzer). MARIA etc. 2 shields, pillar. Rev. 60 ST./EINE etc. 1764	25.00
14	XX E. F. MARK (=½ Conv. thaler). Like No. 15. 1763	80.00

*15	X E. F. MARK (= Conv. thaler). Bust. Rev. Arms. 1764	600.00

GERMAN STATES

HESSE-HANAU-MÜNZENBERG (Cont.)

Wilhelm, Count 1760-85, Landgrave and Elector of Hesse-Cassel as Wilhelm IX (I) 1785-1821

Copper

Fine

*20 I/HELLER. 1768-73 . . . . 3.00

*21 I/KREU/ZER. 1773 . . . . . . 5.00

Billon or Silver

23 I/KREUZER. Arms. Rev. value. 1765 . . . . 5.00

24 I/KREUZER. Like No. 21. 1773 . . . . 5.00

27 5/KR(euzer). HESSEN HANAU MUNTZENBERG. Arms. Rev. value. 1765-66 . . . . 5.00

F-VF

29 5 (Conv. kreuzer). WILHELMUS D.G. LANDG. ET. PR. HER. HASS. COM. HAN. Bust. Rev. IUSTIRT 240 etc. Arms. 1775 . . . . 8.00

31 10 (Conv. kreuzer). WILHELM etc. Bust. Rev. CXX etc. Arms. 1766 . . . . 8.00

33 20 (Conv. kreuzer). Bust. Rev. Arms. 1765, 66 . . . . 12.00

Silver

V.F.

35 XX EINE etc. (= ½ Conv. thaler). Head. Rev. Arms supported. 1765 . . . . 37.50

37 XX EINE etc. (= ½ Conv. thaler). Like No. 35 but armored bust. Bieber Mines. 1770 . . . . 37.50

39 X EINE etc. (= Conv. thaler). Like No. 35 but armored bust 200.00

40 X EINE etc. (= Conv. thaler). Sim. but with EX VISCERIBUS etc. (Bieber Mines). 1769-71 . . . . 130.00

41 X EINE etc. (= Conv. thaler). Head. Rev. Arms/BIBERER/SILBER. 1774-78 . . . . 130.00

41a —. Larger head. 1784 . . . . . 145.00

Gold

V.F.

*42 (ducat). On his marriage to Wilhelmine Caroline of Denmark. 1764 . . . . 1500.00

43 (ducat). P.H. HASS. C.H. Bust. Rev. Arms supported. 1768 . . . . 1200.00

HESSE-HOMBURG, Landgraviate

Founded in 1596 by a younger son of Georg I the Pious, ancestor of the Darmstadt line.

Ludwig 1829-39

Silver

V.F.

1 ½/GULDEN. LUDWIG SOUV. LANDGRAF ZU HESSEN. Bust. Rev. value. 1838 . . . . 75.00

1a —. 1839 . . . . pattern

2 1/GULDEN. Sim. 1838 . . . . 75.00

2a —. 1839 . . . . pattern

Philipp 1839-46

Billon

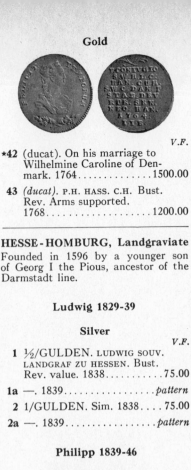

Fine

*3 1/KREUZER. 1840 . . . . 40.00

4 3/KREUZER. Sim. 1840 . . . 55.00

5 6/KREUZER. Sim. 1840 . . . 35.00

Silver

V.F.

6 ½/GULDEN. PHILIPP SOUV. LANDGRAF etc. Head. Rev. value. 1840-46 . . . . 75.00

7 1/GULDEN. Sim. 1841-46 . . 75.00

8 ZWEY (=2)/GULDEN. Head. Rev. value. 1846 . . . . 300.00

Ferdinand 1848-66

Silver

9 EIN (=1) VEREINS-THALER. FERDINAND SOUV. LANDGRAF etc. Head. Rev. arms. 1858-63 . . . . 60.00

HILDESHEIM, Bishopric

In Westphalia, S.E. of Hannover. First coinage in 11th century. Secularized and assigned to Prussia 1803.

Arms: Per pale, gold and red.

Sede Vacante 1761-63

Billon

F-VF

1 I/MARIEN/GROS. Like No. 3. 1762-63 . . . . 3.00

2 I/SCHILLING (=¹⁄₂₈ thaler). Sim. 1763 . . . . 3.00

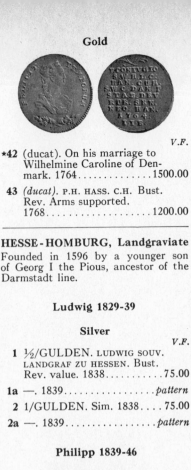

*3 24/EINEN (=¹⁄₂₄)/THALER. 1762-63 . . . . 6.00

3.5 II/MARIEN/GROS. Sim. 1763 . . . . 6.00

4 12/EINEN (=¹⁄₁₂)/THALER. Sim. 1762-63 . . . . 6.00

Silver

6 VI/EINEN (=¹⁄₆)/THALER. Like No. 3. 1763 . . . . 14.00

*8 ⅔ (Reichsthaler). 1761 . . . . . 80.00

Gold

V.F.

*10 ½/PISTOLE (=2½ thaler). Arms. Rev. value. 1763 . . . . 800.00

Friedrich Wilhelm, Freiherr von Westphalen zu Fürstenberg, Bishop of Hildesheim 1763-89, of Paderborn 1782-89

The 1786 copper pfennig is listed under Paderborn.

GERMAN STATES

HILDESHEIM, Bishopric (Cont.)

Billon

Fine

13 24/EINEN (=¹/₂₄)/THALER.
Like No. 17 but no mantle
behind arms. 1763......... 4.00

15 II/MARIEN/GROSCH(en).
Like No. 13. 1763......... 6.00

*17 12/EINEN (=¹/₁₂)/THALER.
1763-65.................. 4.00

18 IIII/MARIEN/GROSCH(en).
Sim. 1763................. 6.00

Silver

F-VF

19 VI/EINEN (=¹/₆)/THALER.
Sim. 1763-64.............12.50

20 ⅓ (Reichsthaler). FRID.
WILH. D.G. EP. HILD. etc. Bust.
Rev. Arms. 1764..........50.00

21 ⅓/REICHS/THALER. Like
No. 17. 1764.............50.00

22 ⅔ (Reichsthaler). Like No.
20. 1764................150.00

V.F.

23 X STÜCK EINE etc. (= Conv.
thaler). Bust. Rev. Arms.
1766, 68................750.00

Gold

*25 1 DUCAT. 1778........1100.00

26 ½/PISTOLE. Arms. Rev.
value. 1763 ....800.00

27 5 THALER. Bust. Rev. Arms.
1764-65................1500.00

28 X THALER. Sim. 1766....RRR

HILDESHEIM, Free City
Became free in 13th century. First
coins minted at end of 15th century.
City absorbed by Prussia 1803.
City arms: Silver, top half of black
eagle. Below: quarterly gold and red.

Copper

Fine

1 I/PFENNIG. City arms.
Rev. value. 1762, 72 .... 8.00

Billon

*2 II/STADT (city)/P(f)ENN(ig).
1748-67.................. 4.50

Fine

4 IIII/STADT/PFENN(ig).
MO. NO. CI(V.) HILDESH. Arms.
Rev. value. 1734-63 .... 6.00

6 24 (=¹/₂₄ thaler). DA PACE
etc. Arms. Rev. HILDESH.
STADT GELD. Orb. 1756-63... 9.00

HOHENLOHE, Counts and Princes
Lands in Bavaria and Württemberg.
First coinage early 15th century. The
family was represented by numerous
branches in the 18th century. All parts
of Hohenlohe were mediatized in 1806.
Hohenlohe arms: Silver, 2 black leop-
ards passant guardant, one over other.

A. HOHENLOHE-INGELFINGEN, Principality.

Philipp Heinrich 1743-81 (prince 1764-81) with Heinrich August 1765-96

Silver

F-VF

2 10 (Conv. kreuzer). Arms on
cwnd. mantle. Rev. value.
1770....................20.00

3 20 (Conv. kreuzer). Sim.
1770....................35.00

Friedrich Ludwig 1796-1806

Silver

VF-EF

5 X/EINE/etc. (= Conv. thaler).
FRIED. LUDWIG FURST ZU
HOHENLOHE INGELFINGEN.
Bust. Rev. value. 1796 ....400.00

Gold

E.F.

7 I/DUCATEN. Like No. 5.
1796..................1500.00

B. HOHENLOHE-KIRCHBERG, Principality.

Christian Friedrich Carl 1767-1806, died 1819

Silver

VF-EF

13 ZWANZIG EINE etc. (=½
Conv. thaler). Like No. 15.
1781, 1804..............120.00

13a —. 1786..............200.00

15 ZEHEN EINE etc. (= Conv.
thaler). CHRIST. FR. CAR. D.G.
S.R.I. PRINC. HOHENL. etc. Bust.
Rev. Arms. 1781........1200.00

C. HOHENLOHE-LANGENBURG, County.
Joint coinage of the rulers of the three
Langenburg sub-branches, Langenburg,
Ingelfingen and Kirchberg, on the 50th
anniversary of the division of Langen-
burg in 1701.

Ludwig of Langenburg 1715-64, Philipp of Ingelfingen 1743-81, and Carl August of Kirchberg 1737-67

Silver

VF-EF

25 (thaler). Like No. 27. Date
1751 in chronogram.......500.00

Gold

V.F.

*27 (ducat). Date 1751 in chrono-
gram...................1100.00

D. HOHENLOHE-NEUENSTEIN-OEHRINGEN, County until 1764, Principality thereafter.

Johann Friedrich II, in Oehringen 1709-65

Silver

VF-EF

32 20 (Conv. kreuzer). Like
No. 42. 1760............. ——

34 40 EINE etc. (=¼ Conv.
thaler). Like No. 42. 1760... ——

36 (½ thaler). Phoenix. Rev.
God's arm crowns female.
On Augsburg Confession bi-
centenary. (1730).......... ——

38 20 EINE etc. (=½ Conv.
thaler). Like No. 42. 1760... ——

E.F.

40 (thaler). IOH. FRIDERICVS
LINEAE HOHENLOH–NEVEN
STEINENSIS etc. Lion holds
arms. Rev. Angel blows trum-
pet. Augsburg Conf. bicent.
Date 1730 in chronogram... ——

42 10 EIN etc. (= Conv. thaler).
IOANN: FRID: COM: DE HOHENL:
etc. Bust. Rev. Arms.
1760.................... ——

Gold

V.F.

44 (ducat). Like No. 42. 1760... ——

Ludwig Friedrich Carl 1765-1805

Billon

F-VF

*48 1 CONVENT(ion) KR(euzer).
1774....................15.00

49 2½ K(reuzer). Sim. 1774...20.00

HOHENLOHE (Cont.)

Silver

VF-EF

51 10 (Conv. kreuzer). FURSTLICH HOHENL. NEUENST. etc. Arms. Rev. 120 EINE etc. 1770, 85..30.00

53 10 (kreuzer). HOHENLOHE NEUENSTEIN etc. Arms. Rev. 10 lines: ZUM . . . TEUTSCHEN SCHULE . . . 1803 . . . . .50.00

55 (10 Conv. kreuzer). No. 65 in silver. 1804 . . . . .25.00

57 20 (Conv. kreuzer). Like No. 51. 1770, 85 . . . . .30.00

59 X EINE etc. (= Conv. thaler). LVD. FRID. CAROL. D.G. PRINC. AB. HOHENL. etc. Bust. Rev. Arms. 1770 . . . . .350.00

60 ZEHEN EINE etc. (= Conv. thaler). Bust. Rev. Arms. 1785 . . . . .350.00

61 X EINE etc. (= Conv. thaler). Bust. Rev. Arms. 1797 . . . .275.00

Gold (ducat = 3.49 gr.)

V.F.

62 (ducat) Bust. Rev. Arms. 1770 . . . . .1200.00

63 (ducat). Bust. Rev. Arms. 1785 . . . . .1200.00

65 (ducat). Bust. Rev. Arms. 1804. On his 81st birthday .1500.00

66 (2 ducats). Sim. 1804 . . . . .1800.00

E. HOHENLOHE-PFEDELBACH, Principality.

Joseph Anton 1745-64

Gold

V.F.

68 (ducat). Bust. Rev. Phoenix. 1747 . . . . .950.00

F. HOHENLOHE-WALDENBURG-SCHILLINGSFÜRST, Principality.

Carl Albrecht 1750-93

Billon

Fine

71 1 Kr(euzer). HOHENLOHE-WALDENBURG etc. Rev. Phoenix. 1768 . . . . .12.00

73 2½ KR(euzer). Like No. 71. 1770 . . . . .16.00

75 V K(reuzer). Like No. 71. 1768, 70 . . . . .25.00

Silver

VF-EF

77 20 EINE etc. (=½ Conv. thaler). Like No. 79. 1770 R.N 90.00

VF-EF

79 10 EINE etc. (= Conv. thaler). CAR: ALB: D: G: PR: REGN: AB HOHENL: ET WALDENB: Bust. Rev. Phoenix. (2 var.). 1757 R.N 450.00

HOHENZOLLERN, Principality

The counts of Hohenzollern in Swabia appeared in the 9th century. A younger line produced the margraves of Brandenburg in Franconia (q.v.) and the kings of Prussia and emperors of Germany.

The elder line was divided into 4 branches in 1576, of which 2, Hechingen and Sigmaringen, survived. These 2 were raised to principalities in 1623. The princes of both lines resigned their sovereignty in favor of Prussia in 1849.

Hohenzollern arms: Quarterly, silver and black.

HOHENZOLLERN-HECHINGEN
Joseph Wilhelm 1750-98

Silver

V.F.

1 (Conv. thaler). IOS: WILH: D: G: PR: DE HOHENZOLLERN etc., bust. Rev. arms. 1783 . . . . .1250.00

Herman Friedrich Otto 1798-1810

Silver

2 (Conv. thaler). HERMAN FRIDER. OTTO D.G. PRINC. DE HOHEN-ZOLLERN etc. Bust. Rev. Arms. 1804 . . . . .1500.00

Friedrich Wilhelm Constantin 1838-49

Billon

Fine

*3 3/KREUZER. 1845-47 . . . . .12.50

4 6/KREUZER. Sim. 1841-47 . . . . .15.00

Silver

VF-EF

5 ½/GULDEN. Like No. 6. 1839-47 . . . . .60.00

6 1/GULDEN. FRIEDRICH W. C. FÜRST ZU HOHENZ. HECH. Head. Rev. value. 1839-47.. 80.00

7 ZWEY (=2) GULDEN. Head. Rev. Arms. 1846-47 . . . . . .350.00

8 2 THALER. Sim. 1844-46 . . . . .1000.00

HOHENZOLLERN-SIGMARINGEN
Carl 1831-48

Copper

F-VF

*1 EIN (=1)/KREUZER. 1842, 46 . . . . .10.00

Billon

2 I/KREUZER. Sim. 1842, 46 . . . . .10.00

3 3/KREUZER. Sim. 1839-47 . . . . .12.50

4 6/KREUZER. Sim. 1839-46 . . . . .12.50

Silver

V.F.

5 ½/GULDEN. Like No. 6. 1838-48 . . . . .50.00

*6 1/GULDEN. Head * Rev. value. 1838-48 . . . . .70.00

7 ZWEI (=2) GULDEN. Head. Rev. Arms. 1845-48 . . . . . .350.00

8 2/THALER. Head. Rev. value. 1841-43 . . . . .650.00

9 2 THALER. Head. Rev. Arms. 1844-47 . . . . .650.00

Carl Anton 1848-49

Silver

10 1/GULDEN. Head. Rev. value. 1848 . . . . .pattern

10a —. 1849 . . . . .90.00

GERMAN STATES

HOHENZOLLERN (Cont.)

*11 ZWEI (=2) GULDEN.   *V.F.*
1848................pattern
11a —. 1849.............600.00

BOTH PRINCIPALITIES UNDER PRUSSIA.

Friedrich Wilhelm IV
1849-61

Copper

*1 EIN (=1)/KREUZER.   *Fine*
1852.................. 7.50

Billon

*2 3/KREUZER. 1852.......20.00
3 6/KREUZER. Sim. 1852...15.00

Silver

4 ½/GULDEN. Like No. 5.   *E.F.*
1852....................45.00

*5 1/GULDEN. FRIEDR. WILHELM
IV KOENIG V. PREUSSEN. Head.
Rev. value. 1852.........65.00

HOLSTEIN, Duchy

South of Schleswig, between Denmark and Germany. First recognizable coinage 14th century. Both Schleswig and Holstein passed by inheritance to Christian of Oldenburg, elected King of Denmark 1448.

In 1533 and 1559 parts of Holstein were split away for the benefit of younger sons of Danish rulers and the lines of Gottorp and Sonderburg were formed.

HOLSTEIN-GOTTORP, Duchy
(Carl) Peter (Ulrich) 1739-62,
Czar of Russia as Peter III 1762,
Killed same year

Silver

*4 (Albertus thaler). (2 var.)   *E.F.*
1753....................750.00

HOLSTEIN SONDERBURG,
Duchy

Friedrich Carl of
Holstein-Plön 1729-61

Silver
       V.F.

11 EIN (=1 Reichs) THALER.
FRIDERICVS CAROLVS D.G.
H. N. D. etc. Bust. Rev. EIN
THALER NACH etc. Arms.
1761, N.D..............450.00

Gold

13 (ducat). Like No. 11 but FIDES
etc. on rev. 1760 R.N.
(2 var.)................1500.00

Holstein-Plön to Denmark 1761.

**For other Holstein coinage,
see Schleswig-Holstein.**

HOLY ROMAN EMPIRE.
See AUSTRIA.

ISENBURG, Counts and Princes

Lands on the Main River east of Frankfurt. First coins 14th century. Various branches existed in the 18th century, of which one, Birstein, was raised to the rank of principality in 1744. All of Isenburg was put under the overlordship of Birstein in 1806. Mediatized to Hesse-Darmstadt 1815.

Monetary System:
108 kreuzers = 1 Reichsthaler.

Carl of Isenburg-Birstein
1806-15

Billon or Silver
       VF-EF

1 6/KREU/ZER. Cwnd. c.
Rev. value in wreath. 1811. 125.00
2 12/KREU/ZER. Like No. 3.
1811...................125.00

*3 16/EINE etc. (=Reichs thaler).   *E.F.*
1811...................900.00

Gold (ducat = 3.49 gr.)

4 DUCAT. Head. Rev. Arms.
1811 (existence doubtful)... ——
5 (2) DUCAT. No. 4 double
thick. 1811.............6000.00

Note: The copper "snipe hellers" issued for Isenburg during the 19th century (Obv. various script monograms. Rev. snipe = long billed bird, all N.D. and w/out denomination), while scarce and interesting, are tokens, not coins.

GERMAN STATES

JEVER, Lordship

N.W. of Wilhelmshaven on the North Sea coast. First coinage 10th-11th centuries.

Monetary System:
8 heller = 4 pfennig = 1 grote;
60 stüber = 72 grote = 1 Reichsthaler.

Friedrich August of Anhalt Zerbst 1753-93

Copper
VG-F

1 1 HELLER. D.G.F.A.P.A. etc. Bust. Rev. IEVER. Arms. 1764 .... 8.50
2 1 PFENNIG. Sim. 1764 .... 8.50

Billon

3 *1 GROTE*. Sim. 1764 ...... 9.00
4 *4 GROTE*. Sim. 1764 ..... 17.50

Silver
F-VF

5 *12 GROTE*. Sim. 1764 ..... 22.00
5a —. 48-P/17-64/15-K under arms. 1764 .... 25.00
7 *(⅔ Reichsthaler)*. D.G. FRIDERICVS AVGVSTVS. P. ANH. — DOMINVS IEVERAE. Bust. Rev. Arms. 1763 R.N 300.00

Jever under Russia 1793-1807
Friedrike Auguste Sophie, Widow of Friedrich August, Administratrix 1793-1807

Copper

Fine

★10 ¼/STÜBER. MON. DYN. IEVER. Lion shield. Rev. value. 1799 .... 8.00

Billon
V.G.

11 *1/STÜBER*. Arms. Rev. value. 1798 .... 8.00
12 *2/STÜBER*. Sim. 1798 ..... 12.00
13 *1/GROTE*. Lion shield. Rev. value. 1798 .... 12.00
14 *3/GROTE*. Sim. 1798 ..... 15.00

Silver
V.F.

15 EIN/HALBER (=½)/ REICHS/THALER. SUB. UMBRA etc. Russian Imp. Eagle. Rev. FRIED AUG SOPH. etc. Value. 1798 .... 90.00
16 EIN (=1)/REICHS/THALER. Sim. 1798 .... 300.00

JÜLICH-BERG
(GÜLICH UND BERG) Duchies

On the Rhine near Cologne. The first count of Jülich lived in 847. Mint right acquired 1237. Jülich united with Berg sporadically from 1348, permanently from 1423. From 1624 to 1801 Jülich-Berg belonged to Pfalz-Neuburg and the successive Electors Palatine (see Pfalz).
  Jülich to France 1801-14, to Prussia 1814 onward.
  See Berg for coins of that duchy after 1801.

Jülich arms: Gold, a black double tailed lion.

Berg arms: Silver, a red lion with blue crown.

Monetary System:
80 stüber = 1⅛ Reichsthaler = 1 Convention thaler.

Düsseldorf mint marks:
A.K. 1749-66; C.L.S. 1767-70; P.M. 1771-83; P.R. 1783-1804.

Carl Theodor, Count Palatine of Sulzbach 1733-99, Elector Palatine 1742-99, Elector of Bavaria 1777-99, in Jülich-Berg 1742-99

Copper

Fine

★1 ¼/STUBER. 1750-51 ...... 5.00

★2 ¼/STUBER. 1765-94 (var.) 3.00
3 ½/STUBER. Sim. 1765-94 .... 3.00

Billon

4 1/STUBER. Like No. 7 1765 .... 6.00
5 2/STUBER. Sim. 1792-94 ... 8.00
6 3/STUBER. CT mon. Rev. value. 1765 .... 8.00

★7 3/STUBER. 1792-94 .... 4.50

Silver
V.F.

8 12 ST(über). CAR. THEODOR D.G. C.P.R. etc. Bust/G.B. Rev. AD NORMAM etc. Arms. 1765-66 .... 25.00

Wildberg Mining Coinage. All with EX VISCERIBUS FODINAE WILD-BERG. Mostly struck at Mannheim but attributable to Jülich-Berg.

12 ⅔ (Reichsthaler). D.G. CAR. TH. C.P.R. etc. Armored bust. Rev. Arms. 1748 .... 85.00
12a —. 1750 .... 95.00
12b —. 1754-55 .... 85.00
13 ⅔ (Reichsthaler). D.G. CAR. THEODOR etc. Draped bust. Rev. 3 shields. 1756-58 .... 95.00
14 (Species thaler). Like No. 12. 1751, 53 .... 325.00
15 (Species thaler). Like No. 13. 1756, 58 .... 550.00

Regular Düsseldorf Coinage

16 10 EINE etc. (= Conv. thaler). CAR THEODOR etc. Draped bust. Rev. 3 shields. 1765 A.K ... 290.00
16a —. Rev. Arms. 1767 C.L.S. 325.00
16b —. Rev. 3 shields. 1771 P.M 275.00
17 10 EINE etc. (= Conv. thaler). Head. Rev. Arms. 1772, 74 P.M 275.00

Gold (ducat = 3.49 gr.)

★18 (ducat). 1749-51 A.K 1250.00
19 (ducat). Bust. Rev. Star of St. Hubert's Order. 1750 A.K 1100.00

★20 (2 ducats). 1750 A.K 1600.00

For other coins of Carl Theodor, see Bavaria and Pfalz.

KAUNITZ-RIETBERG. See Rietberg.

KHEVENHÜLLER. See AUSTRIA (STATES).

KLETTGAU. See Schwarzenburg.

KLEVE. See Cleve.

GERMAN STATES

KNYPHAUSEN, County

In East Friesland. Acquired by the Bentinck family through marriage in the 18th century.

Wilhelm Gustav Friedrich v. Bentinck 1774-1835

Silver

		VF-EF
1	9 grote. G.G.F. BENTINCK S.R.I. COMES. Cwnd. arms. Rev. DYNASTES IN KNIPHAUSEN. Lion. 1807	75.00
2	9 GR(ote). W.G.F etc. . . . IN KNIPHAUSEN. Uncwnd. arms. Rev. Imp. eagle. 1807	125.00

KÖNIGSEGG (KÖNIGSECK), County

In S.W. Bavaria. Mediatized to Bavaria early 19th century.

Franz Hugo 1736-71

Silver

		E.F.
1	(Conv. thaler). S.R.I. COMES A KONIGSEGG etc. Busts of Franz Hugo and 3 brothers. Rev. 22 lines vital statistics. 1759 R.N	900.00

Gold

★2	(ducat). 1756	RRR

KÖLN. See Cologne.

KONSTANZ. See Constance.

KORVEY. See Corvey.

KRUMLAU. See Schwarzenberg.

KURLAND. See POLAND.

LAUENBURG, Duchy

In N. Germany adjacent to Holstein. The duchy of Saxe-Lauenburg was established in 1260. After extinction of the ruling line in 1689, Lauenburg passed through the hands of Brunswick and Prussia into those of Denmark 1816-64.

Frederik VI of Denmark, in Lauenburg 1816-39

Silver

		V.F.
★1	⅔ (Reichsthaler). 1830	140.00

LEININGEN, Counts and Princes

Possessions scattered about the Rhineland, Baden, Bavaria, Hesse and Nassau. Descended from Emicho I (died 1117).

In 1806, when Leiningen was mediatized, the family was represented by 3 main branches, Westerburg, Dagsburg-Hartenburg and Dagsburg-Heidesheim.

Arms: Blue, a red label over 3 silver eaglets.

Carl Friedrich Wilhelm of Leiningen-Dagsburg-Hartenburg 1756-1806, Prince 1779

Billon

		F-VF
1	(pfennig). 1805	22.00
3	III/KREUZER. Like No. 5. 1804	12.00
3a	—. 3 eaglets. Rev. FURSTL. LEIN. L.M. Value. 1805	12.00
5	VI/KREUZER. F.L.L.M., cwnd. shield (3 eaglets). Rev. value. 1804	20.00
5a	—. Like No. 3a. 1805	20.00

LIECHTENSTEIN (LICHTENSTEIN). See AUSTRIA (States).

LIPPE, Principality

Small state in N.W. Germany. First lord of Lippe ruled in 12th century. First coinage 13th century. Rulers elevated to the rank of count in the 16th century. In 1613 Lippe was divided into four branches, of which only Detmold and Alverdissen (later Schaumburg-Lippe) are of importance to this work. The title of prince was conferred upon the counts of Lippe-Detmold in 1720, but was not confirmed until 1789.

Arms: Silver, a red rose.

LIPPE-DETMOLD
Simon August 1734-82

Copper

		Fine
1	I (heller). Like No. 3. 1760	12.00
2	½/PFENNING. SA mon. Rev. value. 1763	12.00
★3	I (pfennig). 1763	9.00
4	I (pfennig). SA mon. Rev. numeral. 1763	9.00
5	II (pfennig). G(rafschaft). LIPP. L. MVNTZ. Rose. Rev. numerals. 1763	14.00
★6	II (pfennig). 1763	9.00
★7	I/HELLER. Rose. Rev. value/ GR.LIPP:/etc. 1767-68	6.00
8	I/PFENNING. Sim. 1767-68	6.00

Billon

★10	2/PFEN(nig). Rose. Rev. value. 1766, 69	6.00
12	I/MATT(ier=4 pfennig= 13 French deniers). Rose. Rev. N.D. LEIPZ. FUS, value/ B.S. 1763	6.00
13	I/MATT(ier). 1766-68	6.00
14	I/MATT(ier). SA mon. in Rose. Rev. GR.LIPP.LAND MUNTZ. Value. 1769	6.00
16	48/EINEN (=¹/₄₈)/THALER. COM. LIPP. &, SA mon. Rev. NACH etc. Value. 1764	7.00
19	I/MARIEN/GROS(chen). SA mon. Rev. value. 1764-68	7.00
20	I/MARIEN/GROS(chen). Like No. 14. 1770	7.00
22	24/EINEN (=¹/₂₄)/THALER. Like No. 16 but COM & N.D. LIPP etc. 1764	7.50

···

LIPPE-DETMOLD (Cont.)

Fine

★24 12/EINEN (=½)/THALER.
SIM. AUG. COM. & N.D. LIPP etc.
Arms. Rev. AD NORMAM etc.,
value. 1764-69 . . . . 8.00

24a —. TAHLER. 1765 . . . . . . .15.00

26 4/MARIEN/GROSCH(en).
COM. ET N.D. LIPP. etc. SA mon.
in rose. Rev. value. 1766 . . .14.00

Silver

V.F.

28 VI/EINEN (=⅙)/THALER.
Head. Rev. value. 1765-70 . .18.50

30 3/EINEN (=⅓)/THALER.
SIM. AUG. COM. ET N.D. LIPP.
etc. Arms. Rev. value.
1772 . . . . .32.00

32 ⅔ (thaler). Like No. 37.
On his 2nd marriage. 1765 . .80.00

32a —. Armored bust. 1765 . . . . .80.00

34 ⅔ (thaler). Bust. Rev. Arms.
1769 . . . . .80.00

36 (thaler). Bust. Rev. QUEM/etc.
in square. On his 41st birthday.
1767 R.N 450.00

Gold

VF-EF

★37 (ducat). 1765 . . . . .1350.00

38 (ducat). Head. Rev. SERVA
IEHOVA etc. Arms. On birth
of heir. 1767 . . . . .1500.00

39 (ducat). SIM: AUG: COM:LIPP:
& CASIM(ira): PRINC(ess) ANH.
Busts of SA and 3rd wife. Rev.
2 hands. 1769 (wedding) . .1500.00

Ludwig Heinrich Adolf, Regent 1782-89 for Friedrich Wilhelm Leopold

Copper

Fine

40 I/HELLER. Like No. 7
1783 . . . . 7.50

Billon

Fine

42 2/PFEN(nig) 1785 . . . . 8.00

44 4/PFEN(nig). Rose.
Rev. value. 1784 . . . . 8.00

46 I/MATT(ier =4 pf.). LHAC
mon. in rose. Rev. GR:LIPP etc.,
value. 1785 . . . . 8.00

48 I/MARIEN/GROS(chen).
Like No. 46. 1784, 86 . . . . . . 8.00

Friedrich Wilhelm Leopold 1782-1802, alone 1789-1802, Prince 1789

Copper

★51 I/HELLER. 1791, 98 . . . . . . 4.00

52 I/PFEN/NING. Sim.
1791 . . . . 4.00

Billon

As Count

54 I/MATTIER (=4 pf.)
GRAFL. LIPP. LANDM. Rose.
Rev. value. 1789 . . . . 8.00

56 I/MARIEN/GROSCHE(n).
Like No. 54. 1789 . . . . 8.00

As Prince

60 1/MATTIER. FURSTL. LIPP.
etc. *Rose.* Rev. value. 1791-
99 . . . . 7.50

62 I/MARIEN/GROSCHE(n).
Like No. 60. 1790-95 . . . . . . 7.50

65 12/EINEN (=½)/THALER.
F.W. LEOPOLD FÜRST ZUR
LIPPE. Rose. Rev. value.
1789-90 . . . . 9.00

Silver

VF-EF

68 (Prize gulden). Arms. Rev.
FRIEDRICH WILHELM LEOPOLD
etc., in field DEM/GUTEN etc.
1793. For flax growers 200.00

Note: The 1796 gold piece is a medal.

Pauline of Anhalt-Bernburg, Widow, Regent 1802-20 for her Son, Paul Alexander Leopold

Copper

F-VF

70 I/HELLER. Rose. Rev. value.
(Like No. 51). 1802-16 . . . . . .2.00

71 1/PFEN/NING. Sim. 1802,
18 . . . . 3.00

72 II/PFEN/NING. Sim.
1802 . . . . 4.00

Billon

F-VF

73 I/MAR(ien)/GROS(chen).
Arms of Lippe and Anhalt.
Rev. I/LIPP. MAR/GROS.
1802-03 . . . . 9.00

73a —. 1804 . . . . 7.00

Paul Alexander Leopold 1802-51, alone 1820-51

Copper

74 I/HELLER. Rose. Rev. value.
(Like No. 51). 1821-40 . . . . . .2.00

74a 1/HELLER. 1826 . . . . 3.00

75 1/PFENNING. Sim. 1820-
25 . . . . 2.00

75a 1/PFENNING. 1824 . . . . . . .3.50

75b 1/PFENNIG. 1828-40 . . . . . .2.00

★76 1½/PFEN/NING.
1821-25 . . . . 5.00

★77 1/PFENNING. 1847 . . . . . . 1.50

78 3/PFENNINGE. Sim.
1847 . . . . 2.00

Billon

★79 ½/SILBER/GROSCHEN.
1847 . . . . 8.50

80 1/SILBER/GROSCHEN.
Sim. 1847 . . . . 7.50

81 2½/SILBER/GROSCHEN.
Sim. 1847 . . . . .10.00

Silver

E.F.

82 2 THALER. Head.
Rev. Arms. 1843 . . . . .350.00

Paul Friedrich Emil Leopold 1851-75

Copper

F-VF

★83 1/PFENNING. 1851, 58 . . . .2.00

84 3/PFENNINGE. 1858 . . . . .3.00

GERMAN STATES

LIPPE-DETMOLD (Cont.)

Billon

F-VF

85 1/SILBER/GROSCHEN.
Like No. 86. 1860......... 6.00

*86 2½/SILBER/GROSCHEN.
1860.................. 9.00

Silver

V.F.

87 EIN (=1) VEREINSTHALER.
Head. Rev. arms.
1860, 66................75.00

LÖWENSTEIN (LOEWENSTEIN)-WERTHEIM, Counts and Princes

In Bavaria and Württemberg. Descended from Ludwig v. Scharfeneck, son by morganatic marriage of Elector Palatine Friedrich I, given the rank of count in 1494. Divided into Virneburg and Rochefort branches in the 17th century. The lands of all branches were mediatized in 1806.

Löwenstein arms: Silver, a lion passant on 4 hillocks, red.

In the list which follows, anonymous coins with a count's coronet are assigned to Virneburg, those with a prince's crown are assigned to Rochefort, and those with neither are catalogued as the joint coinage of both.

LÖWENSTEIN-WERTHEIM-VIRNEBURG, Counts

A. Joint Virneburg coinage.

Billon

Fine

*9 1/KREUZER. 1798........ 9.00

14 10 (Conv. kreuzer). COMITES IN LOEWENST. WERTH. ROCH. VIRNEB., 3 shields. Rev. AD/NORMAM etc. 1767......15.00

B. Johann Ludwig Vollrath 1721-90.

Billon

20 (kreuzer). G.Z.L.W., JLVGZL mon. Rev. Arms. 1772.......12.00

22 3 (kreuzer). Bust. Rev. Arms. 1772................15.00

Silver

F-VF

27 CXX EINE etc. (=10 Conv. kreuzer). JOH. LUD. VOLRATH. COM. IN. LÖW. WERTHEIM. Bust. Rev. Arms. 1767.....20.00

28 LX EINE etc. (=20 Conv. kreuzer). Sim. 1767.......17.50

V.F.

33 X EINE etc. (= Conv. thaler). Bust. Rev. Arms supported. 1766-67................350.00

34 X EINE etc. (= Conv. thaler). Bust. Rev. SUUM CUIQUE in cartouche, lion. 1768, 76...350.00

34a —. 1769................200.00

Gold (ducat=3.49 gr.)

35 (¼ ducat). Arms. Rev. crouching lion/SUUM CUI/QUE. N.D. (1765-84)..........450.00

36 (ducat). Bust. Rev. Lion. N.D. 1600.00

37 (ducat). Bust. Rev. Arms. 1768-71..............1500.00

38 (ducat). Bust. Rev. kneeling figure. 50th year of personal rule. 1780..............1950.00

C. Friedrich Ludwig 1721-96.

Silver

45 XX EINE etc. (=½ Conv. thaler). Like No. 47. 1770..175.00

47 X EINE etc. (= Conv. thaler). FRIEDR. LUD. S.R.I. COM. IN. LOEWENST. WERTH. Bust. Rev. 6 shields. 1768...........450.00

D. Carl Ludwig 1721-99.

Former Nos. 60 and 62 have been tentatively renumbered as 139 and 141. Former No. 64 appears to be No. 14.

Silver

66 20 (Conv. kreuzer). 1770.....35.00

68 XX EINE etc. (=½ Conv. thaler). Like No. 70. 1770..175.00

70 X EINE etc. (= Conv. thaler). CAROL.LUD.S.R.I. COM. IN LOEWENST.WERTH. Bust. Rev. 5 shields. 1770.......250.00

Gold

71 (ducat). Sim. 1767......1750.00

E. Friedrich Carl 1799-1806.

Gold (ducat=3.49 gr.)

*72 (ducat). 1799...........1800.00

73 (2 ducats). Same double thick. 1799.................2500.00

LÖWENSTEIN-WERTHEIM-ROCHEFORT, Principality
Carl (Thomas) 1735-89

Copper

Fine

80 1/PFENNING. CFZL mon. Rev. value. 1781....... 7.50

81 1/KREUZER. Sim. 1767...15.00

82 1/KREUZER. Bust. Rev. value. 1767-69 (var.)......12.00

Billon

87 I/KREUZER. Arms. Rev. value. 1765............ 9.00

89 2/KREUZER. 1767.......35.00

91 (2½ Conv. kr.=3 kr. L.M.). CAROL D.G.S.R.I.P. DE LOEWENST. etc. Bust. Rev. CONV. LAND MÜNZ, arms. 1769....................15.00

93 5 (Conv. kreuzer). Head. Rev. Arms. 1767, 69...........15.00

Silver

V.F.

96 10 (Conv. kreuzer). Head. Rev. Arms. 1767.........17.00

97 10 (Conv. kreuzer). Arms. Rev. AD/NORMAN etc. 1767....................15.00

99 20 (Conv. kreuzer). Head. Rev. Arms. 1762-69......22.00

100 20 (Conv. kreuzer). Like No. 97. 1767............22.00

102 30 (Conv. kreuzer). Bust. Rev. Arms in rhombus. 1767..................32.00

104 XX EINE etc. (=½ Conv. thaler). Like No. 111. 1768.75.00

106 XX EINE etc. (=½ Conv. thaler). Like No. 110. 1769.75.00

108 (Reichsthaler). Bust. Rev. Arms. 1754.............350.00

109 (2 Reichsthaler). Same double thick. 57.6 gr. 1754.....1400.00

110 X EINE etc. (= Conv. thaler). Armored bust. Rev. Arms. 1766-69.................195.00

111 X EINE etc. (= Conv. thaler). Head with draped shoulders. Rev. Arms. 1767, 69......180.00

Gold

*112 (ducat). 1754..........1200.00

GERMAN STATES

LÖWENSTEIN-WERTHEIM (Cont.)

(Dominic) Constantin 1789-1806

Copper

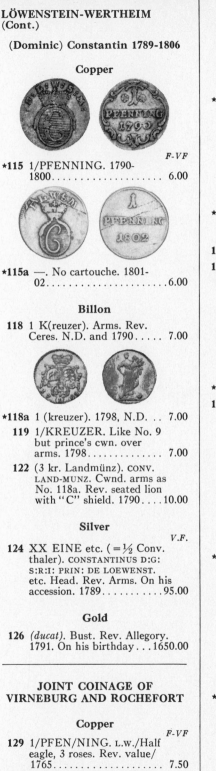

F-VF

★115 1/PFENNING. 1790-
1800.................. 6.00

★115a —. No cartouche. 1801-
02..................... 6.00

Billon

118 1 K(reuzer). Arms. Rev.
Ceres. N.D. and 1790..... 7.00

★118a 1 (kreuzer). 1798, N.D. ... 7.00
119 1/KREUZER. Like No. 9
but prince's cwn. over
arms. 1798.............. 7.00
122 (3 kr. Landmünz). CONV.
LAND-MUNZ. Cwnd. arms as
No. 118a. Rev. seated lion
with "C" shield. 1790.... 10.00

Silver

V.F.

124 XX EINE etc. (= ½ Conv.
thaler). CONSTANTINUS D:G:
S:R:I: PRIN: DE LOEWENST.
etc. Head. Rev. Arms. On his
accession. 1789.......... 95.00

Gold

126 (ducat). Bust. Rev. Allegory.
1791. On his birthday... 1650.00

JOINT COINAGE OF VIRNEBURG AND ROCHEFORT

Copper

F-VF

129 1/PFEN/NING. L.W./Half
eagle, 3 roses. Rev. value/
1765................... 7.50
130 1/PFENNING. L.W. over
arms in 3 shields. Rev. value,
palm branches. 1766..... 6.00
130a —. Arms on cartouche.
1766.................. 6.00

F-VF

130b —. As last but rev. value
in cartouche. 1769-81...... 7.00

★132 1/PFENNING. 1791...... 4.00

★133 1/PFENNING. L.W./Arms
in irregular shield. Rev.
value. 1802, 04 ...... 6.00
133a —. Spade shield. 1804..... 4.00
133b —. Error L.M. 1804....... 5.00

★134 2/PFENNING. 1766...... 5.00
134a —. Like No. 130b.
1776-81................ 7.50

Billon

136 1/PFENNING. Arms.
Rev. value. 1794-95 ...... 7.50

★138 1 "pf" (pfennig symbol).
Arms (eagle over 3 roses).
Uniface. 1798-1804....... 7.00
139 1/KREUZER. Arms. Rev.
value. 1776 .... 4.50

★140 1/KREUZER. Arms. Rev.
value. 1800-06 (3 vars.) ... 6.00
141 (2½ Conv. kr. = 3 kr. L.M.).
NACH D. CONV: FUSS., uncwnd.
3 fold arms. Rev. LOEW:/
WERTH:L/MÜNTZ/1776..... 6.50
142 III/KREUZER. Arms. Rev.
value. 1800-05 (3 vars.) ... 7.50
145 5/KREUZER. Arms. Rev.
value. 1767 .... 9.50

LÜBECK (LUEBECK),

Bishopric

The bishops of Lübeck turned Protestant during the Reformation and moved to Eutin, north of Lübeck, whence they ruled 2 small enclaves in Holstein.

Friedrich August of Holstein-Gottorp 1750-85, Count of Oldenburg 1773, Duke of Oldenburg 1775

Silver

VF-EF

1 (thaler). D.G. EP. LUB. HAER.
NORV. etc. FA mon. Rev. Arms.
1775.................... 300.00
2 (thaler). FRID. AUG. D. G. HAER
N. EP. LUB. etc. ⅓ length bust.
Rev. Arms. 1775.......... 850.00

Gold

V.F.

3 (5 thalers). Sim. but bust to
shoulders. 1776.......... 1500.00

Peter Friedrich Ludwig 1785-1803, Prince of Lübeck 1803, Duke of Lübeck-Eutin 1808, Grand Duke of Oldenburg 1823

Lübeck-Eutin was amalgamated with Oldenburg in this reign. See Oldenburg.

LÜBECK, Free City

On an arm of the Baltic between Holstein and Mecklenburg. Site of an imperial mint in the 12th century. Local coinage from the 13th century. From 1810 to 1815 Lübeck was part of France.

Arms: Per fesse, silver and red.

Monetary Systems: See Hamburg.

Billon

VG-F

★2 I/DREI/LING. 1728-62.... 4.00

★4 I/SCHIL/LING. CIVITATIS
IMPERIALIS. Eagle. Rev. MONETA
NOVA LUBEC. value. 1727-29,
58..................... 3.00
5 I/SCHILLING. Eagle. Rev.
value/LUBISCH. 1789 .... 4.00

GERMAN STATES

LÜBECK (Cont.)

VG-F

*9 4/SCHIL/LING. Eagle. Rev. LUBECKS COURANT GELDT. Arms. 1728-32, 52......... 6.50

Silver

V.F.

10 8/SCHIL/LING. Sim. 1728-52....................12.00

11 16/SCHIL/LING. Like No. 12. 1731-52....................18.00

*12 32/SCHIL/LING. 1731-58..37.50

14 (2 mark = ½ Spec. thaler). No. 19 half thickness. 14.4 gr. 1776....................75.00

16 32/SCHILLINGE. Eagle. Rev. value. 1797.........37.50

18 48 SCHILLING. Eagle. Rev. Arms. 1752..........85.00

19 (4 mark = Spec. thaler). St. John. Rev. Eagle. 1776..225.00

20 *(2 thaler).* 1766........... ——

Gold

22 (ducat). Eagle. Rev. MON AVR/LVBECENS/etc. on tablet. 1790....................950.00

23 (ducat). FRANCISCVS II etc. Eagle. Rev. as last. 1794-1801....................900.00

LUXEMBURG.
See LOW COUNTRIES.

MAINZ (MOGUNTIA),
Archbishopric/Electorate

On the Rhine west of Frankfurt. Site of an archbishopric since 747 and of an imperial mint from Charlemagne through the 11th century. Archiepiscopal coinage from the 11th century. By the Golden Bull of 1356 the archbishops of Mainz were recognized as presidents of the Imperial Electoral College and Arch-Chancellors of the Empire.

Arms: Red, a silver 6-spoked wheel.

Johann Friedrich Carl, Graf von Ostein, Archbishop of Mainz 1743-63, Bishop of Worms 1750-63

Copper

(All struck at Erfurt)

Fine

*1 I/HELLER. 1756-59...... 4.00

1a —. 1760................. 6.00

2 I/PFENNIG. Sim. but many die varieties (cartouches, wreaths, etc.). 1756-61...... 3.50

2a —. Like No. 2b but greyhound to left of arms. 1759-60................. 4.50

*2b —. 1760..................4.75

3 1/PFENNIG. JFC mon. over wheel. Rev. value. 1760.... 4.25

5 II/PFENNIG. I.F.C. etc. 5 fold arms supported by 2 greyhounds. Rev. value. 1759... 5.00

5a —. No hounds. 1759-60.... 5.00

6 II/PFENNIG. J.F.C. mon. on mantle. Rev. value. 1759... 6.00

*8 II/PFENNIG. 1759-60..... 6.00

Fine

9 2/PFENNIG. Like No. 3. 1760-61 (vars.)........... 4.50

9.5 2/PFENNIG. Like No. 5. 1760................. 4.50

10 2/PFENNIG. Like No. 12. 1760................. 4.75

11 2/PFENNIG. Like No. 1. 1760-61............. 4.50

12 3/PFENNIG. I.F.C. etc. Bust. Rev. value. 1759-60....... 4.50

12a —. IOH. FRID. etc. 1760..... 5.00

12b —. Like No. 12a but rev. value in cartouche. 1760-61................. 4.75

12c III/PFENNIG. 1759....... 6.00

13 3/PFENNIG. Like No. 2b. 1759................. 4.50

14 3/PFENNIG. Like No. 5. 1759-60................. 4.00

14a III/PFENNIG. 1759....... 6.50

15 3/PFENNIG. Like No. 15a but rev. no cartouche. 1759-61................. 4.00

*15a 3/PFENNIG. 1761....... 6.00

16 3/PFENNIG. Like No. 16b but rev. no cartouche. 1760................. 6.00

16a —. Obv. also has legend I.F.C. etc. 1760................. 6.50

*16b —. 1760-61............. 5.00

17 3/PFENNIG. Like No. 1. 1760-61................. 4.00

Silver

V.F.

18 (groschen). Like No. 20. 1763....................27.50

19 (⅛ thaler). IOH. FRID. CAR. etc. Arms. Rev. 9 lines: NATUS/ 6 July 1689/etc. On his death. 1763..............37.50

20 (¼ thaler). Sim. but 10 lines. 1763................45.00

21 (½ thaler). IO. FRID. CAR. etc. Bust. Rev. DOCE ME etc. Arms supported. 1760...........90.00

23 (thaler). IOAN. FRID CAROL. etc. Bust. Rev. DOCE ME etc. Arms. 1747-48.................450.00

GERMAN STATES

MAINZ, Archbishopric (Cont.)

Gold (ducat = 3.49 gr.)

V.F.

25 (ducat). Sim. to No. 23.
1745-53 . . . . 950.00
26 (2 ducats). Sim. 1745, 48 . . 1850.00
27 (ducat). Sim. to No. 21.
1759-60 . . . . 900.00
28 (2 ducats). Sim. 1760 . . . . 1800.00

Sede Vacante 1763

Silver

VF-EF

30 (1/8 thaler). St. Martin and
beggar. Rev. CAPITVL METRO-
POLIT. MOGVNTVM. Arms.
1763 . . . . 60.00

★31 (1/4 thaler). Generally sim.
1763 . . . . 60.00
32 (1/2 thaler). Generally sim.
1763 . . . . 85.00
33 (thaler). Sim. but in circle
of 12 shields both sides.
(1763 R.N.) 400.00

Note: Controversy exists as to whether
Nos. 30-33 are medals or coins.

Emerich Joseph,
Freiherr von Breitbach,
Archbishop 1763-74,
Bishop of Worms 1768-74

Copper
(Struck at Erfurt)

Fine

★35 I/HELLER. 1769 . . . . 4.50
36 I/HELLER. E J mon. over
wheel. Rev. value. 1769 . . . . 4.50

★37 I/PFENNIG. Arms. (wheel).
Rev. value/C.M.L.M./1766 . . . 4.50

Fine

38 I/PFENNIG. E.I.D.G. etc.
Arms. Rev. value/SCHEIDE/
etc. 1768-69 . . . . 4.50

★38a —. w/out obv. legend.
1769-70 . . . . 4.50

★38b —. EM. IO. D.G. etc. 1771 . . 4.50
39 II/PFENNIGE. Like No. 37.
1766 . . . . 4.50
40 II/PFENNIG. Like No. 41.
1768 . . . . 4.50

★41 III/PFENNIG. 1768 . . . . 5.00
42 IIII/PFENNIGE. Like No. 37.
1766 . . . . 5.00

Billon

Note: See Erfurt for silver 3 pfennige and 1/48 thaler.

46 1/KREUTZER. Arms. (wheel).
Rev. value. 1765 . . . . 3.00

Silver

V.F.

50 5 (Conv. kreuzer). EMERIC
IOSEPH. D.G. ARCHIEP. MOG. etc.
Arms supported by Basilisk.
Rev. 240 EINE etc. EJC mon. on
pedestal. 1763 . . . . 10.00

52 5 (Conv. kreuzer). EM. IOS.
etc. Arms on pedestal. Rev.
240 etc. rhombus. 1765 . . . . 8.50
53 *5 (Conv. kreuzer).* Sim. but
arms 2 fold. 1767 . . . . 10.00
54 (1/12 thaler). EM. JOS. etc.
Arms. Rev. 10 lines: NATUS
II NOVEMB. 1707 etc. On his
death. 1774 . . . . *(E.F.)* 30.00
56 10 (Conv. kreuzer). Bust.
Rev. 120 EINE etc. 4 fold arms.
1764 . . . . 10.00

V.F.

56a —. Rev. 2 fold arms. 1765-
66 . . . . 10.00
56b —. Rev. 3 fold arms. 1773-
74 . . . . 8.00
58 20 (Conv. kreuzer). Like No.
56 but 60 EINE etc. 1765 . . . . 15.00
58a —. Like No. 56a. 1766 . . . . . . 17.50
58b —. Like No. 56b. 1768, 72 . . 12.50
60 (1/6 thaler). Like No. 54.
1774 . . . . *(E.F.)* 35.00
62 30 (Conv. kreuzer). Like No.
56 but 40 ST. EINE etc. 1765. 22.50
62a —. Rev. 2 shields. 1766 . . . . . 22.50
63 1/8 thaler). Like No. 54.
1774 . . . . *(E.F.)* . 45.00
64 20 EINE etc. (=1/2 Conv.
thaler). Bust. Rev. Arms.
1765 . . . . 85.00
65 20 EINE etc. (=1/2 Conv.
thaler). Like No. 67.
1766 . . . . 95.00
65.5 20 EINE etc. (=1/2 Conv.
thaler). Like No. 68.
1769 . . . . 85.00
66 10 EINE etc. (= Conv. thaler).
Bust. Rev. 4 fold arms. 1764-
65 . . . . 110.00
67 X EINE etc. (= Conv. thaler).
Bust. Rev. 2 fold arms, no
supporters. 1766-68 . . . . 120.00
68 X EINE etc. (= Conv. thaler).
Bust. Rev. Arms supported.
1768-69 . . . . 120.00
69 ZEHEN EINE etc. (= Conv.
thaler). Bust. Rev. oval arms.
1770-71 . . . . 110.00

Gold

70 (ducat). Bust. Rev. 3 fold arms.
1768-71 . . . . 900.00
71 (Rhinegold ducat). Bust.
Rev. AURUM/RHENI/1771
R.N 1800.00

Sede Vacante 1774

Silver

VF-EF

★72 (1/4 thaler). St. Martin.
Rev. Arms. 1774 . . . . 75.00
73 (1/2 thaler). Sim. 1774 . . . . . 75.00
74 (thaler). Sim. 1774 . . . . 90.00

Note: Controversy exists as to whether
Nos. 72-74 are medals or coins.

GERMAN STATES

MAINZ, Archbishopric (Cont.)

**Friedrich Carl Joseph,
Freiherr von und zu Erthal,
Archbishop of Mainz
and Bishop of Worms
1774-1802**

Copper

(Struck at Erfurt)

Fine

*75 1/PFENNIG. Arms. Rev.
value. 1779, 81 . . . . 5.50

76 1/PFENNING. FCIK mon.
Rev. value. 1781 . . . . 8.00

*77 ¼/KREVT/ZER. Bust.
Rev. value. 1795 . . . . 3.00

78 ½/KREVT/ZER. Sim. 1795-
96 . . . . 4.00

Billon or Silver

*80 1 K(reuzer). 1795 . . . . 4.00

87 3 K(reuzer). Like No. 80.
1796 . . . . 6.00

91 5 (Conv. kreuzer). Like No.
80 but 3 fold arms. 1795 . . . . 10.00

92 5 (Conv. kreuzer). CHUR MAINZ.
Arms. Rev. IUS/TIRT. 1795 . . 10.00

Note: See Erfurt for 1/48 thaler, 6
pfennig and groschen coins.

94 10 (Conv. kreuzer). Bust.
Rev. 120 EINE etc. Arms.
1795 . . . . 12.50

94a —. w/out 120 etc. 1795 . . . . . 12.50

95 20 (Conv. kreuzer). Like
No. 94a. 1794 . . . . 20.00

Silver

V.F.

97 XX EINE etc. (= ½
Conv. thaler). Like No. 103.
1795 . . . . 120.00

V.F.

99 ZEHEN EINE etc. (=Conv.
thaler). FRID. CAR. IOS. D.G.
A.E.MOG. etc. Bust r. Rev.
Arms. 1794 . . . . 175.00

99a —. Bust facing. 1794 . . . . . 250.00

100 X EINE etc. (= Conv.
thaler). Bust facing. Rev.
EX VASIS/etc. 1794 R.N.
Contribution thaler 250.00

101 X EINE etc. (= Conv.
thaler). Arms. Rev. value.
(2 vars.). 1794 . . . . 190.00

102 (Conv. thaler). DEUTSCHLANDS
SCHUTZWEHR etc. City view.
Rev. Monument. 1795 . . . 350.00

102a —. Obv. No. 102. Rev. No.
103 . . . . 800.00

102b —. Obv. No. 103. Rev. No.
102 . . . . 800.00

103 ZEHEN EINE (= Conv.
thaler). FRID. CAR. IOS. ERZB.
V. KVRF. etc. Bust. Rev.
Arms. 1796 . . . . 150.00

Gold

104 (ducat). Bust. Rev. Arms.
1795 . . . . 950.00

105 (ducat). Bust. Rev. AVREA
MOGVNTIA. City view. 1795
R.N 950.00

106 (Contribution ducat). Bust.
Rev. SALVS-PVBLICA, arms.
1795 . . . . RR

In 1801 France annexed all of Mainz
lying on the left bank of the Rhine.
Elector Archbishop Carl Theodor von
Dalberg, elected 1802, accepted secularization of the rest of Mainz in 1803
but retained the principality of Aschaffenburg in his capacity as Arch-
Chancellor. He then moved his seat of
government to Regensburg (q.v.),
where he was already bishop. In 1806
he became Prince Primate (q.v.).

MAINZ (MAYENCE), City

Subservient to the archbishopric. Obtained the right to strike local coins
1420. Most frequently encountered are
undated city toll tokens with the wheel
and B.Z. (bridge toll), R.T. (Rhine
Gate) or N.T. (New Gate).

French,
Under General Doyre,
Besieged in Mainz by Prussians

Copper

F-VF

1 1/SOL. Like No. 2. 1793 . . . . 18.00

*2 2/SOLS. 1793 . . . . 18.00

3 5/SOLS. Sim. 1793 . . . . 25.00

MANNHEIM. See Pfalz.

MANSFELD, County

The counts of Mansfeld, a small state
in the silver mining Harz region between Anhalt and Thuringia, appeared
in the 11th century. Their first coinage
was struck toward the close of the 12th
century. In the 15th and 16th centuries
the family became much divided but
all branches except Bornstädt had died
out by 1710.

MANSFELD-BORNSTÄDT
Heinrich, Neapolitan
Prince of Fondi 1717-51,
Prince of the H. R. Empire
and Count of Mansfeld
1717-80

Silver

E.F.

1 (¼ Species thaler). Like
No. 3. 7.2 gr. 1747 . . . . 250.00

2 (½ Species thaler). Sim.
14.4 gr. 1747 . . . . 325.00

3 (Species thaler). D.G. HENR.
S.R.I. & DE FONDI PRINC. etc.
Bust. Rev. Arms. 1747 . . . . 850.00

5 (½ Conv. thaler). HENRI.
S.R.I.P.C. MANSFELD etc. Arms.
Rev. St. George. 14 gr.
1774 . . . . 250.00

6 (Conv. thaler). Sim. 1774 . . 350.00

Gold

VF-EF

8 (ducat). Like No. 3. 1747 . . . . RR

9 (ducat). Like No. 5. 1774 . . 900.00

In 1780 Heinrich's son died and the
Mansfeld male line became extinct.
The Colloredo family [See AUSTRIA
(STATES)] obtained the Mansfeld titles, but Electoral Saxony obtained the
county itself. This passed to Prussia
in 1815, which thereafter struck special
coins with silver from the Mansfeld
mines.

MECKLENBURG (MEGAPOLIS),
Duchy

Along the Baltic Coast between Holstein and Pomerania. First coins 12th
century. Branches of Schwerin and
Strelitz established 1658.

Arms: Gold, a black bull's head.

Monetary Systems: 12 pfenning =
4 dreiling = 2 sechsling = 1 schilling;
48 schilling = 3 mark = 1 (Reichs)
thaler.

MECKLENBURG-SCHWERIN

Duchy until 1815, Grand Duchy thereafter.

GERMAN STATES

MECKLENBURG-SCHWERIN
(Cont.)

Christian Ludwig II
(Regent 1735-47),
As Duke 1747-56

Copper

		Fine
★1	III/PFENING. 1752-55	3.50
1a	—. FR. MECKLENB. 1752	6.00

Billon

4	24/EINEN (=1/24)/THALER (=2 schilling). H.M.S.M. Bull's head. Rev. value. 1754	7.50
5	24/EINEN/THALER. V.G. G.H.Z.M., CL mon. Rev. value./O.H.K. 1754	7.50
7	12/EINEN/THALER (=4 schilling). CHRIST. LVDOV. D.G. DVX MECKLENBVRG. Bull's head. Rev. value. 1750, 52	8.00
9	12/EINEN/THALER. Bust. Rev. value. 1754	8.00

Silver

		F-VF
11	VI EINEN THALER. (=8 schilling). 1752	14.00

★12	VI/EINEN/THALER. 1753-54	15.00
14	8/GUTE/GROSCHEN (=16 schilling). Bust. Rev. value. 1753-54	17.50
16	⅔ (Reichsthaler). Bust. Rev. Arms. 1754	47.50

Gold

		V.F.
19	¼/DUCAT. Bust. Rev. value. 1756	400.00
20	5 TH(aler). Bust. Rev. Arms. 1754	900.00
21	(10 thaler). Bust. Rev. Arms. On birthday of Princess Friederike Luise. 1752	1200.00

Friedrick II 1756-85

Copper

		Fine
22	I/PFENNIG. Buffalo head, no legend. Rev. value. 1758	5.00

		Fine
23	3/PFENNIGE. Sim. 1758	6.00
24	6 PFENNIGE. Sim. 1758	8.50
25	III/PFENNIG. Like No. 26. 1759	3.00
26	6/PFENNIG. F cwnd. Rev. value. 1759	5.00

Billon

28	III/PFENN(ig). F cwnd. Rev. value/COUR/MECK/ SCH/etc. 1763-84	5.00
31	VI/PFENN(ig). Sim. 1763-85	5.00
33	48/EINEN/THALER (=1 schilling). F cwnd./ H.M.S.M. Rev. value. 1760	6.50

★35	1/SCHILLING. 1763-85	2.75
37	2 SCHILLINGE. 1757	8.00
39	24/EINEN/THALER (=2 sch.) Like No. 33. 1760-61	7.00
41	2/SCHILLINGE. Like No. 35. 1763-78	6.00

Silver

		F-VF
43	4/SCHILLINGE. F in cwnd. shell. Rev. value. 1763-83	7.50
45	8/SCHILLINGE. FRIDERICUS D.G. DUX MECLENB. Arms. Rev. value. 1763-64	10.00
47	12/SCHILLINGE. Sim. 1774-77	15.00
49	16/SCHILLINGE. Bull's head shield. Rev. value. 1758	20.00
51	16/SCHILLINGE. Like No. 45. 1763-64	20.00
53	32/SCHILLINGE. Sim. 1763-64	50.00

Gold

		V.F.
55	2/THALER. Bust. Rev. value. 1769-83	1000.00

Friedrich Franz I, 1785-1837,
As Duke 1785-1815

Billon

		Fine
56	III/PFENN(ige). FF cwnd. Rev. III/PFENN. COUR./MECK. SCHW./MUNZE/date. 1787-97	6.00
57	III/PFEN(nige). Like No. 59. 1801-15	4.00
58	VI/PFENN(ige). Like No. 56. 1786-94	5.00

★59	VI/PFEN(nige). 1801-15	4.00

		Fine
★61	1/SCHILLING. Like No. 35 but FF cwnd. 1785-1812	2.50
62	2/SCHILLINGE. 1786	25.00

Silver

		F-VF
63	4/SCHILLINGE. Like No. 43 but FF. 1785, 1809	25.00
66	12/SCHILLINGE. FRIED. FRANZ V.G.G. HERZOG ZU MECKLENB. Arms. Rev. value. 1791, 92	30.00
68	⅓ (Reichsthaler). Arms. Rev. ⅓. 1790	30.00
69	32/SCHILLINGE. Arms (2 vars.). Rev. value. 1797	25.00
70	⅔ (Reichsthaler). Like No. 68. 1789-1810	27.50
71	⅔ (Reichsthaler). Sim. but with DEM VATERLANDE/1813	75.00

Gold

		V.F.
72	2/THALER. Like No. 66. 1792	1400.00
72a	—. 1797	650.00

As Grand Duke 1815-37

Copper

		Fine
73	1/PFENNIG. FF cwnd. Rev. value. 1831	1.50

★74	2/PFENNINGE. 1831	3.00

Billon

		F-VF
75	III/PFEN(nige). Like No. 59. 1816-19	4.00
76	I/DREILING. FF cwnd. Rev. value. 1819-24	3.00
76.4	I/DREILING. Sim. but circular legends both sides. 1828-30	3.00

★76.7	III/PFENNINGE. 1831-36	3.50
77	VI/PFEN(nige). Like No. 59. 1816-17	4.00
78	I/SECHSLING. Like No. 76.7. 1820-24	2.50

MECKLENBURG-SCHWERIN
(Cont.)

F-VF

*78.4 1/SECHSLING. 1829.... 4.50

79 VI/PFENNIGE. Like
No. 76.7. 1831............ 4.50

80 1/SCHILLING. Like
No. 61. 1817............20.00

81 1/SCHILLING. V.G.G.GR.
HZ.V.M.S., cwnd. FF.
Rev. value. 1826-27...... 6.00

81.4 1/SCHILLING. Like
No. 78.4. 1829-37........ 3.50

Silver

V.F.

82 4/SCHILLINGE. Like No. 81.
1826....................10.00

83 4/SCHILLINGE. Head.
Rev. value. 1828.........15.00

83a —. 1829-33.............. 7.50

84 8/SCHILLINGE. Like
No. 81. 1827.............15.00

85 ⅔ (Reichsthaler). Arms.
Rev. value. 1817........150.00

85a —. 1825.................50.00

86 ⅔ (Reichsthaler). Large
bust, legend ends SCHW. Rev.
value. 1825-26............25.00

E.F.

*86a —. Small bust, legend ends
SCHWERIN. 1826........pattern

87 ⅔ (Reichsthaler). Head.
Rev. Arms. 1828.........32.00

87a —. 1829...............65.00

Gold

VF-EF

*88 (ducat). 1830...........pattern

89 ZWEI (=2) THALER.
Sim. (2 vars.). 1830......pattern

90 ZWEI EIN HALB (=2½)
THALER. Head. Rev. Arms.
1831-35.................750.00

VF-EF

91 (5 thaler). Head. Rev. Arms/
D. 28 MAERZ 1828. Mint
Visit................... RRR

92 FÜNF (=5) THALER. Head.
Rev. Arms. 1828-35......800.00

93 ZEHN (=10) THALER.
Sim. 1828-33..........1000.00

Paul Friedrich 1837-42

Billon

F-VF

*94 III/PFENNIGE. PF cwnd.
Rev. value. 1838-42....... 3.50

*95 1/SCHILLING. 1838-42.... 3.75

Silver

V.F.

96 4/SCHILLINGE. Arms.
Rev. value. 1838-39....... 7.50

97 XVIII STÜCK etc. (=⅔
Reichsthaler). Head. Rev.
Arms. 1839-41............35.00

The (4 schillinge) and (8 schillinge)
sized pieces of 1842 (Head. Rev. VOL-
LENDET etc.) on the death of Paul
Friedrich are considered medals.

Gold

VF-EF

*98 ZWEI EIN HALB (=2½)
THALER. 1840.........950.00

99 FÜNF (=5) THALER. Sim.
1840...................1200.00

100 ZEHN (=10) THALER.
Head. Rev. Arms. 1839...1100.00

Friedrich Franz II 1842-83

Copper

Fine

101 3/PFENNIGE. FF cwnd.
Rev. value. 1843-48....... 1.50

101a —. 1852-64A............. 1.00

102 1/PFENNIG. Like
No. 104. 1872........... 1.00

*103 2/PFENNIGE. 1872...... 1.00

Fine

*104 5/PFENNIGE. 1872...... 1.25

Billon

105 III/PFENNIGE. FF cwnd.
Rev. value. 1842-46...... 1.75

106 1/SCHILLING. FF cwnd.
Rev. value. 1842-46...... 2.50

107 48/EINEN/THALER
(=1 schilling). 1848....... 3.00

*107a —. 1852-66A............ 1.25

Silver

V.F.

108 12/EINEN/THALER
(=4 schilling). Head. Rev.
value. 1848.............. 8.50

*109 6 EINEN THALER
(=8 sch.). Head. Rev.
Arms. 1848.............17.50

110 XVIII STÜCK etc. (=32
sch.). Head. Rev. Arms.
1845...................200.00

111 EIN (=1) THALER.
Like No. 109. 1848........35.00

*112 EIN (=1) THALER.
1864....................27.50

113 EIN (=1) THALER.
Sim. but ZUR FEIER etc.
25th year of reign. 1867....65.00

GERMAN STATES

MECKLENBURG-STRELITZ, Duchy and Grand Duchy

Adolf Friedrich IV, Duke 1752-94

Copper

Fine

*1 III/PFEN(nig). 1753-55.....4.50

2 3/GVTE/PFENNING.
AF script. Rev. value. 1760 .. 4.50

*3 III/GUTE/PFENNINGE.
1764-94.................. 3.50

Billon

5 I/SECHS/LING. Like No. 3.
1764, 66 .... 4.00

*7 48/EINEN/THALER (=1
schilling). 1755-57 .... 4.00

9 48/EINEN/REICHS/
THALER (=1 sch.). Like No.
3. 1764, 66 .... 4.00

9a —. 1766. Stars with 6 pts.
flank "48." (=1820 restrike). 7.50

12 24/EINEN/THALER
(=2 sch.). Like No. 7. 1755. 7.00

14 24/EINEN/REICHS/
THALER (=2 sch.). Like No.
3. 1764, 66 .... 7.00

Silver

F-VF

16 *12/EINEN/THALER*
(=4 sch.). Like No. 7. 1754,
56 .... 8.00

18 12/EINEN/REICHS/
THALER (=4 sch.). SALUS
PUBLICA etc. AF mon. Rev.
value. 1763-64 .... 7.00

19 12/EINEN/THALER
(=4 sch.). ADOLPH FRID. IV
etc., arms. Rev. value.
1764..................... 8.00

21 VI/EINEN/THALER
(=8 sch.). Like No. 7.
1754-59.................. 15.00

F-VF

*23 ⅙ (Reichsthaler =8 sch.).
1764...................... 15.00

25 ⅙ *(Reichsthaler =8 sch.).*
1773 .... 16.00

29 8/GUTE/GROSCHEN (=
16 sch.). Head. Rev. value.
1755 .... 17.50

31 8/GROSCHEN (=16 sch.).
Head. Rev. value. 1760 .....16.00

31a —. Bust. 1761............ 16.00

33 ⅓ *(Reichsthaler =16 sch.).*
Bust. Rev. Arms. 1773 .....20.00

35 XVI/GVTE/GROSCHEN
(=32 sch.). Head. Rev. value.
1760 R.N................ 40.00

36 ⅔ (Reichsthaler). Head.
Rev. Arms. 1760.......... 32.50

Gold

V.F.

38 (5 thaler). Head. Rev. Arms.
1754.................. 1200.00

38a —. Bust. 1754.......... 1200.00

Georg, Grand Duke 1816-60

Copper

F-VF

40 1/PFENNIG. Like No. 41.
1838..................... 4.00

*41 1½/PFENNIG. 1838 ...... 4.00

42 III/PFENNIGE. Like No.
43. 1832-47 .... 1.50

42a —. III/PFENNINGE.
1855A, 59A 1.00

Billon

Fine

43 48/EINEN/THALER
(=1 sch.). 1838-47 .... 2.50

*43a —. 1855A, 59A 1.75

Silver

*44 4/SCHILLINGE. Head.
Rev. value. 1846-49 .... 7.50

Friedrich Wilhelm 1860-1904

Copper

F-VF

45 III/PFENNINGE.
FW script. Rev. value. 1862,
64....................... 1.00

*46 1/PFENNIG. 1872....... 2.00

47 2/PFENNIGE. Sim. 1872.. 2.00

48 5/PFENNIGE. Sim. 1872.. 2.00

Billon

49 48/EINEN/THALER
(=1 sch.). Like No. 45. 1862,
64....................... 2.50

Silver

V.F.

50 EIN (=1) THALER.
Head. Rev. Arms. 1870.....45.00

MERGENTHEIM.
See Teutonic Order.

MONTFORT.
See AUSTRIA (STATES).

MÜHLHAUSEN (MUHLHUSINAE), Free City

In Thuringia, N.N.W. of Gotha. Site of an imperial mint during the 12th and 13th centuries. Had its own local coinage from the 16th century through 1767.

Mühlhausen was annexed to Prussia in 1802.

Arms: Silver, top half of black eagle. Mill-rind below.

Copper

F-VF

1 II/LEICHTE (=light) /
PFENNINGE. MVHLHÄVSER/
STADTMVNTZ. Rev. value.
1737..................... 6.50

1a —. MÜHLHÄU/SER. 1767..... 7.00

Billon

2 3 (pfennig). Like No. 3.
1737..................... 6.50

2a —. Like No. 3a. 1767....... 6.50

3 VI (pfennig). Arms. Rev.
value in orb. 1737 .... 6.00

*3a —. 1767.................. 6.00

4 24/EINEN (=¹/₂₄)/THAL(er).
Arms. Rev. CIVIT. IMPERIALIS
MUHLHUSINAE. Value. 1767.. 8.00

GERMAN STATES

MÜHLHAUSEN (Cont.)

Silver

V.F.

5 12/EINEN (=¹/₁₂)/THAL(er).
Sim. 1767................. 9.00

6 ⅔ (Reichsthaler). Sim.
"U"s written "V." 1737....45.00

6a —. with "U"s. 1767.......55.00

7 X EINE etc. (= Conv. thaler).
Arms. Rev. bust of Emp.
Joseph II. 1767..........500.00

MÜNSTER (MONASTERIUM),
Bishopric

In Westphalia. Established in early 9th century. First coinage in 11th century. Secularized 1802.
Arms: Blue, a gold fesse.
Monetary System:
1 schilling = 1/28 thaler; otherwise like contemporary North German.

**Clemens August v. Bayern,
Elector Archbishop of Cologne
1723-61,
Bishop of Münster 1719-61.**

**Also Bishop of Hildesheim,
Osnabrück and Paderborn,
Grand Master of
The Teutonic Order**

Copper

VG-F

2 III/PFEN(nig). CAC mon.
Rev. FURSTL. MUNSTRISCHE
etc. Value. 1736-41........ 3.00

3 III/PFEN(nig). CAC mon.
on cwnd. mantle (like No. 6).
Rev. HOCHFURST MUNST. etc.,
value. 1735-45............. 3.00

4 III/PFEN(nig). Obv. like
No. 2. Rev. like No. 3.
1748-55-*56*.............. 3.00

5 IIII/PFEN(nig). Like No. 2.
1735..................... RR

*6 IIII/PFEN(nig). 1743-45... 4.00

*7 IIII/PFEN(nig). Sim. but
CAC mon. in branches. 1748-
55..................... 4.00

Billon or Silver

Fine

9 48/I (=¹/₄₈)/REICHS/
THAL(er). Like No. 10 *but*
CAC mon. 1723 .... 5.00

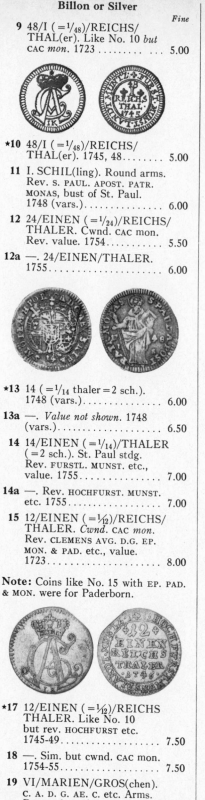

*10 48/I (=¹/₄₈)/REICHS/
THAL(er). 1745, 48........ 5.00

11 I. SCHIL(ling). Round arms.
Rev. S. PAUL. APOST. PATR.
MONAS, bust of St. Paul.
1748 (vars.).............. 6.00

12 24/EINEN (=¹/₂₄)/REICHS/
THALER. CAC mon.
Rev. value. 1754.......... 5.50

12a —. 24/EINEN/THALER.
1755.................... 6.00

*13 14 (=¹/₁₄ thaler = 2 sch.).
1748 (vars.).............. 6.00

13a —. *Value not shown.* 1748
(vars.).................. 6.50

14 14/EINEN (=¹/₁₄/THALER
(= 2 sch.). St. Paul stdg.
Rev. FURSTL. MUNST. etc.,
value. 1755.............. 7.00

14a —. Rev. HOCHFURST. MUNST.
etc. 1755................ 7.00

15 12/EINEN (=¹/₁₂)/REICHS/
THALER. *Cwnd.* CAC *mon.*
Rev. CLEMENS AVG. D.G. EP.
MON. & PAD. etc., value.
1723.................... 8.00

Note: Coins like No. 15 with EP. PAD.
& MON. were for Paderborn.

*17 12/EINEN (=¹/₁₂)/REICHS
THALER. Like No. 10
but rev. HOCHFURST etc.
1745-49.................. 7.50

18 —. Sim. but cwnd. CAC mon.
1754-55................. 7.50

19 VI/MARIEN/GROS(chen).
C. A. D. G. AE. C. etc. Arms.
Rev. value. 1754..........15.00

Note: Former No. 20 (=VI/EINEN/
REICHS/THALER 1754-55) was issued for use in both Cologne and Münster. It is listed as Cologne No. 20.

Sede Vacante 1761

Silver

V.F.

22 R(eichs) ⅙ TH(aler). Like
No. 23. 1761..............35.00

22.5 —. Like No. 23.5. 1761....35.00

*23 R(eichs) ⅓ TH(aler).
St. Paul. Rev. Charlemagne.
1761....................60.00

23.5 —. Sim. but St. Paul in
Cathedral Chapter arms.
1761....................60.00

24 EIN (=1) SPECIES
REICHSTHALER. Münster
cathedral. Rev. Charlemagne.
1761...................275.00

25 (show thaler). St. Paul in
circle of shields. Rev. Charlemagne in same. 1761......*medal*

**Maximilian Friedrich,
Graf v Königsegg-Rothenfels,
Elector-Archbishop of Cologne
1761-84,
Bishop of Münster 1762-84**

Billon or Silver

Fine

26 48/EINEN (=¹/₄₈)/THALER.
MF mon. Rev. value./M.L.M./
1766 .... 5.00

28 I SCHIL(ling =¹/₂₈ thaler).
MF mon. Rev. St. Paul/value/
M.L.M. 1764............. 5.50

*30 12/EINEN (=¹/₁₂)/REICHS/
THALER. 1763-69........ 7.50

Silver

V.F.

32 VI/EINEN (=¹/₆) /REICHS/
THALER. MAX. FRID. D.G. . . .
EPISC. MONAST. etc. Arms.
Rev. value. 1763-64....... 20.00

34 ⅓/REICHS/THALER.
Like No. 32 but arms sup-
ported. 1764-65...........35.00

36 24/MARIEN/GROSCHEN.
Arms. Rev. value. 1763.....45.00

GERMAN STATES

MÜNSTER, Bishopric (Cont.)

V.F.

38 ⅔ (Reichsthaler). MAX. FRID.
D.G.A.E.C. & E. EPISCOP. MON.,
bust. Rev. arms supported.
1764....................60.00

*No. 38 may be identical with Cologne
No. 56.*

Sede Vacante 1801

Billon

VF-EF

★40 1/24 (Reichsthaler). CAPITU.
CATHE. MONAST. Rev. SEDE
VACANTE. 1801............50.00

Silver

★41 ⅓ (Reichsthaler). St. Paul.
Rev. Charlemagne. 1801...100.00

42 ⅔ (Reichsthaler). Sim.
1801..................200.00

43 I SP(ecies)TH(aler). Arms.
Rev. Charlemagne. 1801..2000.00

44 (show thaler). St. Paul in circle
of shields. Rev. Charlemagne
in same. 1801............*medal*

MÜNSTER, Cathedral
Chapter

Copper

VG-F

★1 I/PFENNING. 1790...... 4.50

2 2/PFENNING. Sim. 1790.. 4.50

★3 III/PFENNING. 1739-60... 4.50

VG-F

3a 3/PFENNING. 1787...... 5.00

4 IIII/PFENNING. Like
No. 3 but S.P. under bust.
1739, 62................ 5.00

4a 4/PFENNING. 1787-90.... 6.00

5 VI/PFENNING. Like No. 3
but S. PAULUS/6*P under bust.
1762.................... 6.00

5a —. 6*P only under bust.
1762.................... 6.00

5b 6/PFENNING. Like No. 4a.
1787-90................. 6.00

MÜNSTER, City

Possessed considerable freedom until
1660. Capital of the bishopric from that
year. Local coins 16th-18th centuries.

City arms: Gold, a red fesse.

Copper

(Annual die varieties)

VG-F

1 1 (pfennig). STADT MUNSTER.
Arms. Rev. value. 1740,
50, 58.................. 9.50

2 1½/PFENNING. SM
script mon. Rev. value.
1740, 50, 58..............14.00

★3 II/PFENNING. 1740, 50,
58..................... 7.50

NASSAU, Princes and Dukes

Possessions in the Rhineland. Descended from Walram I, who took the
title of count in 1158. Divided into
Walramian and Ottonian lines 1255.
Each of these was subdivided many
times.

Arms: On a blue field billety with gold,
a gold lion.

I. WALRAMIAN LINE.

A. NASSAU-USINGEN,
Princes from 1668.

Friedrich August 1803-16,
Duke 1806

1. Joint coinage with Prince Friedrich Wilhelm II of Nassau-
Weilburg.

Copper

Fine

★1 ¼/KREU/ZER. 1808-11... 2.00

Fine

1a —. Legend begins upper right.
1809-14................. 2.00

2 ½/KREUZER. Like No. 1a.
1813................... 2.75

3 I/KREU/ZER. Like No. 1.
18-20 mm. 1808-09........ 4.50

3a —. 22-24mm. 1808........ 6.50

3b —. Like No. 1a. 1808-13.... 2.75

Billon

4 III/KREUZER. Obv. like
No. 1. Rev. value. 1810-11.. 3.00

4a —. Obv. like No. 1a. 1809,
12-16................... 3.00

Silver

V.F.

5 5 (Conv. kreuzer) HERZ(OGL.)
NASSAU–CONVENT. MUNZ. Arms.
Rev. 240/EINE etc. 1808....27.50

6 10 (Conv. kreuzer). Sim. but
120/etc. 1809.............40.00

7 20 (Conv. kreuzer). Sim. but
60/etc. (var.). 1809.......30.00

Gold

★8 1/DUCAT. HERZOGTHUM
NASSAU. Arms. Rev. value.
1809..................1000.00

2. Friedrich August, alone.

Silver

9 10 (Conv. kreuzer). Obv.
like No. 12. Rev. Arms.
1809...................60.00

10 20 (Conv. kreuzer). Sim.
1809...................30.00

11 ZWANZIG EINE etc.
(= ½ Conv. thaler). Sim.
1809..................120.00

★12 ZEHN EINE etc. (= Conv.
thaler). Obv. ★. Rev. Arms.
(var.). 1809-15...........175.00

12a —. Rev. DAS/DANKBARE etc.
1812..................300.00

GERMAN STATES

NASSAU (Cont.)

V.F.

12b —. Rev. head of Friedrich Wilhelm (Mint visit 1815)..800.00

Nassau-Usingen was inherited by Weilburg at Friedrich August's death in 1816.

B. NASSAU-WEILBURG.

Carl August 1719-53, Prince 1737

Copper

VG-F

15 IIII/EINEN (= ¼)/ KREUZER CA script mon. divides F–N. Rev. value. 1752....................12.50

16 II/EINEN (= ½)/KREUZER. Sim. 1752................10.00

Billon

18 1/KREUZER. Lion shield divides F–N. Rev. value. 1749.................... 9.00

20 4/KREUZER. 3 shields, F–N above. Rev. value. 1749-51..................13.50

22 XII/KREUZER. Like No. 20. 1750....................27.50

Silver

V.F.

24 *(mining gulden)*. Arms. Rev. ASPERA OBLECTANT, mining scene. 1750.......200.00

25 (mining thaler). CAR. AUG. D.G. PR. NASS. WEILB. Bust. Rev. EX VISCERIBUS etc. Arms. Mehlbach mines. 1752.....500.00

Gold

26 *(ducat)*. Bust. Rev. Arms. 1750....................1100.00

27 1 DUCAT. Arms. Rev. AD LEGEM etc. Knight stdg. 1750.............. 950.00

Friedrich Wilhelm II, Prince 1788-1816

Silver

F-VF

30 10 (Conv. kreuzer). FRIEDRICH WILHELM FÜRST ZU NASSAU. Head. Rev. Arms. 1809.....50.00

31 20 Conv. (kreuzer). Sim. 1809....................50.00

31a —. 1810................50.00

32 ZWANZIG EINE etc. (= ½ Conv. thaler). Sim. 1809...................150.00

F-VF

33 ZEHN EINE etc. (= Conv. thaler). Sim. 1809-15 (var.)..........150.00

C. UNITED NASSAU.

Wilhelm (of Weilburg), Duke of all Nassau 1816-39

Copper

35 ¼/KREU/ZER. Like No. 36. 1817-19 L. 2.00

35a —. Sim. but many obverse legend varieties. 1819, 22 Z. 2.00

★36 1/KREU/ZER. 1817-18.... 3.00

37 EIN (= 1)/KREUZER. Like No. 41. 1830-38........2.00

Billon

38 I/KREUZER. H.N.L.M. Lion shield. Rev. value. 1817-28.................... 4.50

39 I/KREUZER. Like No. 43. 1832-35.................. 4.00

40 III/KREUZER. Obv. like No. 36. Rev. value. 1817-19.................... 4.00

40a —. HERZ. NASS. SCHEID MUNZ. 1822-28.................. 4.00

★41 3/KREUZER. 1831-36..... 4.00

42 6/KREUZER. Like No. 42a but HERZ. NASSAUISCHE etc. 1817-19.................. 4.00

★42a —. 1822-28.............. 4.00

43 6/KREUZER. Like No. 41 but square shield. 1831-37... 3.00

43a —. 1838-39.............. 3.00

Silver

V.F.

44 ½/GULDEN. WILHELM HERZOG ZU NASSAU. Head. Rev. value. 1838-39....... 25.00

V.F.

45 1/GULDEN. Sim. 1838-39..40.00

46 KRONEN THALER. Head. Rev. Arms. 1816.....250.00

47 EIN (=1)/KRONEN/ THALER. Arms. Rev. value. 1817....................200.00

48 KRONEN THALER. Head. Rev. Arms. 1822, 25......200.00

49 KRONEN THALER. Head. Rev. Arms supported. 1831-37....................160.00

49a —. Rev. BESICHT etc. Mint visit. 1831..........(E.F.) 800.00

Gold

★50 (ducat). 1818...........*1800.00*

Adolph, Duke 1839-66 Ousted by Prussia; Later became Grand Duke of Luxemburg 1890-1905

Copper

Fine

51 1/HELLER. Like No. 53 but square shield. 1842........ 3.25

52 1/PFENNIG. NASSAU. Arms and rev. like No. 54. 1859-62.................. 1.25

★53 EIN (=1)/KREUZER. 1842-56................. 1.00

★54 1/KREUZER. 1859-63..... 1.00

Billon

55 1/KREUZER. Arms. Rev. value. 1861.......... 3.50

56 3/KREUZER. Like No. 51. 1839 (pattern), 42-55....... 3.00

57 6/KREUZER. Sim. 1840-55.................... 3.00

Silver

V.F.

58 ½/GULDEN. Head r. Rev. value. 1840-45.......25.00

GERMAN STATES

NASSAU (Cont.)

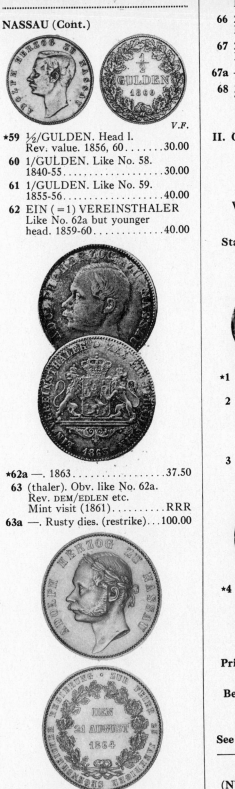

V.F.

*59 ½/GULDEN. Head l.
Rev. value. 1856, 60......30.00

60 1/GULDEN. Like No. 58.
1840-55.................30.00

61 1/GULDEN. Like No. 59.
1855-56.................40.00

62 EIN (=1) VEREINSTHALER
Like No. 62a but younger
head. 1859-60...........40.00

*62a —. 1863..............37.50

63 (thaler). Obv. like No. 62a.
Rev. DEM/EDLEN etc.
Mint visit (1861).........RRR

63a —. Rusty dies. (restrike)...100.00

*64 EIN GEDENKTHALER.
Head laureate. Rev. DEN/21
(error for 24) AUGUST etc. 25th
year of reign. 1864........50.00

V.F.

65 ZWEY (=2) GULDEN. Head.
Rev. Arms. 1846-47.......60.00

66 2/THALER. Head.
Rev. value. 1840........175.00

67 2 THALER. Head.
Rev. Arms. 1844, 54......150.00

67a —. 1847.................275.00

68 ZWEI (=2) VEREINS-
THALER. Head. Rev. arms.
1860...................200.00

II. OTTONIAN LINE.

NASSAU-DIETZ
(ORANGE-NASSAU)
Princes from 1654

**Wilhelm V, Under Regency
1751-66,
Alone in Dietz 1766-1806,
Stadtholder of the Netherlands
1751-95, in Fulda 1803**

Copper

Fine

*1 I/HELLER. O(range) double
N(assau) mon. 1766, 91..... 6.00

2 II/HELLER. Sim. 1766,
91.................... 9.00

Billon

3 1/CONVENT(ion)/KREUZ(er).
Lion shield divides O–N.
Rev. value. 1766......... 7.50

*4 240 EINE etc. (=5 Conv.
kreuzer). FURSTL. ORANIEN
NASS. etc. Lion shield.
Rev. 240 etc. 1766........10.00

**Wilhelm Friedrich,
Prince of Orange-Fulda 1803-10,
Ceded Dietz to Weilburg.**

**Became Prince of Holland 1813,
King of Netherlands
1815-40 as Willem I**

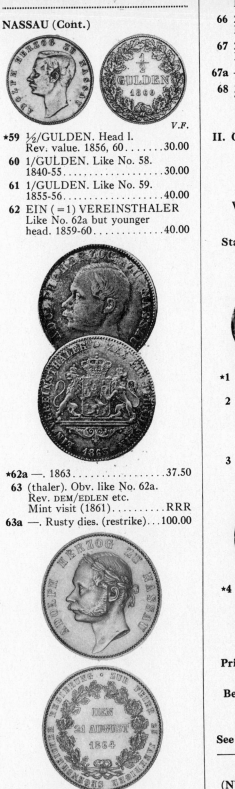

See LOW COUNTRIES.

NÜRNBERG
(NUREMBERG, NORIMBERGA),
Free City

In North Bavaria. Free City 1219. Obtained mint right 14th century. Town annexed to Bavaria 1806.

City arms: 3 devices —

1. Imperial eagle.
2. Harpie (eagle with head and bust of young woman).
3. Parted per pale:
   Dexter – Gold, ½ black eagle.
   Sinister – Bendy of 6, red and silver.

Billon

"pf" is substituted for the pfennig symbol (illustrated at beginning of GERMAN STATES section).

VG-F

1 *1 pf* (=1 pfennig, also called "heller"). Value over arms, date at sides. Rev. blank. 1714-77............ 2.00

3 *1 pf* (=1 pf.) Value over 3rd city device. Rev. Imp. eagle. 1771-77............. 3.00

3a —. 1789................... 3.00

3b —. Rev. blank. 1791-92..... 3.00

6 1 (pfennig). Value, date/2 shields. Rev. blank. 1793 ... 3.00

8 *1 (pfennig).* 1796, 98...... 3.00

10 *1 pf.* Value, date/arms in round shield. Rev. blank. 1806 .... 3.00

11 1 (pfennig). Arms on pedestal, 1 and date at sides. Rev. blank. 1806.............. 3.00

*13 4 pf. 1764-83............. 3.00

17 1 K(reuzer). Value/2 shields/F. Rev. 3 superimposed crosses, STADT MUNTZ. 1750-59...... 3.50

19 1/KREUZER. Arms with mural crown, F in pedestal. Rev. NACH DEM CREIS etc., value. 1763.............. 3.50

*21 1 Kr(euzer). City view. Rev. 3 shields (like No. 84 but N divides 1–Kr). 1773.... 3.50

23 1/KREU/ZER. STADT MUNZ, 2 shields. Rev. value. 1786 .. 3.50

25 1/KREU/ZER. Arms (3rd device). Value. 1796-*99* (var.)................. 3.50

27 1/KREU/ZER. Std. female with shield. Rev. value. 1797.................... 4.00

*34 1/–/KREU/ZER. Father Time. 1799........ 6.00

NÜRNBERG (Cont.)

VG-F

36 1 KR(euzer). City view. Rev. N.L.M., value, arms on pedestal. 1806-07 .... 3.00

36a —. Rev. WANDLE AUF ROSEN (1806) 9.50

37 1/KREUZER. Arms. Rev. NÜRNB L. MUNZ., value. 1806 .... 3.00

40 (2½ Conv. kreuzer = 3 kr. Land münze). Like No. 42 but FRANCISCUS etc. 1764 (var.) 4.50

*42 (2½ Conv. kreuzer). 1767-79. (var.) 4.50

44 3 KR(euzer). Like No. 51. 1806 .... 5.50

*46 K(reuzer)/IIII. 1748-59. (var.) 4.50

48 V K(reuzer). Gen. like No. 46 but CONVENTIONS MUNZ, 240 E.F.M. etc. 1763, 65 .... 7.00

49 V K(reuzer). Sim. but IOSEPHUS etc. 1766 .... 7.00

51 6 KR(euzer). Arms. Rev. NÜRNB SCHEIDE etc., value. 1806-07 .... 7.00

Silver

V.F.

53 10 (Conv. kreuzer). Like No. 57 but IO. but FRANCISCUS etc. Imp. eagle. 1763 ...... 30.00

55 10 (Conv. kreuzer). Like No. 53 but IOSEPHUS etc. 1766 ... 30.00

*57 20 (Conv. kreuzer). 1756-65 .... 15.00

59 20 (Conv. kreuzer). Like No. 55. *1766* 15.00

61 20 (Conv. kreuzer). 3 arms in shield. Rev. IOSEPHUS etc. Imp. eagle. *1767*, 69 .... 15.00

V.F.

63 20 (Conv. kreuzer). SECHZIG etc. Arms in rhombus. Rev. IOSEPHUS etc. Imp. eagle in rhombus. 1772 .... 15.00

65 XX (Conv. kreuzer). LX EINE etc. Arms. Rev. IOSEPHUS etc. Imp. eagle. 1774 ...... 15.00

67 30 (Conv.) Kr(euzer). Arms. Rev. FRANCISCVS etc., Imp. eagle. 1765 .... 65.00

68 *XX EINE etc.* (= ½ Conv. thaler). River god. Rev. eagle. 1760 .... 100.00

69 XX EINE etc. (= ½ Conv. thaler). Like No. 82a. 1766 .. 75.00

71 (Species thaler). City view/NORIMBERGA. Rev. FRANCISCVS etc. Bust of Emp. Franz I. (1745) 175.00

72 X EINE etc. (= Conv. thaler). Sim. but 1754 ..... 150.00

73 X EINE etc. (= Conv. thaler). MONETA NOVA. . . . NORIM etc. Eagle holds 2 shields. Rev. bust of Franz I. 1757-60 .... 120.00

74 10 EINE etc. (= Conv. thaler). Imp. eagle/LEGE VINDICE/ s.s. (N) I.M.F. Rev. bust of Franz I. 1760-63 .... 130.00

75 X EINE etc. (= Conv. thaler). DA PACE etc. Std. female/value/ s.f. Rev. FRANCISCVS etc. Imp. eagle. 1761 .... 125.00

76 X St.E.F. etc. (= Conv. thaler). BENEDICTVS etc. Female at altar. Rev. FRANCISCVS etc. Imp. eagle. Peace of Teschen. 1763 .... 125.00

77 10 EINE etc. (= Conv. thaler). Imp. eagle. s.s.–G.N.R., N below. Rev. bust of Emp. Franz I. 1764 .... 130.00

77a —. With LEGE VINDICE. 1765 .... 130.00

78 X St.E.F. etc. (= Conv. thaler). Like No. 76 but DOMINE CONSERVA etc. 1765 .... 120.00

79 X EINE etc. (= Conv. thaler). Imp. eagle/s(N)R. Rev. bust of Emp. Joseph II. 1765 .... 140.00

80 X EINE etc. (= Conv. thaler). City view/NÜRNBERG. Rev. bust of Emp. Jos. II. 1765 . 130.00

V.F.

V.F.

*81 X EINE etc. (= Conv. thaler). City view/NÜRNBERG. Rev. Imp. eagle with orb on breast. 1768, 80 .... 130.00

81a —. Rev. Imp. eagle with arms on breast. 1765, 68, 79 ..... 130.00

82 X E. FEINE etc. (= Conv. thaler). MONETA . . . NORIMBERG. Arms. Rev. Imp. eagle with arms on breast. 1766 ...... 150.00

82a —. Rev. Imp. eagle with orb on breast. (2 var.). 1766-68, 76 .... 130.00

83 X/EINE etc. (= Conv. thaler). FRANZ DER ZWEITE etc. Bust. Rev. value/3rd city device. 1795 .... (E.F.) 1000.00

Gold (ducat = 3.49 gr.)

Note: The undated coinage with arms, rev. Lamb of God, was struck in 1700.

VF-EF

*84 (½ ducat). 1773 .... 600.00

85 (ducat). VOTA PRIMA etc. Noris (female) stdg./S.P.Q.N. Rev. FRANCISCVS etc. Bust. Homage of 1745 .... 1600.00

86 (ducat). MONETA AVREA . . . NORIMB. Arms. Rev. bust of Emp. Jos. II. 1766 ..... 1500.00

87 (ducat). City view/NÜRNBERG. Rev. head of Emp. Leopold II. 1790 .... 1500.00

*88 (ducat). (1792) 1500.00

89 (ducat). Like No. 90 w/out outer wreath. 1806 .... 1800.00

*90 (2 ducats). 1806 .... RRR

GERMAN STATES

OELS. See Silesia.

OETTINGEN,

Counts and Princes

Lands between Bavaria and Württemberg. Counts of Oettingen first mentioned in the 10th century. Obtained the mint right in the early 14th century. Many family branches from the 14th century. All mediatized early in the Napoleonic era.

Arms: See Rev. No. 4.

OETTINGEN-WALLERSTEIN-SPIELBERG

Johann Aloys I, Prince 1737-80

Billon or Silver

V.F.

2 *1 (kreuzer)*. Bust. Rev. arms. 1759....................17.50

*4 6 (kreuzer). 1759...........25.00

6 XII/KREU/ZER. Arms supported. Rev. value. 1759 ... 30.00

8 ⅔ (Reichsthaler). Like No. 11..............125.00

9 *⅔ (Reichsthaler)*. Like No. 12. 1759.........150.00

11 X/EINE etc. (= Conv. thaler). Bust. Rev. Arms supported. 1759. (2 var.)............500.00

12 X/EINE etc. (= Conv. thaler). Arms supported by 2 hounds. Rev. s: SEBAST(ian) PATRONUS RHAETIAE. St. Sebastian. 1759....................750.00

OLDENBURG,

County, Duchy and Grand Duchy

On the North Sea coast. Independent county the late 12th century until 1667 when it was absorbed by Denmark. Became independent again 1773. Duchy 1775. Annexed to France 1806-07, 10-13. Grand Duchy 1815.

Arms: Gold, 2 red bars.

Monetary Systems:
Until 1857:
5 schwaren = 4 pfennig = 1 grote;
72 grote = 36 mariengroschen = 24 gutegroschen = 1 (Reichs)thaler.

1858-73:
12 schwaren = 1 groschen;
30 groschen = 1 Vereinsthaler.

Friedrich V, King of Denmark 1746-66

Billon

VG-F

2 II/PFEN(nig). Cwnd. FFV. Rev. value/o(ldenburger) L(and) M(ünze). 1764....... 7.50

4 I/GROTE. Like No. 5. 1761-63.................. 6.50

*5 IIII/PFEN(nig). 1762-63... 4.00

6 1½ GROTE. Sim. 1761.... 7.00

7 48/EINEN (=1/48)/THALER. Sim. 1762................. 5.00

8 2/GROTE. Sim. 1761...... 7.00

*9 I/MARIEN/GROS(chen). 1761-63................. 4.00

10 3/GROTE. Sim. 1761...... 9.00

11 24/EINEN (=1/24)/THALER. Sim. 1762................. 7.00

12 4/GROTE. Sim. 1761...... 9.00

13 II/MARIEN/GROSCH(en). Sim. 1761-63............ 7.00

14 12/EINEN (=1/12)/THAL(er). Head. Rev. value. 1761-64 ..12.00

Silver

F-VF

15 VI/EINEN (=1/6)/THALER. Sim. 1761-65............15.00

17 ⅓ (thaler). Like No. 18. 1761-62.................40.00

18 ⅔ (thaler). FRIDERICVS V.D.G. REX D . . . COM. O.D. Head. Rev. NACH. DEM. LEIPZIGER-FVS. Value in field. 1761-65 ..45.00

Friedrich August of Holstein-Gottorp, Bishop of Lübeck (q.v.) 1750-85, Count of Oldenburg 1773, Duke of Oldenburg 1775-85

Peter Friedrich Wilhelm (feeble-minded), Under Regency of Peter Friedrich Ludwig 1785-1823

Oldenburg occupied by France 1806-07, 10-13, raised to Grand Duchy and given Birkenfeld (q.v.) at Congress of Vienna.

Copper

Fine

25 ½/GROTE. Like No. 33. 1802, 16................. 3.50

Billon

27 *1 GROTE*. Arms. Rev. value. 1792..................... 5.00

28 *1 GROTE*. Arms. Rev. value. 1817..................... 6.00

30 *1½ GROTE*. Arms. Rev. value. 1792..................... 5.00

32 2/GROTE. Like No. 33 but obv. leg. 15TH A.D.M.F. 1792. 5.00

*33 2/GROTE. 1815........... 6.00

34 4/GROTE. Like No. 32 but 14½ etc. 1792............ 6.00

35 4 GROTE. *Like No. 33*. 1816, 18..................... 6.00

37 6/GROTE. Elaborate arms. Rev. value/OLD. COUR. MÜNZE. 1816, 18................. 8.00

Silver

39 12/GROTE. Arms. Rev. value. 1816, 18...........15.00

41 3/EINEN (=⅓)/THALER. Arms. Rev. value. 1816, 18...................25.00

Paul Friedrich August 1829-53

Copper

F-VF

*43 1/SCHWAREN. 1846, 52B.................. 1.50

44 ¼/GROTE. Sim. 1846..... 3.00

45 ½/GROTE. Like No. 33. 1831, 35, 40.............. 4.00

46 ½/GROTE. HERZOGTHUM OLDENBURG. Arms. Rev. value. 1846.................... 4.00

GERMAN STATES

OLDENBURG (Cont.)

Billon

47 1/GROTE. GHZ. OLDENB. etc. Arms. Rev. value. 1836 ..... 4.50 *(Fine)*

48 1/GROTE. Sim. but 72 EINEN THALER. 1849-50 .... 4.50

49 3/GROTE. Arms. Rev. value. 1840 .... 6.00

50 4/GROTE. Like No. 48 but 18 EINEN etc. 1840S 6.00

Silver

★51 6/EINEN (=1/6)/THALER. Head. Rev. value. 1846 ..... 30.00 *(V.F.)*

52 EIN (=1) THALER. Head. Rev. Arms. 1846 .... 50.00

★53 2/THALER. Head. Rev. value. 1840 .... 750.00

No. 53 was struck for Birkenfeld. See Birkenfeld for special issues 1848, 58-59.

Nicolaus Friedrich Peter 1853-1900

Copper

54 1/SCHWAREN. Like No. 57 but no obv. legend. 1854, 56 .... 1.50 *(F-VF)*

---

55 1/SCHWAREN. Like No. 57. 1858-69 .... 1.00 *(F-VF)*

56 ½/GROTE. Like No. 54. 1853, 56 .... 1.50

★57 3/SCHWAREN. 1858-69 ... 1.25

Billon

58 1/GROTE. GHZ. OLDENB. etc. Arms. Rev. value. 1853-57 .. 5.00 *(Fine)*

59 ½/GROSCHEN. Sim. 1858-69 .... 3.50

60 1/GROSCHEN. Sim. 2 fold arms. 1858 .... 4.00

60a —. 5 fold arms. 1858-69 .... 4.00

61 3/GROTE. Like No. 58. 1856 .... 5.00

★62 2½/GROSCHEN. 1858 .... 5.00

Silver

63 EIN (=1) VEREINSTHALER. Head. Rev. arms. 1858-66 ... 40.00 *(V.F.)*

OLMÜTZ.
See AUSTRIA (STATES).

ONOLZBACH.
See Brandenburg-Ansbach.

ORANGE-NASSAU.
See Nassau-Orange.

OSNABRÜCK, Bishopric

In Westphalia. Established 804. Obtained the mint right 889. Bishops alternately Catholic and Protestant after 1648. Secularized and absorbed by Brunswick-Lüneburg (Hannover) 1802.

Friedrich, Duke of York, Bishop 1764-1802

Billon

1 III/PFENNIG. Cwnd. F. Rev. value. 1766 .... 9.00 *(VG-F)*

2 IV/PFENNIG. Sim. 1766 .. 10.00

3 VI/PFENNIG. Sim. 1766 ... 12.00

4 XII/PFENNIG. Cwnd. F. Rev. FURSTL. OSNABR. etc., value. 1766 .... 19.00

OSNABRÜCK, City

Semi-independent from the bishopric. Had its own local coinage from the early 16th century until 1805 although it too was absorbed by Hannover in 1802.

Arms: Silver, a red wheel (same as bishopric).

Copper

1 I/HELLER. Like No. 5 but wheel in shield. 1790 .... 8.00 *(VG-F)*

1a —. Like No. 5. 1791, 95, 1805 .... 4.00

2 I/PFENN(ig). Like No. 1. 1790 .... 8.00

3 I/PFENNING. Like No. 5. 1791-1805 .... 4.50

★5 1½/PFENNING. 1791, 95, 1805 .... 4.50

7 2/PFENNING. Like No. 5. 1791-1805 .... 6.00

9 III/PFENNING. STADT OSNABRVCK A(nn)O. Date Wheel. Rev. value. 1704-60 . 6.25

10 III/PFENN(ig). 2 wild men hold wheel. Rev. value. 1790 .... 20.00

11 3/PFENNING. Like No. 5. 1805 .... 7.00

13 IIII/PFENNING. Like No. 9. 1704-60 .... 9.00

OST FRIESLAND.
See East Friesland.

OST PREUSSEN. See POLAND.

PADERBORN, Bishopric

In Westphalia. Founded 795. Obtained mint right 1028. Secularized and assigned to Prussia 1803.

Arms: Red, a gold cross.

Clemens August v. Bayern, bishop 1719-61, apparently struck no coins for Paderborn after 1749. But see Cologne, Münster, etc. for his contemporary coins for other ecclesiastical states.

Sede Vacante 1761-63

Copper

1 III PFENNING. St. Liborius. Rev. value. 1761 .... 6.50 *(Fine)*

2 IIII/PFENNING. Sim. 1761 .... 7.00

3 VI/PFENNING. Sim. 1761 .... 6.75

GERMAN STATES

PADERBORN (Cont.)

Wilhelm Anton, Freiherr von der Asseburg 1763-82

Copper

		Fine
*4	I/PFENNING. 1766-67....	3.25
4a	I/PFENN(ING). 1766.....	3.25

Note: In 1763 certain early Paderborn copper coins were revalidated with a WA (joined) monogram.

Billon

		VG-F
6	4 PFENN(ig). WA mon. Rev. value. 1763	4.00
8	½ MARIEN GROS(chen). 1763	5.50
10	I MATTIER (=4 pfennig = 13 French deniers). 1767....	6.75
12	VI/PFENN(ig). HOCHF. PADERB. etc. WA mon. Rev. value. 1764-65	3.00
15	MARIEN GROSCH(en). Like No. 12. 1763, 66.......	4.00
17	I MARIEN GROSCH(en). 1770, 74..................	4.25
19	II/MARIEN/GROSCH(en). Like No. 12. 1764-66.......	4.25
21	12/EINEN (=½)/THALER. Like No. 4 but arms draped. 1764-67	4.50
21a	—. Arms. 1776	4.50
23	12/EINEN (=½)/THALER. Like No. 12. 1764-65	4.50

Silver

		F-VF
26	VI/EINEN (=⅙)/THALER. Like No. 21. 1764.........	20.00
26a	—. Arms. 1766, 69, 72.....	20.00
28	20/KREUZER. Like No. 21. 1765-67	25.00
30	⅔ (Reichsthaler). Bust. Rev. Arms. 1764, 70......	150.00
32	24/MARIEN/GROSCH(en). Arms. Rev. value. 1765	125.00

		V.F.
34	(thaler). Bust, no legend. Rev. 8 lines: WILHELMUS/ ... /ELECTUS MDCCLXIII/XXV IANUAR. On his election. 1763	385.00

		V.F.
35	X STUCK etc. (= Conv. thaler). WILH. ANT. etc. Bust. Rev. Arms. 1764-65.......	350.00
36	X STUCK etc. (= Conv. thaler). Bust, no legend. Rev. Arms. 1766...........	700.00
37	X EINE etc. (= Conv. thaler). Arms. Rev. St. Liborius. 1767..................	600.00

Gold

38	(ducat). Bust. Rev. Arms. 1776, 77...............	1200.00

*39	5 THALER. 1767......	1300.00

Friedrich Wilhelm, Freiherr von Westfalen zu Fürstenberg, Bishop of Hildesheim (q.v.) 1763-89, of Paderborn 1782-89

Copper

		Fine
40	I/PFENN(ig). FRID. WILH. D. G. EP. HILD ET. PAD. etc. Arms. Rev. value. 1786	3.50

Billon

		VG-F
42	12 EINEN (=½) THALER. Arms. Rev. value. 1783	7.50

Silver

		V.F.
44	XVI/GVTE/GROSCHEN. Arms. Rev. value. 1785	30.00
46	XX EINE etc. (=½ Conv. thaler). Arms. Rev. St. Liborius. 1786............	45.00

Gold

*48	I/DVCAT. 1784.........	1200.00

PALATINATE, RHENISH.
See Pfalz.

PASSAU (PATAVA), Bishopric

In Bavaria near the Austro-Bohemian frontier. Established 738. Obtained the mint right prior to 999. Secularized and divided between Bavaria and Salzburg in 1803.

Arms: Silver, a red wolf rampant.

Joseph Dominic, Graf von Lamberg, Bishop 1723-61

Silver

		E.F.
1	(thaler). IOSEPH DOMINIC D. G. EPISC. PATAV. Bust. Rev. Imp. eagle, arms on breast. 1723.	700.00
2	(thaler). Bust. Rev. Imp. eagle, etc. 1753..........	600.00

Gold (ducat = 3.49 gr.)

		VF-EF
3	(ducat). Bust. Rev. Arms. 1747..................	600.00
4	(5 ducats). No. 2 in gold..	1500.00
5	(6 ducats). No. 2 in gold..	2000.00

Leopold Ernst, Graf von Firmian, Bishop 1763-83

Silver

		V.F.
7	(thaler). LEOP. ERN. D:G. EXEMP. ECCL. PATAVI. EPS. Bust. Rev. Arms. 1767..........	650.00
8	(thaler). D.G. LEOP. ERNEST S.R.E. PRAESB. CARD. DE FIRMIAN. Bust. Rev. Arms. 1779....................	225.00

Gold

		VF-EF
9	(ducat). Bust. Rev. Arms. 1779..................	1350.00

Joseph, Prince of Auersperg, Bishop 1783-95

Silver

10	(thaler). IOSEPH EX PRIN. DE AVERSBERG etc. Bust. Rev. Arms. 1792.........	200.00

PFALZ (RHENISH PALATINATE, RHEINPFALZ)
County

The office of count palatine of the Rhine (Pfalzgraf am Rhein) is first mentioned in the 10th century. First coins 11th century. Capital moved to Heidelberg in the 12th century. Pfalz acquired by Bavaria 1215, assigned to a dispossessed elder branch of the Bavarian (Wittelsbach) House in 1329. Pfalzgraf confirmed as one of the electors of the Holy Roman Empire 1356. In 1410 the Pfalz was divided by 4 brothers, whose descendants effected further subdivisions. The electoral dignity passed from line to line as elder branches died out.

Arms: Black, a gold lion.

GERMAN STATES

PFALZ (Cont.)

I. CHUR (KUR) PFALZ (=ELECTORAL PALATINATE).

**Carl Theodor 1733-99,
Count Palatine of
Pfalz-Sulzbach 1733 (no coins),
Elector Palatine 1742-99,
Elector of Bavaria 1777-99**

Coins of Chur Pfalz for this reign generally are mintmarked A.S. (Anton Schäffer, mintmaster at Mannheim 1744-99).

Copper

VG-F

1 1/ZOLL (=toll)/PFENNIG. CHUR PFALZ, lion shield. Rev. value. 1766 . . . . 3.50

★2 ¼/KREVZ(er). 1773-95 . . . . 3.50

★3 ½/KREVZ(er). 1773-86 . . . . 3.50

Billon or Silver

7 ½ KR(euzer). CHURPFALZ, 3 fold arms. Rev. blank. *1742-50* 7.00
9 ½ KR(euzer). CHURPFALZ, lion shield. Rev. value. 1759 . . . . 7.25
9a (1½ kreuzer). Obv. sim. Rev. blank. 1764 . . . . 7.50
11 EINEN (=1) KREUZER. CHURPFALZ LANDMÜNZ., lion. Rev. value, CT mon. 1746-56 . . . . 8.00
13 1/KREUZ(er). CHUR PFALZ, lion shield. Rev. LAND MUNZ., value. 1762-64 . . . . . . 4.50
15 1 KR(euzer). CHUR PFALZ. 3 fold arms. Rev. CONV(entions). MUNZ., value. 1773 . . . . 5.00
17 1/CONVENT(ions)/KREVZ(er). Like No. 2. 1773-95 . . . . . . 4.75
17a —. W/out CONVENT. 1794 . . . 5.00
21 1/KREUZER. Like No. 2. Rev. value/LANDMUNZ. 1786 . . . . 4.75
23 2/KREU/ZER. CHUR PFALZ, lion shield. Rev. LAND MUNZ., value. 1743-44 . . . . 6.50

VG-F

★23a 2/KR(euzer). 1743-50. (var.) 4.00
25 III KR(euzer). CHUR PFALZ, lion shield. Rev. value/ LANDMUNZ. 1743 . . . . 6.00
27 4/KREUZ(er). CHVR PFALZ, 3 shields. Rev. LAND MVNZ., value. 1746-50 . . . . 5.50

★29 240 EINE etc. (=5 Conv. kreuzer). 1765-74 (var.) 6.00
29a —. As Elector of Pfalz-Bayern. (ex Bavaria No. 60). 1780-89 . . . . 6.00

Silver

Fine

30 10 (Conv. kreuzer). Like No. 31 but D.G. CAR. etc. 1762 . . . . 7.50
31 10 (Conv. kreuzer). Like No. 29 but rev. AD NORMAM etc. Arms. 1763-74 . . . . 6.00
31a —. As Elector of Pfalz-Bayern. (ex Bavaria No. 63). 1778-94 . . . . 8.00
34 XII KR(euzer). D.G. CAR. TH. EL. PALATINUS. Head. Rev. CHVR PFALZ LAND MVNZ. 3 shields. 1746 . . . . 7.50
35 XII/KREU/TZER. D.G. CAR etc. 3 fold arms. Rev. LAND MUNZ., value. 1746 . . . . 7.50
36 XII/KREUZ(er). CHUR PFALZ. 3 fold arms. Rev. LANDMUNZ., value. 1746-48 . . . . 7.50
38 20 (Conv. kreuzer). Like No. 31. *1765* 6.50
38a —. As Elector of Pfalz-Bayern. (ex Bavaria No. 73). 1779-93 . . . . 10.00
40 24 KR(euzer). Like No. 34. 1746 . . . . 8.00
41 *24 KREUZ(er).* Like No. 36. 1746 . . . . 8.00

V.F.

43 40 EINE etc. (=30 Conv. kreuzer). CAR. THEODOR etc. Armored bust. Rev. 3 shields. 1765 . . . . 10.00
44 36 KR(euzer). Like No. 34. 1746 . . . . 18.50
45 36/KREUZ(er). Like No. 36. 1746 . . . . 18.50

V.F.

47 (gulden). CAR. THEODOR D.G. EL. PALATINUS. Bust. Rev. IRRADIAT etc., city view. Homage of Heidelberg. Date (1746) in chronogram 100.00
49 20 EINE etc. (=½ Conv. thaler). Like No. 43. 1762-65 . . . . 37.50
49a —. Head. 1765 . . . . 37.50
51 (ex 49b) (gulden). Like No. 31. 1771-74 . . . . 30.00
51a (ex 49c) —. As Elector of Pfalz-Bayern. 1779-93 . . . . . 30.00
53 (thaler). CAR. THEODOR etc. Bust. Rev. ARCHITHESAVR etc. Arms. 1744 . . . . 450.00
54 (thaler). D.G. C. TH. etc. Bust. Rev. IN PART RHENI etc. Imp. eagle. Vicariat. 1745 . . . . . . 450.00
55 (Conv. thaler). D.G. CAR etc. Head. Rev. 3 shields. 1761 . 190.00
56 (Conv. thaler). Sim. but CAR etc. Head or bust. 1763-65. (var.) 90.00
57 X EINE etc. (= Conv. thaler). Bust. Rev. Arms supported by lion. 1766-67 . . . . 90.00

★58 10 EINE etc. (= Conv. thaler). Bust. Rev. 3 fold arms/A–S. 1768-73 . . . . 80.00
59 (Conv. thaler). Head. Rev. AD NORMAM etc. 3 fold arms. 1773-77 . . . . 80.00
59a —. As Elector of Pfalz-Bayern. (ex Bavaria No. 81a). 1778-95 . . . . 80.00
59b —. Obv. bust. (ex Bavaria No. 82). 1781 . . . . 80.00

GERMAN STATES

PFALZ/CHUR PFALZ (Cont.)

Silver Mannheim
Vicariats Coinage

A. 1790 Vicariat.

E.F.

59.1 10 (Conv. kreuzer). Head/
A.S. Rev. IN PART. etc.,
Imp. eagle with oval
3 fold arms on breast.
(ex Bavaria No. 65).
1790 . . . . 12.00

59.2 20 (Conv. kreuzer). Sim.
(ex Bavaria No. 72).
1790 . . . . 16.00

59.3 (gulden). Sim. but manifold
rectangular arms on eagle's
breast. (ex Bavaria No. 77a).
1790 . . . . 30.00

59.4 (Conv. thaler). Sim. (ex
Bavaria No. 85). 1790 . . . 250.00

B. 1792 Vicariat.

59.6 10 (Conv. kreuzer). Sim.
to No. 59.1 but date in rev.
legend. (ex Bavaria No. 67).
1792 . . . . 12.00

59.7 20 (Conv. kreuzer). Sim.
1792 . . . . 16.00

59.8 (gulden). Like No. 59.1.
(ex Bavaria No. 78). 1792 . 30.00

59.9 (Conv. thaler). Sim. (ex
Bavaria No. 86). 1792 . . . 150.00

Gold (ducat=3.49 gr.)

V.F.

60 (ducat). C. PHIL. THEODOR ET
M. ELISAB AUGUSTA. Conjoined
busts. Rev. 2 shields. Wedding.
1742 . . . . 1300.00

61 (ducat). STADT MANNHEIM.
Lion holds city arms.
Rev. HULDIGET/etc. Homage.
1744 . . . . 950.00

*62 (ducat). Homage of Heidelberg. 1746 . . . . 950.00

63 (Rheingold ducat). CAR. THEODOR
etc. Head or bust. Rev. SIC
FULGENT etc. Mannheim city
view. 1763-67, 78 . . . . 1450.00

64 (ducat). Bust/HOC. AUSPICE.
Rev. INDUSTRIA SORS. Goddess
of luck. N.D. (1764 lottery
prize) 1500.00

65 (ducat). Bust. Rev. 10 fold
arms. 1764 . . . . 1100.00

66 (ducat). Head. Rev. 3 shields.
1769 . . . . 950.00

67 (ducat). Obv. like No. 61.
Rev. BEI/CARL THEODORS/etc.
50th year of reign. 1792 . . . . 900.00

V.F.

68 (5 thaler). Bust. Rev. DOMINUS
etc. 4 cwnd. CTs cruciform.
1748-50 . . . . 1100.00

**For other coins of Carl Theodor see
Bavaria and Jülich-Berg.**

II. PFALZ-(BIRKENFELD-)
ZWEIBRÜCKEN.

Junior surviving branch of the House
of Wittelsbach.

Christian IV,
Count Palatine 1735-75

Copper

VG-F

*1 IIII/EINEN (= ¼) /KREUZER.
P(falz) Z(weibrücken) over
C(hristian) P(falzgraf) mon.
1759-67 . . . . 4.00

2 II/EINEN (= ½) /KREUZER.
Sim. 1759 . . . . 6.00

*3 I/KREUZER. 1774 . . . . 6.00

Billon or Silver

5 1/KR(euzer). Like No. 3.
1765 . . . . 4.50

7 2/KR(euzer). PFALZ ZWEYB.
c4 mon. Rev. value. 1747 . . . 4.50

9 2/KREUZ(er). Obv. Like
No. 1. Rev. value. 1757-63 . . 4.00

11 4/KREUZ(er). Like No. 9.
1759 . . . . 5.50

13 240 EINE etc. (= 5 Conv.
kreuzer). PFALZ ZWEYB. Lion
shield. Rev. value. 1763-*64* . . 6.00

13a —. Rev. IUSTIRT. Value in
rhombus. 1766-*67* 6.00

*15 10 (Conv. kreuzer). 1763-67 . 5.50

Silver

V.F.

17 XII/KREU/ZER. PFALZ.
ZWEYB. Arms. Rev. LANDMUNZ.,
value. 1759 . . . . 7.50

V.F.

19 VI/EINEN (= ⅙ Reichs)/
THALER. CP mon. Rev.
value/P.Z.L.M. 1757 . . . . 15.00

21 20 (Conv. kreuzer). Like No.
15 but head in wreath. 1760-
63, 69 . . . . 10.00

21a —. Like No. 15. 1763 . . . . . . 10.00

21b —. Head in wreath. Rev. 2
shields. 1765-66 . . . . 12.00

24 36/KREUTZ(er). Bust. Rev.
MONET. BIPONT. (=Zweibrücken
money), value. 1747 . . . . 30.00

26 (thaler). Bust. Rev. MONETA
BIPONT. Arms. 1747 . . . . . . 700.00

27 (mining thaler). Bust. Rev. EX
FODINIS BIPONTINO etc. Arms.
Seelberg Mines. 1754 . . . . . . 500.00

28 (Conv. thaler). Head.
Rev. Arms. 1759 . . . . 150.00

28a —. Bust. 1759 . . . . 150.00

29 10 AUF EINE etc. (= Conv.
thaler). Head r. Rev. Arms in
irregular cartouche. 1759 . . . 150.00

29a —. Rev. oval arms. 1759-
63 . . . . 150.00

30 10 AUF etc. (= Conv. thaler).
Head l. Rev. Arms. 1760 . . . 200.00

31 10 AUF etc. (= Conv. thaler).
Head. Rev. Arms. 1765, 75 . . 100.00

Gold

32 *(ducat)*. Bust. Rev. Arms.
1747, 51 . . . . 1000.00

Carl II, 1775-95

Copper

VG-F

34 I/HELLER. Obv. like No. 2
Rev. value. 1788 . . . . 5.00

35 ½/KREVZ(er). Sim. 1788 . . 4.00

36 EIN (=1)/KREUTZER.
Sim. 1788 . . . . 3.50

Gold (ducat=3.49 gr.)

V.F.

40 (ducat). Like No. 41. 1788,
90 . . . . 1250.00

*41 2 (ducats). 1788 . . . . 2500.00

III. RHEIN PFALZ.

Maximilian Joseph in
Birkenfeld-Zweibrücken 1795-99,
Elector of Pfalz-Bayern 1799-1805,
King of Bavaria 1806-25

GERMAN STATES

PFALZ/RHEIN PFALZ (Cont.)

Coins for Rheinpfalz

Copper

1 ½/KREUZ(er). R–P over lion shield. Rev. value. 1802 .... 9.75 *Fine*

2 1/KREUZ(er). Sim. 1802 ...13.50

Silver

★3 X EINE etc. (= Conv. thaler). 1802 ....1950.00 *VF-EF*

POMERANIA (POMMERN), Duchy

District along the Baltic neighboring (now part of) Poland. Annexed by Sweden 1637. Brandenburg-Prussia nibbled away portions in 1648, 1679 and 1720, and finally acquired the residue in 1815.

Arms: Silver, a red griffin.

Monetary Systems:

12 pfennig = 1 schilling;
48 schilling = 24 gute groschen = 1 Reichsthaler.

Adolph Friedrich, King of Sweden 1751-71

I. First Series 1758-61

Billon

2 48/EINEN/THALER (= 1 schilling). Like No. 5. 1760-61 .... 6.50 *VG-F*

★5 24/EINEN/THALER (= 2 sch.). 1759-61 .... 6.00 *VG-F*

Silver

A. Cwnd. AFR mon. Rev. griffin.

8 2 G(ute) GROS(chen). Like No. 12. 1759 .... 7.50 *F-VF*

★12 4 GUTE GROS(chen). 1758-59 ....50.00

17 8 GUTE GROS(chen). Sim. 1758-60 ....75.00

B. Bust. Rev. value.

9 12/EINEN/THALER (= 4 sch.). Like No. 15. 1761 ....12.00

★15 VI/EINEN/THALER (= 8 sch.). 1760-61 ....25.00

19 8/GUTE/GROSCHEN/ COURANT. Like No. 15. 1760-61 ....60.00

The 3 / EINEN / REICHS / THALER 1760 with obv. like No. 15, rev. value in wreath *is a restrike muled with Prussian reverse.*

Gold

★25 5 THALER. Head. Rev. Griffin. 1758 (rare), 59 ....1500.00 *V.F.*

26 10 THALER. Sim. 1759 ..2500.00

II. Second Series 1763-68

Billon

★3 48/EINEN/REICHS/THALER (= 1 sch.). K(Royal) s(wedish) P(omeranian) L(and) M(oney), cwnd. AF mon. Rev. NACH DEM etc., value. 1763 .... 6.50 *VG-F*

6 24/EINEN/REICHS/THALER (= 2 sch.). Like No. 3. 1763 .. 7.00

Silver

★10 12/EINEN/REICHS/THALER (= 4 sch.). Like No. 3 but motto in lieu of K.s. etc. 1763-68 .... 8.00 *F-VF*

★21 ⅓ (Reichsthaler). 1763 .....90.00

23 ⅔ (Reichsthaler). Sim. 1763 ....120.00

Gustav III, King of Sweden 1771-92

Copper

27 3/PFEN/NINGE. Like No. 29. 1776, 92 .... 8.00 *VG-F*

Gustav IV Adolf, King of Sweden 1792-1809

Copper

★29 3/PFEN/NINGE. 1806, 08 .... 6.50

Issues dated 1808 with obv. legend partly spelled out *are patterns.*

POSEN. See POLAND.

PREUSSEN. See Prussia.

GERMAN STATES

PRINCE PRIMATE (FÜRST PRIMAS)

In 1803 the residue of the Archbishopric of Mainz (q.v.) was secularized. Carl v Dalberg, the last archbishop-elector retained the principality of Aschaffenburg in his capacity as Imperial Arch-Chancellor. He moved his seat of government to Regensburg (q.v.) where he was also bishop. In 1806 Napoleon gave him the city of Frankfurt am Main (q.v.) and made him prince primate of the Rhenish Confederation. From 1810 to 1813 he was also grand duke of Frankfurt. At the fall of Napoleon in 1813, Dalberg was stripped of everything except his ecclesiastical rank as bishop of Regensburg.

Copper

Fine

*1 I/HELLER. 1808-12 . . . . . . 5.50

2 I/HELLER. Sim. but GROSH. FRANKF. etc. 1810, 12 . . . . 6.50

Billon

3 I/KREUZER. Like No. 1. 1808-10 . . . . 7.50

Silver

V.F.

4 X EINE etc. (= Conv. thaler). CARL FÜRST PRIMAS. Bust. Rev. Arms. 1808 . . . . 225.00

Silver for Regensburg

5 XX/EINE etc. (= ½ Conv. thaler). CARL FURST PRIMAS DER RHEIN CONFOED. Bust. Rev. value/REGENSBURG. 1809 . . . . 150.00

6 X/EINE etc. (= Conv. thaler). Sim. 1809 . . . . 185.00

7 X EINE etc. (= Conv. thaler). Obv. sim. Rev. Arms/ REGENSBURG. 1809 . . . . 225.00

Gold

8 (ducat). CAROLUS etc. Bust. Rev. PRINC. PRIMAS etc. Arms. 1809 . . . . 1000.00

Gold for Regensburg

9 DUCATUS. CAROL. PR. PR. etc., his bust. Rev. DUCATUS RATISBON, mantled arms. 1809 . . . . pattern?

PRUSSIA (PREUSSEN, BORUSSIA), Kingdom

The largest German State, formerly extending from the Russian border to the French border. Ruled by the Hohenzollern family. In 1701 Elector Friedrich III of Brandenburg was allowed by the Emperor to take the title "King in Prussia." His successors greatly increased their holdings, and in 1871 King Wilhelm I of Prussia became the first emperor of re-united Germany.

Arms: Silver, crowned black eagle, FR script mon. on breast, holding sceptre and orb.

Prussian Mint Marks

A – Berlin, Brandenburg. 1750 to date.
A.E. – Breslau, Silesia. 1743-*51*.
A.G.P. – Cleve, Rhineland. 1742-43.
A.H.E. – See A.E.
A.L.S. – Berlin. 1749.
B – Breslau. 1750-1826.
B – Bayreuth, Franconia. *1796-1803*.
B – Hannover, Hannover. 1866-78.
C – Cleve. 1750-1806.
C – Frankfurt am Main. 1866-79.
C.H.I. – Berlin. 1749-*63*.
D – Aurich, East-Friesland. 1750-1806.
D – Düsseldorf, Rhineland. 1816-48.
E – Koenigsberg, East Prussia. 1750-98.
E.G.N.– Berlin. 1725-49.
F – Magdeburg, Lower Saxony. 1750-1806.
G – Stettin, Pomerania. 1750-1806.
G – Glatz, Silesia. 1807-09.
G.K. – Cleve. 1740-*55*.
S – Schwabach, Franconia. *1792-94*.
W – Breslau. 1743.

Provincial coinages intended for use in one province only are listed elsewhere. See, for example, Brandenburg in Franconia, Cleve, Danzig (POLAND), East Friesland, East Prussia (POLAND), Hohenzollern, Neuchatel (SWITZERLAND), Posen (POLAND), Silesia, and South Prussia (POLAND).

Friedrich II, the Great, 1740-86

I. Coinage for Brandenburg and general circulation throughout the kingdom.

Copper

VG-F

*1 I/PFEN(nig). 1751-55A (var.) 1.50

1a —. 1754F 3.00

2 3/PFEN(nig). Sim. 1752-63 . 3.00

Billon or Silver

3 I/GUTER (=good)/PFEN(nig). Flowery FR mon./date. Rev. value. 1742-43 . . . . 5.00

3a —. Plain FR mon./date. 1768-70 . . . . 4.00

3b —. Rev. value/date. 1772-86 . . . . 3.75

4 3/GUTE/PFEN(nig). Like No. 3. 1742 E.G.N 6.50

4a —. Plain FR mon. divides date. 1764-70A 3.25

4b —. 1764F 6.50

4c —. Like No. 3b. 1772-86A . . . 3.00

5 4/GUTE/PFEN(nig). Like No. 4a. 1764A, 66A 5.00

6 48 EINEN (=¹/₄₈) THALER. Flowery FR mon./G.K. Rev. value/1740 . . . . 50.00

6a —. 1741-49 G.K 4.00

6b —. 1742 A.G.P 4.00

7 48/EINEN/R(eichs)THAL(er). Flowery FR mon./1741. Rev. value/E.G.N. in wreath 4.00

7a —. 1742 A.L.S 5.00

8 48/EINEN/REICHS/ THALER. Obv. like No. 7. Rev. value/E.G.N. 1743-49 . 4.00

8a —. 1749 A.L.S 4.00

10 48/EINEN/REICHS/THALER. Like No. 8. 1750-63 . . . . 4.00

*12 48/EINEN/THALER. Plain FR mon. 1764-80A (var.) 2.75

12a —. Rev. value/date. 1771-79A 3.00

See East Friesland for ¹/₂₄ thaler 1746,48.

14 24/EINEN (=¹/₂₄) /REICHS/ THALER. Flowery FR mon. Rev. value/date. 1751-63 . . . 4.00

14a —. Date on obv. 1751B, 53-55A, 63B 4.50

14b —. Date both sides. 1751B . . 35.00

*15 24/EINEN/THALER. 1764-86 . . . . 2.00

GERMAN STATES

PRUSSIA (Cont.)

Silver

		Fine
16	12/EINEN (=1/12) /REICHS/ THALER. Like No. 3. 1741-46 E.G.N	6.50
17	12/EINEN (=1/12)/REICHS/ THALER. Like No. 19. 1750-55	5.00

★18	12/EINEN/REICHS/ THALER. 1752-86	3.00

★19	VI/EINEN (=1/6) /REICHS/ THALER. 1751-57, 63B	10.00
19a	—. Large bust. 1750-51B	15.00
20	VI/EINEN/REICHS/ THALER. Like No. 18. 1752-56	8.50
20a	—. 1754E, 53G	20.00
21	6/EINEN/REICHS/THALER. Sim. 1764-86	8.50
22	4 EINEN (=1/4) R(eichs) THALER. Bust. Rev. Eagle, trophies. 1750-52	12.50
23	4 EINEN (or R.) THALER. Head. Rev. eagle, trophies. 1764-68	12.50
23a	—. 1764F	25.00
23b	—. Old head. 1786A. On cornerstone laying at Bellevue Castle	125.00
24	1/3 (Reichsthaler). Like No. 30. 1741	30.00
25	3 EINEN (=1/3) R(eichs) THALER. Like No. 22. 1750A, 54	30.00
26	8/GUTE/GROSCHEN. 1753-64A, 58B	17.50

★26a	—. 1753-64. D-G mints	20.00
27	3/EINEN/REICHS/THALER. Head. Rev. value in cartouche. 1758-59A, no mmk. (=Dresden under Prussian occupation)	15.00

		Fine
27a	—. Rev. value in wreath. 1764-75	14.00
27b	—. Old head. 1774-86	12.00
		V.F.
28	2 EINEN (=1/2) R(eichs) THALER. Like No. 22. 1750-52	40.00
28a	—. 1751C	60.00
28.5	(ex 28b) 2 EINEN R(eichs) THALER. Like No. 23. 1764-67	25.00
28.5a	(ex 28c) —. Old head. 1786A. Bellevue Castle cornerstone ceremony	150.00
29	2/3 (Reichsthaler). Like No. 30. 1741	200.00

		E.F.
★30	(Species thaler). 1741	3000.00

		V.F.
★31	EIN (=1) REICHSTHALER. 1750-53	100.00

32	(ex 31a) EIN (=1) REICHS THALER. 1752A	150.00
★32a	(ex 32, 32a, 32b) —. 1761-74	50.00
32c	—. Old head. 1775-86	25.00
32d	—. 17•A•86 ("death thaler")	50.00
		E.F.
33	(Species thaler). Cwnd. bust. Rev. eagle shield. 1755	pattern?
34	EIN (=1) BANCO THALER. Draped bust. Rev. Eagle, trophies	RRR
35	ALBERTVS THALER. Arms. 1766-67	RRR
36	(Levant thaler). Armored bust. Rev. MAR:BRAN: etc. Elaborate arms on eagle's breast. 1766-67	RRR
36a	—. Unclothed bust. 1767	RRR

Gold (ducat = 3.49 gr;

Friedrich d'or = 6.65 gr. = 5 thaler)

All of the following gold coins except No. 37 were struck at Berlin Mint. See Cleve, East Friesland and Silesia for other gold coins of this reign.

		V.F.
★37	(ducat). Homage of Koenigsberg. 1740 R.N	700.00
38	(ducat). Head. Rev. VERITATI/ etc.//HOMAG. BEROL. Homage of Berlin. 1740 R.N	800.00

GERMAN STATES

PRUSSIA (Cont.)

V.F.

★39 (ducat). 1741-45 E.G.N 1500.00
40 (ducat). Bust. Rev. initials
FR in order chain.
1745 E.G.N 1800.00

★41 (ducat). 1745-49 E.G.N 1500.00
41a —. 1749 C.H.I 1800.00
42 (ducat). Head. Rev. cwn./
eagle in branches. 1749
E.G.N 2500.00

★43 1 DVCAT. 1753-54A 650.00
44 (2 ducat). Like No. 42.
1749 E.G.N 3500.00

★45 (½ Friedrich d'or).
1749 C.H.I 650.00
45a —. 1750-52A 400.00
46 (½ Friedrich d'or). Head.
Rev. 2 F's cwnd. 1750A 800.00

★47 (½ Friedrich d'or). 1752A . . 600.00
47a —. 1755A (low grade
gold) 1850.00
47b —. 1756A 550.00

★48 (½ Friedrich d'or). 1765-
74A 400.00

V.F.

48a —. Old head. 1784, 86A 400.00
49 (Friedrich d'or). Like No. 45.
1741-46 E.G.N 900.00
49a —. 1750-52, 59A 750.00
49b —. 1755-56A 950.00
50 (Friedrich d'or). Bust l.
Rev. as last. 1749 A.L.S . . . 1200.00

★51 (Friedrich d'or). 1750A . . . 1200.00
52 (Friedrich d'or). Like No.
47. 1752-63A 850.00
53 (Friedrich d'or). Like No.
48. 1764-76A 850.00
53a —. Old head. 1775-86A 800.00

★54 (2 Friedrich d'or). Like No.
45. 1749 A.L.S 2250.00
54a —. 1750-52A 2000.00
55 (2 Friedrich d'or). Like No.
47. 1753-55A 1500.00
55a —. 1756-57A 2500.00
56 (2 Friedrich d'or). Like No.
48. 1764-75A 1850.00
56a —. Old head. 1776A 1750.00

II. Special coinages. See note preceding No. 1 for list of provincial coinages described elsewhere.

Billon

Former Nos. 60 and 62 have been removed to Silesia and POLAND (East Prussia) respectively.

A. Rhineland/Cleve.

VG-F

64 4/KREU/ZER. Eagle shield.
Rev. value. 1754-55C 7.50

B. Royal Prussian Asiatic Society.

Silver

VF-EF

★66 (piastre). ND (= 1751) . . . . . . RR

C. Westphalia/Lower Saxony.

Billon or Silver

VG-F

70 IIII/PFEN(nig). FR mon.
Rev. value. 1752F 6.00
71 IIII/PFEN(nig). 1764F 6.00
72 I/MARIEN/GROS(chen).
Cwnd. eagle shield. Rev.
value. 1752F 6.25
73 I/MARIEN/GROS (chen).
FR mon. in cwnd. cartouche.
Rev. value. 1764-68F 6.50
74 II/MARIEN/GROS (chen).
Like No. 72. 1752F 7.50
75 II/MARIEN/GROS (chen).
Like No. 73. 1764F 7.50
76 IIII/MARIEN/GROS(chen).
Like No. 72. 1752F 15.00

Friedrich Wilhelm II 1786-97

Copper

80 I/PFENN(ig). Cwnd. FW
script. Rev. value/SCHEIDE/
MÜNZE/date/A. 1788-97. For
Westphalia 2.00

Billon or Silver

81 I/PFENNIG. Like No. 82.
1787-97A 2.25

★82 3/PFENNIGE. FWR mon.
1787-97A 2.50

Silver

Fine

★84 4 GR(oschen = ⅙ Reichsthaler).
1796-98 . . . . 9.50

PRUSSIA (Cont.)

V.F.

★86 3 EINEN (=⅓) R(eichs) THALER. 1786-98........20.00

87 ⅔ (Reichsthaler). FRIEDR. WILH. KOENIG etc., eagle shield. Rev. 18 STUCK etc. ⅔. 1796-97 (2 var.)...............80.00

88 EIN (=1) REICHS THALER. Armored bust. Rev. eagle. 1786-91..................60.00

89 REICHS THALER. Uniformed bust. Rev. eagle in oval shield. 1788A........*pattern*

★90 EIN (=1) THALER. 1790-97.....................100.00

VF-EF

★91 (Albertus thaler). 1797....1500.00

Gold

V.F.

★92 I/DVCAT. 1787, 90A......RRR

★93 (Friedrich d'or). 1786-97...750.00

Friedrich Wilhelm III 1797-1840

I. First Standard:
  24 (gute) groschen =
  1 Reichsthaler (until 1818).

Copper

Fine

95 I/PFENN(ig). Like No. 80. 1799-1806A. For Westphalia..........2.75

★97 1/PFENNIG. 1810-16A... 3.00

98 2/PFENNIGE. Sim. 1810-16A (var.)..........3.00

Billon

★100 1/PFENNIG. 1799-1806A.. 3.00

102 3/PFENNIGE. Sim. 1799-1806A.............3.50

F-VF

★104 4 GR(oschen). 1798-1809A, 02-05B...............10.00

104a —. 1808-09G.............15.00

★105 6/EINEN (=⅙) /REICHS/ THALER. 1810-18........ 8.00

105a —. 1812-14B.............14.00

No. 105 dated 1809A is a pattern.

★106 VIER (=4)/GROSCHEN. 1816-18A, 18D...........15.00

108 DREI EINEN (=⅛) R(eichs) THALER. Like No. 104. 1800-07A...............25.00

108a —. 1809G..............60.00

109 3/EINEN (=⅓)/REICHS/ THALER. Like No. 105. 1809A..................65.00

109a —. 1809G..............90.00

V.F.

111 ⅔ (Reichsthaler). Cwnd. eagle shield. Rev. 18 STÜCK etc., ⅔. 1810A.....75.00

113 EIN (=1) THALER. Bust l. Rev. Arms, wildmen. 1797-1809A, 1799-1803B........45.00

113a —. 1808-09G.............85.00

The 1797-98 with bust r. and FRID. are rare patterns.

114 EIN (=1)/REICHS/THALER. Like No. 105. 1809-16.....35.00

At least 7 varieties of No. 114 exist with blundered legends.

115 1 THALER. Sim. but GOTT/ SCHÜTZE/IHN etc. on rev. Crown Prince's mint visit. 1812A.........(*VF-EF*) 1000.00

PRUSSIA (Cont.)

V.F.

★116 EIN (=1) THALER. The "Kammerherrn Thaler." 1816-17A 200.00

116a —. FRIEDR. WILHELM III KOENIG etc. 1816-22 . . . . . . 30.00

Gold (Friedrich d'or = 6.65 gr. = 5 thaler)

F-VF

★117 (Friedrich d'or). 1797-98A 700.00

★118 (½ Fr. d'or). 1802-16A . . . 550.00

119 (Fr. d'or). Sim. 1798-1816A 600.00

119a —. 1800-05B 1000.00

120 (2 Fr. d'or). Sim. 1800-14A 1200.00

121 (½ Fr. d'or). Like No. 122. 1817A 600.00

★122 (Fr. d'or). 1817-22A 850.00

Note: For other coins of this reign, see Brandenburg - Ansbach - Bayreuth, Silesia, POLAND (East Prussia) and SWITZERLAND (Neuchatel). Pieces not listed in this catalog are patterns, mostly rare, of which there are many varieties, especially circa 1812-19.

II. Second Standard:

30 silbergroschen = 1 thaler (1819/22 onward).

Copper

F-VF

★123 1/PFENNING. 1821-40A . . . 1.00

123a —. 1821-22B 5.00

123b —. 1826B 15.00

123c —. 1821-40D 1.00

124 2/PFENNINGE. Sim. 1821-40A 1.00

124a —. 1821-23B 5.00

124b —. 1823-39D 1.00

124c —. 1833D. Struck in collar . . . . pattern

125 3/PFENNINGE. Sim. 1821-40A 1.50

125a —. 1821-22B 8.00

125b —. 1823-40D 4.00

126 4/PFENNINGE. Sim. 1821-40A 2.75

126a —. 1821-25B 9.00

126b —. 1823-39D 4.00

Billon

127 ½/SILBER/GROSCHEN. Head. Rev. value. 1821-40A 3.00

127a —. 1824-28D 4.00

128 1/SILBER/GROSCHEN. Sim. 1821-40A 3.50

128a —. 1821-40D 5.00

Silver

129 VI EINEN (=⅙) THALER. Head. Rev. Arms. 1822-40A 7.00

129a —. 1823-40D 9.00

V.F.

★130 EIN (=1) THALER. 1823-40 A and D. (var.) 27.50

131 EIN (=1) THALER. Head. Rev. SEGEN DES/etc. Mansfeld mining thaler. 1826-40 . . . . 35.00

132 2 THALER. Head. Rev. Arms. 1839-40A 75.00

132a —. 1841A 150.00

Gold (Friedrich d'or = 6.65 gr.)

V.F.

★133 (½ Fr. d'or). 1825-40A . . . 450.00

134 (Fr. d'or). Sim. 1825-40A 550.00

135 (2 Fr. d'or). Sim. 1825-40A 900.00

Friedrich Wilhelm IV 1840-61

Copper

F-VF

136 1/PFENNING. Like No. 123. 1841-42A 1.50

136a —. 1841-42D 2.50

137 2/PFENNINGE. Sim. 1841-42A 1.50

137a 1841-42D 2.00

138 3/PFENNINGE. Sim. 1841-42A 1.50

138a —. 1841-42D 2.00

139 4/PFENNINGE. Sim. 1841-42A 3.50

139a —. 1841-42D 6.50

140 1/PFENNING. Arms. Rev. value. 1843-45A 1.00

140a —. 1844-45D 1.25

★140b —. Struck in collar. 1846-60A 1.00

140c —. 1846-48D 1.00

141 2/PFENNINGE. Sim. 1843-45A 1.00

141a —. 1844-45D 1.50

★141b —. Struck in collar. 1846-60A 1.00

141c —. 1846-48D 1.50

143 3/PFENNINGE. Sim. 1843-45A 1.50

143a —. 1843-44D 2.00

143b —. Struck in collar. 1846-60A 1.50

143c —. 1846-48D 1.50

143d 3/PFENNIGE. 1850A 20.00

144 4 PFENNINGE. Sim. 1843-45A 3.00

GERMAN STATES

PRUSSIA (Cont.)

	F-VF
144a —. 1844D	8.00
144b —. Struck in collar. 1846-60A	2.00
144c —. 1846-48D	2.50

Billon

145 ½/SILBER/GROSCHEN. Head. Rev. value. 1841-52A 2.50

145a —. Old head. 1853-60A 2.50

★146 1/SILBER/GROSCHEN. 1841-52A 2.00

146a —. 1841-48D 3.50

146b —. Old head. 1853-60A 2.00

★147 2½/SILBER/GROSCHEN. 1842-52A 2.75

147a —. Old head. 1853-60A 2.75

Silver

★148 VI EINEN (=⅙) THALER. 1841-52A 7.50

148a —. 1841-45D 8.50

148b —. Old head. 1853-56A 10.00

★149 VI EINEN (=⅙) THALER. 1858-60A 15.00

V.F.

150 EIN (=1) THALER. Head. Rev. Arms. 1841-52A 20.00

150a —. Old head. 1853-56A 20.00

151 EIN (=1) THALER. Head. Rev. SEGEN DES/etc. Mansfeld mining thaler. 1841-52A 25.00

151a —. Old head. 1853-56A 25.00

151b —. Rev. XXX EIN etc. 1857-60A 25.00

V.F.

152 EIN (=1) VEREINS THALER. Like No. 149. 1857-61 .... 17.50

153 EIN (Vereins) THALER. Like No. 151a. 1857-60 .... 25.00

★154 2 THALER. Head. Rev. Arms. 1841-51A 60.00

154a —. Old head. 1853-56A 75.00

155 ZWEI (=2) VEREINS-THALER. Like No. 149. 1858-59A 140.00

Gold (Friedrich d'or = 6.65 gr.)

156 (½ Fr. d'or). Like No. 158. 1841-49A 600.00

156a —. Old head. 1853A 500.00

157 (Fr. d'or). Sim. 1841-52A .600.00

157a —. Old head. 1853-55A ...500.00

★158 (2 Fr. d'or). 1841-52A 900.00

158a —. Old head. 1853-55A ...900.00

★159 ½/KRONE. 1858A 1650.00

160 1/KRONE. Sim. 1858-60A 1400.00

See Hohenzollern for other coins of this reign.

Wilhelm I 1861-88

Copper

F-VF

★161 1/PFENNING. 1861-73A 1.00

161a —. 1867-73 B, C 1.50

162 2/PFENNINGE. Sim. 1861-71A 1.00

★162a —. 1867-73 B, C 1.50

163 3/PFENNINGE. Sim. 1861-73A 1.00

163a —. 1867-73 B, C 1.50

164 4/PFENNINGE. Sim. 1861-71A 1.50

164a —. 1867-71C 1.50

Billon

165 ½/SILBER/GROSCHEN. Like No. 166. 1861-72A 2.50

165a 1866-73 B, C 2.50

★166 1/SILBER/GROSCHEN. 1861-73A 2.50

166a —. 1866-73 B, C 2.50

167 2½/SILBER/GROSCHEN. Sim. 1861-73A 3.50

167a —. 1867-73 B, C 3.50

Silver

VF-EF

168 VI EINEN (=⅙) THALER. Head. Rev. eagle. 1861-68A 12.50

PRUSSIA (Cont.)

VF-EF

*169 KROENUNGS (Coronation) THALER. Busts of Wilhelm and Augusta. Rev. SUUM CUIQUE, eagle, etc. 1861 . . . 20.00

170 EIN (=1) VEREINS THALER. Like No. 168. 1861-71 . . . . 15.00

171 EIN (=1 Vereins) THALER. Head. Rev. SEGEN DES/etc. Mansfeld mining thaler. 1861-62A 40.00

172 EIN VEREINS THALER. Like No. 168 but laureate head. Victory over Austria. 1866A 35.00

*173 SIEGES (Victory) THALER. Head. Rev. Germania std. Victory over France. 1871A 17.50

174 ZWEI (=2) VEREINS THALER. Head. Rev. eagle. 1861-71 . . . . 140.00

Gold

V.F.

175 ½/KRONE. Like No. 176. 1862-69A 850.00

175a —. 1868B 1250.00

V.F.

*176 1/KRONE. 1861-70 . . . . . 1400.00

PYRMONT, County

S. W. of the city of Hannover. Sporadic coinage from 13th century onward. To Gleichen 1583-1625, to Waldeck thereafter.

Arms: Silver, a red mill-rind (anchor cross).

Carl August Friedrich, Prince of Waldeck-Pyrmont 1728-63

Copper

VG-F

1 I/PFENNIG. Like No. 3. 1761 . . . . 7.00

2 II/PFENNIGE. Sim. 1761 . . 7.00

*3 IIII/PFENNIGE. 1761 . . . . 8.50

Georg, Prince of Pyrmont 1805-12, Prince of Waldeck-Pyrmont 1812-13

Billon

6 24 EINEN (=¹⁄₂₄) THALER. G.F.Z.W.R.F.Z.P. 2 shields on mantle. Rev. value. 1806-07 . . . . 40.00

Silver

VF-EF

7 ZEHN EINE etc. (= Conv. thaler). GEORG PRINZ Z. WALDECK etc. Head. Rev. Arms. 1811 . . . . 1100.00

See Waldeck for other coins.

REGENSBURG (RATISBON), Bishopric

In Bavaria. Coinage from the 10th century, at first jointly with the dukes of Bavaria, then alone. Secularized and ceded to Bavaria 1810.

Arms: Red, a silver bend.

Anton Ignaz, Graf von Fugger zu Glott, Bishop 1769-87

Silver

VF-EF

3 X EINE etc. (= Conv. thaler). ANTON IGNAT. D.G. EPISC. RATISBON. Bust. Rev. Arms. 1786 . . . . 225.00

Gold

4 (ducat). Bust. Rev. Arms. 1770 . . . . 1500.00

Sede Vacante 1787

Silver

9 10 EINE etc. (= Conv. thaler). St. Peter in boat in circle of shields. Rev. REGNANS/etc. . . . . /RATISBONENSIS/etc. 1787 R.N. 175.00

For the 1809 coinage of Bishop Carl von Dalberg, see Prince Primate.

REGENSBURG (RATISBON)

Free City

In Bavaria. Free City 1180-1803. Received mint right 1230. The city was given to Bishop von Dalberg 1803-10, to Bavaria 1810.

Arms: Red, 2 silver keys crossed.

Copper

Fine

*1 H(eller). Uniface. 1677-1802. 3.00

Billon or Silver

*3 1/PFEN/NING. 1747-97 (var.) 3.00

*5 1 (kreuzer). 1754-85 . . . . 4.00

7 (Conv. kreuzer). CONVENTIONS STADT MUNTZ. Crossed keys. Rev. IOSEPHVS etc. Imp. eagle. 1787 . . . . 4.00

9 2 (kreuzer). Like No. 10 but FRANCISCUS I etc. 1754 . . . . . . 4.50

*10 2 (kreuzer). 1767 . . . . 4.50

11 *2 (kreuzer).* 1775, 82 . . . . 4.50

GERMAN STATES

REGENSBURG, Free City (Cont.)

Fine

15 10 (Conv. kreuzer). MONETA NOVA REIP. RATISP. Arms. Rev. FRANCISCUS etc. Imp. eagle. 1754 .... 5.00

17 10 (Conv. kreuzer). Arms/ RATISBONA. Rev. IOSEPHUS II etc. Imp. eagle. 1781 .... 5.00

19 XV (kreuzer). Arms. Rev. bust of Emp. Franz I. N.D. (1745-65) 9.00

21 20 (Conv. kreuzer). Like No. 15. 1754 .... 7.50

23 20 (Conv. kreuzer). Like No. 17. 1774, 75. (var.) 7.75

V.F.

★25 (¼ Conv. thaler). N.D. (1754-55) 27.50

26 40 ST. EINE F.C.M. (=¼ Conv. thaler). Sim. 1754 .... 27.50

Silver

VF-EF

28 *(¼ Conv. thaler)*. Archery Fest. *Like No. 40*. 1788 ..... 65.00

30 (½ Conv. thaler). Like No. 25. N.D. (1754-55) 55.00

30a —. Obv. leg. IN DOMINO etc. RATISBONA below. N.D. (1754-55) 60.00

31 20 ST. EINE etc. (=½ Conv. thaler). Like No. 25. 1754 ... 60.00

33 (gulden) 8 lines: MEMORIAE/ PACIS TERRA/etc. ... RATISBON/—. Rev. globe. 1763 R.N. Peace of Huber- tusburg 75.00

35 XX EINE etc. (=½ Conv. thaler). NON DORMIT. etc. City view. Rev. bust of Emp. Joseph II. 1774, 82 .... 60.00

36 XX ST. EINE etc. (=½ Conv. thaler). Sim. but MONETA etc. in lieu of NON etc. 1775, 81-82 .... 75.00

38 XX EINE F. etc. (=½ Conv. thaler). MONETA REIP. RATISPON. Arms. Rev. IOSEPHVS II etc. Imp. eagle 1784 .... 75.00

40 *(½ Conv. thaler)*. 8 line legend. Rev. target, etc. Archery Fest. 1788 .... 100.00

42 XX ST. EINE etc. (=½ Conv. thaler). City view. Rev. head of Emp. Leopold II. 1791 ... 70.00

44 (Conv. thaler). TALI SUB etc. City view/crossed keys. Rev. bust of Franz I. N.D. 225.00

VF-EF

45 X ST. EINE etc. (= Conv. thaler). Like No. 25. 1754, 56, 62 .... 150.00

46 X ST EINE etc. (= Conv. thaler). Arms. Rev. bust of Franz I. 1759 .... 175.00

47 (Conv. thaler). 8 lines: VOTIS/PRO PACE/etc. Rev. Peace crowns column. 1763 R.N. Peace of Hubertus- burg 300.00

48 (Conv. thaler). Eagle over arms. Rev. bust of Joseph II. 1766 .... 225.00

49 X ST. EINE etc. (= Conv. thaler). Like No. 36. 1766, 75, 80. (var.) 150.00

50 X EINE etc. (= Conv. thaler). DOMINE CONSERVA etc. Arms. Rev. bust of Joseph II. 1773-75. (var.) 120.00

51 (Conv. thaler). TALI SUB etc. City arms/crossed keys. Rev. IOSEPHVS II etc. Imp. eagle. N.D. (1780-90) 400.00

52 (Conv. thaler). 9 lines: SOLEMNIET/etc. Rev. 2 flags, crossbows, etc. 1788 R.N. Archery Fest 750.00

53 X ST. EINE etc. (= Conv. thaler). Like No. 42. 1791 .. 275.00

54 X EINE etc. (= Conv. thaler). Arms. Rev. head of Leopold II. 1791 .... 300.00

55 X EINE etc. (= Conv. thaler). Sunrise over arms. Rev. head of Franz II. 1792 .... 325.00

56 X ST. EINE etc. (= Conv. thaler). City view. Rev. head of Franz II. 1793 .... 275.00

57 (Conv. thaler). LARGIENTE NVMINE. Imp. eagle over city arms. Rev. head of Franz II. 1801-1802 (one date) 450.00

58 (2 thaler). NON DORMIT etc. City view. Rev. bust of Franz I. 51mm. N.D. (1745-65) 850.00

Gold (ducat=3.49 gr.)

I. Undated coins of the reign of Emp. Franz I 1745-65 (all round except where otherwise indicated.)

59 *(1/32 ducat)*. Crossed keys. Rev. Imp. eagle. (1750) 175.00

59a —. Rev. cwnd. R. (1750) .. 175.00

61 *(1/16 ducat)*. Like No. 59a. (1750) 250.00

63 ⅛ (ducat). Like No. 59 .... 275.00

63a —. Klippe (square) 300.00

65 ⅙ *(ducat)*. Like No. 63a .. 350.00

67 ¼ *(ducat)*. Like No. 59 .... 400.00

67a —. Klippe 400.00

69 ¼ *(ducat)*. City view. Rev. bust of Franz I 400.00

71 (½ ducat). Like No. 59 .... 800.00

73 *(½ ducat)*. Like No. 69 .... 650.00

VF-EF

75 DUCATUS (=ducat). DUCATUS RATISBON/City view. Rev. bust 1100.00

77 (ducat). SIBI etc./City view/ RATISBONA. Rev. bust 950.00

79 (2 ducats). Like No. 77 but IN TE etc. in lieu of SIBI etc. 1750.00

81 *(2 ducats)*. Eagle over arms. Rev. bust 2250.00

83 *(3 ducats)*. Like No. 69 .... RRR

85 *(3 ducats)*. Like No. 81 ..... RRR

II. Undated coins of the reign of Emp. Joseph II 1765-90.

87 *(¼ ducat)*. PROSPICIENTE DEO. City view/RATISBONA. Rev. IOSEPH(VS) II etc. Imp. eagle 350.00

89 *(½ ducat)*. RATISBONA. City view. Rev. as No. 87 ...... 500.00

91 (ducat). SIBI etc. City view/ RATISBONA. Rev. as No. 87 . 900.00

93 *(ducat)*. City view. Rev. bust of Joseph II 850.00

95 *(ducat)*. Arms. Rev. bust .. 850.00

★97 (2 ducats) N.D 2000.00

99 (3 ducats). Like No. 95 ..... RRR

The Joseph II 5 and 8 ducat pieces N.D. are medals.

III. Reign of Emp. Leopold II 1790- 92.

101 *(ducat)*. City view. Rev. head of Leopold II. N.D. . 900.00

IV. Reign of Emp. Franz II (1792- 1803).

★103 (ducat). N.D 900.00

REUSS (RUTHENUS), Counts and Princes

In Thuringia. Descended from one Heinrich I v Gleitzberg (d 1045). Ac- quired the confusing habit of naming all male children Heinrich. After many

GERMAN STATES

REUSS (Cont.)

earlier branches died out, Reuss was divided into Elder and Younger lines in 1550.

Arms: Black, gold double tailed lion with right foot on pedestal.

I. ELDER LINE (ÄLTERER LINIE).

Shortly before 1700 the Elder Line adopted a system of numbering in which all successive males received consecutive numbers from 1 to 100, whereupon the cycle was repeated.

A. REUSS (OBER=UPPER) -GREIZ (GREITZ)

Senior branch of the Elder Line, founded 1616.

Heinrich XI, Born 1722, Ruled as Count in Upper Greiz (Under Regency 1723-43), Inherited Lower Greiz 1768, Elevated to Rank of Prince 1778, Died 1800

Copper

VG-F

1 1/HELLER. Reuss lion. Rev. value/G(rafliche) R(euss) P(lauen)/GREI(T)ZER/ L.M. 1760-70 .... 6.00

2 ½/PFENNIG. Sim 1775 ... 7.00

2a —. Rev. value/F(urstliche) R.P./etc. 1787, 89 .... 6.00

3 1/PFENNIG. Like No. 1. 1760-61, 75 .... 4.00

3a —. Like No. 2a. 1787, 89 ... 4.00

4 II/PFENNIG. Like No. 1. 1760-61 .... 6.00

Billon or Silver

9 3 (pfennig). HXIER mon. in cartouche. Rev. 3 in orb on shield. 1763 ...... 6.00

10 —. G.R.P.– G.L.M./arms. Rev. like No. 9. 1764, 69 ...... 5.00

10.5 (ex 10a) —. F.R. PL. G.L.M./ lion. Rev. like No. 9. 1787. 6.00

11 *48/EINEN (=1/48)/THALER. Obv. like No. 9. Rev. value.* 1763 .... 7.50

12 —. Obv. like No. 10. Rev. value. 1769 .... 5.00

12.5 (ex 12a) —. Obv. like No. 10.5. Rev. value in frame. 1787, 89 .... 5.00

*★14 24/EINEN (=1/24)/THAL(er). 1738-39 ....10.00

VG-F

16 24/EINEN/THAL(er). H.D. XI. E.R. G.U.H.V.P. Arms. Rev. value. 1759 ...... 10.00

18 24/EINEN/THALER. H. XI. S.L.R.C. etc. Arms. Rev. CCCXX EINE etc., value. 1763-64 .... 6.50

20 12/EINEN (=1/12)/THALER. Like No. 18 but H.XI.SEN. etc. and CLX etc. 1763 .... 6.50

22 12/EINEN/THALER. D. G. HENR. XI S.L. RVTH etc., arms on mantle. Rev. value. 1789 .... 8.50

24 *VI/EINEN (=1/6)/REICHS/ THALER. Like No. 26.* 1757 .... 15.00

26 VI/EINEN/REICHS/THALER. HENR. XI. S.L. RVTH. COM. etc. Arms under 2 helmets. Rev. LXXX EINE etc., value. 1763 .... 12.50

Silver

V.F.

28 ⅔ (mining thaler). Armored bust. Rev. lion over mining scene. 1754 .... 65.00

30 XX EINE etc. (=½ Conv. thaler). D.G. HENR. XI etc., head. Rev. arms on mantle. 1786 .... 100.00

32 X EINE etc. (= Conv. thaler). Head. Rev. Arms under 2 helmets. 1769 .... 300.00

33 X EINE etc. (= Conv. thaler). Sim. but BERG SEGEN etc. From Neuen Hofnung Mine. 1775 .... 450.00

34 X EINE etc. (= Conv. thaler). Head. Rev. Arms on cwnd. mantle. 1778 .... 250.00

35 X EINE etc. (=Conv. thaler). Like No. 30 but older draped bust. 1790 .... 350.00

Heinrich XIII 1800-17

Copper

Fine

*★37 I/HELLER. 1812, 15 ...... 3.50

38 I/PFENNIG. Like No. 40. 1806, 08 .... 3.00

39 I/PFENNIG. Like No. 37. 1808-16 .... 3.00

*★40 3/PFENNIG. 1805-16 ...... 2.50

Billon

Fine

42 I/GROSCHEN. Like No. 40. 1805, 12 .... 7.50

Silver

V.F.

45 6/EINEN (=⅙)/THALER. V.G.G. HEINR. XIII AELT. REUSS etc., arms on mantle. Rev. value in wreath. 1808 .... 100.00

47 3/EINEN (=⅓)/THALER. Sim. 1809 .... 200.00

49 X EINE etc. (= Conv. thaler). D.G. HENR. XIII S.L. RVTH. etc. Bust. Rev. Arms on mantle. 1806-07 .... 800.00

50 X EINE etc. (= Conv. thaler). Sim. but V.G.G. HEINRICH etc. 1807, 12 .... 450.00

51 EIN/SPECIES/THALER. Bust. Rev. value in wreath. 1812 .... 275.00

Heinrich XIX 1817-36

Copper

Fine

52 I/HELLER. Like No. 37. 1817, 19 .... 3.50

53 I/PFENNIG. Sim. 1817-27 .. 2.00

53a —. 1/PFENNIG. 1828-31 ... 2.00

53b —. Struck in collar. 1831-32 .... 4.00

54 3/PFENNIG. Like No. 40. 1817-31 .... 2.00

54a —. Struck in collar. 1831-33 .... 3.75

Heinrich XX 1836-59

Silver

V.F.

55 EIN (=1) VEREINS-THALER. HEINRICH XX V.G.G. AELT. etc., head. Rev. arms supported. 1858 .... 75.00

56 2 THALER. Head. Rev. Arms on mantle. 1841-51 .... 500.00

Heinrich XXII 1859-1902

Copper

F-VF

*★57 1/PFENNIG. 1864, 68. (2 var.) 2.50

58 3/PFENNIGE. Sim. 1864, 68. (2 var.) 2.50

Billon

Fine

59 1/SILBER/GROSCHEN. Sim. 1868 .... 5.00

REUSS-GREIZ (Cont.)

Silver
V.F.

60 EIN (=1) VEREINS THALER. HEINRICH XXII V.G.G. ALT. etc. Head. Rev. Arms on mantle. 1868.....100.00

B. REUSS UNTER (LOWER) -GREIZ, County

Junior branch of the Elder Line. Founded 1616. Extinct 1768. Lands to Ober-Greiz.

Heinrich III 1733-68

Copper
VG-F

1 1/PFENNIG. h3 in shield. Rev. value/G.R.P. UNTER/ GREIZER/L.M. 1752.........5.00

Billon or Silver

3 III/GUTE/PFENNIGE. G.R.P. UNTER GREIZER L.M. h3 in cwnd. shield. Rev. value. 1752.....................6.50

3a —. H.E.R.III in shield. 1752.. 6.50

6 3 (pfennig). Obv. like No. 3a. Rev. 3 in orb. *1753*, 55.....6.50

6a —. 1763.................6.00

9 VI (pfennig). Obv. like No. 3a. Rev. VI in orb. 1752-58.....6.50

11 48/EINEN (=$^1/_{48}$)/THALER. Obv. like No. 3a. Rev. value. 1763.................7.50

12 48/EINEN/THALER. G.R.P.V.G.L.M./lion. Rev. value. 1763.................8.50

14 24/EINEN (=$^1/_{24}$)/THAL(er). HEINRICH D. III E. REUSS etc. Arms. Rev. NACH DEM etc., value. 1738-39.........8.50

16 24/EINEN/REICHS/THALER. HENR. III SEN. LIN. RUTH etc. Arms. Rev. G.R.P. UNTER GREIZER etc., value. 1753....7.50

18 24/EINEN/THALER. H. III. S.L.R. etc., arms. Rev. CCCXX etc., value. 1763-64.........7.50

20 12/EINEN (=$^1/_{12}$)/THALER. Like No. 16 but Rev. leg. GRAEFL REUS. P. UNTER GRAETZ etc. 1753...........8.50

22 12/EINEN/THALER. Like No. 18. but CLX etc. 1763.................8.25

Silver
F-VF

24 $^1/_8$ SPEC(ies) THAL(er = 4 groschen). HENR. III S.L. RUTH etc. Arms under 2 helmets. Rev. GOTT SEEGNE etc. Mining scene. 1751.........32.50

24a —.... SEN. LIN. etc. Cwnd. arms. 1752-53............30.00

F-VF

26 VI/EINEN (=$^1/_6$)/REICHS/ THALER. Like OBER-GREIZ No. 26 but HEN. III etc. 1763.................20.00

V.F.

28 $^1/_4$ SPECIES THAL(er). Like No. 24a. 1751.........37.50

30 $^2/_3$ (Reichsthaler). Like No. 32. 1759.................50.00

32 X EINE etc. (= Conv. thaler). HENRICUS III S.L. RVTHENOR etc. Bust. Rev. Arms. 1763-64.....................300.00

Gold

34 (ducat). Like No. 32. 1764.................1100.00

II. YOUNGER LINE (JÜNGERER LINIE)

The Younger Line had the custom of beginning its numbering afresh with the first male born in each new century. It was subdivided into 4 branches in 1635 and a further division occurred in 1671.

Arms: In addition to the Reuss lion, certain of the Younger Line branches used a hound's head.

A. REUSS-EBERSDORF

Offshoot of Reuss-Lobenstein, founded 1710. Raised from county to principality 1806. Inherited Lobenstein 1824. Styled Lobenstein-Ebersdorf 1824-49. To Schleiz 1849.

Heinrich XXIV, Count 1747-79

Billon or Silver
VG-F

1 I/PFENNIG. G.R.P.– E.L.M./ arms. Rev. value in frame. 1765.................10.00

3 III/PFENNIG. Sim. 1763.. 9.00

5 48/EINEN (=$^1/_{48}$)/THALER. Sim. 1765.................15.00

7 24/EINEN (=$^1/_{24}$)/THAL(er). Obv. like No. 9. Rev. cccxx EINE etc., value. 1763.....7.50

9 12/EINEN (=$^1/_{12}$)/THALER. HEINRICH XXIV I. REUSS. GR. etc. Arms. Rev. GR. R. PL. EBERSD. etc., value. 1763-64.................10.00

11 VI/EINEN (=$^1/_6$)/THALER. Sim. 1763-64.........17.50

Silver
F-VF

13 3/EINEN (=$^1/_3$)/REICHS-/ THAL(er). Like No. 9. 1763-64.................35.00

15 $^2/_3$ (Reichsthaler). Like No. 17. 1765.............100.00

17 X EINE etc. (= Conv. thaler). Bust. Rev. Arms. 1765-66..200.00

Heinrich LI, Count 1779-1806, Prince 1806-22

Copper
Fine

20 1/PFENNIG. Hound's head in cwnd. shield. Rev. value/ F.R.P./EBERSDORF. 1812.....7.50

21 2/PFENNIG. Sim. 1812....7.50

22 3/PFENNIG. Sim. 1812....9.00

23 4/PFENNIG. Sim. 1812....10.00

Billon

25 *3 PFENNIGE.* 1804.......12.00

27 6/PFENNIG. Like No. 20. 1812.....................14.00

29 8/PFENNIG. Sim. 1812....15.00

31 1/GROSCHEN. HEINRICH LI•I•L•F•REUSS•EBERSDORF. Arms. Rev. value. 1812, 14..15.00

Silver
V.F.

33 EIN (=1)/SPECIES/THALER. Arms. Rev. value. 1812....275.00

See Reuss-Lobenstein-Ebersdorf for coins of the next prince.

B. REUSS-GERA, County

Extinct 1802. To Schleiz.

Heinrich XXX 1748-1802

Copper
VG-F

1 1/PFENNIG. Hound's head. Rev. value/G.R.P. GE/RAISCHE/ L.M./1761.................6.25

2 II/PFENNIG. Sim. 1761...7.50

Billon or Silver

4 *48 EINEN* (=$^1/_{48}$) *THALER.* 1796...........9.50

6 24/EINEN (=$^1/_{24}$)/THALER. H. XXX.I.R.COM. etc. Arms. Rev. value 1763, 64....12.50

8 12/EINEN (=$^1/_{12}$)/THALER. Sim. 1763-64.................10.00

10 VI/EINEN (=$^1/_6$)/REICHS/ THALER. Sim. 1763........25.00

Silver
VF-EF

11 XX. EINE F.M. (= $^2/_3$ Reichsth.) Like No. 12. 1763 R.N......150.00

12 (thaler). HENR. XXX. I.L. RVTH. COM. etc. Arms. Rev. NEGLECTAE etc. 2 figures shaking hands/1763 R.N. On Peace of Hubertusburg....350.00

GERMAN STATES

C. REUSS IÜNGERER LINIE.
See REUSS-SCHLEIZ (after 1849).

D. REUSS-LOBENSTEIN

Branch founded 1635. County until 1790, principality 1790-1824. Extinct 1824. To Ebersdorf.

Heinrich II, Count 1739-82

Copper

		VG-F
1	1/PFENN(ig). Like No. 2. 1760-61	6.00
2	II/PFENNIG. REVS/SCHEIDE/ MVNZE/date. Rev. value. 1760-61	7.00

Billon

| 4 | 48/EINEN (=¹/₄₈)/THALER. G.R.PL.L.L.M./lion. Rev. value in frame. 1771 | 15.00 |
| 6 | 2 GR(oschen). HENR. II. IVN. L. RVTH. etc. Arms. Rev. NON PRETIVM etc. Bridal pair. On marriage of his daughter with Prince of Stolberg. 1759 .....(V.F.) | 35.00 |

Heinrich XXXV, Count 1782-90, Prince 1790-1805

Billon

| *10 | 3/PFENIGE. F.R.P.LOB.S.M. 1804-05 | 7.50 |
| 12 | 48/EINEN (=¹/₄₈)/THALER. Sim. 1805 | 9.50 |

Heinrich LIV, Prince 1805-24

Billon

| 15 | 3/PFENIGE. Like No. 10. 1807 | 8.50 |

E. REUSS-LOBENSTEIN-EBERSDORF, Principality

Heinrich LXXII,
Prince of Reuss-Ebersdorf 1822-24, Inherited Lobenstein 1824, Prince of Reuss-Lobenstein-Ebersdorf 1824-49, Abdicated in Favor of Schleiz 1849

Copper

		F-VF
*1	1/PFENNIG. 1841, 44	3.50

		F-VF
2	3/PFENNIGE. Sim. 1841, 44	4.00

Billon

| 3 | ½/SILBER/GROSCHEN. Sim. 1841 | 10.00 |
| 4 | 1/SILBER/GROSCHEN. Sim. 1841, 44 | 7.00 |

Silver

		VF-EF
5	2 THALER. HEINRICH LXXII JÜNG LIN. FÜRST REUSS. Head. Rev. Arms. 1840, 47	400.00
6	ZWEI (=2) THALER (on edge). Obv. sim. Rev. ZUR FEIER etc. Arms. 25th year of reign. 1847	1100.00

F. REUSS-SCHLEIZ (SCHLEITZ), County until 1806, Principality 1806-1918.

Heinrich XII, Count 1744-84

Billon or Silver

		VG-F
5	24/EINEN (=¹/₂₄)/THALER. HENR. XII I.L.R.COM. etc. Arms. Rev. value. 1763-64	6.00
7	12/EINEN (=¹/₁₂)/THALER. Sim. but HENRICUS XII etc. 1763	8.00
9	VI/EINEN (=¹/₆)/REICHS/ THALER. Sim. 1763	15.00

Silver

		V.F.
11	III/EINEN (=¹/₃) /REICHS/ THALER. Sim. 1763	Rare
13	²/₃ (Reichsthaler). Like No. 15. 1763	100.00
14	²/₃ (Reichsthaler). Like No. 16. 1764	120.00
15	X EINE etc. (= Conv. thaler). HEINRICH D. XII I. REUSS etc. Bust. Rev. AUF KRIEGES LAST etc. Arms. On Peace of Hubertusburg. 1763	225.00
16	X EINE etc. (= Conv. thaler). Obv. like No. 15. Rev. IN IESV etc. Arms. 1764	225.00

Gold

| 17 | (ducat). AUF KRIEGES LAST. Cwnd. GRXII mon. Rev. FOLGT etc. Arms. 1763. Peace of Hubertusburg | 1500.00 |
| 18 | (ducat). Like No. 16. 1764 | 1850.00 |

Heinrich XLII, Count 1784-1806, Prince 1806-18, Acquired Gera 1802

Copper

		Fine
20	3/PFENNIG. Lion in oval shield. Rev. value/F.R.P./ SCHLEIZER etc. 1815-16	4.50

Billon

		Fine
22	I/GROSCHEN. Sim. but lion/crane in oval shield. 1815	7.50
22a	—. Uncwnd. lion. 1816	10.00
22b	—. Cwnd. lion. 1816	20.00

Heinrich LXII, Prince 1818-54. Acquired Lobenstein-Ebersdorf 1849. Became the only reigning prince of Reuss Younger Line.

Copper

| 25 | ½/PFENNIG. Arms, no legend. Rev. value. 1841A | 17.50 |

*26	1/PFENNIG. 1841, 47	6.50
27	1/PFENNIG. Sim. but FÜRSTENTHUM REUSS IÜNGERER LINIE. 1850	2.75
28	3/PFENNIGE. Like No. 26. 1841, 44	5.00
29	3/PFENNIGE. Like No. 27. 1850	6.00

Billon

30	1/SILBER/GROSCHEN. Like No. 26. 1841-46	5.00
31	1/SILBER/GROSCHEN. Like No. 27. 1850	6.00
32	2/SILBER/GROSCHEN. Like No. 27. 1850	10.00

Silver

		VF-EF
33	2 THALER. HEINRICH LXII IÜNG etc. Head. Rev. Arms. 1840-54	400.00
34	ZWEI (=2) THALER (on edge). Obv. as last. Rev. ZUR FEIER etc. Arms. 25th year of reign. 1843	1000.00

Heinrich LXVII, Prince 1854-67

Copper

		F-VF
*35	1/PFENNIG. 1855-64	2.00
36	3/PFENNIGE. Sim. 1855-64	2.50

Billon

		Fine
37	1/SILBER/GROSCHEN. Sim. 1855	8.00
38	2/SILBER/GROSCHEN. Sim. 1855	15.00

GERMAN STATES

REUSS-SCHLEIZ (Cont.)

Silver

V.F.

39 EIN (=1) VEREINS-
THALER. HEINRICH LXVII
v.G.G. etc., head. Rev. arms.
1858, 62................60.00

Heinrich XIV, Prince 1867-1913

Copper

F-VF

40 1/PFENNIG. Like No. 41.
1868................. 2.25

*41 3/PFENNIGE. 1868...... 4.00

Silver

V.F.

42 EIN (=1) VEREINS-
THALER. Head. Rev. arms.
1868....................60.00

RIETBERG (RITPERG),
County

In Westphalia on the River Ems. First
coins circa 1481-1516. Rietberg was acquired through marriage by Maximilian
Ulrich von Kaunitz in 1699. Mediatized to Westphalia 1807.

Wenzel Anton, Count 1758-64,
Prince 1764-94

Copper

VG-F

1 I/PFEN(nig). WA script mon.
divides date. Rev. RITBERGISCHE,
etc., value. 1766..........30.00

2 II/PFEN(nig). Sim. 1766...40.00

ROSTOCK, City

On the Baltic in Mecklenburg. Obtained the mint right in 1325.

Arms: Parted per fesse.
Chief: Blue, gold griffin.
Foot: Per fesse, silver and red.

Monetary System:
12 pfennig = 1 schilling;
48 schilling = 1 thaler.

Note: There are many varieties each
of most Rostock coins.

Copper

Fine

*1 I/PFENNING. 1782 (var.). 4.50

1a —. ROSTOCKER MUNZE
(MUNZ, MUNTZ). 1793-97
(var.)................. 4.75

2 I/PFENNING. ROSTOCKER
MUNZE. Griffin shield or like
No. 2a. Rev. value on tablet.
1798 (var.)............... 5.50

*2a —. No tablet. 1798-1802.... 4.00

4 I/PFENNING. Like No. 2a
but ROSTOCKER begins at
8 o'clock. 1802, 05........ 5.00

4a —. No circle between legend
and griffin. 1805, 15, 24..... 4.00

5 1/PFENNIG. Griffin, no
legend. Rev. value. 1848.... 6.00

*7 III/PFENING. 1744-59.... 7.50

7a —. CIVITATIS ROSTOCH.
1750.................... 7.75

8 III/PFENNING. CIVITATIS
ROSTOCK. Griffin. Rev. value.
1760-61................. 7.50

9 III/PFENNING. Griffin
rampant/ROST. Rev. value.
1761.................... 6.50

10 3/PFENNING. Like No.
4a. 1815, 24.............. 2.75

10a 3 PFENNINGE. 1843..... 2.50

*11 3/PFENNINGE. Sim. but
griffin shield. 1855....... 2.50

12 3/PFENNINGE. Like No. 10a.
1859................... 2.50

12a —. 1862, 64............. 2.50

14 6/PFENNING. Like No. 9.
1761-62................ 6.75

Gold

V.F.

16 *(ducat).* Like No. 17 but
Franz I. 1762............1200.00

17 (ducat). MONETA AUREA
ROSTOCHIENSIS. Griffin shield.
Rev. IOSEPHVS II etc. Imp.
eagle. 1783.............1100.00

18 (ducat). Sim. but Franz II.
1796...................1000.00

ST. ALBAN, Priory

In Mainz. Given mint right 1518.

Gold

VF-EF

1 (gold gulden). SANCTUS
ALBANUS MARTYR. St. Alban
stdg. Rev. donkey shield.
1778-80................950.00

SACHSEN. See Saxe and Saxony.

SALM, County

On the German-French-Belgian frontier. First mentioned in the 11th century. The ruling family was divided
into many branches and struck few
coins.

Arms: Black, a silver leopard.

Friedrich III, Prince of
Salm-Kyrburg 1779-94

Silver

V.F.

2 (10 Conv. kreuzer). Like No. 8
but AD NORMAM etc. added to
Rev. 1780.................47.50

5 (Conv. thaler). Like No. 2.
1780...................1100.00

6 (Conv. thaler). Sim. but smaller
head, no mantle behind arms.
1782...................750.00

Gold

*8 (ducat). 3.49 gr. 1780, 82.1350.00

10 (Carolin). Head. Rev.
Arms. 9.7 gr. 1782.......1850.00

SAXE (SACHSEN)
ALTENBURG, Duchy

In Thuringia. Created in 1826 for the
erstwhile duke of Saxe-Hildburghausen
during the reshuffle following the extinction of the Saxe-Gotha-Altenburg
line.

GERMAN STATES

SAXE ALTENBURG (Cont.)

Saxon arms: Barry of 10, black and gold with green crown opened diagonally across it.

Monetary System:
10 pfennig = 1 neugroschen;
30 neugroschen = 1 thaler.

Joseph 1834-48

Copper

	F-VF
1 1/PFENNIG. Like No. 7. 1841	5.75
2 I/PFENNIG. Like No. 11. 1843	6.00
3 2/PFENNIGE. Like No. 7. 1841	6.00
4 II/PFENNIGE. Like No. 11. 1843	7.50

Billon

5 ½/NEU-/GROSCHEN. Like No. 7. 1841-42	8.00
6 1/NEU-/GROSCHEN. Sim. 1841-42	8.00

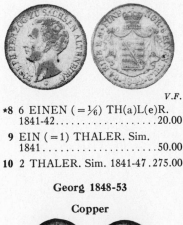

*7 2/NEU-/GROSCHEN. N.D	45.00
7a —. 1841	8.75

Silver

	V.F.
*8 6 EINEN (=⅙) TH(a)L(e)R. 1841-42	20.00
9 EIN (=1) THALER. Sim. 1841	50.00
10 2 THALER. Sim. 1841-47	275.00

Georg 1848-53

Copper

	Fine
*11 I/PFENNIG. 1852	4.00
12 II/PFENNIGE. Sim. 1852	5.00

Silver

	V.F.
13 2 THALER. GEORG HERZOG ZU SACHSEN ALTENBURG, head. Rev. arms. 1852	350.00

Ernst I 1853-1908

Copper

	F-VF
14 I/PFENNIG. Like No. 11. 1856, 58	3.75
14a —. 1857	4.50
14b —. 1861-65	4.50
15 II/PFENNIGE. Sim. 1856	6.00

Silver

	V.F.
16 EIN (=1) VEREINSTHALER. ERNST HERZOG ZU SACHSEN ALTENBURG, head. Rev. arms. 1858, 64, 69	40.00

SAXE (SACHSEN)-COBURG-SAALFELD, Duchy

In Thuringia. Founded 1680 as Saxe-Saafeld by the 7th son of Ernst the Pious of Saxe-Gotha. Obtained Coburg 1735.

Franz Josias
(Previously Joint Ruler With His Elder Brother, Christian Ernst 1729-45), Alone in Coburg-Saalfeld 1745-64, Regent in Weimar 1749-55

Copper

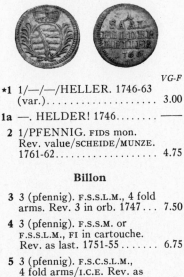

	VG-F
*1 1/—/—/HELLER. 1746-63 (var.)	3.00
1a —. HELDER! 1746	—
2 1/PFENNIG. FIDS mon. Rev. value/SCHEIDE/MUNZE. 1761-62	4.75

Billon

3 3 (pfennig). F.S.S.L.M., 4 fold arms. Rev. 3 in orb. 1747	7.50
4 3 (pfennig). F.S.S.M. or F.S.S.L.M., FI in cartouche. Rev. as last. 1751-55	6.75
5 3 (pfennig). F.S.C.S.L.M., 4 fold arms/I.C.E. Rev. as last. 1764	6.75
5a —. No obv. legend. 1764	7.00
6 VI (pfennig). F.S.S.M., 4 fold arms. Rev. VI in orb. 1746	7.50
7 6 (pfennig). Obv. like No. 4. Rev. 6 in orb. 1751	7.00

	VG-F
7a VI (pfennig). 1754	7.00
8 VI (pfennig). 1756, 60	7.00
9 VI (pfennig). FI in cartouche. Rev. F.S.S.L.M., VI in orb. 1761	7.00
10 48/EINEN (=¹⁄₄₈)/THALER. Obv. like No. 5. Rev. value. 1764	8.50
11 24/EINEN (=¹⁄₂₄)/REICHS THALER. FVRSTL. S. SALF etc. F.I. mon. Rev. NACH DER LEIPZIGER etc., value. 1746-48	9.25
11a —. Rev. NACH CHVRFURSTL. etc. 1751-58	9.00

*12 24/EINEN (=¹⁄₂₄)/THALER. 1763	9.00
12a 24 EINEN REICHS THALER. 1764	9.00
13 12/EINEN (=¹⁄₁₂)/REICHS/THALER. Like No. 11. 1746	11.00
14 12/EINEN/THALER. Like No. 12. 1763	11.00
14a 12 EINEN REICHS THALER. 1764	11.00

Silver

	V.F.
16 ⅙ (Reichsthaler). FRANCISCUS IOSIAS D.G.D.S. COBURG SAALFELD. Bust. Rev. Arms. 1764	22.50
18 (¼ Conv. thaler). Bust. Rev. pyramid. On his death. 1764	50.00
20 X EINE etc. (= Conv. thaler). Like No. 16	450.00

Gold (ducat = 3.49 gr.)

22 ¼ (ducat). FI mon. in cartouche. Rev. Arms. 1752	400.00
23 DUCATVS (=ducat). Lion holds FI mon. cartouche. Rev. DVCATVS SAALFELDENSIS. 1746, 49	1250.00

Ernst Friedrich 1764-1800

Copper

	Fine
24 ½/PFENNIG. Like No. 24a but Rev. value/SCHEIDE/MUNZ/1772	4.50

*24a —. 1798-1800	4.75
25 1/PFENNIG. Like No. 24. 1770-72, 98	3.50
26 1½/PFENNIG. Like No. 24. 1772	4.25
26a —. Like No. 24a. 1799	4.75

GERMAN STATES

SAXE-COBURG-SAALFELD (Cont.)

I. For Saalfeld.

Billon
VG-F

27 I/PFENNIG. 4 fold arms with Saxon center shield/I.C.K. Rev. value. 1765 . . . . 6.50

28 3 (pfennig). Obv. as last but with F.S.C.S.L.M. Rev. 3 in orb. 1764-65 . . . . 6.75

29 48/EINEN (=1/48)/THALER. Obv. as last. Rev. value. 1765-91 . . . . 6.50

30 24/EINEN (=1/24)/THALER. Like No. 35 but arms as on No. 27. 1764-72 . . . . 9.00

30a 24/EINEN/REICHS/THALER. Like No. 35. 1765 . . . . 9.50

30b 24/EINEN/REICHS/THALER. Like No. 30. 1774 . . . . 9.50

32 12/EINEN (=1/12)/REICHS/THALER. Like No. 35. 1764 . . . . 9.50

33 12/EINEN/THALER. Like No. 30. 1765-71 . . . . . . 9.50

33a —. 1774 . . . . 9.50

*35 12/EINEN/THALER. 1775-85 . . . . 9.50

II. For Coburg.

Billon or Silver
Fine

37 I/CONV(entions)/KREUZER. E.F.D.G. D.S. C.S. Arms as on No. 27. Rev. value. 1765, 67 . . . . 5.50

39 (2½ Conv. kreuzer). 1765 . . . . 9.25

40 5 (Conv. kreuzer). ERN. FRID. D.G. D.S. COBURG S. Arms as on No. 27. Rev. IVSTIRT/ 240 etc. 1765 . . . . 14.00

42 20 (Conv. kreuzer). Bust. Rev. Arms. 1765 . . . . 25.00

III. For both districts.

Silver
V.F.

43 XX EINE etc. (=½ Conv. thaler). Like No. 45. 1765 . . . 70.00

45 X EINE etc. (= Conv. thaler). Bust. Rev. Arms. 1764, 65 . 195.00

Gold
V.F.

46 (mining ducat). Bust. Rev. EX AVRO etc. View of Reichmannsdorf. 1766 . . . . 1900.00

Franz 1800-06

I. For Saalfeld.

Copper
Fine

47 I/PFENNIG. Like No. 64. 1804-05 . . . . 3.50

47a —. H.S.C.—S.L.M. 1805 . . . . . . 4.50

48 III/PFENNIG. Like No. 47. 1806 . . . . 3.00

Billon

49 3/PFENNIG. Like No. 54. 1804-06 . . . . 4.00

52 48/EINEN (=1/48)/THALER. Different 4 fold arms with Saxon centershield. Rev. value. 1804 . . . . 5.00

52a —. 1805 . . . . 5.00

*54 24/EINEN (=1/24)/THALER. 1805 . . . . 5.00

II. For Coburg.

Billon

56 1/PFENIG. H.S.C.L.M. Saxon arms. Rev. value. 1805 . . . . 4.50

57 I/KREUZER. Sim. but H.S.C.S.L.M. 1805 . . . . 6.00

58 III/KREUZER. Sim. but oval arms. 1804 . . . . 5.00

58a —. Pointed arms. 1804-05 . . 5.00

*59 III/KREUZER. 1805 . . . . . . 6.00

59a —. LAND M. 1805 . . . . 6.00

60 VI/KREUZER. Like No. 57. 1804-05 . . . . 6.00

61 VI/KREUZER. Like No. 59a. 1805 . . . . 6.00

III. For both districts.

Silver
V.F.

62 X/EINE etc. (= Conv. thaler). Arms. Rev. value. 1805 . . . 475.00

Ernst I, Duke of Saxe-Coburg-Saalfeld 1806-26, of Saxe-Coburg-Gotha 1826-44

I. For Saalfeld 1806-26.

Copper
Fine

63 1/HELLER. Saxon arms. Rev. H.S.C.S.S.M., value. 1808-24 (var.) 3.75

64 1/PFENNIG. H.S.C.S.S.M. Saxon arms. Rev. value. 1808-26 (var.) 3.75

65 III/PFENNIG. Sim. 1807-08 . . . . 4.50

65a 3/PFENNIG. 1821-26 . . . . . . 4.50

Billon

66 6/PFENNIG. Like No. 69 but H.S.C.S. 1808-20 . . . . 6.50

67 1/GROSCHEN. Sim. 1808, 10, 18 . . . . 6.00

II. For Coburg.

Copper

68 1/HELLER. Like No. 69. 1809 . . . . 4.50

*69 1/PFENNIG. 1809 . . . . 4.00

70 2/PFENNIGE. Sim. 1810 (var.) 3.50

70a —. 1817-18 . . . . 3.50

71 4/PFENNIGE. Sim. 1809-20 . . . . 7.50

Billon

73 1/PFENIG. Like No. 56. 1808 . . . . 5.00

74 I/KREUZER. Like No. 69 but H.S.C. 1808-20 . . . . 6.00

74a —. H.S.C.S 1824-26S 5.00

75 3/KREUZER. Sim. H.S.C. 1808-20 . . . . 4.50

75a —. H.S.C.S. 1821-26 . . . . 6.00

76 6/KREUZER. Sim. H.S.C. 1808-20 . . . . 6.00

76a —. H.S.C.S. 1821-26 . . . . 6.00

*77 10 (Conv.)/KREUZER. 1820 . . . . 22.50

GERMAN STATES

SAXE-COBURG-SAALFELD (Cont.)

Fine

77a —. With LICHTENBERG.
1824.....................22.50

79 XX/KREUZER. Like No.
77 but pointed shield. 1807
in rev. wreath (var.).......20.00

79a —. 1807 below wreath......25.00

80 20/KREUZER. Like No. 77.
1812-20..................17.50

80a —. Like No. 77a. 1823-26...16.00

III. For both districts.

Silver

VF-EF

81 ZEHN EINE etc. (= Conv.
thaler). Bust. Rev. Arms.
1817.....................300.00

81a —. EIN SPECIESTHALER on
edge. 1817................350.00

82 EIN (=1) KRONTHALER
(on edge). Bust. Rev. Cwn.,
sceptre, sword. 1825......1000.00

82a —. No value on edge
(=pattern or restrike.)
1825.....................Rare

SAXE-COBURG-GOTHA

Ernst I 1826-44

I. Coinage on the 1763 Convention Standard.

Copper

Fine

★83 1/PFENNIG. 1833-37......1.50

84 1½/PFENNIGE. Sim. 1834-
35......................3.00

85 2/PFENNIGE. Sim. 1834-
35......................1.75

86 3/PFENNIGE. Sim. 1834...2.50

Billon

86.5 1/KREUZER (script). Like
No. 87. 1827ST............6.00

87 1/KREUZER. Cwnd. *Ɛ*.
Rev. H.S.C.G., value. 1827-
30......................5.00

88 1/KREUZER. Arms. Rev.
value. 1831-37.............3.50

89 1/GROSCHEN. Arms.
Rev. value. For Gotha.
1837.....................7.50

89.5 3/KREUZER (script).
Like No. 87. 1827ST........7.50

90 3/KREUZER. Like No. 87.
1827-31..................4.00

91 3/KREUZER. Like No. 88.
1831-37..................3.75

Fine

92 6/KREUZER. Like No. 87.
1827-30..................5.00

93 6/KREUZER. Like No. 91.
1831-37..................3.50

Silver

V.F.

94 10 (Conv. kreuzer). Head
Rev. Arms. 1831-34.......25.00

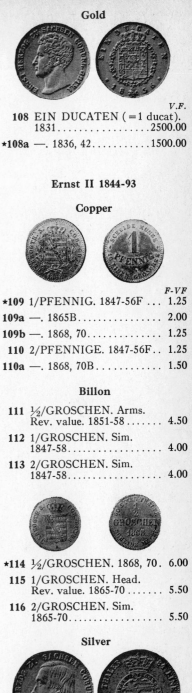

★94b —. 1835-37.............25.00

95 20/KREUZER. Arms. Rev.
value (& GOTHA). 1827....40.00

95a —. (UND GOTHA). 1827-30 .35.00

96 20 (Conv. kreuzer). Like No.
94. 1831, 34.............30.00

96a —. 1835-36.............30.00

97 ZWANZIG EINE etc. (=½
Conv. thaler). Like No. 94.
1830-34..................60.00

97a —. 1835................80.00

98 (Kronthaler). Like No. 82a
but different titles. 1827..600.00

99 ZEHN EINE (=Conv. thaler).
Like No. 94. 1828........RRR

99a —. 1829................500.00

99b —. 1832-33............Rare

99c —. 1835..............1000.00

II. Coinage on the 1838 Convention Standard.

Copper

Fine

100 1/PFENNIG. Like No. 109.
1841....................2.00

101 2/PFENNIGE. Sim. 1841..3.00

Billon

101.3 (ex 91a). 3/KREUZER.
Arms. Rev. value. (For
Coburg). 1838............6.00

101.6 (ex 93a) 6/KREUZER.
Sim. 1838................5.00

102 ½/GROSCHEN. Arms.
Rev. value. 1841, 44......5.00

103 1/GROSCHEN. Sim. 1841.12.50

104 2/GROSCHEN. Sim. 1841,
44......................10.00

Silver

V.F.

105 6 EINEN (=⅙) THALER.
Head. Rev. Arms. 1841-43 .35.00

106 EIN (=1) THALER. Head.
Rev. Arms. 1841-42.......60.00

107 2 THALER. Sim. 1841-
43.....................225.00

Gold

V.F.

108 EIN DUCATEN (=1 ducat).
1831....................2500.00

★108a —. 1836, 42...........1500.00

Ernst II 1844-93

Copper

F-VF

★109 1/PFENNIG. 1847-56F ... 1.25

109a —. 1865B..............2.00

109b —. 1868, 70............1.25

110 2/PFENNIGE. 1847-56F.. 1.25

110a —. 1868, 70B...........1.50

Billon

111 ½/GROSCHEN. Arms.
Rev. value. 1851-58.......4.50

112 1/GROSCHEN. Sim.
1847-58.................4.00

113 2/GROSCHEN. Sim.
1847-58.................4.00

★114 ½/GROSCHEN. 1868, 70. 6.00

115 1/GROSCHEN. Head.
Rev. value. 1865-70.......5.50

116 2/GROSCHEN. Sim.
1865-70.................5.50

Silver

V.F.

★117 6 EINEN (=⅙) THALER.
1845-55 (var.)............25.00

118 6 EINEN THALER. Head.
Rev. Arms on cwnd. mantle.
1864....................25.00

119 6 EINEN THALER. Head.
Rev. DEN/29 IANUAR/1869.
25th year of reign....(E.F.) 40.00

120 EIN (=1) THALER. Head.
Rev. Arms. 1846-52 (var.) .45.00

GERMAN STATES

SAXE-COBURG-GOTHA (Cont.)

V.F.

121 EIN VEREINSTHALER. Like No. 118. 1862, 64, 70 .40.00

122 EIN VEREINSTHALER. Like No. 119. 1869 . . . . . . .75.00

123 2 THALER. Head. Rev. Arms. 1847 . . . . .300.00

123a —. 1854 . . . . .200.00

SAXE-EISENACH, Duchy

In Thuringia. Independent under a collateral line of the House of Saxe-Weimar 1662-1741. To Weimar thereafter.

Friedrich III of Saxe-Gotha-Altenburg, Regent in Eisenach 1749-55 During the Minority of Ernst August II Constantin of Saxe-Weimar-Eisenach

Copper

VG-F

1 1/HELLER. Like No. 2. 1750-55 . . . . 3.00

*2 1/PFENNIG. FDS mon. 1750-55 . . . . 3.25

3 1/GUTER/PFENNIG. FDS mon. Rev. value. F.S.E.O.V.L.M. 1750-55 . . . . . . 4.50

4 1½/PFENNIG. Like No. 2. 1751-53 . . . . 5.00

5 II/PFENNIG. Sim. 1750-55 . . . . 5.00

Billon

6 3 (pfennig). FDS mon. Rev. 3 in orb. 1751 . . . . 7.50

7 3 (pfennig). F in cwnd. cartouche. Rev. 3 in orb. 1751-55 . . . . 6.25

8 VI (pfennig). Arms as No. 9a. Rev. M.N. ISEN. etc., VI in orb. 1751-55 . . . . 7.75

9 24/EINEN (=1/24)/THALER. Arms. Rev. value. 1752 . . . . .13.00

*9a —. 1753-55 . . . . 9.00

9b —. Rev. FVRSTL. S. WEIMAR V. EISEN. etc., 24 in orb. (Mule). 1756 . . . . .17.50

Silver

V.F.

10 (¼ *Species thaler*). Bust of Friedrich III. Rev. Genius with arms and altar. 1755. 2nd centenary of religious liberty 70.00

11 ⅔ (*Reichsthaler*). Bust. Rev. Arms. 1755 . . . . .150.00

12 (thaler). FRIDERICUS III etc. Bust. Rev. 11 lines: IN/ MEMORIAM/ . . . /DUCATUS ISENACENSI/etc. 1755 R.N., in circle of shields 375.00

13 (2 thaler). Same double thick. 1755 R.N 850.00

Gold

14 (*ducat*). Bust. Rev. Felicitas stdg. 1752 . . . . .1200.00

15 (*ducat*). Bust. Rev. Arms. 1754 . . . . .1200.00

SAXE-GOTHA-ALTENBURG, Duchy

In Thuringia. Founded 1680 by the eldest son of Ernst the Pious. Extinct 1825. Lands divided among the other branches 1826.

Friedrich III 1732-72, Also Regent in Eisenach 1749-55

Copper

VG-F

*1 1/HEL/LER. 1738-45 . . . . . . 2.75

2 HELLER. Helmeted Saxon arms. Rev. F.S./GOTHA. V./ ALTENB./HELLER. 1744-50 . . . 2.75

*3 I/HELLER. 1761-70 . . . . . . 3.50

4 I/HELLER. SGVA mon. Rev. value. 1770 . . . . 4.50

5 I/PFENNIG. Like No. 2. Rev. value/F.S.G.V.A./L.MVNTZ/ 1747 . . . . 3.25

5a —. MVTNZ. 1747 . . . . 6.50

6 I/PFENNIG. Cwnd. script F. Rev. value/H.S.G.V.A.L.M. 1753-70 . . . . 4.25

7 I½/PFENNIG. Sim. 1733-37 . . . . 4.50

8 I½/PFENNIG. Like No. 5. 1744-50 . . . . 4.50

9 I½/PFENNIG. FRIEDER. HERZ. Z.S. Saxon arms. Rev. H.S.G.V.A.L.M., value. 1752-61 . . . . 4.50

VG-F

10 3/PFENNIGE. Arms. Rev. value. 1761 (var.) 4.50

Billon

11 2/PFENN(ig). Arms. Rev. value. 1752 . . . . 7.00

12 3/PFENN(ig). Sim. 1752-53 . . . . 7.00

13 VI (pfennig). Cwnd. script F. Rev. VI in orb. 1735-49 . . . . . 7.50

14 6/PFENN(ig). Arms. Rev. value. 1752-59 . . . . 7.50

*15 1/48 (thaler). 1767-72 . . . . . . 4.75

*16 24/EINEN (=1/24) THA/ LER. 1752-56 . . . . 7.75

*17 (1/24 thaler). 2nd Centenary Religious Peace. 1755 R.N . .19.00

18 1/24 (thaler). H.S.G.V.A.L.M. Arms. Rev. value. 1762 . . . . . 7.50

19 24/EINEN/THALER. Arms. Rev. CCCXX etc., value. 1763-71 . . . . 7.50

Silver

V.F.

*20 (1/24 thaler). On his death. 1772 . . . . .13.00

21 12/EINEN (=1/12)/THALER. Like No. 19 but CLX etc. 1763-64 . . . . 7.00

22 (1/12 thaler). Like No. 20. Double thick, milled edge. 1772 . . . . .22.00

23 (1/6 thaler). Bust. Rev. like No. 17 rev. 1755 R.N 18.50

24 1/6 (thaler). Bust. Rev. Arms. 1757-58 . . . . .18.50

25 80 EINE etc. (=1/6 thaler). Head. Rev. Saxon arms. 1761-62 . . . . .18.50

GERMAN STATES

SAXE-GOTHA-ALTENBURG (Cont.)

V.F.

25a —. ⅛ (thaler). Rev. manifold arms. 1764-65 . . . . 18.50

26 (⅛ thaler). Bust. Rev. IN MEMOR etc. Arms. 2nd Cent. Rel. Peace. 1755 . . . . 29.00

27 XXXX EINE etc. (= ⅛ thaler). Like No. 25a. 1765-66 . . . . . 40.00

28 XX EINE etc. (= ⅔ Reichs thaler). Sim. but arms supported. 1764 . . . . 40.00

29 (thaler). Bust. Rev. TORQVE DONATVS etc. Arms. Order of Garter bestowed on F. III. 1741 R.N 450.00

30 (thaler). Bust. Rev. PIETATE etc. Arms. 2nd Cent. Rel. Peace. 1755 R.N 450.00

31 X EINE etc. (= Conv. thaler). Like No. 28. 1764 . . . . 125.00

32 X EINE etc. (= Conv. thaler). Head. Rev. Arms. 1765, 68.140.00

Gold (ducat = 3.49 gr.)

33 (ducat). Bust. Rev. PIETATE etc. Arms. 1732 . . . . 1100.00

34 (ducat). Bust. Rev. IN MEMOR etc. Arms. 2nd Cent. Rel. Peace. 1755 R.N 1100.00

35 (2 ducats). Like No. 23. 1755 R.N 2200.00

Ernst Ludwig 1772-1804

Silver (lowest value billon)

★36 24/EINEN (=1/24) /THALER. 1773 . . . . 12.00

37 XXX EINE etc. (=light gulden). ERNESTVS D.G. GOTHAN SAXONVM DVX. Bust. Rev. Arms 1774 . . . . 65.00

V.F.

★38 XX EINE etc. (=½ Conv. thaler). Head. Rev. Arms. 1774, 76 . . . . 65.00

39 XV EINE etc. (=light thaler). Like No. 37. 1774 . . . . 130.00

40 X EINE etc. (= Conv. thaler). Like No. 38. 1775, 76 . . . . . . 90.00

SAXE-HILDBURGHAUSEN

In Thuringia. Founded 1680 by Ernst IV, 6th son of Ernst the Pious. During the 1826 reshuffle the duke of Hildburghausen exchanged it for Altenburg (see Saxe-Altenburg).

Ernst Friedrich III Carl 1745-80

Copper

VG-F

★1 1/HELLER. EFC mon. 1759-66 . . . . 4.25

3 (heller). Arms. Rev. blank. 1772 . . . . 4.50

★3a 1/H(ildburg)H(ausen)/ HELLER. 1772-78 . . . . 4.50

4 1/PFENNIG. Saxon arms, trophies. Rev. value/H.S. HILD.B.H./L.M./1759 . . . . 4.50

5 3/PFENNIGE. Saxon arms. Rev. value/H.S.H.H./S.M./ 1763 . . . . 5.00

I. Kreuzer Standard.

Billon or Silver

7 2/PFENNIG. 1769 . . . . 12.00

★9 1 (kreuzer). ERN. FRID. CAR. D.G.D.S.&. 1753, 58 . . . . 5.50

9a —. Rev. I in cartouche. 1760 . . . . 5.50

VG-F

11 I/CONVENTI/ONS/ KREUZER. EFC mon. Rev. value. 1765 . . . . 7.50

12 *I CONVENT./KREUZER.* Arms. Rev. value. 1774-78 . . 7.50

13 2/KREUZ(er). SACHSEN HILDBURGH. Arms. Rev. value. 1761 . . . . 7.75

14 2½ (Conv. kreuzer). Like No. 14a but HILDBHAUS CONV. MUNZ. 1768 . . . . 13.00

★14a —.1770 . . . . 8.75

15 4/KREUZ(er). Like No. 13. 1761 . . . . 12.50

16 300 EINE etc. (=4 Conv. kreuzer). Head. Rev. Arms. 1763 . . . . 13.00

19 5 KR(euzer). EFC mon. Rev. IVSTIRT/240/etc. 1765 . . . . 9.75

20 240 EINE etc. (=5 Conv. kreuzer). Arms. Rev. 240 etc. IUS/TIRT/1770 . . . . 13.00

21 6 (kreuzer). Bust. Rev. LAND MUNZ. Arms. 1759 . . . . 13.00

22 *10 (kreuzer).* 1759 . . . . 17.50

23 10 (kreuzer). Bust r. in wreath. Rev. PIETATE etc. Arms. 1760 . . . . 17.50

24 10 (Conv. kreuzer). Head in wreath. Rev. 120 EINE etc. Arms. 1769 . . . . 17.50

25 20 (kreuzer). Bust l. Rev. PIE-TATE etc. Arms. 1760 . . . . . . 24.00

26 20 (kreuzer). Bust in wreath. Rev. PIETATE etc. Arms. 1766 . . . . 24.00

27 20 (Conv. kreuzer). Like No. 24 but LX ST. etc. 1769 . . 24.00

II. Groschen Standard.

★29 24/EINEN (=1/24) /REICHS/ THALER. 1759-60 . . . . 8.00

29a 1/GROSCHEN. 1760 . . . . . . 19.50

31 24 (=1/24 Reichsthaler). Saxon arms. Rev. LAND MUNZ, 24 in orb. 1760 . . . . 12.50

32 24/EINEN/REICHS/THALER. Cwn. F/H.H.S.M. Rev. value. 1760, 64 . . . . 13.00

34 (groschen). Head. Rev. IN MEM./NATAL./FRIDERICI/ PRINC.HERAED/SAXON. 1763 R.N. On birth of heir 29.00

GERMAN STATES

SAXE-HILDBURGHAUSEN (Cont.)

VG-F

★36 12/EINEN (=1/12) /REICHS/ THALER. 1758, 60........14.50

38 XII EINEN REICHS THALER. Bust r. or l. Rev. Arms. 1759................14.50

40 VI/EINEN/REICHS/ THALER. EFC mon. Rev. value. 1758 ....15.00

41 VI/EINEN/REICHS/ THALER. Bust. Rev. value. 1758......................15.00

42 1/6 (Reichsthaler). Bust. Rev. Arms. 1758...........28.50

Silver

V.F.

44 1/3 *(Reichsthaler)*. 1760......40.00

46 2/3 (Reichsthaler). Bust. Rev. Arms supported by wildmen. 1758.............65.00

46a —. Rev. oval arms. 1758 ...75.00

47 2/3 (Reichsthaler). Armored bust. Rev. PIETATE etc. knight std. 1759...........75.00

48 2/3 (Reichsthaler). Draped bust. Rev. ZWANZIG etc. knight std. 1760...........55.00

50 ZEHEN etc. (= Conv. thaler). Like No. 48. 1760..........90.00

51 ZEHEN etc. (= Conv. thaler). Head. Rev. Arms. 1763. (On Peace of Hubertusburg)185.00

52 ZEHEN etc. (= Conv. thaler). Head. Rev. lion holds arms. 1769....................190.00

Gold

54 *(ducat)*. Bust. Rev. Arms. 1771..................1100.00

Joseph Friedrich, Prince Regent 1780-84 (Joint Regent 1784-87)

Copper

VG-F

55 1/—/HELLER. Like No. 3a. 1781, 84. Klippe........... 5.50

Billon or Silver

56 I CONVENTIONS KREUZER. Cwnd. IF mon. between H–H. *Rev. value*. 1781 .... 7.75

58 2½ (Conv. kreuzer). H.H.Z.S. H.H. etc. Cwnd. IF mon. Rev. 48/CONVENT/THALER. 1781....................12.50

VG-F

60 20 (kreuzer). V.G.G. IOSEPH FR. H.Z.S. etc. Bust. Rev. LX EINE etc. Arms. 1781.......20.00

V.F.

62 ZEHEN EINE etc. (= Conv. thaler). Bust. Rev. knight stdg. 1781...............350.00

63 X EINE etc. (= Conv. thaler). Nude bust. Rev. knight stdg. N.D....................175.00

Friedrich, Under Regency 1780-84, Joint Regent 1784-87, Alone 1787-1826, Thereafter Duke of Saxe-Altenburg

Copper

65 1/—/HELLER. Like No. 3a. 1787-88. Klippe............ 6.00

65a —. Round. Date on Rev. 1788, 1804-06 (var.)........ 4.00

★66 1/Heller. 1808-18.......... 1.75

★67 1/HELLER. 1820-25....... 1.75

67a Rev. 1/8/KREUZER. 1825.. 3.50

68 II/H(eller). Script F. Rev. II/H.H./S.M. 1791...... 4.00

69 I/PFENNIG. H.S.H.HAUESI. S.M. Saxon arms. Rev. value. 1823-26.................. 2.50

69.5 1/PFENNIG. H.S.H.H. Saxon arms. Rev. value. 1826 .....*10.00*

70 1/4/KREUZER. Cwnd. F. Rev. value. 1825 .... 1.75

71 1/4/KREUZER. H.S.H.H. Saxon arms. Rev. value. 1825 ..... 1.75

72 1/2/KREUZER. Like No. 66. 1808-09.................. 3.00

73 1/2/KREUZER. HERZOGTHUM HILDBURG etc. Arms. Rev. value/L.M. 1823 (var.)...... 3.75

73a —. Rev. KREUZER LAND MUNZE, 1/2. 1823........... 3.75

Billon

74 1 KREUZER. H–H over Saxon arms. Rev. I/KREUZER/LAND/ MUNTZ. 1784-1811.......... 5.00

78 1/48 (Reichsthaler). Saxon arms. Rev. H.S.H.S.M., 1/48. 1788.................... 6.00

VG-F

★79 48/EINEN (=1/48) /THALER. 1788.................... 6.00

81 *1/GROSCHEN*. Arms. Rev. value. 1788 .... 7.25

82 *1/GROSCHEN*. Cwnd. F. Rev. value. 1790 .... 7.50

83 3/KREUZER. Like No. 86. 1808-20.................. 8.00

★86 6/KREUZER. 1808-18.....10.00

88 6/KREUZER. Cwnd. script F in branches. Rev. H.S.H.H., value. 1820-25.............10.00

93 *20 (kreuzer)*. Head. Rev. Arms. 1796...............*(Fine)* 40.00

SAXE-MEININGEN

(Also known as SAXE-COBURG-MEININGEN 1735-1826.)

In Thuringia (included much of Henneberg). Founded by Bernhard III, 3rd son of Ernst the Pious. Acquired Hildburghausen 1826 in exchange for its portion of Coburg.

Anton Ulrich 1746-63

Copper

VG-F

1 I/—/HELLER. Saxon arms. Rev. I/MEINING/HELLER/ date. 1755-61............. 6.50

2 1/HELLER. Like No. 5. 1761.................... 6.50

★3 I/—/HELLER. Hen r. or l. For Henneberg. 1761-62.... 7.00

4 2/—/HELLER. Like No. 1. 1761....................12.00

★5 3/HELLER. AV mon. 1761.. 7.00

Charlotte Amalia of Hesse, Regent 1763-75

Copper

8 1/—/HELLER. Like No. 3. 1768................. 7.50

9 1/—/HELLER. Like No. 1. 1769................... 5.50

SAXE-MEININGEN (Cont.)

Billon

VG-F

11 I/—/CONVENT(ion)/
KREUZER. CHARL:AMA:D.G.
D.S. TVTRIX. REGENS. Arms.
Rev. I/S. MEINING/etc.
1765 . . . . 12.50

11a —. Rev. I/S. COB. MEIN./etc.
1771 . . . . 12.50

13 5 K(reuzer). V.G.G. CARL
AMALIA etc. Arms. Rev.
SACHSEN COB. MEINING. etc.
IVSTIRT/240/etc. 1765 . . . . . . 23.00

Carl, Under Regency 1763-75, Alone 1775-82

Billon

15 I/—/CONVENT(ion)/
KREUZER. Arms btwn. SC-M.
Rev. I/S. COB.MEIN./value.
1781 . . . . 13.00

Gold

V.F.

16 *(ducat).* C(arl &) L(ouise) mon.
Rev. legend. Wedding.
1780 . . . . 1350.00

16.5 *(2 ducats).* 2 shields. Rev.
legend. Wedding. 1780 . . . . 2200.00

Georg I 1782-1803

Billon

*17 I/KREVZER. 1786-94 . . . . . 6.50

18 1/—/CONVENT(ion)/
KREUZER. Like No. 15.
1794 . . . . 8.50

Silver

V.F.

19 X EINE etc. (=Conv. thaler).
GEORG etc. His bust. Rev.
LOUISE ELEANORE etc. His
wife's bust. N.D. (on his
death 1803) 300.00

Bernhard Erich Freund, Under Regency of his Mother, Louise Eleanore v. Hohenlohe, 1803-21

Copper

Fine

21 1/HELLER. Like No. 25.
1814 (var.) 3.50

22 ¼ KREUZER. Obv. like
No. 25. Rev. like No. 33.
1812-18 . . . . 3.50

23 1/PFENNIG. Like No. 25.
1818 . . . . 5.50

Fine

24 ½ KREUZER. Like No. 22.
1812-18 . . . . 3.50

*25 1/KREUZER. 1814, 18 . . . . . 3.00

Billon

26 1/KREUZER. H.S.C.M. Arms.
Rev. value. 1808, 12 . . . . 5.00

27 3 (kreuzer). S.COB. MEIN. Arms.
Rev. 480 EINE etc., 3 in wreath.
1808, 12-13 . . . . 9.00

28 6 (kreuzer). Like No. 27 but
240 etc. 1808, 12-13 . . . . 10.00

Silver

29 20/KREUZER. Bust of Louise
Eleanore. Rev. value. 1812 . . RRR

Bernhard Erich Freund, Alone 1821-66

Acquired Hildburghausen and Saalfeld
in exchange for his part of Coburg during the 1826 reshuffle.

Copper

30 ⅛ KREUZER. Like No. 33.
1828 . . . . 2.75

31 ¼ KREUZER. Like No. 22.
1823 . . . . 4.00

*33 ¼ KREUZER. 1828-32 . . . . 2.50

33a —. MEININGEN. 1829 . . . . 7.50

34 1/PFENNIG. Obv. like No. 33.
Rev. like No. 25. 1832-
35 (var.) 2.50

*35 1/PFENNIG. 1839, 42 . . . . . 2.00

36 ¼/KREUZER. Like No. 42.
1854 . . . . 2.50

37 1/PFENNIG. Sim.
1860-66 . . . . 1.50

38 ½ KREUZER. Like No. 33.
1828-32 . . . . 2.00

39 2/PFENNIG. Like No. 34.
1832-35 . . . . 2.00

40 2/PFENNIGE. Like No. 35.
1839, 42 . . . . 1.75

41 ½/KREUZER. Like No. 42.
1854 . . . . 1.75

Fine

*42 2/PFENNIGE. 1860-66 . . . . 1.00

43 1/KREUZER. Like No. 34.
1828-30 (var.) 2.50

43a —. HERZOG. 1831-35 . . . . 2.00

44 1/KREUZER. Like No. 35.
1842 . . . . 2.25

45 1/KREUZER. Like No. 42 but
w/out SCHEIDEMÜNZE.
1854 . . . . 2.50

Billon

47 1/KREUZER. Like No. 54.
1828-30 . . . . 3.50

48 1/KREUZER. Arms btwn.
branches. Rev. value. 1831-
37 . . . . 3.00

49 1/KREUZER. HERZOGTH.—
S.MEINING. Arms. Rev. value.
1839 . . . . 3.00

*50 1/KREUZER. 1864, 66 . . . . . 3.25

51 3/KREUZER. Like No. 54.
1827-30 . . . . 5.00

52 3/KREUZER. Like No. 48.
1831-37 . . . . 4.00

53 3/KREUZER. Like No. 49.
1840 . . . . 5.00

*54 6/KREUZER. 1827-30 . . . . . 6.00

55 6/KREUZER. Like No. 48.
1831-37 . . . . 4.00

56 6/KREUZER. Like No. 49.
1840 . . . . 5.00

Silver

F-VF

57 ½/GULDEN. Head.
Rev. value. 1838-41 . . . . 15.00

57a —. 1843, 46 . . . . 15.00

57b —. 1854 . . . . 18.00

V.F.

58 ZWANZIG EINE etc. (=½
Conv. thaler =gulden from
Saalfeld mines). Head. Rev.
SEGEN DES/etc. 1829 . . . . . . 200.00

GERMAN STATES

SAXE-MEININGEN (Cont.)

V.F.

★59 EIN (=1) GULDEN. Head.
Rev. date/cwn. 1830-33.....90.00

★59a —. 1835-37..............85.00

60 1/GULDEN. Like No. 57.
1838-41...............35.00

60a —. 1843, 46..............30.00

60b —. 1854................35.00

★61 EIN (=1) VEREINSTHALER.
1859-66................40.00

62 ZWEY (=2) GULDEN. Head.
Rev. Arms. 1854..........60.00

63 2/THALER. Head. Rev.
value. 1841.............400.00

64 2 THALER. Head. Rev.
Arms. 1843, 46..........300.00

64a —. 1853-54.............300.00

Georg II 1866-1914

Copper

F-VF

65 1/PFENNIG. Like No. 42.
1867-68.................1.00

---

66 2/PFENNIGE. Sim.

F-VF

1867-70................1.00

Silver

V.F.

67 EIN (=1) VEREINSTHALER.
Head. Rev. Arms. 1867....100.00

SAXE-WEIMAR-EISENACH
(SAX. VINAR. ISENAC.)

In Thuringia. Ruling line descended
from Wilhelm IV of Middle-Weimar,
an older brother of Ernst the Pious,
ancestor of the other Saxon ducal families.

Ernst August II
Constantin 1748-58

Under regency 1748-55. Franz Josias
of Saxe-Coburg-Saalfeld, regent in Weimar 1749-55. Friedrich III of Saxe-
Gotha-Altenburg, regent in Eisenach
1749-55 (see Saxe-Eisenach).

**I. Weimar under regency of Franz
Josias 1749-55.**

Copper

VG-F

★1 I/HELLER. FIDS mon. 1750-
54....................2.75

2 I/PFENNIG. FIDS mon.
Rev. value/F.S. WEIMAR/etc.
1750-54................2.75

2a —. Rev. value/F.S.W. OBERV./
etc. 1755...............2.75

3 1½/PFENNIG. Like No. 2.
1750...................3.50

4 II/PFENNIG. Sim. 1750,
52....................3.00

Billon

5 3 (pfennig). F.S.W.O.–V.L.M.
FI in shield. Rev. 3 in orb.
1751, 53................6.00

6 VI (pfennig). Sim. 1752, 54..6.00

7 24/EINEN (=¹⁄₂₄)/REICHS/
THALER. FVRSTL. S. WEIMAR
etc. Rev. NACH CHUR etc.,
value. 1751, 53...........8.00

8 12/EINEN (=¹⁄₁₂)/REICHS/
THALER. Sim. 1753.......12.00

**II. Ernst August II Constantin,
alone 1755-58.**

Copper

★9 1/HELLER. EAC mon. 1756-
58 (var.)...............2.00

VG-F

10 1/PFENNIG. Sim. 1756-
57....................2.00

11 1/GUTER/PFENNIG. Sim.
1756-57................2.50

11a —. Obv. FDS mon. Mule with
Eisenach coin. 1757.......15.00

12 II/PFENNIG. Like No. 9.
1756-57................3.00

13 II/GUTE/PFENNIG. Sim.
1756-57................3.00

Billon

14 3 (pfennig). EAC mon. Rev.
F.S.W.V.E.L.M., 3 in orb. 1756-
58....................6.00

15 VI (pfennig). Sim. 1756-58..6.50

★16 24 (=¹⁄₂₄ Reichsthaler).
1756-57................9.50

Silver

Fine

18 ⅙ (Reichsthaler). EAC mon.
Rev. Arms. 1756..........32.00

19 ⅓ (Reichsthaler). EAC mon.
in shield. Rev. FURSTL. S.
WEIMAR etc. Arms. 1756....45.00

V.F.

21 ⅔ (Reichsthaler). Like No.
19. 1756...............110.00

23 ⅔ (Reichsthaler). ERN. AVG.
CONSTANTIN etc. Bust. Rev.
IVSTITIA etc. Arms. 1757...135.00

25 (Speciesthaler). Bust. Rev.
Arms. 1756 R.N. (on edge).
On his entry into rule....220.00

Gold (ducat = 3.49 gr.)

27 (ducat). Bust. Rev. LAETISSIMVS
etc. Eisenach city view.
Homage of Eisenach.
1756..................1450.00

28 (ducat). EAC mon. Rev.
Hilaritas stdg. Entry into rule.
1756..................1100.00

29 (ducat). Bust. Rev. Hilaritas.
1756..................1100.00

30 5 THALER. Bust. Rev. Arms,
value. N.D.............1750.00

Anna Amalia of Brunswick,
Regent 1758-75
For Her Son, Carl August

Copper

VG-F

31 1/HELLER. Saxon arms.
Rev. value/F.S.W.U.E./L.M./
1760..................2.25

32 1/GUTER PFEN(nig). Sim.
1761-62................2.50

33 2/GUTE.PFEN(nig). Sim.
1760..................2.50

GERMAN STATES

SAXE-WEIMAR EISENACH
(Cont.)

★34 3/GVTE PFEN(nig). Sim.
1760-62................ 4.25

Billon

35 3 (pfennig) Saxon arms.
Rev. 3 in orb /F.S. 1760..... 4.00

★36 3 (pfennig). 1763-64....... 2.75

37 VI (pfennig). ADS mon.
Rev. as No. 36 but VI in orb.
1759-60................ 6.00

38 VI (pfennig). Like No. 35.
1760................... 6.00

39 VI (pfennig). Like No. 36.
1763-64............... 6.00

40 24/EINEN (=1/24)/THALER.
F.S.W.V.E.O.V.M. A script and
Saxon arms. Rev. CCCXX etc.,
value. 1763-64............ 6.50

41 12/EINEN (=1/12)/THALER.
Sim. but CLX etc. 1763-64... 6.75

Silver

F-VF

42 1/6 (Reichsthaler). AADS script
mon. Rev. F.S.W.U.E. etc.
Saxon arms. 1763......... 17.50

42a —. Rev. 4 fold arms with
Saxon centershield. 1763-64..17.50

★43 1/3 (Reichsthaler).
1763-65................35.00

V.F.

45 2/3 (Reichsthaler =) 60X
(kreuzer). AADS script mon.,
F.S.W.U.E. etc. Rev. Arms.
1760...................60.00

46 2/3 (Reichsthaler). Bust. Rev. Saxon
arms. 1763...............60.00

V.F.

★46a —. Rev. manifold arms.
1763-65................55.00

49 EIN (=1) REICHSTHALER/
(=) 90X (kreuzer). Like No.
45 but F.S.W.U.E. etc. on Rev.
1760...................750.00

50 10 EINE etc. (= Conv. thaler).
Like No. 46a. 1763-65.....135.00

Gold (ducat = 3.49 gr.)

52 *(ducat)*. Bust. Rev. Arms.
1764...................1450.00

53 5 TH(aler). Bust. Rev. Arms.
1764...................1750.00

Carl August 1758-1828, Alone 1775-1828
(Grand Duke 1815-28)

Copper

Fine

55 1/HELLER. Like No. 57
1790-1813 (var.).......... 4.50

56 1/PFENNIG. Sim. 1790-
1813 (var.)................ 2.75

★57 1½/PFENNIG. 1799, 1807.. 4.25

58 2/PFENNIGE. Sim. 1790-
1813................... 3.75

59 3/PFENNIGE. Sim. 1791-
1807 (var.).............. 4.00

60 4/PFENNIGE. Sim. 1810-
13.................... 5.50

★61 1/PFENNIG. 1821-26...... 1.75

Fine

62 1½/PFENNIG. Sim. 1824.. 2.50

63 2/PFENNIGE. Sim. 1821,
26..................... 2.50

64 3/PFENNIGE. Sim. 1824... 3.00

65 4/PFENNIGE. Sim. 1821,
26..................... 4.00

Billon

66 VI (pfennig). Saxon arms.
Rev. S.W.U.-E., VI. 1790..... 9.00

67 48/EINEN (=1/48)/THALER.
Like No. 57. 1794-1814..... 6.50

68 48/EINEN/THALER. Sim.
but G.H.S.W.E. 1815........ 6.00

69 48/EINEN/THALER. Like
No. 61. 1821-26........... 4.00

70 24/EINEN (=1/24)/THALER.
Like No. 57. 1794-1814..... 6.50

71 24/EINEN/THALER. Like
No. 68. 1815............. 9.00

72 24/EINEN/THALER. Like
No. 61. 1821-26........... 4.00

72a —. ENIEN. 1821.........10.00

Silver

V.F.

74 XX/EINE etc. (=½ Conv.
thaler). CARL AUGUST H.Z.S.
WEIMAR etc. Arms. Rev. value.
1813...................75.00

75 X/EINE etc. (= Conv. thaler).
Sim. 1813...............175.00

76 10 EINE etc. (= Conv. thaler).
GROSHERZOGTHUM SACHSEN.
Arms. Rev. DEM/VATERLANDE/
1815...................300.00

Carl Friedrich 1828-53

Copper

Fine

77 1/PFENNIG. Like No. 61.
1830................... 2.00

78 1½/PFENNIG. Sim. 1830.. 2.50

79 2/PFENNIGE. Sim. 1830 .. 2.50

80 3/PFENNIGE. Sim. 1830... 2.75

81 1/PFENNIG. Like No. 91.
1840-51................. 1.00

82 3/PFENNIGE. Sim. 1840.. 3.00

Billon

83 48/EINEN (=1/48)/THALER.
Like No. 61. 1831.......... 4.00

84 24/EINEN (=1/24)/THALER.
Sim. 1830............... 4.00

85 ½/SILBER/GROSCHEN.
Like No. 91. 1840......... 3.50

86 1/SILBER/GROSCHEN.
Sim. 1840............... 3.00

Silver

V.F.

87 EIN (=1) THALER. Head.
Rev. Arms. 1841..........45.00

88 2 THALER. Head. Rev. Arms.
1840-48.................225.00

GERGERMAN STATES

SAXE-WEIMAR-EISENACH
(Cont.)

Carl Alexander 1853-1901

Copper

F-VF

89 1/PFENNIG. Like No. 91.
1858, 65 . . . . 1.00

90 2/PFENNIGE. Sim.
1858, 65 . . . . 1.75

Billon

★91 ½/SILBER/GROSCHEN.
GROSSHERZOGTH. SACHSEN W.E.
1858 . . . . 3.00

92 1/SILBER/GROSCHEN.
Sim. 1858 . . . . 4.00

Silver

V.F.

93 EIN (=1) VEREINSTHALER.
Head. Rev. arms. 1858-70 . . . 45.00

94 2 THALER. Head. Rev.
Arms. 1855 . . . . 350.00

SAXONY (SACHSEN)
Electoral Duchy Until 1806,
Kingdom 1806-1918

At the time of the Reformation, Saxony, in S.E. Germany, was one of the more powerful states in Central Europe. Ravaged in the religious wars of the 17th century, it was further drained by the cost of supporting two successive dukes, Friedrich August I and Friedrich August II, as kings of Poland.

The Polish connection terminated in 1763, but was renewed again when King Friedrich August I became grand duke of Warsaw as Napoleon's ally.

Saxony was forced to cede half its territory to Prussia at the Congress of Vienna 1815.

See POLAND for other coins of the Saxon rulers 1733-63 and 1807-15.

Arms:

Saxony: Barry of 10, black and gold, with green crown opened diagonally across it.

Electoral Saxony: Per pale.

　Dexter: Crossed swords on a field divided black and silver per fesse;

　Sinister: Saxony.

Mint marks:

　　B – Dresden, Prussian occupation. 1756-59.

　　B – Dresden. 1861-72.
　　C – Dresden. 1779-1804.
E.C., E.D.C. – Leipzig. 1753-63.
　　　　　　Dresden. 1764-78.
　　F – Dresden. 1845-58.
F.W.oF – Dresden. 1734-63.
　　G – Dresden. 1833-44.
　　H – Dresden. 1804-12.
　I.C. – Dresden. 1779-1804.
I.D.B. – Dresden, Prussian occupation. 1756-59.
I.E.C. – Dresden. 1779-1804.
I.F.oF – Leipzig. 1763-65.
I.G.G. – Leipzig. 1752.
I.G.S. – Dresden. 1716-34.
I.G.S. – Dresden. 1813-32.
　　L – Leipzig. 1761-62.
　　S – Dresden. 1813-32.
S.G.H. – Dresden. 1804-12.

Friedrich August II 1733-63

(King of Poland as August III 1733-63. See that country for his coins with that title.)

Billon

VG-F

★1 pf (=1 pfennig). 1734-56 . . . . 2.50

2 3 (pfennig). Sim. 1734-55 . . . 2.50

2a —. Rev. 3 in cartouche.
1763 . . . . 4.25

3 3/PFENNIG. c(hur) s(achsen)/
SCHEID/MUNTZ. Rev. value,
date. 1761-62 . . . . 2.50

4 48/EINEN (=1/48)/THAL(er).
Obv. like No. 1. Rev. value.
1734 . . . . 4.75

4a —. THALER. 1734-56,
61, 63 . . . . 3.00

4b —. 1757B 6.00

5 48/EINEN/THALER.
AR mon. Rev. value. 1753 . . . 4.00

6 VI/PFENNIG. Like No. 3.
1761-62 . . . . 2.75

7 24/EINEN (=1/24)/THAL(er).
Like No. 7a. 1734 . . . . 5.00

★7a —. THALER. 1734-56.
F.W.oF 4.25

VG-F

7b —. Obv. legend ends & VIC.
1745. Vicariat 12.00

7c —. 1756-57. I.D.B 5.00

7d —. Rev. CCCXX etc., value.
1763 . . . . 4.75

★8 1 gl (=1 groschen). 1740.
Vicariat 7.00

9 1 gl (=1 groschen). Like
No. 73. 1741-42. Vicariat . . . 7.00

11 24/EINEN/THALER.
Like No. 5. 1753 . . . . 6.75

12 24/EINEN/THAL(er).
Like No. 12a. 1753-54 . . . . . . 4.50

★12a —. THALER. 1753-62
(var.) 4.50

13 I/GROSCHEN. Like No. 3.
1762 . . . . 4.50

Silver

14 12/EINEN (=1/12)/THALER.
Like No. 7a. 1734-55, 62 . . . . 6.00

14a —. Obv. legend ends & VICARIVS.
1745. Vicariat 18.00

15 (2 groschen). 8 lines: CAROLI/
UTRIUSQUE/etc. . . ./1738 R.N.
Rev. CORONAM etc. Arm from
clouds, altar, 2 hearts. On
marriage of Princess Maria
Amalia to King Carlo of
Naples 18.00

16 2 gl (=2 groschen). Like No.
73. Vicariat. 1741-42 . . . . . . 17.50

18 (2 groschen). 8 lines: LUDOVICI/
DELPHINI/etc. . . ./1747 R.N.
Rev. AMOR MUTUUS. 2 hearts,
arms of France and Poland-
Saxony. On marriage of Princess
Maria Josepha with the Dauphin of France 18.00

★19 (2 groschen). Marriage of
Prince Friedrich Christian.
1747 R.N. 18.00

20 XII/EINEN/THALER.
Bust. Rev. value. 1762 . . . . . 10.00

GERMAN STATES

SAXONY (Cont.)

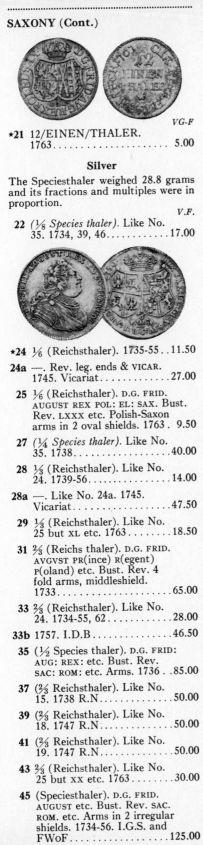

VG-F

★21 12/EINEN/THALER. 1763 .... 5.00

Silver

The Speciesthaler weighed 28.8 grams and its fractions and multiples were in proportion.

V.F.

22 (⅛ *Species thaler*). Like No. 35. 1734, 39, 46 .... 17.00

★24 ⅙ (Reichsthaler). 1735-55 .. 11.50

24a —. Rev. leg. ends & VICAR. 1745. Vicariat 27.00

25 ⅙ (Reichsthaler). D.G. FRID. AUGUST REX POL: EL: SAX. Bust. Rev. LXXX etc. Polish-Saxon arms in 2 oval shields. 1763 . 9.50

27 (¼ *Species thaler*). Like No. 35. 1738 .... 40.00

28 ⅓ (Reichsthaler). Like No. 24. 1739-56 .... 14.00

28a —. Like No. 24a. 1745. Vicariat 47.50

29 ⅓ (Reichsthaler). Like No. 25 but XL etc. 1763 .... 18.50

31 ⅔ (Reichs thaler). D.G. FRID. AVGVST PR(ince) R(egent) P(oland) etc. Bust. Rev. 4 fold arms, middleshield. 1733 .... 65.00

33 ⅔ (Reichsthaler). Like No. 24. 1734-55, 62 .... 28.00

33b 1757. I.D.B 46.50

35 (½ Species thaler). D.G. FRID: AUG: REX: etc. Bust. Rev. SAC: ROM: etc. Arms. 1736 . . 85.00

37 (⅔ Reichsthaler). Like No. 15. 1738 R.N 50.00

39 (⅔ Reichsthaler). Like No. 18. 1747 R.N 50.00

41 (⅔ Reichsthaler). Like No. 19. 1747 R.N 50.00

43 ⅔ (Reichsthaler). Like No. 25 but XX etc. 1763 .... 30.00

45 (Speciesthaler). D.G. FRID. AUGUST etc. Bust. Rev. SAC. ROM. etc. Arms in 2 irregular shields. 1734-56. I.G.S. and FWoF 125.00

V.F.

45a Rev. leg. ends. VICARIUS. 1745. Vicariat 170.00

45b —. 1757. I.D.B 90.00

46 (shooting thaler). Cwnd. A double R mon. Rev. VNA–META–OMNI–BVS, cwnd. A's, target. Klippe. 1740 .... (*E.F.*) 240.00

47 (Species thaler). Like No. 8. 1740, 45. Vicariat 165.00

48 (Species thaler). Like No. 73. 1741. Vicariat 135.00

49 (Mining Species thaler). Like No. 45 but DER SEEGEN etc. 1756-62. F.W.oF 180.00

49a —. 1757. I.D.B 260.00

50 X EINE etc. (= Conv. thaler). Like No. 45. 1763 .... 50.00

E.F.

51 2 TH(aler) COUR(ant). Bust of FA II. Rev. MEMORIAE etc. Monument to FA I. 1733 R.N 475.00

53 (2 Speciesthaler). No. 45 double thick. 1736-37 ...... 550.00

54 (2 Species thaler). No. 47 double thick. 1740 .... 600.00

Gold (ducat = 3.49 gr.)

V.F.

57 ¼ (*ducat*). Like No. 61. 1734. I.G.S 450.00

57a —. 1735-43. F.W.oF 400.00

59 ½ (*ducat*). Sim. 1735-43, 56. F.W.oF 400.00

61 (ducat). D.G. FRID. AUGUST etc. Bust. Rev. SAC. ROM etc. Arms. 1734 .... 1100.00

61a —. 1735-63. F.W.oF 850.00

61b —. 1745. F.W.oF. on the Vicariat 1000.00

61c —. 1757. I.D.B 850.00

63 (ducat). Like No. 15. 1738 R.N 950.00

64 (ducat). Like No. 8. 1740. Vicariat 1000.00

65 (ducat). Like No. 73. 1741, 42. Vicariat 800.00

66 (ducat). Elector on horseback. Rev. DECUS etc., flying eagle. 1745 R.N 800.00

67 (ducat). Like No. 19. 1747 R.N 1000.00

68 (*2 ducats*). Cwn. Rev. legend. On 1734 Coronation 2200.00

69 (*2 ducats*). Like No. 61a. 1735-39. F.W.oF 1850.00

71 (*3 ducats*). 1738. F.W.oF .... RRR

72 (*4 ducats*). 1738. F.W.oF .... RRR

V.F.

★73 (5 ducats). 1742. Vicariat ... RRR

Friedrich Christian, Elector Oct. 5-Dec. 7, 1763

Billon

Fine

75 24/EINEN (= 1/24)/THALER. Like No. 76. 1763 .... 3.75

★76 12/EINEN (= 1/12)/THALER. 1763 .... 6.00

Silver

V.F.

77 XX EINE etc. (= ½ Conv. thaler). Bust. Rev. Arms. 1763 .... 50.00

78 X EINE etc. (= Conv. thaler). Sim. 1763 .... 65.00

Gold

79 (ducat). Sim. 1763 .... 900.00

Xaver, Prince Regent 1763-68 for Friedrich August III

Billon

Fine

★80 24/EINEN (= 1/24)/THALER. 1764-68 .... 6.00

81 12/EINEN (= 1/12)/THALER. Sim. 1764-68 .... 8.00

Silver

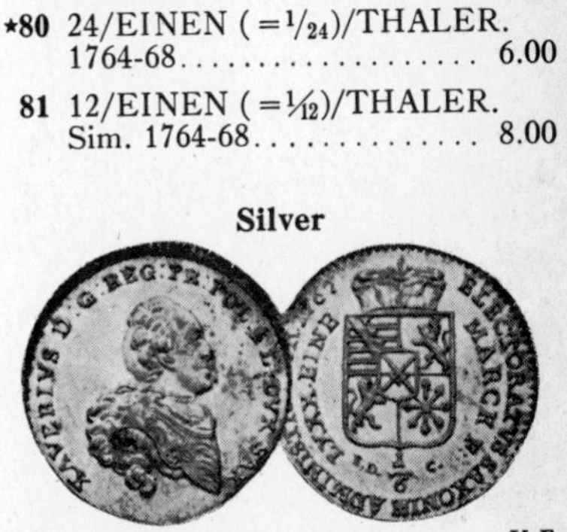

V.F.

★82 ⅙ (Reichsthaler). 1764-67 . . 15.00

GERMAN STATES

SAXONY (Cont.)

V.F.

83 ⅓ (Reichsthaler). Sim. 1764-66 .... 24.00

84 ⅔ (Reichsthaler). Sim. 1764-68 .... 35.00

85 X EINE etc. (= Conv. thaler). Sim. 1764-68 .... 60.00

86 X EINE etc. (= Conv. thaler). Bust. Rev. ZUR ERMUNTERUNG etc. Mining scene. Foundation of Freiberg Mining Academy. 1765 .... (*E.F.*) 700.00

Gold

87 (ducat). Like No. 82. 1766-68 .... 800.00

Friedrich August III 1763-1827

I. As Elector 1763-1806.

Copper

VG-F

***90** I/HELLER. 1778-1806 .... 2.00

91 I/PFENNIG. Sim. 1772-1806 (var.) 2.25

***92** III/PFENNIGE. Sim. 1799-1806 .... 2.75

Billon

93 I/PFENNIG. Sim. 1764 .... 8.50

93a —. 1765 .... 2.75

94 III/PFENNIG. Arms in irregular shield, no branches. Rev. value. 1764 .... 5.00

95 III/PFENNIG. Like No. 90. 1765-93 .... 2.50

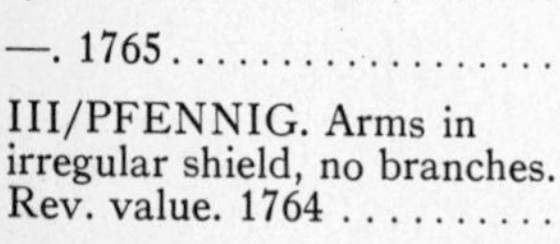

***96** 1/KREUZER for Henneberg. 1765, 80 .... (*Fine*) 8.50

97 48/EINEN (=1/48)/THALER. Like No. 90. 1764-1806 .... 3.00

VG-F

***98** 24/EINEN (=1/24)/THALER. 1764-1806 .... 4.00

99 5 KR(euzer). FA script mon. in rhombus. Rev. IVSTIRT/240 etc. For Henneberg. 1765 .... (*Fine*) 24.00

***100** 12/EINEN (=1/12)/THALER. 1764-1801 .... 4.00

Silver

V.F.

***102** CLX EINE etc. (=2 groschen). Vicariat. 1790 .... 8.50

104 CLX EINE etc. (=2 groschen). Bust. Rev. Imp. eagle. Vicariat. 1792 .... 8.50

***106** LXXX EINE etc. (=⅙ Reichsthaler). 1764-68 .... 12.00

108 LXXX EINE etc. (=⅙ Reichsthaler). Like No. 113. 1803-05 .... 12.00

110 XL EINE etc. (=⅓ Reichsthaler). Like No. 106. 1764, 67 .... 17.50

111 ⅓ (Reichsthaler). Sim. but older head. 1780-90 .... 17.50

112 ⅓ (Reichsthaler). Like No. 102. Vicariat. 1790 .... 18.00

***113** ⅓ (Reichsthaler). 1791-1802 .... 17.50

V.F.

114 ⅓ (Reichsthaler). Like No. 104. Vicariat. 1792 .... 22.50

116 XX EINE etc. (=⅔ Reichsthaler). Like No. 106. 1764 .... 24.00

117 ⅔ (Reichsthaler). Young bust. Rev. 2 oval shields. 1765-68 .... 19.50

118 ⅔ (Reichsthaler). Head. Rev. as last. 1769-86 .... 27.50

120 ⅔ (Reichsthaler). Like No. 102. Vicariat. 1790 .... 25.00

121 ⅔ (Reichsthaler). Like No. 113. 1791-1806 .... 19.50

122 ⅔ (Reichsthaler). Like No. 104. Vicariat. 1792 .... 21.50

124 X EINE etc. (= Conv. thaler). Like No. 106. 1764 .... 55.00

125 X EINE etc. (=mining Conv. thaler). Sim. but D. SEEGEN etc. 1763-64 .... 120.00

126 X EINE etc. (= Conv. thaler). Like No. 106 but young bust. 1765-68 .... 30.00

127 X EINE etc. (= mining Conv. thaler). Sim. but DER SEEGEN etc. 1765-68 .... 55.00

E.F.

128 X EINE etc. (= Conv. thaler). Like No. 126 but ZUR BELOHNUNG etc. 1765 .... 250.00

129 X EINE etc. (= Conv. thaler). Head of FA III. Rev. of No. 86. 1765 .... 300.00

130 (Conv. thaler). Bust of FA III. Rev. bust of Xaver/ZUR BELOHNUNG etc. 1766 .... 300.00

130a —. Head of FA III. 1766 .... 500.00

V.F.

131 X EINE etc. (= Conv. thaler). Like No. 111. 1769-90 (var.) 27.50

132 X EINE etc. (= mining Conv. thaler). Sim. but DER SEEGEN etc. 1769-90 .... 45.00

133 X EINE etc. (= Conv. thaler). Head. Rev. ZUR BELOHNUNG etc. Wreath, beehive, etc. 1780 .... (*E.F.*) 300.00

134 X EINE etc. (= Conv. thaler). Like No. 102. Vicariat. 1790 .... 85.00

135 X EINE etc. (= Conv. thaler). Like No. 113. 1791-1806 .... 32.00

136 X EINE etc. (=mining Conv. thaler). Sim. but DER SEEGEN etc. 1791-1806 .... 80.00

137 X EINE etc. (= Conv. thaler). Like No. 104. Vicariat. 1792 .... 110.00

E.F.

138 V EINE etc. (=2 Conv. thaler). Like No. 128. 1765 .... 400.00

139 (2 Conv. thaler). No. 130 double thick. 1766 .... 600.00

SAXONY (Cont.)

E.F.

140 V EINE etc. (=2 Conv.
thaler). Like No. 133.
1780.................550.00

Gold (ducat=3.49 gr.)

V.F.

141 I/PFENNIG (=¼ ducat).
No. 93a in gold. 1765.....475.00

142 (ducat). Young head.
Rev. Arms. 1764-90......750.00

145 (ducat). Bust. Rev. Arms.
1791-1806..............800.00

146 (ducat). Like No. 104.
Vicariat. 1792.........850.00

148 5 THALER. Like No. 154.
1777-82................950.00

150 5 THALER. Bust. Rev. Arms.
1802, 06...............950.00

152 10 THALER. Like No. 154
but armored bust. 1777-
78....................1250.00

★154 10 THALER. 1779-90...1250.00

156 10 THALER. Like No. 150.
1791-1806.............1100.00

II. Friedrich August 1763-1827, as King Friedrich August I 1806-27.

See POLAND for other coins of this reign.

Copper

Fine

★157 I/HELLER. 1813........ 2.25

158 I/PFENNIG. Sim. but
pearl borders both sides.
1807...................2.00

158a —. Trefoil border on obv.
1808...................1.50

158b —. Like No. 157. 1811-22.. 1.50

159 1/PFENNIG. Like No. 161.
1825...................3.50

160 III/PFENNIGE. Like No.
157. 1807-23...........3.00

Fine

★161 3/PFENNIGE. 1825...... 3.00

162 4/PFENNIGE. Like No.
157. 1808-10........... 3.00

Billon

163 48/EINEN (=1/48)/THALER.
Like No. 157. 1806-15..... 4.00

164 ACHT (=8)/PFENNIGE.
Sim. 1808 (pattern).......20.00

165 8/PFENNIGE. Sim. 1808-
09, 11.................5.00

166 24/EINEN (=1/24)/THALER.
Like No. 169. 1816-18..... 4.50

167 24/EINEN/THALER.
Like No. 170. 1819-22..... 5.00

167a —. FRIEDR. 1823.......... 7.00

★168 24/EINEN/THALER. 1824-
27.....................5.00

169 12/EINEN (=1/12)/THALER.
Like No. 170 but REX
SAXONIAE. 1806-18........5.00

169a —. VGVST. 1809..........27.00

★170 12/EINEN/THALER. 1819-
21.....................7.00

170a —. FRIEDR. 1823.........12.50

171 12/EINEN/THALER. Like
No. 168. 1824-27..........7.00

Silver

V.F.

172 ⅙ (Reichsthaler). Like No.
192. 1806-17...........12.50

173 ⅙ (Reichsthaler). Like No.
194. 1825..............25.00

174 ⅙ (Reichsthaler). Old head.
Rev. VOLLENDET/D. 5 MAI.
1827. On his death........20.00

V.F.

★175 ⅓ (Reichsthaler).
1806-17................17.50

175a —. FEIN. 1808...........90.00

175b —. ACHTZIG. 1808.......120.00

176 ⅓ (Reichsthaler). Like
No. 184. 1818, 21.........50.00

177 ⅔ (Reichsthaler). Like
No. 192. 1806-17..........30.00

178 ⅔ (Reichsthaler). Like
No. 184. 1821 (pattern)....RRR

178a —. 1822................80.00

179 ZEHN EINE etc. (=mining
Conv. thaler). Like No. 136.
1807 (pattern)......(E.F.) 500.00

180 ZEHN EINE etc. (= Conv.
thaler). Like No. 192.
1806-16................35.00

180a —. GOTT SEGNE etc.
on edge. 1816...........50.00

181 ZEHN EINE etc. (=mining
Conv. thaler). Sim. but DER
SEEGEN etc. ZEHN etc. left
to right. 1807-12.........65.00

181a —. right to left. 1811-16...85.00

182 (Conv. thaler). Head. Rev.
K.S. BERGAKADEMIE etc.,
DEM FLEISSE. 1815..(E.F.)1200.00

★183 ZEHN etc. (= Conv. thaler).
"Pyjama thaler." 1816....400.00

184 ZEHN etc. (= Conv. thaler).
Sim. but military bust l.
1817-21................35.00

SAXONY (Cont.)

V.F.

185 ZEHN etc. (=mining Conv. thaler). Sim. but DER SEGEN etc. 1817-21............50.00

186 ZEHN etc. (= Conv. thaler). Like No. 193. 1822-23.....40.00

187 ZEHN etc. (=mining Conv. thaler). Sim. but DER SEGEN etc. 1822-23............60.00

188 ZEHN etc. (= Conv. thaler). Like No. 200. 1824-27.....35.00

189 ZEHN etc. (=mining Conv. thaler). Sim. but DER SEGEN etc. 1824-27............60.00

189a —. Circle btwn. arms and outer legends. 1824.......150.00

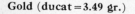

*190 X E.F.M. (= Conv. thaler). 1827....................85.00

190a —. SEGEN etc. (on edge). 1827....................175.00

Gold (ducat = 3.49 gr.)

*191 (ducat). 1806 (mule).....800.00

*192 (ducat). 1806-22........650.00

V.F.

*193 (ducat). 1823..........1000.00

194 (ducat). Like No. 200. 1824-27.................650.00

195 FÜNF (=5) THALER. Like No. 192. 1806-17....950.00

196 FÜNF (=5) THALER. Like No. 184. 1818......1500.00

197 FÜNF THALER. Like No. 200. 1825-27........850.00

198 ZEHN (=10) THALER. Like No. 192. 1806-17...1250.00

199 ZEHN THALER. Like No. 184. 1818.........2000.00

*200 ZEHN THALER. 1825-27.................1250.00

Anton 1827-36

Copper

Fine

201 1/PFENNIG. Like No. 202. 1831-33.............2.00

*202 3/PFENNIGE. 1831-33...3.50

202a —. Obv. leg. KOEN. SAECHS etc. 1834G..............3.00

Billon

203 24/EINEN (=¹/₂₄)/THALER. ANTON V.G.G.KOEN. V. SACHS. Arms. Rev. value. 1827-28.................7.50

204 12/EINEN (=¹/₁₂)/THALER. Sim. 1827-28............7.50

204a —. 1829-32.............3.75

Silver

V.F.

205 ⅙ (thaler). Head. Rev. Arms. 1827-29.................20.00

V.F.

*206 ⅙ (thaler). Sim. but D. 6 IUNI 1836. On his death...................20.00

207 ⅓ (thaler). Like No. 205. 1827-30.................40.00

208 ⅔ (thaler). Sim. 1827-29...55.00

209 ZEHN etc. (= Conv. thaler). Sim 1827-36............30.00

210 ZEHN etc. (= Mining Conv. thaler). Sim. but SEGEN etc. 1828-36.................90.00

E.F.

211 (Prize Conv. thaler). Head. Rev. K.S. BERGAKADEMIE etc. 1829.................2000.00

212 (Prize Conv. thaler). Head. Rev. K.S. FORSTINSTITUTE etc. 1830.................RR

213 (Prize Conv. thaler). Head. Rev. DEM/FLEISSE/etc. 1830...................RR

V.F.

214 ZEHN etc. (on edge = Conv. thaler). Heads of Anton and Friedrich August. Rev. VEREINTEN etc. New Constitution. 1831...........80.00

215 ZEHN etc. (= Conv. thaler). Like No. 206. 1836.......80.00

215a —. SEGEN etc. (on edge). 1836.................250.00

Gold

217 (ducat). Like No. 218. 1827-28.................800.00

217a —. 1829-36...........700.00

*218 FÜNF (=5) THALER. 1827-28...............1500.00

218a —. 1829-36.............900.00

219 ZEHN (=10) THALER. Sim. 1827-28..........1400.00

219a —. 1829-36.........1100.00

Friedrich August II 1836-54

Monetary System after 1839:

10 pfennig =1 neugroschen;
30 neugroschen =1 thaler.

GERMAN STATES

SAXONY (Cont.)

Copper

220 1/PFENNIG. Like No. 221 but no obv. legend. 1836-38G.................. 2.25

*221 1/PFENNIG. 1841-54..... 1.75

222 2/PFENNIGE. Sim. 21mm. 1841.................... 8.00

222a —. 19.7mm. 1841-54..... 1.75

*223 3/PFENNIGE. 1836-37....3.00

Billon

*224 ½/NEU/GROSCHEN. 1841-54................. 2.50

225 1/NEU/GROSCHEN. Sim. 1841-54............ 2.50

226 2/NEU/GROSCHEN. Sim. 1841-54............ 2.75

Silver

V.F.

227 12 EINEN (=1/12)/THALER. FRIEDRICH AUGUST etc. Arms. Rev. value. 1836........12.50

228 FÜNF (=5) N(eu)GR(oschen). Head. Rev. Arms. 1841-50.. 9.00

228a 6 EINEN (=⅙) THALER. 1851-52................20.00

229 LXXXIV EINE etc. (on edge, =⅙ thaler). Like No. 231. On his death. 1854....10.00

230 3 EINEN (=⅓) THALER. Like No. 228a. 1852-54....17.50

*231 XLII EINE etc. (on edge, =⅓ thaler). On his death. 1854.................35.00

V.F.

232 ZEHN etc. (= Conv. thaler). Head. Rev. Arms. 1836-38..50.00

233 X EINE etc. (= Mining Conv. thaler). Sim. but SEGEN etc. 1836-38......120.00

234 (thaler). Head. Rev. DEM PRINZEN/ALBERT ERNST/etc. Royal mint visit. 1839 (E.F.)...RR

235 EIN (=1) THALER. Head. Rev. Arms. 1839-49......22.50

235b —. 1850-54.............20.00

236 XIV EINE etc. (=mining thaler). Sim. but SEGEN etc. 1841-49.................80.00

236a —. 1850-54.............60.00

237 XIV EINE etc. (on edge, = thaler). Head. Rev. Justice and Love, sorrowing. On his death. 1854.............40.00

237a —. SEGEN etc. (on edge, = mining thaler). 1854......65.00

238 2 THALER. Like No. 235. 1839-54.................80.00

239 (Prize 2 thaler). Head. Rev. K.S. BERGAKADEMIE etc. 1841.....(E.F.) 2000.00

240 (Prize 2 thaler). Head. Rev. K.S. ACADEMIE FUR FORST etc. 1847.....(E.F.) Rare

241 VII EINE etc. (on edge, =2 thaler). Like No. 237. 1854.................175.00

Gold

242 (ducat). Head. Rev. Arms in branches. 1836-38.......1000.00

243 FÜNF (=5) THALER. Sim. 1837-39............1000.00

244 ZEHN (=10) THALER. Sim. 1836-39............1100.00

245 ZWEI UND EIN HALB (=2½) THALER. Head. Rev. Arms on mantle. 1842-54.....................900.00

246 FÜNF (=5) THALER. Sim. 1839-54..........800.00

247 ZEHN (=10) THALER. Sim. 1839-54...........950.00

Johann 1854-73

Copper

F-VF

248 1/PFENNIG. Like No. 249. 1855-59F.............. 1.00

248a —. 1861B.............. 4.00

*249 2/PFENNIGE. 1855-59F.. 1.50

249a —. 1861B.............. 4.00

250 1/PFENNIG. Like No. 251. 1862-73................. 1.00

F-VF

*251 2/PFENNIGE. 1862-73... 1.50

252 5/PFENNIGE. Sim. 1862-69................. 2.50

Billon

Fine

253 ½/NEU/GROSCHEN. Like No. 224. 1855-56..... 2.50

254 1/NEU/GROSCHEN. Sim. 1855-56F........... 2.50

254a —. 1861B............. 6.00

255 1/NEU/GROSCHEN. Like No. 251. 1863-67..... 2.50

256 1/NEU/GROSCHEN. Head. Rev. value. 1867-73...... 2.50

257 2/NEU/GROSCHEN. Like No. 224. 1855-56..... 2.75

258 2/NEU/GROSCHEN. Like No. 251. 1863-66..... 3.00

259 2/NEU/GROSCHEN. Like No. 256. 1868-73..... 2.75

Silver

V.F.

*260 6 EINEN (=⅙) THALER. 1855-56................12.00

261 6 EINEN (=⅙) THALER. Head. Rev. arms in ribbon. 1860-71.................10.00

262 3 EINEN (=⅓) THALER. Like No. 260. 1856........25.00

*263 3 EINEN THALER. 1858-59.................15.00

264 3 EINEN THALER. Sim. but no mantle. 1860.......20.00

265 EIN (=1) THALER. Head. Rev. Arms. 1854..........35.00

266 XIV EINE etc. (=mining thaler). Sim. but SEGEN etc. 1854.................55.00

267 EIN (=1) THALER. Head. Rev. GEPRAEGT/IN GEGENWART/ etc. Royal mint visit. 1855..............(E.F.) 100.00

268 EIN (=1) THALER. Like No. 260. 1855-56.........17.50

GERMAN STATES

SAXONY (Cont.)

269 XIV EINE etc. (=mining
thaler). Sim. but SEGEN etc.
1855-56 . . . . .50.00

270 EIN (=1) VEREINS-
THALER. Like No. 263.
1857-59 . . . . .20.00

271 XXX EIN etc. (=mining
thaler). Sim. but SEGEN etc.
1857-58 . . . . .50.00

272 EIN (=1 mining) THALER.
Head. Rev. SEGEN DES
BERGBAUS, arms supported
by miners. 1858-61 . . . . .32.00

272a —. BERGBAUES. 1861-67 . . . .25.00

272b —. 1868-71 . . . . .25.00

273 EIN (=1) VEREINS-
THALER. Head. Rev.
arms supported by lions.
1860-61 . . . . .20.00

273a —. Circle btwn. legend
and arms. 1861-71 . . . . .15.00

★274 EIN (=1) THALER.
Victory over France. 1871 . .40.00

275 2 THALER. Like No. 260.
1855-56 . . . . .75.00

276 (Prize 2 thaler). Head.
Rev. DEM/FLEISSE etc.
1857F 1500.00

276a —. 1857B 1200.00

277 ZWEI (=2) VEREINS-
THALER. Like No. 263.
1857-58 . . . . .65.00

277a —. 1858 THAELR 75.00

277b —. DOPPELTHALER. 1859 . . .75.00

278 ZWEI (=2) VEREINS-
THALER. Like No. 273a.
1861 . . . . .75.00

★279 XV EIN etc. (on edge, =2
thaler). 2 busts★. Rev.
1822/1872. Golden wedding.
1872 . . . . .85.00

279a —. No legend on rim.
1872 . . . . .350.00

Gold

280 ½/KRONE. Head.
Rev. value. 1857-70 . . . . .900.00

281 1/KRONE. Sim.
1857-71 . . . . .800.00

SAYN, County

The counts of Sayn in the Rhineland
are first mentioned in the 12th century. They had a sporadic coinage from
the 13th century and acquired possessions in various parts of west Germany.
Divided in 1605 into the branches of
Sayn-Sayn, Sayn-Wittgenstein and
Sayn-Berleburg.

Arms: Red, an uncwnd. double-tailed
lion guardant.

SAYN-ALTENKIRCHEN

Offshoot of Sayn-Sayn. To Saxe-
Eisenach 1686-1741. To Brandenburg-
Ansbach 1741-91. To Prussia 1791-
1803. To Nassau 1803.

Monetary System:
60 stüber =90 Convention kreuzer =
108 kreuzer landmünze =1 Reichsthaler.

Carl Wilhelm Friedrich, Margrave of Brandenburg Ansbach (q.v.), in Sayn-Altenkirchen 1741-57

Copper

1 I/PFENNING. Like No. 2.
1752-53 . . . . 7.00

★2 ¼/STVBER. Arms of Brandenburg and Sayn. 1752-57 . . 5.00

Billon

4 1 STVBER. 1752 . . . . ——

6 4/KREUZER. 4 fold arms.
Rev. value in cartouche.
1756 . . . . .12.50

8 3/STUBER. CAR.GUIL. FRID.
etc. . . . . c(omes).s(ayn). ET.
w(ittgenstein). Like No. 2.
1752, 57 . . . . 7.25

10 VI (kreuzer). Bust. Rev. COM
SAYN ET WITTG. 2 shields.
1751-55 . . . . 9.00

12 XII/EINEN (=1⁄12)/REICHS/
THALER. CARL WILH. FRIED.
etc. C.S.&W. 4 fold arms.
Rev. value. 1755 . . . . .12.00

★14 XII/KREV/ZER. 1753, 55 .12.50

Silver

18 ZEHEN etc. (= Conv. thaler).
CAR. WILH. etc. . . . C.S.&W.
Bust. Rev. 4 fold arms, Brandenburg eagle centershield,
2 eagle supporters.
17 A(ltenkirchen)55 . . . . . .400.00

Christian Friedrich Carl Alexander of Brandenburg-Ansbach 1757-91

Copper

20 ¼/STVBER. Like No. 2.
1758 . . . . 4.75

Billon or Silver

22 1 (kreuzer). Bust. Rev. 2 arms.
1758 . . . . 8.00

24 5 (Conv. kreuzer). 1764 . . . . . . ——

26 VI (kreuzer). CHR. FR. CAR.
AL. etc. Like No. 10. 1758 . . . 8.50

28 10 (Conv. kreuzer). 1764 . . . . . ——

30 XII KREV/ZER. CHR. FR. etc.
Like No. 14. 1757 . . . . .17.00

32 VI EINEN (=1⁄6) THALER.
CFCA mon. Rev. value/
B.O.S.L.M. 1757 . . . . .17.00

34 20 (Conv. kreuzer). 1764 . . . . ——

SCHAUMBURG (SCHAUENBURG), County

In N.W. Germany. United with Holstein 1106-1290, again independent
1290-1640. Divided between Hesse-
Cassel and Lippe-Alverdissen in 1640.

Arms: Red, a silver nettle. Centershield parted per fesse silver and red.

SCHAUMBURG-HESSEN

The Cassel portion, subordinate to
Hesse-Cassel.

Friedrich II of Hesse-Cassel 1760-85

Copper

1 I/GUTER (good)/PFENN(ig).
Cwnd. F(riedrich) L(andgraf)
mon. Rev. value. 1769 . . . . . 6.50

★2 I/GUTER/PFENN(ig).
1772-85 . . . . 2.75

2a —. PFENNIG. 1783 . . . . 4.00

GERMAN STATES

SCHAUMBURG-HESSEN (Cont.)

Wilhelm of Hesse-Cassel
1785-1821

Copper

I. As Landgrave Wilhelm IX 1785-1803.

VG-F

3 I/GUTER/PFENNIG. Sim. but w–Arms–L. 1787-1803 . . 4.00

II. As Elector Wilhelm I 1803-21.

4 I/GUTER/PFENNIG. Sim. but w–Arms–K(urfürst) under electoral bonnet. 1804-15.... 4.00

4a —. Under royal crown. 1816-21 .... 4.00

Wilhelm II of Hesse-Cassel
1821-47

Copper

I. Alone 1821-31.

5 I/GUTER/PFENNIG. Like No. 4a. 1824-30 .... 4.00

II. Under Regency 1831-47.

6 I/GUTER/PFENNIG. Sim. 1832 .... 5.75

SCHAUMBURG-LIPPE
The Lippe portion erected into a county independent of Lippe.

Wilhelm I Friedrich Ernst,
Count 1748-77

Copper

VG-F

1 1/PFENNING. 1750 ...... 4.75

Billon

3 IIII/PFEN(nig). Nettle. Rev. SCHAUMB. LAND MUNTZ, value. 1750 .... 6.00

5 *I/MARIEN/GROS(chen)*. Like No. 3. 1750 .... 12.50

7 *24/EINEN (=1/24)/THALER.* Like No. 3. 1750 .... 12.00

Silver

V.F.

9 1/3 (Reichsthaler). Like No. 13. 1761 .... 35.00

11 (2/3 Reichsthaler). WILHELM FR. E. D.G. S.R.I. COM. IN SCH. C. & N.D. LIPP. etc. 1748. Bust. Rev. Arms. URENDO. etc. On his accession 75.00

V.F.

13 2/3 (Reichsthaler). WILHELMUS I DEI GRAT: C: REG: IN SCHAUMB. Head. Rev. Arms. 1761..... 60.00

15 (Species thaler). Like No. 11. 1748 .... 450.00

17 EIN (=1) R(eichs) THAL(er). Obv. like No. 13. Rev. Arms. 1765 .... 85.00

Gold

19 I DUCAT. Like No. 20 but arms helmeted. 1762 ..... 1000.00

★20 X THALER. 1763 ...... 1750.00

Philip II Ernst 1777-87

Gold

★25 (ducat). 1777 .... 1000.00

26 (ducat). Bust. Rev. Tablet. 1783 .... 1250.00

Georg Wilhelm, Count of Schaumburg-Lippe, Under Regency of His Mother Juliane Wilhelmine v. Hessen-Philippsthal and Ludwig, Count of Wallmoden-Gimborn, 1787-1807

Billon

Fine

30 IIII/PFEN(nig). Nettle. Rev. GR. SCH. LIPP etc., value. 1802 .... 5.00

32 I/MARIEN/GROS(chen). Like No. 30. 1802 .... 7.00

Silver

V.F.

34 X/EINE etc. (= Conv. thaler). GRAFL. SCHAUMBURG LIPP etc. Arms. Rev. value on tablet. 1802 .... 250.00

Georg Wilhelm, Alone, As Prince 1807-60

Copper

Fine

★36 I/GUTER/PFENNIG. 1824, 26 .... 2.25

Fine

37 1/PFENNIG. Like No. 40. 1858 .... 2.25

38 2/PFENNIGE. Sim. 1858.. 2.00

39 3/PFENNIGE. Sim. 1858... 2.00

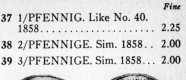

★40 4/PFENNIGE. GW mon. 1858 .... 3.00

Billon

41 4/PFENN(ig). Obv. like No. 36. Rev. FÜRSTL. SCHAUMB. LIPP. etc., value. 1821 ...... 4.00

41a —. 1828 .... 4.00

42 I/MARIEN/GROSCH(en). Sim. 1821, 28 .... 4.00

43 24/EINEN (=1/24)/THALER. Sim. 1821, 26............. 5.50

Silver

V.F.

44 XX/EINE etc. (=1/2 Conv. thaler). GEORG WILH. REG. FÜRST etc. Head. Rev. value. 1821 .... 70.00

Billon

F-VF

45 1/2/SILBER/GROSCHEN. Like No. 46. 1858 .... 4.00

★46 1/SILBER/GROSCHEN. 1858 .... 6.50

47 12/EINEN (=1/12)/THALER. GEORG WILHELM etc. Head. Rev. value. 1858 .... 10.00

Silver

V.F.

48 EIN (=1) VEREINSTHALER. Head. Rev. Arms. 1860..... 60.00

49 EIN DOPPEL (=2) THALER. Head. Rev. NACH/FÜNZIG etc. 50th year of reign. 1857... 250.00

Gold

★50 ZEHN (=10) THALER. 1829 .... *2000.00*

GERMAN STATES

SCHAUMBURG-LIPPE (Cont.)

Adolf Georg 1860-93

Silver

		V.F.
51	EIN (=1) VEREINSTHALER. Head. Rev. Arms. 1865	60.00

SCHLESIEN. See Silesia.

SCHLESWIG-HOLSTEIN, Duchies

Border area between Denmark and Germany. See Holstein. To Denmark until 1864 when annexed by the German Confederation.

Arms:
Schleswig: Gold, 2 blue lions passant.
Holstein: Red, silver nettle.

Monetary System: 12 pfennig = 4 dreiling = 2 sechsling = 1 schilling; 60 schilling = 1 Speciesthaler (Speciedaler).

Christian VII,
King of Denmark 1766-1808,
In Schleswig-Holstein 1784-1808

Copper

		VG-F
1	1/DREILING. Like No. 2. 1787	4.50

| ★2 | 1/SECHSLING. CR VII mon. 1787 | 4.50 |

Billon

| 3 | 2/SECHSLING. Like No. 4. 1787-1800 | 7.00 |

| ★4 | 2½/SCHILLING. 1787-1801 | 6.00 |
| 5 | 5/SCHILLING. Sim. 1787-1801 | 6.00 |

Silver

		Fine
6	10/SCHILLING. Sim. 1787-89, 96	15.00

		Fine
★7	20 SCHILLING. 1787-1808	22.00
8	40 SCHILLING. Sim. 1787-1808	38.00
9	60 SCHILLING. Sim. 1787-1808	(V.F.) 65.00

Gold

		V.F.
11	(ducat). Wildman stdg. Rev. MON AUR./ALTONAV/ AD LEGEM/IMPERII. 1771	800.00

Friedrich VI,
King of Denmark 1808-39

Billon or Silver

		Fine
20	2½/SCHILLING. Like No. 4 but FR VI mon. 1809, 12	6.00

| ★21 | 8/REICHS/BANK/ SCHILLING. 1816-19 | 10.00 |

| ★22 | 16/REICHS/BANK/ SCHILLING. Sim. 1816, 18. | 15.00 |
| 22a | —.1/12 SP added. 1831, 39 | 15.00 |

Christian VIII,
King of Denmark 1839-48

See DENMARK for coins of his reign with double denominations in Danish and German.

Provisional Government 1848-51

Copper

| ★23 | 1/DREILING. 1850 | 4.00 |
| 24 | 1/SECHSLING. Sim. 1850-51 | 4.00 |

SCHMALKALDEN

City and district in western Thuringia. Part of Henneberg until 1583, to Hesse-Cassel (q.v.) thereafter.

Wilhelm VIII of
Hesse-Cassel 1751-60

Copper

		VG-F
1	I/—/HELLER. Cwnd. WL script mon. Rev. I/SCHMALK/HELLER/ 1754	15.00

SCHÖNAU, Lordship

On the lower Rhine.

Johann Gottfried,
Freiherr von Blanche

Copper

		VG-F
★1	IIII (heller). Imp. eagle, lion shield on breast. Rev. R.HERRS/ SCHONAW/IIII. 1755	25.00

SCHWARZBURG, Princes

Very old Thuringian family. First coinage 12th century. After many divisions, two lines, Sondershausen and Rudolstadt, founded in 1552, emerged. The counts of Sondershausen and Rudolstadt were raised to the rank of prince in 1709 and 1710, respectively.

Arms: Gold, a black Imp. eagle with red prince's crown in gold shield on breast. Fork and comb below.

SCHWARZBURG-RUDOLSTADT
Johann Friedrich 1744-67

Copper

		VG-F
1	1/PFENNIG. JF mon. Rev. value/F. SCHWARZB./RUD. L.M./date. 1751-52	3.50
1a	—. Rev. value/F.S. RUDOL/ STADT. L.M. 1751-52	3.50
1b	—. Rev. value/F. SCHWARZB./ RVDOLSTADT/LAND MVNZ/date. 1752-53	3.50

★1c	—. Rev. L./MUNTZ. 1752-61	3.00
2	II/PFENNIG. Like No. 1c. 1760-61	3.50
3	3/PFENNING. J.F. mon. Rev. value/F.S.R.L.M. 1761-62	4.50

SCHWARZBURG-RUDOLSTADT
(Cont.)

Billon
VG-F

5 3 (pfennig). F.S.R.L.M., JF mon.
Rev. 3 in orb. 1751-52...... 6.00

7 3 (pfennig). Like No. 5 but
JF in shield. 1764........... 8.00

9 VI (pfennig). Like No. 5.
1752.................... 6.50

12 VI (pfennig). F.S.R.L.M., JF mon.
in shield or cartouche. Rev.
VI in orb. 1753-61-*66*...... 8.00

12a —. F.S.R.L.M. on Rev. 1762.. 7.50

15 48/EINEN (=1/48)/THALER.
Obv. like No. 7. Rev. value.
1764, 66................. 6.50

17 24/EINEN REICHS/THALER.
FVRSTL. SCHWARZB. RVDOLSTADT
LAND MVNZ. JF in cartouche.
Rev. Imp. eagle. 1752-57.... 8.00

19 24/EINEN (=/1/24)/THALER.
FVRSTL. SCHW. RVDOL. CONV.
MVNTZ, Imp. eagle. Rev. value/
CCCXX/EINE etc. in wreath.
1763.................... 8.00

19a —. Rev. CCCXX EINE etc.
around rim, no wreath.
1763-64................. 8.00

21 12/EINEN REICHS/THALER.
Like No. 17. 1753......... 9.50

22 12/EINEN (=1/12)/THALER.
Like No. 19a but rev. CLX
EINE etc. 1763-66........ 9.00

Silver
V.F.

24 *LXXX EINE etc.* (=1/6 thaler).
Bust. Rev. Imp. eagle.
1764................... 35.00

26 XX EINE etc. (=1/2 Conv.
thaler). Like No. 28. 1764... 50.00

28 X EINE etc. (= Conv.
thaler). IOANNES FRIDERICVS.
D.G. P.S.RUD. etc. Bust. Rev.
Arms. 1764-65........... 175.00

Ludwig Günther IV 1767-90

Copper
VG-F

30 I/HELLER. LG mon.
Rev. value. 1769.......... 5.00

31 ½/PFENNIG. Sim. 1783... 4.00

*32 1/PFENNIG. 1772........ 3.50

Billon

VG-F

*34 VI (pfennig). 1779-86...... 5.00

Silver
V.F.

37 X EINE etc. (= Conv. thaler).
D.G. LVDOVICVS GVNTHERVS
P. SCHWARZB. RVD. Bust.
Rev. Arms. 1768.......... 150.00

38 X EINE etc. (= Conv. thaler).
Bust. Rev. IN MEMORIAM/etc.
Marriage of Crown Prince.
1780................... 125.00

39 X EINE etc. (= Conv. thaler).
Bust. Rev. Arms supported.
1786................... 175.00

Friedrich Carl 1790-93

Copper
VG-F

41 ½/PFENNIG. FC mon.
Rev. value. 1792......... 5.00

42 1/PFENNIG. FC mon. Rev.
value/F.S. RUDOL/STADT. L.
MUNTZ/1792.............. 4.00

Billon

*44 VI (pfennig). 1792........ 5.00

Silver
V.F.

46 XX EINE etc. (=1/2 Conv.
thaler). Like No. 48. 1791... 50.00

48 X EINE etc. (= Conv. thaler).
D.G. FRID. CAROLUS PR.
SCHWARZB. RUD etc. Bust.
Rev. Arms. 1791.......... 125.00

Ludwig Friedrich II 1793-1807

Copper

Fine

*50 1 Pf(ennig). 1801-02...... 5.00

51 3 Pf(ennig). Sim. 1804...... 7.00

Billon

53 6 Pf(ennig). Like No. 50.
1800-04................. 5.00

54 I/GROSCHEN. Sim. 1803.. 6.00

Gold

V.F.

*55 DUCATEN (=ducat).
1803................... 1500.00

Friedrich Günther,
Under Regency 1807-14

Copper
Fine

57 2/PFENNIGE. FG mon. in
wreath. Rev. F.S.R.S.M./
value. 1812.............. 5.00

58 3/PFENNIGE. Sim. 1813.. 7.00

59 4/PFENNIGE. Sim.
1812-13................. 5.00

Billon

60 6 Pf(ennig). Like No. 50.
1808................... 5.00

60a —. Altered dies. 1812-13.... 4.50

61 I/GROSCHEN. Like No. 50.
1808................... 7.00

61a —. Altered dies. 1812.... 7.00

Silver
VF-EF

62 EIN (=1) SPECIES THALER.
FRIEDRICH GÜNTHER FÜRST
ZU SCHWARZBURG RUDOLSTADT.
Head. Rev. value. 1812-13.. 200.00

The 1812 Species thaler with bust in
uniform is a rare pattern.

Friedrich Günther,
Alone 1814-67

Copper
Fine

63 I/PFENNIG. Like No. 57.
but mon. cwnd. 1825....... 4.00

64 3/PFENNIGE. Sim. 1825.. 4.00

I. Coinage for the Lower
(Northern) Lordship.

Copper

65 1/PFENNING. FURSTENTH.
SCHWARZBURG R. Arms. Rev.
value. 1842.............. 4.00

66 2/PFENNINGE. Sim. 1842. 4.00

67 3/PFENNINGE. Sim. 1842. 6.00

Billon

68 ½/SILBER/GROSCHEN.
Sim. 1841............... 20.00

69 1/SILBER/GROSCHEN.
Sim. 1841............... 20.00

GERMAN STATES

SCHWARZBURG-RUDOLSTADT (Cont.)

Silver

V.F.

70 EIN (=1) VEREINSTHALER. Head. Rev. Imp. eagle. 1858-59..................50.00

70a —. 1862-63..............50.00

70b —. 1866..............35.00

★71 EIN VEREINSTHALER (on edge). On 50th year of reign. 1864...............70.00

72 2 THALER. Head. Rev. Arms. 1841, 45..........250.00

II. Coinage for the Upper (Southern) Lordship.

Copper

Fine

73 ⅛/KREUZER. Like No. 74. 1840, 55................. 3.50

★74 ¼/KREUZER. 1840-56.... 2.50

74a —. Rev. SCHEIDEMÜNZE added. 1857-66........ 2.00

75 ½/KREUZER. Like No. 74. 1840...................30.00

76 1/KREUZER. Sim. 1840... 2.00

76a —. Like No. 74a. 1864-66... 2.00

Billon

77 3/KREUZER. Like No. 78. 1839-46.............. 8.50

77a —. With SCHEIDEMÜNZE. 1866..................17.50

★78 6/KREUZER. 1840-46..... 7.00

78a —. Like No. 77a. 1866......14.00

Silver

V.F.

79 ½/GULDEN. Head. Rev. value. 1841-46.............27.50

80 1/GULDEN. Sim. 1841-46..20.00

81 ZWEY (=2) GULDEN. Head. Rev. Arms. 1846.........500.00

Albert 1867-69

Copper

F-VF

82 ¼/KREUZER. Like No. 74a. 1868.................... 2.00

83 1/KREUZER. Sim. 1868... 1.50

Silver

V.F.

84 EIN (=1) VEREINSTHALER. ALBERT FÜRST ZU SCHWARZBURG. Head. Rev. Imp. eagle. 1867...................40.00

SCHWARZBURG-SONDERSHAUSEN

Christian Günther III, In Ebeleben 1750-58, In Sondershausen 1758-94

Billon

VG-F

2 3/PFEN/NIG. CG mon. Rev. value/1764.......... 6.00

4 48/EINEN (=¹/₄₈)/THALER. Sim. 1764................. 5.00

6 24/EINEN (=¹/₂₄)/THALER. C.G.F.– Z.S.S., Imp. eagle on cartouche. Rev. value. 1763.10.00

8 12/EINEN (=¹/₁₂)/THALER. Sim. but CHRIST. GUNTH. F.Z. SCHW. SONDERSH. 1763..12.50

9 —. Imp. eagle not on cartouche. 1763-64....... 6.00

Silver

V.F.

10 ⅙ (Reichsthaler). 1764.....30.00

12 ⅓ (Reichsthaler). Sim. 1764...................40.00

14 ⅔ (Reichsthaler). Like No. 10. 1764.................65.00

16 X EINE etc. (= Conv. thaler). Like No. 10. 1764........600.00

Günther Friedrich Carl II 1835-80

Copper

Fine

18 1/PFENNIG. Like No. 21. 1846, 58.................. 2.00

19 3/PFENNIGE. Sim. 1846, 58, 70.............. 2.00

Billon

20 ½/SILBER/GROSCHEN. Sim. 1846, 51, 58.......... 6.00

★21 1/SILBER/GROSCHEN. Fine 1846-70................. 6.00

Silver

V.F.

22 EIN (=1) VEREINSTHALER. Head. Rev. Imp. eagle. 1859, 65, 70.............45.00

23 2 THALER. Head. Rev. Arms. 1841, 45, 54.............275.00

SCHWARZENBERG, Princes

Franconian family elevated to princely rank and given the mint right in 1670. Acquired Kletgau and Sulz (in Baden) by marriage 1687. Also possessed Gimborn (in Rhineland-Westphalia, sold to Wallmoden 1789) and Krumlau (acquired 1719) in Bohemia.

Joseph (Adam) 1732-82

Silver

V.F.

1 I KR(euzer). Arms. Rev. I KR. NACH DEM CONVENT. FUS. 1765...................35.00

2 (Species thaler). IOSEPH. D.G. S.R.I. PR. IN SCHWARZENBERG. Bust. Rev. Arms. 1741....350.00

3 X EINE etc. (= Conv. thaler). Bust. Rev. Arms. 1766....175.00

Gold (ducat=3.49 gr.)

VF-EF

4 (ducat). Bust. Rev. Arms. 1768...................1250.00

5 (10 ducat). No. 2 in gold. 1741....................RRR

Johann (Nepomuk) 1782-89

Silver

V.F.

6 20 (Conv. kreuzer). IOH. D.G. S.R.I. PRINCEPS IN SCHWARZENBERG. Bust. Rev. Arms. 1783..................45.00

7 (Conv. thaler). Sim. 1783..200.00

Gold (ducat=3.49 gr.)

E.F.

8 (ducat). Sim. 1783.......1000.00

9 (10 ducat). No. 7 in gold. 1783....................RRR

SCHWERIN. See Mecklenburg.

SIEGMARINGEN (SIGMARINGEN). See Hohenzollern.

GERMAN STATES

SILESIA (SCHLESIEN), Duchy

Former German district between Czechoslovakia and Poland, now part of Poland. Acquired piecemeal by Austria at various times, notably 1526 and 1675. Taken by Prussia 1740.

Arms: Gold, a black eagle with a silver bar or crescent or crescent and star on its breast.

Monetary System:
12 pfennige = 5 denare = 4 gröschel (= greschel) = 3 kreuzer = 2 poltura. 90 kreuzer = 1 Reichsthaler.

Breslau mint marks:
W or A.E. or A.H.E. until 1750; B – 1750-1826.

See Prussia for similar coins and list of other Prussian provinces.

Friedrich II, The Great, King of Prussia, 1740-86

Billon

VG-F

1 1/DENAR. FR mon./A.H.E. Rev. value/SCHEIDE/MUNTZ/W divides date. 1746-47 .... 6.00

3 1 GRÖSCHEL. FR mon. Rev. eagle. 1752-57B 5.50

5 EIN (=1)/GRÖSCHEL. FR mon. Rev. value. 1769-84B 6.00

7 1 (kreuzer). Armored bust. Rev. eagle in cwnd. cartouche. 1745-63 .... 5.00

8 1/KREVTZER. Cwnd. FR mon. Rev. value. 1752B 7.50

9 1 KREUTZER. FRIDERIC BORUSS. REX. Bust. Rev. eagle. 1752-57B 3.50

10 —. Sim. but obv. head. 1766-67 .... 3.50

11 1 KREUTZER. Sim. 1771-86 .... 3.00

12 POLTURA. Bust. Rev. eagle. 1744A.E 10.00

13 2 GRESCHEL. Sim. 1745 .. 5.00

14 2 GRÖSCHEL. Sim. 1745-49A.E., 50-54B 3.00

★15 ZWEY (or ZWEI)/GRÖSCHEL. 1771-86B 3.00

17 3 (kreuzer). Like No. 7. 1743A.E 8.00

19 3 (kreuzer). Bust. Rev. flying eagle. 1752B 7.00

21 3 (kreuzer). Armored bust. Rev. MONETA ARGENTEA, 2 eagle shields. 1752-56B-63B 6.00

VG-F

23 3 (kreuzer). Cwnd. head. Rev. MONETA ARGENT., eagle. 1764-65B 6.00

24 3 (kreuzer). Head. Rev. MONETA ARGENT., eagle. 1771-86 A or B 4.00

Note: No. 24, especially when struck at Berlin, is often listed as 3 grosze for East Prussia. The East Prussian grosze and the Silesian kreuzer were equivalent to each other in the Prussian monetary system.

24a —. D. 20 AUGUST in lieu of MONETA ARGENT. 1781B. On birthday of Count von Hoym, Governor of the Jewish population of Breslau...... RRR

26 VI (kreuzer). Type of No. 7. 1743-47A.E. 7.50

27 VI (kreuzer). Like No. 33. 1755-56B 7.50

★28 VI (kreuzer). 1755-57B 8.50

30 XV (kreuzer). Armored bust. Rev. eagle in cwnd. cartouche. 1743-46 .... 20.00

31 18 (kreuzer). Armored bust. Rev. MONETA ARGENT. REG: PRUSS. 1752-53B .... ——

Dietzel lists the above coin under Silesia but his illustration looks like an 18 groszy from the Koenigsberg (East Prussia) mint.

32 18 (kreuzer). Cwnd. bust with sword. Rev. MONETA ARGENTEA, eagle. 1753-58B, 58-59A ... 12.50

No. 32 dated 1758-59A was former Prussia No. 60, and also would have been the equivalent of 18 groszy in East Prussia.

33 (ex 32a) 18 (kreuzer). Cwnd. fat-faced armored bust. Rev. cwnd. circular 4 fold arms with eagle center shield. (Parody of Polish-Saxon coinage.) 1755-56B 15.00

Gold (ducat = 3.49 gr.,
5 thalers = Friedrich d'or = 6.65 gr.)

V.F.

★36 (ducat). 1743W 850.00

36a —. 1743-48 A.H.E 800.00

V.F.

★37 1 DUCAT. 1754, 57B 850.00

★38 (½ Friedrich d'or). 1750-53B 500.00

39 (½ Fr. d'or). Like No. 43. 1765-75B 450.00

39a —. Old head. 1776-77B ... 1250.00

★40 (Fr. d'or). 2 vars. 1744-48 A.E 1100.00

★41 (Fr. d'or). 1746-49 A.E 900.00

41a —. 1750 A.E 1000.00

★42 (Fr. d'or). 1750-57, 64B 850.00

★43 (Fr. d'or). 1764-75B 750.00

★43a —. 1776-86B 600.00

GERMAN STATES

SILESIA (Cont.)

V.F.

43b —. No. 43a with D. 20 AUGUST 1781B (see No. 24a).......RRR

44 (2 Fr. d'or). Like No. 41. 1747-49 A.H.E..........2600.00

45 (2 Fr. d'or). Like No. 42. 1751-52B.............1500.00

Friedrich Wilhelm II 1786-97

Copper

VG-F

*47 ½/KREUZER. 1788-97B... 2.50

Billon

49 1/GROESCHEL. Cwnd. FWR mon. Rev. value. 1787-97B...............4.00

*51 1 KR(euzer). 1787-97B..... 4.50

Friedrich Wilhelm III 1797-1840

Mint Marks: A – Berlin; G – Glatz.

Copper

53 ½/KREUZER. Like No. 47. 1806A...................4.00

54 1/KREUZER. Eagle in oval. Rev. value/SCHLES. 1810A .. 3.00

Billon

*56 1/GRÖSCHEL. FWR mon. 1805-06A, 08-09G..........4.00

*57 1 KR(euzer). 1806A, 08G... 5.00

See POLAND (East Prussia) No. 60 for the III (grosze) with bust, rev. MON. ARGENT., eagle 1800-07A, 07-08G, which passed for 3 kreuzer in Silesia.

Fine

60 9/KREUZER. Bust. Rev. SCHLES.L.M., eagle. 1808G...20.00

Fine

61 18/KREUZER. Sim. 1808G.................50.00

See Prussia for other similar coins.

SILESIA-WÜRTTEMBERG-OELS, Duchy

The small duchy of Oels in Silesia was acquired through marriage by Silvius Nimrod of Württemberg in 1647. His branch line continued until 1792, in which year Oels went to Brunswick-Wolfenbüttel.

Carl Christian Erdmann 1744-92

Silver

V.F.

1 EIN (=1) REICHSTHALER. CAROL. CHRIST. ERDM. DUX WURTEMB. OLSN etc. Bust. Rev. Arms. 1785.........185.00

SINZENDORF, Counts

Old Austrian family which acquired the title of Hereditary Treasurer of the Empire and held the burgraviates of Reineck near Andernach (to France 1801) and Winterreiden.

Johann Wilhelm 1742-66

Gold

VF-EF

*1 (ducat). 1753............1200.00

SOLMS, Counts and Princes

Family first mentioned in the 12th century, with possessions on both sides of the Lahn between Wetzlar and Weilburg. Divided into two lines, Braunfels and Lich, in 1409. Each of these were later subdivided into a multiplicity of branches. All of the branches acquired the mint right about 1552. All were mediatized during the Napoleonic era.

Arms: Gold, uncwnd. blue lion.

SOLMS-LAUBACH, County

A branch of Solms-Lich. Founded by Otto I, died 1522.

Christian August 1738-84

Silver (lower values billon)

VF-EF

5 10 (Conv. kreuzer). GRAEF ZU SOLMS LAUBACH. CA mon. Rev. CXX etc., lion with rose. 1762.................60.00

9 30 (Conv. kreuzer). V.G.G. CHRIST. AUG. GRAF ZU SOLMS LAUBACH. Arms. Rev. IN/MEM. NEPOT./CAR. CHRIST. FRID./ etc. Death of grandchild. 1768.................60.00

VF-EF

11 30 (Conv. kreuzer). Obv. like No. 9. Rev. DEN/ZWEITEN/ ENCKEL/etc. Birth of grandchild. 1769...............60.00

13 30 (Conv. kreuzer). V.G.G. CHRISTIAN etc. DEN III ENCKEL etc. Rev. XL EINE etc. DEN VIII BRAUNFELSISCHEN ENCKEL etc. Birth of 2 grandchildren. 1770....................60.00

15 (Speciesthaler). CHRISTIAN AUGUST GRAF ZU SOLMS etc. Bust r. Rev. cherub with LAVBACH over the city. N.D. 550.00

16 (Species thaler). Bust of Chr. Aug. Rev. bust of Elisabetha Amalia. His first marriage. 1738..............550.00

17 (Species thaler). Bust of Elis. Am. Rev. IN MEM etc., angel holds arms. Death of 1st wife. 1748..................550.00

18 (Species thaler). CHRIST AVG etc. Busts of Chr. Aug. and his 3rd wife, Dorothea Wilhelmina in 2 medallions. Rev. ICH HABE etc., sarcophagus. Her death. 1754..............550.00

19 X EINE etc. (= Conv. thaler). V.G.G. CHRISTIAN etc. Arms. Rev. ZUM/GEDAECHTNIS/etc. 1767.................550.00

20 X EINE etc. (= Conv. thaler). Obv. like No. 19. Rev. CONIUNCTIO FELIX. 2 cherubs over shields. Marriage of his heir to a Princess of Isenburg. 1767...............400.00

21 X EINE etc. (= Conv. thaler). Obv. like No. 19. Rev. CHRISTIANS WERCK., view of new salt mine. 1768.......350.00

22 X EINE etc. (= Conv. thaler). OTTO GRAF ZU SOLMS etc. His 16th century bust. Rev. pyramid with PA/TRI/etc. 1770. In memory of Count Otto I...................400.00

23 X EINE etc. (= Conv. thaler). Bust of Chr. Aug. Rev. SORGEN LOOS., hunting lodge. 1770...............400.00

24 X EINE etc. (= Conv. thaler). Bust of Chr. Aug. Rev. cherub with LAUBACH over city. N.D. (=1770)...........300.00

Gold

V.F.

26 EIN (=1) DUC(at). Bust. Rev. Arms. 1761........1750.00

SONDERSHAUSEN.

See Schwarzburg.

SPEYER (SPEIER, SPIRES), Bishopric

In the Pfalz. Reestablished 610 AD. Obtained mint right 11th century. Divided between France and Baden 1802. To Bavaria 1814.

GERMAN STATES

SPEYER (Cont.)

Arms: Blue, a silver cross.

Franz Christoph, Freiherr von Hutten, Bishop 1743-70

Copper
VG-F

1 II/PFENNIG. Arms under Cardinal's hat/B(ishopric) s(peyer). Rev. value/LAND-MUNZ/1765 . . . . 6.00

2 I/KREUTZER. Sim. 1765 . . 6.50

Gold
V.F.

5 (ducat). FRANCIS CHRIST. D.G. EP. SPIR. etc. Bust. Rev. Homage ceremony at Bruchsal. 1745 . . . . 1100.00

August, Graf von Limburg-Gehmen-Styrum, Bishop 1770-97

Silver (lower values billon)

7 240 EINE etc. (=5 Conv. kreuzer). AUGUSTUS D.G. EP. SPIR. etc. 3 arms. Rev. value. 1772 . . . . 16.50

8 10 (Conv. kreuzer). Obv. sim. Rev. CXX etc. in shield. 1770 . 16.50

10 20 EINE etc. (=½ Conv. thaler). Like No. 12. 1770 . . 85.00

12 10 EINE etc. (= Conv. thaler). AUGUSTUS D.G. EP. SPIR. etc. Arms in 3 shields. Rev. Minerva and 3 cherubs. On his accession. 1770 . . . . 200.00

Gold

14 (ducat). Like No. 12. 1770 . 1100.00

STOLBERG, Counts

Stolberg, a rich silver mining district in the Harz mountains of central Germany, had its own coinage from the 11th century. The ruling family represented in this catalog acquired possession in 1222. After numerous divisions and reunions, the lines of Wernigerode and Stolberg were established in 1641. Each of these were thereafter further subdivided. All were finally absorbed by Prussia.

Arms: Gold, a black stag, with or w/out cwnd. pillar.

STOLBERG-ELDER LINE (STOLBERG-WERNIGERODE), County Christian Ernst 1710-71

Silver
V.F.

5 (½ thaler). Like No. 10. 1725 . . . . 70.00

V.F.

7 (½ thaler). Obv. sim. Rev. cwnd. arms. 1738 . . . . 70.00

10 (thaler). CHRISTIANUS. ERNESTUS. COMES. IN. STOLBERG etc., stag. Rev. helmeted arms. 1724-25 . . . . . 225.00

11 (thaler). Bust. Rev. flaming altar /NACH FUNFZIG etc. 50th year of reign. 1760 . . . . 225.00

12 (thaler). Arms. Rev. flaming altar etc. 50th year. 1760 . . . 550.00

Gold

14 (ducat). Head. Rev. stag. 1730 . . . . 1000.00

15 (ducat). Stag. Rev. Arms. 1742, 59 . . . . 950.00

16 (ducat). Bust. Rev. stag. 1768 . . . . 950.00

Heinrich Ernst II 1771-78

Gold

20 (ducat). HENR. ERNST GR. Z. STOLB. etc. Head. Rev. stag. 1778 . . . . 1800.00

Christian Friedrich 1778-1824

Gold
VF-EF

24 I DUCATEN (=ducat). CHRISTIAN FRIDR: GRAF ZU STOLBERG etc. stag. Rev. value on tablet. 1784, 95 . . 2000.00

★25 I/DUCAT. Golden Wedding. 1818 . . . . 1500.00

Heinrich XII 1824-54

Gold

★26 EIN (=1) DUCAT. 1824 . . . . 1500.00

STOLBERG-YOUNGER LINE (STOLBERG-STOLBERG and STOLBERG-ROSSLA), Counties Christoph Ludwig II zu Stolberg 1738-61

I. Alone.

Gold (ducat =3.49 gr.)
V.F.

1 (1/32 ducat). CL mon. Rev. stag, column. N.D. 175.00

V.F.

2 (1/16 ducat). Sim. N.D 175.00

3 (⅛ ducat). Sim. N.D 200.00

4 (¼ ducat). Sim. N.D 250.00

II. With Friedrich Botho zu Rossla 1739-68.

Silver
F-VF

6 48/EINEN (=1/48)/THALER. GOTT SEEGNE U. ERHALTE UNSERE BERGWERK. stag, column. Rev. value. 1739-56 . . . . 6.00

7 24/EINEN (=1/24)/THALER. Obv. as last. Rev. CHR. LUDEWIG U. FR(IEDR.) BOTHO GR. Z. ST(OLB.) etc., value. 1741-50 . . . . 8.00

8 12/EINEN (=1/12)/THALER. Sim. 1746-50 . . . . 12.50

9 ⅙ (Reichsthaler). Arms. Rev. stag, column. 1740-46 . . . . . 17.50

10 LXXX EINE etc. (=⅙ Reichsthaler). On 2nd Centenary Religious Peace. 1755 . . . . 17.50

12 ⅓ (Reichsthaler). Like No. 9. 1746 . . . . 35.00

13 ⅔ (Reichsthaler). Sim. 1741-45 . . . . 50.00

14 XXIV/MARIEN/GROSCH(en). Value. Rev. stag. 1741-47 . . . 50.00

15 (Species thaler). Like No. 9. 1746 . . . . (V.F.) 550.00

Gold (ducat =3.49 gr.)
V.F.

17 (⅛ ducat). Like No. 20. N.D 200.00

18 (¼ ducat). Sim. N.D 250.00

19 (½ ducat). Sim. 1745-50 . . 400.00

★20 (ducat). 1740-57 . . . . 800.00

21 (2 ducats). Sim. 1743 . . . . . 1750.00

22 (4 ducats). Sim. 1743 . . . . . . RRR

Friedrich Botho zu Rossla 1739-68

I. Alone.

Gold (ducat =3.49 gr.)

25 (⅛ ducat). FB mon. Rev. stag, column. N.D. (=1761-68) . . 200.00

26 (¼ ducat). Sim. N.D. (=1761-68) 275.00

II. With Carl Ludwig zu Stolberg 1761-1815.

Silver
F-VF

28 24/EINEN (=1/24)/THALER. F.B.U.C.L.G.Z. STOLB. etc., stag, column. Rev. value. 1763-64 . . . . 8.00

GERMAN STATES

STOLBERG-YOUNGER LINE (Cont.)

F-VF

29 *24 EINEN THALER*. Like No. 31. 1766.............. 8.00

30 12/EINEN (=1/12)/THALER. Like No. 28 but F. BOTHO etc. 1763-64.................... 8.00

31 12/EINEN/THALER. Like No. 7 but FR. BOTHO V. CARL. LVDEWIG etc. 1766.......... 8.00

32 1/6 (Reichs thaler). Arms. Rev. stag, column. 1763-64..16.50

33 1/3 (Reichsthaler). Sim. 1764.....................27.00

35 *XX EINE etc.* (=1/2 Conv. thaler). Like No. 39. 1763...40.00

37 2/3 (Reichsthaler). Like No. 40. 1764..................47.50

39 X EINE etc. (= Conv. thaler). Oval arms. Rev. stag, column. 1763....................175.00

40 X EINE etc. (= Conv. thaler). Elaborate arms. Rev. stag, column. 1764. (var.)........95.00

Gold (ducat=3.49 gr.)

V.F.

41 *(1/2 ducat)*. Like No. 42. 1762, 66.................750.00

★42 (ducat). 1762-66..........950.00

43 *(2 ducats)*. Sim. 1764.....2250.00

Carl Ludwig zu Stolberg 1761-1815

I. Alone.

Gold

45 *(ducat)*. Bust. Rev. Arms. 1796..................1000.00

II. With Heinrich Christian Friedrich zu Rossla 1768-1810.

Copper

F-VF

47 I/PFENNIG. Stag, column. Rev. value/SCHEIDE/MUNTZ/ date/Z. 1799-1801.......... 4.50

Silver

V.F.

48 24/EINEN (=1/24)/THALER. Like No. 7 but CARL LVD. V. H. CHRIST. FR. GR. Z. STOLB. etc. 1771.................... 8.00

50 1/3 *(Reichsthaler)*. Like No. 52. 1770-90...............25.00

52 2/3 (Reichsthaler). Arms (cwnd. or helmeted). Rev. stag, column. 1768-96..........45.00

V.F.

54 1 1/3 (Reichsthaler). Helmeted arms. Rev. stag, column. 1796...................200.00

Gold (ducat=3.49 gr.)

56 *(1/2 ducat)*. Stag, column. Rev. Arms. 1768 (small or broad planchet)..........1200.00

56a —. 1770................900.00

57 (ducat). Sim. 1768-96......900.00

STRALSUND, Town

On the Baltic. Had its own coinage circa 1325-1763. Belonged to Sweden 1637-1815.

Arms: Arrowhead pointing upward.

Monetary System:
12 pfennig=3 witten=2 sechsling= 1 schilling; 48 schilling=1 thaler.

Billon

F-VF

1 I/WITTEN. Date/cwnd. arrowhead. Rev. value/ S(tralsund) S(tadt) M(ünz). 1763.....................14.50

2 I/SECHS/LING. Sim. 1763.14.50

STRASSBURG (STRASBOURG, ARGENTINIUM), Bishopric

In Alsace, on the French-German border. Established about 4th century. Bishops obtained the mint right in 873. In 1789 the bishopric was secularized and annexed to France.

Arms: Red, a silver bend.

Louis Constantine, Prince de Rohán, Bishop 1756-79

Copper

F-VF

1 EIN (=1)/KREUTZER. LUD. CAR(dinal) DE ROHAN D.G. EPUS. ET PS ARGENT. Arms. Rev. value. 1773 ....12.00

Billon or Silver

4 5 (kreuzer). Like No. 12. 1773....................12.00

6 XII (=1/12) TH(aler). Like No. 10. 1759.............12.00

8 10 (kreuzer). Like No. 12. 1773.....................15.00

★10 VI (=1/6) TH(aler). 1759...22.00

12 20 (kreuzer). Arms. Rev. MONETA etc. ARGENTINENSIS. Arms. 1773...............25.00

V.F.

16 *(1/2 thaler)*. Like No. 10. 1760....................65.00

V.F.

18 (thaler). Like No. 10. 1759-60.....................400.00

TECKLENBURG-RHEDA.

See Bentheim.

TEUTONIC ORDER (DEUTSCHER ORDEN)

Knightly brotherhood established during the Third Crusade, 1198. Acquired considerable territories in East Prussia by conquest from the heathen Prussians in the late 13th-early 14th centuries. The Order struck coins in and for East Prussia until 1525 when the then Grand Master turned Protestant and took title as the first hereditary duke of Prussia. At this time the Catholic members retired to Mergentheim, where the Teutonic Order continued until its suppression (and the absorption of its lands by Württemberg) in 1809.

Arms: Silver, a black cross. Black eagle on gold centershield.

Clemens August von Bayern, Grand Master 1732-61

(Also ruled and struck coins in other ecclesiastical states. See Cologne).

Silver

VF-EF

5 (groschen). C.A.D.G. etc. Arms. Rev. 9 lines: NATUS/17 AUG. 1700/ELECTUS/IN SUPR. ADM. PRUSS/etc. On his death. 1761.....................22.50

9 40 EINE etc. (=30 kreuzer). Like No. 5. 1761...........50.00

13 (1/2 Species thaler). CLEM AUG etc. Double CA mon. Rev. ELISABETHA PATRONA ORDINIS TEUTONICI. St. Elisabeth. 1750...................175.00

Carl Alexander, Duke of Lorraine, Grand Master 1761-80

Billon

F-VF

15 1 KR(euzer). Cross of Order, Lorraine middleshield (see No. 19). Rev. value/NACH DEM/ CONVENT/FVS/W 1776 E..... 7.00

17 2 1/2 KR(euzer). Like No. 15. 1776.................... 7.50

★19 5 (Conv. kreuzer). 1776..... 9.50

Silver

V.F.

21 120 EINE etc. (=10 Conv. kreuzer). C.A.D.G. etc. Arms. Rev. 9 lines: NATUS . . . 1712 ELECTUS IN SUPR. ADM. PRUSS. etc. On his death. 1780.....11.00

GERMAN STATES

TEUTONIC ORDER (Cont.)

V.F.

23 20 (Conv. kreuzer). D.G. CAROL. ALE. DUX etc. Bust. Rev. SUP. ADM. BOR. etc. Arms. 1776..11.00

25 40 EINE etc. (=30 Conv. kreuzer). Like No. 21. 1780..40.00

27 XX E.F. etc. (=½ Conv. thaler). Like No. 23. 1776...85.00

29 X EINE etc. (= Conv. thaler). Like No. 23. 1776........375.00

30 *(2 Conv. thaler). No. 29 double thick.* 1776........650.00

Gold

32 *(ducat).* Bust. Rev. Arms. 1765..................1000.00

TRIER (TREVES), Archbishopric

Near the German-Luxemburg border. Bishopric elevated to archbishopric in 9th century. Mint right obtained 10th century. Archbishop confirmed as one of the seven imperial electors in 1356. In 1802 Trier was secularized and divided between France and Nassau. Most of it went to Prussia in 1814.

Arms: Silver, a red cross.

Monetary System:
4 pfennig = 1 kreuzer;
120 Conv. kreuzer =
144 kreuzer Landmünze = 72 albus
(Petermenger) = 6 kopfstuck =
2 Conv. gulden = 1 Species
or Convention thaler.

Franz Georg, Graf von Schönborn-Puckheim, Archbishop 1729-56

(Also bishop of Worms.)

Copper

VG-F

1 I/PFENNI(N)G. Bonnetted F(ranz) G(eorg) c(hurfürst) mon. Rev. value. 1748-50 ... 4.00

2 II/PFENNING. Sim. 1748-49.................. 4.00

3 IIII/PFENNING. Sim. 1748-50.................. 4.25

Billon

5 2 PFENNIG. Like No. 1. 1731.................. 4.00

6 *2 PFENNIG.* Sim. 1733, 43.................. 4.00

7 II PFENNIG. Sim. 1744-49.................. 4.00

9 ½ PETER MENGEN. Arms. Rev. value. 1747-50, N.D ... 4.00

11 EIN (=1) KR(euzer). Obv. like No. 1. Rev. Arms. 1730-45.................. 4.75

Silver

E.F.

13 *(½₂ Species thaler).* Like No. 19. 1756............50.00

15 (⅟₁₆ Species thaler). Like No. 19. 1756............60.00

17 ½ *KOPFSTUCK.* Like No. 20. 1734........ *(F-VF)* 20.00

19 (⅛ Species thaler). FRAN. GEORG etc. Arms. Rev. 10 lines: NATUS 25 JUNI 1682 ELECTUS ELECTOR etc. On his death. 1756..................70.00

20 EIN (=1)/KOPFSTUCK. FRAN GEORG D.G. AR. EP. ET EL. TREV. etc. Arms. Rev. value. 1734............. *(F-VF)* 20.00

21 (½ Species thaler). Like No. 19. 1756..........200.00

Gold (ducat = 3.49 gr.)

V.F.

23 (ducat). Bust. Rev. Arms. 1735, 50, 52............2000.00

24 *(2 ducats).* Sim. 1735-52.....RRR

Johann Philipp, Freiherr von Walderdorf, Archbishop 1756-68

Copper

VG-F

25 I/PFENNING. Like No. 28. 1757-62.................. 3.00

26 II/PFENNING. Sim. 1757-62.................. 4.00

27 III/PFENNING. Sim. 1761..................15.00

★28 IIII/PFEN(N)ING. JPC mon. 1757-64.................. 2.50

29 1/KREUTZER. Sim. but Rev. value/LAND/MUNZ/1761 ....30.00

30 VI/PFENNING. Like No. 28. 1761.............25.00

Billon

32 (Petermenger). JOAN. PHIL. D.G. etc. Arms. Rev. MONETA NOVA TREVIRENSIS. St. Peter with book and key. 1758-62...... 5.00

★34 III/PETERMENGER. 1760...................10.00

VG-F

34a III (Petermenger). Sim. 1760.................. 6.00

36 240 (=5 Conv. kreuzer). Like No. 34. 1760............. 7.00

37 240 (= 5 Conv. kreuzer). 1761, 62.............. 7.00

39 240 (=5 Conv. kreuzer). Bonnetted JPC mon. Rev. NACH DEM etc. Arms. 1763-64..... 7.00

40 240 EINE etc. (=5 Conv. kreuzer). St. Peter/CHVR TRIER. Rev. value, IVS/TIRT. 1765 .. 7.00

Silver

E.F.

41 (½₂ Species thaler). Like No. 42. 1768.............50.00

★42 (⅟₁₆ Species thaler). On his death. 1768..............75.00

46 (⅛ Conv. thaler). Like No. 42. 1768..............60.00

V.F.

★43 10 (Conv. kreuzer). 1760....12.50

43a —. 120 EINE etc. added. 1760-61..................12.50

44 10 (Conv. kreuzer). Bust in wreath. Rev. Arms on pedestal. 1763-65, N.D..............10.00

45 VI/EINEN (=⅙)/THALER. JPC mon. Rev. value. 1757-58..................20.00

45a —. With 100 EINE etc. 1757.20.00

47 20 (Conv. kreuzer). Like No. 43. 1760.............25.00

49 20 (Conv. kreuzer). Like No. 44. 1765.............18.50

51 40 EINE etc. (=30 Conv. kreuzer). Like No. 43. 1760..27.00

53 20 EINE etc. (=½ Conv. thaler). Bust. Rev. EX FODINIS VILLMARIENSIBUS. Arms. Vilmar mining gulden. 1757, 61....190.00

55 20/EINE etc. (=½ Conv. thaler). Like No. 59a. 1760, 62.....................140.00

57 20 EINE etc. (=½ Conv. thaler). Like No. 53 but EX FODINIS BERNCASTELIANIS. Berncastel mining gulden. 1761.....................170.00

59 10/EINE etc. (= Conv. thaler). Bust. Rev. Arms supported. 1757...................140.00

GERMAN STATES

TRIER (Cont.)

V.F.

59a —. 1760-61 . . . . 100.00
59b —. 1762-63 . . . . 100.00
59c —. 1764 . . . . 100.00
60 10 EINE etc. (= Conv. thaler).
Sim. but no supporters.
1765 . . . . 125.00

Gold (ducat = 3.49 gr.)

62 (ducat). Bust. Rev. VNIONE
MIRIFICA etc. Arms. Date
(1759) in chronogram . . . . . . RRR
63 *(ducat)*. Sim. but w/out
VNIONE etc. 1760-62 . . . . . . 2250.00
64 (2 ducats). Like No. 62.
(1759) . . . . RRR

Clemens Wenzel,
Prince of Saxony-Poland,
Archbishop 1768-94

(Also bishop of Augsburg.)

Copper

VG-F

66 I/PFENNIG. CWC mon.
Rev. value. 1789/G.M. 2.25
67 II/PFENNIG. Sim. 1789 . . . 3.50
68 IIII/PFENNIG. Sim. 1789. 3.50

Billon

70 1/KREUZER. CWC mon.
Rev. value/TRIER/L.M./
1794 . . . . 3.75
72 1/ALBUS. Like No. 70 but
Rev. value/TRIERISCH.
1789-91 . . . . 3.75
74 *5 (Conv. kreuzer)*. Arms.
Rev. value. 1770-71 . . . . 5.00
76 3/ALBUS. Arms. Rev. KUR
TRIER LAND MUNZ, value.
1789-93 . . . . 5.00

Silver

V.F.

78 20 (Conv. kreuzer). CLEMENS
WENC. D.G. A. E. TREV. etc.
Bust. Rev. AD NORMAM etc.
Arms. 1769 . . . . 22.50
79 LX EINE etc. (=20 Conv.
kreuzer). AD NORMAM etc. Arms.
Rev. value. 1769 . . . . 22.50
81 *20 (Conv. kreuzer)*. 1771 . . . . 22.50
83 20 EINE etc. (=½ Conv.
thaler). Bust. Rev. Arms.
1770, 73 . . . . 65.00
85 X EINE etc. (= Conv. thaler).
Bust r. Rev. Arms supported.
1768 . . . . 235.00
86 X EINE etc. (= Conv. thaler).
Bust l. Rev. Arms. 1769 . . . 135.00
87 10 EIN etc. (= Conv. thaler).
Bust r. Rev. oval arms.
1771 . . . . 135.00

V.F.

88 X EINE etc. (= Conv. thaler).
Bust r. Irregular arms.
1773 S.C 135.00
88a —. 1773 G.M 150.00
89 X EINE etc. (= Conv. thaler).
Bust. Rev. EX VASIS etc. Arms.
Date (1794) in chronogram.
War Contribution . . . . *(E.F.)* 175.00

Gold

90 (ducat). Bust. Rev. EPISC.
AUG. etc. Arms. 1770 . . . . 2250.00

ULM, Free City

In Württemberg. First mentioned 854.
Became a free city 1155 and obtained
the mint right 1398. Annexed to Bavaria 1803, given to Württemberg 1809.

Arms: Per fesse, black and silver.

Monetary System:
7 kreuzer Stadt münze (city money) =
5 Convention kreuzer.

Copper

VG-F

3 EIN (=1)/KREUTZER.
ULM/arms. Rev. value. 1772-
73 . . . . 6.00

Billon

7 KREUZER. ULM KREUZER.
1767, Arms. Rev. Imp. eagle. 8.00
9 III ½ K(reuzer Stadtmünze).
2½ K(reuzer Conv. münze).
Like No. 11. 1758 . . . . 12.00
11 VII K(reuzer Stadtmünze).
5 K(reuzer Conv. münze).
ULM. Arms. Rev. FRANC. I etc.
Imp. eagle. 1758 . . . . 12.00

★13 5 (Conv. kreuzer). 1767 . . . . . 15.00

VORDER-OESTERREICH.
See AUSTRIA (HAPSBURG LANDS).

WALDECK (UND PYRMONT),
Princes

The counts of Waldeck, whose lands
bordered on Hesse, were a 13th century
offshoot of the line of counts of Schwalenberg. Their first coinage appeared
in the same century. Waldeck acquired
Pyrmont (q.v.) in the 16th century.
The Eisenberg line represented in this
catalog became princes in 1712.

Arms: Gold, a black star with six
(early) or eight (later) points.

Carl August Friedrich
1728-63

Copper

VG-F

1 I (pfennig). FURSTL. WALDECK
LANDMUNTZ. Double c(arl) mon.
Rev. ANNO DOMINI—, I in
cartouche. 1730-61 . . . . 2.50
2 II (pfennig). Sim. 1730 . . . . . 3.50
3 II/PFENNIGE. Obv. sim.
Rev. value/date. 1751-59 . . . 3.50
4 III (pfennig). Like No. 1.
1730 . . . . 3.75
5 III/PFENNIGE. Like No. 3.
1751-61 . . . . 3.50
6 IIII (pfennig). Like No. 1.
1730 . . . . 7.50
7 VI (pfennig). Sim. 1730 . . . . . 6.50

See Pyrmont for other copper coinage of this reign.

Billon

9 *1 KREUZER*. Like No. 1.
1730 . . . . 8.00

★12 VI/PFEN(nig). Double C mon.
1740-*55* 6.00
16 *24/EINEN (=1/24)/THALER*.
Arms. Rev. value. 1732, 37 . . 6.00
19 *12 EINEN (=1/12) THALER*.
Like No. 16. 1732, 37 . . . . 8.00

Silver

V.F.

23 ⅔ (Reichsthaler). CAROLUS D.G.
PR. WALDECC. Bust r. Rev.
Arms. 1733-34 . . . . 110.00
26 *(⅔ Reichsthaler)*. Bust l.
Rev. Arms. 1752 . . . . 100.00
28 (Speciesthaler). CAROL AUG.
FRID. D.G. Bust r. Rev. ARDUA
etc. Arms. 1741 . . . . 450.00
29 (Speciesthaler). CAROL D.G.
P. WALD. C. P. Bust l. Rev.
ARDUA etc. Arms. 1752 . . . . 350.00

Gold (ducat = 3.49 gr.;
Carolin = 9.7 gr.)

F-VF

30 (¼ ducat). Head. Rev. ARDUA
etc. Arms. 1741, 60, 61 . . . . 450.00
31 (½ ducat). Head. Rev. Arms.
1736 . . . . 900.00
32 (ducat). Like No. 30. 1731-
50 . . . . 1500.00
33 *(ducat)*. Bust l. Rev. Arms.
1762 . . . . 1500.00
34 *(ducat)*. Bust r. Rev. Arms.
1762 . . . . 1500.00
35 *(2 ducats)*. Head. Rev. Arms.
1750 . . . . 2250.00
36 (¼ Carolin). Bust. Rev. MONETA
AUREA WALDE., *Double C* mon.
cruciform, arms. 1735 . . . . . 1000.00

GERMAN STATES

WALDECK (Cont.)

F-VF

37 (½ *Carolin*). Head. Rev. Arms, initials. 1734...........1350.00

38 (½ *Carolin*). Like No. 36. 1735................2000.00

39 (*Carolin*). Head r. Rev. Arms. 1734................2250.00

40 (*Carolin*). Like No. 36. 1734................1800.00

41 (*Carolin*). Head l. Rev. Arms. 1750................2250.00

41.5 (*10 ducats*). Bust. Rev. Arms. 1752................RRR

Friedrich 1763-1812

Copper

VG-F

42 I/PFENNING. Like No. 42a but w/out obv. legend. 1773-99................ 1.50

★42a —. 1780-96............. 2.00

42b —. Sim. but Rev. SCHEIDE/MUNTZ omitted. 1809-10.... 2.75

43 I/PFENNING. FURST WALDECK etc. Arms. Rev. as No. 42a. 1781-99................ 3.50

43a —. Rev. as No. 42b. 1809.. 2.75

43b —. Rev. I/PFENNIG. 1810... 7.50

44 III/PFENNIGE. Obv. like No. 42a but LAND MUNZ. Rev. value. 1781............. 6.50

44a —. FURSTL. WALDECK SCH. MVNZ. 1781-1810........... 5.00

44b —. Like No. 42. 1797-98.... 4.00

45 III/PFENNIGE. Like No. 43a. 1781-1809............. 5.00

45a —. No obv. legend. 1810.... 6.00

★46 ½/GROSCHEN. 1809...... 5.00

Silver

V.F.

50 *10 KREUZER*. Arms. Rev. value. 1763................22.00

53 IV/EINEN (=¼)/THALER. FRIDERICUS PR. WALDECCIAE etc. Arms. Rev. value. 1810................70.00

V.F.

57 10 EINE etc. (= Conv. thaler). FRIED.D.G.PR.WALD. etc. Head. Rev. VIRTVTE etc. Arms. 1781................350.00

59 X EINE etc. (= Conv. thaler). Like No. 53. 1810........375.00

59a —. FRIDERICUS D. G. PR. etc. 1810................600.00

Gold

F-VF

61 (*ducat*). Like No. 57. 1781................2250.00

Georg, In Pyrmont 1805-12, In Waldeck-Pyrmont 1812-13

See Pyrmont for his other coins.

Silver

V.F.

★62 IV/EINEN (=¼)/THALER. 1812-13................450.00

Obv.   Nos. 63, 64

VF-EF

★63 X EINE etc. (on edge = Conv. thaler). 1813...........1000.00

Rev.   Nos. 63, 64

★64 KRONTHALER (on edge). 1813................1000.00

64a —. WALDECKISCHER etc. (on edge). 1813.........1200.00

64b —. Stars in lieu of value on edge. 1813................1200.00

Georg Heinrich 1813-45

Copper

Fine

65 I/PFENNIG. GH script. Rev. value. 1816-17........ 5.00

66 I/PFENNIG. Like No. 43b. 1816-17................. 7.00

67 I/PFENNIG. Arms of Waldeck-Pyrmont, no legend. Rev. value. 1821. (var.)........ 2.25

68 I/PFENNIG. F.W.S.M. Arms on mantle. Rev. value. 1825.. 2.25

★69 1/PFENNIG. 1842-45...... 2.00

70 III/PFENNIG(E). Arms of W-P on mantle. Rev. value. 1819. (var.).............. 3.75

70a —. Rev. value/SCHEIDE/MUNZE. 1819................. 3.75

71 3/PFENNIGE. Like No. 70a. 1824-25................. 3.75

72 3/PFENNIGE. Like No. 69. 1842-45................. 3.00

73 ½/MARIEN/GROSCHEN. FURSTL. WALDECK LANDMUNZE. Arms. Rev. value. 1825..... 9.00

Billon

★74 I/MARIEN/GROSCH(en). 1814, 20................. 5.00

74a —. Obv. no legend, star shield. 1820.................30.00

74b —. Obv. no legend, W-P arms on mantle. 1820, 23........ 6.50

75 24/EINEN (=¹⁄₂₄)/THALER. Like No. 74b. 1818-19.....12.50

76 1/SILBER/GROSCHEN. GEORG HEINRICH FÜRST Z. WALDECK U. P. Arms. Rev. value. 1836, 39........... 4.00

77 1/SILBER/GROSCHEN. Like No. 87. 1842-45....... 3.00

78 2/MARIEN/GROSCH(en). Like No. 74b. 1820-28. (var.)................. 6.00

Silver

V.F.

79 6/EINEN (=⅙) /THALER. Like No. 76. 1837-45.....17.00

80 3/EINEN (=⅓)/THALER. GEORG etc. 2 fold arms. Rev. XLII etc., value. 1824......30.00

80a —. Obv. of No. 80. Rev. of No. 81 (mule). 1824........40.00

GERMAN STATES

WALDECK (Cont.)

V.F.

81 3/EINEN/THALER. No legend.
9 fold arms. Rev. value (w/out
XLII etc.). 1824...........50.00

82 EIN (=1)/KRONEN/
THALER. Value. Rev. palm
tree. 1824...............350.00

83 2/THALER. Arms. Rev. value.
1842, 45.................500.00

Emma, Regent 1845-52
For Georg Victor

Silver

VF-EF

*84 2/THALER. Obv. *.
Rev. value. 1847........1400.00

Georg Victor, Alone, 1852-93

Copper

F-VF

85 1/PFENNIG. Like No. 69.
1855, 67.................2.00

86 3/PFENNIGE. Sim.
1855, 67.................2.00

Billon

*87 1/SILBER/GROSCHEN.
1855, 67.................5.00

Silver

V.F.

88 EIN (=1) VEREINSTHALER.
Head. Rev. Arms. 1859, 67..65.00

89 2 THALER. Sim. 1856....450.00

WALLMODEN-GIMBORN.
See Gimborn.

WEIMAR. See Saxe-Weimar.

WERDEN UND HELMSTAEDT,
Twin Abbeys

Werden (in the Ruhr) and Helmstaedt
(east of Brunswick-Wolfenbüttel) were
united at an early date and received
the mint right in 974. They were secularized in 1803.

Anselm von Sonius, 1757-74

Silver

E.F.

10 (thaler). ANSELMUS D.G. S.R.I.
ABBAS WERDINENSIS etc. Arms.
Rev. S. LUDGERUS etc. Saint in
clouds over 2 abbeys. 1765.550.00

WEST FRIESLAND.
See LOW COUNTRIES.

WESTPHALIA (WESTFALEN)
Kingdom

Parts of Hesse-Cassel, Brunswick, Hildesheim, Paderborn, Halberstadt, Osnabrück, Minden, etc., erected by Napoleon into a kingdom for his brother,
Hieronymus (Jerome) 1807-13. In 1813-
14 Westphalia was redistributed to its
former secular rulers.

Hieronymus Napoleon 1807-13

I. Coinage on the German Stan-
dard.

A. Clausthal Mint.

Copper

Fine

1 I/PFENNING. HN mon
Rev. value. 1808..........4.00

2 II/PFENNING. Sim. 1808,
10......................6.00

Billon

3 IIII/PFENN(ig). HN mon.
Rev. NACH DEM etc., value.
1808....................30.00

3a —. 1809...............10.00

4 I/MARIEN/GROS(chen).
Sim. 1808, 10...........10.00

5 12/EINEN (=1/12)/THALER.
Sim. 1808-10............10.00

Silver

V.F.

6 1/6 (Reichsthaler). HIERONYMUS
NAPOLEON. Arms. Rev. KOENIG
etc. 1/6. 1808, 12........100.00

6a —. 1810...............50.00

7 2/3 (Reichsthaler). Like No. 7a
but HIERONYMUS begins at
1 o'clock. 1808, 10........80.00

V.F.

*7a —. 1809-10.............60.00

*8 (2/3 Reichsthaler). 1811.....200.00

9 2/3 (Reichsthaler). Obv. like
No. 8. Rev. like No. 7a but
LEIPZIGER instead of REICHS.
1811-13.................75.00

*10 10 ST. EINE etc. (= Conv.
thaler). Laureate head r. Rev.
*. Mansfeld mines. 1811...350.00

B. Brunswick Mint.

Silver

11 VI/EINEN (=1/6)/THALER.
Obv. like No. 6. Rev. 80 STUCK
etc., value. 1809-13B.......27.50

WESTPHALIA (Cont.)

V.F.

★12 XXIIII/MARIEN/
GROSCH(en). 1810.......80.00

Gold

13 V/THALER. Obv. like No. 6.
Rev. value. 1810.......1850.00

14 V/THALER. Bare head.
Rev. value. 1811.......2500.00

14a —. Laureate head.
1811-13...............1500.00

15 X/THALER. Like No. 13.
1810....................RRR

16 X/THALER. Like No. 14.
1811.................3000.00

16a —. Like No. 14a.
1811-13.............2250.00

C. Cassel Mint.

Billon
Fine

17 24/EINEN (=¹⁄₂₄)/THALER.
HN mon. Rev. value. 1807-
09F.....................7.00

17a —. 1809C...............7.00

Silver
V.F.

18 VI EINEN (=⅙) THALER.
Like No. 11. 1808-10F, 09-
13C....................35.00

VF-EF

19 X/EINE etc. (= Conv. thaler).
HIERONYMUS NAPOLEON. Arms.
Rev. value. 1810...........RR

VF-EF

★20 X/EINE etc. (= Conv. thaler).
1810-13.................175.00

II. Coinage on the French Standard.

Cassel (C) and Paris (J) Mints.

Copper
Fine

21 1/CENT(ime). Like No. 24.
1809, 12C................2.00

22 2/CENT(imes). Sim. 1808-
12C.....................2.50

22a —. 1808J...............*pattern*

23 3/CENT(imes). Sim. 1808-
12C.....................2.50

23a —. 1808J...............*pattern*

★24 5/CENT(imes). 1808-12C...5.00

24a —. 1808-09J............*pattern*

Billon

25 10/CENT(imes). Sim. but
HN cwnd. 1808-12C........6.00

25a —. 1808J...............*pattern*

26 20/CENT(imes). Sim. 1808-
12C.....................7.00

26a —. 1808J...............*pattern*

Silver
V.F.

27 ½/FRANK. Like No. 29.
1808J...................150.00

28 1/FRANK. Sim. 1808J....250.00

V.F.

★29 2/FRANK. 1808J........150.00

30 5/FRANK. Sim. but head l.
1808J...................350.00

30a —. 1809J...............300.00

Gold
VF-EF

31 5/FRANK. Sim. 1813C....750.00

32 10/FRANK. Sim. 1813C...750.00

33 20/FRANK. Sim. Edge: GOTT
ERHALTE etc. 1808-09J.....800.00

33a —. 1808-11. Eagle's head
and C...................750.00

33b —. 1809 Horse's head and
C.......................750.00

33c —. No edge inscription.
(restrikes)................——

34 40/FRANK. 1813C.......RRR

34a —. 1813C. No edge inscription.
(restrike)................——

WIED, Counts and Princes

Noble family in the Rhine-Lahn district first mentioned 11th century. First known coins 14th century. Divided into branches of Wied-Runkel and Wied-Neuwied in 1698. Lands of both branches mediatized during the Napoleonic era.

Arms: Gold, a red pale charged with a peacock.

Monetary System: 12 pfennig = 3 kreuzer Landmünze = 1 groschen; 60 stüber = 24 groschen = 1 Reichsthaler.

WIED-NEUWIED
Friedrich Alexander,
Count 1737-86, Prince 1786-91

Copper
VG-F

1 (pfennig). Miner. Rev. LOUISEN/
GLUCK (mine). 1749.......17.50

2 I/PFENNING. FFAW mon. Rev.
value/LANDMUNTZ/1753.....8.50

★3 (¼ stüber). FFAW mon. Rev.
mine windlass. 1748-50.
(var.)...................5.50

GERMAN STATES
···

WIED-NEUWIED (Cont.)

VG-F

4 ¼/STVBER. FFA mon. Rev. LANDMVNZ, value. 1749-51 .. 5.50

5 (¼ stüber). FFAW mon. Rev. AEREA etc., windlass. 1749 R.N. 5.50

6 ¼/STUBER. GOTT SEGNE DAS BERGWERCK. Mining scene. Rev. BERG MUNTZ, value. 1750 .... 5.50

7 ¼/STVBER. Obv. like No. 6/ ALEXANDER. Rev. GRAFL. WIED etc., value. 1752 .... 5.50

Billon

10 *3 PFENNING.* Arms. Rev. value. 1751 .... 6.00

12 *4 PFENNING.* Arms. Rev. value. 1751 .... 8.00

*14 ½/STVBER. 1752 .... 6.00

15 *1 KREUZER.* 1751 .... 6.00

16 I/STVBER. Like No. 14. 1752, 61 .... 5.00

18 *2 STVBER.* Like No. 14. 1752-53, *58* 6.00

20 *1/24 (thaler).* Bust. Rev. DECENTE etc., peacock in cartouche. 1750-51 .... 6.00

22 4/KREU/ZER. Like No. 14. 1751 .... 8.00

24 4/KREU/ZER. Like No. 34. 1753 .... 8.00

26 3/STVBER. Like No. 14. 1752, 54 .... 8.00

28 *4 STVBER.* Bust. Rev. value. 1752 .... 8.00

29 *5 (kreuzer).* Bust. Rev. Arms. 1750 .... 12.00

30 240 (=5 Conv. kreuzer). 4 fold arms. Rev. GW mon. on "240" pedestal. 1764 ...... 12.00

32 12/EINEN (=1/12)/REICHS/ THALER. FRID. ALEX. COM. WEDAE. Bust. Rev. value. 1757 .... 12.00

33 *12 EINEN THALER.* Bust. Rev. value. 1786 .... 12.00

*34 XII/KREV/ZER. 1754-57 .. 17.50

Silver

Fine

36 ¼ GULDEN. Bust. Rev. DECENTE etc. View of Neuwied. 1753 .... 17.50

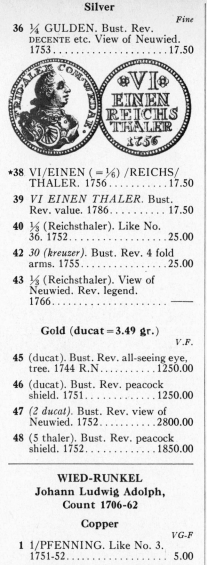

*38 VI/EINEN (=⅙) /REICHS/ THALER. 1756 .... 17.50

39 *VI EINEN THALER.* Bust. Rev. value. 1786 .... 17.50

40 ⅓ (Reichsthaler). Like No. 36. 1752 .... 25.00

42 30 (kreuzer). Bust. Rev. 4 fold arms. 1755 .... 25.00

43 ⅓ (Reichsthaler). View of Neuwied. Rev. legend. 1766 .... ——

Gold (ducat = 3.49 gr.)

V.F.

45 (ducat). Bust. Rev. all-seeing eye, tree. 1744 R.N 1250.00

46 (ducat). Bust. Rev. peacock shield. 1751 .... 1250.00

47 *(2 ducat).* Bust. Rev. view of Neuwied. 1752 .... 2800.00

48 (5 thaler). Bust. Rev. peacock shield. 1752 .... 1850.00

WIED-RUNKEL
Johann Ludwig Adolph, Count 1706-62

Copper

VG-F

1 1/PFENNING. Like No. 3. 1751-52 .... 5.00

2 1/GVTER (good)/PFENNING. Sim. 1752 .... 6.00

*3 ¼/STVBER. G(raf) W(ied) mon. 1751-58 .... 4.50

Billon

5 1/KREU/ZER. IOH. LUD. ADOL. G.Z. WR I.V.C. Bust. Rev. G. WR etc., value. 1758 .... 7.00

7 *1 STVBER.* Bust. Rev. double arms. 1758 .... 7.00

10 *2 STVBER.* Cwnd. mon. 1758 .... 8.00

12 *3 (kreuzer).* Like No. 7. 1758. 8.00

14 *4 KREUZER.* 3 shields. Rev. value. 1758 .... 10.00

VG-F

16 VI (kreuzer). Like No. 7. 1758 .... 13.50

Silver

*18 VI/EINEN (=⅙) /THALER. 1758 .... 28.00

Christian Ludwig, Count 1762-91, Prince 1791

Silver

VF-EF

20 (thaler). CHRIST: LUD: COM: WED: etc. Busts of Chr. Ludw. and Charlotte Sophie. Rev. view of Runkel. On his marriage. 1762 R.N .... RR

WISMAR, City

On the Baltic. Belonged to Sweden 1648-1803, to Mecklenburg-Schwerin 1803 on. Local coinage from the 13th century until 1854.

Arms: Per pale.

Dexter: Gold, right half of black (Mecklenburg) buffalo head.
Sinister: Barry of 4, black and white.

Monetary System:

12 pfennig = 1 schilling.

Under Sweden

Copper

VG-F

*1 III/PFENING. 1721-99 .... 5.75

2 6/PFENNING. Arms. Rev. value. 1762 .... 6.50

Under Mecklenburg-Schwerin

Copper

3 III/PFENING. Like No. 1. 1824-45 .... 2.50

3a —. MOHETA. 1835 .... 4.00

4 3/PFENNINGE. Helmeted arms. Rev. value. 1854 ..... 4.25

WÜRTTEMBERG,
Dukes, Electors and Kings

In South Germany between Baden and Bavaria. The counts of W. acquired a sizeable portion of Swabia at the death of Conradin Hohenstaufen in 1268. They obtained the mint right in 1374, became dukes in 1495, electors in 1803 and kings in 1806.

GERMAN STATES

WÜRTTEMBERG (Cont.)

Arms:
Württemberg: Gold, 3 black stag horns.
Teck: Lozengy, black and gold.
Württemberg (Hereditary Flagbearer of the Empire): Blue, gold flag charged with black eagle.

Carl Eugen,
Under Regency 1737-44,
Duke 1744-93

Coins of 1744-93

Billon

VG-F

2 ½ (kreuzer). *Arms.* Rev. blank. 1747........ 4.50

5 ½ (kreuzer). Stag horns in round shield. Rev. ½. 1766...... 3.50

7 ½ (kreuzer) Obv. like No. 5 Rev. blank. 1768-87........ 3.50

9 ½ (kreuzer). Cwnd. oval arms. Rev. ½. 1791............ 4.00

12 1 K(reuzer). Double c(arl) mon. Rev. Arms. 1744-45....... 3.50

14 *1 K(reuzer). 1749*......... 3.50

★16 1 (kreuzer). 1758-70....... 3.75

18 *1 (kreuzer). 1785, 90, 91*..... 3.75

25 III (kreuzer). Double c mon. Rev. Arms. 1746.......... 4.50

26 3 K(reuzer). Sim. 1746..... 3.50

26a 3 (kreuzer). Rev. WURTEMBERG LAND MUNZ. Arms. 1746..... 4.75

28 3 (kreuzer). Bust. Rev. WURTEMBERG LAND MUNZ. 4 fold arms. 1747.......... 4.75

28a 3 K(reuzer). WURTEMBERG deleted. 1758............... 2.50

★30 48/EINEN/CONVENT./ THALER (=3 kr. Landmünze =2½ Conv. kreuzer). 1767-92. (var.)............... 2.50

34 4 (kreuzer). CAROLUS etc. 3 shields. Rev. COM. MON. etc. Arms. 1760............... 5.75

36 6 K(reuzer). Like No. 26. 1746.................... 6.00

37 6 K(reuzer). Like No. 28. 1747-50................ 4.75

VG-F
37a —. Like No. 28a. 1758..... 5.00

40 240 EINE etc. (=5 Conv. kreuzer =6 kr. Landmünze). CAROLUS etc. Bust. Rev. Arms. 1769.............. 5.00

40a 5 (Conv. kreuzer). 1790.... 5.00

42 *(10 Conv. kreuzer).* Bust. Rev. Arms. 1763.......... 6.50

★43 10 (Conv. kreuzer). 1764.... 6.50

44 10 (Conv. kreuzer). Sim. but 4 fold arms. 1765, 90....... 6.50

★48 15 K(R)(euzer). 1746-59 (var.).................. 8.00

Silver

50 VI/EINEN (=⅙) /REICHS/ THALER. Bust. Rev. value. 1758.................... 25.00

51 VI/EINEN/REICHS/ THALER. Double CE mon. Rev. value. 1758......... 40.00

53 *20 (kreuzer). 1744*......... 10.00

56 20 (Conv. kreuzer). Like No. 43. 1763-64............... 7.50

57 20 (Conv. kreuzer). Like No. 44. 1765, 67, 75.......... 7.50

58 20 (Conv. kreuzer). Bust. Rev. Arms. 1768, 74....... 7.50

59 20 (Conv. kreuzer). Bust in rhombus. Rev. PROVIDE etc. Arms supported. 1769...... 10.00

61 20 (Conv. kreuzer). Bust in rhombus. Rev. Imp. eagle in rhombus. 1770............ 7.50

V.F.
64 (¼ thaler). Bust. Rev. PROVIDE etc. 5 fold arms. 1744....... 75.00

66 (½ thaler). Like No. 64. 1744...................... 300.00

69 ⅔ *(Reichsthaler). 1759*..... 300.00

72 (thaler). Like No. 64. 1746. 375.00

72a —. Rev. Arms on mantle. 1748................... 550.00

73 10 F M (= Conv. thaler). Bust. Rev. helmeted arms. 1759.................... 200.00

73a —. Rev. cwnd. squared arms. 1760................... 165.00

V.F.
74 10 AUF etc. (= Conv. thaler). Bust. Rev. Arms. 1760-66. (var.).................. 135.00

75 10 EINE etc. (= Conv. thaler). Bust. Rev. Arms supported. 1768.................... 175.00

76 10 EINE etc. (= Conv. thaler). Bust. Rev. Arms. 1769-84. (var.).................. 175.00

77 (2 thaler). Like No. 64. 1744............. (E.F.) 850.00

Gold

78 (ducat). Bust. Rev. cwnd. arms. 1744-91, N.D..... 1450.00

79 (ducat). Bust. Rev. helmeted arms. 1746............. 1450.00

80 (ducat). c(arl) and F(riederike) mon. in shield. Rev. altar. 1749. Celebrating his 1748 wedding............... 1200.00

Ludwig Eugen 1793-95

Billon

VG-F
82 ½ (kreuzer). LUDOV. EUGEN D.G. DUX WIRT. Bust. Rev. ½. N.D................. 12.00

84 1 (kreuzer). Obv. like No. 82. Rev. Arms. 1794.......... 6.00

86 48/EINEN/CONVENT./ THALER (=3 kreuzer Landmünze). Arms. Rev. value 1794.................... 7.00

Silver

E.F.
★90 (Conv. thaler). 1794...... 550.00

Gold

V.F.
92 (ducat). Like No. 90. 1794................. 1500.00

GERMAN STATES

WÜRTTEMBERG (Cont.)

Friedrich I Eugen 1795-97

Billon

VG-F

95 1/KREUTZER. F.E.H.Z.W.
Arms. Rev. value. 1796 ..... 7.00

97 48/EINEN/CONVENT./
THALER (=3 kr. Landmünze).
FRID. EUG. D.G. DUX. W. Arms.
Rev. value. 1796 .... 7.00

Silver

V.F.

99 60 EINE etc. (=20 Conv.
Kreuzer). Head r. Rev. 60 etc.
Arms. 1796 .... 60.00

103 (Conv. thaler). Head l. Rev.
Arms/TERT. DUCAT/SECULAR.
300th year duchy. 1795 .... 425.00

Friedrich 1797-1816

I. As Duke Friedrich II 1797-1803.

Billon

VG-F

106 ½ (kreuzer). F II. Rev. ½.
1798 .... 4.50

108 1/KREUTZER. F II. Rev.
value. 1799-1802 .... 4.50

110 3 (kreuzer). F II. Rev. Arms
in heart shield. 1798-99 .... 5.00

110a —. Rev. round shield. 1800-
02 .... 5.00

112 6 (kreuzer). Like No. 110.
1799 .... 6.00

Silver

V.F.

116 (20 Conv. kreuzer). FRIDERICUS
II D.G. DUX WIRTEMB. ET T.
Bust. Rev. CUM DEO etc. Arms.
1798-99 .... 40.00

116a 20 (Conv. kreuzer). 1798 ... 40.00

119 (Conv. thaler). Like No. 120.
1798. (2 vars.) ...... (E.F.) 800.00

E.F.

★120 (2 Conv. thaler). 1798 ... 1500.00

II. As Elector Friedrich I 1803-06.

Billon

Fine

122 1 KR(euzer). CHURF. WURT.
etc., F II mon. Rev. Arms.
1803-04 .... 3.00

122a —. Cwnd. F II mon. 1805 .. 3.00

124 III/KREUZER. Like No.
122. 1803-06 .... 3.00

126 VI/KREUZER. Like No.
122. 1803-05 .... 6.00

Silver

V.F.

128 10 (Conv. kreuzer). FRID. II
D.G. DUX WURT. . . . ELECTOR.
Bust. Rev. CUM DEO etc. Arms.
1805 .... 20.00

130 20 (Conv. kreuzer). Like No.
128. 1805 .... 40.00

132 (½ Conv. thaler). Like No.
128. 1805 .... 150.00

134 (Conv. thaler). Like No. 128.
1803 .... 750.00

Gold

136 *(ducat)*. Bust. Rev. legend
in wreath. 1803, 04 ...... *1950.00*

137 (ducat). FRIED. II HERZ. V.
WURT. V. CHURFURST. Bust r.
Rev. CUM DEO etc. Arms.
1804 .... 1500.00

III. As King Friedrich I 1806-16.

Billon

Fine

138 ½ (kreuzer). Cwnd. FR mon.
Rev. ½. 1812-16, N.D 3.00

139 I/KREUZER. Cwnd. FR mon.
Rev. value. 1807-16 .... 2.50

140 III/KREUZER. Like No.
142. 1806 .... 7.50

141 III/KREUZER. Like No.
143. 1807-14 .... 3.00

Fine

★142 VI/KREUZER. Electoral
arms. 1806 .... 9.00

★143 VI/KREUZER. Royal arms.
1806-14 .... 3.75

Silver

V.F.

144 10 (Conv. kreuzer). Obv. like
No. 155. Rev. AD NORMAM
etc., oval arms. 1808-09 .... 30.00

145 10 (Conv. kreuzer). FRID(ERICH)
KOENIG VON WURTEMB. Head r.
Rev. NACH DEM etc., oval arms.
1812. (2 var.) 22.50

146 20 (Conv. kreuzer). Like No.
144. 1807-10 .... 25.00

147 20 (Conv. kreuzer). FRIDERICH
I KOENIG etc. Head l. Rev.
NACH DEM etc., oval arms.
1810, 12 .... 25.00

147a —. Rev. AD NORMAM etc.
(Mule with No. 146). 1810 .. 37.50

148 20 (Conv. kreuzer). Like No.
145. 1812 .... 25.00

149 (Conv. thaler). FRIDERICUS
D. G. REX WURT. S.R.I. AR. etc.
Rev. electoral arms (see No.
142). 1806 .... 900.00

149a —. REX WURTEMBERG(IAE).
1806. (2 var.) 650.00

150 (Conv. thaler). Like No.
149a but royal arms. 1809.
(2 var.) 900.00

151 KRONEN THALER (on edge).
Obv. like No. 149a. Rev.
like No. 157. 1810 .... 950.00

152 KRONEN THALER (on edge).
Sim. but FRIEDRICH I KOENIG
etc. 1810 .... 950.00

153 KRONEN THALER (on edge).
Head l. Rev. sim. 1810 ... 250.00

153a —. 1811 .... 550.00

154 KRONEN THALER (on edge).
Head r. Rev. sim. 1812 ... 350.00

Gold (ducat =3.49 gr.)

VF-EF

★155 (ducat). 1808 .... 1500.00

WÜRTTEMBERG (Cont.)

VF-EF

156 (ducat). Like No. 157.
1813 . . . . 1850.00

★157 (Carolin or Friedrich d'or).
1810 . . . . 2600.00

Wilhelm I 1816-64

Copper

Fine

158 ¼/KREUZER. Like No. 159
but w/out SCHEIDE MUNZE.
1842-56 . . . . 1.75

★159 ¼/KREUZER. 1858-64 . . . 1.00

160 ½/KREUZER. Like No. 158.
1840-56 . . . . 1.00

161 ½/KREUZER. Like No. 159.
1858-64 . . . . 1.00

Billon

162 ½ (kreuzer). Cwnd. w. Rev.
½. 1818, N.D. (=1818) . . . 4.00

163 ½ (kreuzer). Arms. Rev.
SCHEIDE etc. ½. 1824-37 . . . 2.00

★164 I/KREUZER. 1818.
(2 var.) 4.00

165 1 K(reuzer). Head. Rev.
Arms. 1824-38 . . . . 2.75

166 1/KREUZER. KONIGR.
WURTTEMBERG. Arms. Rev.
value. 1839-42 . . . . 2.00

166a —. KONIGR. WURTTB. 1842-
57 . . . . 1.25

166b —. Like No. 205,
K. WÜRTTEMBERG etc.
1857-64 . . . . 1.00

167 III/KREUZER. Like No.
164. 1818. (2 var.) 5.00

168 3 K(reuzer). Head. Rev.
round arms. 1823-25 . . . . 5.00

168a —. Pointed arms. 1826-37 . . 3.00

Fine

169 3/KREUZER. Like No. 166.
1839-42 . . . . 3.00

169a —. Like No. 166a. 1842-56 . 2.00

170 VI/KREUZER. Like No. 164.
1817-18 . . . . 5.00

170a —. 1819, 21 . . . . 5.00

171 6 K(reuzer). Like No. 168.
1823-25. (var.) 6.00

171a —. Like No. 168a. 1825-37. 3.00

172 6/KREUZER. Like No. 166.
1838-42 . . . . 3.00

172a —. Like No. 166a. 1842-56 . 2.00

Silver

V.F.

173 10/KREUZER. Head. Rev.
value. 1818 . . . . 15.00

174 10 (kreuzer). Head. Rev.
round arms. 1823 . . . . 30.00

175 12 K(reuzer). Head. Rev.
round arms. 1824 . . . . 25.00

175a —. 1825 . . . . 30.00

176 20/KREUZER. Like No. 173.
1818 . . . . 20.00

177 20 (kreuzer). Like No. 174.
1823 . . . . 32.50

178 24 K(reuzer). Like No. 175.
1824-25 . . . . 40.00

★179 ½/GULDEN. 1838-64 . . . . 20.00

★180 EIN (=1) GULDEN.
1824 . . . . 65.00

181 EIN GULDEN. KOENIG VON
etc. Head. Rev. pointed arms.
1825 . . . . 120.00

181a —. KOENIG V. etc. 1825 . . . 60.00

182 1/GULDEN. Like No. 179.
With VOIGT under head. 1838-
56 . . . . 35.00

182a —. With A.D. under head.
1837-38 . . . . 35.00

182b —. w/out VOIGT. 1839-41 . . 35.00

182c —. 1848 over 1846 . . . . ——

E.F.

★183 EIN GULDEN (on edge).
25th year of reign. 1841 . . . . 50.00

★184 EIN GULDEN (on edge).
King's mint visit. 1844 . . . 450.00

★185 (gulden). Laureate head.
Rev. legend. Queen's mint
visit. 1845 . . . . ——

V.F.

★186 EIN (=1) VEREINSTHALER.
Head. Rev. Arms. 1857-
64 . . . . 25.00

186.5 2 GULDEN. Head r.
Rev. round arms
1823 . . . . (E.F.) pattern?

187 ZWEI (=2) GULDEN.
Like No. 180. Head 25mm.
high. 1824 . . . . 150.00

187a —. Head 31mm. high.
1824 . . . . 350.00

188 ZWEI (=2) GULDEN.
Like No. 181. 1825 . . . . 175.00

189 ZWEY (=2) GULDEN. Head.
Rev. Arms. 1845-56 . . . . . . 60.00

190 EIN (=1)/CONVENTIONS/
THALER. Head l. Rev.
value. 1817 . . . . 500.00

GERMAN STATES

WÜRTTEMBERG (Cont.)

V.F.

190a —. Head r. 1818........350.00
191 EIN (=1)/KRONEN/
THALER. Head l. Rev.
value. 1817............600.00
191a —. Head r. 1818........350.00
192 KRONEN THALER. Head.
Rev. pointed arms. 1825-
37........................80.00
193 KRONENTHALER (on edge).
Head. Rev. HANDELSFREIHEIT
etc. 1833................80.00
194 2/THALER. Head. Rev.
value. 1840-55........125.00
195 VII EINE etc. (=2 thaler,
on edge). Head. Rev. heads
of Carl and Olga. Wedding
of Crown Prince. 1846....200.00

Gold

★196 (ducat). 1818..........1400.00
197 1 DUCATEN (=ducat).
Head l. Rev. Arms. 1840-
48......................700.00
198 FÜNF (=5) GULDEN.
Head r. Rev. pointed arms.
1825....................900.00
198a —. 1824, 35..........1000.00
198b —. 1839............1400.00
199 ZEHN (=10) GULDEN.
Sim. 1824-25..........=2250.00
200 (10 gulden). Head. Rev. IN
DES/KOENIGS/etc. Royal
mint visit. 1825..........RRR
201 VIER (=4) DUCATEN
(on edge). No. 183 in gold.
1841....................1000.00
202 VIER DUCATEN (on edge).
No. 184 in gold. 1844......RR

**Nos. 201 and 202 w/out values
shown are restrikes.**

Karl I 1864-91

Copper

F-VF

203 ¼ KREUZER. Like No. 159.
1865-72................1.00
204 ½ KREUZER. Sim.
1865-72................1.00

Billon

★205 1 KREUZER. 1865-73.... 1.25

Silver

V.F.

206 ½/GULDEN. Head. Rev.
value. 1865-66..........25.00

★206a —. 1867-69............25.00
206b —. 1870-71............25.00
207 EIN (=1) VEREINS-
THALER. Head. Rev. Arms
supported, antlers hang.
1865...................225.00

★207a—. Antlers extend into legend.
1865-67................30.00
207b —. 1868-70............35.00

★208 XXX EIN etc. (on edge,
=1 thaler). Victory over France.
1870-71 (one coin).......35.00

E.F.

★209 ZWEI (=2) THALER. Head.
Rev. Ulm Cathedral. 37 gr.
1869, 71...............500.00
209a —. 33.5gr.(Restrikes)(*Unc.*)25.00

WÜRZBURG (WIRCEBURG, HERBIPOLIS), Bishopric

In Franconia. Established in 741. Acquired the mint right in the 11th century. Secularized and given to Bavaria
1803. Erected into a grand duchy for
Ferdinand of Tuscany-Salzburg 1806-
14. Returned to Bavaria 1814. Patron:
Saint Kilian.

Arms of Würzburg:
Red, 3 gold points.

**Arms of Duchy of (Eastern) Fran-
conia:** Red and silver flag on leaning
gold lance.

Monetary System:
(Courtesy of Hans-Dietrich Kahl.)
144 kreuzer (2⅖ gulden) rhein, =120
Conv. kreuzer (2 Conv. gulden) =96
kreuzer or 44⅘ schillinger (1⅗ gulden) fränk. =1 Conv. thaler.
504 heller =252 pfenninge fränk. =84
dreier (körtlinge) =28 schillinger =
60 kreuzer fränk. =1 guter (fränk)
gulden =1⅕ gulden (75 kreuzer) conventionsmünze = 1½ gulden (90
kreuzer) rhein. *Rhein. =Rhenish;*
fränk = Franconian.

The so-called "death groschen" are
medals.

Carl Philipp, Freiherr von Greiffenklau, Bishop 1749-54

Copper

VG-F

1 ½/PFENNING. CP mon.
Rev. ½/WIRZBURG/PFENNING/
1751....................2.75

★2 4/EINEN (=¼)/LEICHTERN
(=light)/KREUTZER. 1752-
53......................2.75

GERMAN STATES

WÜRZBURG (Cont.)

VG-F

★3 I/LEICHTER/KREUTZER.
1753.................... 3.00

Billon

★6 (schillinger). 1751......... 6.00

Silver
E.F.

8 (death groschen). Obv. like
No. 6. Rev. 10 lines: NATUS
etc. 1754.................30.00
V.F.

10 10 EINE etc. (= Conv. thaler).
CAROL: PHILIPP. D.G. EP. HERB.
etc. Bust. Rev. Arms. 1754.. ——

Gold

11 (gold gulden). Bust. Rev.
SINCERE etc. Arms, S.P.Q.W.
N.D. (1749 homage).....1100.00

12 *(gold gulden).* Arms. Rev.
griffin. N.D.............1200.00

Adam Friedrich,
Graf von Seinsheim,
Bishop of Würzburg 1755-79
(Also bishop of Bamberg, q.v.)

Copper
VG-F

14 ½/PFEN/NING. WIRZBURG
SCHEIDE MUNZ. Cwnd. AFF mon.
Rev. value. 1760-61..... 2.75

15 ½/PFEN/NING. Cwn. over
2 shields. Rev. value.
1761-64, N.D............. 2.75

16 ½ K(reuzer). Sim. but cartouches both sides. 1762,
N.D..................... 2.75

Billon

19 3 (pfenninge). Arms, 3 in orb.
Rev. blank. 1759-63..... 3.50

21 84 (=1 körtling). Cwn. over
3 shields. (Würzb., E. Francon.
and Seinsheim). Rev. 84 in
orb, M—P at sides. 1764..... 4.50

23 622½ EINE etc. (=schillinger).
Arms. Rev. SUSCIPE etc.
Madonna. 1763........... 7.00

VG-F

25 (2 kreuzer fränk.). CON-
VENTIONS LANDMÜNZ. AF mon.
Rev. Arms/M(W)P. 1764-65.. 6.00

28 (death groschen). ADAM FRID.
D.G. EP. BAM. ET WIRCEB. etc.
Cwnd. arms. Rev. 9 lines:
NATUS etc. 1779......*(E.F.)* 20.00

30 300 EINE etc. (=4 Conv.
kreuzer). Like No. 23. 1763.. 6.50

32 V K (=5 Conv. kreuzer).
AF mon. Rev. NACH DEM etc.
Arms/M(W)P. 1764-65....... 4.50

Silver

V.F.

★35 10 (Conv. kreuzer).
Rev. 1760................. 9.00

37 10 (Conv. kreuzer). Bust.
Rev. Arms. 1762-66....... 9.00

39 20 (Conv. kreuzer). Like No.
35. 1760, 63...............11.00

41 20 KREUZER. AD. FRIDER.
etc. Arms of Bam. Würz. Rev.
AD LEGEM etc., value. 1761..12.00

43 20 (Conv. kreuzer). Like No.
43a but Rev. SECHZIG etc. Arms.
1762.....................12.00

★43a —. 1763-76..............10.00

43b —. Bust in wreath.
1764-69..................10.00

45 ZWANZIG EINE etc. (=½
Conv. thaler). Like No. 51.
1760.....................45.00

46 XX EINE etc. (=½ Conv.
thaler). Bust. Rev. PATRONA
FRANCONIAE. Madonna stdg.
1761.....................45.00

48 20 EINE etc. (=½ Conv.
thaler). Like No. 46 but
Madonna std. 1765........45.00

49 *20 EINE etc. (=½ Conv. thaler).*
Bust. Rev. Arms sup-
ported. 1764-65..........45.00

50 (Conv. thaler). Rev. Bust.
11 lines: ADAMUS/HIC EST/etc.
Date (1760) in chronogram.500.00

51 ZEHEN EINE etc. (= Conv.
thaler). Bust. Rev. mantled
arms supported/G.N.(W)P.B.
1760. (var.).............150.00

52 X EINE etc. (= Conv. thaler).
Like No. 46. 1760........150.00

V.F.

53 10 EINE etc. (= Conv. thaler).
Like No. 48. 1763........125.00

53a —. 1764-65, 73-79........125.00

55 10 EINE etc. (= Conv. thaler).
Like No. 49. 1763-77.....125.00

56 X EINE etc. (= Conv. thaler).
Bust. Rev. ADAM FRID etc. Bishop
stdg. by arms. 1766......650.00

Gold (ducat =3.49 gr.)
VF-EF

57 (gold gulden). Bust. Rev.
PROSPERE etc. Arms/S.P.Q.W.
Homage of Würzburg. 1755.950.00

58 (gold gulden). Fame over arms.
Rev. BE/NEDI =/etc. 3 females.
N.D. (ca. 1757).........1000.00

59 *(gold gulden).* Bust. Rev.
dove, Franconia stdg. Peace
of Hubertusburg. 1764....950.00

60 EIN (=1) GOLDGULDEN.
Bust. Rev. palm tree/S.P.Q.W.
1773-78..................900.00

61 (ducat). Bust. Rev. Arms.
1755-70..................950.00

62 DUCATUS (=ducat). Bust in
rhombus. Rev. Arms in rhombus. 1772................950.00

63 DUCAT. Bust in rhombus.
Rev. Madonna in rhombus.
1773-79..................950.00

Franz Ludwig,
Freiherr von Erthal,
Bishop of Würzburg 1779-95
(Also bishop of Bamberg.)

Billon

VG-F

★66 84 (=1 körtling). 1794..... 4.50

69 (½ death groschen). Like No.
74. 1795.................11.00

★72 (schillinger). 1794-95....... 5.00

Silver
V.F.

74 (death groschen). FRANC. LUD.
D.G. EP. BAM. ET. WIRCEB.,
cwnd. arms. Rev. 9 lines:
NATUS etc. 1795...........15.00

76 20 (Conv. kreuzer). Bust with
ermine mantle. Rev. round
arms on cwnd. mantle. *1779.*
Taken out of circulation at re-
quest of bishop's brother, the
elector of Mainz, who claimed
ermine mantles were electoral
privilege.................45.00

GERMAN STATES

WÜRZBURG (Cont.)

V.F.

78 20 (Conv. kreuzer). Bust. Rev. S. KILIANUS etc. St. stdg. 1785-87 . . . . .12.50

80 20 (Conv. kreuzer). Bust. Rev. B.–W. arms. 1788-91 . . . . . . .12.50

83 LX/EINE etc. (=20 Conv. kreuzer). Like No. 92. 1795 . . . . .15.00

85 10 EINE etc. (= Conv. thaler). FRANC. LUDOV. D.G. EP. WIRC. etc. Bust. Rev. oval arms on cwnd. mantle. 1779 . . . .250.00

86 10 EINE etc. (= Conv. thaler). FRANC. LUDOV. D.G. EP. BAMB. ET. WIRC. etc. Bust. Rev. irreg. arms on cwnd. mantle. 1779-84 .75.00

87 X EINE etc. (= Conv. thaler). Bust. Rev. St. Kilian and 2 companions. 1785 . . . . .100.00

88 10 E. FEINE etc. (= Conv. thaler). Bust. Rev. PATRONA etc. Madonna std. 1786 . . . .100.00

89 X EINE etc. (= Conv. thaler). Bust. Rev. MERCES LABORUM. Angel, book, globe, prize. 1786-91 . . . . .250.00

89a —. 1794 . . . . .400.00

90 X EINE etc. (= Conv. thaler). Bust. Rev. S. KILIANUS etc. His statue. 1790 . . . . .150.00

91 X/EINE etc. (= Conv. thaler). Bust. Rev. PRO PATRIA, value. 1794-95 . . . . .125.00

92 X/EINE etc. (= Conv. thaler). Arms. Rev. PRO PATRIA, value. 1794-95 . . . . .125.00

93 V EINE etc. (=2 Conv. thaler). Like No. 89. 1786-91 . . . . . .600.00

Gold

94 EIN (=1) GOLD GULDEN. Bust. Rev. palm tree. 1779 . . . . .1000.00

95 EIN GOLD GULDEN. Bust. Rev. St. Kilian. 1786 . . . . .1000.00

96 EIN GOLD GULDEN. Bust. Rev. Arms. 1786-94 . . . . . . .900.00

97 EIN GOLD/GULDEN. Bust. Rev. St. Burkhard. 1790 . .1000.00

98 DUCAT. Like No. 87. 1785 . . . . .1000.00

99 ZWEY (=2) GOLD/GULDEN. Like No. 95. 1786 . . . . . .1600.00

Georg Carl, Freiherr von Fechenbach, Bishop 1795-1803

Billon

VG-F

★102 84 (=1 körtling). 1795 . . . . 3.50

VG-F

102a —. Arms/date. 1796-99 . . . . 2.50

★104 (schillinger). 1795-96 . . . . . . 3.50

Silver

V.F.

107 20 (Conv. kreuzer). Arms. Rev. PRO PATRIA, LX/EINE etc. 1795. (var.) 15.00

108 60 EINE etc. (=20 Conv. kreuzer). Bust. Rev. PRO PATRIA. Arms. 1795 . . . . . . 15.00

110 20 (Conv. kreuzer). Obv. of No. 108. Rev. of No. 107. 1795 . . . . 15.00

111 20 (Conv. kreuzer). Bust. Rev. Madonna. 1795 . . . . . . 15.00

112 20 (Conv. kreuzer). Bust. Rev. 3 saints. 1795 . . . . 15.00

114 20 (Conv. kreuzer). Bust. Rev. Arms. 1796 . . . . 15.00

117 X EINE etc. (= Conv. thaler). Bust. Rev. PRO PATRIA. Arms. 1795 . . . . .150.00

118 X/EINE etc. (= Conv. thaler). Bust. Rev. PRO PATRIA, value. 1795. (var.) 150.00

Gold

119 EIN (=1) GOLD GULDEN. Arms. Rev. palm tree. 1795 . . . . .950.00

★120 EIN GOLD/GULDEN. *1795, 98* 1250.00

121 EIN CAROLIN. Bust. Rev. Arms. 1795 . . . . . . .1900.00

Ferdinand, Grand Duke 1806-14

(Archduke of Austria, ex-grand duke of Tuscany, elector of Salzburg.)

Bronze

Fine

★151 1/VIERTEL (=¼) /KREUZER. 1811 . . . . 4.00

152 ½/KREUZER. Sim. 1810, 11 . . . . 4.00

Billon

Fine

153 I/KREUZER. Sim. (vars. with G.W.L.M. on obv. or rev.). 1808 . . . . 6.00

154 III/KREUZER. Sim. 1807-09 . . . . 6.50

155 VI/KREUZER. Sim. 1807-09 . . . . 6.50

The 20 kreuzer 1808-10 does not exist.

Gold

V.F.

157 (gold gulden). FERDINDUS D.G. H.B.R. PR. A.A.D. SAL. Bust. Rev. Arms. Salzburg type. 20.5mm. 1806 . . . . .950.00

158 EIN (=1) GOLD GULDEN. Obv. sim. Rev. palm tree, Wurzb. shield. (Mule). 20.5mm. 1809 . . . . .1250.00

159 EIN GOLD GULDEN. Bust, legend ends WIRCEBVR-GENSIS. Rev. like No. 158. 1809 . . . . .950.00

★160 EIN GOLD/GULDEN. 1812 . . . . .1250.00

161 EIN (=1) GOLD GULDEN. Head. Rev. oval arms. 1813 . . . . .1250.00

162 EIN GOLD GULDEN. Head. Rev. Arms leaning against altar, 3 burning hearts. 1814 . . . . .1450.00

UNVERIFIED DATA

Note: Throughout this catalog, any uncertain, indefinite or unconfirmed information is shown in *italic type*. Such material may be, for example, coin descriptions, dates and prices, names of rulers, or supplementary notes. Further information to confirm or correct *material in italics* should be sent to the author at the following address:

William D. Craig
c/o Whitman Coin Supply Division
1220 Mound Avenue
Racine, Wisconsin 53404, U.S.A.

NOTES

GIBRALTAR

British fortress at the straits leading from the Mediterranean into the Atlantic.

Monetary System:
24 quarts (quartos) = 1 real.

Victoria 1837-1901

Copper

Fine

1 HALF QUART. Like No. 3. 1842 . . . . 4.00

2 ONE QUART. Sim. 1842 . . . 5.00

★3 TWO QUARTS. 1842 . . . . . . 7.50

Nos. 1-3 dated 1841, 60 or 61 did not circulate.

A number of Gibraltar tradesmen's tokens exist from the period 1802-20.

GOLD COAST

Former British colony on the Gulf of Guinea on the West Coast of Africa (now Ghana).

Monetary System:
8 tackoe = 1 ackey.

Administration of the African Company 1750-1821

Proofs exist in silver and copper.

George III 1760-1820

Silver

E.F.

1 (tackoe). Like No. 2. 16mm. 1796 . . . . 160.00

★2 (2 tackoe). 1796 . . . . 240.00

3 (4 tackoe). Sim. 23mm. 1796 . . . . 375.00

4 (ackey). Sim. but arms supported. 1796 . . . . 800.00

5 ½ ACKEY. Like No. 6. 1818 . . . . 225.00

E.F.

★6 1 ACKEY. 1818 . . . . 475.00

GREAT BRITAIN, KINGDOM

Situated off the coast of Europe, separated from it by the English Channel and the North Sea.

Coins for England, Scotland and Wales only are listed here. Those for Ireland and the lesser islands are catalogued under the place of issue.

Monetary System:
4 farthings = 1 penny;
12 pence = 3 groats = 1 shilling;
20 shillings = 4 crowns = 1 pound (sovereign).

George II 1727-60

Copper

VG-F

1 (farthing). Like No. 1a but young bust. 1730-39 . . . . 1.50

2 (½ penny). Sim. 29mm. 1729-39 . . . . 1.75

★1a (farthing). 1741-54 . . . . 1.00

2a (½ penny). Sim. 1740-54 . . . . 1.75

Silver

I. Maundy Issues

VF-EF

3 1 (penny). Young bust. Rev. MAG. BRI. etc., value. 1729-60 . . . . 6.00

4 2 (pence). Sim. 1729-60 . . . . . 3.50

5 3 (pence). Sim. 1729-60 . . . . . 12.00

6 4 (pence). Sim. 1729-60 . . . . . 12.00

II. Regular Issues

A. Young Bust.

F-VF

7 (6 pence). Bust. Rev. 4 shields cruciform. 23mm. 1728-41 . . . 10.00

8 (shilling). Sim. 29mm. 1727-41 . . . . 10.00

9 (½ crown). Sim. 35mm. 1731-41 . . . . 35.00

10 (crown). Sim. 40mm. 1732-41 . . . . 130.00

B. Old Bust.
(Same coin diameters as Nos. 7-10)

F-VF

7a (6 pence). Like No. 8b but w/out LIMA. 1743-58 . . . . 4.00

7b —. LIMA under bust. 1745-46 . . . . 7.50

8a (shilling). Like No. 7a. 1743-58 . . . . 4.00

★8b —. LIMA under bust. 1745-46 . . . . 10.00

9a (½ crown). Like No. 7a. 1743-51 . . . . 30.00

9b —. LIMA under bust. 1745-46 . . . . 25.00

10a (crown). Like No. 7a. 1743-51 . . . . (V.F.) 130.00

10b —. LIMA under bust. 1746 . . 150.00

Silver coins of 6 pence and larger are found with and w/out roses and plumes in angles of the shields.

Gold (guinea = 8.4 gr.)
First Regular Issue

V.F.

11 (½ guinea). Young head. Rev. Arms. 1728-39 . . . . . . 500.00

12 (guinea). Sim. 1727-38 . . . . . 500.00

13 (2 guineas). Sim. 1734-39 . 1000.00

14 (5 guineas). Sim. 1729-41 . . 1700.00

E. I. C. Issues

11a (½ guinea). Like No. 11 but E(ast) I(ndia) C(ompany) under head. 1729-39 . . . . . . 1000.00

12a (guinea). Sim. 1729-32, 39 . . 600.00

14a (5 guineas). Sim. 1729 . . . . 2000.00

Mature Head

11b (½ guinea). Mature head. Rev. Arms. 1740-46 . . . . 500.00

11c —. LIMA under head. 1745 . 1200.00

12b (guinea). Like No. 11b. 1739-46 . . . . 500.00

12c —. LIMA under head. 1745 . 1000.00

13a (2 guineas). Like No. 11b. 1739-40 . . . . 700.00

Old Head

11d (½ guinea). Old head. Rev. Arms. 1747-60 . . . . 225.00

12d (guinea). Sim. 1747-60 . . . . 300.00

13d (2 guineas). Sim. 1748, 53 . . . . 1100.00

14c (5 guineas). Sim. but LIMA under head. 1746 . . . . 2250.00

14d (5 guineas). Sim. 1748, 53 . . . . 2100.00

GREAT BRITAIN

George III 1760-1820

Copper

A. First Issue.

VG-F

15 (farthing). GEORGIUS III REX.
Bust. Rev. Britannia std.
24mm. 1771-75 . . . . 2.00

18 (½ penny). Sim. 9-11 gr.
28mm. 1770-75 . . . . 1.50

Note: Lightweight counterfeits of No.
18 are common, often having blundered
legends and earlier or later dates. Such
bad pieces weigh less than 8 gr.

B. Second Issue.

★21 (penny). The "Cartwheel."
37mm. 1797 . . . . 5.00

23 (2 pence). Sim. 40.6mm.
1797 . . . . 7.50

★16 1 FARTHING. 1799 . . . . . . 1.25

19 (½ penny). Sim. 31mm.
1799 . . . . 1.25

★17 (farthing). 1806-07 . . . . 1.25

20 (½ penny). Sim. 29mm.
1806-07 . . . . 1.25

22 (penny). Sim. 35mm.
1806-07 . . . . 2.00

Silver

I. Maundy Issues
(Bust. Rev. Value.)

A. Young Bust.

VF-EF

24 1 (penny). 1762-86 . . . . 5.00

25 2 (pence). 1762-86 . . . . 5.00

26 3 (pence). 1762-86 . . . . 4.50

27 4 (pence). 1762-86 . . . . 12.00

B. Mature Bust.

24a 1 (penny). 1792 . . . . 5.00

25a 2 (pence). 1792 . . . . 25.00

26a 3 (pence). 1792 . . . . 27.50

27a 4 (pence). 1792 . . . . 35.00

C. Older Bust.

24b 1 (penny). 1795-1800 . . . . . . 3.00

25b 2 (pence). 1795-1800 . . . . . . 5.00

26b 3 (pence). 1795-1800 . . . . . . 7.00

27b 4 (pence). 1795-1800 . . . . . 15.00

D. Last Bust.

★24c 1 (penny). 1817-20 . . . . 5.00

25c 2 (pence). 1817-20 . . . . 6.00

26c 3 (pence). 1817-20 . . . . 15.00

27c 4 (pence). 1817-20 . . . . 17.50

II. Regular Issues

F-VF

28 (6 pence). Like No. 31.
1787 . . . . 4.00

29 (6 pence). Like No. 32.
1816-20 . . . . 3.00

30 (shilling). Bust. Rev. shields
cruciform (The Northumber-
land shilling). 1763 . . . *(V.F.)* 100.00

★31 (shilling). 1787 . . . . . . *(E.F.)* 10.00

31a —. "Dorrien & Magens."
1798 . . . . *(E.F.)* RRR

★32 (shilling). 1816-20 . . . . 5.00

V.F.

★33 (½ crown). 1816-17 . . . . 18.00

33a —. Smaller head. 1817-20 . . . 15.00

★34 (crown). 1818-20 . . . . 37.50

III. Emergency Issues

Foreign silver, usually Spanish and
Spanish-American, countermarked with
oval (1797-99) or octagonal cmk. (1799-
1804).

8 reales = 4s9d (1797-1800); = 5s (1800-
04) = 1 dollar.

35 (⅛ dollar). Oval cmk . . . . . . Rare

36 (¼ dollar). Oval cmk . . . . . . Rare

36a —. Oct. cmk . . . . Rare

37 (½ dollar). (Usually Spanish).
Oval cmk 150.00

37a —. Oct. cmk . . . . Rare

GREAT BRITAIN

★38 (dollar). Oval cmk. 100.00

★38a —. Oct. cmk. 200.00

Counterfeits exist of the foregoing
countermarked coins.

IV. Bank of England.

Silver Token Coinage

39 18 PENCE. Like No. 40.
1811-12 . . . . 12.00

39a —. Like No. 40a. 1812-16 . . . 10.00

★40 3 SHILL(ings). 1811-12 . . . . 20.00

V.F.
★40a —. 1812-16 . . . . 17.50

★41 FIVE SHILLINGS. 1804 . . . 75.00

Gold (guinea = 8.4 gr.)

VF-EF
42 (¼ guinea). Head. Rev. Arms.
1762 . . . . 120.00

43 (⅓ guinea). Head. Rev. crown.
1797-1800 . . . . 100.00

43a —. Rev. cwn./date. 1801-
13 . . . . 80.00

44 (½ guinea). Like No. 42.
1762-86 . . . . 200.00

45 (½ guinea). Head. Rev. spade
shield. 1787-1800 . . . . 180.00

46 (½ guinea). Head. Rev. Arms
in garter. 1801-13 . . . . 180.00

47 (guinea). Like No. 42.
1761-86 . . . . 220.00

48 (guinea). Like No. 45.
1787-99 . . . . 190.00

VF-EF
49 (guinea). Like No. 46.
"Military Guinea." 1813 . . . 750.00

The 2 and 5 guineas of this reign
never circulated.

★50 (½ sovereign). 1817-20 . . . . . 75.00

★51 (sovereign). 1817-20 . . . . . . 200.00

The 2 and 5 sovereigns were patterns.

George IV 1820-30

Copper

(image)

VG-F
★52 (farthing). 1821-26 . . . . 1.00
52a —. Like No. 54. 1826-30 75
53 (½ penny). Like No. 54.
29mm. 1825-27 . . . . 1.50

(image)

★54 (penny). 1825-27 . . . . 4.00

See Malta for the ⅓ farthing and
Ceylon for the ½ farthing.

GREAT BRITAIN

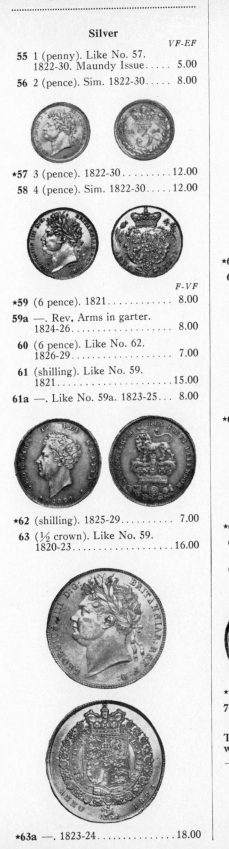

Silver

		VF-EF
55	1 (penny). Like No. 57. 1822-30. Maundy Issue.....	5.00
56	2 (pence). Sim. 1822-30.....	8.00
★57	3 (pence). 1822-30........	12.00
58	4 (pence). Sim. 1822-30.....	12.00

		F-VF
★59	(6 pence). 1821..........	8.00
59a	—. Rev. Arms in garter. 1824-26.................	8.00
60	(6 pence). Like No. 62. 1826-29.................	7.00
61	(shilling). Like No. 59. 1821.................	15.00
61a	—. Like No. 59a. 1823-25...	8.00

★62	(shilling). 1825-29.........	7.00
63	(½ crown). Like No. 59. 1820-23.................	16.00

★63a	—. 1823-24..............	18.00

		F-VF
★64	(½ crown). 1824-29.......	16.00
65	(crown). Head. Rev. St. George. 1821-22.................	25.00

Gold

		V.F.
★66	(½ sovereign). 1821......	450.00
★67	(½ sovereign). 1823-25....	200.00
68	(½ sovereign). Like No. 70. 1825-28.................	200.00
69	(sovereign). Head. Rev. St. George. 1821-25.............	250.00
★70	(sovereign). 1825-30......	275.00
70.5	(2 sovereigns). Like No. 69. 1823.................	600.00

The 2 and 5 sovereign coins of 1826 were not intended for circulation.

William IV 1830-37

Copper

		Fine
71	(farthing). Like No. 72. 21.5mm. 1831, 34-37......	2.00

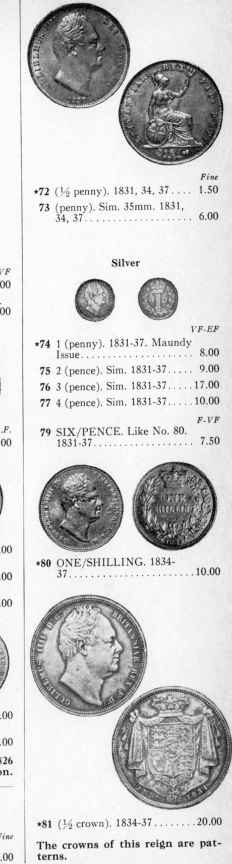

		Fine
★72	(½ penny). 1831, 34, 37....	1.50
73	(penny). Sim. 35mm. 1831, 34, 37.................	6.00

Silver

		VF-EF
★74	1 (penny). 1831-37. Maundy Issue.................	8.00
75	2 (pence). Sim. 1831-37.....	9.00
76	3 (pence). Sim. 1831-37....	17.00
77	4 (pence). Sim. 1831-37.....	10.00

		F-VF
79	SIX/PENCE. Like No. 80. 1831-37.................	7.50

★80	ONE/SHILLING. 1834-37......................	10.00

★81	(½ crown). 1834-37........	20.00

The crowns of this reign are patterns.

GREAT BRITAIN

Gold

V.F.

⋆82 (½ sovereign). 1834......400.00
82a —. 19mm. 1835-37.......210.00
83 (sovereign). Sim. 22mm.
1831-37.................300.00

The 1831 2 sovereign is a pattern.
See Malta for the ⅓ farthing, Cey-
lon for the ¼ farthing, Ceylon and
Jamaica for the 1½ pence, and
British Guiana for the Britannia 4
pence of this reign.

GRENADA.
GUADELOUPE. See CARIBBEAN
ISLANDS AND TERRITORIES.

GUATEMALA

In Central America. Together with
neighboring areas, constituted the
Spanish Captaincy General of Guatemala 1524-1821. Annexed to Mexico
1821-23. Part of the Republic of Central America 1823-47. Independent republic thereafter.

Mint Marks:
G or G–G (Guatemala 1733-76)
NG (Nueva Guatemala 1777 onward.)

Monetary System:
16 reales = 1 escudo (scudo).

I. Under Spain.

Felipe V 1700-24-46

Cob Silver

V.G. (crude)

1 (½ real). Like No. 3.
1733-46.................12.50
2 I (real). Sim. 1733-46.......10.00

⋆3 2 (reales). PHILIP. V etc.
Rev. like No. 11. On irregular
planchet. 1733-46..........17.50
4 4 (reales). Sim. 1733-46.....85.00
5 8 (reales). Sim. 1733-46.....90.00

Gold

V.F. (crude)

5.5 8 (escudos). Bust. Rev.
INITIUM etc. Arms. 1741,
43..................... ——

Fernando VI 1746-59

Silver

A. Cob Type.

V.G. (crude)

6 (½ real). Like No. 10 but on
irregular planchet. 1747-
53.....................15.00
6.5 I (real). Sim. 1747-53......10.00
7 2 (reales). Sim. 1747-53.....15.00
7.5 4 (reales). Sim. 1747-53.....75.00
8 8 (reales). Sim. 1747-53....80.00

B. Milled Type.

F-VF

9 (½ real). Like No. 11.
1754-60.................32.50
10 I (real). Sim. but FERDIND. VI.
1754-60.................37.50

⋆11 2 (reales). FERD. VI etc.
1755-60.................50.00
12 4 (reales). Like No. 10.
1754-60.................125.00
13 8 (reales). Sim. 1754-60....100.00

Gold

V.F.

14 1 (escudo). Bust. Rev. INITIUM
etc., arms. Crude. 1751-55 ....RR
14a —. Like No. 15a. 1757.......RR
15 8 (escudos). Like No. 14.
1750. Crude.................RR

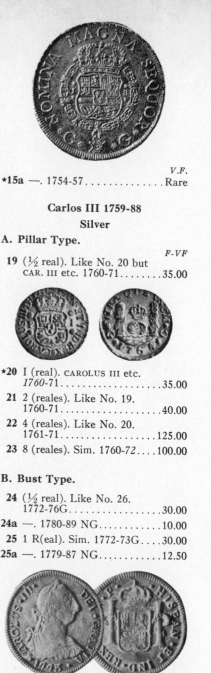

V.F.

⋆15a —. 1754-57.............Rare

Carlos III 1759-88
Silver
A. Pillar Type.

F-VF

19 (½ real). Like No. 20 but
CAR. III etc. 1760-71.......35.00

⋆20 I (real). CAROLUS III etc.
1760-71.................35.00
21 2 (reales). Like No. 19.
1760-71.................40.00
22 4 (reales). Like No. 20.
1761-71.................125.00
23 8 (reales). Sim. 1760-72....100.00

B. Bust Type.

24 (½ real). Like No. 26.
1772-76G.................30.00
24a —. 1780-89 NG...........10.00
25 1 R(eal). Sim. 1772-73G....30.00
25a —. 1779-87 NG...........12.50

⋆26 2 R(eales). 1772-76G.......25.00
26a —. 1777-87 NG...........10.00
27 4 R(eales). Sim. 1772-76G .175.00
27a —. 1777-87 NG...........65.00
28 8 R(eales). Sim. 1772-76G..250.00
28a —. 1777-87 NG...........150.00

Gold
A. Crude Local Portraits.

30.5 (4 escudos). Like No. 32a.
1765.................Unique
32 8 (escudos). Bust of
Fernando VI. Rev. like
No. 15a. 1761.........Unique

GUATEMALA

V.F.

★32a (8 escudos). Young bust of
Carlos III. 1765-70
(var.) *4500.00*

B. Older Standard Bust.

29 1 S(cudo). Like No. 33.
1778, 83 . . . . RR

30 2 S(cudos). Sim. 1783, 85 . . . . . RR

31 4 S(cudos). Sim. 1778-83 . . . . . RR

33 8 S(cudos). CAROL. III etc. Rev.
like No. 32a. 1778-87 . . . . . 2500.00

Carlos IV 1788-1808

Silver

A. Castle/Lion.

F-VF

36 ¼ (real). G–castle–¼.
Rev. lion. 1796-1808 . . . . 10.00

B. Bust of Carlos III.

37 (½ real). CAROLUS IV etc.
Bust of Carlos III. Rev. arms
btwn. pillars. 1789-90 . . . . . . 15.00

38 1 R(eal). Sim. 1789-90 . . . . . . 25.00

39 2 R(eales). Sim. 1789-90 . . . . 30.00

40 4 R(eales). Sim. 1789-*90* . . . 150.00

★41 8 R(eales). 1789-90 . . . . 150.00

C. Bust of Carlos IV.

F-VF

43 (½ real). Like No. 45.
1790-1807 . . . . 7.50

44 1 R(eal). Sim. 1791-1807 . . . . 7.50

★45 2 R(eales). 1790-1807 . . . . . . 10.00

46 4 R(eales). Sim. 1790-1807 . . 60.00

47 8 R(eales). Sim. 1790-1808 . . 75.00

Gold

A. Bust of Carlos III.

V.F.

48 1 S(cudo). CAROL IV etc.
Bust of Carlos III.
Rev. arms. 1789-*91* . . . . RR

49 2 S(cudos). Sim. 1789-90 . . . . . RR

50 4 S(cudos). Sim. 1789 . . . . RR

51 8 S(cudos). Sim. 1789-90 . . 1500.00

B. Bust of Carlos IV.

52 1 S(cudo). CAROL IIII etc. His
bust. Rev. Arms. 1794-
1801 . . . . 250.00

53 2 S(cudos). Sim. 1794 . . . . . 400.00

54 4 S(cudos). Sim. 1794-1801 . 800.00

★55 8 S(cudos). 1794-1801 . . . . 1000.00

Fernando VII 1808-33,
In Guatemala 1808-21

Silver

A. Castle/Lion.

F-VF

62 ¼ (real). Like No. 36.
1809-22 . . . . 5.00

B. Bust of Carlos IV.

F-VF

63 (½ real). Like No. 67,
FERDIND. VII etc.
1808-10 . . . . 15.00

64 1 R(eal). Sim. 1808-10 . . . . . 20.00

65 2 R(eales). Sim. 1808-10 . . . . 25.00

66 4 R(eales). Sim. 1808-10 . . . . 75.00

★67 8 R(eales). 1808-10 . . . . 125.00

C. Bust of Fernando VII.

68 (½ real). Like No. 70.
1808, 1811-22 . . . . 7.50

69 1 R(eal). Sim. 1811-21 . . . . . . 7.50

★70 2 R(eales). 1808, 1811-22 . . . 8.00

71 4 R(eales). Sim. 1808,
1811-21 . . . . 30.00

72 8 R(eales). Sim. 1808-22 . . . . 40.00

Gold

V.F.

★73 1 S(cudo). 1817-*18* 500.00

74 2 S(cudos). Sim.
1808, *11*, 17 . . . . 1200.00

75 4 S(cudos). Sim. 1813, 17 . 2000.00

76 8 S(cudos). Sim. 1808-17 . . 1500.00

II. As a state in the Republic of Central America.

Mint mark: N.G. or G.

For similar coins with other mint marks
see C(osta) R(ica) and Honduras (T).

GUATEMALA

Silver

F-VF

*91 ¼ (real). Mountains/date.
Rev. G–tree–¼. 1824-50.... 4.00

92 ½ R(eal). Like No. 93.
1824.................... 15.00

*93 1 R(eal). 1824, 28......... 12.50

*94 1 R(eal). ESTADO
DE GUATEMALA. 1829 ...... 150.00

95 8 R(eales). Like No. 93.
1824-51............. (V.F.) .37.50

Gold

V.F.

111 ½ E(scudo). Like No. 113.
1824-26, 43.............. 75.00

112 1 E(scudo). Sim. 1824-25 .250.00

*113 2 E(scudos). 1825-47..... 175.00

114 4 E(scudos). Sim. 1824-
26.................... 4000.00

*115 8 E(scudos). Sim. 1824-
25.................... 6500.00

Countermarked Silver

The following countermarks occur on
Spanish-American cobs or on coins of
the independent South American republics (usually of Bolivia or Peru).

Note: The pieces listed below are most
often found with holes (see illustration
of No. 124), and prices are for coins
with such defects.

F-VF (cmk.)

121 (real). Cmkd. like No. 124..Rare
122 (2 reales). Sim........... 75.00
123 (4 reales). Sim......... 150.00

*124 (ex 101) (8 reales). Cmkd.
sun/3 mountains in 7mm.
circle. ND (ca. 1838-40)... 50.00

124a —. Sim. but sun over
1 mountain............ 125.00

*134 (8 reales). Obv. cmkd. like
No. 124. Rev. cmkd. star
over bow and arrow...... 100.00

GUIANA — See BRITISH GUIANA,
FRENCH GUIANA, VENEZUELA.

GUINEA

Portuguese possession on the coast of
West Africa.

José I 1750-77

The copper V, X, XX and XL (réis)
dated 1752-57, of Brazilian type but
with legends ending GUINEÆ are now
listed under ANGOLA. "Guinea" was
then a general term for all the west
central African coast; and Angola, as
the largest Portuguese settlement, appears to have been the intended desti-
nation for most of this issue. The coins
were used to a lesser extent in Portuguese Guinea, as well as Brazil.

UNVERIFIED DATA

Note: Throughout this catalog, any
uncertain, indefinite or unconfirmed information is shown in *italic type.* Such
material may be, for example, coin descriptions, dates and prices, names of
rulers, or supplementary notes. Further
information to confirm or correct *material in italics* should be sent to the
author at the following address:

William D. Craig
c/o Whitman Coin Supply Division
1220 Mound Avenue
Racine, Wisconsin 53404, U.S.A.

HAITI. See CARIBBEAN ISLANDS AND TERRITORIES.

HARAR

East African sultanate founded in 1647. Conquered by Egypt in 1877 but regained its independence in 1885. Conquered by and absorbed into Ethiopia in 1887.

Monetary System:
22 mahallak = 1 ashrafi.

'Abd al-Shakur
AH1197-1209 (=1783-94)

Billon

VG-F

*6 (¼ *ashrafi*). SULTAN/'ABD/AL-SHAKUR. Rev. MADINAT (=city)/ HARAR/date. 0.3-0.4 gr. 11-12mm. AH1197, 1202..... ——

Ahmad II
AH1209-36 (=1794-1821)

'Abd al-Rahman
AH1236-40 (=1821-25)

'Abd al-Karim
AH1240-50 (=1825-34)

Abu Bakr II
AH1250-68 (=1834-52)

Anonymous Issues

Brass

F-VF

*10 (*mahallak*). Islamic creed: LA ILAH/ILLA ALLAH. Rev. MUHAMMAD/RASUL/ ALLAH, date at left. 0.2 gr. 7-9 mm. AH1222, 27......25.00

10a —. 0.13 gr. 5-7mm. ND ...15.00

Billon

G-VG

*14 (*mahallak*). MADINAT/AL-HARARI. Rev. BI-TARIKHI (=in the year)/date. 1.4-2.3 gr. 12-14mm. AH123x, 124x............20.00

Brass

Fine

14a (*mahallak*). Sim. 0.5-0.6 gr. 10-11mm. AH1257-58......35.00

Silver

Fine

*18 (¼ *ashrafi*). Like No. 14. 2.7 gr. 17mm. AH*125x*..... ——

Muhammad II
AH1272-92 (=1856-75)

Brass

*21 (*mahallak*). AL-SULTAN/ MUHAMMAD IBN 'ALI. Rev. IBN AL-SULTAN/ 'ABD AL-SHAKUR/date. 0.35 gr. 9-11mm. AH1274.........25.00

24 —. Obv. sim., date at bottom. Rev. MADINAT/AL-HARAR. 0.35 gr. *9*-12mm. AH*1276*, 79.........17.50

*24a (ex 27) —. Date moved to rev. 10-14mm. AH1284....12.50

Silver

30 (*mahallak*). Like No. 24a. 0.13-0.20 gr. 10mm. AH1288.................25.00

'Abd-Allah II
AH1302-04 (=1885-87)

Brass

*35 (mahallak). AL-'ABD/AL-DA'IF/ date. Rev. DURIBA/FI/MADINAT/ HARAR. 15-19mm. AH1303-04 (var.).................15.00

HONDURAS

Part of the Spanish Captaincy-General of Guatemala until 1821. To Mexico 1822-23. A state in the Republic of Central America 1823-47. Independent republic thereafter.

Mint: T(egucigalpa).

Monetary System:
16 reales =1 escudo.

Fernando VII of Spain, In Honduras 1808-21

Silver

7 *8 R(eales).* Bust. *Rev. Arms.* Crude. 1813.............. ——

Agustín Iturbide, Emperor of Mexico 1822-23

Silver
G-VG

9 2 R(eales). ENPER. AGUSTIN 1823. Bust. Rev. same as No. 14..................RRR

Provisional Government 1823

Silver

11 (½ real). T.L./1823. Rev. cross with arms of Castile (castle) and Leon (lion) in corners. 1823......................RRR

*13 2 R(eales). 1823............RR

*14 2 R(eales). 1823............RR

15 2 R(eales). Obv. of No. 13. Rev. of No. 14. 1823.......RRR

17 2 R(eales). Obv. of No. 14. Rev. PROVISIONAL etc. Cross with castles, lions in corners. 1823...................RRR

As a state in the Republic of Central America

For similar coins with other mint marks see C(osta) R(ica) and Guatemala (N.G.).

Silver
VG-F

21 ½ R(eal). Like No. 23. 1830-31..................35.00

22 1 R(eal). Sim. 1830-31...... 7.50

HONDURAS

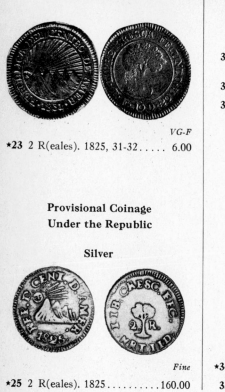

VG-F

★23 2 R(eales). 1825, 31-32 . . . . . 6.00

Provisional Coinage
Under the Republic

Silver

Fine

★25 2 R(eales). 1825 . . . . 160.00

As the Independent State (Estado) of Honduras

Base Silver or Bronze

V.G.

31 ½ R(eal). Like No. 34.
1832-33, 45 . . . . 20.00

32 1 R(eal). Sim. 1832-*53* 12.50

33 2 R(eales). Sim. 1832-55 . . . . 3.50

Fine

★34 4 R(eales). 1849-57 . . . . 5.50

35 8 R(eales). Sim. 1856-61 . . . . 10.00

HUNGARY.
See AUSTRIA (Hapsburg Lands).

UNVERIFIED DATA

Note: Throughout this catalog, any uncertain, indefinite or unconfirmed information is shown in *italic type*. Such material may be, for example, coin descriptions, dates and prices, names of rulers, or supplementary notes. Further information to confirm or correct *material in italics* should be sent to the author at the following address:

William D. Craig
c/o Whitman Coin Supply Division
1220 Mound Avenue
Racine, Wisconsin 53404, U.S.A.

INDIA

South Asian sub-continent governed at the beginning of the 18th century by the Mughal emperor resident at Delhi. Europeans, the British, Danes, Dutch, French and Portuguese, had established trading settlements here in the 16th century, but these were still small and scattered along the coast.

In the 18th century the power of the emperors declined rapidly. The British, the French, and a quantity of native adventurers hastened to fill the void. The French were decisively beaten by the British, who then obtained large concessions for themselves, while at the same time a multitude of native states were also being carved from the supine empire.

Thereafter, anarchy in one state after another led to British intervention until at last, in the mid 19th century, the British East India Company had built a new empire "in a fit of inattention."

A burst of Indian nationalism, the Great Indian Mutiny of 1857-58, led to final deposition of the last shadow Mughal emperor and the end of the British Company's rule (India came directly under the British Crown).

Monetary Systems:
Hindu System (South India):

20 cash = 1 faluce (fulus);
3360 cash = 168 faluce = 42 fanams = 1 pagoda.

Moslem System:

192 pie = 64 paisa (pice, pysa) = 16 annas = 1 rupee;
14 to 16 rupees = 1 mohur (mohar).

Other denominations and their relative values will be mentioned in the text as they appear.

Denominations were rarely shown on Indian coins (except by Europeans) until the late 19th century. Accordingly, most silver and gold passed by weight. The rupee weighed 10.7-11.6 gr., while the mohur weighed 10.7-11.4 gr. Their fractions and multiples were in proportion.

The Indians had an unfortunate habit of striking many of their silver and gold coins from dies meant for a larger denomination with the result that often much of the legend is off the coin.

As might be anticipated, the Mughul coinage was struck at a multitude of mints, many of which turned to state coinage as the local ruler achieved virtual independence from Delhi.

I. COINS OF THE MUGHAL EMPERORS.

Ahmad Shah Bahadur, Emperor
1161-67AH (=1748-54AD)

Silver
                                         V.G.

10 (½₂ rupee). Like No. 15. Dates mostly off planchet...10.00

*15 (rupee)..................7.50

Mints for silver:

Akbarabad
Akbarnagar 1164-66
Allahabad
Azimabad ★ 1162-67
Balwantnagar
Bareli 1166-67
Burhanpur 1164
Dera
Etawa yr. 5
Farrukhabad
Imtiyazgadh
Jahangirnagar yrs. 5-7
Jaipur Sawai 1161
Katak yrs. 1-7 (same posthumous yrs. 8-88 struck by Mahrattas at Orissa)
Khanbayat
Lahore 1162-64
Muhammadabad Banaras 1161-67
Multan 1163
Muradabad
Murshidabad 1162-67
Sarhind 1161-62
Shahjahanabad 1161-67

Gold
                                         Fine

16 (¹⁄₆₄ mohur). Legend. Rev. blank...............22.50

*22 (mohur). **Mints:** Akbarabad★ (Agra) yr. 2; Allahabad yr. 3; Burhanpur 1166...........95.00

Alamgir II, Emperor
1167-73AH (=1754-59AD)

Former Nos. 25 and 27 were issued by Alamgir I, d. 1707.

Silver
                                         V.G.

31 (¹⁄₃₂ rupee). Like No. 36. Various mints and dates, mostly off planchet.........2.50

35 (½ rupee). Like No. 36.....4.50

*36 (rupee)..................3.00

Mints for silver:

Ahmadabad yrs. 3-6
Ahmadnagar-Farrukhabad
Akbarabad yrs. 2-3
Akbarnagar★ 1167
Allahabad 1168-69
Aurangnagar
Azimabad 1167-73
Balwantnagar 1171
Bareli 1168-73
Burhanpur
Dera
Etawa 1168
Gwalior yr. 4
Imtiyazgadh yr. 1
Indrapur
Jahangirnagar yrs. 2-5
Jaipur Sawai yr. 3
Khanbayat yr. 6
Kora yr. 3
Lahor 1169-72
Machhlipatan 1168
Mahindrapur
Muhammadabad Banaras 1167-72
Multan
Muradabad yrs. 2-5
Murshidabad 1167-71
Najibabad yrs. 2-6
Narwar 1173
Sarhind 1171
Shahjahanabad 1167-73
Surat yr. 5

Gold
                                         Fine

39 (½ hun = ½ pagoda). Legend both sides. Imtiyazgadh Mint. 1.6 gr....................25.00

40 (hun). Sim. 3.3 gr..........40.00

41 (¹⁄₆₄ mohur). Like No. 47....20.00

45 (¼ mohur). Sim. 45.00

*47 (mohur). **Mints:** Azimabad yr. 3; Jaipur Sawai★ yrs. 5-8; Lahor 1172; Muhammadabad Banaras yr. 3; Shahjahanabad yrs. 2-6...................95.00

48 (mohur). Legends in and around square, each side. Shahjahanabad 1168......110.00

Shah Jahan III, Emperor
1173-74AH (=1759-60AD)

Silver
                                         V.G.

55 (½ rupee). Azimabad. N.D. 5.00

*56 (rupee). **Mints:** Ahmadabad; Akbarabad; Azimabad (Patna) 1173-74; Maha-Indrapur★ 1174; Surat..............5.00

INDIA

MUGHAL COINAGE (Cont.)

Gold

Fine

★67 (mohur). **Mints:** Azimabad★;
Maha-Indrapur 1174......100.00

Shah Alam II, Emperor
1173-1221AH (=1759-1806AD)

In the reign of Shah Alam II many of the latter-day Indian native states became independent and acquired the coinage right. The process was gradual and many states commenced by striking Shah Alam coins with a special mint mark. The British and French companies did the same thing. Accordingly see II EUROPEAN COINAGE FOR INDIA, and III COINS OF THE NATIVE STATES, for other coins similar to those which follow. Especially look elsewhere for coins with (fictitious) regnal years after 49.

Copper

Fair-G

★71 *(dam).* 14.7-18.5 gr........ 1.50

Mints for copper:

Bareli yrs. 34-35
Chhachrauli ★ yr. 42
Daulatabad
Kanan yr. 40
Kharpur yr. 40
Mahindrapur yr. 42
Najibabad yrs. 3-12
Saharanpur yrs. 33-42
Shahjahanabad

Silver

V.G.

81 (1/32 rupee). Like No. 86.
Various dates and mints.
Dates mostly off planchet... 3.50

82 (1/16 rupee). Sim. 3.50

83 (1/8 rupee). Sim. 3.00

84 (1/4 rupee). Sim. 2.50

85 (1/2 rupee). Sim. 3.00

V.G.

★86 (rupee)................. 3.50

86a —. Broad (31mm)........ 6.00

Mints for silver:

Ahmadabad yrs. 15-21
Ahmadnagar Farrukhabad yrs. 15-39
Ajmer Daru-l-khair yrs. 6-14
Akbarabad Mustaqirru-l-khilafat yrs. 2-47
Allahabad 1174-92
Anwala (Aonla) yr. 3
Asafabad Ujhani 1189
Asafnagar 1189-90
Azimabad (Patna) yrs. 2-6
Balanagar-garh yrs. 31-35
Balwantnagar yrs. 25-26
Bareli (=Qita Bareli,
    under Nawab Viziers of Awadh 1774-1801.
    Name changed in AH1209-11 from Qita
    Bareli to Asafabad Bareli.)
Brajindrapur (Bharatpur) yr. 34
Burhanpur Daru-s-Sarur yrs. 3-4
Daulatabad 1184
Etawa yr. 22
Gokulgarh yrs. 17-30
Hathras yr. 30
Jahangirnagar yrs. 2-4
Jaipur Sawai yr. 34
Jammun Daru-l-aman yr. 24
Khujista Bunyad 1186
Konch yrs. 25-31
Kora yrs. 2-20
Machhlipatan yr. 14
Maha Indrapur yrs. 4-16
Muhammadabad Banaras yrs. 1-16
    (for coins with regnal years 17 and later,
    plus fish symbol, see sections II British
    and III Awadh)
Muradabad yrs. 4-18
Murshidabad yrs. 2-19
Mustafabad yr. 2
Muzaffargarh ★ yrs. 39, 47
Najibabad yrs. 3-33
Narwar
Sagar Ravishnagar yrs. 25-45
Shahjahanabad Daru-l-khilafat yrs. 2-48
Ujjain Daru-l-fath yrs. 24-44

Gold

Fine

91 (1/64 mohur). Like No. 86....22.50

93 (1/16 mohur). Like No. 86....37.50

95 (1/4 mohur). Like No. 86....45.00

97 (mohur). Like No. 86......95.00

97a —. Broad. (Var.)........200.00

Mints for gold:

Ahmadabad
Ahmadnagar-Farrukhabad yr. 31
Azimabad yrs. 2-5
Ilahabad 1195
Jaipur Sawai yr. 15
Kora yrs. 2-3
Maha-Indrapur (Bharatpur) yrs. 2-10
Muhammadabad Banaras
Najibabad yrs. 5-25
Shahjahanabad Daru-l-khilafat yrs. 2-24

Bidar Bakht, Pretender
1202-03AH (=1788AD)

Silver

★106 (rupee). Ahmadabad 1203..15.00

Gold

Fine

★117 (mohur). Shahjahanabad
Daru-l-khilafat 1202★;
1203...................150.00

Muhammad Akbar II, Emperor
1221-53AH (=1806-37AD)

Copper

Fair-G

121 *(pysa).* Like No. 123.
Ahmadabad yr. 12. 7.6 gr... 2.00

★123 *(1/2 anna).* Shahjahanabad
yrs. 4-12. 11.4 gr.......... 1.50

Silver

VG-F

131 (1/32 rupee). Like No. 136.
Various dates and mints,
mostly off planchet........ 2.50

★136 (rupee). **Mints:** Ahmadabad
yr. 11 (yr. 12 struck by British);
Shahjahanabad Daru-l-
khilafat yrs. 3-30......... 4.00

Gold

Fine

★147 (mohur). Shahjahanabad
Daru-l-khilafat yrs. 1-6...140.00

INDIA

MUGHAL COINAGE (Cont.)

Bahadur Shah II, Emperor
1253-74AH (=1837-58AD)
Deposed 1858

Silver

*156 (rupee). Shahjahanabad
Daru-l-khilafat yr. 3 ...... 15.00 **Fine**

II. EUROPEAN COINAGE
FOR INDIA.

A. British East India Company.

The British first acquired possessions in India in the 17th century (Madras 1639, Bombay 1661, Fort William by Calcutta 1690). For convenience the British Company's coinage covered by this catalog is collected under four main headings, corresponding to the three Presidencies (administrative districts of Madras, Bombay and Bengal, plus the general British coinage for all India).

As "John Company" acquired new territories in the 18th century, it took over several native mints and built other new ones. The crude coins familiar to the natives were not quickly changed, but the AH and/or regnal dates on Mughal-type issues usually became "frozen" or permanently fixed. The frozen dates can serve as "mint marks" for quick identification (flans are often too small to show the mint name), but their main purpose was to stop the native practice of discounting older coins on the theory that they had lost weight or were more likely to be counterfeit.

Note: British India has been substantially revised and completely renumbered for the third edition in the light of F. Pridmore, *The Coins of the British Commonwealth of Nations*, Part 4, India vol. 1 (Spink 1975).

Revised Numbering:

Old	New	Old	New
6-23	463-494	120-120.2	416-417
32-43	830-844	121-126	445-449a
51-64	701-720	128-129	541-542
70	Ceylon	135-137	421-426
75-76	521-522	141-148	452-459
77-79	440-442	149-159	750-779a
84-86	852-854b	161-162	805-806
91-95	407-411	171-174	554-560
96-100	435-439	175-187	565-568,
102-106	531-535		681-682a
110-114	431-434	190-193	581-584
116-119	530-533a	196-200	575-579

Old	New	Old	New
205-207	586-588	247-279	661-678a
208-210	687-689	291-297	694-698
211-213	591-593	300.1-305	865-879
231-239	642-659		

1. Madras Presidency.

The city of Madras (Fort St. George, founded 1640) was headquarters for the East India Company's presidency on the Coromandel (southeast) coast. Dump-type coins (handmade, with irregular thick flans smaller than their dies) were struck at Madras 1643-1807, Cuddalore (Fort St. David) ca. 1691-1754, and Masulipatam ca. *1761*-1808. Machine-made coins were struck at Soho (England), Madras and Calcutta.

Monetary System:

80 cash = 1 fanam;
to 1802: 36 fanam = 1 pagoda;
1802-17: 42 fanam = 1 pagoda;
1817 on: 45 fanam = 1 pagoda;

192 pai = 48 pice = 16 annas = 1 rupee;
3½ rupees = 1 pagoda.

(a) General issues.

Dump Copper

*407 (cash). Balemark, CVEI in angles. Rev. *Persian legend*, date in double square. AH1212 (=1797) .... 6.50 **V.G.**

410 (5 cash). Like No. 411 but rev. date in 2 lines. Ca. 3.1 gr. 1755-*1804* 5.00

*411 (10 cash = dudu). Balemark with GCE (usually appears CCE). Rev. date btwn. wavy lines. Ca. 6.3 gr. 1755-*1806* 3.50

Similar but heavier coins were struck 1691-*1753*. Coins with uncertain dates are worth less than prices shown.

Dump Silver

416 (fanam). Like No. 417. ND (0.9 gr. = 1765-1807) ...... 4.50 **Fine**

*417 (2 fanam). Vishnu stdg. Rev. 2 interlinked C's. ND (1.8 gr. = 1765-1807) 6.00

Similar but larger and heavier coins were struck 1689-1763.

Dump Gold
F-VF

421 (pagoda). Half figures of 3 gods stdg. Rev. grained field. 3.4 gr. 12-14mm. ND (1740-1807) 50.00

Coins with smaller full-standing figures were struck earlier or by non-British authorities.

426 (pagoda). Obv. like No. 421. Rev. star in grained border. 3.4 gr. 10-11mm. ND (1740-1807) 60.00

Machine-Struck Copper

*431 I CASH. 1803 .... 1.00 **Fine**

432 V CASH. Like No. 433. 1803 .... 1.50

*433 X CASH. 6.5 gr. 1803, 08 .. 1.50

433a — 4.6 gr. 1808 .... 1.50

434 XX CASH. Sim. 12.9 gr. 1803, 08 .... 2.00

434a — 9.3 gr. 1808 .... 1.75

435 2½ CASH. Like No. 438. 16mm. ND (1807) .... 2.50 **V.G.**

436 V CASH. Sim. 20mm. ND. 1.75

437 X CASH. Sim. 23mm. ND. 1.25

*438 XX CASH. Value in Persian/English. Rev. value in Telugu/Tamil. ND (1807) 1.75

439 XL CASH. Sim. 35mm. ND 3.50

440 1 pai. Like No. 441. 18mm. 1825, 33 .... 1.75 **Fine**

*441 2 pai. 1825 .... 2.50

INDIA

BRITISH - Madras (Cont.)

Fine

442 4 pai. Sim. 27mm.
1824-25................ 2.75

Machine-Struck Silver

*445 FANAM. Star with or w/out
crossed branches below.
Rev. star, value in Telugu
and Tamil. 9-10mm. ND
(1807-08)............... 8.50

*445a —. Sim. but garter border,
rev. ribbon border
(1808-12)............... 3.50

446 DOUBLE FANAM. Like
No. 447a but plain borders.
12-13mm. ND (1807-08).. 6.00

446a —. Like No. 447a. 14-16mm.
ND (1808-12)........... 3.00

447 FIVE FANAMS. Like
No. 447a but plain borders.
17-18mm. ND (1807-08).. 9.00

*447a —. Persian value, English
value on garter. Rev. Telugu
value, Tamil value on
ribbon. ND (1808-12).... 5.50

For similar TWO ANNAS and FOUR AN-
NAS see Nos. 541-542.

448 QUARTER PAGODA.
Like No. 448a but obv.
ribbon border, rev. no
ribbon. ND (1807-08).....17.50

Fine

*448a —. Temple, garter border.
Rev. Vishnu, ribbon border.
ND (1808-12).......... 12.50

449 HALF PAGODA. Like
No. 448. ND (1807-08)....65.00

449a —. Like No. 448a.
ND (1808-12)...........45.00

Nos. 449-449a were struck over cut-
down Spanish dollars, traces of which
often show.

Machine-Struck Gold

V.F.

452 PAGODA. Like No. 448a.
17-18mm. ND (1808-15)...60.00

453 TWO PAGODAS. Sim.
20-21mm. ND (1808-15)...90.00

456 (¼ mohur). ENGLISH EAST
INDIA COMPANY, lion (like
No. 431). Rev. Persian
legend. 2.9 gr. 17mm.
ND (1819)..............70.00

457 (⅓ mohur). Sim. but lion
on shield. 3.9 gr. 19mm.
ND (1820)..............55.00

458 (½ mohur). Like No. 456.
5.8 gr. 21mm. ND (1819)..100.00

459 (mohur). Sim. but arms
like No. 433. 11.6 gr.
28mm. ND (1819)......140.00

(b) Coins with Arkat (Arcot) name.

The Nawab of Arcot gave the Company the right to copy his coins with
Persian "struck at Arkat" legend in
1742. British dump issues bear a lotus
blossom mint mark. They were struck
at Madras, Cuddalore and Calcutta,
but cannot be distinguished by mint.
   For other silver dumps with either
Arkat name or lotus mmk. see Nos.
512-514 and French India Nos. 24-76.

Dump Silver

VG-F

463 (½ rupee). Like No. 464.
Yr. 1 (=1748-49)......... —

464 (rupee). In name of Ahmad
Shah Bahadur (like Mughal
No. 15). Rev. like No. 469.
11.4 gr. Yrs. 1-4......... —

465 (¹⁄₁₆ rupee). Like No. 469.
Yr. 6.................... *7.00*

466 (⅛ rupee). Sim. Yr. 6..... *7.00*

467 (¼ rupee). Sim. Yr. 6..... *7.00*

468 (½ rupee). Sim. Yr. 6..... *5.00*

*469 (rupee). In name of Alamgir
II. Rev. yr.–ARKAT legend,
lotus mmk. 11.4 gr. Yrs. 2-6
(=1755-59 but struck with
frozen yr. 6 to 1807)..... 5.00

Prices are for coins with legible regnal
years.

Machine-Struck Silver

This series bears legends as No. 460
(shortened on the ¹⁄₁₆, ⅛, ¼ and 2
rupees and ¼ mohur). All have frozen
date AH1172 (=1758-59) and regnal
yr. 6 of Alamgir II (varieties with 1176
or yr. 2 are scarce errors). Struck at
Madras (mmk. lotus) and Calcutta
(mmk. rose).

(i) Lotus mmk. (=Madras).

F-VF

480 (¹⁄₁₆ rupee). Like No. 481a.
0.7 gr. 10mm. (1820-35)... 2.00

481 (⅛ rupee). Sim. 1.5 gr.
16.5mm. (1807)..........*Rare*

*481a —. 13.5mm. (1812-35).... 2.00

482 (¼ rupee). Sim. 3.0 gr.
16.5mm. (1807)..........*Rare*

482a —. Struck in collar.
17.5mm. (1812-35)...... 2.50

483 (½ rupee). Like No. 483c
but not struck in collar. 6.0
gr. 22mm. (1807-*12*)......*10.00*

483a —. Struck in collar.
22mm. (1812-35)........ 3.00

484 (rupee). Like No. 464.
12.1 gr. 26-28mm.
(1807-12).............. 5.00

484a —. Struck in collar.
28mm. (1812-35)........ 4.00

*485 (2 rupees). Like No. 483
but cruder dies. 24.2 gr.
38-41mm. (1807-12)....120.00

No. 485 was struck over Spanish dollars, traces of which often show.

INDIA

BRITISH - Madras (Cont.)

(ii) Rose mmk. (=Calcutta).

F-VF

480c (1/16 rupee). Like No. 481a.
10mm. (1823-25)........ 2.00

481c (1/8 rupee). Sim. 13.5mm.
(1823-25)............. 2.00

482c (1/4 rupee). Sim. 17.5mm.
Reeded edge. (1823-25)... 2.50

482d —. Plain edge. (1830-35).. 2.50

★483c (1/2 rupee). Reeded edge.
(1823-25)............. 3.00

483d —. Plain edge. (1830-35).. 3.00

484c (rupee). Sim. 28mm.
Reeded edge. (1823-25)... 4.00

484d —. Plain edge. (1830-35).. 4.00

Gold

All with lotus mmk. (=Madras).

492 (1/4 mohur). Like No. 481a.
17.5mm. (1817-18)........*RR*

493 (1/2 mohur). Like No. 483c.
22mm. (1817-18)..........*RR*

494 (mohur). Sim. 28mm.
(1817-18).............175.00

(c) Northern Circars.

Districts along the "Golconda Coast" northeast of Madras, ceded to the British East India Company by the Nizam of Hyderabad in 1766. Native-type coins were struck at Masulipatam, and machine-made coins at Soho (England) and Madras.

Monetary System:
192 dubs =48 fanams =4 rupees =
1 Madras pagoda.

(i) Coins with Machhlipatan (Masulipatam) name.

Dump Copper

V.G.

504 (1/2 dub). Like No. 506.
6.6-6.9 gr. 16mm......... 4.00

V.G.

506 (dub). Persian "struck at Machhlipatanbandar." Rev. date legend. 13-14 gr. 20mm. AH*1175-1222* (=*1761-1807*)........... 5.00

507 —. Sim., with English M on rev. AH1218 (=1803)..... 7.50

Dump Silver

512 (1/4 rupee). Like No. 514. AH1200, 10............. —

513 (1/2 rupee). Sim. AH1198-1204............ —

514 (rupee). In name of Alamgir II. Rev. Persian "struck at Machhlipatan," date. Lotus mmk. AH1197-1213 (=1783-99)............. —

The above types are easily confused with Nos. 467-469, which also use lotus mmk. For earlier issues see French India Nos. 66, 76.

(ii) General machine-struck issues.

Copper

VG-F

★521 96/TO ONE (=$1/96$) RUPEE (=1/2 dub). 1794, 97..... 2.00

522 48/TO ONE (=$1/48$) RUPEE (=dub). Sim. 1794, 97... 3.50

V.G.

★530 (1/4 dub). Telugu legend. Rev. Tamil legend. ND (1807).............15.00

531 (1/2 falus = 1/2 dub). Generally like No. 535. 5 gr. 23mm. 1807 (in Persian numerals)........ 4.50

★531a 1/2 DUB. Obv. sim. Rev. Telugu legend/English value. 5 gr. 26mm. 1808........ 5.50

532 (falus =dub). Sim. but no English value. 10 gr. 26mm. 1807.................. 5.50

V.G.

532a I DUB. Like No. 531a but thicker. 10 gr. 26mm. 1808................. 5.50

533 (2 falus =2 dubs). Like No. 531. 20 gr. 39-40mm. 1807..................20.00

532a 2 DUBS. Like No. 531a. 20 gr. 35-37mm. 1808....15.00

★535 (regulating dub). Persian: "This coin and 3 falus make 1 fanam." Rev. sim. in Telugu (5 lines) and Tamil. 7.5 gr. 26-27mm. 1807-08....... 6.00

No. 535 was used to adapt Nos. 530-533a to both rupee and pagoda systems.

Silver

Fine

541 TWO ANNAS. Like No. 447a. 1.5 gr. 16mm. ND (1808).............25.00

542 FOUR ANNAS. Sim. 3 gr. 17mm. ND (1808)....... 40.00

---

2. Bombay Presidency.

The island of Bombay on India's west coast was ceded to the British by Portugal in 1661. It became a major seaport and (1687) the seat of the East India Company's west coast government. Coins were struck for the Bombay area and for the Company's trading settlements on the Malabar (southwest) Coast: dumps struck at Bombay except where otherwise shown; machine-made coins struck at Bombay, Calcutta, and in England.

Monetary System:
192 pie =64 pice =16 annas =1 rupee;
15 rupees =1 mohur.

(a) Bombay minor coinage.

Issues listed here were struck primarily for use in the immediate vicinity of Bombay.

Tin Alloy

Good

554 1/4/PICE. Like No. 555. 18-19mm. ND (1757)......25.00

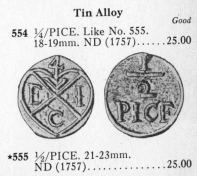

★555 1/2/PICE. 21-23mm. ND (1757)..............25.00

INDIA

BRITISH - Bombay (Cont.)

558 (½ pice). Like No. 559.
27-28mm. ND (1754)......25.00
Good

★559 (pice). G–R/crown/BOMB.
Rev. AUSPICIO/etc./date
or ornament. 32-35mm.
1717-71, ND............12.50

560 (2 pice). Sim. 37-40mm.
1717-71, ND............15.00

Dump Copper

565 ¼ (pice). Like No. 566.
10-11mm. ND (1773)...... *4.00*
VG (Crude)

★566 ½ (pice). 14-15mm.
ND (1773).............. *4.00*

567 I/PICE. Obv. sim. Rev.
value/BOMB/date. 18mm.
1773-88.............15.00

568 (2 pice). Obv. sim. Rev. like
obv. of No. 559, date below.
23mm. 1773-83........... 6.50

Prices for Nos. 567-568 are for coins
with legible dates. Pridmore says dates
after 1773 are probably forgeries.

570 (pice). Native coins cmkd.
BOMB/1788 in 9 x 14mm.
rectangle............. ——

575 (¼ pice). Like No. 577.
2.6 gr. 13-14mm. 1816-25... 5.00

576 (½ pice). Sim. 5.3 gr.
14-16mm. 1802-27........ 3.00

VG (Crude)

★577 (pice). Balemark/date.
Rev. scales/Persian ADIL
(=just). 10.6 gr. 17-20mm.
1802-29................ 3.00

578 2 (pice). Sim., value above
ADIL. 21.2 gr. 19-23mm.
1802-04................ *7.50*

578a (2 pice). Sim., no value
shown. 1808-29.......... 4.50

579 4 (pice). Like No. 578.
42.5 gr. 24-27mm. 1802-04.. *12.50*

Machine-Struck Copper

581 (½ pice). Like No. 583.
20mm. 1791, 94.......... 3.00
Fine

582 (pice). Sim. 25mm.
1791, 94................ 3.50

★583 (1½ pice). 9.7 gr. 29mm.
1791................... 3.50

584 (2 pice). Sim. 13 gr. 30mm.
1791, 94............... 3.00

★586 (½ pice). 1804.......... 2.75

587 (pice). Sim. 26mm. 1804... 3.25

588 (2 pice). Sim. 31mm. 1804.. 3.25

See NETHERLANDS EAST INDIES
for other coins dated 1804 which use
these arms.

591 PIE. Sim. 18mm. 1831, 33.. 1.25

★592 QUARTER ANNA. Sim.
Obv. with EAST INDIA
COMPANY. 1830, 32....... 2.50
Fine

592a —. Obv. no legend. 1833... 1.50

593 HALF ANNA. Like No. 592.
31mm. 1834............. 3.00

(b) Coins with Bombay or Munbai name.

Coins in this group bear English BOM-
BAY or Persian MUNBAI (=Bombay).
Dumps have normal regnal years to the
death of Alamgir II (in his yr. 6 =1759),
thereafter they bear his legend with
frozen yr. 9 (=1762!) to ca. 1778. Also
see No. 592 with both Bombay and
Tellicherry legends.

Dump Silver

Fine

★621 ς (=¹/₅ rupee=fanam). In
name of Shah Jahan II
(AD1719), value in center.
Rev. MUNBAI legend. 2.25 gr.
ND (ca. 1727-96). Struck
for Tellicherry............ 7.50

An earlier version of No. 621, on larger
flan and with 5 not inverted, was struck
1719-30. Cruder copies of both varieties
on small flans are native issues.

629 (rupee). In name of Ahmad
Shah Bahadur (like Mughal
No. 15). Rev. like No. 639.
11.5 gr. Yrs. 4-6 (=1751-
53)...................*18.00*

635 (¹/₅ rupee=fanam). Like
No. 639. 2.2 gr. Frozen
yr. 9. (struck 1774-75 for
Tellicherry)............. *7.50*

637 (¼ rupee). Like No. 639a.
2.8 gr. Yr. 9........... ——

638 (½ rupee). Like No. 639.
5.7 gr. Yrs. 2, 5, 9....*10.00*

638a —. *Like No. 639a. Yr. 9...* ——

639 (rupee). Like No. 640 but
dump. 11.5 gr. Yrs. 2, 5
(=1755, 58)............*15.00*

639a —. Crescent mmk. added
on obv. Yr. 9...........

INDIA

BRITISH - Bombay (Cont.)

Machine-Struck Silver

F-VF

★640 (rupee). In name of Alamgir II. Rev. MUNBAI legend. ND (struck at Calcutta 1810-13 *for Malabar Coast settlements*)..............20.00

Gold

642 (¼ mohur). ENGLISH EAST INDIA COMPANY, arms. Rev. BOMBAY/1765. 2.7 gr. 17mm.................*125.00*

643 (½ mohur). Sim. 5.5 gr. 20mm. 1765...........*175.00*

644 (mohur). Sim. 10.9 gr. 23mm. 1765............*325.00*

★649 15 RUP(ee)s (=mohur). In name of Alamgir II. 1770..................*400.00*

655 (gold rupee =¹/₁₅ mohur). Like No. 659. 0.76 gr. 8-10mm. Yr. 9........*30.00*

657 (¼ mohur). Sim. *3.8 gr.* 13-15mm. *Yr. 9*..........*50.00*

658 (*½ mohur*). *Sim. 5.8 gr.*....——

★659 (mohur). Like No. 640 but dump. 11.5 gr. AH1188 (=1774), frozen yr. 9......*80.00*

(c) Coins with Surat name.

A city on the Gulf of Cambay north of Bombay, Surat was the site of the first British foothold in India 1612-13. The Company acquired its native mint in 1800, and struck coins with this mint name at Surat, Bombay and Calcutta. **Dates:** All coins bear frozen regnal year 46 of Shah Alam II (=1803-04). Surat coins with earlier dates are Mughal or native issues.

Mint marks on dump issues often were intended to be "secret" (=privy marks), indicating changes in standards as well as mint of origin. The following chart is derived from IV Pridmore:

Mint marks involve the 3 diamonds and 4 dots in center line of obverse. (This is No. 664 with mmk. 1.)

1	∴	◇◇	Surat 1800-15
2	∴	◇◇	Bombay 1801-02
3	∴	◇◇	Bombay 1802
4*	∴	◇◇	Bombay 1803-24
4b	∴	◇◇	Bombay 1803-24
5*	∴	◇◇	Bombay 1825-31
5b	∴	◇◇	Bombay 1825-31
6	∴	◇◇	Bombay 1800-24
7	∴	◇◇	**and** 1825 Bombay 1825
8	∴	◇◇	**on rev.** Bombay 1825-31
9	∴	◇◇	Unknown

*Crown also may be inverted (Pridmore's 4a, 5a).

Dump Silver

Fine

661 (⅛ rupee). Like No. 663. 1.4 gr. 10-12mm. Mmks. 1, 6, 8, 9.............5.00

662 (¼ rupee). Sim. 2.9 gr. 13-14mm. Mmks. 1, 6, 8...5.00

★663 (½ rupee). In name of Shah Alam II. Rev. yr. 46–SURAT legend. 5.8 gr. 15-17mm. Mmks. 1, ★6, 7, 8, 9.......4.50

★664 (rupee). Sim. 11.6 gr. 17-20mm. Mmks. 1, 6, 7, ★8, 9. 4.00

Dump Gold

F-VF

665 (gold rupee =¹/₁₅ mohur). Like No. 664. 0.77 gr. 7-8mm. Mmks. 1, *2*, 4b, 5b........*30.00*

667 (⅓ mohur ="panchia"). Sim. 3.9 gr. 14-15mm. Mmks. 1, 2, 3, 4, 5........*50.00*

F-VF

★669 (mohur). Sim. 11.6 gr. 16-19mm. Mmks. 1, *2*, ★4, 5...*85.00*

Machine-Struck Silver

In this series, mint marks no longer follow the chart above No. 661.

676 (¼ rupee). Like No. 677. 17mm...................2.50

★677 (½ rupee). Legends like No. 663. Plain edge, struck in collar. 23mm. (Bombay 1832-35)................2.75

678 (rupee). Sim. but reeded edge, not struck in collar. 11.6 gr. 26-27mm. (Calcutta 1823-24)................4.50

678a —. Like No. 678. 28mm... 3.75

(d) Malabar Coast issues.

Coins listed here are believed to be for various British East India Company trading settlements on India's west coast. Definite attribution is not possible on the basis of present knowledge. See IV Pridmore, pp. 139-143.

Dump Copper

V.G.

681 (½ pice). Like No. 682. 1.6-2.0 gr. 10-15mm. 1710-85....................5.00

681a —. 0.9-1.2 gr. 8-9mm. (1)803....................*4.00*

★682 (pice). Balemark. Rev. date. 3.2-5.9 gr. 16-20mm. 1705-79...................*4.50*

★682a —. 2.2-2.9 gr. 10-12mm. 1803, 07..............4.00

684 (*2 pice*). Balemark both sides. 9.6-10.6 gr. 19mm. ND....................——

INDIA

BRITISH - Bombay (Cont.)

687 ½ pice. Like No. 689. *V.G.*
3.7 gr. 17-18mm. 1820-21 .. 6.50

688 pice. Sim. 7.5 gr. 19-20mm.
1820-21 .... 6.00

688a (pice). Like No. 689a.
1829 .... ——

★689 ½ anna. Balemark/date.
Rev. scale/Nagari value/
date. 15 gr. 23-24mm.
1820-21. For southern
Concan 8.00

689a (½ anna). Rev. scale/date
in western numerals.
Cruder. 1828-29 .... 10.00

Silver

Pridmore says that No. 640, the machine-struck Bombay rupee, was most
likely issued for this area.

(e) Tellicherry.

Seaport north of Calicut in the Canna-
nore district; site of the East India
Company's first major trading settlement on the Malabar Coast (1683). Despite their legends, coins listed here
were struck at Calicut (mint acquired
by the Company ca. 1790).

Silver

Fine

★694 (fanam = ⅕ rupee). T(ellicherry 17)99/Persian legend/
AH1214. Rev. Persian
"struck at Tellicherry" 6.00

★695 (fanam). Persian "struck at
Munbai (Bombay), reign of
Shah Alam." Rev. scale/
T(ellicherry)/1805 .... 7.00

Gold

689 (pagoda). Like No. 694 but
obv. date in western numerals
at bottom. 1809 .... 65.00

3. Bengal Presidency.

A large territory in northeast India,
site of British trading settlements from
1633. British *de facto* rule followed bat-
tles against native forces in 1757 and
1764, and Bengal came to be the largest
and most prosperous of the Company's
three Presidencies.

Coins were struck at Calcutta, Banaras, Dacca, Falta, Farrukhabad, Murshidabad, Patna and Sagar.

Monetary System:
192 pie = 64 pice (pai sikka) =
16 annas = 1 rupee;
12 to 17 rupees = 1 mohur.

(a) General copper coinage.

Listed here are all Bengal coppers without mint names, regardless of whether
their circulation was general or if it was
regional.

(i) Prinsep coinage.

Coins struck 1781-84 under contract by
John Prinsep at Falta (Fultah) near
Calcutta.

701 (⅟₁₆ anna). Like No. 702.   *V.G.*
1.8 gr. 14-16mm. AH1195/
yr. 22 .... 2.50

★702 (⅛ anna). Shah Alam II
legend/AH1195 (= 1781).
Rev. yr. 22 legend. 3.6 gr.
17-20mm 1.75

703 (¼ anna). Sim. 7.3 gr.
21-24mm. 1195/yr. 22 ..... 2.00

704 (½ anna). Sim. 14.6 gr.
25-29mm. 1195/yr. 22 ..... 3.00

(ii) Year 37 and 45 coinage.

These pieces bear frozen yr. 37 (= 1795,
first issue date) or 45 (= 1802-03, copied
from Farrukhabad silver, q.v.) of Shah
Alam II.

705 (½ pai sikka). Like No. 706.
5.8 gr. 23-24mm. Yr. 37.
(1795) 7.50

705a —. 4.3 gr. (1796-ca. 1800) .. 4.00

★706 (pai sikka = pice). Shah   *V.G.*
Alam yr. 37 legend. Rev.
value in Bengali/Persian/
Hindi. 11.6 gr. 29-30mm.
(1795) 5.00

706a —. 8-9 gr. 27-30mm.   *VG-F*
(1796-1809) 1.75

706b —. 6.5 gr. 26.5-28mm.
(1809-29) 1.50

706d —. 6.5 gr. 25.5-26mm.
(1829-30) 1.50

★706e —. 23mm. Struck in collar.
(1831-35) .... *(F-VF)* 1.25

708 (pai sikka). Sim. but dated
yr. 45 (= 1802-03). 6.5 gr.
24mm. (Farrukhabad
1816-*20*) *4.00*

709 (2 pai sikka). Sim. 13 gr.
28mm. Yr. 45 .... *10.00*

★710 (½ pai sikka). Obv. like
No. 706. Rev. value in
Persian/Nagari. 3.1 gr.
17mm. Yr. 37 (= 1795,
struck at Calcutta 1808-09
for Banaras) *10.00*

711 (pai sikka = pice). Sim.
6.2 gr. 24mm. Yr. 37 .... *15.00*

712 (2 pai sikka). Sim. 12.4 gr.
29mm. Yr. 37 .... *15.00*

(iii) Year 37 and 45 trisul pice.

Similar coins with trisul (trident) mint
mark.

★714 (pai sikka = pice). Obv. like
No. 706. Rev. value in
Persian/Hindi. Trisul both
sides. 22-26mm. Yr. 37
(Banaras 1815-21) 2.50

714a —. Circle around border.
19-23mm. (1821-27) 3.00

714b —. Neater engraving. Rev.
trisul has crossbar. 23-24mm.
(1827-29) 3.75

INDIA

BRITISH - Bengal (Cont.)

716 (pai sikka). Sim. but dated
yr. 45. Trisul both sides.
(Farrukhabad 1820-24,
Sagar 1826-33) . . . . 3.75 *(VG-F)*

716a —. Obv. trisul, rev. 6-pointed
star. (Sagar 1833-35) 5.00

(iv) Final Bengal issue.

★**718** ONE/PIE. Value in English/
Bengali. Rev. value in
Persian/Nagari. ND
(1831-35) . . . . *(V.F.)* 1.25

720 HALF/ANNA. Sim.
28mm. ND 3.00

No. 706e is generally considered part
of this group.

(b) Coins with Kalkatah (Calcutta) name.

The city of Calcutta grew up around
small settlements controlled by the
East India Company from 1690. Its
mint opened in 1757, striking native-
style dumps with Persian name "Alinagar Kalkatah;" this was soon shortened to "Kalkatah." After about 1766
the silver and gold struck there bore
the names of other Company mints.

Dump Copper

723 10 to 5 annas (=½ anna).
Like No. 724. 14.5 gr. 21mm.
AH1188 (=1774) . . . . — *V.G.*

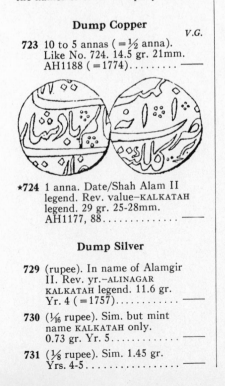

★**724** 1 anna. Date/Shah Alam II
legend. Rev. value–KALKATAH
legend. 29 gr. 25-28mm.
AH1177, 88 . . . . —

Dump Silver

729 (rupee). In name of Alamgir
II. Rev. yr.–ALINAGAR
KALKATAH legend. 11.6 gr.
Yr. 4 (=1757) . . . . —

730 (1/16 rupee). Sim. but mint
name KALKATAH only.
0.73 gr. Yr. 5 . . . . —

731 (⅛ rupee). Sim. 1.45 gr.
Yrs. 4-5 . . . . —

---

732 (¼ rupee). Sim. 2.9 gr.
Yr. 4 . . . . *V.G.*

733 (½ rupee). Sim. 5.8 gr.
Yr. 4 . . . . —

734 (rupee). Sim. 11.6 gr. AH1171-
72/yr. 5 (=1757-58) . . . . . . —

739 (rupee). In name of Shah
Alam II. Rev. like No. 729.
1176/yr. 4 (=1762-63) . . . . . —

Dump Gold

744 (mohur). Like No. 729.
11.1 gr . . . . RRR

747 (¼ mohur). Like No. 730.
2.8 gr . . . . RRR

748 (½ mohur). Sim. 5.5 gr . . . . RRR

749 (mohur). Sim. 11.1 gr.
AH1171, 74/yrs. 5-6
(=1758, 61) . . . . RRR

(c) Coins with Murshidabad name.

Control of the important city of Murshidabad passed to the Company in a
1765 grant by the Mughal emperor.
Coins dated before AH1179/yr. 7 are
Mughal issues (see section I). Mint
closed 1777-92 and permanently in
1797, but coins with this name were
struck continuously at Calcutta ca.
1766-1835.

(i) Dump Coinage.

On dumps the AH dates (when visible)
show normal annual changes, but regnal years became "frozen" permanently
in yr. 19 (=1777). Murshidabad and
Calcutta strikings are indistinguishable
(but yr. 19 = Calcutta only). Silver was
struck to 1793, gold to 1789.

Dump Silver

750 (1/16 rupee). Like No. 754.
0.73 gr. Yrs. 9-19 . . . . 7.50 *VG-F*

751 (⅛ rupee). Sim. 1.45 gr.
Yrs. 7-19 . . . . 7.50

752 (¼ rupee). Sim. 2.9 gr.
Yrs. 9-19 . . . . 7.50

753 (½ rupee). Sim. 5.8 gr.
Yrs. 8-19 . . . . 7.50

★**754** (rupee). In name of Shah
Alam II. Rev. yr.–MURSHIDA-
BAD legend. 11.6 gr.
AH1179-1205 (=1765-90)/
yrs. 7-19 . . . . 5.00

Dump Gold

758 (½ mohur). Sim., with
c(alcutta) in rev. field.
5.82 gr. Yr. 7 . . . . RRR *F-VF*

---

759 (mohur = 14 rupees). Sim.
11.64 gr. AH1180/yr. 8
(=1766-67) . . . . RR *F-VF*

760 (1/16 mohur). Like No. 754
(legends often shortened).
0.77 gr. AH1182-1203
(=1769-89)/yrs. 10-19 . . . . 40.00

761 (⅛ mohur). Sim. (legends
often shortened). 1.55 gr.
1182-1203/yrs. 10-19 . . . . . 40.00

762 (¼ mohur). Sim., full
legends. 3.09 gr. 1182-1203/
yrs. 10-19 . . . . 50.00

763 (½ mohur). Sim. 6.18 gr.
1182-83/yrs. 10-15 . . . . 65.00

764 (mohur = 16 rupees). Sim.
12.37 gr. 1182-1202/
yrs. 10-19 . . . . 85.00

(ii) Machine-struck coinage.

This series bears legends as No. 754
(shortened on the ¼ rupee and ¼ mohur). All have frozen yr. 19 (=1777) of
Shah Alam II; AH dates, when used,
are similarly frozen.

Silver

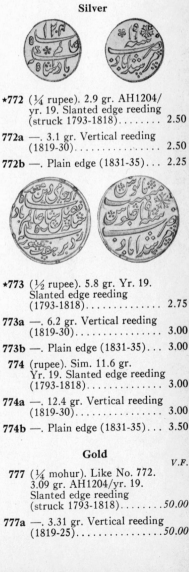

★**772** (¼ rupee). 2.9 gr. AH1204/
yr. 19. Slanted edge reeding
(struck 1793-1818) 2.50

772a —. 3.1 gr. Vertical reeding
(1819-30) 2.50

772b —. Plain edge (1831-35) . . . 2.25

★**773** (½ rupee). 5.8 gr. Yr. 19.
Slanted edge reeding
(1793-1818) 2.75

773a —. 6.2 gr. Vertical reeding
(1819-30) 3.00

773b —. Plain edge (1831-35) . . . 3.00

774 (rupee). Sim. 11.6 gr.
Yr. 19. Slanted edge reeding
(1793-1818) 3.00

774a —. 12.4 gr. Vertical reeding
(1819-30) 3.00

774b —. Plain edge (1831-35) . . . 3.50

Gold

777 (¼ mohur). Like No. 772.
3.09 gr. AH1204/yr. 19.
Slanted edge reeding
(struck 1793-1818) . . . . 50.00 *V.F.*

777a —. 3.31 gr. Vertical reeding
(1819-25) 50.00

INDIA

BRITISH - Bengal (Cont.)

778 (½ mohur). Like No. 773. *V.F.*
6.18 gr. AH1202/yr. 19.
Slanted edge reeding
(1793-1818)............*65.00*

778a —. 6.63 gr. Vertical reeding
(1819-25)................*65.00*

779 (mohur). Sim. 12.36 gr.
1202/yr. 19. Slanted edge
reeding (1790-1818, 25-35).
Var...................*85.00*

779a —. 13.26 gr. Vertical reeding
(1819-25)................*85.00*

(d) Coins with Jahangirnagar name.

An honorary title for the city of Dacca
(today capital of Bangladesh), controlled by the East India Company from
1765. Mint closed 1773-91 and 1797 on.
Coins dated before AH1179/yr. 7 are
Mughal issues.

Dump Silver

794 (rupee). Like No. 754 but
rev. Persian JAHANGIRNAGAR
etc. 11.6 gr. AH1183/yr. 10.RRR

(e) Coins with Patna and Azimabad names.

Patna (= Azimabad) was the third of
the major cities granted to the Company in 1765. Mint closed 1773-91 and
1797 on. Coins dated before AH1179/
yr. 7 are Mughal issues.

Copper

V.G.

★805 One Ann(a)s. Patna/Post/
value/1774. Rev. Persian
AZIMABAD/value. Issued to
buy postage............60.00

806 Two Ann(a)s. Sim. 1774...75.00

Pridmore considers the above pieces to
be tokens.

Dump Silver

814 (rupee). Like No. 754 but
rev. Persian AZIMABAD etc.
11.6 gr. AH1179-83/yrs. 7-11
(var.)...................*RR*

Dump Gold

F-VF

815 (⅟₁₆ mohur). Sim. but shortened legends. 0.77 gr. 12mm.
AH1182/yr. 10............*RRR*

---

817 (¼ mohur). Like No. 814. *F-VF*
3.07 gr. 1182/yr. 10.......*RRR*

819 (mohur). Sim. 11.1 gr.
Yr. 10.................*RRR*

(f) Coins with Muhammadabad Banaras name.

The city and district of Banaras (Bena-
res, Varanasi) in western Bengal were
ceded to the British by the Nawab Vi-
zier of Awadh (Oudh) in 1775. Coins
bearing mint name Muhammadabad
Banaras (Banaras only on some copper)
were struck to *ca. 1807* (copper) and
1819 (silver and gold). Later issues did
not bear these names, and are listed
elsewhere. Mint closed 1830.

Dates and mint marks:

1. Coins dated before yr. 17 lack fish
mmk. and are Mughal issues. See section I.

2. British issues begin with yr. 17 (=
1775-76) of Shah Alam II, and use as
mint mark the **outline** of a fish.

3. Copper and gold have normal regnal
years and (on gold) AH dates.

4. All silver bears frozen yr. 17; from
yr. 20 coins bear additional "true" year
(became frozen in yr. 49 = 1806).

5. Similar coins dated yrs. *17-26* with
mmk. a **solid** fish are native issues. See
section III (Awadh).

Dump Copper

825 falus (= pice). SHAH ALAM/ *V.G.*
value, fish mmk. Rev. MU-
HAMMADABAD BANARAS, date.
9-10 gr. yrs. 17, 19.......*4.00*

★826 —. Sim. but rev. BANARAS,
date. Trisul mmk. added both
sides. Yrs. 28, 35, 49......*3.00*

Dump Silver

Fine

830 (⅟₁₆ rupee). Like No. 834.
0.71 gr. Yrs. 17+20-49....*10.00*

831 (⅛ rupee). Sim. 1.42 gr.
Yrs. 17+20-49..........*7.50*

832 (¼ rupee). Sim. 2.83 gr.
Yrs. 17+20-49..........*7.50*

833 (½ rupee). Sim. 5.67 gr.
Yrs. 17+20-49..........*10.00*

★834 (rupee). In name of Shah *Fine*
Alam II, fish mmk. Rev.
yr.–MUHAMMADABAD BANARAS
legend. 11.33 gr. AH1190-
1229/yrs. 17+20-49......5.00

Dump Gold

839 (mohur). Sim. but w/out
frozen yr. 17. 10.9 gr.
1209, 13/yrs. 37, 41
(=1795, 99)............*150.00*

Machine-Struck Silver

842 (¼ rupee). Like No. 844 but
shortened legends. 17mm.
AH1229/yrs. 17+49...... —

843 (½ rupee). Like No. 844.
20mm. 1229/yrs. 17+49.....*RR*

★844 (rupee). Like No. 834 but
broad coin, reeded edge.
AH1229 (frozen)/yrs. 17+
49 (struck 1815-19)......17.50

(g) Coins with Farrukhabad name.

The city and district of Farrukhabad
in north-central India was acquired by
the East India Company in 1801. Silver
with this mint name was struck at Farrukhabad 1805-24, Calcutta 1818-35,
Banaras 1820-29 and Sagar (Saugor)
1825-35. Farrukhabad copper coins
bear no mint name (see Nos. 708-09,
716).

Dates: All coins bear frozen yr. 45 of
Shah Alam II (=1803, when mint was
authorized).

Machine-Struck Silver

F-VF

852 (¼ rupee). Like No. 853
but shortened legends. Obv.
rosette at top, no AH date.
2.8 gr. Yr. 45. Slanted edge
reeding. (ca. 1807-18).....3.50

852a —. 2.9 gr. Vertical reeding
(1819-24)...............3.50

★852b —. Sim. but obv. AH1204
at top. Vertical reeding
(Calcutta and Banaras
1819-30)...............3.00

852c —. Plain edge (Calcutta
1831-33)...............3.00

INDIA

F-VF

*853 (½ rupee). In name of
Shah Alam II. Rev. yr.–
FARRUKHABAD legend. 5.6 gr.
Yr. 45. Slanted edge reeding
(ca. 1807-18)............. 5.00

853a —. 5.8 gr. Vertical reeding
(1819-30)................ 4.00

853b —. Plain edge (1831-33)... 4.00

854 (rupee). Sim. 11.2 gr. yr. 45.
Slanted edge reeding
(1805-18)................ 5.50

854a —. 11.68 gr. Vertical
reeding (1819-35)........ 4.00

854b —. Plain edge (1831-35)... 4.50

---

4. British East India Company coinage for all India.

William IV 1830-37

Copper

F-VF

865 1/12/ANNA. Like No. 868.
1835, 48................. .75

866 ½/PICE. Sim. 1853....... 1.50

867 ONE/QUARTER/ANNA.
Sim. 1833-58............. 1.00

*868 HALF/ANNA. 1833-45.... 1.50

Silver

872 ¼/RUPEE. Like No. 874.
1835.................... 3.00

873 HALF/RUPEE. Sim. 1835. 3.50

F-VF

*874 ONE/RUPEE. 1835...... 5.00
The 1834 rupee is a pattern.

Gold

E.F.

878 ONE MOHUR. Like
No. 879. 1835.......... 175.00

878a —. Restrike.......(Proof) 100.00

V.F.

*879 TWO MOHURS. 1835.... —
879a —. Restrike........(Proof) 175.00
Many restrikes (especially in proof)
exist of Nos. 878-879.

B. DANISH INDIA (=Tranquebar).

Former Danish colony on the S.E.
coast of India. Initially governed by
the Danish East India Company
(D.O.C.) and then by the Danish Asiatic Company (D.A.C.). Sold to the
British East India Company in 1845.

Monetary System:

640 kas (cash) = 8 Royaliner
 (or fano = fanam) = 1 rupee;
18 Royaliner = 1 Speciesdaler.

Note: Because flans were usually smaller the dies, one or two digits of a coin's
date are often missing. If the date is
thereby made uncertain, the value is
reduced by about 40%.

Frederik V 1746-66

Copper

G-VG

1 1 (kas). Like No. 3. 1761...RRR

2 2 (kas). Sim. 1761........50.00

*3 4 (kas). Cwnd. F5.
Rev. DAC mon./value.
1761, 63................10.00

Silver

VG-F

4 1/ROYALIN. Like No. 5.
1755-66, ND (var.)........100.00

*5 2/ROYALINER. 1755-66,
ND (var.)...............100.00

Christian VII 1766-1808

Copper

G-VG

6 1 KAS. Cwnd. c7. Rev. Value.
1768-80.................27.50

7 2 (kas). Cwnd. c7. Rev. Cwn./
DAC/2. 1768-80...........27.50

8 4 (kas). Sim. 1767-77.......8.00

*9 IV/KAS. 1782-1807........6.50

9a —. Error VI. 1797-1800....20.00

10 10 KAS. Cwnd. double c7 mon.
Rev. Cwn./DAC/value/1768.70.00

11 X KAS. Sim. 1768-77......40.00

12 X/KAS. Like No. 9.
1782-90.................20.00

Silver

VG-F

13 1/ROYALIN. Cwnd. c7 mon.
Rev. like No. 5. 1767-1807..27.50

14 2/ROYALINER. Sim.
1767-1807................27.50

Gold

V.F.

15 (pagode). Cwnd. c7 mon. in
oval on granulated surface.
Rev. Indian deity. ND
(1789)...................RRR

Modern counterfeits of No. 15 exist in
both gold and silver.

INDIA

DANISH INDIA (Cont.)

Frederik VI 1808-39

Copper

		V.G.
*16	1/KAS. 1819	40.00
17	IV/KAS. Sim. 1815-39	9.00
17a	—. (Error) VI for IV. 1824	60.00
18	X/KAS. Sim. 1816-39	20.00

Silver

		Fine
19	I/FANO. Sim. 1816, 18	125.00

| *20 | 2/FANO. 1816, 18 | 125.00 |

Christian VIII in Tranquebar 1839-45

Copper

		V.G.
21	IV/KAS. Like No. 22. 1840-45	12.50

| *22 | X/KAS. 1842 | 40.00 |

C. FRENCH INDIA.

France acquired various possessions on both coasts of India in the 17th century. During the 18th century wars the French came near to besting the British in India, but were finally restricted to certain small coastal settlements while the British went on to conquer the subcontinent.

Monetary Systems:

4 caches (cash, kas) = 1 doudou;
64 biches (pice) = 1 rupee;
2 royalins = 1 fanon (Pondichéry);
5 (heavy) fanons = 1 rupee (Mahé).

1. Coins with Arkat (Arcate, Arcot) mint name.

In 1736 the French obtained rights to copy the native coinage with "struck at Arkat" legend. French issues were struck at Pondichéry, and bear a crescent mint mark to left of regnal year on rev. For other coins with Arkat mint name and lotus mmk., see section A, British India. *Native Arket silver issues with other mmks. also exist.*

Dump Silver

		Fine
24	(¼ rupee). Like No. 26. Yr. 3	20.00

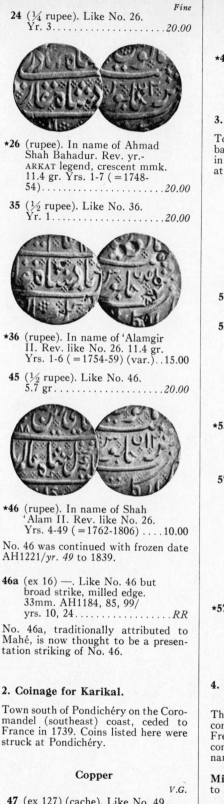

| *26 | (rupee). In name of Ahmad Shah Bahadur. Rev. yr.-ARKAT legend, crescent mmk. 11.4 gr. Yrs. 1-7 (= 1748-54) | 20.00 |
| 35 | (½ rupee). Like No. 36. Yr. 1 | 20.00 |

| *36 | (rupee). In name of 'Alamgir II. Rev. like No. 26. 11.4 gr. Yrs. 1-6 (= 1754-59) (var.) | 15.00 |
| 45 | (½ rupee). Like No. 46. 5.7 gr | 20.00 |

| *46 | (rupee). In name of Shah 'Alam II. Rev. like No. 26. Yrs. 4-49 (= 1762-1806) | 10.00 |

No. 46 was continued with frozen date AH1221/*yr. 49* to 1839.

| 46a | (ex 16) —. Like No. 46 but broad strike, milled edge. 33mm. AH1184, 85, 99/ yrs. 10, 24 | RR |

No. 46a, traditionally attributed to Mahé, is now thought to be a presentation striking of No. 46.

2. Coinage for Karikal.

Town south of Pondichéry on the Coromandel (southeast) coast, ceded to France in 1739. Coins listed here were struck at Pondichéry.

Copper

		V.G.
47	(ex 127) (cache). Like No. 49. 0.6-0.8 gr	10.00
48	(ex 128) (½ doudou). Sim. 1.7-2.0 gr	6.00

		V.G.
*49	(ex 129) (doudou). Tamil KA/RIK/KAL. Rev. like No. 123. 3.2 gr	5.00

3. Coinage for Mahé.

Town south of Tellicherry on the Malabar (southwest) coast, ceded to France in 1726. Coins listed here were struck at Pondichéry.

Louis XV 1715-74
Louis XVI 1774-93
Louis XVIII 1815-24

Copper

| 51 | (¼ biche). Like No. 53. 1.1-1.4 gr. *1753, 67, 69* | 10.00 |
| 52 | (½ biche). Sim. 2.2-3.6 gr. 1731-85 | 7.50 |

| *53 | (biche). *4.4-6.4 gr.* 1730-90 | 6.00 |

Silver

| 57 | (fanon = ⅕ rupee). Urdu FRANSWA KAMPANI. Rev. date/ PURCHERI (= Pondichéry). 1731-35 | 40.00 |

		Fine
*57a	—. Sim. but FRANS/KANPANI. Rev. date/P(ondichéry =)/ BHULCHERI. 2.25 gr. 1738-1820	10.00

4. Coins with Machhlipatan (Mazulipatam) mint name.

The city of Machhlipatan on the Golconda (east) coast was held by the French 1749-59, then passed to British control. For other coins with this mint name see British India.

Mint mark: Trident (*= lotus blossom)* to left of regnal year.

Dump Copper

Copper dabous (dubs) were also struck.

INDIA

FRENCH INDIA (Cont.)

Dump Silver

Fine

66 (rupee). In name of Ahmad Shah Bahadur. Rev. yr.– MACHHLIPATAN legend, *lotus* mmk. 11.4 gr. Yr. 4 (=1751)............30.00

76 (rupee). In name of 'Alamgir II. Rev. like No. 66. AH1167, 73/yrs. 1, 6 (=1754, 59)..............30.00

5. Murshidabad (Moxoudabat).

Although the French had coinage rights at Murshidabad 1738-65, their issues apparently are indistinguishable from the Mughal coinage struck there concurrently. For coins with this mint name prior to *AH1179* (=1765) see section I, Mughal Empire; for later coins (including former Nos. 91-97) see British India.

6. Pondichéry.

City south of Madras on the Coromandel (southeast) coast. Settled by French 1683; soon became their chief Indian possession. Several times occupied by British 1761-1816. Site of French mint 1700-1841.

(a) Undated issues ca. 1720-1837.

Copper

See MAURITIUS for former Nos. 101-102.

V.G.

121 (cache). Like No. 123. 1.6 gr..................7.50

122 (½ doudou). Sim. 2.1 gr... 5.00

*123 (doudou). Single fleur de lis. Rev. Tamil PUDU/CHHE/RI. 4.2 gr....................3.00

Former Nos. 127-129 have been relocated. See Nos. 47-49.

Silver

Note: Style and size of designs vary greatly on Nos. 131-133a. Flans are often smaller than the dies, thus coins must be attributed by weight. Pieces showing complete design (as illustration of No. 133a) are worth substantially more than the prices shown.

Fine

131 (½ fanon). Like No. 133a but crown decorated with pearls. 0.7 gr..................7.50

132 (fanon). Sim. 1.5 gr....... 7.50

132a —. Crown like No. 133a...*10.00*

Fine

133 (2 fanons). Like No. 131. 2.7-3.0 gr..............*12.50*

**133a —. Crown decorated with flowers or stars.........7.50

Gold

V. Fine

137 (ex 131) *(pagode)*. Like No. 133a. *2.25 gr*.........*Rare*

139 (ex 112) (pagode). Hindu goddess. Rev. small crescent mmk., grained field around. 3.4....................90.00

Former No. 114 has been relocated as No. 164. Former No. 113 is not French; see section III, Native States (Mysore No. 68).

(b) Dated issues.

Louis Philippe 1830-48

Copper

VG-F

*141 (doudou). Gallic cock. Rev. like No. 123. 1836.... 6.00

Silver

Fine

143 (½ fanon). Like No. 145. 0.7 gr. 9-10mm. 1837......10.00

144 (fanon). Sim. 1.5 gr. 11-13mm. 1837..........10.00

*145 (2 fanons). Crown. Rev. Gallic cock. 3 gr. 13-16mm. 1837..........15.00

7. Surat (Surate).

The French had coins struck at the native Surat mint 1749-59. This coinage apparently cannot be distinguished from the native issues of the period. For former No. 156 see section III, Native States (Surat).

---

8. Coinage for Yanaon (Yanam).

A French settlement on the Golconda coast northeast of Machhlipatan. No. 164 was struck at Pondichéry for trade here.

Gold

V. Fine

164 (ex 114) (pagode). 3 Hindu deities. Rev. like No. 139. 3.4 gr.................100.00

D. NETHERLANDS POSSESSIONS IN INDIA.

The Netherlands United East India Company acquired a number of coastal trading sites in South India in the 17th century. These were ceded to the British at various times, the last in 1824.

1. Cochin.

On the Malabar (West) Coast in South India. Acquired from Portugal 1669. Occupied by British 1795-1814, ceded to them in 1814.

Monetary System:
After 1724: 8 bazarucos = 4 duits = 1 stuiver.

Tin

Good

5 8 (= ⅛ stuiver). 8/voc mon. Rev. pear-shaped shield. N.D. (1724-95)................5.00

Copper

V.G.

11 (½ rasi). Degenerate figure of Kali in pearl border. Rev. lazy J/13 dots. 5.5 gr. N.D. (18th century)............10.00

For trade with Muscat.

12 (rasi). Sim. 11 gr. N.D. (18th century)............7.50

Silver

Fine

*20 (fanam). Sim. to No. 11 but w/out pearl borders, O(ostindische) C(ompagnie) over the lazy J. .31-.38 gr. N.D. (=1782-91)..............5.00

For later issues see section III, Native States (Cochin).

0.100 Gold

25 (fanam). Like No. 11 w/out pearl borders. .35-.38 gr. N.D. (=1740-80)..............15.00

2. Negapatnam.

On the Coromandel (East) Coast of South India. Taken from Portugal 1658. Ceded to British Company 1784.

No Negapatnam copper or silver identifiable to the period after 1750.

INDIA

NETHERLANDS INDIA (Cont.)

Gold
F-VF

31 (Porto Novo pagoda). Four
armed deity. Rev. Grains. 3.4 gr.
N.D. (1745-84 at Negapatnam,
1760-1800 at Tuticorin).....60.00

3. Pulicat.

On the Coromandel (East) Coast. Acquired 1610. Mint opened at Fort Gelria 1615. Occupied by British 1781-84,
1795-1818. Ceded to British Company
1824.

Monetary System:
10 cash = 1 stuiver.

Copper
Good

41 (cash). p/VOC mon. Rev. PALICA
or PALCATE around G(elria),
date. 1.6 gr. 1742, 43,
65.................Very Rare

42 (2 cash). Sim. 3.3 gr.
1780.................Very Rare

**Other Pulicat coins and cmks. an-
tedate the period covered by this
catalog.**

4. Tuticorin.

Acquired from Portugal 1658. *Ceded
to the British Company 1795.*

0.365-0.406 Gold
F-VF

51 (fanam). Degenerate Kali.
Rev. degenerate Nagari legend.
.35-.38 gr. N.D. (=1675-
1793).................17.50

E. PORTUGUESE INDIA.

Former Portuguese possessions on the
West Coast of India.

Monetary Systems:
750 bazarucos = 600 réis = 10 tangas =
2 pardao (xerafins) = 1 rupia;
15 réis (Diu) = 12 réis (Goa) = 1 atiá;
600 réis (Diu) = 400 réis (Goa).

1. Damão.

North of Bombay on the Gulf of Cambay.

José I 1750-77

Note: Several coins traditionally attributed to Diu and Goa have been reassigned to Damão by Damião Peres,
*Catálogo das Moedas indo-portuguesas
do Museu Numismático Português* (vol.
II, 1964).

Tutenaga (tin-lead alloy)
VG (crude)

2 *(2 bazarucos). Like No. 3.*
1.8 gr. 13mm. *ND*........ ──

VG (crude)

★3 *(5 bazarucos).* 4 gr. 1770....25.00

5 *(10 bazarucos).* Sim. 6.6 gr.
25-27mm. 1770...........35.00

★6 *(10 bazarucos).* 5.2-6.9 gr.
26-30mm. ND, 1775.......40.00

Gold

9 (5 xerafins). Like No. 10.
2.84 gr. 16mm. 1755......*600.00*

★10 (ex 65) (10 xerafins). 5.68 gr.
19mm. 1755, *57*..........*800.00*

Maria II 1834-53

Copper

Fine

★21 15 R(éis). No wreaths.
1843.................14.00

22 30/R(éis). Like No. 23.
1840.................17.50

★23 60/R(éis). 1840...........30.00

Pedro V 1853-61

Copper

31 15 R(éis). Like No. 21.
1854.................14.00

32 30/R(éis). *Like No. 23.*
1854.................17.50

2. Diu (Dio).

On the opposite side of the Gulf of
Cambay from Damão. All tutenaga issues, and copper to 1799, have mint
mark D–O (or D–α, O–D, O–α) at sides
of arms.

José I 1750-77

Tutenaga (tin-lead alloy)

VG (crude)

★56 (5 bazarucos). 3.5-4.5 gr.
21-23mm. 1765, 68, 77.....15.00

57 (10 bazarucos). Sim.
Ca. 26mm. 1777..........25.00

58 (20 bazarucos). Sim.
14-18 gr. 33-35mm.
1765, 68, 77.............20.00

Copper

60 (½ atiá). Like No. 73. 4.5 gr.
18-20mm. 1767-68........10.00

61 (ex 51) (atiá). Sim. 9 gr.
22-24mm. 1767-68, 77......8.00

Silver
F (crude)

63 (pardao). Sim., with rays
from ends of cross. 5.9 gr.
17-18mm. *1765*...........80.00

64 (rupia). Sim. 11.8 gr.
22-23mm. 1765-71........65.00

Gold

Former No. 65 has been reassigned to
Damão. See No. 10.

Maria I and Pedro III 1777-86

Copper

71 (¼ atiá). Like No. 73. 2.2 gr.
14-15mm. 1778...........10.00

★73 (atiá). 9 gr. 1778...........8.00

Silver

★77 RVPIa. 10.65 gr. 1781......100.00

INDIA

PORTUGUESE-Diu (Cont.)

Maria I, alone 1786-1807

Tutenaga

VG (crude)

90 *(3 bazarucos).* Like No. 93.
2.8 gr. 16-17mm. 1800......15.00

91 *(5 bazarucos).* Sim. 3.4-5.0 gr.
20-23mm. 1799-1801.......10.00

92 *(10 bazarucos).* Sim. 7.6-9.3 gr.
25-28mm. 1799-1800......6.00

★93 (20 bazarucos). Sim. 15-20 gr.
32-37mm. 1799-1801......8.00

Copper

95 (ex 81) (½ atiá). Like
No. 73. 4.5 gr. 17-19mm.
1787, 99.................7.50

96 (ex 82) (atiá). Sim. 7.4-8.1 gr.
21-23mm. 1799...........7.50

Silver

F (crude)

98 150 (réis). Like No. 100 but
rev. value, DIO, date around
cross. 1806................45.00

99 300 (réis). Sim. 1806......55.00

★100 600 (réis=rupia). Arms in
irregular shield. Rev. value/
cross/DIO. 1806..........55.00

Counterfeits of No. 100 are common.

João VI, as Prince Regent 1807-18

Tutenaga

111 *(5 bazarucos).* Like No. 93.
20.5mm. 1807...........*exist?*

113 *(20 bazarucos).* Like No. 93.
1807...................*exist?*

Copper

VG (crude)

★116 (ex 105) 30/Reis. Cwnd.
oval arms. Rev. value.
1818.................25.00

117 (ex 106) 60/Reis. Sim.
1818.................35.00

See Nos. 258-259 for similar coins without dates.

João VI, as King 1818-26

Copper

Former Nos. 121-124 now appear to be badly struck specimens of Nos. 271-278.

Pedro IV 1826-28

Tutenaga

F (crude)

131 (5 bazarucos). Like No. 133.
3.5-4.8 gr. 19-22mm.
1827-28................15.00

132 (10 bazarucos). Sim.
5.5-8.0 gr. 27-29mm.
1827...................20.00

★133 (20 bazarucos). 15-24 gr.
33-36mm. 1827-28........20.00

Maria II 1834-53

Copper

★141 ½ ATIA. 1851..........*pattern*

142 ATIA. Sim. 1851........*pattern*

Silver

148 600 (réis). Like No. 100.
1841.................150.00

Counterfeits of No. 148 are common.

Pedro V 1853-61

Silver

V.F.

★155 150 (réis). 1859..........50.00

156 300 (réis). Sim. 1859......65.00

---

3. Goa.

South of Bombay. Largest of the Portuguese possessions.

José I 1750-77

Tutenaga (tin-lead alloy)

VG (crude)

161 5 (bazarucos). Like No. 162.
1760...................20.00

★162 10 (bazarucos). Arms, G(O)A.
Rev. value. 1760, 69.....25.00

163 15 (bazarucos). Sim.
1760, 69.................25.00

164 II (réis). Obv. sim.
Rev. value. ND (1769)....20.00

★165 IV (réis). 1769...........20.00

166 VI (réis). Sim. 1769......20.00

167 (ex 162.5) XII (réis). Sim.
1769...................20.00

Copper

★168 dez (=10)/reis. ND
(1752-58).............8.00

169 doze (=12)/re(i)s. Sim.
ND....................10.00

170 vinte (=20)/re(i)s. Sim.
ND....................8.00

171 (ex 178) Meia (=½)/tanga.
Sim. ND...............10.00

171a 30/R(éis). Sim. ND......8.00

172 (ex 179) Tanga. Sim. ND..15.00

172a 60/R(eis). Sim. ND......15.00

173 *3 R(éis). Like No. 175.
ND(1768)*................12.50

174 (ex 171) 6 R(éis). Sim.
1762-69................7.50

★175 12 R(éis). 1762-69........10.00

INDIA

PORTUGUESE - Goa (Cont.)

VG (crude)

177 30 R(éis). Sim. 1759-74....12.50

180 5 R(éis). Sim. 1774.......20.00

181 (ex 173) 10 R(éis). Sim.
1774.................15.00

182 (ex 176) 20 R(éis). Sim.
1770-74.................15.00

Silver

F (crude)

185 (tanga = 60 réis). Cwnd. arms.
Rev. like No. 186. 1.16 gr.
13-14mm. ND...........45.00

★186 60 (réis). Cwn./value.
Rev. cross. 1.16 gr. 13-14mm.
ND.................45.00

Peres assigns Nos. 185-186 to the reign
of João V*(struck ca. 1733-40?)*

187 30 (réis). Like No. 188.
0.58 gr. 9-11mm. 1751-64..45.00

★188 60 (réis). Head btwn.
branches. Rev. cwn./value
btwn. branches. 1.16 gr.
11-13mm. 1751, 56, 60.....55.00

189 (60 réis). Obv. sim.
Rev. arms. 1756.........60.00

Nos. 187-189 often omit branches and
first two digits of date. Crudeness of
portraits permits attribution of coins
dated 1751 to either João or José.

★190 (½ pardao). IOZE–PH I.R.P.,
young head. Rev. arms.
2.9 gr. 1753-64..........65.00

191 (pardao). Sim. 5.9 gr.
17-19mm. 1753-62........75.00

191a —. Sim. but IOZE. PRIM.
1761.................90.00

192 (rupia). Like No. 190.
11.8 gr. 21-24mm. 1751-57..75.00

★193 MEIO (= ½) Pardao. Older,
cruder head. 2.64 gr.
1775-77.................35.00

F (crude)

194 Pardao. Sim. 5.3 gr.
17-18mm. 1775-76.......35.00

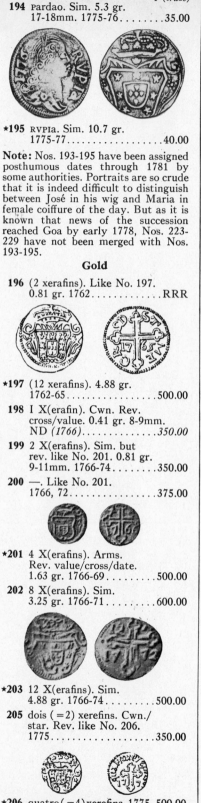

★195 RVPIa. Sim. 10.7 gr.
1775-77.................40.00

Note: Nos. 193-195 have been assigned
posthumous dates through 1781 by
some authorities. Portraits are so crude
that it is indeed difficult to distinguish
between José in his wig and Maria in
female coiffure of the day. But as it is
known that news of the succession
reached Goa by early 1778, Nos. 223-
229 have not been merged with Nos.
193-195.

Gold

196 (2 xerafins). Like No. 197.
0.81 gr. 1762............RRR

★197 (12 xerafins). 4.88 gr.
1762-65.................500.00

198 I X(erafin). Cwn. Rev.
cross/value. 0.41 gr. 8-9mm.
ND *(1766)*.............*350.00*

199 2 X(erafins). Sim. but
rev. like No. 201. 0.81 gr.
9-11mm. 1766-74........350.00

200 —. Like No. 201.
1766, 72.................375.00

★201 4 X(erafins). Arms.
Rev. value/cross/date.
1.63 gr. 1766-69.........500.00

202 8 X(erafins). Sim.
3.25 gr. 1766-71.........600.00

★203 12 X(erafins). Sim.
4.88 gr. 1766-74.........500.00

205 dois (= 2) xerefins. Cwn./
star. Rev. like No. 206.
1775.................350.00

★206 quatro (= 4) xerefins. 1775.500.00

207 oito (= 8) xerefins. Sim.
1775.................600.00

208 doze (= 12) xerefins. Sim.
1775-77.................500.00

Maria I, With Pedro III 1777-86; Alone 1786-1807
(Under Regency 1799-1807)

Copper

*It is believed that Nos. 210-220 may be
distinguished from undated copper issues
of the previous reign by the shield style
and by the way in which the denomination is written.*

VG (crude)

210 1½/Reis. Like No. 213.
ND.................. ——

211 3/Reis. Sim. ND.........15.00

212 4½/Reis. Sim. ND.......15.00

★213 6/Reis. Arms in irregular
shield. Rev. value. ND....10.00

214 *10/Reis.* Sim. ND........ ——

215 12/Reis. Sim. ND.........10.00

216 20/Reis. Sim. ND.........10.00

218 30/Reis. Sim. ND.........10.00

220 60/Reis. Sim. but rev.
value in wreath. ND......17.50

★217 vinte (= 20)/reis.
1787.................15.00

219 Meia (= ½)/tanga. Sim.
1787.................20.00

221 Tanga. Sim. 1787........20.00

Silver

**A. Young bust with bonnet.
Rev. arms in style of previous
reign.**

F (crude)

★223 MeIO (= ½) Pardao.
1780.................75.00

224 Pardao. Sim. 1779-80......75.00

225 RVPIa. Sim. 1778-81.......75.00

INDIA

···

PORTUGUESE-Goa (Cont.)

B. Young draped bust. Rev. as above.

F (crude)

226 MEIO (=½) Pardao. Like
No. 228. 1781............65.00

227 150 R(éis). Sim. but legend
like No. 232. 1782........65.00

★228 Pardao. 1781............65.00

229 RVPIA. Sim. 1781........75.00

C. Busts of Maria and Pedro. Rev. arms in irregular shield.

230 30 R(éis). Like No. 232.
0.53 gr. 10-11mm. 1784....——

231 60 R(éis). Sim. 1.06 gr.
12mm. 1785.............50.00

★232 150 R(éis). 1782-86......35.00

233 PARDAO. Sim. but arms
like No. 228. 1782........50.00

233a —. Like No. 232. 1782-87..25.00

234 RVPIA. Sim. 1782-87.....30.00

D. Older bust in widow's veil.

235 60 R(éis). Like No. 237.
ND....................——

236 150 R(éis). Sim. 1787-97...35.00

★237 PARDAO. 1787-97........50.00

238 RVPIA. Sim. 1787-95.....40.00

E. Aged bust with bonnet.

239 60 R(éis). Like No. 242.
1801-03................60.00

240 150 R(éis). Sim. 1796.....60.00

240a 150 re(i)s (or RES). Sim.
1798-1806..............45.00

241 PARDAO. Sim. 1796-1806.40.00

★242 RVPIA. Sim. 1796-1806...25.00

Gold

F-VF (crude)

243 doze (=12) xerefins.
Like No. 208. 1778-*80*....750.00

244 *1 X(erafin). Like
No. 247*.................——

244.5 *2 X(erafins). Sim*.......——

245 4 X(erafins). Sim.
1795, 1803.............600.00

246 8 X(erafins). Sim.
1787, 95...............850.00

247 12 X(erafins). Like No.
203 but arms in irregular
shield. 1779-1806........500.00

★247a 12 X(erafins). Like No.
203 *(mule)*. 1781........700.00

João VI, as Prince Regent 1807-18

Copper

VG (crude)

251 3/Reis. Like No. 256.
ND.................... 7.50

252 4½/REIS. Sim. ND...... 7.50

253 6/Reis. Sim. ND......... 5.00

254 7½/Reis. Sim. ND....... 5.00

254a 7¾/Reis. Sim. ND.......10.00

255 10/Reis. Sim. ND......... 7.50

★256 12/Reis. Cwnd. oval arms.
Rev. value. ND.......... 7.50

257 15/Reis. Sim. ND......... 7.50

258 30/Reis. Sim. ND......... 7.50

259 60/Reis. Sim. ND........20.00

See Nos. 116-117 for sim. coins dated
1818.

Silver

F (crude)

261 MEI (=½) x(erafin).
Like No. 263. 1818........75.00

262 PARDAO. Sim. 1808-18...60.00

★263 RVPIA. Bust. Rev. oval arms.
1807-18.................25.00

Gold

265 8 X(erafins). Oval arms.
Rev. like No. 244. 1819...850.00

266 12 X(erafins). Sim.
1808-15.................500.00

João VI, as King 1818-26

Copper

VG (crude)

271 3/Reis. Like No. 279. ND..15.00

272 4½/Reis. Sim. ND........10.00

273 6/Reis. Sim. ND.........10.00

274 7½/Reis. Sim. ND........10.00

275 9/Reis. Sim. ND......... 7.50

275a NOVE (=9)/Reis. Sim.
ND....................10.00

276 10/Reis. Sim. ND........ 7.50

277 12/Reis. Sim. ND........ 5.00

278 15/Reis. Sim. ND........ 5.00

★279 30/Reis. Arms on cwnd.
globe. Rev. value. ND.....10.00

280 60/Reis. Sim. ND........20.00

Silver

F (crude)

285 TANGA. Like No. 288.
11-12mm. 1819, 23........85.00

286 MEI (=½) X(erafin).
Sim. 15-17mm. 1818-23....85.00

287 PARDAO. Sim. 1818-25...85.00

★288 RVPIA. Bust. Rev. arms
on cwnd. globe. 1818-26...65.00

Gold

F-VF (crude)

289 1 X(erafin). Arms on cwnd.
globe. Rev. like No. 244.
0.4 gr. 8mm. 1819........——

290 *4 X(erafins). Sim*.........——

291 12 X(erafins). Sim.
1819, 24, 25............1100.00

PORTUGUESE-Goa (Cont.)

Pedro IV 1826-28
Silver

F *(crude)*

300 *PARDAO*. Like No. 301.
   N.D. .65.00

★301 *RVPIA*. 1827-28. . . . . . . .85.00

Miguel 1828-34
Copper
(Mostly struck over older coins.)

★310 ½ T(anga). Arms. Rev. A(sia)
   P(ortugueza)/½ T. ND. . . 6.00
311 T(anga). Sim. ND. 10.00
311a —. Cmkd. 60 Rei. N.D. . . .10.00

Cmkd. Copper

315 P(ortaria) R(egistrada No.).
   809 in circle cmkd. on ½
   tanga. 8.00
316 PR809 in circle. Cmkd. on
   tanga. 8.00

Silver

318 MEI (=½) X(erafin). Like
   No. 320. 14-16mm. 1831. . . ——
319 PARDAO. Sim. 1831. . . . .100.00

★320 *RVPIA*. 1829-33. . . . . .85.00

Maria II 1834-53
Copper

The 3, 5, 10, 30 and 60 R(éis) of 1834
with arms in wreath, rev. value in
wreath (former Nos. 323-331) are rare
patterns, as are similar 150, 300 and
600 R(éis) in silver.

VG-F

333 3/R(eis). Like No. 335.
   ND, 1845-48. . . . . .10.00
334 4½/R(eis). Sim. 1845-47. . .10.00

VG-F

★335 6/R(éis). ND, 1845-48. . . . .10.00
336 7½/R(éis). Sim.
   ND, 1845-48. . . . . .15.00
337 10/R(éis). Sim. 1845. . . . . .20.00
338 I2/R(éis). Sim. ND. 10.00

★338.2 I5/R(éis). Sim. but
   rev. value in wreath.
   ND. 15.00
338.5 30 (réis =)/½/T(anga).
   Sim. ND. 15.00
338.7 60 (réis =)/T(anga).
   Sim. ND. 25.00

Cmkd. Copper (1846)
Various copper coins:

★339 Cmkd. 15 (reis) in circle. . .15.00
340 Cmkd. 30 (reis) in circle. . .15.00
341 Cmkd. 60 (reis) in circle. . .45.00

Silver

Fine

345 PARDAO. Like No. 346
   1839-41. . . . . .60.00

★346 *RVPIA*. 1839-41. . . . . .60.00

★348 MEIO (=½) /P(ardao).
   Head. Rev. Value. 1845-49 .40.00
349 PARDAO. Sim. 1845-49. . .40.00
350 RVPIA. Sim. 1845-49. . . . .45.00
352 PARDAO. Like No. 353.
   1851. . . . . .100.00

Fine

★353 RUPIA. 1850-51. . . . . . . .100.00

Gold

V.F

356 12 X(erafins). Arms in
   wreath. Rev. like No. 244.
   1840-41. . . . . .1250.00

Pedro V 1853-61
Silver

Fine

★361 60/R(éis). 1858. . . . . .45.00
362 MEIO (=½)/P(ardao).
   Like No. 364. 1857-60. . . . .60.00
.363 PARDAU. Sim. 1857-61. . .60.00

★364 RUPIA. 1856-61. . . . . .35.00

Luiz I 1861-89
Silver

371 PARDAU. Like No. 372.
   1868. . . . . .75.00

★372 RUPIA. 1866-69. . . . . .45.00

UNVERIFIED DATA

Note: Throughout this catalog, any
uncertain, indefinite or unconfirmed information is shown in *italic type*. Such
material may be, for example, coin descriptions, dates and prices, names of
rulers, or supplementary notes. Further
information to confirm or correct *material in italics* should be sent to the
author at the following address:

William D. Craig
c/o Whitman Coin Supply Division
1220 Mound Avenue
Racine, Wisconsin 53404, U.S.A.

Indian State Mint Marks

Bhopal	Bundi, Kotah	Jaipur	Dewas
Bhopal	Jhalawar	Jodhpur	Indore
Bikanir	Bhartpur, Narwar	Jodhpur	Indore
Chhatarpur Orissa	Bikanir	Jodhpur	Mewar
Gwalior	Jaipur	Jodhpur	Narwar
Srinagar, Jalaun	Jodhpur	Karauli	Tonk
Alwar	Alwar	Karauli	Datia
Dholpur	Bhopal	Karauli	Dholpur
Gwalior	Bhartpur	Kishangarh	Jalaun, Kuchawan
Saugor	Dholpur, Tonk	Jhalawar	Jodhpur
Datia	Gwalior	Tonk	Seondha
Datia	Jaipur	Bikanir	Srinagar, Kunch
Datia	Srinagar, Jalaun, Kunch, Mandla	Bikanir	Bikanir
Dewas	Tonk	Bikanir	Jhansi
Gwalior	British East India Co.	Dewas	Karauli
Jalaun, Mandla	Bhartpur	Rewah	Mewar
Jhansi	Mewar	Saugor	Mewar
Bijawar, Chhatarpur	Mewar	Bikanir	Poona
Bikanir	Tonk	British East India Co.	Seondha
Jalaun	Datia	Dewas, Indore	Indore
Datia, Orchha	Kunch, Mandla, Saugor	French East India Co.	Jaipur
Gwalior	Ajmir	Bundi, Kotah	Tonk
Gwalior	Alwar		Awadh, British East India Co.
	Dewas		

III. Coins of the Native States.

A high proportion of states which struck coins in the 18th-20th centuries came into existence in the 18th century as the Mughal Empire weakened. The first coins of such states were generally copies of Mughal types, mostly those of Shah Alam II who was on the throne when many began coining, with only a symbol or Persian mint name to distinguish them. During Shah Alam's reign 80 mints were striking money in his name, mostly operated or farmed by semi-independent or independent rulers.

In many states this Shah Alam type coinage continued for 50 years after his death, and in many places was only halted after the Indian Mutiny when the last Mughal emperor at Delhi was deposed.

INDIA

AHMADABAD

City in west India. Former Mughal mint taken by Marathas in 1752. Leased to Baroda (q.v.) 1800-14, 1817-18. British mint 1818-35.

Mint marks: rayed diamond (see rev. of No. 36) plus (1) under Marathas: ankus (elephant goad) and sometimes "scissors" (compare Poona); (2) under British: flower in place of ankus.

I. Under Marathas 1752-1800, 1814-17.

A. In name of Alamgir II, 1754-59.

Silver
Fine

10 (rupee). Persian legends. AH117x/yr. 6............10.00

B. In name of Shah Jahan III, 1759-60.

Silver

15 (rupee). Persian legends. 117x/yr. 1............15.00

C. In name of Shah Alam II, 1759-1806.

Copper
V.G.

20 (paisa). Persian legends. Dates off flan.............. 4.00

Silver

Fine

★25 (rupee). Persian legends. 1188-97/yrs. 15-27........ 7.50

★26 (rupee). Sim. Nagari "RaM." Yr. 3x................10.00

Gold

28 (mohur). Like No. 25. 1202/yr. 29.............. ——

D. In name of Muhammad Akbar II, 1806-37.

Silver
Fine

34 (½ rupee). *Like No. 37*..... 5.00

Fine

★36 (rupee). Persian legends. Mmks. ankus and "scissors" (compare Poona No. 25). 12xx/yr. 8.............10.00

37 (rupee). Sim., w/out scissors mmk. Yr. 9.............. 7.50

II. Under Baroda 1800-14, 17-18.
See Baroda.

III. Under British East India Company, 1818-35.

Copper
V.G.

40 (paisa). Persian legends. AH1234/yr. 12........... 5.00

Silver

Fine

★45 (rupee). Md. Akbar II legends. Flower mmk. 1234, 43/ yr. 12................... 7.50

AJMIR

Regular mint of the Mughal emperors until 1731, when chief of Jodhpur (q.v.) gained virtually full control as viceroy. Ceded to Marathas 1759, retaken by Jodhpur 1787-92. To Gwalior (q.v.) 1792-1818, then ceded to the British.

I. Under Jodhpur 1731-59.
See Jodhpur.

II. Under Marathas 1759-87.

Copper
G-VG

10 (paisa). Sim. to No. 15..... 4.00

Silver

15 (rupee). In name of Shah   Fine
Alam II. AH1178/yrs. 6, 10................... 7.50

★16 —. Sim. Rev. symbol vertical line through 3 dots. 1188-90/ frozen yr. 14.............. 7.50

17 —. Sim. Rev. symbol vertical line through 2 dots. 1196-98/ frozen yr. 24.............. 7.50

Gold   G-VG

25 (mohur). *Like No. 15*....... ——

III. Under Gwalior 1792-1818.
See Gwalior.

ALMORA (Almorah)

Town in north India held by the Gurkhas of Nepal AD1790-1815.

Mint mark: "footprints of Vishnu."

Copper

Good

★5 (paisa). Unread Persian legends. *Ca. late 18th-early 19th cent.* Vars................ 5.00

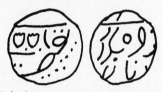

★10 (paisa). In name of Girvan Yuddha of Nepal. (AD1790-1815)................... 5.00

ALWAR

State in Rajputana, N.W. India. Founded by Pratap Singh, starting with 2½ villages in 1772. Southern half of state acquired late 18th century; northern half in 1803-06. Rulers became maharajas 1887.

Mint: Rajgarh.

Pratap Singh 1772-91
Bakhtawar Singh 1791-1815
Bani Singh 1815-57

A. In name of Shah Alam II, 1759-1806.

Copper
Good

5 (paisa). Sim. to No. 10. Yr. 28.................... 3.00

Silver

7 (⅛ rupee). Like No. 10..... ——

8 (¼ rupee). Sim............ ——

9 (½ rupee). Sim............ ——

10 (rupee). Yrs. 5-19......... ——

B. In name of Muhammad Akbar II, 1806-37.

Copper

15 (paisa). Like No. 20. Yr. 16.................... 4.00

INDIA

ALWAR (Cont.)

Silver

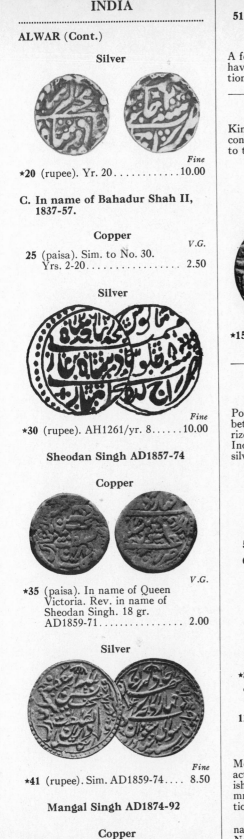

Fine

*20 (rupee). Yr. 20 . . . . 10.00

C. In name of Bahadur Shah II, 1837-57.

Copper

V.G.

25 (paisa). Sim. to No. 30.
Yrs. 2-20 . . . . 2.50

Silver

Fine

*30 (rupee). AH1261/yr. 8 . . . . . . 10.00

Sheodan Singh AD1857-74

Copper

V.G.

*35 (paisa). In name of Queen
Victoria. Rev. in name of
Sheodan Singh. 18 gr.
AD1859-71 . . . . 2.00

Silver

Fine

*41 (rupee). Sim. AD1859-74 . . . . 8.50

Mangal Singh AD1874-92

Copper

45 (paisa). Like No. 51 . . . . Rare

Silver

Fine

51 (rupee). Obv. like No. 41.
Rev. in name of Mangal
Singh. AD1874-76 . . . . 15.00

A few specimens of No. 51 are said to
have been struck yearly for presentation 1877-91.

ARAKAN

Kingdom along the Bay of Bengal,
conquered by Burma in 1784. Ceded
to the British company 1826.

Maha Samada Raja, Last King AD1782-84

Silver

Good

*15 (rupee). 9.5 gr. Yr. 1144
Arakanese (=AD1782) . . . . . ——

ARCOT (Arkat, Carnatic), Nawabs of

Possessions on the east coast of India
between Madras and Calcutta. Authorized both British and French East
India Companies to strike Arcot type
silver and gold.

Muhammad Ali (Wala-djah) AH1165-1209 (=AD1752-95)

Copper

Good

5 (¼ paisa). Arcot. AH1201 . . 2.00
6 (¼ paisa). Trichinopoly
(Nathernagar). ND.,
AH1202-07 . . . . 1.50

*8 (½ paisa). AH1201-09 . . . . . . 2.00
9 (½ paisa). Elephant.
Carnatic. AH1202 . . . . 2.50
12 (paisa). AH1201-08 . . . . 2.25

Silver

Most coins with Arkat mint name were
actually struck elsewhere by the British (lotus mmk.) and French (crescent
mmk.). These pieces are listed in section II, European Coinage for India.
  Native silver coinage with Arkat
name *has different mmks. and is scarcer.*
No listing of these issues is presently
available to the author.

Oumdat-l-omara
AH1209-16 (=AD1795-1801)

Copper

Fine

21 (½ paisa). Arcot. AH1212 . . 2.50
23 (paisa). Arcot. AH1212-14 . . 2.25

ASSAM

Kingdom neighboring Burma. Parceled
out amongst several sub-kingdoms, that
of the Ahoms (Assam proper), the
Kochs, Rangpur, Matak and Jaintiapur.

**Nearly all Assamese coins except
the smallest are octagonal.
Saka dates = AD less 78.**

(a) Assam (Ahom Kingdom).

Kings adopted the Hindu religion in
the 18th century and thereafter took
both Hindu and Shan names.
  Occupied by Burma 1816-24. Annexed to British India 1825.

Surempha, alias Rajesvara Simha
Saka 1673-91 (=AD1751-69)

Silver

Fine

3 (1/16 rupee). 2 line legend
each side. Round. ND 4.00
4 (⅛ rupee). 3 line legends.
Square. ND 3.00
5 (¼ rupee). Sim. Oct.
Saka 1674-90 . . . . 3.00
6 (½ rupee). Sim. Oct.
ND 6.00

*7 (rupee). Saka 1674-90 . . . . . . 7.50
8 (rupee). Like No. 20.
Oct. AD1751 . . . . *15.00*
10 (¼ rupee). Like No. 12.
Square. ND 10.00
12 (rupee). Persian legends in lieu
of Bengali. Rangpur Mint.
Square. Saka 1674 . . . . 15.00

*12a ——. Oct. Saka 1685 . . . . 12.50

Gold

F-VF

14 (1/16 mohur). Oct. ND 25.00

INDIA

ASSAM (Cont.)

		F-VF
*15	(⅛ mohur). ND	35.00
15a	—. Square. ND	40.00
16	(¼ mohur). Like No. 16a but octagonal. Saka 1677-78	45.00

*16a	—. Saka 1678	60.00
17	(½ mohur). Sim. Oct. ND	75.00
18	(mohur). Sim. Oct. Saka 1674-90	150.00
19	(mohur). Like No. 12a. Oct. Saka 1685	175.00

*20	(mohur). Ahom legends. AD1751	175.00

Sunyeopha, alias Lakshmi Simha
Saka 1691-1702 (=AD1769-80)

Silver

		Fine
21	(¹/₁₆ rupee). 2 line legends. Round. ND	3.50
22	(⅛ rupee). Sim. Oct. ND	4.00
23	(¼ rupee). Like No. 25. Saka 1692-1702	3.00
24	(½ rupee). Sim. ND	5.00

*25	(rupee). Saka 1692-1700	7.00

Gold

		F-VF
27	(¹/₁₆ mohur). Oct. ND	25.00
28	(⅛ mohur). Oct. ND	35.00
29	(¼ mohur). 3 line legend. Rev. Saka/1692-1702	60.00
30	(½ mohur). Oct. ND	75.00
31	(mohur). Oct. Saka 1698-1701	150.00

Suhitpanpha, alias Guarinatha Simha
Saka 1702-17 (=AD1780-95)

Silver

		Fine
32	(¹/₃₂ rupee). 2 line legends. Round. ND	3.00
33	(¹/₁₆ rupee). Oct. ND	3.50
34	(⅛ rupee). Like No. 32. Oct. ND	3.50
35	(¼ rupee). 3 line legend. Rev. Saka/date/regnal year. Oct. Saka 1703-17	3.50

*36	(½ rupee). ND., years 5-8*	5.00
37	(rupee). Like No. 43. Saka 1703-17	6.50

Gold

		F-VF
38	(¹/₃₂ mohur). Oct. ND	25.00
39	(¹/₁₆ mohur). Oct. ND	25.00
40	(⅛ mohur). Oct. ND	35.00
41	(¼ mohur). Oct. Saka 1703-16	60.00
42	(½ mohur). Like No. 36. ND	75.00

*43	(mohur). Saka 1705-10	150.00
44	(mohur). Ahom legends. Oct. ND	175.00

Kamalesvara Simha
Saka 1717-32 (=AD1795-1810)

Silver

		Fine
46	(⅛ rupee). 2 line legends. ND	4.00
48	(½ rupee). 4 line legends. Oct. ND	7.50

		Fine
*49	(rupee). Saka 1720	10.00

Gold

		F-VF
52	(⅛ mohur). Oct. ND	50.00
55	(mohur). Oct. Saka 1720	175.00

Chandrakanta Simha Narendra
Saka 1732-39, 41-42
(=AD1810-18, 19-20)

Silver

		Fine
56	(¹/₃₂ rupee). 2 line legends. Oval. ND	3.00
57	(¹/₁₆ rupee). Sim. Oct. ND	3.50
58	(⅛ rupee). Sim. Round. ND	3.50
59	(¼ rupee). Oct. Saka 1741-42	6.00
60	(½ rupee). 3 line legends. Round. ND	7.00

*61	(rupee). Saka 1741-42	12.00

Brajnatha Simha
Saka 1739-40 (=AD1818-19)

Silver

68	(¹/₃₂ rupee). 2 line legends. ND	2.50
69	(¹/₁₆ rupee). Sim. ND	3.00
70	(⅛ rupee). Sim. ND	3.50
71	(¼ rupee). 3 lines. Rev. 2 lines. Saka 1739-40	4.50

*72	(½ rupee). ND	5.00
73	(rupee). Sim. but 4 line legends. Saka 1739-40	7.50

Gold

		F-VF
76	(⅛ mohur). Oct. ND	40.00
79	(mohur). Like No. 73. Saka 1739-40	150.00

INDIA

ASSAM (Cont.)

Jogesvara Simha
Saka 1743 (= AD1821)

Silver

		Fine
82	(⅛ rupee). Oct. ND	4.00
83	(¼ rupee). Oct. Saka 1743	4.00

*84	(½ rupee). ND	7.50
85	(rupee). Oct. Saka 1743	10.00

(b) Assam (Koch Kingdom = Cooch Bihar).

Kingdom founded in a portion of Assam in the 15th century. Divided into western and eastern Koch Kingdoms circa 1581.

Western Kingdom
Upendra Narayana
AD1715-64

Silver

		Fine
*101	(½ rupee). ND	7.50

Devendra Narayana
AD1764-66

Silver

111	(½ rupee). 3 lines. Rev. 4 lines. ND	10.00

Dhairyendra Narayana
AD1766-71, 80-83

Silver

121	(½ rupee). 3 lines. Rev. 4 lines. ND	10.00

Rajendra Narayana
AD1771-73

Silver

131	(½ rupee). 3 lines. Rev. 4 lines. ND	10.00

Darendra Narayana
AD1773-80
Harendra Narayana
AD1783-1839

Silver

		Fine
151	(½ rupee). 3 lines. Rev. 4 lines. ND	5.00

Swendra Narayana
AD1839-47

Silver

161	(½ rupee). 4 lines each side. ND	5.00

Gold

		F-VF
165	(mohur). Sim. ND	200.00

Narendra Narayana
AD1847-63

Silver

		Fine
171	(½ rupee). 4 lines. Rev. 4 lines in square. ND	5.00

Gold

		F-VF
173	(mohur). Sim. ND	200.00

(c) Jaintiapur.

Kingdom in Assam. Annexed by the British Company 1835.

Bar Gosain II
Saka 1653-92 (= AD1731-70)

Silver

		Fine
175	(¼ rupee). Like No. 177. Saka 1653	20.00
177	(rupee). 4 line legends. Saka 1653-56	15.00

Chattra Simha
Saka 1692-1704 (= AD1770-82)

Silver

180	(rupee). Sim. Saka 1696	17.50

Jitra Narayana
Saka 1704-07 (= AD1782-85)

Silver

183	(rupee). Sim. Saka 1704	20.00

Bijaya Narayana
Saka 1707-12 (= AD1785-90)

Silver

186	(ex 181) (rupee). Sim. 9.4 gr. Saka 1707	15.00

Ram Simha II
Saka 1712-54 (= AD1790-1832)

Silver

		Fine
189	(¼ rupee). Sim. Saka 1712	20.00
191	(rupee). Sim. 7.3-9.4 gr. Saka 1712	17.50

(d) Matak.

Kingdom in Assam.

Sarvananda Simha, Raja
Saka 1715-17 (= AD1793-95)

Silver

		Fine
201	(1/16 rupee). 2 line legends. ND	4.00
202	(⅛ rupee). 3 line legends. ND	4.50
203	(¼ rupee). Sim. Oct. Saka 1715-16	4.50
204	(½ rupee). Sim. Oct. ND	5.00

*205	(rupee). Saka 1716-17	10.00

Gold

		F-VF
208	(¼ mohur). Oct. Saka 1716	75.00
209	(½ mohur). Oct. ND	100.00
210	(mohur). Oct. Saka 1715	175.00

(e) Rangpur.

Kingdom in Assam.

Bharatha Simha, Raja
Saka 1713-15, 18-19
(= AD1791-93, 96-97)

Silver

		Fine
211	(1/16 rupee). 2 line legends. ND	5.00

INDIA

ASSAM (Cont.)

		Fine
212	(⅛ rupee). *3 line legends.* Oct. ND	5.00
213	(¼ rupee). *Sim.* Oct. Saka 1713-19	6.00
214	(½ rupee). Sim. ND	7.50

★215	(rupee). Saka 1713-15, 18-19	10.00

Gold

		F-VF
217	(⅛ mohur). Oct. ND	50.00

AWADH (Oudh)

Kingdom in N.E. India. Ruling dynasty founded by a Persian adventurer, S'adat Khan, who became a wazir of the Mughal Empire and, in 1720, Subahdar of Awadh. Domains included Awadh, Ghazipur, Banaras (lost to the British Company 1775), Gorakhpur, Ilahabad, Kora and Rohilkhand. The rulers of Awadh were known as Nawab-Wazirs until 1819, and as kings thereafter.

Awadh was annexed to British India 1856/58.

I. Mughal Coinage to *1775.*

See section I, Mughal Emperors, for coins with mint name Muhammadabad Banaras dated through AH1189/yr. 16 of Shah Alam II. These coins do not bear a fish mint mark.

Note: The dates AH1168 (=AD1754) or 1179 (=AD1765) are sometimes given as the end of Mughal control.

II. British Coinage 1775-1819.

All coins struck by the British with mint name Muhammadabad Banaras have as mmk. a fish in linear or outline form. See section II (British) for these issues.

III. Coins of the Nawab-Wazirs 1777-1819.

About 1776 the capital of Awadh was moved from Banaras to Lakhnau (Lucknow), and a new mint opened there. Coins retained the mint name Muhammadabad Banaras, but a solid fish mmk. (see No. 6) distinguishes them from the simultaneous British issues.

Asaf al-Daula
AH1189-1212 (=AD1775-97)
Wazir Ali
AH1212-13 (=AD1797-98)
Sa'adat Ali
AH1213-30 (=AD1798-1814)
Ghazi al-Din Haidar, as Nawab
AH1230-34 (=AD1814-19)

Copper

		G-VG
2	(falus). Like No. 6. AH1208, 33/frozen yr. 26	3.00

Silver

		Fine
3	(⅛ rupee). Like No. 6. 14mm. AH1215/yr. *26*	3.50

★6	(rupee). Shah Alam II legend. Rev. mint name, solid fish mmk. 1191-1234/yrs. 18-26 (yr. 26 frozen from AH1199)	3.50
6a	—. 28mm. 1216, yr. 26	15.00

Gold

		F-VF
10	(mohur). Sim. 1230/yr. 26	150.00

Note: See Nos. 125-135 for similar issues dated 1229/yr. 26 with mint name Suba Awadh.

IV. Kings of Awadh 1819-56.

Coins struck during this period use the mint name Lakhnau.

Ghazi al-Din Haidar, as King AH1234-43 (=AD1819-27)

A. In name of Shah Alam II.

Copper

		G-VG
13	(falus). Like No. 22. AH1234/yr. 26	2.00

Silver

		Fine
★22	(rupee). Shah Alam II legend. Rev. new royal arms. AH1234/(frozen) yr. 26	8.00

B. In his own name.

Copper

		V.G.
★33	(ex 15, 16) (falus). Ghazi al-Din legend. Rev. arms. 1235-40	1.50

Silver

		Fine
35	(¹⁄₁₆ rupee). Sim. 10mm. AH1235	4.00
36	(ex 24) (⅛ rupee). Sim. 14mm. 1235	4.00
37	(¼ rupee). Sim. 16mm. 1236	4.00
38	(½ rupee). Sim. 20mm. 1240	7.50

★39	(ex 28, 34) (rupee). Sim. 1234-43	5.00

Gold

		F-VF
43	(ex 39) (¼ mohur). Sim. *16mm.*	65.00

★45	(ex 41) (mohur). Sim. 1239	125.00

Nasir al-Din Haidar AH1243-53 (=AD1827-37)

A. In name of Sulayman Jah.

Copper

		V.G.
47	(ex 49) (falus). Like No. 52. 1243-44	2.00

Silver

		Fine
★52	(ex 56) (rupee). 1243-45	8.00

B. In his own name.

Copper

		V.G.
★56	(ex 50) (falus). 1245-50	1.50

INDIA

AWADH (Cont.)

Silver

Fine

58 ($1/16$ rupee). Like No. 62. 11mm. 1250. . . . . 4.50

59 ($1/8$ rupee). Sim. 14mm. 1248. . . . . 3.50

60 ($1/4$ rupee). Sim. 16mm. *1247-50*. 4.50

★62 (rupee). AH1246-53. . . . . 5.00

Gold

F-VF

69 (mohur). Sim. Yr. 3. . . . . . . 150.00

Muhammad Ali Shah
AH1253-58 (=AD1837-42)

Copper

V.G.

72 (falus). Like No. 79. 1254-55. . . . . 2.50

Silver

Fine

77 ($1/4$ rupee). Sim. 16mm. 125x. 4.50

★79 (rupee). AH1253-58 (var.). . . 6.00

Gold

F-VF

86 (mohur). Sim. 1253-58. . . . . 150.00

Amjad Ali Shah
AH1258-63 (=AD1842-47)

Copper

V.G.

★95 (falus). AH1258. . . . . 2.00

Silver

Fine

97 ($1/16$ rupee). Sim. 11mm. 4.00

98 ($1/8$ rupee). Sim. 14mm. 1262-63. . . . . 5.00

Fine

★101 (rupee). AH1258-63. . . . . . 6.00

Gold

F-VF

107 ($1/2$ mohur). Sim. 100.00

108 (mohur). Sim. 150.00

Wajid Ali Shah
AH1263-72 (=AD1847-56)
Deposed by British

Copper

V.G.

109 ($1/8$ *falus*). Like No. 124. . . . 5.00

110 ($1/4$ falus). Sim. 14mm. 1270. . . . . 3.00

111 ($1/2$ falus). Sim. 17mm. 1271. . . . . 3.00

112 (falus). Sim. 22mm. *1267-72*. 2.50

Silver

Fine

115 ($1/8$ rupee). Like No. 124. 13mm. 1269-71. . . . . 5.00

116 ($1/4$ rupee). Sim. 16mm. 1265. . . . . 5.00

117 ($1/2$ rupee). Sim. 19mm. 1268, 71. . . . . 7.50

118 (rupee). Sim. 1263-72. . . . . . 5.00

Gold

F-VF

120 ($1/16$ *mohur*). Like No.124. . 50.00

121 ($1/8$ mohur). Sim. 50.00

122 ($1/4$ mohur). Sim. 60.00

123 ($1/2$ mohur). Sim. 85.00

★124 (mohur). 1263-64. . . . . 100.00

V. Rebel Coinage 1857-58.

The following coins were struck during the famous Indian Mutiny, which began in Lakhnau in mid-1857.

Brijis Qadr, Nawab-Wazir
AH1273-74 (=AD1857-58)

Copper

V.G.

125 (falus). Like No. 130. AH1229/yr. 26. . . . . *4.00*

Silver

Fine

127 ($1/8$ rupee). Like No. 130. 1229/yr. 26. . . . . 7.50

129 ($1/2$ rupee). Sim. 1229/ yr. 26. . . . . *10.00*

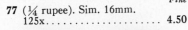

★130 (rupee). Like No. 6 (in name of Shah Alam II) but mint name Subah Awadh. Fictitious date AH1229/yr. 26. . . . . . . 5.00

Gold

F-VF

135 (mohur). Sim. 1229/ yr. 26. . . . . *200.00*

BAHAWALPUR

State in northwest India ruled by a dynasty of Nawabs.

Copper

V.G.

★5 (falus). AH1195-97. . . . . 5.00

10 (falus.) Lion right. Rev. Persian legend. ND. . . —

★15 (falus). Round or square. AH1248-7x. 5.00

Silver

Fine

20 (rupee). AH1275-86 (=Yeoman D1). 10.00

BAJRANGGARH

State in Gwalior, north-central India.

Jai Singh, Maharaja

AD1797-1818

Silver

3 ($1/8$ rupee). Sanscrit legends each side. ND. 2.50

★4 ($1/4$ rupee). Sim. ND. 3.00

5 ($1/2$ rupee). Sim. ND. 4.00

INDIA

BAJRANGGARH (Cont.)

Fine

*6 (rupee). Sanscrit legends.
Yrs. 20-29. (var.).......... 7.50

6a —. Symbols added: obv.
bow and arrow, rev. lotus.
ND.................... 5.00

Gold

F-VF

13 (mohur). Like No. 6.
Octagonal. ND..........200.00

Barmawal. See Sailana.

BARODA

Maratha state in western India. The ruling line was descended from Damaji, a Maratha soldier, who received the title of "Distinguished Swordsman" in 1721 (hence the scimitar on most Baroda coins). The Baroda title "Gaik-wara" comes from "gaikwar" or cow herd, Damaji's father's occupation. Baroda was acquired in 1732.

Mints: Ahmadabad (1800-14, 17-18), Amreli *(from ca. 1818)*, Baroda, Petlad.

Anand Rao
AH1215-35 (=AD1800-19)

A. In name of Shah Alam II.

Coins dated with regnal years of Anand Rao.

Copper

G-VG

10 (paisa). Sim. to No. 18..... 4.00

Silver

Fine

14 (½ rupee). Like No. 17.
Yr. 4 of Anand...........10.00

17 (rupee). Persian legends.
Rev. Nagari "Ma," scimitar
(=Baroda mint). Yrs. 3-4
of Anand...............10.00

18 (rupee). Sim. Rev. Nagari "A"
(=Petlad). Yrs. 3-4.......10.00

19 (rupee). Sim. Rev. Nagari
"Ga(ikwar)," ankus (=Ahmad-
abad). Yr. 4..............10.00

**B. In name of Muhammad
Akbar II.**

Coins dated with regnal years of Md.
Akbar.

Copper

G-VG

21 (paisa). Like No. 27. 9.8 gr.
1227, 33/yrs. 7, 14........ 2.00

Silver

Fine

24 (⅛ rupee). Like No. 27.
12mm. 1234.............. 4.00

26 (½ rupee). Sim. 1226-28.... 4.00

*27 (rupee). Rev. Nagari "A,"
scimitar (=Baroda). 1227-34/
yrs. 1-14 of Md. Akbar..... 6.00

*28 (rupee). Rev. like No. 19.
(Ahmadabad). Yrs. 6, 11....10.00

Sayaji Rao II
AH1235-64 (=AD1819-47)

**A. Anonymous issue
(Amreli mint).**

Copper

V.G.

29 (paisa). Nagari "Sa(yaji)
Ga(ikwar)" with elephant,
crescent, katar or sword. ND,
1252-57/yrs. 12-26........ 2.00

**B. In name of Muhammad
Akbar II.**

Coins dated with regnal years of Md.
Akbar. Baroda mint.

*31 (½ paisa). 4.3 gr. Yrs. 35, 40 2.00

*33 (paisa). Rev. Nagari "Sa*Ga*"
and mmks. scimitar, stalk, flag,
cross, sun, lotus or shaded ball.
10.2 gr. 1236-60/yrs. 16-41.. 2.50

Silver

Fine

35 (⅛ rupee). Like No. 38.
1248.................... 3.00

36 (¼ rupee). Sim. 123x/
yr. 18................... 3.00

37 (½ rupee). Sim. 1239-41/
yrs. 24, 40.............. 3.50

Fine

*38 (rupee). Rev. Nagari "Sa."
1238-59/yrs. 18-39........ 5.00

Ganpat Rao
AH1264-73 (=AD1847-56)

**A. Anonymous issue
(Amreli mint).**

Copper

V.G.

39 (paisa). Nagari "Sri/GaG,"
sun, lotus, sword. 1266/
yr. 3 *(43?)*.............. 2.50

**B. In name of Muhammad
Akbar II.**

Coins dated with regnal years of Md·
Akbar. Baroda mint.

Copper

41 (½ paisa). Like No. 33 but
Nagari "Ga." 5 gr. 1269.... 2.00

42 (paisa). Sim. 10 gr. Yr. 46.. 2.00

Silver

Fine

45 (¼ rupee). Like No. 27 but
Nagari "Ga." 126x......... 3.00

46 (½ rupee). Sim. *ND*....... 3.00

47 (rupee). Sim. 1265/
yrs. 44, 46.............. 6.00

Khande Rao
AH1273-87 (=AD1856-70)

**A. Anonymous issues
(Amreli mint).**

Copper

V.G.

*49 (paisa). Nagari "Sri/KhG"
or "SaL/Kh," scimitar, jhar
1277/yr. 7.............. 3.50

**B. In name of Muhammad
Akbar II.**

Coins dated with regnal years of Md.
Akbar. Baroda mint.

Copper

51 (½ paisa). Like No. 60.
4.2 gr. *ND*............. 2.00

52 (paisa). Sim. 8.4 gr. yr. 52... 2.50

INDIA

BARODA (Cont.)

Silver

		Fine
58	(¼ rupee). Like No. 59. 1273	3.00
59	(½ rupee). Like No. 27 but Nagari "Kha." (Baroda). ND	4.00
60	(rupee). Sim. 127x/yr. 53	6.00

C. In name of "Commander of the Special Band" (= the Gaikwar). Baroda Mint.

Copper

		V.G.
62	(½ paisa). Like No. 63. 3.4 gr. 1275	2.00

★63	(paisa). Nagari "KhGa," scimitar. 7-8 gr. 1274-76	2.00
63a	—. Sim., plus horse's hoof. 1281-85	2.00
64	(2 paisa). Sim. 15 gr. ND, 1284	4.00

Silver

		Fine
66	(⅛ rupee). Like No. 63. ND	2.50
67	(¼ rupee). Sim. 1278	2.50

★69	(½ rupee). Sim. 1275, 78	3.50
70	(rupee). Sim. 1274-87	6.00
74	(½ rupee). Like No. 77	——

★76	(rupee). Nagari legend. Rev. Persian legend. 1287	15.00
77	(rupee). Obv. sim. Rev. diff. legend. ND	——

Malhar Rao
AH1287-92 (= AD1870-75)

Copper

80	(½ paisa). Like No. 81. 1288	2.00

		Fine
★81	(paisa). Nagari "MaGa," scimitar, shaded ball. (Baroda). 7.6-8.6 gr. 1288-90	2.00
82	(2 paisa). Sim. 16.1 gr. 1288-89	4.00

Silver

87	(¼ rupee). Like No. 90. 13mm. 1290	3.00
88	(½ rupee). Sim. 1287-90	3.50
89	(rupee). Sim. 1288-90	5.00

★90	(2 rupee). Nagari "MaGa," scimitar. (Baroda). 1288	75.00

BELA (Beylah)

State in Baluchistan.

Copper

		V.G.
★5	falus. AH1271-85	5.00

★10	falus. ND. Struck by Mahmud Khan of Kalat	7.50

BHARTPUR

State in Rajputana, N.W. India. Founded in 1707 during the anarchy following the death of Emperor Aurangzeb. Considerably expanded in 1760 and again in the late 18th century.

Mint Names: Maha Indrapur to AH 1206/yr. 34 of Shah Alam II; Braj Indrapur thereafter. Victoria rupees struck at Bhartpur and Dig, both with Braj Indrapur honorific.

Usual symbols on coins are katar and star.

Badan Singh	AD1723-56
Suraj Mal	AD1756-63
Jawahir Singh	AD1763-68
Ratan Singh	AD1768-69
Kehri Singh	AD1769-77
Ranjit Singh	AD1777-1805
Randhir Singh	AD1805-23
Baldeo Singh	AD1823-25
Durjan Singh	AD1825-26
Balwant Singh	AD1826-52
Jaswant Singh	AD1852-93

A. In name of Ahmad Shah, 1748-54.

Silver

		Fine
4	(rupee)	10.00

B. In name of Alamgir II, 1754-59.

Silver

8	(rupee). AH1171/yr. 4	10.00

Gold

9	(mohur). Yr. 4	——

C. In name of Shah Jahan III.

Silver

12	(rupee). AH1174/yr. 1	25.00

Gold

15	(mohur). Sim. 1174/yr. 1	——

D. In name of Shah Alam II, 1759-1806.

Copper

		V.G.
★16	(ex 5) (½ paisa). Braj Indrapur. 5.6-6.5 gr. 120x-1x/yr. 40	2.00
17	(paisa). Maha Indrapur. 9.4 gr. Yr. 47	4.00

INDIA

BHARTPUR (Cont.)

		V.G.
*18	(2 paisa). Braj Indrapur. 18-19 gr. AH1215/yr. 49	3.00

Silver

		Fine
20	(rupee). Maha Indrapur. 1176-1206/yrs. 4-34	5.00
20a	—. Braj Indrapur. 1207-31/ yrs. 34-58	5.00

Gold

		F-VF
21	(mohur). Maha Indrapur. 1175-8x/yrs. 2-10	150.00

E. In name of Muhammad Akbar II, 1806-37.

Silver

		Fine
23	(¼ rupee). Like No. 25	4.00
24	(½ rupee). Sim	4.00

**25	(rupee). AH1224-70	5.00

Gold

		F-VF
32	(mohur). Like No. 25. Yr. 1 (=1806)	125.00

F. In name of Bahadur Shah II, 1837-57.

Copper

		Fine
38	(paisa). *Like No. 45.* AH1279/yr. 9	3.00

Silver

*45	(rupee). Samvat 1912/ yr. 18 (=1855)	10.00

G. In name of Queen Victoria and Jaswant Singh.

Copper

		Fine
51	(½ paisa). Like No. 60. 9.3 gr. ND. (=1858)	4.00
52	(paisa). Sim. 18.2 gr. 1858	5.00

Silver

57	(⅛ rupee). Like No. 60	10.00
58	(¼ rupee). Sim. 1859	15.00
59	(½ rupee). Sim	15.00

*60	(rupee). Rev. vars. 1858-71. Bhartpur and Dig mints	22.50

Gold

		F-VF
67	(mohur). Like No. 60 but w/out name of Jaswant Singh. Indrapur mint. 1858-59	200.00

BHAUNAGAR

State in Rajputana, N.W. India. Dynasty founded by Bhausinghji of the Gohel Clan of Rajputs. Rulers bore title "Thakur." The mint is said to have been closed by the British in 1840.

Monetary System: See Kutch.

A. In name of Shah Jahan I (1628-58).

Copper

		G-VG
13	(¼ trambiyo). *Like No. 15.* 1.0 gr	——
14	(trambiyo). Sim. 4.2 gr. ND	——

*15	(dokdo). Shah Jahan legend. Rev. Persian BHAUNAGAR/ Nagari BAHADUR/sword. 7-8 gr. ND	3.50

*15a	—. Nagari SRI on panel added to rev	3.50
20	(dhinglo). *Like No. 15*	——

B. In name of Shah Alam II.

Copper

		G-VG
25	(dokdo). *Shah Alam legend. Rev. like No.15*	——

C. In name of Muhammad Akbar II.

Copper

30	(dhinglo). *Md. Akbar legend. Rev. like No. 15*	——

BHOPAL

Central Indian state founded by Dost Muhammad, an Afghan officer of Aurangzeb, who seized Bhopal in 1690 and made himself independent.

Mints: Bhopal, Daulatgarh.

Kudsia Begam AH1235-53 (=AD1819-37)
Sikandar Begam AH1264-85 (=AD1847-68)
Shah Jahan Begam AH1285-1319 (=AD1868-1901)

A. In name of Shah Alam II, 1759-1806.

Silver

		Fine
12	(rupee). Yrs. 1-48 (=1759- 1806). Bhopal	7.50

B. In name of Muhammad Akbar II, 1806-37.

Silver

24	(⅛ rupee). Like No. 27. 12mm. Yr. 18	4.00
25	(¼ rupee). Sim. Yr. 13	4.00

*27	(rupee). Yrs. 5-33. Daulatgarh	6.00

C. Anonymous Issues.

Copper

		V.G.
20	(paisa). Persian BHOPAL. Rev. date in circle. Yrs. 25, 29 of Md. Akbar	2.00

*20a	—. Rev. blank. ND	2.00

INDIA

BHOPAL (Cont.)

V.G.

★21 (paisa). Date/BHOPAL.
Rev. whisk. Yr. 28........ 2.00

★21a —. Rev. blank. 1255...... 2.50

★35 pau (=¼) anna. Date/
BHOPAL. Rev. value. 7.6 gr.
1269, 73............... 2.00

36 nim (=½) anna. Sim.
15.6 gr. 1278............ 3.00

37 yek (=1) anna. Sim.
31 gr. 1271, 76........... 3.50

39 (ex 53) pau (=¼) anna.
Like No. 41. 7.5 gr.
1285-1303............... 1.50

40 (ex 54) nim (=½) anna. Sim.
15 gr. 1286-130x.......... 1.75

★41 (ex 57) yek (=1) anna. Persian
SH/BHOPAL. Rev. date/value.
31 gr. 1285, 89........... 4.00

Silver
Fine

44 (ex 40) (⅛ rupee). Like
No. 47. 1275, 88........ 2.25

45 (¼ rupee). Sim. 1275-88.... 2.25

46 (½ rupee). Sim. 1275-92.... 3.00

★47 (ex 43, 63) (rupee). Persian
legends. 1271-93. Bhopal.... 4.00

Fine

60 (⅛ rupee). Sim. but modified
dies. 1294-1306........... 2.25

61 (¼ rupee). Sim. 1294-1302.. 2.50

62 (½ rupee). Sim. 1294-1306.. 3.00

★64 (rupee). Persian legends.
1293-1306............... 4.00

Gold
F-VF

66 (ex 50) (mohur). Like No. 47.
1283...................125.00

D. In name of Shah Jahan Begam.

Copper
V.G.

71 pau (=¼) anna. Name/value.
Rev. date/BHOPAL. 7.6 gr.
1302-05................. 1.50

★72 nim (=½) anna. 15 gr.
1302, 04................. 1.50

73 yek (=1) anna. Sim. 31 gr.
1302-06.................. 4.00

BIJAWAR

State in Bundelkhand District, north-
central India. Its ruler's title was
"Sawai Maharaja." Mint was closed in
1897.

Ratan Singh AD1810-

Silver

Fine

★15 ("Ratan Shahi" rupee).
Shah Alam II legend. Yr. 4.. 7.50

BIKANIR

State in Rajputana. Rulers descended
from Jodha, founder of Jodhpur. Mint
opened about 1760. All coins until 1859
are in name of Alamgir II, except that
nazrana (presentation) rupees of the
first three rulers are in the name of
Shah Alam II. All ordinary rupees bear
the current ruler's symbol plus those of
his predecessors.

Gaj Singh AD1746-87

Copper
V.G.

5 (paisa). Sim. to No. 10.
Rev. trident.............. 3.00

Silver

Fine

★10 (rupee). Alamgir legend,
obv. trident symbol at left.
AH1167-*12xx*/yrs. 1-37 of
Shah Alam.............. 6.00

11 (nazrana rupee). Shah Alam
legend. Rev. trident. AH114
(error)............(F-VF) 30.00

Surat Singh AD1787-1828

Copper
V.G.

12 (½ *paisa*). *Like No. 13.
ND*..................... 3.00

13 (paisa). Sim. to No. 17.
Rev. flag. Yr. 42.......... 3.00

Silver

Fine

★17 (rupee). Like No. 10, plus
rev. flag. 1204-29/yrs. 28-52
of Shah Alam............ 4.50

18 (nazrana rupee). Like
No. 11 plus rev. flag.
1121 (error)........(F-VF) 30.00

Ratan Singh AD1828-51

Copper
V.G.

22 (½ paisa). *Like No. 23. ND*. 2.00

Fine

★23 (paisa). Rev. turban star.
15-17 gr. ND, 1228........ 1.50

Silver

★32 (rupee). Like No. 10, plus
rev. flag and turban star.
1229 (frozen)/yrs. 21-41 of
Muhammad Akbar II...... 5.00

INDIA

BIKANIR (Cont.)

33 (nazrana rupee). Like No. 11 plus rev. turban star. 1124 (error)...............30.00 *F-VF*

Sardar Singh AD1851-72

A. In name of Alamgir II.

Silver

Fine

34 (rupee). Like No. 10 but obv. w/out trident. Rev. trident, flag, turban star, umbrella. 1229 (frozen)/yrs. 18, 21 of Bahadur Shah II........... 7.50

34a (nazrana rupee). Sim. 29mm. 1229/yr. 21........(*F-VF*) 30.00

B. In name of Queen Victoria.

Copper

V.G.

35 (paisa). Like No. 41. 7.2-7.8 gr. Frozen dates AD1859/Samvat 1916...... 1.50

Silver

Fine

38 (1/8 rupee). Sim. 11mm. 1859/S. 1916............. 3.00

39 (1/4 rupee). Sim. 15mm. 1859/S. 1916............. 3.00

40 (1/2 rupee). Sim. 18mm. 1859/S. 1916............. 4.00

*41 (rupee). Victoria legend. Rev. turban star, umbrella, trident, flag. AD1859/ S. 1916................. 5.00

41a (nazrana rupee). Sim. 30mm. 1859/S. 1916........(*F-VF*) 30.00

Dungar Singh AD1872-87

Copper

V.G.

45 (paisa). Like No. 50. Frozen AD1859/S. 1916........... 2.00

Silver

Fine

*50 (rupee). Like No. 41, plus rev. fly whisk to r. of umbrella. Frozen 1859/S. 1916.. 5.00

50a (nazrana rupee). Sim. 30mm. 1859/S. 1916........(*F-VF*) 30.00

Ganga Singh AD1887-1943

Copper

V.G.

55 (paisa). Like No. 60. Frozen AD1859/S. 1916.......... 3.00

Silver

Fine

58 (1/4 rupee). Sim. 14mm. 1859/S. 1916............. 4.00

59 (1/2 rupee). Sim. 18mm. 1859/S. 1916............. 5.00

*60 (rupee). Like No. 50, plus rev. diff. type fly whisk to r. of umbrella. Frozen AD1859/ S. 1916................. 5.00

60a (nazrana rupee). Sim. 30mm. 1859/S. 1916.......(*F-VF*) 30.00

For other coins of Ganga Singh, see Yeoman, *Modern World Coins.*

BROACH (Bharuch)

Town in west India ruled by a line of Nawabs 1736-72. To British 1772-83 and 1803 on, to Sindhia (Gwalior) 1783-1803.

Nek Nam Khan AD1754-68
Imtya-ud-Daula AD1768-72

Copper

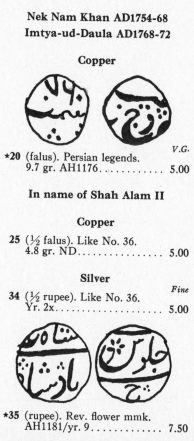

V.G.

*20 (falus). Persian legends. 9.7 gr. AH1176............ 5.00

In name of Shah Alam II

Copper

25 (1/2 falus). Like No. 36. 4.8 gr. ND............... 5.00

Silver

Fine

34 (1/2 rupee). Like No. 36. Yr. 2x................... 5.00

*35 (rupee). Rev. flower mmk. AH1181/yr. 9............. 7.50

Fine

*36 (rupee). Rev. mmk. cross of St. Stephen. Struck under British. Yr. 2x............ 7.50

BUNDI

State in Rajputana, N.W. India. Chiefs called Maharao Rajas.

Mint marks: bent-stemmed flower and *umbrella* (compare Kotah).

I. In name of Shah Alam II, AD1759-1806.

Copper

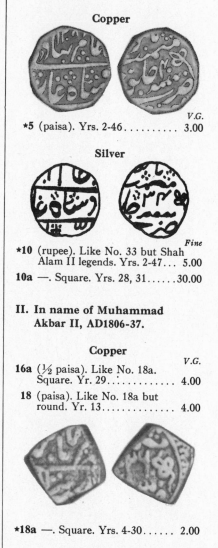

V.G.

*5 (paisa). Yrs. 2-46.......... 3.00

Silver

Fine

*10 (rupee). Like No. 33 but Shah Alam II legends. Yrs. 2-47... 5.00

10a —. Square. Yrs. 28, 31......30.00

II. In name of Muhammad Akbar II, AD1806-37.

Copper

V.G.

16a (1/2 paisa). Like No. 18a. Square. Yr. 29..:......... 4.00

18 (paisa). Like No. 18a but round. Yr. 13............. 4.00

*18a —. Square. Yrs. 4-30...... 2.00

Silver

Fine

24 (1/4 rupee). Like No. 30. Yr. 23................... 5.00

INDIA

BUNDI (Cont.)

		Fine
*30	(rupee). Yrs. 1-32	5.00
30a	—. Square. Yrs. 5, 19	30.00
30b	—. Round, broad strike. 31mm. Yrs. 24, 32	30.00

Gold

		F-VF
*33	(mohur). Yr. 19	125.00

III. In name of Bahadur Shah II.

Silver

		Fine
*40	(rupee). Yrs. 5-8	10.00

Notes:
1. For similar issues see Kotah Nos. 28, 30.
2. The VICTORIA QUEEN Bundi types are listed in Yeoman, *Modern World Coins.*

CANNANORE

In S.W. India on the Malabar coast.

The Ali Rajas
("Lords of the Deep"),
Sovereigns of the
Laccadive Islands

Silver

		Fine
*10	(¹/₅ rupee). AH1144-1203 (=AD1731-88) and blundered dates including AH1231	5.00

CHAMBA

State in north India. To Sikhs 1809-47. Returned to the Raja by the British in 1848.

Charhat Singh AD1808-44

Copper

		V.G.
15	(paisa). Nagari legend/trident and double C's. Rev. sim. 8.5-9.0 gr. ND	5.00

Lakar Shah, Rebel AD1844

Copper

20	(paisa). Like No. 15 but no tridents. 4.5-7.3 gr. ND	7.50

Sri Singh AD1844-70

Copper

25	(paisa). Like No. 15 but degenerate legends. Crude. 3.9-6.8 gr. ND	4.00

CHHATARPUR

State in Bundelkhand, north-central India. Established 1806. Mint open 1816-82.

Jagat Singh AD1854-

Silver

		Fine
*15	(Raja Shahi rupee). Shah Alam II legends and sunflower. Fictitious dates AH1192, 1212, years 11-25	5.00

CHHOTA UDAIPUR (East)

Formerly one of the non-Aryan Chota Nagpur states of Bengal.

Copper

		V.G.
*40	*(paisa)*. 7.4 gr. Saka 1787	3.00
41	*(2 paisa)*. Sim. 13.4-14 gr.	4.00

CHHOTA UDAIPUR (West)

State in west India. Under British protection from 1822.

Motisinghi AD1881-1906

Copper

		V.G.
20	*1/paisa*. Date. Rev. value/ scimitar. Circular Gujerati legends both sides. 15mm. Samvat 1948	4.50

		V.G.
22	2/paisa. Sim. 22mm. Samvat 1948	5.00

COCHIN

On the Malabar (west) Coast, at the southern tip of India. Taken from the Netherlands by the British Company in 1795. See II Netherlands possessions in India for similar coins prior to that date.

Monetary System:
puttun (puttan)=fanam;
6 puttuns=5 annas.

Silver

		Fine
1	(puttun). Like No. 2. .324 gr. ND. (=1795-1850)	1.50

*2	(2 puttuns). Sun and moon/ lazy J/12 dots. Rev. line, dots, conch shell. 1 gr. ND. (=1795-1850)	2.75
5	(puttun). Siva seated. Rev. like No. 2. .52 gr. (=1856-58)	2.50

*6	(2 puttuns). Sim. 1 gr	3.50

Cooch Behar.
See Assam (Koch Kingdom).
Cutch. See Kutch.

DATIA

State in north-central India, governed by a Maharaja. Founded in 1735 by Bhagwan Das, son of Narsingh Deo of Orchha.

Parachat AD1802-39
Vijaya Bahadur AD1839-57
Govind (Bhowani) Singh
AD1857-1907

A. In name of Shah Alam II.

Copper

		V.G.
*21	(Tegh Shahi paisa). 16 gr. Yr. 1	2.00

INDIA

DATIA (Cont.)

	V.G.
⋆22 (½ Gaja Shahi paisa). 6.5 gr. Yr. 4x	3.00
23 (G. S. paisa). Sim. 12 gr. Yrs. 3x-4x	2.00

Silver

	Fine
25 (¼ Raja Shahi rupee). Like No. 27	2.50
26 (½ R.S. rupee). Sim	3.00

⋆27 (R.S. rupee). Frozen AH1178/ yr. 6 (ca. AD1802-39)	3.50
35 (⅛ Gaja Shahi rupee). Like No. 38. Yrs. 2, 4, *22 and others*	2.00
36 (¼ G.S. rupee). Like No. 38. 1317/yr. 23	2.50
37 (½ G.S. rupee). Like No. 38. *1215-1313*	3.00

⋆38 (G.S. rupee). Copy of Orchha coinage, identified by dots around right point of elephant goad on obv. Fictitious dates AH1215-1313/yrs. 19-46. *(19th cent. to 1904)*	3.50

B. In name of Muhammad Akbar II.

Silver

45 (G.S. rupee). Sim. to No. 38. AH1270/yr. 33	——

Deccan, Nizams of:
See Hyderabad.

DEWAS

Two Maratha states in west-central India. The two rajas, each with a palace in Dewas city, ruled distinct territories (Senior Branch, Junior Branch). Descended from two brothers, Tukoji and Jiwaji who were given Dewas in 1726 by Peshwa Baji Rao as a reward for army services.

Semi Official Copper Struck at Allote, Dewas Senior Branch

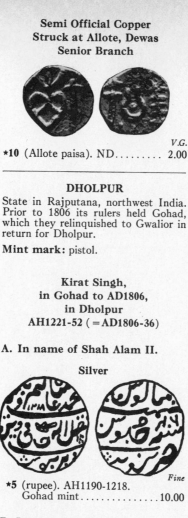

	V.G.
⋆10 (Allote paisa). ND	2.00

DHOLPUR

State in Rajputana, northwest India. Prior to 1806 its rulers held Gohad, which they relinquished to Gwalior in return for Dholpur.

Mint mark: pistol.

Kirat Singh, in Gohad to AD1806, in Dholpur AH1221-52 (=AD1806-36)

A. In name of Shah Alam II.

Silver

	Fine
⋆5 (rupee). AH1190-1218. Gohad mint	10.00

B. In name of Muhammad Akbar II.

Silver

12 (rupee). Like No. 12a (vars.). Mint name Dholpur. 1221-25	10.00

⋆12a —. Mint name Gohad (actually Dholpur). 1226-52.	7.50

ELICHPUR

Town in Berar, central India.

Anonymous Copper

	V.G.
10 (paisa). *Tiger left.* 10.8 gr. (ca. AD1832-67)	3.00
10a (paisa). Sim., *tiger right*	5.00
15 (1½ paisa). Sim. to No. 10. 15.0 gr. AH1250	5.00

GARHWAL

State in north India. Held by Ghurkhas of Nepal 1803-15. Silver coins weigh 1.7-2.3 grs. probably because of trade with Tibet. Copper coins weigh 3.5-5.4 grs.

Mint: Srinagar.

Pradip Shah AD1717-72

Copper

	V.G.
⋆5 (paisa). Persian legends. ND., Samvat 1827, yr. 25 (of P.S.)	4.00

Silver

	Fine
10 (timasha). In name of Shah Alam II. His yrs. 1-15	7.50

Lallat Shah Samvat 1829-38 (=AD1772-81)

Copper

	V.G.
⋆15 (paisa). Persian legends. Samvat 1830-31	4.00

Silver

	Fine
⋆20 (timasha). In name of Shah Alam II. Rev. dates. AH1189-92/Samvat 1832-37	7.50

Parduman Shah Samvat 1842-60 (=AD1785-1803)

Copper

	V.G.
25 (paisa). Persian legends. Samvat 1835-53	3.00

Girvan Yuddha of Nepal Samvat 1860-72 (=AD1803-15)

Copper

⋆30 (paisa). Persian legends. Vars. ND., Samvat 1872 (=AD1815)	5.00

INDIA

GARHWAL (Cont.)

Silver

A. In names of Shah Alam II and Girvan Yuddha.

★35 (timasha). Persian legends. *1191/Samvat (18)66*....... 7.50 *Fine*

B. In names of Muhammad Akbar II and Girvan Yuddha.

★37 (timasha). Persian legends. Vars. Yr. 1, Samvat (18)66-70................. 7.50

C. In name of Girvan Yuddha alone.

★40 (timasha). Persian legends. ND (AD1813-15).........10.00

Gohad. See Dholpur.

GWALIOR (=Sindhia)

State in central India. Founded by Ranoji, who became slipper bearer (whence family name, "Sindhia") to Balaji Vishvanath, the first Maratha Peshwa, in 1714. Capital originally Ujjain (=Daru-l-fath), but transferred to Gwalior in 1810.

Mints: Ajmir, Basoda, Bhilsa, Burhanpur, Chanderi, Dahod (Dohad), GakhaKota, Gwalior Fort, Isagarh, Jamgaon, Jawad, Jhansi, Lashkar, Mandisor, Narwar, Nathgarh, Raghugarh, Rajod, Shadorah, Sheopur, Sipri, Ujjain.

Mints were operated either directly by the Sindhias or by their feudatories.

Most coins are in the name of the Mughal emperor, and are unattributable to Sindhia chiefs except by dates (which are sometimes spurious). During the regency of Baija Bao 1827-33, several mints began to add Nagari letters to the coins to identify the Gwalior rulers.

Jiyaji AH1158-73 (=AD1745-59)
Jankoji AH1173-75 (=AD1759-61)
Mahadji Rao
AH1175-1209 (=AD1761-94)

Daulat Rao
AH1209-43 (=AD1794-1827)
Baija Bao, Regent
AH1243-49 (=AD1827-33)
Jankoji Rao
AH1243-59 (=AD1827-43)
Jayaji Rao
AH1259-1302 (=AD1843-86)

I. Ajmir mint.

To Gwalior 1792-1818. For earlier issues see Ajmir. Mint mark: vertical line through 2 dots.

Silver
Fine

5 (rupee). Sim. to No. 10 but w/out jhar or Nagari SRI. Frozen AH1203/yr. 31...... 5.00

★10 (rupee). Shah Alam II legends. Rev. jhar, Nagari SRI, Ajmir mmk. Frozen 1203/yr. 31... 5.00

II. Basoda mint.

To Gwalior from 1817.

Jankoji Rao 1827-43

Silver

★20 (rupee). Md. Akbar II legend. Rev. Nagari JANA/KUJI, mmks. 1252, 74(!)/yr. 32.........10.00

III. Bhilsa mint.

Mint mark: frozen date AH(12)25.

Jayaji Rao 1843-86

Silver

30 (¼ rupee). Like No. 32. Frozen AH(12)25.......... 3.00
31 (½ rupee). Sim. (12)25..... 3.00

★32 (rupee). Shah Alam II legends. Rev. Nagari JI, bow and arrow. (12)25.............. 4.50

IV. Burhanpur mint.

To Gwalior 1778-1860.

A. In name of Shah Alam II.

Copper
V.G.

40 (paisa). Persian legends, mmk. 5-pointed leaf. Square. ND (1795)............... 4.00
40a —. Round to irregular shape. (1805).................... 3.00

Silver
Fine

45 (¼ rupee). Like No. 47. AH1214.................. 4.00
46 (½ rupee). Sim. 1214...... 5.00

★47 (rupee). 1197-1276........ 7.00

B. In name of Alyjah Bahadur (title of Sindhia chiefs).

Copper

V.G

★50 (paisa). AH1260, 73-75..... 4.00

V. *Chanderi mint.*

Silver

60 (rupee). Persian legends. Cannon mmk. Yr. 7........ —

VI. Dahod (=Dohad) mint.

Feudatory to Gwalior. Administered by British.

Copper

★70 (paisa). 6.4 gr. Samvat 1912. 5.00

VII. Gwalior Fort mint.

Operated from 1777. To British 1844-1853.

A. In name of Muhammad Shah.

Gold
F-VF

75 (⅓ mohur). Mint name "Shahjahanabad." Frozen AH1130/yr. 2 (struck 1795)...................200.00

INDIA

GWALIOR (Cont.)

75a —. Sim., with Nagari SRI for Baija Bao. (1827)........225.00 *F-VF*

75b —. Sim., with Nagari JA for Jankoji. (1834)..........225.00

75c —. Sim., with Nagari JI for Jayaji. (1843)...........200.00

B. In name of Shah Alam II.

Copper
V.G.

80 (Tegh paisa). Sim. to No. 87. Yrs. 40-49...............2.00

Silver
Fine

85 (Tegh rupee). Sim. to No. 92. 1191-1221/yrs. 19-49......7.50

C. In name of Muhammad Akbar II.

Copper

V.G.

★87 (ex 15) (Tegh paisa). Obv. mmk. dagger. Yrs. 2-59.....2.00

Silver

Fine

★92 (ex 27) (Tegh rupee). Mmks. obv. flower, rev. dagger. 1222-41..................5.00

★95 (ex 40) (rupee). Sim., rev. Nagari SRI for Baija Bao. Frozen yr. 23 (1829-33).....6.00

★100 (ex 52) (rupee). Sim., rev. Nagari JA(nkoji), bow and arrow pointing up or down. 1244/yr. 23..................5.00

110 (1/16 rupee). Sim., rev. Nagari JI for Jayaji. 9mm. Yr. 23..3.00

Fine

111 (1/8 rupee). Sim. 11mm. Yr. 23.................3.00

112 (1/4 rupee). Sim. 13mm. Yr. 23.................3.00

113 (1/2 rupee). Sim. 15mm. Yr. 23.................3.50

114 (rupee). Sim. 18-20mm. Yr. 23.................5.00

★114a (ex 65) —. 25-27mm. For nazrana (presentation). 125x/yr. 23 ......(*F-VF*).25.00

VIII. Isagarh mint.

Silver

125 (1/4 rupee). Like No. 127...5.00

126 (1/2 rupee). Sim............5.00

★127 (rupee). 1248-52..........5.00

IX. Jawad mint.
Taken from Bhim Singh of Mewar.

Copper

V.G.

★130 (paisa). With Nagari J for Jankoji Rao. ND.........4.00

★135 (paisa). Nagari JI for Jayaji. Vars. ND....4.00

X. Jhansi mint.
To Gwalior 1865-86. For earlier issues see Jhansi.

Silver

Fine

★140 (rupee). Shah Alam II legends, Nagari JI for Jayaji. AH1282-85...............6.00

XI. Lashkar mint.

Silver
Fine

145 (1/8 rupee). Like No. 148. Yr. 17..................2.00

146 (1/4 rupee). Sim. Yr. 17....2.00

147 (1/2 rupee). Sim. Yr. 17....3.00

★148 (rupee). Shah Alam II legends. Yrs. 16-22 of Md. Akbar (=1821-27).......4.00

Baija Bao 1827-33

155 (1/4 rupee). Sim., with Nagari SRI for Baija Bao. Frozen Yr. 23..................3.00

156 (1/2 rupee). Sim. Yr. 23....3.50

★157 (rupee). Yr. 23...........5.00

Jankoji Rao 1827-43

Copper
V.G.

160 (1/2 paisa). Like No. 161. Yrs. 23-38...............2.00

★161 (ex 45) (paisa). Shah Alam II legends. Mmks. obv. trident, rev. scepter, spearhead. Yrs. 23-38..........2.00

Silver
Fine

165 (1/8 rupee). Like No. 148, with Nagari J(ankoji). Frozen yr. 23.............3.00

166 (1/4 rupee). Sim. Yr. 23....3.00

167 (1/2 rupee). Sim. Yr. 23....3.00

★168 (rupee). Yr. 23..........4.00

Jayaji Rao 1843-86

Copper
V.G.

170 (ex 57) (1/2 paisa). Like No. 171. 5 gr. Yr. 23......1.50

INDIA

GWALIOR (Cont.)

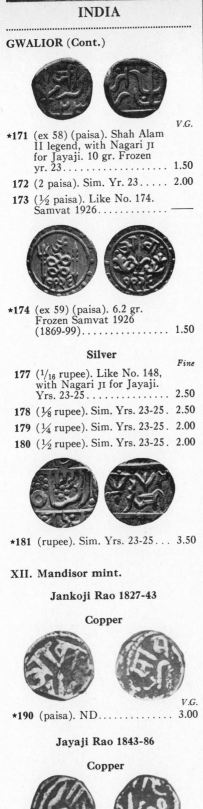

V.G.

★171 (ex 58) (paisa). Shah Alam II legend, with Nagari JI for Jayaji. 10 gr. Frozen yr. 23 . . . . 1.50

172 (2 paisa). Sim. Yr. 23 . . . . . 2.00

173 (½ paisa). Like No. 174. Samvat 1926 . . . . ——

★174 (ex 59) (paisa). 6.2 gr. Frozen Samvat 1926 (1869-99) 1.50

Silver

Fine

177 (1/16 rupee). Like No. 148, with Nagari JI for Jayaji. Yrs. 23-25 . . . . 2.50

178 (⅛ rupee). Sim. Yrs. 23-25 . 2.50

179 (¼ rupee). Sim. Yrs. 23-25 . 2.00

180 (½ rupee). Sim. Yrs. 23-25 . 2.00

★181 (rupee). Sim. Yrs. 23-25 . . . 3.50

XII. Mandisor mint.

Jankoji Rao 1827-43

Copper

V.G.

★190 (paisa). ND 3.00

Jayaji Rao 1843-86

Copper

★195 (paisa). Samvat 1921-27 . . . 3.00

XIII. Narwar mint.

To Gwalior in 1805. For earlier issues see Narwar.

Copper

V.G.

198 (paisa). Shan Alam II legends. Rev. mmk. katar. *Frozen AH1230* 2.50

Silver

Fine

★200 (½ rupee). 1230/yr. 21 . . . . 6.00

201 (rupee). Sim. 1228-30/yrs. 7-9 . . . . 5.00

XIV. Rajod mint.

Copper

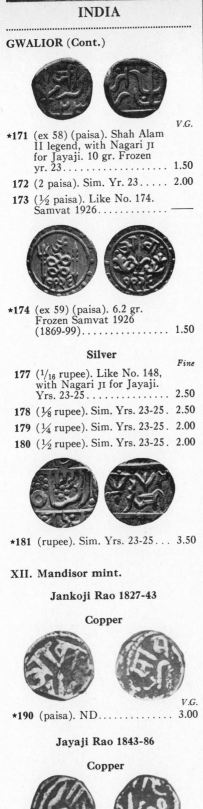

V.G.

★218 (paisa). 10-14 gr. Samvat 1930 . . . . 5.00

219 (paisa). Sim. 7-13 gr. Samvat 1936 . . . . 5.00

220 (paisa). Sim. 10-13 gr. Samvat 1940 . . . . 5.00

XV. Shadorah (Sadhorah) mint.

Mint mark:
Cannon (also see Nos. 235-240).

Copper

222 (paisa). Sim. to No. 225. ND 3.00

Silver

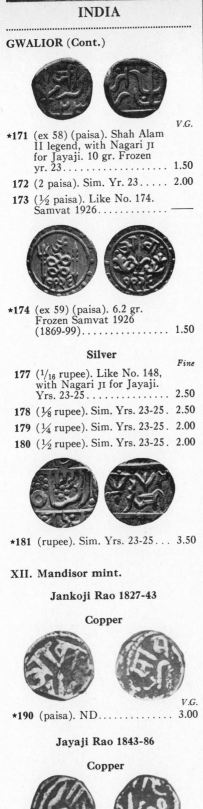

Fine

★225 (rupee). Md. Akbar II legends, cannon to r. ND . . 7.50

226 (rupee). Sim., cannon to l. AH1228-31/yrs. 8-11 . . . . . . 7.50

XVI. Sheopur mint.

Mint mark:
Cannon (also see Nos. 222-226).

Silver

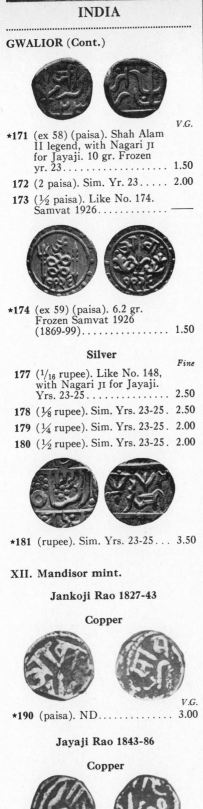

Fine

★235 (rupee). Md. Akbar II legends. Frozen AH1228/ yrs. 7-27 . . . . 7.50

★240 (rupee). Nagari JI(yaji). 1270-76 and yr. 15 . . . . 7.50

XVII. Ujjain mint.

Gwalior mint from 1726.

Copper

V.G.

250 (paisa). Sim. to No. 259. Square. Yrs. 45-51 . . . . 2.00

Silver

Fine

256 (⅛ rupee). Like No. 259. Yr. 5x 3.00

257 (¼ rupee). Sim. Yrs. 20-86 . 3.00

258 (½ rupee). Sim. Yrs. 20-86 . 3.00

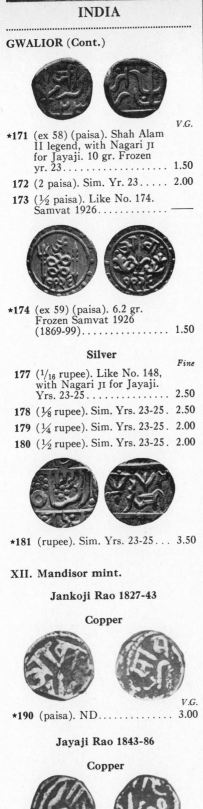

★259 (ex 10) (rupee). Shah Alam II legends, no Nagari letters. AH1176-1215/yrs. 3-99 . . . . 4.00

Copper

V.G.

265 (paisa). Like No. 250, with Nagari SRI for Baija Bao. 14 gr. Square. Yr. 23 . . . . . . 2.50

270 (paisa). Sim., with J(ankoji). Square. Yr. 31 . . . . 2.50

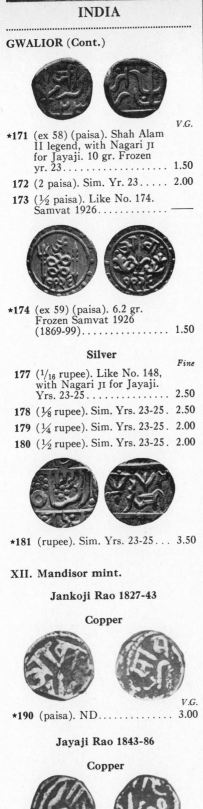

★275 (paisa). Sim., with JI for Jayaji Rao. Square or round. AH1262-93 . . . . 2.00

INDIA

HYDERABAD (=Haidarabad)

Largest Indian state, located in south-central India. Ruling family founded by Asaf Jah, a Turcoman soldier of Aurangzeb, who was appointed Sub-ahdar of the Deccan (central India) in 1713 with the title of Nizam.

Asaf Jah and his successors until 1857 were generally known as Nizams of the Deccan. They coined in the name of the emperor until that year.

After the Indian Mutiny the Deccan title gave way to that of Hyderabad.

The gold pieces of this state are said to have been produced for ceremonial and jewelry purposes rather than as legal tender.

I. General State Coinage.

Mints:
Aurangabad (=Khujista Bunyad), Haidarabad (=Farkhunda Bunyad).

Nizam Ali Khan
AH1175-1218 (=AD1761-1803)

Silver

		Fine
25	(rupee). Shah Alam II legend with Persian "N(izam)." Farkhunda Bunyad mint. 1193/yr. 19 (of N.A.)	—

Sikandar Jah
AH1218-44 (=AD1803-29)

Copper

		V.G.
*40	(paisa). Shah Alam II legend. Rev. 2-bladed sword. 11.6 gr. 1217-18	2.00
42	(paisa). *Sim.* but Md. Akbar II legend. 1221-37	2.00

Silver

		Fine
46	(¼ rupee). Like No. 48	—
47	(½ rupee). Sim	—

*48	(rupee). Muhammad Akbar II legend. Rev. sword. *Haidarabad mint.* 1222-42	6.00

		Fine
51	(¼ rupee). Like No. 53. AH1242	4.00
52	(½ rupee). Sim. 1242	5.00

*53	(rupee). Md. Akbar II legend with Persian "S(ikandar)." Rev. 2-bladed sword, Farkhunda Bunyad Haidarabad. 1225-44/yrs. 4-25	5.00

Gold

		Fine
56	(¹⁄₁₆ mohur). Sim	—
57	(⅛ mohur). Sim	—
58	(¼ mohur). Sim	—
59	(½ mohur). Sim	—
60	(mohur). Sim	—

Nasir-ud-Dowla
AH1244-73 (=AD1829-57)

A. In name of Muhammad Akbar II.

Copper

		V.G.
61	(paisa). Md. Akbar legend and Persian "N(asir)." AH1250	2.00

Silver

		Fine
64	(ex 61) (¼ rupee). Like No. 53 but with Persian "N(asir)." 1251, 73	3.50
65	(ex 62) (½ rupee). Sim. 1249-51	4.00
66	(ex 63) (rupee). Sim. 1244-53	5.00

Gold

		F-VF
68	(ex 70) (¹⁄₁₆ mohur). Sim	20.00
69	(ex 71) (⅛ mohur). Sim	25.00
70	(ex 72) (¼ mohur). Sim	40.00
71	(ex 73) (½ mohur). Sim	65.00
72	(ex 74) (mohur). Sim. 1246	100.00

B. In name of Bahadur Shah II.

Copper

		V.G.
73	(paisa). Bahadur Shah legend and Persian "N(asir). Rev. sword, Khujista Bunyad. AH1262-72	2.00

Silver

		Fine
75	(¹⁄₁₆ rupee). Like No. 79. 1272	3.00
76	(⅛ rupee). Sim. 1272	3.00

		Fine
77	(ex 64) (¼ rupee). Sim. 1256-74	3.00
78	(ex 65) (½ rupee). Sim. 1257-73	3.75

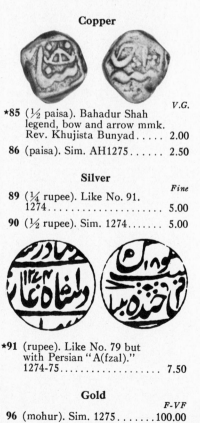

*79	(ex 68) (rupee). Bahadur Shah legend and Persian "N(asir)." Rev. like No. 53. 1256-73	4.50

Gold

		Fine
80	(¹⁄₁₆ mohur). Like No. 68	—
81	(⅛ mohur). Sim	—
82	(¼ mohur). Sim	—
83	(½ mohur). Sim	—
84	(mohur). Sim	—

Afzal-ud-Daula
AH1273-85 (=AD1857-69)

A. In name of Bahadur Shah II.

Copper

		V.G.
*85	(½ paisa). Bahadur Shah legend, bow and arrow mmk. Rev. Khujista Bunyad	2.00
86	(paisa). Sim. AH1275	2.50

Silver

		Fine
89	(¼ rupee). Like No. 91. 1274	5.00
90	(½ rupee). Sim. 1274	5.00

*91	(rupee). Like No. 79 but with Persian "A(fzal)." 1274-75	7.50

Gold

		F-VF
96	(mohur). Sim. 1275	100.00

B. In name of Asaf Jah (founder of Hyderabad dynasty).

INDIA

HYDERABAD (Cont.)

Copper

		V.G.
106	(paisa). *Sim. to No. 109. AH1272-82*	2.00

Silver

		Fine
109	(ex 92) (⅛ rupee). "Halli Sicca" coinage. Asaf Jah legend, "92" and date. Rev. Hyderabad mint. Like No. 118	3.00
110	(ex 93) (¼ rupee). Sim. 1276-83	3.00
111	(ex 94) (½ rupee). Sim. 1276-79	3.50
112	(ex 95) (rupee). Sim. 1274-85	4.50

Gold

		V.F.
114	(ex 99) (1/16 *mohur*). Sim.	25.00
115	(ex 100) (⅛ mohur). Sim. 1279-81	35.00
116	(ex 101) (¼ mohur). Sim. 1281	50.00
117	(ex 102) (½ mohur). Sim. 1281	75.00

★118	(ex 103) (mohur). 1281-82	125.00

II. Feudatory States Under Hyderabad.

A. Gadwal, Rajas of.

Silver

		Fine
20	(rupee). Shah Alam II legend. Rev. Akarwan (=Gadwal) mint. Yr. 11 (=AH1183)	10.00

B. Godavery.

Copper

		V.G.
30	(paisa). AH1273	3.00

C. Narayanpett, Rajas of.

Coins have frozen date AH1186 on obverse.

Silver

		Fine
37	(⅛ rupee). Like No. 40, with Nagari "Go" on obv. 1252	5.00

Fine

40	(rupee). Shah Alam II legend and Nagari "Go" or "Ti." Rev. Dilshadabad mint and Nagari "L" or "K." 1186, 1245, 52	7.50

D. Issues of Pestonji Meherji.

A Bombay Sahukar (chief). Coins were struck at Aurangabad.

Silver

		Fine
57	(⅛ rupee). Like No. 60. Yr. 4	——
59	(½ rupee). Sim. AH1256/ yr. 4	——
60	(rupee). Bahadur Shah II legend, star. Rev. mmk. sword. 1256/yr. 4	——

E. Shorapur, Rajas of.

Copper

		V.G.
63	(paisa). Symbols both sides	3.00
65	(½ paisa). 5.9 gr. *ND*	4.00
66	(paisa). Sim. 10.2 gr. AH1262	4.00

F. Wanparti, Rajas of.

Silver

		Fine
80	(rupee). Muhammad Akbar legend and Nagari "J." Rev. Persian legend and Nagari "Ra." AH1235/yr. 14	10.00

INDORE (Holkar State)

Maratha state in central India. Founded by Mulhar Rao Holkar (d. AD1765) who was rewarded in 1728 by the Peshwa for services with lands which became the nucleus of Indore. Other districts were thereafter wrested from the emperor by Mulhar Rao and his successors. Ahalya Bai moved the capital to Indore, which she renamed Mulharnagar.

Mints: Maheshwar, Mulharnagar.

I. In name of Shah Alam II.

A. Mulharnagar mint.

Copper

		V.G.
★3	(paisa). Mmk. sunface (=Holkar symbol). 5-7.2 gr. AH1209/yr. 30	2.00
4	(paisa). Like No. 6. 9.6 gr. Yr. 88 of Holkars	3.00
5	(paisa). Sim. 19 gr. 1243-44, yr. 88 of Holkars	3.00

		V.G.
★6	(ex 90) ½ anna. Shah Alam legend and leaf. Rev. legend and bull. 12-17 gr. 1261-86/ yrs. 97-113	3.00

Silver

		Fine
7	(ex 95) (⅛ rupee). Like No. 10. 10mm. AH1279-89	2.00
8	(ex 96a) (¼ rupee). Sim. 11-14mm. 1234-95	2.00
8a	(ex 96) —. Broad, thin flan. 25mm. 1280/yr. 110 of Holkars	15.00
9	(ex 97a) (½ rupee). Sim. 15mm. 1228-95	2.00

★9a	(ex 97) —. Broad thin flan. 27mm. 1280/yr. 110	20.00

★10	(rupee). Shah Alam legend. Rev. sunface mmk. 1185-1296/yrs. 15-122	4.00
10a	—. Broad thin flan. 28mm. 1280/yr. 110	30.00

B. Maheshwar mint.

Silver

14	(¼ rupee). Like No. 16. 1214, 19/yr. 44	5.00
15	(½ rupee). Sim. 1203-05	5.00

★16	(rupee). Like No. 10 (with Mulharnagar mint name) but rev. mmks. leaf and *vase*. 1186-1217/yrs. 29-46	6.50

INDIA

INDORE (Cont.)

II. In name of Holkars of Indore.

Nos. 3-16 were the regular issues of the following two reigns, and Nos. 52-112 were probably all for nazrana (presentation) or other commemorative occasions.

Jaswant Rao
AH1212-26 (=AD1797-1811)

Silver

Fine

★**52** (nazrana rupee). Jaswant legends (in Nagari). Saka 1728 (=AD1806).........40.00

★**58** (nazrana rupee). Persian legends, in names of Md. Akbar II and Jaswant. AH1222/yr. 2............30.00

Tukoji Rao II
AH1260-1304 (=AD1844-86)

Copper

V.G.

80 (paisa). Like No. 100. Saka 1780...............*20.00*

82 (paisa). Like No. 102. Saka 1788/Samvat 1923....*20.00*

Silver

Fine

★**100** (rupee). Saka 1780 (=AD1858).............35.00

102 (rupee). Sim. Saka 1788/ Samvat 1923 (=AD1866)..30.00

Fine

★**110** (rupee). Sword and lance on obv. Saka 1788 and AH1289, 95.............20.00

112 (rupee). Sim. but sword and lance below sunface. AH1287/Samvat 1934.....25.00

III. Coinage for Sironj.

A Holkar feudatory possession AD1754-98, then to Tonk (q.v.).

Silver

150 (rupee). Alamgir II legends. AH1168/yr. 1...........15.00

160 (rupee). Shah Alam II legends. 1172-1200........10.00

Jaintiapur. See Assam.

JAIPUR

State in Rajputana, N.W. India. The ruling maharajas were of ancient lineage. The Jaipur symbol was the Jhar, or 6-leafed spray. Coins on broad thin flans (e.g., Nos. 5a, 46, 112a, etc.) were struck primarily for nazrana (presentation) use.

Mints: Jaipur, Madhopur, both with title "Sawai" (=superior).

Isvari Singh AD1743-60
Madho Singh AD1760-78
Pratap Singh AD1778-1803
Jagat Singh II AD1803-18
Mohan Singh AD1818-19
Jai Singh III AD1819-35
Ram Singh AD1835-80

A. In name of Ahmad Shah.

Silver

Fine

5 (rupee). 21mm. Yrs. 2-6....10.00

★**5a** —. 33mm. AH1166/yr. 6.... ——

B. In name of Alamgir II.

Silver

Fine

★**21** (rupee). Alamgir II legends. Yrs. 1-6................. 7.50

Gold

25 (mohur). Sim. 117x/yr. 6... ——

C. In name of Shah Alam II.

Copper

V.G.

★**29** (ex 15) (paisa). Rev. jhar. 17 gr. Yrs. 12-44.......... 2.00

★**29a** —. 29mm. Yrs. 34, 37.....10.00

31 (paisa). Sim. Rev. star-shaped flower. Yrs. 22-31. Sawai Jaipur............. 2.50

Silver

Fine

★**36** (rupee). Rev. jhar. 1208-14/ yrs. 34-40. Sawai Jaipur.... 5.00

36a —. 32mm. 1208/yr. 34...... ——

Gold

40 (mohur). Sim. Yr. 15....... ——

D. In name of Muhammad Akbar II.

(1) Sawai Jaipur mint.

INDIA

JAIPUR (Cont.)

Copper

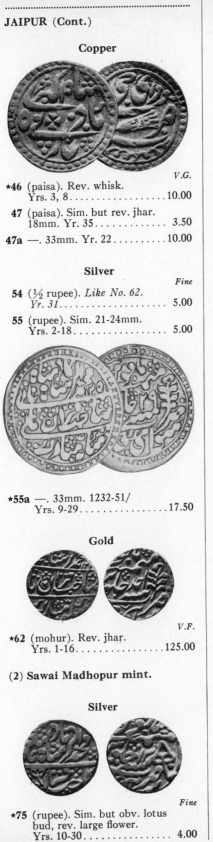

V.G.

★46 (paisa). Rev. whisk. Yrs. 3, 8 .... 10.00

47 (paisa). Sim. but rev. jhar. 18mm. Yr. 35 .... 3.50

47a —. 33mm. Yr. 22 .... 10.00

Silver

Fine

54 ($\frac{1}{2}$ rupee). *Like No. 62. Yr. 31* 5.00

55 (rupee). Sim. 21-24mm. Yrs. 2-18 .... 5.00

★55a —. 33mm. 1232-51/ Yrs. 9-29 .... 17.50

Gold

V.F.

★62 (mohur). Rev. jhar. Yrs. 1-16 .... 125.00

(2) Sawai Madhopur mint.

Silver

Fine

★75 (rupee). Sim. but obv. lotus bud, rev. large flower. Yrs. 10-30 .... 4.00

E. In name of Bahadur Shah II.

(1) Sawai Jaipur mint.

Copper

V.G.

85 (paisa). Rev. jhar. 18-20mm. Yrs. 13-16 .... 3.00

85a —. 32mm. Yrs. 13, 17 ...... 10.00

Silver

Fine

89 ($\frac{1}{16}$ rupee). Like No. 100. 11mm. Yr. 7 .... 3.50

90 ($\frac{1}{8}$ rupee). Sim. 15mm. Yr. 18 .... 2.00

92 ($\frac{1}{2}$ rupee). Sim. 18mm. Yr. 5 .... 4.00

93 (rupee). Sim. 21-23mm. Yrs. 3-12 .... 5.00

Gold

V.F.

★100 (mohur). Rev. jhar. Yrs. 13, 19 .... 100.00

(2) Sawai Madhopur mint.

Silver

Fine

102 (rupee). Mmks. like No. 75. Yrs. 10-18 .... 5.00

F. In names of Queen Victoria and Ram Singh.

Copper

V.G.

104 (ex 107) (old paisa). Like No. 105. 18 gr. 30mm. AD1870/Yr. 35 .... 2.00

★105 (new paisa). Rev. jhar. 6 gr. Yrs. 37-45 of Ram Singh 1.25

105a —. 28mm. AD1872, 80/ Yrs. 37, 45 .... 6.00

Silver

Fine

110 ($\frac{1}{4}$ rupee). Like No. 112a but dump. 15-17mm. Yrs. 21-44 .... 2.50

111 ($\frac{1}{2}$ rupee). Sim. 18-20mm. Yrs. 21-45 .... 3.50

112 (rupee). Sim. 21-23mm. Yrs. 21-45 .... 4.00

Fine

★112a —. Rev. jhar. 27-29mm. AD1870/Yr. 35 of Ram Singh 10.00

Gold

V.F.

★119 (mohur). Sim. Yrs. 21-45 . . 100.00

JAISALMIR

State in Rajputana, N.W. India. Rulers styled maharawals.

A. Anonymous issue.

Copper

V.G.

4 (dodia $= \frac{1}{40}$ anna). Short Persian legend. Rev. Trident. 2.9 gr. ND. *(1660-1836)* 1.50

B. In name of Muhammad Shah, AD1719-48.

Silver

Fine

7 ($\frac{1}{8}$ rupee). Like No. 10. Yr. 22 .... 3.00

8 ($\frac{1}{4}$ rupee). Sim. Yr. 22 ..... 4.00

9 ($\frac{1}{2}$ rupee). Sim. Yr. 22 ..... 4.00

★10 (rupee). Mmk. = symbols in rev. exergue. Frozen date AH1152/yr. 22 .... 6.00

C. In name of Queen Victoria.

Silver

23 ($\frac{1}{8}$ rupee). Like No. 26. Yr. 22 .... 3.00

24 ($\frac{1}{4}$ rupee). Sim. Yr. 22 ..... 4.00

25 ($\frac{1}{2}$ rupee). Sim. Yr. 22 ..... 4.00

★26 (rupee). Rev. mmks. like No. 10. Frozen yr. 22 (= 1858) 6.00

INDIA

JAISALMIR (Cont.)

Fine

27 (⅛ rupee). Sim. Rev. with additional mmks. bird and umbrella. Yr. 22 . . . . 3.00

28 (¼ rupee). Sim. Yr. 22 . . . . . 4.00

29 (½ rupee). Sim. Yr. 22 . . . . . 4.00

30 (rupee). Sim. Yr. 22 . . . . 6.00

Gold

F-VF

32 (⅛ mohur). Like No. 27. Yr. 22 . . . . .75.00

33 (¼ mohur). Sim. Yr. 22 . . .100.00

34 (½ mohur). Sim. Yr. 22 . . .175.00

35 (mohur). Sim 150.00

JALAUN

Maratha state in north-central India. Partly annexed to British Bundelkhand in the early 19th century.

Mints: Jalaun, *Srinagar.*

Copper

V.G.

5 (paisa). Like No. 15. 14.1 gr. Yr. 53 . . . . 1.50

Silver

Fine

★15 (rupee). Shah Alam II legends. "Balashahi" coinage with trident and cruciform rosette. Yrs. 17-55 (=AD*1775*-1818). (Var.) 4.00

Jammu. See Kashmir.

JANJIRA

Island near Bombay. Dynasty of Nawabs dates from 1489. The copper coins are very crude.

Sidi Ibrahim Khan II
AD1789-92, AD1804-26

Copper

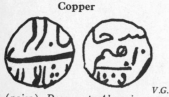

V.G.

★5 (paisa). *Degenerate Alamgir II legend.* Rev. Ibrahim legend. 7 gr. ND 3.50

Sidi Muhammad Khan
AD1826-48

Copper

V.G.

15 (paisa). *Obv. sim.* Rev. Muhammad legend. ND 4.00

Sidi Ibrahim Khan III
AD1848-79

Copper

★20 (paisa). *In his own name.* AH1284-85 . . . . 2.00

Silver

Fine

★25 (rupee). Coin of Poona cmkd. Nagari J(anjira) 10.00

JHALAWAR

State in Rajputana, N.W. India. Originally part of Kotah. Established in memory of services to Kotah of Zalim Singh, long-time administrator of that state. His grandson was given Jhalawar in 1837 with the title of Raj Rana.

Mint marks: branch and triangular tree-like ornament (sim. to Kotah), mint name Jhalawar.

Madan Singh AD1837-47
Prithvi Singh AD1847-75
Zalim Singh AD1875-96

A. In name of Bahadur Shah II.

Coins dated from founding of Jhalawar (yr. 1 = AD1837).

Copper

V.G.

★21 (paisa). 18 gr. Yrs. 1-21 . . . . . 2.50

Silver

Fine

25 (⅛ rupee). Like No. 28. Yrs. 1-21 . . . . 3.00

Fine

26 (¼ rupee). Sim. Yrs. 1-21 . . . 3.50

27 (½ rupee). Sim. Yrs. 1-21 . . . 4.00

★28 (rupee). Yrs. 1-21 . . . . 5.00

B. In name of Queen Victoria.

Coins dated from start of her reign in India (yr. 1 = AD1857-58).

Copper

V.G.

30 (½ paisa). Like No. 31. 9 gr. *ND* 3.00

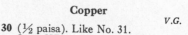

★31 (paisa). 18 gr. Yrs. 1-34 . . . . . 3.00

Silver

Fine

34 (⅛ rupee). Like No. 37a but dump. 13mm. Yrs. 1-37 . . . . . 3.00

35 (¼ rupee). Sim. 14mm. Yrs. 1-37 . . . . 3.50

36 (½ rupee). Sim. 17mm. Yrs. 1-34 . . . . 4.00

37 (rupee). Sim. 19-22mm. Yrs. 1-37 . . . . 5.00

F-VF

★37a —. 27-28mm. For presentation. Samvat 1915/yrs. 5, 15 . . . .30.00

JHANSI

North-central India. Ruled by the Maratha Peshwa 1766-1817. Acquired by the British Company in the latter year.

Mint: Balwantnagar (= Jhansi).

Copper

V.G.

★10 (paisa). Persian Shah Alam II legends. 16.8 gr. ND., yr. 5 . . 2.00

INDIA

JHANSI (Cont.)

Silver

<table>
<tr><td></td><td></td><td align="right">Fine</td></tr>
<tr><td>18</td><td>(¼ rupee). Like No. 20. Yr. 2x</td><td align="right">5.00</td></tr>
</table>

<table>
<tr><td>★20</td><td>(rupee). Partial dates AH(117)4-(122)4</td><td align="right">4.00</td></tr>
</table>

JIND

Gold

<table>
<tr><td></td><td></td><td align="right">F-VF</td></tr>
<tr><td>20</td><td>(mohur). Legend each side. (AD1840-65)</td><td align="right">100.00</td></tr>
</table>

JODHPUR (=Marwar)

State of Marwar in Rajputana, northwest India, founded in 1459. Better known by the name of its capital, Jodhpur. Its rulers were maharajas.

Mints: Ajmir (to 1759), Jodhpur *(1753-*1947), Merta *(1774-1833,* 1864-71), Nagore *(1757-*1872), Pali (to *ca. 1900),* Sujat (1807-88). With exceptions as noted, mint name on coins is Jodhpur regardless of actual place of minting.

Note: Dates and regnal years on many Jodhpur coins are fictitious, with little or no relationship to the reigns named on the coins. Blundered dates occur frequently.

Bijy (Vijaya) Singh AD1752-92
Bhim Singh AD1792-1803
Man Singh AD1803-43
Takht Singh AD1843-73

I. Anonymous issues.

Copper

<table>
<tr><td></td><td></td><td align="right">V.G.</td></tr>
<tr><td>★15</td><td>(Amir Shahi paisa). Uniface. 16.5 gr. Ca. 1650 - 18th century</td><td align="right">2.00</td></tr>
</table>

<table>
<tr><td></td><td></td><td align="right">V.G.</td></tr>
<tr><td>★21</td><td>(paisa). 20-21 gr. AH1192-1205/yrs. 34-64 of Shah Alam II (ca. 1778-1822)</td><td align="right">2.00</td></tr>
</table>

II. In name of Ahmad Shah Bahadur.

Silver

<table>
<tr><td></td><td></td><td align="right">Fine</td></tr>
<tr><td>23</td><td>(rupee). Ahmad legend. Rev. like No. 25. 1165/yr. 5. Jodhpur mint</td><td align="right">Rare</td></tr>
<tr><td>24</td><td>(rupee). Sim. 1161. Ajmir mint (on coin)</td><td align="right">—</td></tr>
</table>

III. In name of Alamgir II.

Silver

<table>
<tr><td>25</td><td>(rupee). 1170-80/yrs. 3-6. Jodhpur mint</td><td align="right">15.00</td></tr>
<tr><td>26</td><td>(rupee). 117x/yr. 6. Ajmir mint (on coin)</td><td align="right">—</td></tr>
</table>

<table>
<tr><td>★27</td><td>(rupee). Yr. 5. Nagore mint (on coin)</td><td align="right">25.00</td></tr>
</table>

IV. In name of Shah Alam II.

Silver

<table>
<tr><td>29</td><td>(½ rupee). Like No. 31</td><td align="right">—</td></tr>
</table>

<table>
<tr><td>★30</td><td>(rupee). 1192-1218/yrs. 20-45. "Jodhpur" (Jodhpur, Pali, Sujat)</td><td align="right">4.50</td></tr>
<tr><td>30a</td><td>—. Square. 1218/yr. 45</td><td align="right">25.00</td></tr>
</table>

<table>
<tr><td>★31</td><td>(rupee). 1203/yr. 31. Ajmir mint (on coin)</td><td align="right">5.00</td></tr>
<tr><td>33</td><td>(rupee). Rev. like No. 26. 1194-1218. Nagore mint (on coin)</td><td align="right">12.50</td></tr>
</table>

<table>
<tr><td></td><td></td><td align="right">Fine</td></tr>
<tr><td>★34</td><td>(rupee). Rev. jhar (=Sujat ca. 1848-59). 1204, 64/ yrs. 23, 43</td><td align="right">6.00</td></tr>
<tr><td>35</td><td>(rupee). 1188. Merta mint</td><td align="right">25.00</td></tr>
</table>

Gold

<table>
<tr><td></td><td></td><td align="right">F-VF</td></tr>
<tr><td>40</td><td>(mohur). Like No. 30. 1218/yr. 45 and others. Jodhpur mint</td><td align="right">125.00</td></tr>
</table>

V. In name of Muhammad Akbar II.

Copper

<table>
<tr><td></td><td></td><td align="right">V.G.</td></tr>
<tr><td>★50</td><td>(paisa). 22.5 gr. Yrs. 22, 31</td><td align="right">4.00</td></tr>
</table>

Silver

<table>
<tr><td></td><td></td><td align="right">Fine</td></tr>
<tr><td>55</td><td>(rupee). Obv. mmk. upside down Nagari G (=Jodhpur ca. 1826-59). Yrs. 22-23</td><td align="right">10.00</td></tr>
<tr><td>56</td><td>(rupee). 1222. Nagore mint (on coin)</td><td align="right">20.00</td></tr>
</table>

Gold

<table>
<tr><td></td><td></td><td align="right">F-VF</td></tr>
<tr><td>59</td><td>(mohur). Like No. 55. (Jodhpur ca. 1826-59)</td><td align="right">150.00</td></tr>
</table>

VI. Takht Singh AD1843-73.

A. In names of Victoria and Takht Singh.

Silver

<table>
<tr><td></td><td></td><td align="right">Fine</td></tr>
<tr><td>63</td><td>(rupee). Mmks. jhar, rev. sword. Yrs. 22, 52. (Jodhpur 1858-59)</td><td align="right">5.00</td></tr>
<tr><td>63a</td><td>—. Rearranged legends. Yrs. 22, 52 (Jodhpur 1860-69)</td><td align="right">5.00</td></tr>
</table>

<table>
<tr><td>★63b</td><td>—. (ex 70) Sim., rev. with Nagari legend added. Yrs. 16, 22, 52 (Jodhpur 1859-69)</td><td align="right">5.00</td></tr>
<tr><td>67</td><td>(rupee). Sim. to No. 63. Rev. mmks. Katar, Nagari LA. Yr. 16 (Sujat)</td><td align="right">7.50</td></tr>
<tr><td>67a</td><td>—. Sim., rev. with Nagari legend added. Yr. 16 (Sujat 1869)</td><td align="right">7.50</td></tr>
</table>

INDIA

JODHPUR (Cont.)

Gold

F-VF

69 (mohur). Like No. 63.
Yr. 22 (Jodhpur 1858-59)..100.00

B. In names of "Queen of India" etc. (=Victoria) and Takht Singh.

All coins bear true mint names on rev.

Silver

Fine

*73 (rupee). Jodhpur mint.
Rev. mmks. jhar and sword.
Samvat 1926, 28......... 5.00

74 (rupee). *Sim. but Nagore mint.
Rev. mmk. sword only.*
Samvat 1926.............*15.00*

75 (rupee). Sim. but Pali mint.
Rev. mmks. as Jodhpur.
S. 1926/yr. 45............... 5.00

*76 (rupee). Sujat mint.
Rev. mmks. as Jodhpur.
S. 1926, 28............... 7.50

Gold

F-VF

77 (mohur). Like No. 73.
Jodhpur mint. S. 1926.....125.00

VII. Jaswant Singh AD1873-95.

A. In name of Queen Victoria only.

Copper

V.G.

*82 (paisa). 20-21 gr. S. 1941-47
and yrs. 61, 65............ 2.00

B. In names of Queen Victoria and Jaswant Singh.

Silver

Fine

87 (⅛ rupee). Like No. 90..... 3.50

Fine

88 (¼ rupee). Sim............ 3.50

89 (½ rupee). Sim. S. 1945.... 4.00

*90 (rupee). Mmks. jhar, rev.
sword. S. 1924, 34-50, AH1293,
yr. 22. Jodhpur........... 5.00

91 (rupee). Sim. Rev. mmks.
jhar and sword. S. 1930-44.
Pali..................... 5.00

92 (rupee). Sim. Rev. mmks.
as Jodhpur. S. 1929-38,
AH1291. Sujat............ 7.50

Gold

F-VF

95 (¼ mohur). Like No. 90.
AH1293. Jodhpur..........75.00

96 (½ mohur). Sim. 1293.....100.00

97 (mohur). Sim. AH1293,
S. 1943.................125.00

JUNAGADH (Junagarh)

State on Kathiawar peninsula in west India. Dynasty of Nawabs founded in 1735 by Sher Khan Babi, a soldier of fortune. All coins except No. 25 have AH and Samvat (S.) dates on rev.

Monetary System: See Kutch.

Bahadur Khan I
AH1226-56 (=AD1811-40)
Hamid Khan II
AH1256-68 (=AD1840-51)
Mahabat Khan II
AH1268-1300 (=AD1851-82)

Copper

V.G.

20 (dokdo). Sim. to No. 28.
AH1239-48/S. *1880*-89...... 4.00

Silver

Fine

25 (kori). Indian salutations
to Hindu gods both sides.
(AD1819). Withdrawn by
Muhammadan Nawab......Rare

27 (½ kori). Like No. 28. 2.3 gr.
AH1236-80/S. 1877-1920.... 3.00

*28 (kori). Md. Akbar II legends.
4.4 gr. AH1235-80/
S. 1875-1920............. 2.50

For similar coins in the name of Mahabat Khan II, see Yeoman, *Modern World Coins.*

KALAT (Qilat)

A state in Baluchistan.

Mehrab Khan
AD1816-39

Copper

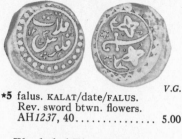

V.G.

*5 falus. KALAT/date/FALUS.
Rev. sword btwn. flowers.
AH*1237*, 40.............. 5.00

Khudadad Khan, 2nd Reign
AD1864-*93*

Copper

*10 falus. In the name of *Khudadad's grandfather* Mahmud
Khan. AH1290-95......... 2.50

KARAULI

State in Rajputana, N.W. India. The maharajas of Karauli first struck coins in the reign of Manak Pal.

Manak Pal AD1772-1804
Harbaksh Pal AD1804-38
Pratap Pal AD1838-48
Nar Singh Pal AD1848-53
Madan Pal AD1853-69

A. In names of Mughal Emperors.

Silver

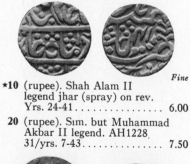

Fine

*10 (rupee). Shah Alam II
legend jhar (spray) on rev.
Yrs. 24-41............... 6.00

20 (rupee). Sim. but Muhammad
Akbar II legend. AH1228
31/yrs. 7-43............. 7.50

*40 (rupee). Sim. but Bahadur
Shah II legend. Yrs. 13, 15.. 7.50

INDIA

KARAULI (Cont.)

B. In name of Queen Victoria.

Copper
V.G.

45 (paisa). Like No. 50 but
no jhar on rev. AD1852
(error)/yr. 13............. 4.00

Silver
Fine

49 (½ rupee). Like No. 50
AD1852 (error)/yr. 13...... 9.00

*50 (rupee). AD1852 (error),
59/yrs. 7-14.............. 7.50

C. In name of Empress Victoria.
Arjun Pal AD1875-86

Copper
V.G.

54 (½ paisa). Like No. 65.
10 gr. 1886/yr. 11 of Arjun.. 3.00

55 (paisa). Sim. 18 gr.
1881-86/yrs. 10-11........ 3.00

Silver

Fine

*65 (rupee). Rev. Nagari A(rjun).
1884-86.................. 7.50

Bhanwar Pal AD1886-1927

Copper
V.G.

69 (½ paisa). Like No. 80.
9 gr. Yrs. 1-2............. 3.00

70 (paisa). Sim. 18 gr.
1886-93/yrs. 1-2.......... 3.00

Silver
Fine

78 (¼ rupee). Like No. 80.
1896.................... 7.50

79 (½ rupee). Sim. 1893...... 7.50

*80 (rupee). Rev. Nagari
BH(anwar). 1888-93........ 6.00

KASHMIR

State in extreme northern India. Part
of Afghanistan (q.v.) 1752-1819, under
Sikhs of Punjab 1819-46, locally ruled
by Dogra Rajas thereafter. Separate
coinages were struck for the districts
of Jammu and Ladakh.

There is great variety in the Kashmir
and Jammu coinage, notably in the
Sikh issues where types and legends
were not standardized. Most common
symbol is the large leaf also used on
Punjabi issues; others include star, flag,
sword, lotus and trident.

Mints: Generally coins must bear mint
names (in Persian) Khitta Kashmir or
Srinagar, or (in Gurmukhi) Kasamara.
Otherwise, see Punjab.

Dates are in Samvat Era (=AD +
57).

I. Under Sikhs of Punjab.

Ranjit Singh, in Kashmir
AD1819-39
Kurrun Singh AD1839-40
Sher Singh AD1840-43
Dulip Singh AD1843-46

Copper

V.G.

**10 (falus). Persian and/or
Gurmukhi legends, leaf or
other symbols. Many vars.
ND and Samvat 1877-
1901................ 2.00-4.00

Silver
Fine

40 (¼ rupee). Like No. 42..... 4.50

42 (rupee). Persian legends.
Samvat 1876-1903........ 6.00

45 (rupee). Gurmukhi legends.
Samvat 189x............. ——

II. Under Dogra Rajas.

Gulab Singh, Raja
of Jammu AD1839-56,
in all Kashmir AD1846-56
Ranbir Singh AD1857-85
Rertab Singh AD1885-1925

Copper

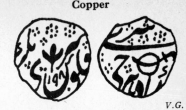

V.G.

*55 (falus). Generally like No. 10.
Many vars. Samvat 1906-08. 3.50

60 nim (=½) anna. Like No. 61.
S. 1920................. 3.00

61 yek (=1) anna. S. 1920..... 4.00

65 (⅓) falus. Like No. 66.
S. 1920-28.............. 1.50

66 falus. Date in cartouche.
S. 1920-31.............. 2.00

70 (¼ paisa). Generally like
No. 99. With initials JHS.
Samvat 1935-41.......... 2.00

71 (½ paisa). Sim. S. 1935-41.. 1.50

72 (paisa). Sim. S. 1936-38..... 2.50

Silver
Fine

79 (⅛ rupee). Like No. 82.
S. 1905................. 5.00

80 (¼ rupee). Sim. S. 1904.... 5.00

81 (½ rupee). Sim. S.1904.... 5.00

82 (rupee). Like No. 87 but w/out
JHS on obv. S. 1904-05...... 7.50

84 (⅛ rupee). Like No. 87.
S. 1925................. 7.50

85 (¼ rupee). Sim. S. 1922, 25.. 7.50

86 (½ rupee). Sim. S. 1914-29.. 7.50

*87 (ex 82) (rupee). Persian
legends. Obv. leaf, sword,
JHS. 10 gr. S. 1907-29....... 7.50

98 (½ rupee). Sim. but rev.
Takari legend. S. 1928-50... 6.00

99 (rupee). Sim. 7 gr.
S. 1926-51.............. 5.00

III. Coinage for Jammu.

District in southern Kashmir. Anonymous coinage under the Dogra Rajas.

Copper
V.G.

110 (falus). Persian legends,
leaf on obv. Vars.
Samvat 1894-98.......... 3.00

115 (paisa). Persian legend, leaf.
Rev. Gurmukhi legend,
sometimes sword. Vars.
7 gr. S. 1879-1927........ 2.00

118 *(paisa)*. Obv. sim. Rev.
Takari legend. 3 gr.
S. 1930-48.............. 2.00

INDIA

KASHMIR (Cont.)

IV. Coinage for Ladakh (=Botaan).

District in eastern Kashmir.

Monetary system: timasha (3 masha) =Tibet ½ sho=approx. ¼ rupee.

A. Under Afghans AD1776-1819.

Silver

Fine

125 (timasha). Degenerate
Persian legends. 2.5-2.7 gr.
ND, *AH1185* .... —

130 (timasha). In name of
Mahmud Shah Durrani.
Rev. like No. 125. 2.2-2.5 gr.
ND (ca. *1813-16*) *10.00*

135 (timasha). Obv. sim.
Rev. like No. 145.
ND (ca. *1816*-19) *10.00*

B. Under Dogra Rajas from AD1834.

Copper

V.G.

★**140** (paisa). Persian legend.
Rev. Nagari legend.
S. 1924-31 .... 4.50

Silver

Fine

★**145** (timasha). Nagari "Raja
Gulab Singh." Rev. Persian
"struck in Botaan," katar.
1.8-2.0 gr. ND (*1846*-57)... 7.50

150 (timasha). Persian legend.
Rev. Tibetan legend.
S. 1928 .... *Rare*

KISHANGARH

State in Rajputana, N.W. India.
Founded by Maharaja Kishan Singh,
a son of Udai Singh of Jodhpur. Earliest
coinage in the reign of Shah Alam II.

A. In name of Shah Alam II.

Copper

V.G.

4 (paisa). Sim. to No. 10
3.6 gr. AH119x/yr. 25 ...... 5.00

V.G.

5 (paisa). 17.5 gr. *Yr. 45* 2.00

Silver

Fine

8 (¼ rupee). Like No. 10.
1198/yr. 24 .... 10.00

★**10** (rupee). Shah Alam legend.
Rev. jhar. Vars. 1197-98/
yrs. 24-25 .... 10.00

Gold

F-VF

17 (mohur). Like No. 10.
(ca. *AD1800-38*) *150.00*

B. In name of Muhammad Akbar II.

Copper

V.G.

25 (paisa). 17.5 gr. ND 2.00

C. In names of Queen Victoria and Prithvi Singh, AD1857-79.

Silver

Fine

★**35** (rupee). Queen Victoria legend.
Rev. Prithvi legend, jhar.
AD1858-59/frozen yr. 24
of Shah Alam 8.50

KOLHAPUR

Maratha state in S.W. India between
Goa and Bombay. Independent 1731.
Ruled by rajas. Said to have struck
Satara type coppers. Mint closed ca.
1850.

Silver

Fine

15 (½ rupee). Like No. 16.
ND (1759 – ca. 1850) 4.00

★**16** (rupee). Shah Alam II legends.
ND (1759 – ca. 1850) 5.00

Fine

★**25** (rupee). Persian legends.
AD1821 .... 10.00

KOTAH

State in Rajputana, northwest India.
Ruled by branch of the Bundi family.

Mint marks: bent-stemmed flower
and *umbrella* (same as Bundi) plus 4
small triangles cruciform below flower.

A. Early 19th Century Gold.

F-VF

25 (½ mohur). *Persian Mughal
legends each side. (ca. 1800-
57)* 100.00

26 (mohur). *Sim. (ca. 1800-
57)* 150.00

B. In name of Shah Alam II, AD1759-1806.

Silver

Fine

★**28** (rupee). Yr. 45 .... 7.50

C. In name of Muhammad Akbar II, AD1806-37.

Silver

★**30** (rupee). Yrs. 12, 16 .... 7.50

D. In name of Bahadur Shah II, AD1837-57.

Silver

32 (rupee). 20-22mm. Yr. 18 ... 7.50

32a —. 26-29mm. For presentation.
Yrs. 16, 19 .... 35.00

INDIA

KOTAH (Cont.)

E. In name of Queen Victoria, AD1857-1901.

Copper

		V.G.
34	(½ paisa). Like No. 35. Yrs. 37, 39	2.50

| ★35 | (paisa). 18.2 gr. Yrs. 15-51 | 2.50 |

The copper coins are usually much dumpier than shown.

Silver

		Fine
39	(⅛ rupee). Like No. 42. Yrs. 27-37	2.50
40	(¼ rupee). Sim. 12mm. Yrs. 29-37	3.00
41	(½ rupee). Sim. 15mm. Yrs. 18-36	3.50
42	(rupee). Sim. 19-22mm. Yrs. 2-44	7.50

| ★42a | —. 26-29mm. For presentation. Yrs. 7-44 | 35.00 |

Gold

		F-VF
50	(mohur). Like No. 42. Yr. 15 (ca. AD1872)	150.00

KOTLA-MALER
(Maler-Kotla)

State in the Punjab founded by an Afghan in the 15th century. Coins are imitations of a rupee of Ahmad Shah Durrani, year 4, struck at the Sirhind mint, and except for the last ruler, contain the chief's initial on the reverse. The chiefs were called Ra'is until 1821, Nawabs thereafter.
For similar issues see Patiala.

Umar Khan AD1768-78

Silver

		Fine
5	(rupee). Sim. to No. 15. Initial 'ain on reverse	7.50

Asadullah Khan AD1778-82

Silver

		Fine
10	(rupee). Sim. Initial alif on reverse straight instead of curved	7.50

Amir Khan AD1821-45

Silver

15	(rupee)	5.00

Sube Khan (Mahbub Khan) AD1845-59

Silver

| ★20 | (rupee). Initial mim on reverse | 7.50 |

Sikandar Ali Khan AD1859-71

Silver

30	(rupee)	4.00

Ibrahim Ali Khan AD1871-1908

Silver

35	(¼ rupee). Like No. 40. 13mm	8.50
40	(rupee)	5.00

Ahmad Ali Khan AD1908-192x

Silver

50	(rupee). In the name of the Nawab	4.00

KUCHAWAN

Semi-independent state within Jodhpur. Rajputana, N.W. India. Ruler called Thakur.

Mughal Type Silver (AD1788-1857)

		Fine
15	(¼ rupee). Like No. 17. Fictitious AH1203, yr. 31 of Shah Alam II	7.50
16	(½ rupee). Sim	7.50

| ★17 | (rupee). Copy of Ajmir rupee of Shah Alam II. Fictitious AH1203. Yr. 31 | 10.00 |

Kesri Singh AD1857-

Silver

		Fine
28	(¼ rupee). Like No. 30. 1863	6.00
29	(½ rupee). Sim. 1863	6.00

| ★30 | (rupee). Queen Victoria legend. AD1863 | 9.00 |

KUNCH
Maratha Mint.

Silver

		Fine
★15	(rupee). Shah Alam II legend. Yrs. 28, 31 (=AD1785, 88)	6.00

KUTCH

State in N.W. India, founded in the 15th century, consisting of a peninsula north of the Gulf of Kutch. Its rulers, called Raos, were a branch of the Rajputs. First coinage 1617.

Monetary System:
48 trambiya = 24 dokda = 16 dhingla = 1 silver kori (=4.6 gr.).

There is no historical relation between the kori and the rupee.

Lakhpatji AD1752-62

Copper

		V.G.
8	(dhinglo). Sim. to No. 17. ND	—

Silver

		Fine
10	(½ kori). Like No. 11. AH1165	15.00

| ★11 | (kori). In name of Ahmad Shah Durrani. 1165 | 15.00 |
| 12 | (kori). Sim. to No. 22. ND | — |

Gohodaji II AD1761-78

Copper

		V.G.
15	(½ trambiyo). Like No. 22. 1.1 gr. ND	Rare
16	(trambiyo). Like No. 17. 4.5 gr. ND	3.00

INDIA

KUTCH (Cont.)

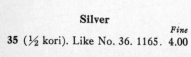

		V.G.
*17	(dokdo). 8.5 gr. ND	3.00
18	(dhinglo). Sim. 13 gr. ND	3.50

Silver

		Fine
20	(¼ kori). Like No. 22. 1.1 gr. ND	——
21	(½ kori). Sim. ND	12.50

*22 (kori). ND 12.50

Rayadhanji II AD1778-1814

Copper

		V.G.
25	(trambiyo). Like No. 26. 4 gr. ND	2.00
*26	(dokdo). 7.8 gr. ND	2.00
27	(dhinglo). Sim. 12.8 gr. ND	2.50

Silver

		Fine
28	(¼ kori). Like No. 30. ND	——
29	(½ kori). Sim. ND	7.50

*30 (kori). ND 7.50

Bharmalji II AD1814-19

Copper

		V.G.
*31	(trambiyo). 4 gr. ND	5.00
32	(dokdo). Sim. 8 gr. ND	——
33	(dhinglo). Sim. 12 gr. ND	——

Silver

		Fine
35	(½ kori). Like No. 36. 1165	4.00

---

*36 (kori). AH1165 (fictitious)... 4.00

Desalji II
AH1234-77/Samvat 1875-1916
(=AD1819-60)

A. First Issue.

Copper

		V.G.
38	(trambiyo). Like No. 40. 4.2 gr. ND	1.50
39	(dokdo). Sim. 8.7 gr. ND	2.00
40	(dhinglo). 12.9 gr. ND	2.50

B. In names of Muhammad Akbar II and Desalji.

Copper

41	(trambiyo). Like No. 43. 4 gr. AH1234/S. 1880	4.00
42	(dokdo). Sim. 8 gr. AH1234/S. 1880	4.00

*43	(dhinglo). Persian/Nagari legends. Rev. Persian legend. 12 gr. AH1234/S. 1880	4.50
45	(trambiyo). Like No. 47. 4 gr. AH1255-62	1.50
46	(dokdo). Sim. 8 gr. 1255-62	1.50

*47 (dhinglo). 12 gr. 1255-62 .... 2.00

Silver

		Fine
52	(½ kori). Like No. 53. AH1234/S. 1875-87	——

*53	(kori). AH1234 (frozen)/ S. 1875-87	3.50
55	(½ kori). Like No. 56. S. 1892	......
55a	—. Like No. 56a. AH1252/S. 1894	......

		Fine
*56	(ex 53a) (kori). AH1250-52/S. 1892-93	7.50

*56a —. AH1252/S. 1894 ...... 7.50

| 58 | (½ kori). Like No. 59. S. 1895-1902 | —— |
| 58a | —. Like No. 59a. AH1262-63/S. 1903-04 | —— |

*59 (kori). S. 1895-1902 .... 3.50

*59a —. AH1262-63/S. 1903-04 .. 5.00

C. In names of Bahadur Shah II and Desalji.

Copper

		V.G.
61	(trambiyo). Like No. 62. 4 gr. AH1263-66	5.00
61a	—. Like No. 63a. 1267-74	1.50

*62	(dokdo). 8 gr. 1263-66	5.00
62a	—. Like No. 63a. 1267-74	1.50
63	(dhinglo). Like No. 62. 12 gr. 1263-66	5.00

*63a —. 1267-74 .... 2.00

Silver

		Fin
65	(½ kori). Like No. 66. S. 1909-14	3.50

INDIA

KUTCH (Cont.)

		Fine
*66	(kori). S. 1909-16........	3.00

Gold

		E.F.
67	(25 kori). Like No. 66. S. 1912-15...............	70.00

MALABAR COAST

West coast at southern tip of India. Generally corresponds with Cochin (q.v.).

Silver

		Fine
10	(fanam). Degenerate figure of Kali. Rev. Lazy J, dots. .39 gr. (18th-19th centuries).	3.50

Base Gold

		F-VF
20	(fanam). Sim. .38 gr. (18th-19th centuries).......	10.00

MALDIVE ISLANDS

Coral atolls southwest of India, with capital and mint at Malé (Mahlé).
Monetary System: 120 lari = 1 rupee. Recent study by Panish indicates that only the ½ larin and 2 lari were struck after billon was replaced by copper ca. AH1184 (=1770). Coin weights became very irregular at that time, leading to postulation of other denominations by earlier writers.

Muhammad Imad al-Din III
AH1163-68 (=AD1750-55)

Billon

		VG-F
4	(larin). Like No. 7. 4.8 gr. AH1163-66...............	8.00

*7	(2 lari). Sultan's name. Rev. his titles/date/mint. 9.6 gr. 1163-68...........	6.00

Hasan Izz al-Din
AH1173-80 (=AD1759-67)

Billon

| 12 | (larin). Like No. 14. 4.8 gr. 1173............... | 8.00 |

		VG-F
*14	(2 lari). Sultan's name. Rev. his titles, date. 9.6 gr. 1173, 77.................	8.00

Muhammad Ghiyas al-Din
AH1180-87 (=AD1767-73)

Copper

		V.G.
*16	(½ larin). Sultan's name. Rev. his titles, date. 2.3-2.5 gr. 1184, 86.........	4.00

Billon

		VG-F
17	(larin). Sim. 4.8 gr. 1180....	7.50
18	(2 lari). Sim. 9.6 gr. 1182....	7.50

Muhammad Muiz al-Din
AH1188-92 (=AD1774-78)

Copper

		V.G.
21	(½ larin). Like No. 16 but Md. Muiz. 2.4 gr. ND, 1188.................	5.00
24	(2 lari). Sim. (vars.). 9.6 gr. 1189.................	6.00

Hasan Nur al-Din I
AH1192-1213 (=AD1778-98)

Copper

*26	(½ larin). Like No. 16 but Hasan. 1.5-2.3 gr. 1194-1202.................	3.50
28	(2 lari). Sim. 9.6 gr. 1197-1207.................	5.00

Gold

35	(mohur). Sim. 12.4 gr. 1207.....................	RRR

Muhammad Muin al-Din
AH1213-50 (=AD1798-1834)

Copper

41	(½ larin). Like No. 16 but Md. Muin. 1.4-2.3 gr. 1216-48.................	3.50

		V.G.
*43	(2 lari). 9.6 gr. 1214......	6.00

Muhammad Imad al-Din IV
AH1250-1300 (=AD1834-82)

Copper

46	(½ larin). Like No. 16 but Md. Imad. 1.1-3.5 gr. 1257-98..................	3.50
48	(2 lari). Sim. 8.2-9.0 gr. 1294, 98.................	5.00

MANDLA

District in east-central India. Conquered by the Marathas, who deposed Mandla's Gond-Rajput king in 1781. Site of Maratha Mint. Ceded to British Company by the Peshwa in 1818.

Silver

		Fine
*10	(Balashahi rupee). Shah Alam legend. Yrs. 28-36....	6.00

MANIPUR

State of the Burmese frontier in northeast India. Deprived of its independence in 1891 following the massacre of certain British subjects. Its rulers were Rajas.

Monetary System:
880 to 960 sel = 1 rupee to AD1838;
420 to 480 sel = 1 rupee after AD1838.

A. Anonymous issues.
Recent study by Pridmore and Rhodes indicates that the sels bearing Nagari letters cannot yet be attributed safely to specific reigns. Therefore the arrangement in the first two editions of this book has been abandoned.

Bell Metal

		V.G.
1	(sel). Like No. 2 but SRI....	3.00

*2	(ex 30, 50) (sel). Nagari. MA. Rev. blank............	3.00
4	(sel). Sim. but KA..........	4.00
6	(sel). Sim. but RA..........	4.00
8	(sel). Sim. but LA..........	4.00
9	(sel). Sim. but KU..........	4.00

INDIA

MANIPUR (Cont.)

Gaura Singh
Saka 1678-86 (=**AD1756-64**)

Silver

Fine

23 (rupee). Saka 1678 .... ——

Gold

26 (mohur). Sim. 12.8 gr. Saka 1678 .... ——

27 (¼ mohur). Like No. 29. 2.9 gr. ND .... ——

28 (½ mohur). Sim. 5.8 gr. Saka 1684 .... ——

29 (mohur). 11.6 gr. Saka 1684. ——

Jai Singh
Saka 1686-1720 (=**AD1764-98**)

Silver

32 (½ rupee). ND .... ——

Gold

36 (mohur). Saka 1694 .... ——

Chaurajit Singh
Saka 1725-34 (=**AD1803-12**)

Silver

55 (¼ rupee). Like No. 56. Saka 1726, 29 .... ——

56 (½ rupee). Saka 1726 ...... ——

57 (rupee). Sim. Saka 1728-34.. ——

Marjit Singh
Saka 1734-41 (=**AD1812-19**)

Gold

76 (mohur). Saka 1741 .... ——

Gambhir Singh

Gold

86 (mohur) .... ——

MARATHA (Mahratta) CONFEDERATION

The Marathas are a Hindu people resident in central India, linked chiefly by language (Mahratti). A Maratha leader, Sivaji, rebelled against the Mughals in 1657 and by 1750 his successors had created a loose empire (confederation) covering much of north-central India. Its king, a descendant of Sivaji, resided at Satara in the West, but had little power. Most authority was in the hands of his chief minister, the Peshwa, who resided at Poona, also in the West. Subservient to the Peshwa as head of the Maratha race, but independent in much else, were a host of militant great nobles including the rulers of Baroda, Dewas, Gwalior and Indore and the Bhonsla rajas.

The Maratha power was destroyed in three wars with the British Company, 1775, 1803 and 1818, after each of which certain districts were ceded.

Mints:
Maratha coinage was struck at a considerable number of mints. The Peshwa coined at Poona. The Bhonsla rajas coined at Katak in Orissa and at Nagpur (coins say Surat). Other Maratha mints include Ahmadabad, Ajmir, Jalaun, Jhansi, Kolhapur, Kunch, Mandla, Nasik, Nipani, Satara, Saugor (Sagar) and Tanjore. See also Baroda, Dewas, Gwalior and Indore.

Matak. See Assam.

MEWAR (=Udaipur)

State in Rajputana, N.W. India. Capital: Udaipur.

Mints:
Bhilwara, Chitor, Jawad, Udaipur.

Pratap Singh II AD1752-54
Raj Singh II AD1754-61
Ari Singh II AD1761-73
Hammir Singh II AD1773-78
Bhim Singh II AD1778-1828
Jawan Singh AD1828-38
Sirdar Singh AD1838-42

Semi-Official Copper
(AD1760-1910)

V.G.

0.5 (½ *paisa*). Like No. 1. 1.5 gr. ND 1.50

1 (Dhingla paisa). Brief Persian legend. Rev. trident. 3 gr. ND 1.25

2 (Trisulia paisa). Trident. Rev. double trident. 5.3 gr. ND... 1.25

★3 (Bhilwara paisa). Rude Shah Alam legends. 14.3-17.3 gr. ND 1.50

★4 (paisa). Jawad mint. Vars. ND (early 18th century).... 3.00

Silver

Fine

22 (1/16 rupee). Like No. 26. ND 2.50

23 (⅛ rupee). Sim. ND 2.50

24 (¼ rupee). Sim. ND 2.50

25 (½ rupee). Sim. ND 3.00

★26 (Chitori rupee). Shah Alam II legend. ND 4.50

32 (Udaipuri rupee). Like No. 26 but Jhar (spray) and star added to obv. ND 5.00

38 (Bhilwari rupee). Copy of Shah Alam II Shahjahanabad rupee. ND 6.00

44 (Chandori rupee) *10.00*

Swarup Singh AD1842-61

Silver

85 (1/16 New Chandori rupee). Like No. 89. ND 1.50

86 (⅛ N.C. rupee). Sim. ND... 1.75

87 (¼ N.C. rupee). Sim. ND... 2.00

88 (½ N.C. rupee). Sim. ND... 2.50

★89 (N.C. rupee). ND 4.00

Gold

F-VF

101 (mohur). Sim. ND 100.00

MYSORE

Large state in S. India. Governed until 1761 by various Hindu dynasties. A Muhammadan interlude ensued 1761-99 under the adventurer Haidar Ali and his son, Tipu Sultan. Hindu rule was restored 1799-1868.

(a) Hindu Rulers Prior to AD1761.
Issued coins 17th century through 1761.

Copper

INDIA

MYSORE (Cont.)

Types: Obv. elephant, lion, tiger or Kanarese numerals of value. Rev. lattice work or legend.

Gold

Fanams 0.324 gr. Vishnu standing. Rev. legend.

(b) Muhammadan Rulers.

Haidar Ali
AH1174-97 (=AD1761-82)

Copper

		V.G.
*50	(paisa). 12.2 gr. AH1195-96. ND	3.00

Gold

		F-VF
60	(fanam). Like No. 68. .37 gr. ND	20.00
63	(½ pagoda). Like No. 68. 1.7 gr. ND	60.00

| *65 | (½ pagoda). Vishnu std. Rev. Persian н(aidar) on grains. ND | 60.00 |

| *68 | (pagoda). Siva and Parvati. Rev. н(aidar) on grains. ND | 35.00 |

| *70 | (pagoda). Muhammad Shah legend. 2.7 gr. AH1194 | 60.00 |

Tipu (Tipoo) Sultan
AH1197-1214 (=AD1782-99)

Dates from AD1787 onward are Mauludi (solar years from Muhammad's birth=AM) years 1215-27, and are written right to left.

Copper

Tipu coined at several mints and there exist many varieties of his copper, elephants right or left, tails up, tails down, on plain field or with rosettes, etc.

		V.G.
*100	(⅛ paisa). 1.2 gr. AM1218-26. ND	5.00

| *105 | (¼ paisa). 2.7-3.2 gr. AH1198-1201, AM1215-26 | 2.50 |

| *110 | (½ paisa). 5.5-5.7 gr. AH1200-01, AM1215-26 | 2.50 |

| *115 | (paisa). 10.8-11.5 gr. AH1197-1200, AM1215-27 | 3.00 |

| *120 | (2 paisa). 21-23 gr. AM1218-26 | 10.00 |

Silver

		Fine
130	(½₂ rupee). *Like No. 133*	10.00
131	(1/16 rupee). Sim. AM1221-25	7.50
132	(⅛ rupee). Sim.	7.50

| *133 | (¼ rupee). AM1217-22 | 6.00 |
| 134 | (½ rupee). Like No. 135. AM1216-19 | 5.00 |

		Fine
*135	(rupee). AH1200, AM1216-23	5.00
136	(2 rupees). Sim. AH1200, AM1216	30.00

Gold

Monetary System:
40 fanams =4 pagodas =1 mohur.

		F-VF
*150	(fanam). н(aidar's Persian initial). Rev. legend. .35 gr. AH1198-1200, AM1215-22	12.50
151	(pagoda sultani). 3.4 gr. Sim. 1198	40.00

| *151a | —. AH1200, AM1216 | 40.00 |

| *155 | (pagoda Farouki). AM1216-21 | 35.00 |
| 156 | (½ mohur). Like No. 157. AM1217-19 | 95.00 |

| *157 | (mohur). AM1217-18 | 140.00 |

(c) Hindu Dynasty Restored.

Monetary System:
20 cash =1 paisa.

Krishna Raja Wodeyar
(b 1793) AD1799-1868

Copper

		V.G.
*170	(5 cash). Rev. Nagari legend. 2.7 gr. ND	10.00

INDIA

MYSORE (Cont.)

		V.G.
171	V CASH. Like No. 177. ND	3.00
171a	—. Like No. 177a. ND	3.00
171b	—. Like No. 177b. ND	2.50
174	X CASH. Like No. 177. 4.5 gr. ND	7.50
174a	—. Like No. 177a. ND	5.00
174b	—. Like No. 177b. ND	5.00
177	(ex 177b) XX CASH. Like No. 177a but rev. only 2 lines of Kanarese. ND	2.50

★177a	(ex 177) —. Elephant, Kanarese SRI above. Rev. 3-line Kanarese legend, English value. ND	2.00
177b	—. Sim. but Kanarese CHAMUNDI added above elephant. ND	2.50
180	XL CASH. Like No. 177. ND	10.00

★185	(6¼ cash). ND	2.50
186	(12½ cash). ND	5.00

★187	XXV CASH. ND	4.00
190	211 (=2½ cash). Like No. 193. 1 gr. 1839-43	3.00
191	5 (cash). Sim. 2 gr. 1833-43	2.50
192	10 (cash). Sim. 4.4 gr. 1833-43	2.25

		Fine
★193	XX CASH. 1833-43	2.50

Note: The English legends on Nos. 171-193 are often blundered. Such errors command little or no premium.

Silver

		Fine
199	(1/32 rupee). Like No. 201. 6mm. AH1215	6.00
200	(1/16 rupee). Sim. 9mm. ND	3.50

★201	(⅛ rupee). Chamundi dancing. Rev. Kanarese script	3.00

★202	(¼ rupee). Sim. but rev. Persian. AH1214-48	4.00
205	(¼ rupee). Like No. 207. Partial AH dates	3.00
206	(½ rupee). Sim	4.00

★207	(rupee). *Arcot type* Shah Alam II legends. MM crescent (Mysore). AH1214-48	6.00

Gold

		F-VF
208	(fanam). Like No. 210. ND	7.50
209	(½ pagoda). Sim. ND	20.00

★210	(pagoda). Siva and Parvati. ND	35.00

NABHA

State in the Punjab founded in the 18th century. The distinctive Raja's symbol is on the left of the reverse.

Jaswant Singh AD1783-1840

Silver

		Fine
★20	(rupee). In name of Ahmad Shah Durrani. Rev. egret plume symbol. Samvat 1877, 83, 93	10.00

Bharpur Singh AD1846-63

Silver

		Fine
40	(rupee). In name of Govind Singh. Rev. leaf symbol. Samvat 1907, 17, 20	10.00

Hira Singh AD1871-

Silver

★50	(rupee). Obv. sim. Rev. katar symbol. Samvat 1928-29	10.00

NAGPUR

District and city in central India subject to Maratha Bhonsla rajas. (See also Orissa.) Acquired by the British Company in 1853.

Silver

		Fine
★16	(rupee). In name of Ahmad Shah Bahadur. Crude copy of Mughal issue with Surat mint name	7.50

NARWAR

State in Gwalior. To Sindhias of Gwalior in 1805.

Kachwaha Dynasty (Before Maratha Conquest)

Copper

		V.G.
★10	(paisa). Shah Alam II legend. AH1215	2.50

Silver

		Fine
23	(¼ rupee). Like No. 25. AH1207/yr. 3x	5.00

★25	(rupee). Shah Alam II legend. 1106 (sic)/yrs. 9-47, 1201-08/yrs. 29-35	7.50

INDIA

NASIK

Town in west India. A Maratha mint.

Silver

Fine

★20 (rupee). Shah Alam II legends.
AH1229-30............... 10.00

NAWANAGAR (Navanagar)

State on the Kathiawar peninsula, west-central India. Founded 1540 by Jam Raval. Its rulers, called Jams, were Rajputs. Coins are degenerate copies of a 16th century Gujerati issue, with frozen date AH978 (=1570). For similar issues see Kutch and Porbandar.

Monetary System: See Kutch.

Anonymous Copper

V.G.

15 (dokdo). Like No. 21. AH978.
(late 16th-mid 19th cent.)... 1.50

Anonymous Silver

Fine

20 (½ kori). Like No. 21.
2.3 gr. AH978............ 2.50

★21 (kori). Debased Persian legends plus rev. Nagari SRI JAM (compare Porbandar No. 38). 4.6 gr. AH978 (late 16th-mid 19th cent.)................. 3.00

Note: For similar machine-struck issues see Yeoman, *Modern World Coins*.

Nepal. See NEPAL.

NIPANI

Maratha Confederation mint in S.W. India.

Silver

Fine

★10 (rupee). Crude Shah Alam II legend, 4 and 5 ptd. stars on rev. ND. (AD*1759*-1818) ... 7.00

ORCHHA

State in north-central India founded by Rudra Pratap. His successors were maharajas.

The Orchha coinage was called "Gaja Shahi" because of the "gaja" or mace which was its symbol.

See Datia for copies of the Orchha issues.

**Vikramajit Mahendra AD1796-1817
Dharam Pal AD1817-34
Tej Singh AD1834-42
Hamir Singh AD1848-74
Pratip Singh AD1874-1930**

A. In name of Shah Alam II.

Copper

V.G.

24 (½ paisa). Like No. 32..... 3.00

25 (paisa). Sim. 16.6 gr.
AH1155-1286............. 2.50

Silver

Fine

29 (⅛ rupee). Like No. 32.
Yr. 4x................... 2.50

30 (¼ rupee). Sim. 1211-51.... 3.00

31 (½ rupee). Sim. 1211-15.... 4.00

★32 (rupee). Mmks: obv. ankus, rev. mace. AH1211-*45,57* ... 6.00

B. In name of Muhammad Akbar II.

Copper

V.G.

38 (paisa). Like No. 42.
yr. 3x................... 3.50

Silver

Fine

42 (rupee). *Like No. 32* but Md. Akbar legend.
AH1232-1321............. 6.00

ORISSA

District in east India on the Bay of Bengal. The Bhonsla rajas of the Maratha confederation operated a mint at Katak in Orissa, coining posthumous rupees of Mughal Emperor Ahmad Shah Bahadur (AH1161-67).

Copper

V.G.

5 (paisa). Maratha legends, trisula. 9.2 gr. ND........ 2.00

Silver

Fine

★16 (rupee). Ahmed Shah legends. Fictitious years 8-88....... 6.00

PANNA

State in central India. Chiefs were Rajas. Mint mark: running Hanuman (monkey god). Mint: Kukureti.

Copper

V.G.

★10 (paisa). Shah Alam II legends. ND............. 5.00

PARTABGARH (Pratapgarh)

State in Rajputana, N.W. India, governed by a maharawa. Mint opened 1784.

Salim Singh AD1784-

Silver

Fine

15 (½ old Salim Shahi rupee). Like No. 16. Yrs. 26, 29 (of Shah Alam II = AD1784, 87)............. 3.50

★16 (O.S.S. rupee). Shah Alam II legends. Frozen AH1199/ yrs. 26, 29 of S.A. 6.00

Sawant Singh, Circa AD1820

Silver

26 (⅛ O.S.S. rupee). Like No. 29. 1236/yr. 45.............. 3.50

27 (¼ O.S.S. rupee). Sim. 1236/yr. 45.............. 3.00

28 (½ O.S.S. rupee). Sim. 1236/yr. 45.............. 3.50

INDIA

PARTABGARH (Cont.)

★29 (O.S.S. rupee). Shah Alam II
legends. Frozen dates 1236/
yr. 45 . . . . *Fine* 6.00

★29a—. Square. 1236/yr. 45 . . . . . 25.00

Udaya Singh AD1864-90

Copper

★35 (paisa). Sunface with hands.
Rev. Nagari legend. 7.4-7.7 gr.
Samvat 1935 (=AD1878) . . . *V.G.* 2.00

37 (paisa). Sunface/2 swords.
Rev. Samvat 1943 (=AD1886)
and legend in oval 2.00

Silver

41 (⅛ new Salim Shahi rupee).
Like No. 44. (1870) . . . . *Fine* 2.00

42 (¼ N.S.S. rupee). Sim.
(1870) 2.75

43 (½ N.S.S. rupee). Sim.
(1870) 3.50

★44 (N.S.S. rupee). Queen Victoria
legend. Fictitious date 1236/
yr. 45 (struck 1870) 6.00

44a —. Square. 1236/yr. 45 . . . . . 30.00

Rasanath Singh AD1890-1929

Copper

50 (paisa). Samvat 1953
(=1896) 4.00

PATIALA

State in the Punjab. In the mid-18th
century the Raja was given his title
and mint right by Ahmad Shah Durrani of Afghanistan, whose coin he

---

copied. The rulers became maharajas in
1810.

Mint mark: stylized Persian yr. 4,
with Raja's personal symbol to its left.

Amar Singh AD1765-81

Silver

10 (rupee). Sim. to No. 30.
Rev. yr. 4 and flower
symbol . . . . *Fine* 10.00

Sahib Singh AD1781-1813

Silver

20 (rupee). Sim. Rev. yr. 4
and *flower* 10.00

Karm Singh AD1813-45

Silver

30 (rupee). In name of Ahmad
Shah Durrani. Rev. yr. 4
and sword 7.50

Narindar Singh AD1845-62

Silver

40 (rupee). Sim. Rev. yr. 4
and spear head 10.00

POONA

City in southwest India, seat and chief
mint of the Peshwa, leader of the Maratha Confederation. To British in 1818;
mint closed ca. 1834-35.

Coin dates are in one of two eras:
AH (in Arabic numerals) or Fasli (in
Nagari numerals). Fasli date + 590 =
AD date.

Mint marks: battle axe, Nagari SRI,
ankus (elephant goad), *scissors or spec-
tacles.*

Copper

10 (paisa). *Like No. 25.*
ND *(1774-1818)* . . . . *V.G.* 2.00

Silver

16 (rupee). Like No. 22.
Rev. mmk. battle axe.
ND (AD1787) . . . . *Fine* 12.50

19 (rupee). Sim. Rev. mmk.
Nagari SRI. AH1206, 11 . . . . 12.50

★22 (rupee). In name of Ali
Gauhar (pre-accession name of
Shah Alam II). Rev. mmk.
ankus. AH1225, 29 and
yrs. 11-15 . . . . 10.00

No. 22 was also struck at Alibagh, Wad-
goan and Wai.

22a —. Sim. Fasli 1232-44
(=AD1822-34). Struck by
British . . . . *Fine* 10.00

★25 (rupee). Sim. Rev. mmk.
scissors. Fasli 1230-44
(=AD1820-34). Struck by
British 10.00

See Ahmadabad No. 36 for coin with
similar mmk.

PORBANDAR

State on Kathiawar peninsula, W. India. Its rulers, called Ranas, established
themselves about the 10th century.
Coins are degenerate copies of a 16th
century Gujerati issue, with frozen date
AH978 (=1570). For similar issues see
Kutch and Nawanagar.

Monetary System: See Kutch.

Copper

30 (½ trambiyo). Like No. 38.
1.9 gr. AH978 . . . . *V.G.* 5.00

31 (trambiyo). Sim. 3.9 gr.
AH978 . . . . 3.00

32 (dokdo). Sim. 7.6 gr.
AH978 . . . . 3.00

Silver

36 (¼ kori). Like No. 38.
1.2 gr. AH978 . . . . *Fine* 6.50

37 (½ kori). Sim. 2.3 gr.
AH978 . . . . 4.50

★38 (kori). Debased Persian legends
plus rev. Nagari SRI RANA
(compare Navanagar No. 21).
4.6 gr. AH978 (late 16th-
late 19th cent.) 3.50

PUNJAB, Sikhs of

State N.W. India. Capital: Lahore.
Conquered and annexed Kashmir (q.v.)
1819. After a period of anarchy 1839-
46, Punjab was itself annexed by the
British 1849.

Mints: Amritsar, Anandgarh, Derajat
(from ca. 1819), Lahore, Multan (ca.
1777 and 1818 on), Peshawar (from
1834).

Ranjit Singh AD1799-1839
Kurrun Singh AD1839-40
Sher Singh AD1840-43
Dulip Singh AD1843-49

INDIA

PUNJAB (Cont.)

A. Amritsar mint.

Silver

                           Fine

19 (½ rupee). Like No. 20.
S. 1880.................. 8.00

19a —. Like No. 20a. S. 1884
(frozen) with 1886, 92...... 8.00

20 (rupee). S. 1856-85........10.00

*20a —. Obv. true dates S. 1886-
1904. Frozen date S. 1884
or 1885 on rev...........10.00

Gold

                           F-VF

24 (mohur). Like No. 20.
S. 1861.................150.00

B. Lahore mint.

Silver

*63 (rupee). S. 1822-34........ —

*66 (rupee). S. 1857-64........ —

C. Multan mint.

Silver

85 (rupee). S. 1875-99........ —

D. Peshawar mint.

Silver

*98 (rupee). S. 1894.......... —

RADHANPUR

State on Kathiawar peninsula. Its rulers, members of the Babi family, received Radhanpur from the emperor in 1723. They were raised to the rank of Nawab under Muhammad Shah.

Anonymous Copper

                         V.G.

30 (paisa). Crude, thick, uniface.
ND.....................1.50

Zorawar Khan AD1825-74

Copper

34 (¼ anna). AH1285........ 2.50

Silver

                         Fine

37 do (=2) anna. Like No. 40.
1.4 gr. AD1871/AH1288....10.00

38 chahar (=4) anna. Sim.
2.9 gr. 1871/1288.........15.00

39 hasht (=8) anna. Sim.
5.8 gr. 1871/1288.........20.00

*40 yek (=1) rupee. Queen Victoria legend. Rev. Zorawar
legend. 1871/1288..........17.50

Gold

                         F-VF

48 (mohur). Head of Queen
Victoria. Rev. Persian legend.
AH1277.................275.00

Rangpur. See Assam.

REWAH

State in eastern north-central India. Governed by a maharaja.

Jai Singh Deo AD1809-35

Copper

                         V.G.

*20 (paisa). 6.8 gr. Samvat 1890. 2.00

*21 (paisa). 8.8-12.6 gr. ND.... 1.75

22 (2 paisa). Sim. ND........ 3.00

Vishvanath Singh AD1835-43

Copper

                         V.G.

31 (paisa). Like No. 20. 7.8 gr.
ND.....................2.00

*34 (2 paisa). Nagari legend.
Rev. Sree/rama/dheka/ree.
16.8 gr. ND.............. 3.00

Raghuraj Singh AD1843-80

Copper

*45 (paisa). Lion. Rev. Agent/
Bushby/Sahep. Samvat
1906...................7.50

46 (2 paisa). Sim.
Samvat 1906............. 7.50

SAILANA

State in west central India. Governed by rajas, cadets of the House of Ratlam from which Sailana branched in 1709.

A. Anonymous Issue.

Copper

                         V.G.

5 (paisa). Persian legend.
Rev. flag (tip points up or
down). 5.8 gr. ND........ 1.50

II. Dule Singh AD1850-95.

Copper

*41 (paisa). Samvat 1937/sword.
Rev. Trident............. 2.50

III. Coinage for Barmawal.

Feudatory state of Sailana. Mint closed 1881.

Copper

61 (paisa). ND.............. 5.00

INDIA

SALUMBA

State in Rajputana, N.W. India. Feudatory to Mewar.
Struck copper coins.

SATARA

Seat of the "King" of the Maratha Confederation. In west India, south of Poona.

Copper

		V.G.
18	(½ paisa). Like No. 20. 5.7 gr. ND	3.00

*20	(paisa). Nagari legends. Obv. has single horizontal line. 8.8-12.8 gr. ND (late 18th cent.)	2.50
20a	—. Obv. has double horizontal line. (late 18th-early 19th cent	2.00

SAUGOR (Sagar)

Chief town in the Maratha District of Saugor, north-central India. Conquered by the Peshwa 1735. Mint operated 1779-1832. Ceded to British Company 1818.

Copper

		V.G.
10	(paisa). Like No. 20. 16.5 gr. Yr. 37	1.50

*12	(paisa). ND	1.50

Silver

		Fine
*20	(rupee). Shah Alam II legends. Yrs. 25-55	4.00

SEONDHA

Town in Datia State, north-central India. Symbol: cannon.

Copper

		V.G.
*10	(paisa). Persian legends, cannon on obv. 10.6-13.7 gr. ND, yrs. 2-15 (early 19th cent.)	3.00

SHAHPUR (Shapura)

State in Rajputana, N.W. India, feudatory to Mewar.

Copper

		V.G.
10	(paisa). Shah Alam II legends in bungled Persian. ND. (1759-1857)	1.50

Silver

		Fine
20	(¼ rupee). Like No. 22. ND. (1754-1857)	3.00
21	(½ rupee). Sim. ND. (1754-1857)	4.00

*22	(rupee). Shah Alamgir II legends copied from his Shahjahanabad coinage, Trisul MM. ND. (1754-1857)	6.00

Gold

		F-VF
29	(mohur). Like No. 22. ND. (1754-1857)	75.00

SIND

Area west of Rajputana, much of which came under the rule of the Talpur Amirs. Originally fiefs of the Afghan Durranis, the Amirs assumed independence ca. 1783 and came under British protection in 1839.

Mints: Bhakkar, Hyderabad Sind, Shikarpur (after 1824).

A. Bhakkar mint.

Silver

		Fine
10	(rupee). In name of Mahmud Shah Durrani. Sometimes with bird, hare or lion. Many vars. AH1241-65	10.00

B. Hyderabad Sind mint.

Silver

25	(rupee). In name of Timur Shah Durrani. 1198-1257	10.00

C. Shikapur mint.

Copper

		V.G.
35	(falus). AH1250-58	3.50

SIRMUR

State in north India. Ruled by a family of Rajas descended from the Rajputs of Jaisalmir. Lost their state to Ghurkas 1803, restored 1815. Capital and mint: Nahan.

Girvan Yuddha of Nepal AD1799-1816

Copper

20	(½ paisa). Like No. 21. 20mm. AH1227	

*21	(paisa). 1227	

Fath Prakash AD1815-

Copper

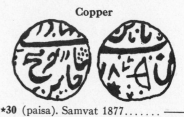

*30	(paisa). Samvat 1877	—

SITAMAU

State in west-central India founded 1660 as an offshoot of Ratlam.

Raj Singh AD1820-

Copper

		V.G.
*40	(paisa). Legend. Rev. Trisul. 9.8 gr. ND	2.00

SRINAGAR
in Bundelkhand

Town in east-central India founded in the early 18th century by Mohan Singh. The Srinagar coinage was very popular and was used extensively in neighboring states.

INDIA

SRINAGAR (Cont.)

Copper

*10 (Balashahi paisa). Persian legends, trident on obv., dagger on rev. 13.9-15.6 gr. Yr. 5... .75

10a —. Square............... 2.50

Silver

*25 (Srinagri rupee). Like No. 10 but snowflake instead of dagger. AH1212/yrs. 38-39........ 2.00

SURAT

Town on Gulf of Cambay on west coast of India. Maratha Mint until 1818. (See also Surat coins of the British and French Companies).

Silver

25 (rupee). Yr. 2............ 4.50

TANJORE

A Maratha state in south India, established ca. 1764. Became a British protected state in 1776; passed to the East India Company in 1855.

Gold

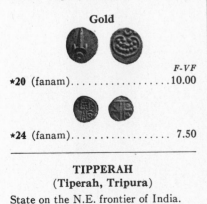

*20 (fanam)................10.00

*24 (fanam)................ 7.50

TIPPERAH
(Tiperah, Tripura)

State on the N.E. frontier of India.

Krishna Manikya Deva and
Dschanavi Maha Devi

Silver

10 (rupee). Saka 1682
(=AD1760)............... 9.00

Gold

20 (mohur). Legends each side.
(AD1700-1800)............ ——

King Rama Simha Manikya
AD1806

Silver

*30 (rupee). 5 line legend in square. Rev. Lion with trident. Saka 1728............... ——

Note: Chota (Chhota) Udaipur was independent of Tipperah, and has therefore been listed separately.

TONK

State partly in Rajputana and partly in central India. Founded by a Pathan, Amir Khan, who received Sironj (1798) and Tonk (1806) for his services to Jaswant Rao Holkar and took the title of Nawab. Tonk was later augmented by gifts from the British. Capital moved from Sironj to Tonk city in 1873.

Mints: Sironj (to ca. 1896), Tonk (ca. 1873-1934).

Amir Khan
AH1212-50 (=AD1798-1834)
Wazir Muhammad Khan
AH1250-81 (=AD1834-64)

A. In name of Muhammad
Akbar II.

Copper

*45 (paisa). Md. Akbar legend. Rev. horse/Sironj. AH1225-26...................... 2.50

*50 (paisa). Obv. sim. Rev. mint legend, rosettes and pearl necklace. 16 gr. 1253....... 2.00

*60 (rupee). Like No. 50 but w/out pearl loop. 1235-69... 5.00

B. In names of Empress Victoria and Wazir Muhammad Khan.

Silver

*75 (rupee). 1276-80.......... 5.00

TRAVANCORE

State in extreme southwest India. Mint established in ME965 (=1789-90).

Monetary System:

16 cash (kasu) =1 chakram (chuckram) =0.32-0.39 gr. silver;
8 chakram =2 fanam =1 anantaraya =0.32 gr. gold;
52½ fanam =1 pagoda (hun, varaha).

Dates:

Malabar era (ME)+824-25 =AD date.

Bala Rama Varma I
ME973-86 (=AD1798-1810)

Silver

*10 (½ chakram). Sankha (conch shell). Rev. hexagram. ND. (1809-10)................ 4.00

*11 (chakram). ND (ca. 1600-1860)............ 1.00

*12 (2 chakram). Like No. 10 but rev. with legend around hexagram. ND (1809-10)...... 6.00

Gold

19 (½ anantaraya). Like No. 22. ND (1790-1830)..........12.50

....

TRAVANCORE (Cont.)

22 (anantaraya). Generally like No. 11. ND (1790-1860).... **F-VF** 8.00

Note: Coins like Nos. 11 and 22 with leaf sprays on obv. are later issues. See Yeoman, *Modern World Coins.*

Rani Parvathi Bai, Regent
ME990-1004 (=AD1815-29)

Copper

V.G.

25 (cash). Like No. 27. 10mm. ME991-97................ 1.50

26 (2 cash). Sim. 12mm. ME999-97................ 2.50

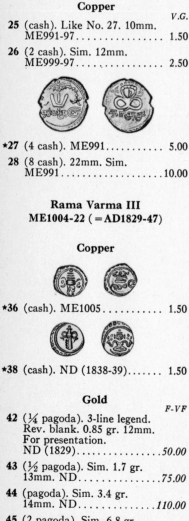

27 (4 cash). ME991........... 5.00

28 (8 cash). 22mm. Sim. ME991................... 10.00

Rama Varma III
ME1004-22 (=AD1829-47)

Copper

36 (cash). ME1005........... 1.50

38 (cash). ND (1838-39)....... 1.50

Gold

F-VF

42 (¼ pagoda). 3-line legend. Rev. blank. 0.85 gr. 12mm. For presentation. ND (1829)................. *50.00*

43 (½ pagoda). Sim. 1.7 gr. 13mm. ND................. *75.00*

44 (pagoda). Sim. 3.4 gr. 14mm. ND................. *110.00*

45 (2 pagoda). Sim. 6.8 gr. 15mm. ND................. *170.00*

WAI (Vai)

In the domain of the Maratha Peshwa in western India.

For the coin previously listed here see Poona.

UNVERIFIED DATA

Note: Throughout this catalog, any uncertain, indefinite or unconfirmed information is shown in *italic type.* Such material may be, for example, coin descriptions, dates and prices, names of rulers, or supplementary notes. Further information to confirm or correct *material in italics* should be sent to the author at the following address:

William D. Craig
c/o Whitman Coin Supply Division
1220 Mound Avenue
Racine, Wisconsin 53404, U.S.A.

NOTES

IONIAN ISLANDS—See BALKANS

IRELAND (HIBERNIA)

Island west of England under British dominion during the period covered by this catalog.

Monetary System:
4 farthings = 1 penny;
12 pence = 1 shilling;
20 shillings = 1 pound.

George II 1727-60

Copper

		VG-F
1 (farthing). Like No. 2a but young head. 1737-44		4.50
1a —. Old head. 1760		3.50
2 (½ penny). Like No. 1. 1736-46		4.50

★2a —. Mature head. 1747-55		3.50
2b —. Old head. 1760		4.00

George III 1760-1820

Copper

		Fine
3 (farthing). Like No. 6. 1806		2.00
4 (½ penny). GEORGIVS III REX. Young head, short hair. Rev. Harp. 30mm. 1766, 69 (2 vars.)		3.50
4a —. Head, long hair. 1774-82 (83 = counterfeit)		3.50
5 (½ penny). Like No. 6. 1805		2.50

★6 (penny). 1805 .... 3.50

Silver

Bank of Ireland Token Coinage

		Fine
7 FIVE/PENCE. Like No. 8. 1805-06		4.00

★8 TEN/PENCE. 1805-06 ..... 5.00

		V.F.
★9 10 PENCE. 1813		8.00

		F-VF
10 XXX PENCE. Like No. 11. 1808		15.00

		VF-EF
★11 SIX SHILLINGS. 1804		80.00

George IV 1820-30

Copper

		Fine
12 (½ penny). Like No. 13. 1822-23		2.50

		Fine
★13 (penny). 1822-23		3.50

ISLE OF MAN

In the Irish Sea between England and Ireland.

Monetary System:
14 pence (Manx) = 1 shilling (English).

James Murray, Duke of Atholl, 1736-65

Copper

		V.G.
1 (½ penny). Cwnd. AD mon. Rev. STABIT etc. Triquetra. 25mm. 1758		6.50
2 (penny). Sim. 29.5mm. 1758		5.00

George III of England 1760-1820

Copper

		VG-F
3 (½ penny). Like No. 5. 1786		4.00

★4 (½ penny). 1798, 1813		3.00

ISLE OF MAN

		VG-F
★5	(penny). 1786	6.50
6	(penny). Like No. 4. 1798, 1813	5.00

Victoria 1837-1901

Copper

		Fine
7	(farthing). Like No. 9. 1839	5.00
8	(½ penny). Sim. 28mm. 1839	3.00

★9	(penny). 1839	5.00

NOTE: Nos. 7-9 dated 1841, 59 or 60 did not circulate.

ISLES DU VENT.
See CARIBBEAN ISLANDS AND TERRITORIES.

· 301 ·

ITALY

Until 1859-61 Italy was divided into a number of separate states, all independent except the Austrian Kingdom of Lombardy-Venetia. In 1859-61 the Kingdom of Sardinia absorbed the other states excepting only Venetia and that portion of the Papal States situated around Rome. The Kingdom of Italy was established in 1861, with Vittorio Emanuele II of Sardinia as king. The new kingdom acquired Venetia in 1866 and the residual Papal territory in 1870.

MONETARY SYSTEMS GENERALLY:

Most of the Italian monetary units prior to Napoleon bore some relation, distant or close, to the once universal Carolingian system, namely: 12 denari = 1 soldo; 20 soldi = 1 lira. Commencing with the Napoleonic era the decimal system, 100 centesimi = 1 lira, spread over the land and finally became the national coinage. The gold zecchino (= ducat) and doppia (= 2 ducats) were popular into the 19th century. Beyond this, diversity between states was such that it has proven necessary to describe the systems of each state separately.

A peculiarity of many Italian coins is that the unit appears before the numeral of value, viz: SOLDI 10 (= 10 Soldi).

ALESSANDRIA

City in Piedmont (NW Italy). Besieged 1746, on which occasion the Sardinian defenders struck coins.

Carlo Emanuele III, King of Sardinia 1730-73

Billon
VG-F

1 S(ol)di 10 (= 10 S.) Eagle with Savoy arms on breast. Rev. BLOC/ARCISALEX/GUB/MARCHIO/ DE/CARALIO/1746 . . . . —

ANCONA, City

Principal city in the Marches (central east coast of Italy). Formerly a republic, but became part of the Papal States in the late 14th century.

Ancona fell to the French in 1797. Thereafter, it was part of the Roman Republic 1798-99, of the Papal States 1799-1808, of the Napoleonic Kingdom of Italy 1808-14, of the Papal States 1814-48, of the Roman Republic 1848-49, of the Papal States 1849-60, and of the Kingdom of Italy 1860 onward.

Monetary System:

5 quattrini = 1 baiocco;
100 baiocchi = 1 scudo.

Pius VI (= Sextus), Pope 1775-99

Copper
VG-F

1 VN (= 1)/BAIOCCO. PIVS SEXTVS PON. M. etc. Arms. Rev. Value/ANCONA/1796, N.D. 10.00

2 DVE (= 2)/BAIOCCHI. Sim. 1796. . . . . 10.00

*3 BAIOCCHI/DVE E MEZZO (= 2½ B.). 1796 . . . . 10.00

Roman Republic 1798-99

Copper

6 DVE (= 2)/BAIOC/CHI. REPVBBLICA ROMANA, fasces/ A(ncona). Rev. Value. N.D. . . 10.00

6a —. REP. ROM. ANCONA. N.D. . . 17.50

Base Silver

Papal types restruck during siege of 1799.
Fine

9 (½ Scudo). Papal States No. 89a. 1778A (= 1799) . . . . —

10 (Scudo). Papal States No. 91. 1780A (= 1799) 300.00

Roman Republic 1848-49

Cast Copper
F-VF

12 1/BAIOCCO. REPUBBLICA ROMANA. Fasces. Rev. Value. 1849A 5.00

13 3/BAIOCCHI. Sim. 1848A 40.00

ASCOLI, City

In the Marches. Acquired by the papacy in 1426.
Monetary System: See Ancona.

Pius VI 1775-99

Copper
VG-F

1 UN (= 1)/QVATTRINO. PIVS SEXT. P.M. etc. Arms. Rev. Value/ASCOLI/1797 . . . . 50.00

VG-F

2 MEZZO (= ½) /BAIOCCO. Sim. 1797 . . . . 25.00

3 VN (= 1) /BAIOCCO. Sim. 1797, yr. XXIII, N.D. 25.00

4 BAIOCCHI/DVE E MEZZO (= 2½ B.). S.P. APOST. etc. St. Peter. Rev. Value/ASCOLI/ 1797. N.D. 20.00

*5 BAIOC(chi)/CINQVE (= 5 B.). 1797-99 . . . . 30.00

Roman Republic 1798-99

6 (quattrino). Fasces divides R-R. Rev. ASCO/LI. N.D. 75.00

7 MEZZO (= ½)/BAIOCCO. Obv. sim. Rev. value/ASCOLI. N.D. 50.00

*8 DVE (= 2)/BAIOCCHI (or BAIOC/CHI). REPVBLICA ROMANA. Fasces. Rev. Value/ ASCOLI. N.D. 25.00

BELGIOJOSO, Princes

The counts and later princes of Belgiojoso in Lombardy were of the Barbiani family. In 1769 Count Antonio da Barbiano was created a prince of the Empire and given the coinage right.

Antonio I, Prince 1769-79

Silver
E.F.

1 (scudo). Like No. 2. 1769 . . 800.00

ITALY

BELGIOJOSO (Cont.)

Gold

*2 (zecchino). 1769......... — *E.F.*

BOLOGNA (BONONIA), City

Site of a famous university in northern Italy. Acquired by the papacy in 1506. Governed 1796-97 by a local revolutionary republic which merged into the Cispadine Republic. To the Cisalpine Republic 1797-1802, to the Italian Republic 1802-05 and the Kingdom of Italy 1805-14. Restored to the papacy 1815-59. Thereafter, to Italy.

Arms of Bologna: See Rev. of No. 39.

Monetary System:

Until 1777:
6 quattrini = 1 bolognino;
12 bolognini = 1 giulio = 1 bianco;
80 to 108 bolognini = 1 scudo.

After 1777:
6 quattrini = 1 bolognino = 1 baiocco;
30 baiocchi = 6 grossi = 3 giuli =
3 Paoli = 1 testone;
100 baiocchi = 1 scudo;
30 Paoli = 3 scudi = 1 doppia.

Benedict XIV, Pope 1740-58

Copper
V.G.

1 (quattrino). BONO/NIA/DOCET/ date. Rev. Lion stdg. with pennant. 1740-58.......... 1.50

2 MEZZO (=½) BOLOGNINO. BONONIA DOCET. Arms. Rev. Lion, value. 1740-56....... 1.50

2a —. MEZO. 1740.......... 3.00

Billon

G-VG

*3 (2 bolognini). 1742-56..... 2.00

4 (4 bolognini). Sim. but bust l. A(nno) II (=1741-42), 1744-54..................... 2.50

Silver
Fine

5 CINQVE (=5) /BOLOGNI/ NI. Bolognese arms. Rev. Value, date. 1740-58........ 5.00

Fine

6 12 (bolognini). BENEDICTVS XIV P. MAX. Bust. Rev. BONONIA MAT. etc. Lion with arms, pennant. 1740-42......... 13.50

7 12 (bolognini). Bust. Rev. BONONIA DOCET. Lion with pennant. 1743-54......... 10.00

8 (scudo = 108 bol.). Arms. Rev. BONONIA DOCET. Cross. 1740....................175.00

9 (scudo = 108 bol.). Bust l. Rev. PASTORE/etc. .... /BONONIENSIS/1741 R.N...600.00

10 (scudo = 108 bol.). BENEDICT XIV P.M. BONON. A. XVII. Bust. Rev. VNVM/etc. (1756-57)..125.00

10a —. Rev. PATRIA/etc. (1756-57)......................125.00

Nos. 9, 10 and 10a are probably medals.

Gold (zecchino = 3.45 gr.)
E.F.

11 (zecchino). BENEDICTVS etc. Bust. Rev. PATRI PATRIAE. Felsina stdg. A(nno) II (=1741-42)..................... —

12 ZECCHINO. Arms. Rev. BONONIA DOCET. Lion. 1746.................... —

13 (zecchino). Arms. Rev. BONONIA DOCET. Cross. 1751........ —

14 (2 zecchini). Like No. 11. A II (=1741-42).......... —

15 (10 scudi). No. 10 in gold. A.XVII (=1756-57)....... —

Clement XIII, Pope 1758-69

Silver
VG-F

16 CINQVE (=5) /BOLOGNI/NI. Like No. 5. 1765..........10.00

*17 12 (bolognini). 1759-68..... 8.00

Gold
E.F.

18 *ZECCHINO.* Arms. Rev. *BONONIA etc.,* Lion. 1758-69................. —

Sede Vacante 1769

Silver
Fine

19 (40) or 40 (bolognini = ½ scudo). SEDE VACANTE. Arms. Rev. BONONIA etc. Cross. 1769....50.00

Clement XIV, Pope 1769-74

Silver
VG-F

20 CINQVE (=5) /BOLOGNI/NI. Like No. 5. 1769, 71..... 7.50

21 12 (bolognini). CLEME XIV P.M. Bust. Rev. BONO DOCET. Lion. 1773....................13.50

V.F.

22 (½ scudo =40 bol.). Arms. Rev. BONONIA etc. Cross. 1769, 73.................30.00

Gold

23 ZECCHINO. Arms. Rev. BONONIA etc. Lion. 1771.... —

Sede Vacante 1774-75

Silver

24 80 (bolognini). SEDE VACANTE. Arms. Rev. S. PETRON(IO) PROT(ECTOR) BON(ON). St. P. kneeling. 1774-75 R.N. (var.)...................275.00

Pius VI, Pope 1775-99, In Bologna 1775-96

Copper

F-VF

*25 (quattrino). PIVS VI PONT. M. Arms. Rev. BONO/NIA/DOCET/ date. 1778-84.............. 2.00

26 QVATTRINO. PIVS/etc. Rev. BONON. etc. Lion. 1795-96...................... 4.00

27 MEZZO (=½) BOLOGNINO. BONONIA DOCET. Arms. Rev. Lion, value. 1777......... 5.00

28 MEZZO (=½) BAIOCCO. PIVS etc. in wreath. Rev. Arms in 2 shields, city arms at r. under lion's head. 1781....... 5.00

29 MEZ(zo =½) BAI(occo). Like No. 26. 1795-96 R.N... 2.00

30 BAIOCCO. PIVS VI (or SEXTVS) etc. Lily plant. Rev. BONON(IA) DOCET. Arms. 1780. (var.)... 6.00

31 BAIOCCO. PIVS etc. in wreath. Rev. as last. 1781........ 6.00

32 BAIOCCO. Like No. 28. 1784.................... 5.00

33 BAIOCCO I. Like No. 26. 1795-96 R.N............. 2.25

34 BAIOCCHI 2. Sim. 1795-96 R.N.................... 4.00

ITALY

BOLOGNA (Cont.)

Billon

V.G.

35 (2 baiocchi). PIVS VI etc. Bust.
Rev. S. PETRON. BON. PROT.
St. P. stdg. 1.2-1.8 gr. 1778-
96........................ 2.00

36 B(aiocchi) IIII. PIVS VI etc.
Keys. Rev. as last. 1778.... 5.00

37 B(aiocchi) 4 (or 4 baiocchi).
Like No. 35. 3.0-3.5 gr. 1778-
96, N.D................... 2.25

Silver

Fine

38 CINQVE (=5) /BOLOGNI/NI.
Like No. 5. 1777........... 6.00

★39 B(aiocchi) 5. Lily plant.
Rev. Bolognese arms. 1777-
83...................... 4.50

40 B(aiocchi) 5. PIVS etc. Arms.
Rev. S. PETRON. BON. PROT.
Bust of St. P. 1778........ 4.50

41 B(aiocchi) 5. PIVS etc. Papal
arms. Rev. Bolognese arms.
1778-80.................. 3.00

42 B(aiocchi) 5. Obv. Like No. 39.
Rev. like No. 40. 1796...... 4.00

43 10 (baiocchi). PIVS etc. Arms.
Rev. PRAESID. ET. DECVS. BONON.
Madonna. 1781, 85......... 4.00

43a —. 1786................... 4.50

44 12 (baiocchi). PIVS etc. Bust.
Rev. BONONIA etc. Lion.
1795.................... 8.00

45 20 (baiocchi). PIVS etc. Arms.
Rev. BONON etc. Lion. 1777..10.00

45a —. 1778-80.............. 5.00

45b —. 1786-93.............. 5.00

F-VF

46 30 (baiocchi). PIVS etc. Bust.
Rev. BONONIA etc. Arms.
1777-92..................15.00

47 30 (baiocchi). Bust. Rev.
ADVENTVS etc. Temple/BONONIA.
1782....................30.00

48 (½ scudo). PIVS SEXTVS etc.
Arms. Rev. S. PETRONIVS
BONONIAE. etc. St. P. stdg.
AN(no) III (=1777-78)....30.00

49 50 (baiocchi). Sim. but PIVS
VI and St. P. std. 1778-95.
(var.)...................17.50

50 50 (baiocchi). Like No. 47.
1782....................40.00

F-VF

51 80 (bolognini). Like No. 49.
1775, AN(no)I............75.00

51a —. With ANNO IVBILAEI.
1775....................150.00

52 100 (baiocchi). PIVS VI etc. Arms.
Rev. St. P. stdg. 1777-80.
(var.)...................75.00

53 100 (baiocchi). Like No. 47.
1782....................80.00

54 100 (baiocchi). PIVS VI etc. Arms.
Rev. St. P. std. 1795.......70.00

Gold (zecchino = 3.4 gr.)

E.F.

55 100 (baiocchi). Like No. 60.
N.D...................... —

56 (½ zecchino). Sim. 1786..2250.00

57 (zecchino). Sim. 1778-87,
N.D.....................950.00

58 (zecchino). Like No. 47.
1782.................... —

59 (2 zecchini). Like No. 60.
1786-87...............1950.00

★60 ZECCH(ini) 5. 1787...... —

61 ZECCH(ini) 10. Sim. 1786-
87...................... —

62 (15 Paoli). PIVS etc. Lily plant.
Rev. City arms in one shield,
no legend. 2.7 gr. 1778....1200.00

63 P(aoli) 15. Obv. sim. Rev. BON.
DOCET. 2 shields. 1778-79...300.00

63a (15 Paoli). 2.7 gr. 1786-91..275.00

64 P(aoli) 30. Sim. 1778-85...400.00

64a (30 Paoli). 5.4 gr. 1786-92..350.00

64b 1 DOP(pia). 1787-88......450.00

65 P(aoli) 60. Sim. 1778-81...950.00

65a (60 Paoli). 10.9 gr. 1786-87,
A•XIII (=1787)..........900.00

65b 2 DOP(pie). 1787-96......850.00

66 4 DOP(pie). Sim. 1786-87.1650.00

Revolutionary Government
1796-97

7½ baiocchi = 1 carlino.

Copper

Fine

67 MEZZO (=½)/QVATTRINO.
BONON. DOCET. Lion. Rev.
Value/1796...............10.00

Billon

VG-F

67.3 VN (=1)/CARLINO.
COMVNITAS ET SENATVS BONON.
Arms. Rev. Value.
N.D. (1796)............. 7.50

67.4 DVE (=2)/CARLINI.
Sim. N.D. (1796)........ 7.50

Silver

V.F.

68 P(aoli) 5. POPVLVS ET SENATVS
BONON. Arms. Rev. Madonna
and child over city. 1796-97.45.00

69 P(aoli) 10. Sim. 1796-97....80.00

69a (10 Paoli). COMMVNITAS ET
SENATVS. 1796 and 1796
R.N. 225.00

See Cispadine Republic for 1797 20
lire coin from Bologna mint.

Regular coins of the Napoleonic
Kingdom of Italy 1807-13, of the
Papacy 1815-59, of the Roman Re-
public 1849, and of Sardinia/Italy
1859-61 (see Emilia) were struck at
Bologna with B mint mark.

CISALPINE REPUBLIC
(REPUBBLICA CISALPINA)

Founded by the French February 19,
1797, by the combination of Lombardy
with the then Cispadine Republic
(q.v.). Absorbed into the Italian Republic 1802.

Monetary System:

20 soldi = 1 lira; 6 lire = 1 scudo.

Silver

V.F.

★1 SOLDI 30. ANNO IX
(=1801)................65.00

ITALY

CISALPINE REPUBLIC (Cont.)

*2 SCUDO/DI LIRE SEI   *E.F.*
(=6 lire). ANNO VIII
(=1800)...............250.00

CISPADINE REPUBLIC (REPUBLICA CISPADINA)

Short-lived government set up in Bologna, Ferrara, Modena and Reggio, October 16, 1796–February 19, 1797. On the latter date these districts were joined with Lombardy to form the Cisalpine Republic.

Gold
VF-EF

1 (20 lire). REPVBLICA CISPADINA
etc. Quiver, flags. Rev. Madonna.
1797..................... ——

CIVITAVECCHIA, City

In the Papal States, lying N.W. of Rome, on the Tyrrhenian Seacoast.

Monetary System:
100 baiocchi = 1 scudo.

Pius VI, Pope 1775-99
Copper
VG-F

5 BAIOCCHI/DUE E MEZZO
(=2½ B.). St. Peter.
Rev. Value/CIVITA/VECCHIA.
30mm. 1796-97............ 7.50

5a —. 25mm. 1797........... 7.50

6 BAIOC(chi)/CINQVE (= 5B.).
Madonna. Rev. Value/
CIVITA/VECCHIA. 1797...... 7.50

Roman Republic 1798-99
Copper
VG-F

11 DVE (=2)/BAIOC/CHI.
REPUBBLICA ROMANA. Fasces.
Rev. Value. C(ivítavecchia).
N.D. (1798-99)...........15.00

12 DVE/BAIOC/CHI. Both
sides like Rev. of No. 11.
N.D. 15.00

CLITUNNO, Department

Under the Roman Republic 1798-99 (q.v.).

Copper

1 VN (=1)/BAIOCCO.
REPVBBLICA ROMANA, Fasces.
Rev. Value/CLITVN/NO.
N.D. 50.00

2 DVE (=2)/BA/IOCCHI.
REPV(BL). ROM. (DP). CLITUNNO.
Fasces. Rev. Value. N.D. ..35.00

CORSICA, Island

Napoleon's birthplace in the Mediterranean. Mostly under the control of Genoa until 1768, to France thereafter.

Monetary System:
12 denari = 1 soldo; 20 soldi = 1 lira.

Theodor, Baron Neuhof "King" of Corsica for 8 months in 1736.

Copper
V.G.

1 S(ol)DI/DVE E/M (=2½ S.).
Like No. 2. 1736...........30.00

*2 SOLDI/CINQVE (=5 S.).
1736...................25.00

Silver
Fine

3 (½ scudo). THEODORVS REX
CORSICE. Head. Rev. Madonna.
1736 (**18th century copy**).100.00

Republic of Corsica
General Pasquale Paoli
1762-68

Arms: Sailor's head. Supporters: 2 sea gods.

Billon
V.G.

4 8/DENARI. Like No. 7.
1762-68.................10.00

---

5 1/SOLDO. Cap on pole.   *V.G.*
Rev. Value. 1768..........17.50

6 2/SOLDI. Like No. 7. 1762-
68.....................10.00

*7 4/SOLDI. 1762-68......... 7.50

Silver
VG-F

8 10/SOLDI. Sim. 1762-64....17.50

9 20/SOLDI. Sim. 1762-68....15.00

EMILIA

A former Papal province containing Bologna and Ferrara. Acquired by Sardinia in 1859.

Monetary System:
100 centesimi = 1 lira.
B(ologna Mint).

Silver
VF-EF

1 C(entesimi) 50. VITTORIO
EMANUELE II. Head. Rev. DIO
PROTEGGE L'ITALIA. Arms/B.
1859...................30.00

2 L(ira) 1. Sim. 1859........50.00

3 L(ire) 2. Sim. 1859-60.....300.00

4 L(ire) 5. Sim. 1859-60....1000.00

Gold
E.F.

5 LIRE 10. Obv. As last. Rev.
REGIE PROVINCIE DELL'EMILIA.
Value/B. 1860............ ——

6 LIRE 20. Sim. 1860....... ——

For other coins of Vittorio Emanuele II, see Sardinia and Tuscany.

FANO, City

In the Marches (Central Italy). Acquired by the Papacy in 1462.

Monetary System:
100 baiocchi = 1 scudo.

Pius VI, Pope 1775-99
Copper
VG-F

1 BAIOCCHI/DVE E. MEZZO
(=2½ B.). S.P. APOST. etc.
St. Peter. Rev. Value/FANO.
1797...................25.00

ITALY

FANO (Cont.)

VG-F

★2 BAIOC(chi)/CINQVE (=5 B.).
1797.....................25.00

FERMO, City

In the Marches. Held by the Papacy
intermittently from the late 14th century, permanently from 1513.

Monetary System:
5 quattrini = 1 baiocco;
100 baiocchi = 1 scudo.

Pius VI, Pope 1775-99

Copper

1 MEZZO (=½)/BAIOCCO.
PIVS PAPA VI etc. Rev. Value/
FERMO or FERMANO. 1797-
98..................... 7.50

★2 BAIOCCHI/DVE E MEZZO
(=2½ B.). 1796-97........ 5.00

3 BAIOC(chi)/CINQVE(= 5 B.).
Like Fano No. 2 but FERMO.
1797-99.................. 5.00

Billon

4 BAIOCCHI/SESSANTA
(=60 B.). PIVS etc. Arms.
Rev. Value/FERMO. 1799....40.00

Provisional Republic 1798

Copper

Fine

★5 MEZZO (=½)/BAIOCCO.
ANNO PMO REIP. FIRM. City arms.
Rev. Value/FERMO. 1798....12.50

Roman Republic 1798-99

Copper

6 VN/QVATRINO. REPVBLICA
ROMANA. Fasces. Rev. Value/
FERMO. N.D..............20.00

7 MEZZO (=½)/BAIOCCO.
ANNO/PMO/DELLA REP/ROMANA.
Rev. Value/FERMO. N.D.
(1798-99)................12.00

8 MEZZO (=½)/BAIOCCO.
Like No. 6. N.D...........10.00

9 VN (=1)/BAIOCCO. ANNO
PMO DELLA REPVB around,
ROMA/NA in center. Rev. Value/
FERMO. 1798, N.D. 10.00

10 VN (=1)/BAIOCCO. REPVBLICA
ROMANA around, ANNO/I in
center. Rev. Value/FERMO.
1798, N.D. 10.00

11 VN (=1)/BAIOCCO. Like
No. 6. N.D...............15.00

12 DVE (=2) /BAIOCCHI.
Like No. 6. 1798, N.D.....10.00

13 DVE (=2) /BAIOCCHI.
Like No. 9. 1798, N.D.....10.00

14 DVE (=2) /BAIOCCHI.
Like No. 10. 1798.........10.00

FERRARA, City

In Emilia (NE Italy). To the Papacy
1598-1859, with the usual Napoleonic
and 1848-49 interruptions.

Monetary System:
6 quattrini = 1 baiocco.

Benedict XIV, Pope 1740-58

Copper

V.G.

0.5 (quattrino). Arms of Benedict
XIV (see Papal States No. 27).
Rev. St. Peter/FERRARA
(or FERRARIE). N.D. 7.50

1 (quattrino). St. George.
Rev. FERRARIAE. 1744...... 5.00

2 (quattrino). Arms. Rev. FER/
RARI/AE. 1744-48, N.D.
(var.)................... 2.00

3 MEZZO (=½)/BAIOCCO.
BENEDICT XIV P.M. etc. Arms.
Rev. Value/FERRARA. (var.).
1744-51, A(nno) IV-XI,
N.D..................... 2.00

4 1/BAIOCCO. Sim. 1744-51,
A. IV-XII, N.D. (var.)..... 5.00

FOLIGNO (FVLIGNO), City

In Umbria, Central Italy. To the Papal
States with the usual Napoleonic and
republican interruptions.

Pius VI, Pope 1775-99

Copper

Fine

1 (quattrino) PIVS SEXTVS
etc., Arms. Rev. St.
Feliciano stdg. A(nno)
XX (=1794-95) 35.00

2 MEZZO (=½)/BAIOCCO.
Obv. sim. Rev. Value/DI/
FOLIGNO (FVLIGNO). N.D. ..20.00

3 VN (=1) BAIOCCO. Sim.
1794-95, N.D. 15.00

4 DVE (=2)/BAIOCCHI.
Sim. 1795, N.D. 15.00

5 BAIOCCHI/DVE E MEZZO
(=2½ B.). St. Peter. Rev.
Value/FVLIGNO. 30mm.
1796-97..................10.00

5a —. 25mm. 1797...........15.00

6 BAIOC(chi)/CINQVE (=5B.).
Madonna. Rev. Value/
FVLIGNO. 1797............15.00

Roman Republic 1798-99

Copper

VG-F

7 QVATRINO. S. FELICIANO.
St. stdg. Rev. Value. N.D. ..15.00

8 MEZZO (=½)/BAIOCCO.
DE FVLIGNO. Star. Rev. Value.
N.D. ....RRR

GENOA (GENOVA), Republic

Important seaport and its environs in
N.W. Italy. First doge (dux) appointed
1339. Corsica, which had belonged to
Genoa, was taken by France in 1768.
Genoa was transformed by Napoleon
into the Ligurian Republic 1798-1805.
Thereafter it was part of France 1805-
14. The republic was restored in 1814,
but on January 1, 1815 Genoa was absorbed by Sardinia.

Monetary System:
12 denari = 1 soldo;
20 soldi = 10 parpagliola =
5 cavallotto = 1 lira (Madonnina).

Copper

V.G.

1 D(enari) I. Value. Rev. Cross.
N.D. (1752)............... 5.00

2 D(enari) 2. Sim. N.D.
(1752)................... 3.00

2a 2 (denari). N.D. (1752)..... 5.00

3 3 (denari). Sim. N.D.
(1752)................... 3.00

4 D(enari) 4. ½ length bust of
Madonna. Rev. D-4 in angles
of cross. N.D. (1752)...... 7.00

5 D(enari)/QUATRO (=4 d.).
Arms (cross). Rev. Value (var.).
1768-81.................. 1.50

5a —. QUATTRO. 1793-97.... 1.25

ITALY

GENOA (Cont.)

Billon
G-VG

6 (8 denari). DVX ET GVB REIP GENV. Arms. Rev. ET REGE EOS. Madonna. (var.). 1699-1756 .... 1.25

6a —. Us in lieu of Vs. (var.). 1768-96 .... 1.00

7 S(oldi) 2. Like No. 6. 1710-49 .... 1.50

8 S(oldi) 4. Obv. sim. Rev. EX PROBITATE etc. St. George. 1736-56 .... 1.75

9 SOLDI/CINQUE (=5 s.). St. George (no legend). Rev. Value. 1792 .... 2.75

9a —. DUX ET G. R. GEN. St. Geo. 1792-93 .... 1.75

10 SOLDI/IO. Like No. 10a. 1792 .... 2.75

★10a SOLDI/DIECI (=10 S.). 1792-97 .... 2.50

Silver
F-VF

11 (lira). DVX ET GVB REIP. GENV. Arms. Rev. SVB TVVM etc. Immaculate Conception. 4.5 gr. 1745-50 .... 30.00

12 L(ira) I. Like No. 16a. 1793-95 .... 12.50

13 (2 lire). Like No. 11. 8.8 gr. 1747-51 .... 55.00

14 L(ire) 2. Like No. 16a. 1792-96 .... 35.00

15 L(ire) 4. Sim. 1792-97 .... 60.00

16 L(ire) 8. Like No. 16a but cruder. 1792-93 .... 85.00

F-VF
★16a L(ire) 8. 1793-97 .... 80.00

Gold
V.F.

17 (12½ lire). DUX ET GUB REIP. GENU. Arms. Rev. ET REGE EOS. Madonna. 3.5 gr. 1758-67 .... ——

18 (25 lire). Sim. 7.0 gr. 1758-67 .... ——

19 (50 lire). Sim. 14. gr. 1758-67 .... ——

20 (100 lire). Sim. 28 gr. 1758-67 .... ——

21 L(ire) 12. Sim. 1793-95 .... ——

22 L(ire) 24. Sim. 1792-95 .... ——

23 L(ire) 48. Sim. 1792-97 ... 2250.00

24 L(ire) 96. Sim. 1792-97 ... 2750.00

Genoa as the Ligurian Republic (Repubblica Ligure) 1798-1805

Copper
VG-F

25 D.3 (=3 denari) R(epublic) L(igure) A(nno) V (=5 =1802). Rev. Cross 15.00

Billon
V.G.

26 SOLDI/10 REPUBBLICA LIGURE etc. Arms. Rev. Value. 1798-99 .... 5.00

Silver
F-VF

27 L(ira) 1. Like No. 30. 1798 .. 30.00

28 L(ire) 2. Sim. 1798 .... 25.00

29 L(ire) 4. Sim. 1798-1804 .... 90.00

★30 L(ire) 8. 1798-1804 .... 135.00

Gold
V.F.

31 L(ire) 12. REPUBBLICA LIGURE. Date, Liguria std. Rev. Fasces. 1798 .... ——

32 L(ire) 24. Sim. 1798 .... ——

33 L(ire) 48. Sim. 1798-1804 . 2250.00

34 L(ire) 96. Sim. 1798-1805 . 2750.00

During the French occupation of Genoa 1805-14, regular French issues were struck there 1813-14 with mint mark C.L.

Republic Restored April-December 1814

Copper

35 D(enari)/QUATTRO. Arms. Rev. Value. 1814 .... 2.50

Billon

F-VF
★36 S(oldi) 2. 1814 .... 3.00

★37 S(oldi) 4. 1814 .... 4.00

Silver

★38 SOL(di) 10. 1814 .... 5.00

38a —. JANVENSIS 6.00

After the absorption of Genoa by Sardinia on January 1, 1815, Sardinian coins with a fouled anchor mint mark were struck here to 1860.

GORIZIA (GÖRZ), County
At the head of the Adriatic Sea. To Austria 1500. Now in Italy.
Monetary System: 20 soldi = 1 lira.

Maria Theresia 1740-80

Copper
VG-F

1 ½/SOLDO. Like No. 2. 1741-43, 61-62 .... 1.25

ITALY

GORIZIA (Cont.)

VG-F

★2 1/SOLDO. Görz arms. Rev.
Value in cartouche. 1741-70 . 1.00

Joseph II, Alone 1780-90

Copper

3 ½/SOLDO. Sim. 1783-90 . . . 1.50
4 1/SOLDO. Sim. 1783-90 . . . . 1.25

Leopold II 1790-92

Copper

5 ½/SOLDO. Sim. 1791-92 . . . 1.50
6 1/SOLDO. Sim. 1791-92 . . . . 1.50

Franz II 1792-1835

Copper

7 ½/SOLDO. Sim. 1793-1801 . 1.50
8 1/SOLDO. Sim. 1793-1802 . . 1.25
9 2 SOLDI. Sim. 1799-1802 . . . 1.50

Billon

★10 15/SOLDI. 1802 . . . . 7.00

GUBBIO (EUGUBIA)

City in Romagna, central Italy, belonging to the Papal States.

Monetary System:
Same as Papal States.

Benedict XIV, Pope 1740-58

Copper

V.G.

0.1 QVAT/TRINO. Arms.
Řev. Value/GVB./1740 . . . . . 30.00
0.2 (quattrino). BEN(ED)(ICTVS)
XIV etc. Arms. Rev. St. Peter.
ND, yr. III 3.00
0.3 (quattrino). Sim. but Rev.
St. Paul. ND, yr. III 2.50
0.4 (quattrino). Sim. but Rev.
SS.Peter and Paul. N.D. . . . 7.50
1 (quattrino). Obv. sim.
Rev. S. VBALDVS EP(ISCO)
(EVGVB.) St. stdg. N.D. 2.00

V.G.

2 MEZZO (=½)/BAIOC/CO.
Arms. Rev. Value. Yr. II . . . 4.00
2a —. Rev. MEZZO/BAIOCCO/
GUBBIO. 1743-51 . . . . 2.00
2b —. Rev. MEZ/BAIOC/CO/GVB.
1752-54 . . . . 2.50
3 VN (=1)/BAIOCCO. Arms.
Rev. Value/GVB(BIO) (var.)
1740-58 . . . . 2.00

Clement XIII, Pope 1758-69

Copper

8 (quattrino). CLE. XIII etc. Arms.
Rev. St. Peter. N.D. 4.00
9 (quattrino). Sim. but
Rev. St. Paul. N.D. 4.00
11 (quattrino). Sim. but
Rev. St. Ubaldus. N.D. 2.50
12 MEZ(ZO) (=½)/BAIOCCO.
Arms. Rev. Value/GVBBIO.
1759-60 . . . . 3.00
13 VN (=1)/BAIOCCO. Sim.
1759 . . . . 3.50

Clement XIV, Pope 1769-74

Copper

VG-F

20 (quattrino). CLEM XIV etc.
Arms of Ben. XIV. Rev.
St. Paul. N.D. 75.00
21 (quattrino). Sim. but
Rev. St. Ubaldus. N.D. 75.00
22 (quattrino). Sim. but
Rev. St. Peter. N.D. 75.00

Pius VI, Pope 1775-99

Copper

31 MEZZO (=½)/BAIOCCO.
PIVS SEXTVS etc. Arms.
Rev. Value/GVBBIO. N.D. . . 4.00
32 VN (=1)/BAIOCCO. Sim.
N.D. 4.00
33 DVE (=2)/BAIOCCHI.
Sim. (var.). N.D. 5.00
34 BAIOCCHI/DVE E MEZZO
(=2½ B.). St. Peter. Rev.
Value/GVBBIO. 1796 . . . . 4.00
34a —. DI/GVBBIO. 1796 . . . . . . .Rare
35 BAIOC(chi)/CINQVE (=5 B.).
Madonna. Rev. Value/GVBBIO.
1797 . . . . 5.00

Under the Roman
Republic (q.v.) 1798-99

Copper

41 MEZZO (=½)/BAIOCCO.
Value/GVBBIO. Rev. same.
N.D. 25.00
42 DVE (=2)/BAIOCCHI.
Fasces. Rev. Value/GVBBIO.
N.D. 20.00

ITALIAN REPUBLIC
(REPUBBLICA ITALIANA)

Created in 1802 out of the Cisalpine
Republic (q.v.) with some additions.
Converted into the Kingdom of Italy
in 1805. Capital: Milan. Years 1-4 of
the republic = 1802-05.

Napoleon Bonaparte,
President 1802-05

The coins of the Italian Republic, in
two distinct series, (i) ANNO II, and
(ii) 1804, are all very rare patterns. See
Pagani, **Prove e Progetti** (Milano
1957), Nos. 433-466.

ITALY, Kingdom
(REGNO D'ITALIA)

The Italian Republic was converted
into a kingdom for Napoleon's benefit
at the time he became emperor of
France. It endured from 1805 to 1814
and then was broken up and returned
to the former rulers of its parts.

Monetary System:
100 centesimi = 20 soldi = 1 lira.

Mints:
B(ologna); M(ilan) and V(enice).

Patterns and Essays:
Pieces of 1806, those dated 1807 with
ML mon. beside date, 1807 copper with
head right, and the 1808M 25 centesimi, are patterns or essays, all very
scarce or rare.

Napoleon I 1805-14

Copper

Fine

1 CENTESIMO. Like No. 3.
1807-13 . . . . 3.00
1a —. 1808M. Error.
IMPERAPORE 15.00
2 3 CENTESIMI. Like No. 3.
1807-13 . . . . 5.00

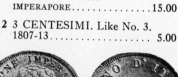

★3 SOLDO. 1807-13 (vars.) 5.00

Billon

G-VG

★4 10 CENT(esim)I
(="parpagliola"). 1803-13 . . . 2.00

ITALY

ITALY, Kingdom (Cont.)

Silver

F-VF

5 5 SOLDI. Like No. 6. 1808-14 .... 5.00

*6 10 SOLDI. 1808-14 .... 5.00

7 15 SOLDI. Sim. 1808-14 .... 25.00

8 1 LIRA. Like No. 9. 1808-14 .... 10.00

*9 2 LIRE. 1807-14 .... 30.00

10 5 LIRE. Sim. 1807-14 ...... 45.00

Gold

11 20 LIRE. Like No. 9 but head l. 1808-14 .... 225.00

12 40 LIRE. Sim. 1807-14 .... 450.00

LIGURIAN REPUBLIC (REPUBBLICA LIGURE). See GENOA.

LOMBARDY-VENETIA
Kingdom

In North Italy. Consisted mainly of the former duchies of Milan and Mantua and the former Republic of Venice, all restored to Austria at the fall of Napoleon (1814). Ceded piecemeal to the new kingdom of Italy (Lombardy-Milan 1859, Venice 1866).

Monetary System:

1814-56: 100 centesimi = 20 soldi = 20 Austrian kreuzer = 1 lira; 6 lire = 2 fiorino = 1 scudo = 1 Conventions thaler.

1857-66: 100 new soldi = 100 new kreuzer = 1 fiorino (Austrian florin or gulden).

Mints:

A – Vienna; B – Kremnitz; M – Milan; V – Venice.

Franz I, Emperor 1792-1835, In Lombardy-Venetia 1814-35

Copper

VG-F

*1 1/CENTESIMO. 1822, 34 .. .75

2 3/CENTESIMI. Sim. 1822, 34 .... .85

3 5/CENTESIMI. Sim. 1822, 34 .... 1.00

Nos. 1-3 dated 1822 from A (Vienna) Mint are patterns.

Silver

F-VF

*4 ¼ LIRA. 1822-24 .... 12.50

4a —. 1843V 15.00

5 ½ LIRA. Sim. 1822-24 ..... 15.00

No. 4a is a mule struck in 1848 by the provisional government of Venice.

No. 5 of 1821 is a pattern.

V.F.

6 LIRA. Like No. 10 but Rev. legend begins LOMB. ET VEN. etc. 1822-25 .... 30.00

7 (½ scudo). Like No. 10. 14 gr. 1822-27 .... 75.00

8 (scudo). Sim. 1821-32 ..... 175.00

Gold

9 (zecchino). S.M. VENEI. FRANC. I. Doge kneeling before St. Mark. Rev. Christ stdg. N.D. (1815) 1250.00

*10 (½ sovrano = 20 lire). 1820-31 .... 375.00

10a —. 1835 .... 400.00

11 (sovrano = 40 lire). Sim. 1820-31 .... 750.00

11a —. 1835 .... 1650.00

Ferdinand, Emperor 1835-48

Copper

Fine

12 1/CENTESIMO. Like No. 1. 1839, 43, 46 .... 1.00

13 3/CENTESIMI. Sim. 1839, 43, 46 .... 1.25

14 5/CENTESIMI. Sim. 1839, 43, 46 .... 1.50

Silver

V.F.

15 ¼ LIRA. Like No. 4 but head of Ferdinand. 1837-44 ..... 17.50

16 ½ LIRA. Sim. 1837-44 .... 20.00

17 LIRA. Like No. 6 but head of Ferdinand. 1837-44 ..... 30.00

18 (½ scudo). Like No. 10 but head of Ferdinand. 14 gr. 1837-46 .... 75.00

19 (scudo) Sim. 1837-46 ..... 115.00

Gold

20 (½ sovrano = 20 lire). Sim. 1837-48 .... 700.00

20a —. 1849M 800.00

21 (sovrano = 40 lire). Sim. 1837-48 .... 2250.00

Lombardy Revolutionary Provisional Government March-August 1848

Silver

*22 5/LIRE. 1848 .... 50.00

Gold

23 20/LIRE. Sim. 1848 ...... 1300.00

24 40/LIRE. Sim. 1848 ...... 2000.00

Other coins of the Provisional Government are trial pieces.

See Venice for the 1848-49 revolutionary coinage of that half of the kingdom.

Austrians Restored Franz Joseph 1848-1916, In Lombardy-Venetia 1848-66

Copper

Fine

25 1/CENTESIMO. Like No. 1. 1849, 50, 52 .... 1.50

26 3/CENTESIMI. Sim. 1849, 50, 52 .... 1.10

ITALY

LOMBARDY-VENETIA (Cont.)

Fine

27 5/CENTESIMI. Sim. 1849,
50. . . . . 1.50

28 10/CENTESIMI. Sim.
1849. . . . . 1.60

29 1/CENTESIMO. Like No. 32.
1852. . . . . 1.00

30 3/CENTESIMI. Sim. 1852. . 1.00

31 5/CENTESIMI. Sim. 1852. . 1.00

★32 10/CENTESIMI. 1852V. . . 1.50

33 15/CENTESIMI. Sim.
1852V. 4.50

Nos. 32-33 1852M exist and are rare.
There is a dispute whether they are
patterns.

34 5/10 (soldo). Like No. 35.
1862. . . . . .1.00

★35 1 (soldo). 1862. 50

Silver

V.F.

36 ½ LIRA. Like No. 4 but head
of Franz Joseph. 1854-55. . . .10.00

37 LIRA. Like No. 39 but Rev.
legend begins LOMB etc. 1852-
58. . . . . .35.00

38 (½ scudo). Like No. 39.
1853. . . . . .60.00

★39 (scudo). 1853. . . . . *(VF-EF)* 275.00

Gold

V.F.

40 (½ sovrano = 20 lire). Sim.
5.67 gr. 1854-56. . . . . .2600.00

41 (sovrano = 40 lire). Sim.
1853-56. . . . . ——

LUCCA (LUCA, LUCENSIS)

In N.W. Tuscany on the Gulf of Genoa.
Mint opened by the Lombards in 650
A.D.

I. Republic 1369-1799.

Arms of the Republic:
LIBERTAS on a bend.

Monetary System:
2 quattrini = 1 duetto;
3 quattrini = 1 soldo;
12 soldi = 6 Bolognini = 2 grossi =
1 Barbone;
25 soldi = 1 Santa Croce;
2 scudi d'oro = 1 doppia.

Copper

Fine

1 MEZZO (= ½)/SOLDO. Arms.
Rev. Value. 1734-90. . . . . . . 3.00

Billon

G-VG

2 (duetto) RESPUBLICA
LUCENSIS, L–U–C–A. Rev.
SANCTUS PETRUS, St. Peter.
1682-1790 (var.). 2.00

3 (soldo). RESPUBLICA LUCENSIS,
Arms. Rev. SANTVS PAVLINVS, St.
Paul. 1681-1758 (var.). 4.00

**Nos. 2 and 3 are often found cmkd.
with the city arms supported by
panther.**

4 BOLOGNINO. City arms
on branch with 9 leaves.
Rev. St. Peter. 1717, 90. . . . 4.00

★4a —. Restrike. 6 leaves.
1790 (= 1835). . . . . . . *(V.F.)* 6.00

Silver

Fine

5 (½ grosso). RESPUB. LUCEN.
2 shields. Rev. SANCT. VULTUS.
His bust. 1.5 gr. 1732-66,
N.D. 4.50

6 (½ grosso). Arms of the Republic. Rev. Arms of the
city/1768. 1.3 gr. 6.00

7 (Barbone). CIVITAS LVCENSIS.
Arms. Rev. SANCTUS VULTUS.
His bust. 2.8 gr. 1732-51. . . .20.00

8 (Barbone). RESPVB. LVCENS.
Arms. Rev. IVSTITIA ET PAX.
Justice. 1757. . . . . .18.00

F-VF

★9 (25 soldi). 1668-1756. . . . . . .35.00

★10 (scudo). 1735-54. . . . . .60.00

10a —. Arms supported. 1753-
56. . . . . .55.00

Gold (doppia = 5.5 gr.)

11 (½ doppia). Like No. 12.
1749. . . . . .800.00

★12 (doppia). 1749-50. . . . . . .1250.00

ITALY

LUCCA (Cont.)

                                      F-VF
13 (doppia). Generally like No. 3.
1758 . . . . ——

14 (2 doppie). Like No. 12.
1748 . . . . ——

II. French Occupation 1799-1805.

No coins.

III. Principality of Lucca and Piombino 1805-14.

Lucca and neighboring Piombino were erected into a principality for Napoleon's sister, Elisa Bonaparte 1805-14, and her husband, Felix Baciocchi 1805-10. Elisa was also her brother's viceroy in all Tuscany with the title of Grand Duchess, 1809-14.

Monetary System:
100 centesimi = 1 franco.

Felix and Elisa 1805-10

Copper
                                       Fine
21 3/CENTESIMI. Like No. 24 but 2 busts left. 1806 . . . . 5.00

22 5/CENTESIMI. Sim. 1806 . . 5.00

Silver
                                       F-VF
23 1/FRANCO. Like No. 24. 1805-08 . . . . 25.00

*24 5/FRANCHI. 1805-08 . . . . . . 60.00

IV. Provisional Government 1814-17.

No coins.

V. Duchy of Lucca 1817-47.

Monetary System:
3 quattrini = 1 soldo; 20 soldi = 1 lira.

Maria Luisa di Borbone (Ex Queen of Etruria, See Tuscany), Duchess of Lucca 1817-24

Carlo Lodovico di Borbone (Ex King of Etruria) Duke of Lucca 1824-47

Copper
                                       VG-F
31 1/QUATTRINO. ducato/di/ lucca. Rev. Value. 1826 . . . . 3.00

32 MEZZO (= ½)/SOLDO. ducato etc., cwn. Rev. Value. 1826, 35 . . . . 3.00

33 2/QUATTRINI. ducato etc. Lily-shield. Rev. Value. 1826 . . . . 2.50

34 1/SOLDO. carlo etc. . . . duca di lucca. Cwnd. lys. Rev. Value. 1826, 41 (var.) . . 2.00

35 5/QUATTRINI. carlo etc. Arms. Rev. Value. 1826 . . . . . 5.00

Billon

36 2/SOLDI. ducato etc. Arms. Rev. Value. 1835 . . . . 5.00

37 3/SOLDI. ducato etc. CL mon. Rev. Value. 1835 . . . . 35.00

38 5/SOLDI. ducato etc. Arms. Rev. Value. 1833, 38 . . . . 4.00

Silver
                                       F-VF
39 10/SOLDI. Head. Rev. Value. 1833, 38 . . . . 15.00

40 LIRA. Sim. 1834-38 . . . . 25.00

*41 2 L(ire). 1837 . . . . 45.00

In 1847 Carlo Lodovico became duke of Parma and ceded Lucca to Tuscany.

MACERATA, City

In the Marches.

Monetary System:
5 quattrini = 1 baiocco;
100 baiocchi = 1 scudo.

I. As part of the Papal States.

Pius VI, Pope 1775-99

Copper
                                       VG-F
1 BAIOC(chi)/CINQVE (= 5 B.). pivs papa sextvs etc. Value/ macerata. Rev. sancta etc. Madonna. 1797-98 . . . . 7.50

Billon
                                       Fine
2 BAIOCCHI SESSANTA (= 60 B.). pivs sextvs etc. Arms. Rev. Value/macerata/ 1799 . . . . 37.50

II. Under the Roman Republic 1798-99.

Copper

3 QVATRI/NO. a.i.d.l.i. Fasces. Rev. Value/macer. N.D 40.00

4 MEZZO (= ½)/BAIOCCO. Sim. but a(nno) i della lib(erte) ital(iane). Rev. Value/ macera/ta. N.D. 35.00

MALTA

An island in the Mediterranean lying south of Sicily. Governed from 1550 to 1798 by the Knights of St. John of Jerusalem. To France 1798-1800, to Great Britain thereafter.

Much of the independent Maltese coinage, particularly the minor series, is crude.

Arms of the Order: Maltese cross.

Monetary System:
6 piccioli = 1 grano;
20 grani = 2 carlini = 1 taro;
12 tari = 1 scudo;
30 tari = 1 pezza or oncia.

Emmanuel Pinto, Grand Master 1741-73

Pinto arms: 5 crescents, 2-1-2.

Copper
                                       V.G.
1 (grano). f. emanuel pinto m.m.h.h. Arms. Rev. in hoc signo etc. Cross. 1743-73 . . . 2.50

2 V (grani). Arms. Rev. 2 hands. 1748-57 . . . . 2.50

3 X (grani). Sim. 1742-57 . . . . . 3.00

*4 XX (grani). Head of St. John r. 1742 . . . . 12.50

4a —. Head l. 1752-62 . . . . 15.00

Silver

                                       VG-F
*7 (2 tari). 1741 . . . . 7.50

ITALY

MALTA (Cont.)

VG-F

8 *T(ari) 4*. Bust r. Rev. Arms.
1741 . . . . 7.50

8a —. Bust l. N.D 7.50

*10 T(ari) 4. Bust. Rev. Arms.
1756-68 . . . . 15.00

Fine

12 (7½ tari). Like No. 19.
N.D. 20.00

14 (scudo). Bust. Rev. Arms.
1741-54 . . . . .35.00

14a —. Bust r. 1764 . . . . .35.00

16 T(ari) XV. Like No. 19.
1756-72 . . . . .35.00

17 (2 scudi). Bust l. Rev. Arms.
38.5mm. 1741 . . . . .75.00

18 S(cudi) 2. Bust l. Rev. Arms of
Order and Pinto in 2 shields.
1764 . . . . .75.00

19 T(ari) XXX. Arms. Rev. NON
SVRREXIT etc. St. John stdg.
with banner. 1756-68 (var.) . .40.00

Gold (zecchino = 3.5 gr.)

V.F.

20 (zecchino). Bust l. Rev. Arms.
N.D., 1742 . . . . .700.00

21 (2 zecchini). Sim. N.D.,
1742 . . . . .1100.00

22 (4 zecchini). Sim. N.D.,
1742 . . . . .1750.00

22.3 (5 zecchini). Sim. N.D.,
1742 . . . . .3000.00

22.7 (10 zecchini). Sim. N.D.,
1742 . . . . ——

23 S(cudi) V. Like No. 19.
1756 . . . . .450.00

24 S(cudi) X. Sim. 1756-63 . . .475.00

25 S(cudi) XX. 2 shields.
Rev. St. John. 1764 . . . . . .1000.00

26 S(cudi) 20. Bust r. or l.
Rev. Arms. 1764-72 . . . . . .1100.00

Francisco Ximenez de Texada, Grand Master 1773-75

Arms: Per pale, tower and lion.

Silver

V.G.

30 (2 tari). Arms. Rev. Cross.
1774 . . . . 5.00

V.G.

31 T(ari) 4. Bust. Rev. Arms.
1774 . . . . 7.50

VG-F

*32 S(cudo) 1. 1773-74 . . . . .20.00

33 S(cudi) 2. Bust. Rev. 2 shields.
1773-74 . . . . .40.00

Gold

V.F.

34 S(cudi) X. Bust in circle.
Rev. 2 shields. 1773 . . . . . . .950.00

34a —. No circle. 1774 . . . . . . .800.00

34b —. Rev. Arms of Order only.
1774 .800.00

35 S(cudi) 20. Like No. 34.
1773 . . . . .1200.00

35a —. Like No. 34b. 1774 . . . .1400.00

Emmanuel de Rohan, Grand Master 1775-97

Arms: 9 lozenges, 3-3-3.

Copper

VG-F

36 (grano). Arms. Rev. Cross.
1776 . . . . 2.00

37 G(rano) I. F. EMMANUEL DE
ROHAN M. Arms. Rev. NON AES
etc. Value. 1776-85 (var.) . . . 2.00

37a —. Value/date. 1785-86 . . . . . 3.00

38 P(iccioli)/XV. Arms. Rev.
Value. 1776 . . . . 6.00

39 V (grani). Arms. Rev. 2 hands.
1776-90 . . . . 3.00

40 X (grani). Sim. 1776-88 . . . . . 5.00

*41 T(aro) I or (taro). 1786,
N.D. (var.) 10.00

41a T(aro) I. Rev. Legend
CONCVTIATIS etc. in lieu of
NON etc. N.D 12.00

Silver

F-VF

42 T(aro) I. Arms. Rev. Value.
1777 . . . . 3.00

43 (2 tari). Arms. Rev. Cross.
1776-79 . . . . 3.00

F-VF

*44 T(ari) 4. Arms. Rev. Value.
1776, 79 . . . . 4.00

46 T(ari) VI. Sim. 1776-80 . . . . . 6.00

47 S(cudo) I. Bust. Rev. winged
arms. 1776 . . . . .45.00

48 S(cudo) I. Bust. Rev. Arms.
1796 . . . . .25.00

49 T(ari) XV. Bust. Rev. 2 shields.
1776 . . . . .40.00

50 T(ari) XV. Like No. 47.
1779 . . . . .40.00

50a T(ari) 15. 1781 . . . . .30.00

51 T(ari) XXX. Like No. 49.
1777 . . . . .75.00

52 T(ari) XXX. Like No. 47.
1779 . . . . .50.00

52a T(ari) 30. 1781-96 . . . . .45.00

53 S(cudi) 2. Like No. 48.
1796 . . . . .25.00

Gold

V.F.

54 S(cudi) 5. Like No. 49.
1779 .600.00

55 S(cudi) 10. Sim. 1778-82 . . .850.00

56 S(cudi) 20. Sim. 1778-82 . .1350.00

Ferdinand, Freiherr von Hompesch, Grand Master 1797-98

Silver

VF-EF

57 *T(ari) 15*. Like No. 58.
1798 . . . . .30.00

58 T(ari) 30. FERDINANDVS
HOMPESCH M.M. Bust. Rev.
Arms on Imp. eagle. 1798 . .100.00

**No. 58 with a dot beneath the bust
is said to be a restrike issued during the French occupation.**

Gold

E.F.

59 *S(cudi) 20*. Arms on Imp. eagle.
Rev. St. John. Misdated
1778 . . . . ——

Siege and Blockade 1798-1800

Emergency coinage of French defenders under General Vaubois. Cut silver
and gold of various weights cmkd.
lion in oval. Rev. 3 lines: issue No./
Value in scudi, carlini and grani/as-
sayer's mark. All very rare.

ITALY

MALTA (Cont.)

Under Great Britain
1800 Onward

Monetary System:

12 "grani" = 4 farthings = 1 penny.

George IV 1820-30
Copper

F-VF

*60 (⅓ farthing). 1827........ 4.00

William IV 1830-37
Copper

VG-F

*61 (⅓ farthing). 1835........ 2.00

MANTUA (MANTOVA), Duchy

In Lombardy. To the Gonzaga family 1328-1708. To Austria 1708-97. Part of the Cisalpine Republic 1797-1802, of the Italian Republic 1802-05, and of the Napoleonic Kingdom of Italy 1805-14. To Austria as part of the Kingdom of Lombardy-Venetia 1814-66.

Mantua mint closed 1758. Later issues of the duchy were struck at Milan.

Monetary System:

12 denari = 2 sesini = 1 soldo; 20 soldi = 1 lira.

Maria Theresia of Austria
1740-80

Copper

V.G.

1 SESINO. Cross. Rev. SESINO/ DI. MAN/TOVA. 1750-58...... 2.00

2 SOLDO. Sun and rays. Rev. SOLDO/etc. 1750-58........ 3.00

3 SOLDONE (=2 soldi). Aust. arms. Rev. SOLDONE/ etc. 1750-58.............. 4.00

Silver

VG-F

4 S. 5 (=5 soldi). Like No. 8. 1750-55.................. 3.00

5 S. V (=5 soldi). Sim. 1756-57.................... 5.00

6 S. 10 (=10 soldi). Sim. 1750-56...................... 5.00

7 S. X (=10 soldi). Sim. 1757. 5.00

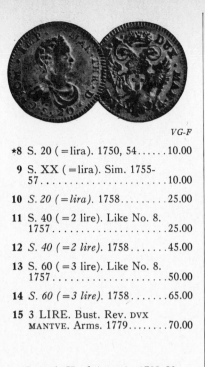

VG-F

*8 S. 20 (=lira). 1750, 54...... 10.00

9 S. XX (=lira). Sim. 1755-57.................... 10.00

10 *S. 20 (=lira). 1758........ 25.00

11 S. 40 (=2 lire). Like No. 8. 1757.................... 25.00

12 *S. 40 (=2 lire). 1758...... 45.00

13 S. 60 (=3 lire). Like No. 8. 1757.................... 50.00

14 *S. 60 (=3 lire). 1758...... 65.00

15 3 LIRE. Bust. Rev. DVX MANTVE. Arms. 1779........ 70.00

Joseph II of Austria 1780-90

His coinage for Milan was also used in Mantua.

Leopold II of Austria 1790-92

Silver

16 MEZZA (=½)/LIRA. Like No. 17. 1791.......... 18.00

*17 UNA (=1)/LIRA. 1791.... 22.00

Franz II of Austria
1792-97, 1814-35

Copper

19 ½/SOLDO. Arms. Rev. ½/SOLDO/DI/MANTOVA/ 1793.................... 4.00

Silver

Fine

20 SOLDI. 20 (=lira). FRANC. II. D.G. etc. ... MANT. Arms. Rev. 2 reliquaries/value. 1796. Struck by Austrian defenders during siege of the city by the French.............. 125.00

Blockade and Siege of 1799
Coined by the French Defenders

Cast Bell-Metal

Fine

*31 UN (=1)/SOLDO. A(nno) 7 (=1799)................. 25.00

Billon

32 SOLDI/-/-/V (=5 S.). Sim. but w/out branches. AN.VII (=1799)........... 35.00

33 X/SOLDI. Sim. ANNO VII (=1799)................. 40.00

See AUSTRIA — Nos. 188a, 191a and 192a for the 1848 Mantua siege coins.

MASSA-CARRARA
(di Lunigiana), Duchy

Small state in Tuscany. Marquis of Massa given the mint right in 1559. Raised to principality 1568, to duchy 1663.

Monetary System:

3 quattrini = 1 soldo; 20 soldi = 1 lira.

Maria Beatrice D'Este,
Wife of
Archduke Ferdinand of Austria
Duchess 1790-96, 1814-29

Copper

1 UN (=1)/QUATTRINO. Like No. 2. 1792.......... 10.00

*2 DUE (=2)/SOLDI. 1792... 12.50

Billon

V.G.

3 4/SOLDI. Sim. 1792....... 6.00

4 X/SOLDI. Sim. 1792....... 7.50

Massa was absorbed by Modena in 1829.

ITALY

MATELICA, City

In the Province of Macerata, Papal States.

Monetary System:
5 quattrini = 1 baiocco;
100 baiocchi = 1 scudo.

Pius VI 1775-99

Copper

VG-F

1 VN (=1) /QVATRINO. PIVS SEX. P.M. etc. Arms. Rev. Value/MATELI/CA. A(nno) XXIII (=1797-98)........22.50

2 MEZZO (=½) BAIOCCO. Sim. A(nno) XXIII (=1797-98)....................25.00

3 BAIOCCHI/DVE E MEZZO (=2½ B.). S.P. APOST. etc. St. Peter. Rev. Value/ MATELICA/1797...........15.00

4 BAIOC(chi)/CINQVE (=5 B.). PIVS PAPA etc. Value/MATELI/CA. Rev. SANCTA etc. Madonna. 1797....................35.00

MILAN (MILANO, MEDIOLANUM, MAILAND), Duchy

In Lombardy. Acquired by Spain 1535. Ceded to Austria 1713. Became part of the Cisalpine Republic 1797, of the Italian Republic 1802, and of the Kingdom of Italy 1805-14. Back to Austria as part of Lombardy-Venetia 1814-59.

Arms: The "Biscia" (coiled snake devouring child).

Monetary System:
12 denari = 6 sestini = 3 quattrini = 2 sesini = 1 soldo;
20 soldi = 8 parpaglioli = 1 lira;
6 lire = 1 scudo.

Crocione = Kronenthaler.

Mint marks:
M or no MM – Milan; W – Vienna;
S – Schmöllnitz.

Maria Theresia of Austria 1740-80

Copper

1 UN (=1)/SESTINO. Like No. 9. 1777, 79...... 2.00

2 (quattrino). Bust. Rev. MEDIO. DUX ET. Arms. 1750....... 3.50

4 UN (=1)/QVATTRINO. Like No. 9. 1776-79........ 2.00

5 (quattrino). Bust. Rev. MEDIOL. etc. Arms. N.D. (=1778-80)....................... 3.50

8 SESINO. Bust. Rev. MEDIOL. etc. Value. N.D. (1776-77).. 5.00

VG-F

★9 MEZZO/(=½)/SOLDO. 1776-79.................. 1.50

The 1773 soldo is a pattern.

★10 UN (=1)/SOLDO. Bust. Rev. Value. 1776-79....... 2.00

11 SEI (=6)/QUATTRINI. Sim. 1776.................. 8.00

Silver

I. Filippo Series. Irregular, .958 fine. Filippo = 27.8 gr.

F-VF

12 (⅛ Filippo). Bust. Rev. MEDIOLANI DUX ET C. Arms. 3.45 gr. 1741, 44..........30.00

13 (¼ Filippo). Sim. 6.95 gr. 1741, 44..................40.00

14 (½ Filippo). Sim. 13.9 gr. 1741, 44, 49..............85.00

14a —. No. 15 half thickness. 1741....................200.00

15 (Filippo). Sim. 1741-49....375.00

16 (2 Filippi). No. 15 double thick. 55 gr. 1741, 44..........800.00

II. Coinage Modernized.

Fine

17 (2½ soldi). Bust. Rev. MLNI/ DUX/date. 1.4 gr. 1749-63... 1.75

18 S(oldi) V. Sim. 1749-63.... 2.00

19 (½ lira). MARIA THERESIA/ . . . / MEDIOLANI/21 IAN 1741. Rev. Lion, arms. Investiture as duchess. 1.8 gr.......... 8.00

★20 X (soldi) 1762, 67.........10.00

21 10 (soldi). Sim. 1766.......10.00

22 X (soldi). Veiled bust. Rev. MEDIOL. DUX. Biscia in wreath. 1771, 74..................10.00

22a —. Rev. Arms. 1773.......12.00

23 (lira). Investiture as duchess. Like No. 19. 3.7 gr. 1741....45.00

Fine

24 XX (soldi). Like No. 20. 1762, 67..................16.00

The 20, 30 and 60 soldi of 1763 are patterns.

III. Final Silver Series.

The V and X soldi and (½ lira), (1 lira) and (6 lire) 1777 are patterns.

31 5/SOLDI. Biscia in shield. Rev. Value. 1778-80........ 8.00

33 MEZZA (=½) LIRA. Like No. 38. 1778-80...........12.00

34 UNA (=1) LIRA. Sim. 1778-80.....................25.00

F-VF

35 (3 lire). Sim. 1777-80......60.00

36 (6 lire). Sim. 23 gr. 1778-80.....................125.00

Gold

(zecchino = 3.47 gr. = 14 lire 10 soldi; doppia = 6.3 gr. = 24 lire)

V.F.

37 (zecchino). Bust of Mar. Ther. Rev. St. Ambrose. N.D..... —

★38 (zecchino). 1778-80........950.00

39 (doppia). Sim. 1778-80....2750.00

40 (2 doppie). Sim. 1778-79.... —

Joseph II of Austria 1780-90

Silver

Fine

41 5/SOLDI. Biscia shield. Rev. Value. 1780-87........ 5.00

★42 MEZZA (=½) LIRA. 1781-87..................... 9.00

43 UNA (=1) LIRA. Sim. 1781-90.................... 10.00

F-VF

44 (3 lire). Sim. 1781-86......50.00

45 (6 lire). Sim. 23 gr. 1781-86.....................125.00

Pieces dated 1781 with bust, rev. LANGOBARD/FIDES/etc., are homage ceremony medals.

ITALY

MILAN (Cont.)

Gold (zecchino = 3.47 gr.)

V.F.

46 (zecchino). Bust. Rev. Arms.
1781-84...................375.00
47 (doppia). Sim. 1781-85.....850.00

Types of the Austrian Netherlands

Struck at Milan (mmk. M) as trade coins. See LOW COUNTRIES for similar coins with other mmks.

Silver

F-VF

48 (½ Crocione). Head.
Rev. like No. 59.
14.72 gr. 1786-90M.......18.00
49 (Crocione). Sim. 1786-
90M....................35.00

Gold (sovrano = 11.06 gr.)

V.F.

50 (½ sovrano = 1 souverain d'or
in Aust. Neth.). Like No. 51.
1787-90M................85.00

*51 (sovrano). 1786-90M......175.00

Leopold II of Austria 1790-92

Silver

Fine

52 UNA (= 1) LIRA. Head.
Rev. MEDIOLANI ET MANT. DUX.
Arms. 1790-91...........15.00

Types of the Austrian Netherlands

F-VF

53 (½ Crocione). Like No.
54. 1791M................25.00

V.F.

*54 (Crocione). Obv. *.
Rev. like No. 59.
1791-92M................75.00

Gold (sovrano = 11.06 gr.)

V.F.

55 (¼ sovrano). Like No. 56.
1791M................. ——

*56 (½ sovrano). 1790-92M....375.00
57 (sovrano). Sim. 1790-92M.2000.00

Franz II of Austria, 1792-1835, In Milan 1792-97/1800

Silver

Fine

58 SOLDI 30. Head. Rev. Arms.
1792-1800...............15.00
58a —. MEDILANI. 1794.....40.00

Pieces dated 1792 with bust, rev. LAN-
GOBARD/etc., are homage ceremony
medals.

Types of the Austrian Netherlands

Silver

F-VF

*59 (Crocione). 1792-1800M....27.50

Gold (sovrano = 11.06 gr.)

V.F.

60 (½ sovrano). Head. Rev. like
No. 56. 1800M.........3750.00
61 (sovrano). Sim. 1793-
1800M...............1200.00

MODENA (MUTINA), Duchy

In upper Italy. The town of Modena, which began coining in the 13th century, came into the hands of the d'Este family shortly afterward. The rulers of Modena were given the rank of duke in 1452. From 1796 to 1813 Modena was part of the Napoleonic complex. Thereafter, until 1859 when it was absorbed into the new kingdom of Italy, Modena was governed by the House of Austria-Este. No coins were struck after 1796.

Monetary Systems:
12 denari = 2 sesini = 1 soldo =
1 bolognino;
20 Bolognini = 10 Muraglioli =
4 Giorgini = 3 Capellone = 1 lira;
3 small scudi = 1 Tallero.

Francesco III d'Este, 12th Duke 1737-80

Copper

VG-F

*1 (sesino). Head r. Rev. 6 fold
arms, eagle centershield. No
legends. 16-18mm. 0.8-1.0 gr.
N.D.....................2.50
2 SOL/DO. Lily. Rev. Value.
19mm. 1.5-2.3 gr. N.D......1.50
3 BOLO/GNINO. d'Este eagle.
Rev. Value. N.D...........1.50

Billon

V.G.

4 DA DUE/BOLOG (= 2
Bolognini). NOBILI AESTEN.
Arms. Rev. Value/MOD/date.
1740-47.................2.00
5 B.4 (= 4 Bolognini). FRANC. III
MUT. R.M. DUX. Bust. Rev.
NOBILITAS AESTENSIS. Eagle.
1739....................3.00
6 (5 soldi). NOBILITAS ESTENSIS.
Eagle. Rev. S. CONTARDUS
ESTENSIS. St. stdg. 1740-62..2.75
7 DA. BOLOG/SEI. DEN/OTTO
(= 6B8d = Capellone). FRANCIS
III M.R. M.D. Bust. Rev. Value.
1750-51.................4.00
8 (10 soldi). Like No. 11.
2-3.2 gr. 1738...........4.50

Fine

9 (lira). Sim. 5.4-6.2 gr.
1738-39................15.00

F-VF

10 (lira). Obv. sim. Rev. QUEM
GENUIT etc. Madonna. For
Reggio. 1739.............45.00

*11 (2 lire). 10.6-11.5 gr. 1738...65.00

ITALY

MODENA (Cont.)

Silver
F-VF

12 (scudo). Obv. sim. Rev. VETERIS etc. Arms. 1739..........350.00

Ercole (Hercules) III d'Este, 13th Duke 1780-96

Driven out by French and died in exile 1803.

Copper

Eklund attributes an anonymous undated sesino to this reign (No. 246: eagle, rev. value), but CNI places it before the period covered by this catalog.

V.G.

13 DENARI/QVATTRO (=4 denari). Cwnd. lily. Rev. Value. N.D. (var.).... 3.50

14 UN (or VN=1) /SOLDO. Date in wreath or cartouche. Rev. Value in same. 1783-84. (var.)................. 3.50

15 UN (or VN=1) /BOLOGNI/NO. d'Este eagle. Rev. Value. 1783-84................... 3.50

Billon

16 DA DUE/BOLOGNI/NI (=2 B.) Eagle. Rev. Value. 1783-84................... 6.00

Silver

V.F.

*17 (small scudo). 9 gr. 1782-83 .80.00

18 (2 scudi). Sim. 18 gr. 1782-83.....................100.00

19 (3 scudi). Sim. 27 gr. 1782-83.....................170.00

20 (Tallero). Bust. Rev. DEXTERA etc. Arms. 1795-96.......190.00

MONACO, Principality

On the Mediterranean near the French-Italian border. Ruled by the Genoese Grimaldi family since 968.

Monetary System:
100 centimes=1 franc.

Honoré V 1819-41

Copper or Brass

F-VF

*1 CINQ (=5)/CENTIMES. Cast Brass. Large or small (*) head. 1837................12.00

1a —. Struck Copper. 1837-38..10.00

2 UN/DECIME (=10 Centimes). Struck Copper or Brass. Sim. 1838................12.00

Note: Nos. 1, 1a and 2 were engraved by BORREL (see name under head). Specimens by ROGAT are patterns.

Silver

E.F.

*3 5 FRANCS. 1837.........400.00

Other silver denominations and gold of the reign of Honoré V are patterns.

MONTALTO, City

In the Province of Ascoli, The Marches, Papal States.

Monetary System:
100 baiocchi=1 scudo.

Pius VI, Pope 1775-99

Copper
VG-F

1 BAIOCCHI/DVE E MEZZO (=2½ B.). S.P. APOST. etc. St. Peter. Rev. Value/ MONTALTO/1797............15.00

2 BAIOC(chi)/CINQVE (=5 B.). PIVS PAPA etc. Value/MONTALTO. Rev. SANCTA etc. Madonna. 1797....................25.00

MURANO, Community

In the Republic of Venice. Given, at an early date, the right to strike silver oselle (New Year presentation pieces, weight about 10 gr.), and from the same dies, gold 4 zecchini. These pieces, which list the names and show the arms of Murano aristocracy, generally with the current Venetian doge's name and COMVNITAT MVRIANI, were struck almost yearly during the 18th century up to 1796. They could pass for coins, but were not intended to circulate and are therefore not listed here. They are scarce and desirable.

NAPLES and SICILY (TWO SICILIES), Kingdom

The foot and shank of Italy's boot and the adjacent island of Sicily. Founded 1130.

The kingdom was wrested from Austria by Don Carlos of Bourbon, son of Philip V of Spain, in 1733-34. In 1735 Carlos was recognized as king of Naples and Sicily.

The two parts used the same money of account, but the grana, carlini and tari of Naples were each worth two Sicilian ones. Coins for Naples alone, or for the entire kingdom, are listed here. Coins for Sicily alone are listed under that island.

Monetary System of Naples:

6 cavalli=1 tornese;
240 tornesi=120 grana=12 Carlini=
6 (Naples) tari=1 piastra;
5 grana=1 cinquina;
100 grana=1 ducato (tallero).

Carlo (Carlos) IV di Borbone 1734-59

(Later Carlos III of Spain 1759-88)

Copper

*1 3 (cavalli). CAR. D.G. UTR. VG-F SIC. REX. Bust. Rev. 3. 1755-57................... 2.50

ITALY

NAPLES (Cont.)

VG-F

2 4 (cavalli). Sim. but Rev. 4.
1751-57 .... 2.50

2.5 (tornese). Bust. Rev.
HILA/RI/TAS. 20mm.
1754-57 .... 2.00

3 9 (cavalli). Bust. Rev. 9.
1756-57 .... 6.00

5 (grano). Like No. 2.5.
27mm. 1756-57 .... 2.00

7 (3 tornesi). CAR. D.G. UTR.
SIC. ET HIER. REX. Bust.
Rev. PUBLICA/LAETI/TIA.
1756-57 .... 2.00

Silver

Fine

10 5 (grana). *Bust.* Rev. 5.
1735 .... 5.00

12 (5 grana). 1751 .... 4.50

★13 (5 grana). Rev. Abundantia.
1755-59 .... 4.50

15 (Carlino). CAR. etc. Bust.
IN HOC etc. Cross. 1755 ..... 7.00

19 G(rana) 60. Like No. 23.
1734-49 .... 30.00

21 (60 grana). Like No. 24.
1747 .... 45.00

★22 G(rana) 60. 1750-54 .... 40.00

F-VF

23 G(rana) 120. CAR: D: G: REX
NEA(P): etc. Arms. Rev. DE
SOCIO PRINCEPS. Poseidon re-
clines, Vesuvius in background.
1734-49 .... 45.00

F-VF

24 (piastra). Busts of Carlo and
Maria Amalia. Rev. FIRMATA
etc. Female and child. On birth
of Prince Philip. 1747 ...... 90.00

25 G(rana) 120. Like No. 22.
1750-54 .... 50.00

Gold

V.F.

26 D(ucati) 2. Like No. 28.
1749-54 .... 850.00

27 D(ucati) 4. Sim. 1749-59 ... 900.00

28 D(ucati) 6. CAR. D.G. UTR. etc.
Bust. Rev. Arms. 1749-55 . 1100.00

28a —. CAR. D.G. SIC. ET HIE.
REX HIS. IN. 1752 .... 1200.00

**Ferdinando IV (III in Sicily)
1759-1825,
Ousted from Naples (but not Sicily)
1799, 1805-15
Adopted Title Ferdinando I,
King of Two Sicilies, 1816**

First Period: 1759-99

Copper

VG-F

29 C(avalli) 3. Bust. Rev. Cross.
1788-92 .... 1.25

★31 C(avalli) 4. 1788-93 .... 3.00

33 TOR/NESE. Bust. Rev.
Value/C.6. 1788-92 .... 2.00

37 C(avalli) 9. Bust. Rev.
Tower. 1788-93 .... 4.00

39 VN (=1) /GRANO. FERDINAN
IV. SICILIAR etc. Bust. Rev.
VN/GRANO/(=)CAVALLI/12.
1788-97 .... 5.00

★43 (3 tornesi). Bust. Rev.
PVBLICA/COMMODI/TAS.
1788-93 .... 7.50

VG-F

45 T(ornesi) 5. Arms in wreath.
Rev. cwnd. T.5/date. 1797-
98 .... 5.00

49 OTTO (=8) /TORNESI.
Head. Rev. value 1796-97 ... 12.00

51 TORNESI/10. Sim.,
but cwn. over value. 1798 ... 12.00

Silver

F-VF

★53 (Carlino). *1788-98* 5.00

55 G(rana) 20. 1787-92 .... 5.00

★57 G(rana) 20. 1795-98 .... 5.00

59 G(rana) 50. Bust. Rev. arms.
1784-85 .... 25.00

60 G(rana) 60. Young bust
with small head. Rev. broad
arms. 1760 .... 25.00

61 G(rana) 60. Older bust with
large head. Rev. narrower
arms. 1785-94 .... 25.00

61a —. Head. 1795-96 .... 25.00

63 DUCATO. FERDINAN IV D.G.
SICILIAR etc. Bust. Rev. oval
arms. 1784-85 .... 45.00

64 GR(ana) 120. Bust. Rev. arms.
1766 .... 55.00

64a —. Smaller bust. 1767 ...... 55.00

65 (piastra). Busts of Ferd. and
Maria Carolina. Rev. Queen
and child. On birth of princess.
1772 .... (V.F.) 75.00

66 G(rana) 120. Bust. Rev. Arms.
1784-85 .... 45.00

66a —. Sprays over arms. 1786-
94 .... 45.00

66b —. Head (like No. 98). 1795-
98 .... 45.00

V.F.

67 (piastra). Busts of Ferd. and
Maria Carolina. Rev. PRO
FAVSTO etc. Vesuvius, 2 dieties.
1791 .... 100.00

68 (piastra). Obv. sim.
Rev. SOLI etc. Sun, earth,
zodiac. 1791 .... 100.00

ITALY

NAPLES (Cont.)

Gold

V.F.

69 D(ucati) 2. Bust. Rev. Arms.
1762 . . . . 650.00

71 D(ucati) 2. Older bust.
Rev. Arms. 1771 . . . . 650.00

73 D(ucati) 4. Like No. 69.
1760-67 . . . . 700.00

74 D(ucati) 4. Like No. 71.
1768-82 . . . . 700.00

75 D(ucati) 6. Like No. 69.
1759-67 . . . . 750.00

76 D(ucati) 6. Like No. 71.
1768-82 . . . . 750.00

76a —. Still older bust. 1783-
85 . . . . 1500.00

Neapolitan Republic
(Parthenopean Republic, Repubblica Napolitana)

Revolutionary government in Naples
23 January-13 June 1799 (year 7).

Copper

Fine

81 TORNE/SI/QVAT/TRO
(=4 T.). Fasces. Rev. Value.
ANNO SETTIMO (=yr. 7). . . . 7.50

82 TOR/NESI/SEI (=6 T.).
Sim. Yr. 7 . . . . 7.50

Silver

83 CAR/LINI/SEI (=6 C.).
Like No. 84. Yr. 7 . . . . 45.00

★84 CAR/LINI/DODI/CI (=12 C.)
Liberty stdg. Rev. Value.
Yr. 7 . . . . 135.00

For coins of the Royal Neapolitan occupation of Rome 1799-1800, see Papal States.

Ferdinando IV,
Restored in Naples 1799-1805

Copper

91 C(avalli) 3. Bust. Rev. Cross.
1804 . . . . 2.50

92 C(avalli) 4. Bust. Rev. Grapes.
1804 . . . . 5.00

Fine

93 TOR/NESE. Bust. Rev.
Value/C.6./1804 . . . . 5.00

94 C(avalli) 9. Bust. Rev. Castle.
1801, 04 . . . . 6.00

94.5 VN/GRANO. Like No. 39.
1800 . . . . 35.00

95 TOR/NESI/4. Bust.
Rev. Value. 1799-1800 . . . . . 5.00

96 TOR/NESI/6. Sim.
1799-1803 . . . . 10.00

Silver

F-VF

97 G(rana) 60. Like No. 99.
1805 . . . . 40.00

★98 G(rana) 120. Head. Rev. Arms.
1799-1802 . . . . 50.00

★99 G(rana) 120. Head. Rev. spade
shield. 1805 . . . . 60.00

Joseph Napoleon,
King of Naples (not Sicily)
1806-08

(Afterward King of Spain)

Silver

VF-EF

★100 G(rana) 120. Head.
Rev. Arms. 1806-08 . . . . . . 200.00

Gioacchino Napoleone
(Marshal Joachim Murat, Napoleon's brother-in-law, King of Naples (not Sicily) 1808-15

I. First Monetary System:
120 grana = 12 Carlini = 1 piastra.

Copper

Fine

101 GRANA/2. Head l. Rev.
Value. 1810 . . . . 35.00

102 GRANA/3. Sim. 1810 . . . . . 35.00

102a 3/GRANA. 1810 . . . . 35.00

Silver

V.F.

★103 DODICI (=12) /CARLINI.
Head l. Rev. Value. 1809-
10 . . . . 250.00

The 1810 with head to right is a rare pattern.

II. Second Monetary System:
100 centesimi = 1 franco.

Gold

104 FRANCHI/40. Head l.
Rev. value. 1810 . . . . . . Ex. Rare

III. Third Monetary System:
100 centesimi = 1 lira.

Bronze

105 3/CENTESIMI. Head l.
Rev. Value. 1813 . . . . 900.00

106 5/CENTESIMI. Sim.
1813 . . . . 900.00

107 10/CENTESIMI. Sim.
1813 . . . . 900.00

107a —. Overstruck TOR/NESI/6
by Bourbons 850.00

Silver

108 MEZ(za = ½)/LIRE. Head r.
Rev. value. 1812, 13 . . . . . . 40.00

109 1/LIRA. Sim. 1812, 13 . . . . 30.00

110 2/LIRE. Sim. 1812, 13 . . . . 50.00

ITALY

NAPLES (Cont.)

V.F.

★111 5 LIRE. Head r. Rev. Arms.
1812, 13 . . . . .300.00

Gold

112 20/LIRE. Head l. Rev. Value.
1813 . . . . .500.00

113 40/LIRE. Sim. 1813 . . . .800.00

Ferdinando, Again Restored in Naples 1815-25

I. As Ferdinando IV 1815-16.

Copper

F-VF

114 CINQUE (=5)/TORNESI.
Cwnd. head l. Rev. Value.
1816 . . . . .10.00

115 OTTO (=8)/TORNESI.
Sim. 1816 . . . . .25.00

Silver

V.F.

116 G(rana) 10. Like No. 118.
1815-16 . . . . .15.00

117 G(rana) 60. Sim. 1816 . . . . .50.00

★118 G(rana) 120. Bust.
Rev. Arms. 1815-16 . . . . . .100.00

Note: 120 grana of this reign with R(is-tampato) beside date are struck over coins of Joseph Napoleon and Murat. Worth 200% more.

II. As Ferdinando I, King of Two Sicilies 1816-25.

Copper

F-VF

119 1/TORNESE. Cwnd. head l.
Rev. Value in wreath.
1817 . . . . .3.00

F-VF

120 QUATTRO (=4)/TORNESI.
Sim. but no wreath.
1817 . . . . .15.00

121 CINQUE (=5)/TORNESI.
Sim. 1816-18 . . . . 4.00

121a TORNESI/CINQUE (=5 T.).
Obv. sim. Rev. cwn./value.
1819 . . . . 8.00

122 OTTO (=8)/TORNESI.
Like No. 120. 1816-18 . . . . .35.00

123 TORNESI/DIECI (=10 T.).
Like No. 121a. 1819 . . . . . . .20.00

Silver

V.F.

★124 G(rana) 10. 1818 . . . . .12.00

125 G(rana) 60. Sim. 1818 . . . . .50.00

126 G(rana) 120. Sim.
1817-18. (var.) 40.00

Gold

127 DUCATI 3. Cwnd. head l.
Rev. Genius with lily-shield.
1818 . . . . .500.00

128 DUCATI 15. Sim. 1818 .2250.00

129 DUCATI 30. Sim. 1818 . . . ——

Francesco I 1825-30

Copper

F-VF

130 TORNESE/UNO (=1 T.).
Like No. 133. 1827 . . . . 5.00

131 TORNESI/DUE (=2 T.).
Sim. 1825-26 . . . . 6.00

132 TORNESI/CINQUE (=5 T.).
Sim. 1826-27 . . . . .12.50

F-VF

★133 TORNESI/DIECI (=10 T.).
FRANCISCVS I D.G. REGNI VTR.
SIC. etc. Head. Rev. Cwn.
over value. 1825 . . . . 7.50

Silver

134 (10 grana). Head. Rev. oval
arms. 18.5mm. 1826 . . . . . . .10.00

135 G(rana) 20. Like No. 137.
1826 . . . . .25.00

136 G(rana) 60. Sim. 1826 . . . . .60.00

V.F.

★137 G(rana) 120. Head.
Rev. Arms. 1825-28 . . . . . . .40.00

Gold

138 DUCATI 3. Head. Rev. Genius
with lily-shield. 1826 . . . . . . ——

139 DUCATI 6. Sim. 1826 . . . . ——

140 DUCATI 15. Sim. 1825 . . . ——

141 DUCATI 30. Sim. 1825-
26 . . . . ——

Ferdinando II 1830-59

A. Head Without Beard.

Copper

F-VF

★142 MEZZO (=½)/TORNESE.
FERD. II etc. 1832-47 . . . . . . 3.50

143 TORNESE/UNO (=1 t.).
Sim. 1832-36 . . . . 3.00

143a —. Older head. 1838-48 . . . .4.00

ITALY

NAPLES (Cont.)

F-VF

144 TORNESE/UNO E MEZZO
(= 1½ t). Sim. 1832-40.... 8.00

145 TORNESI/DUE (= 2 t).
Sim. but FERDINANDUS II etc.
1832, 35 ....15.00

146 TORNESI/TRE (= 3 t).
Sim. 1833-38............ 8.00

147 TORNESI/CINQUE (= 5 t).
Sim. 1831-41............10.00

148 TORNESI/DIECI (= 10 t).
Sim. 1831-39............10.00

Silver

★149 GRANA CINQUE (= 5 g).
1836-47 .... 6.00

150 G(rana) 10. Like No. 153.
1832-35 .... 9.00

150a —. Obv. legend broken
over head. 1835-39....... 9.00

★151 G(rana) 20. Sim. 1831-39 .. 6.00

V.F.

152 G(rana) 60. Like No. 153.
1831-34 ....40.00

152a —. Obv. legend broken
over head. 1835-39.......37.50

★153 G(rana) 120. 1831-35......35.00

153a —. Obv. legend broken
over head. 1835-39.......25.00

Gold

154 DUCATI 3. Young head.
Rev. Genius holding lily-shield.
1831-35 ....1100.00

154a —. 1837.............1100.00

155 DUCATI 6. Sim. 1831-35.1600.00

V.F.

156 DUCATI 15. Sim. 1831... ——

157 DUCATI 30. Sim.
1831-35 .... ——

B. Head With Beard.

Copper

F-VF

★142a MEZZO (= ½)/TORNESE.
FERD. II etc. 1848-54..... 3.00

143b TORNESE/UNO (= 1 t).
Sim. 1845-59........... 3.50

144a TORNESE/UNO E MEZZO
(= 1½ t). Sim. 1844-48... 8.00

144b —. Older head.
1849-54 .... 8.00

★145a TORNESI/DUE (= 2 t).
Sim. 1838-59........... 4.00

146a TORNESI/TRE (= 3 t).
Sim. 1839-58........... 8.00

147a TORNESI/CINQUE (= 5 t).
Sim. 1841-45...........10.00

147b —. Older head.
1846-59 ....10.00

148a TORNESI/DIECI (= 10 t).
Young head. 1839-51
(2 var.)................10.00

148b —. Older head. 1851-59 ..10.00

Silver

149b GRANA CINQUE (= 5 g).
Like No. 149 but bearded
head. 1848-53 .... 6.00

150b G(rana) 10. Like No. 153b.
1838-46 .... 6.00

150c —. Older head. 1847-59... 5.00

151b G(rana) 20. Like No. 153b.
1839-59 .... 6.00

V.F.

152b G(rana) 60. Sim.
1841-45 ....40.00

152c —. Older head. 1846-59...30.00

V.F.

★153b G(rana) 120. Young bearded
head. Rev. like No. 151.
1840-51 ....20.00

153c —. Older head.
1851-59 ....20.00

Gold

154b DUCATI 3. Young bearded
head. Rev. like No. 154.
1839-40 ....950.00

154c —. 1842-48...........900.00

154d —. Older head
1850-56 ....900.00

155b DUCATI 6. Like No. 154b.
1840 ....1500.00

155c —. 1842-56..........1350.00

156c DUCATI 15. Like
No. 154c. 1842-47........ ——

156d —. Older head.
1848-56 .... ——

157b DUCATI 30. Like
No. 154b. 1839-40....... ——

157c —. 1844-54............ ——

157d —. Older head.
1854, 56............... ——

Francesco II 1859-61

Copper

VF-EF

★158 TORNESI/2. Head.
Rev. Lily/value. 1859.....12.00

159 TORNESI/10. Sim. 1859..17.50

Silver

160 G(rana) 20. Like No. 161.
1859 ....20.00

ITALY

NAPLES (Cont.)

VF-EF

*161 G(rana) 120. Head.
Rev. Arms. 1859.........60.00

In 1860-61 Sicily and then Naples were absorbed into the new kingdom of Italy.

NEAPOLITAN REPUBLIC.

See NAPLES and SICILY.

ORBETELLO (REALI PRESIDII)

Small domain in Tuscany which belonged to the kingdom of Naples and Sicily until 1808.

Monetary System:

60 quattrini = 1 lira.

Ferdinando IV, King of Naples and Sicily 1759-1808

Copper

VG-F

1 QVATTRINO/I. Like No. 2.
1782-98.................15.00

*2 QVATTRINI/II. 1782-98...15.00

3 QVATTRINI/IIII. Sim.
1782-98..................15.00

PALMA NOVA

Strong place in Venetia on Illyrian frontier. Ceded by Austria to France 1806, back to Austria 1814.

Monetary System:

100 centesimi = 1 lira.

Emergency Coinage of French Defenders 1814

Billon

Pagani says the 25 cent. of Palma Nova is probably a pattern, possibly unique.

F-VF

*2 CENT(esim)! 50. 1814.....85.00

PAPAL STATES (STATI PONTIFICI, STATES OF THE CHURCH)

Area in Central Italy governed by the Pope. Invaded by France in 1797. Converted into the Roman Republic 1798-99. Occupied by Neapolitan troops 1799-1800. Returned to the Pope 1800. Absorbed piecemeal into the Napoleonic kingdom of Italy 1805-09. Back to the Papacy 1814-48. Again converted through revolution into the Roman Republic 1848-49. Back to the Papacy 1849-70. Bologna, The Marches, and Umbria to the new kingdom of Italy 1860, Rome and environs (the Patrimony of St. Peter) to Italy 1870.

Monetary System until 1866:

5 quattrini = 1 baiocco;
30 baiocchi = 6 grossi = 4 Carlini = 3 giulio = 3 Paoli = 1 testone;
100 baiocchi = 1 scudo;
30 Paoli = 1 doppia.

Mints (except as otherwise identified): A(ncona) until 1798; B(ologna) until 1859; R(ome) until 1870.

Benedict XIV, Pope 1740-58

Copper

VG-F

1 QVAT/TRINO. BENEDICT XIV P.M. etc. Arms. Rev. Value/ ROM(ANO)/date. 1740-42.... 1.75

1a QVATRINO/ROMANO.
1751-52..................1.50

1b QVATRI/NO. 1752-56
(var.)....................1.50

See Gubbio for undated quattrini with SS. Peter or Paul or both.

VG-F

*4 QVATTRINO. BENED. XIV etc.
Arms. Rev. QVATTRINO ROMANO.
Holy Door. 1750 (var.)..... 2.50

5 MEZZO (=½)/BAIOCCO.
Like No. 1. 1740-55........ 1.50

6 MEZZO BAIOCCO. Like
No. 4. 1750.............. 1.75

7 VN (=1)/BAIOCCO. Like
No. 1. 1740-43. N.D........ 2.00

7a —. ROMANO. 1751-58....... 2.50

Billon

G-VG

8 DVE (=2) BAIOC/CHI.
Like No. 9. 1746-49........ 2.50

*9 QVAT/TRO (=4) BAIOC/CHI.
1747-48.................. 2.75

10 VN (=1) /CARLINO. BENED.
XIV. etc. Arms. Rev. Value/
ROMANO. 1747-51........... 3.00

11 DVE (=2) /CARLINI. Sim.
1747-52.................. 3.25

Silver

F-VF

12 (½ grosso). BENEDICT XIV etc.
Arms. Rev. BENE/FAC/HVMILI.
.5-.6 gr. A(nno) I.......... 5.00

12a —. Rev. BEATI/PAVPERES.
A(nno) I, III, VIII........ 3.50

12b —. Rev. VIATORI etc. Holy
Door, open. 1750.......... 4.50

12c —. Rev. APERVIT etc. Holy Door
closed. 1750............. 5.00

13 (½ grosso). Arms. Rev.
MODECUM/IVSTO. 1757...... ——

14 (grosso). BENEDICTVS XIIII etc.
Arms. Rev. PAVPERI/PORRIGE/
MANVM. 1.1-1.4 gr. 1740..... 5.00

15 (grosso). BENEDICT(vs) XIV etc.
Arms. Rev. S. PETRVS etc. St.
Peter. A(nno) I-X......... 2.25

15a —. Rev. PAVPERI/etc. A(nno) I,
1741.................... 4.00

15b —. Rev. SACROSAN etc.
1741.................... 6.00

15c —. Rev. DISPERSIT/etc. A(nno)
II, 1742-43.............. 3.50

ITALY

PAPAL STATES (Cont.)

F-VF

15d —. Rev. EDENT/etc. A(nno)
II 5.00

15e —. Rev. NOVIT/etc. A(nno)
III-IV 4.00

15f —. Rev. OCVLI/etc. 1743-44,
A(nno) IV 3.25

15g —. Rev. S. PAVLVS etc. St. Paul.
A(nno) IV-VIII 2.50

15h —. Rev. MACVLA etc. Madonna.
A(nno). VII-VIII 4.00

15i —. Rev. TIBI etc. St. Peter.
1748 . . . . 4.25

15j —. Rev. VT/ALAT/etc. A(nno)
IX-X, 1748-49 . . . . 3.00

15k —. Rev. ACCIPIVNT etc. Holy
Door open. 1750 . . . . 3.25

15l —. Rev. APERVIT etc. Holy
Door closed. 1750 . . . . 3.50

15m —. Rev. TOTA etc. Madonna.
A(nno) XII-XVI 2.75

16 (giulio). BENEDICT XIV etc.
Arms. Rev. SACROSANC/etc.
1741 R.N 5.00

★17 (2 giulio). Bust. Rev. Holy
Church std. 5.3 gr. 1753-57
R.N 12.50

18 (testone). BENEDICT XIV etc.
Arms. Rev. PRINCIPES VRBIS
etc. SS Peter and Paul.
1746 R.N 45.00

19 (½ scudo). Like No. 17.
13.1 gr. 1753-54 R.N 60.00

20 (scudo). Sim. 1753-54 R.N . 200.00

Gold (zecchino = 3.4 gr.)

V.F.

21 (¼ zecchino). BEN. XIV. Keys.
Rev. S. PETRVS, St. Peter.
1741-42, N.D 250.00

23 (½ zecchino). Like No. 27 but
Rev. DEDIT etc. Arms. 1740. 300.00

23a —. Like No. 27. 1740-55 . . 250.00

23b —. A. IVB. 1750 . . . . 700.00

24 (zecchino). Like No. 23 but
BENED. XIIII etc. 1740 . . . . 350.00

24a —. Rev. DE REPENTE etc.
1740 . . . . 350.00

25 (zecchino). Like No. 27.
1741-56 . . . . 300.00

25a —. A. IVB. 1750 . . . . 600.00

V.F.

★27 (2 zecchini). 1748 . . . . ——

Sede Vacante 1758

Silver

VF-EF

28 (grosso). Like No. 29. 1758 . . 15.00

★29 QVINTO·DI·SCV(do = 1/5
scudo). 1758 R.N 25.00

30 MEZ(zo = ½) SCV(do). Sim.
1758 R.N 65.00

31 SCVDO. Sim. 1758 R.N . . . 150.00

Gold

V.F.

32 (zecchino). SEDE VACANTE.
Holy Church std. Rev. VBI etc.
Arms. 1758 . . . . 1650.00

Clement XIII, Pope 1758-69

Copper

Fine

33 QVATRI/NO. CLEM. XIII etc.
Arms. Rev. Value/ROMANO.
A(nno) I, 1758-59 . . . . 3.50

34 MEZZO (= ½) BAIOCCO.
Sim. but ROM. 1758-59,
A(nno) I 4.00

35 VN (=1) BAIOCCO. Like
No. 33. 1758-59, A(nno) III. 6.00

See Gubbio for quattrini with SS
Peter or Paul.

Silver

★36 (½ grosso). 1760-61 . . . . 4.00

37 (grosso). CLEM. XIII etc. Arms.
Rev. SACROSAN/etc. 1758 . . . . 5.00

37a —. Rev. DA/PAVPERI. 1758 . . 5.00

37b —. Rev. MISERICORS/etc. 1760 5.00

37c —. Rev. VTERE/etc. 1762-
67 . . . . 2.25

Fine

38 (giulio). Like No. 48. 2.6 gr.
N.D 6.00

38a —. Rev. THESAVRIZATE/etc.
1761 . . . . 6.00

38b —. Rev. OBLECTAT/etc.
1763-65 . . . . 3.00

39 (2 giulio). CLEM. XIII etc.
SACROSAN/etc. Rev. like
No. 44 Rev. 5.2 gr. 1758 . . . . 10.00

40 (2 giulio). Like No. 48.
1758-59, 66-69 . . . . 5.00

41 (2 giulio). Like No. 44.
1760-66 . . . . 5.50

42 (30 baiocchi). CLEMENS XIII etc.
Arms. Rev. S. PETRVS S. PAVLVS,
2 saints. 1761-67 R.N 45.00

V.F.

43 (½ scudo). Like No. 48.
13.2 gr. 1759 . . . . 75.00

★44 (½ scudo). 1760 . . . . 175.00

45 (scudo). Like No. 48. 26.4 gr.
1759 . . . . (VF-EF) 250.00

Gold (zecchino = 3.4 gr.)

46 (½ zecchino). Sim.
1758, 67 . . . . 300.00

47 (zecchino). Sim. 1758-69 . . . 300.00

★48 (2 zecchini). 1759, 66 . . . . . 1250.00

Sede Vacante 1769

Silver

VF-EF

49 (giulio). Like No. 50. 2.6 gr.
1769 R.N 15.00

ITALY

PAPAL STATES (Cont.)

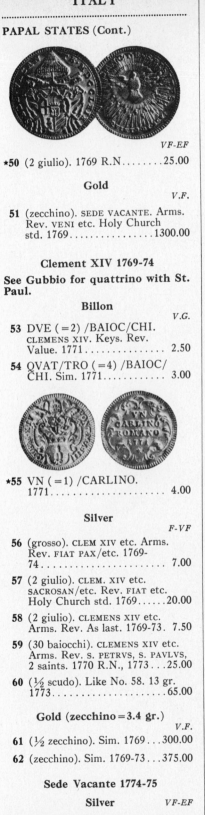

VF-EF

★50 (2 giulio). 1769 R.N. 25.00

Gold
V.F.

51 (zecchino). SEDE VACANTE. Arms.
Rev. VENI etc. Holy Church
std. 1769 . . . . .1300.00

Clement XIV 1769-74
**See Gubbio for quattrino with St.
Paul.**

Billon
V.G.

53 DVE (=2) /BAIOC/CHI.
CLEMENS XIV. Keys. Rev.
Value. 1771 . . . . 2.50

54 QVAT/TRO (=4) /BAIOC/
CHI. Sim. 1771 . . . . 3.00

★55 VN (=1) /CARLINO.
1771 . . . . 4.00

Silver
F-VF

56 (grosso). CLEM XIV etc. Arms.
Rev. FIAT PAX/etc. 1769-
74 . . . . 7.00

57 (2 giulio). CLEM. XIV etc.
SACROSAN/etc. Rev. FIAT etc.
Holy Church std. 1769 . . . . . .20.00

58 (2 giulio). CLEMENS XIV etc.
Arms. Rev. As last. 1769-73. 7.50

59 (30 baiocchi). CLEMENS XIV etc.
Arms. Rev. S. PETRVS, S. PAVLVS,
2 saints. 1770 R.N., 1773 . .25.00

60 (½ scudo). Like No. 58. 13 gr.
1773 . . . . .65.00

Gold (zecchino = 3.4 gr.)
V.F.

61 (½ zecchino). Sim. 1769 . . .300.00

62 (zecchino). Sim. 1769-73 . . .375.00

Sede Vacante 1774-75

Silver
VF-EF

63 (giulio) SEDE VACANTE 1774 R.N.
Arms. Rev. VENI etc. Dove.
2.6 gr 15.00

VF-EF

64 (2 giulio). Sim. 5.2 gr.
1774 R.N. 25.00

65 (½ scudo). Sim. 13.2 gr.
1774 R.N 75.00

Gold
V.F.

66 (zecchino). SEDE VACANTE.
Arms. Rev. VENI etc. Holy
Church std. 1774 . . . . .850.00

Pius VI, Pope 1775-99

Copper
Fine

67 QVATRI/NO. PIVS SEXTVS etc.
Arms. Rev. Value/ROMANO.
A(nno) IX-XII 3.00

67a —. Rev. VN/QVATTRINO/
ROMANO. A. XXIII 4.00

68 MEZZO (=½) /BAIOCCO.
Like No. 67. A. IX-XVI 2.00

★68a —. PIVS SEXT. etc. A. XXIII,
1797 . . . . 3.00

69 VN (=1) /BAIOCCO. Like
No. 67. A. VIII-XX 2.00

69a —. Like No. 68a. A. XXIII . . 3.00

70 DVE (=2) /BAIOCCHI. Like
No. 67. A. XI-XXIII 2.50

70a —. 1797 . . . . 3.00

71 BAIOCCHI/DVE E MEZZO
(=2½ B.). St. Peter. Rev.
Value/ROMANI. (2 var.).
1795 . . . . .10.00

71a —. St. Peter bust r. 1796 . . .10.00

71b —. St. Peter bust l.
30mm. 1796-97 . . . . 5.00

71c —. 25mm. 1797 . . . . 4.00

★72 BAIOC/CHI/CINQVE
(=5 B.). PIVS SEXTVS etc. Value.
Rev. SANCTA etc. Madonna.
(Rome Mint) 1797-99 . . . . . . 7.50

**For similar provincial coins from
A(ncona), Ascoli, Fano, Fermo,
Foligno, Gubbio, Macerata, Ma-
telica, Montalto, Pergola and San
Severino, see those places.**

Billon
G-VG

73 VN (=1) /BAIOCCO. PIVS
SEXTVS P.M. Keys. Rev. Value/
ROMANO. 1780-82 . . . . 1.50

74 DVE (=2) /BAIOC/CHI.
PIVS SEXTVS. Keys. Rev. Value.
1777-78, 94 . . . . 1.50

75 QVAT/TRO (=4) /BAIOC/
CHI. Like No. 74. 1777, 93-
94 . . . . 1.75

76 VN (=1) /CARLINO. PIVS
SEXTVS etc. Arms. Rev. Value/
ROMANO. 1777-96 . . . . 2.00

76a —. w/out ROMANO. 1777 . . . . 3.00

77 OTTO (=8) /BAIOC/CHI.
Like No. 74. 1793 . . . . 4.00

78 DVE (=2) /CARLINI. Like
No. 76. 1777-96, A(nno) VII-
XI 3.25

Fine

79 DODI/CI (=12) /BAIOC/CHI.
Like No. 74. 1793 . . . . 4.25

80 VENTICIN/QVE (=25)
/BAIOCCHI. PIVS SEXTVS etc.
Keys. Rev. Value. 1795-96 . . 5.00

F-VF

81 BAIOCCHI/SESSANTA
(=60 B.). PIVS SEXTVS etc.
Arms. Rev. Value. 1795-99 . .50.00

81a —. 1793 (error) 75.00

Silver

82 (grosso). PIVS VI etc. Arms.
Rev. APERVIT etc. Holy Door.
1775 . . . . 5.00

83 (grosso). PIVS SEXTVS etc. Arms.
Rev. AVXILIVM/etc. 1777-83. 2.50

★83a —. PIVS SEXT. etc. A(nno)
X-XIII 3.00

★84 (giulio). Arms. Rev. Holy Door.
1775 . . . . 6.00

85 (2 giulio). PIVS VI etc. SACROSAN/
etc. Rev. Like No. 93 Rev.
1775 . . . . 7.00

86 (2 giulio). Like No. 93. 5.2 gr.
1775 . . . . 7.00

86a —. PIVS SEXTVS etc. 1783-
96 . . . . 5.00

87 (2 giulio). PIVS VI etc. Bust.
Rev. As last. 1776-77 . . . . 6.00

87a —. PIVS SEXTVS etc. 1777-
84 . . . . 5.00

ITALY

PAPAL STATES (Cont.)

F-VF

88 (30 baiocchi). PIVS SEXTVS etc. Arms. Rev. SANCTVS PETRVS SANCTVS ANDREAS, 2 saints. 1785-96..............20.00

89 (½ scudo). Like No. 93. 13.2 gr. 1775-77...........50.00

89a —. Like No. 86a. 1778-80, 96........................30.00

90 (½ scudo). Like No. 87a. 1777.....................50.00

91 (scudo). Like No. 86a. 1780..25.00

See Ancona for No. 89a 1778A and No. 91 1780A, both base silver.

Gold (zecchino = 3.4 gr.)

V.F.

92 (½ zecchino). Sim. 1796...600.00

★93 (zecchino). 1775-76.......350.00

93a —. Like No. 86a. 1783-84..325.00

94 P(aoli) 15. FLORET etc. Lily plant. Rev. APOSTOLOR etc. St. Peter. 1776-84........275.00

94a (½ doppia). 2.7 gr. 1787...275.00

95 P(aoli) 30. Sim. 1776-85...400.00

95a (doppia). 5.4 gr. 1786-92...450.00

96 P(aoli) 60. Sim. 1777.....1450.00

See Roman Republic for coins of the Papal States 1798-99.

Neapolitan Occupation of Rome 1799-1800

During the era of the Roman Republic Neapolitan forces twice occupied Rome, first for 16 days in 1798, and second, after putting an end to the Republic, from September 30, 1799 until entry of the new pope.

Ferdinando IV of Naples

Silver

VF-EF

101 (½ scudo). FERDINANDUS/ IV/N. ET. S. R. Rev. DEFENSORI RELIGIONIS. Holy Church stdg. 1800..................1000.00

102 (scudo). Sim. but –/NEAP. ET. SIC. REX/. 1800 R.N...1200.00

103 (scudo). Sim. but –/UTR. SIC./ REX. Rev. AUXILIUM etc. Church std. 1800........1000.00

Pius VII, Pope 1800-23, In Rome 1800-09, In all of the Papal States 1814-23

Copper

Fine

106 QUATTR(ino). Like No. 109 but rev. SACR. BASILIC: etc. 1801 RN...............3.00

107 QVATTR(ino). Like No. 109. 1802 RN.............2.00

107a QVATTRINO. Sim. 1816-22 R.N.............2.00

107.5 VN/QVATTRINO. PIVS VII etc., Arms. Rev. Value/ 1816 R.N./B.............5.00

108 M(ezzo = ½) BAI(occo). Like No. 106. 1801 R.N...3.25

★109 M(ezzo = ½) BAI(occo). PIVS/SEPTIMVS/etc. Rev. PONTIFICATVS etc. 1802, 16-22 RN...........2.00

109a MEZZO B(aiocc)o. 1816, 22 R.N.............2.00

110 VN (=1) /BAIOCCO. PIVS VII etc. Arms. Rev. Value/ ROMANO. A(nno) I.......7.50

111 BAIOCCO. Like No. 106. 1801 R.N.............4.00

112 BAIOCCO. Like No. 109. 1802, 16 R.N.............2.25

Silver

F-VF

★113 (grosso). PIVS VII etc. Arms. Rev. PAVPERI/etc. 1815, 1816-17 R.N.............2.50

114 (giulio). Sim. but Rev. AVXILIVM etc. Holy Church std. 2.7 gr. 1817 R.N......4.00

115 (2 giulio). Sim. 5.3 gr. 1816, 18.....................4.50

116 (30 baiocchi). PIVS VII etc. Arms. Rev. S. PETRVS S. PAVLVS, 2 saints. 1802 R.N., 1803..............30.00

117 (½ scudo). Like No. 114. 13 gr. 1800-03, 1816.......30.00

V.F.

118 (scudo). Sim. but Rev. SVPRA etc. Holy Church std. 1800..................150.00

★119 (scudo). Arms. Rev. Holy Church (like No. 114). 1802-18.....................35.00

120 (scudo). Bust. Rev. Holy Church std. 1816..........(VF-EF) 3500.00

Gold

★121 (doppia). A(nno) I-XXIV (=1800-23)............325.00

Note: Some exceedingly rare coins of regular French types (mmk. cwnd. R) were struck at Rome 1812-13. Example:

Sede Vacante 1823

Silver

VF-EF

★122 (2 giulio). 1823 R.N......20.00

123 (½ scudo). Sim. 13.1 gr. 1823 R.N...............30.00

124 (scudo). Sim. 26.2 gr. 1823, 1823 R.N..............100.00

ITALY

PAPAL STATES (Cont.)

Gold
V.F.

125 (doppia). SEDE etc. Arms.
Rev. PRINCEPS etc. St. Peter.
1823 R.N. 1500.00

Leo XII, Pope 1823-29

Copper

125.5 QVATTRINO. LEO XII etc.
Arms. Rev. Value/ROMANO.
1824. . . . . 4.50

*126 QVATRINO.
1824-25. . . . . 4.50

126a —. ROM. 1826. . . . . 7.50

127 MEZZO (= ½)/BAIOCCO.
Like No. 125.5. 1824B. 7.50

127a —. Like No. 126a. 1825-
26R. 6.00

Silver

E.F.

*128 (scudo). Bust. Rev. Holy
Church std. 1825-26. . . . . .200.00

Gold
VF-EF

129 (doppia). LEO XII etc. Arms.
Rev. PRINCEPS etc. St. Peter.
A(nno) I-II. 1000.00

130 (2 zecchini). Arms. Rev.
POPVLIS etc. Holy Church
std. 1825. . . . . .2000.00

**A(nno) II with Rev. SVPRA etc. is
an essay.**

131 (2 zecchini). Bust. Rev.
SVPRA etc. Holy Church stdg.
1828. . . . . .1200.00

Sede Vacante 1829
Silver

E.F.

*132 (½ scudo). 1829 R.N. 100.00

133 (scudo). Sim. 1829 R.N. . .200.00

Gold
VF-EF

134 (doppia). Obv. sim. Rev.
PRINCEPS etc. St. Peter.
1829 R.N. 1000.00

Pius VIII, Pope 1829-30

Copper
V.F.

135 QVATTRINO. PIVS VIII etc.
Arms. Rev. Value/ROMANO.
1829. . . . . .10.00

*136 MEZZO (= ½) /BAIOCCO.
Sim. 1829. . . . . .10.00

137 BAIOCCO. Sim. 1829. . . . .10.00

Silver

VF-EF

*138 B(aiocchi) 30. PIVS VIII etc.
Bust. Rev. s. EXVP. . . . etc.,
2 saints. 1830. . . . . .50.00

VF-EF

*139 (scudo). Bust. Rev. ISTI etc.
SS Peter and Paul. 1830. .125.00

No. 139 in gold is a rare presentation
piece.

Sede Vacante 1830-31

Silver
E.F.

141 BAJ(occhi) 30. SEDE etc. Arms.
Rev. VENI etc. Dove. 1830
R.N. 50.00

142 (scudo). Sim. 1830 R.N. . . .125.00

Gold
VF-EF

143 DOPPIA. Sim.
1830 RN. 2250.00

Gregory XVI, Pope 1831-46

Copper
Fine

144 QVATTRINO. Like No. 145a
but Rev. Value/ROMANO/
1831. . . . . 2.50

144a —. Like No. 145a. 1835-
44. . . . . 2.00

145 MEZZO (= ½) /BAIOCCO.
Like No. 144. 1831-34. . . . . 2.50

*145a —. 1835-45. . . . . 2.00

146 BAIOCCO. Like No. 144.
1831-32. . . . . 2.50

146a —. Like No. 145a. 1835-
45. . . . . 2.00

Silver
V.F.

147 5/BAIOCCHI. Arms. Rev.
Value. 1835-46. . . . . 3.00

148 10/BAIOCCHI. Sim. 1836-
46. . . . . 3.00

149 BAI(occhi) 20. Bust. Rev.
Arms. 1834. . . . . 7.00

*150 20/BAIOCCHI. 1835-46. . . 5.00

PAPAL STATES (Cont.)

V.F.

151 BAI(occhi) 30. Like No. 149. 1834 . . . . 30.00

152 30/BAIOCCHI. Like No. 150. 1836-46 . . . . 25.00

153 BAJ(occhi) 50. Bust. Rev. St. Romuald. 1832, 34 . . . . . 45.00

154 50/BAIOCCHI. Like No. 150. 1835-46 . . . . 37.50

155 (scudo). Bust. Rev. LVMEN etc. Presentation in the Temple. 1831-34 . . . . 75.00

156 SCVDO. Like No. 150. 1835-46 . . . . 75.00

Gold

*157 DOPPIA. 1833-34 . . . . . 2000.00

158 SCVDI/2.50. Bust. Rev. Value. 1835-46 . . . . 450.00

159 SCV(di) 5. Bust. Rev. PRINCIPES etc. SS Peter and Paul. 1834 . . . . ——

160 5/SCVDI. Like No. 158. 1835-46 . . . . 1200.00

161 10/SCVDI. Sim. 1835-46. 2250.00

Sede Vacante 1846
Silver

E.F.

*162 SCVDO. Arms. Rev. NON RELINQVAM etc. Dove. 1846 R.N 175.00

Gold

163 5 SC(udi). Sim. 1846 R.N . . . . ——

Pius IX, Pope 1846-78

Ousted by republicans 1848-49. Bologna, The Marches and Umbria lost to Italy 1860. Remainder of Patrimony of St. Peter to Italy 1870.

I. Baiocchi/Scudo System.

Copper

F-VF

164 1/QVATTRINO. Like No. 171. 1851R, 54B 4.00

F-VF

165 MEZZO (= ½) /BAIOCCO. Sim. 1847-49 . . . . 3.50

166 ½ BAIOCCO. Sim. 1850-52 . . . . 2.00

167 BAIOCCO. Sim. 1846-49 . . . 4.00

168 1/BAIOCCO. Sim. 1850-53 . . . . 3.00

169 2/BAIOCCHI. Sim. 1848-49 . . . . 5.00

169a —. 1850-54 . . . . 5.00

170 5/BAIOCCHI. Sim. 1849-50 . . . . 7.00

170a —. 1850-54 . . . . 7.00

For other 1848-49 coins from Rome and Bologna Mints, see Roman Republic.

Silver

*171 5/BAIOCCHI. (.900 fine) 1847-57 . . . . 3.50

171a —. (.800 fine) 1858-64 . . . . 2.50

171b —. (.835 fine) 1865-66 . . . . 2.50

172 10/BAIOCCHI. Sim. (.900 fine) 1847-56 . . . . 2.50

172a —. (.800 fine) 1858-64 . . . . 2.50

172b —. (.835 fine) 1865-66 . . . . 2.50

173 20/BAIOCCHI. Bust. Rev. Value in wreath. 1848-56 . . . . 3.75

173a —. (.800 fine) 22.8 mm. 1858 . . . . 3.75

173b —. (.800 fine) Like No. 174. 24.5mm. 5.71 gr. 1858-65 A.XIX 3.75

173c —. (.835 fine) 5.33 gr. 1865 ANXX—1866 . . . . 3.75

V.F.

*174 50/BAIOCCHI. 1850-57 . . . 50.00

175 SCVDO. Sim. 1846-56 . . . . . 75.00

Gold

176 1/SCVDO. Sim. 14mm. 1853-57 . . . . 250.00

176a —. 16mm. 1858-65 . . . . . . 250.00

177 SCVDI 2.50. Sim. 1848-63 . . . . 350.00

178 5/SCVDI. Sim. 1846-54 . . 1750.00

179 10/SCVDI. Sim. 1850, 56R . . . . ——

II. New Monetary System:
100 centesimi = 20 soldi = 1 lira.

Copper

F-VF

180 1/CENTESIMO. Like No. 182. 1866-68 . . . . 5.00

181 ½/SOLDO. Sim. 1866-67 . . 2.00

182 1/SOLDO. Like No. 182a but smaller bust. 1866 . . . . . 2.00

*182a —. 1866-67 . . . . 1.50

183 2/SOLDI. Sim. 1866-67 . . . 2.50

184 4/SOLDI. Sim. 1866-69 . . . 4.00

Silver

The silver 4 soldi 1868 is a pattern.

186 5/SOLDI. Like No. 188a. 1866-67 . . . . 2.25

187 10/SOLDI. Sim. 1866-69 . . . 4.00

188 1/LIRA. Sim. 1866 . . . . 2.50

*188a —. Large bust. 1866-69 . . . 4.00

189 2/LIRE. Sim. 1866-70 . . . . 10.00

190 2½/LIRE. Sim. 1867 . . . . 45.00

191 5/LIRE. Sim. 1867, 70 . . . 70.00

Gold

V.F.

192 5/LIRE. Sim. 1866-67 . . . 1350.00

193 10/LIRE. Sim. 1866-69 . . . 475.00

194 20/LIRE. Sim. 1866-70 . . . 200.00

195 50/LIRE. Sim. 1868, 70 . . . ——

196 100/LIRE. Sim. 1866-69 . . . ——

PARMA, PIACENZA (PLAC.) and GUASTALLA (VAST.), Duchies

The first coins of Parma, in N. Italy, were struck in the reign of Charlemagne. The city, and later duchy, to which Piacenza and Guastalla had been added, passed through numerous hands until it came into those of the Spanish Bourbons in the early 18th century.

Monetary Systems:
Until 1802:
12 denari = 2 sesini = 1 soldo;
20 soldi = 1 lira; *7 lire = 1 ducato.*
After 1815:
100 centesimi = 1 lira.

ITALY

PARMA (Cont.)

Filippo di Borbone 1737-65, Title Confirmed 1748

Silver
V.F.

2 (Filippo). PHILIPPUS D.G. HISPAN. INFANS. Head. Rev. PARMAE PLAC. ET VASTAL. DUX. Arms. 1751...................1800.00

Ferdinando di Borbone 1765-1802

Copper
VG-F

3 SESINO. FERD. I. H. I. D. G. PAR. PLAC. ET VA. DVX. Arms. Rev. SESINO/DI/PARMA. (var.). 1783-98...................5.00

Billon
G-VG

4 SOLD. V (= 5 S.). Arms. Rev. VITAM PRAEST PVR. Madonna. 1784-85............4.50

5 SOLDI. V. VITAM etc. Madonna. Rev. Value/PARMA. 1792-99..................3.50

6 SOLDI. X. Arms. Rev. S. HILARIVS. PARM. PROT. St. Hilary. 1784-95............5.00

★7 SOLDI. XX. 1783-97.......7.50

Silver
Fine

8 LIRE/TRE (=3 lire). Head. Rev. Value/DI/PARMA. 1790-96......................75.00

9 LIRE/SEI (=6 lire). Sim. 1795-96...................250.00

10 (1/14 ducato). Like No. 15. 1.7 gr. 1784, 86............35.00

11 (1/7 ducato). Sim. 3.5 gr. 1784-87..................40.00

V.F.

12 (½ ducato). Like No. 14. 12.6 gr. 1784.............90.00

13 (½ ducato). Like No. 15. 1786-90..................60.00

14 (ducato). FERDINANDVS I. HISPAN. INFANS. Head. Rev. D.G. PARMAE etc. DVX. Arms in order chain. 25.6 gr. 1784 ..350.00

15 (ducato). Sim. but oval arms. 1786-99..................200.00

Gold (zecchino = 3.4 gr.; doppia = 7.2 gr.)
V.F.

16 (zecchino). Like No. 14. 1784...................350.00

17 (½ doppia). Sim. but diff. shield. 1785-97............125.00

18 (doppia). Like No. 14. 1784 200.00

18a —. Like No. 17. 1786-96...150.00

19 (3 doppie). Like No. 17. 1786..................3000.00

20 (4 doppie). Like No. 14. 1784..................1200.00

20a —. Like No. 17. 1787-96..1000.00

21 (6 doppie). Like No. 17. 1786..................3500.00

22 (8 doppie). Like No. 14. 1784..................2000.00

22a —. Like No. 17. 1786-96..1800.00

Parma was part of France 1802-14.

Maria Luigia (Marie Louise of Austria, Napoleon's Wife), Duchess of Parma 1815-47

Bronze
F-VF

23 1/CENTESIMO. MARIA LUIGIA etc. Arms. Rev. DUCHESSA DI PARMA etc. Value. 1830.....10.00

24 3/CENTESIMI. Sim. 1830...10.00

★25 5/CENTESIMI. Sim. 1830..10.00

Silver

★26 5 SOLDI. Head. Rev. cwnd. ML mon. 1815, 30........12.00

27 10 SOLDI. Sim. 1815, 30...12.00

28 1 LIRA NUOVA (new lira). Like No. 30. 1815.........30.00

29 2 LIRE. Sim. 1815........50.00

F-VF

★30 5 LIRE. 1815, 21, 32......80.00

Gold
V.F.

31 20 LIRE. Sim. but circle btwn. rev. legend and arms. 1815, 32...................1350.00

32 40 LIRE. Sim. 1815, 21...600.00

Carlo II di Borbone, Duke of Lucca 1815-47, In Parma 1848-49. Abdicated.

Carlo III di Borbone 1849-54 Assassinated.

Copper
VF-EF

33 Cent(esimo) 1. CARLO III INFANTE DI SPAGNA. Head. Rev. DUCA DI PARMA etc. Arms...................700.00

34 Cent(esimi) 3. Sim. 1854...700.00

35 Cent(esimi) 5. Sim. 1854...700.00

Roberto di Borbone, Under Regency of his Mother, Luisa Maria, 1854-59

Driven out 1859 at formation of new kingdom of Italy.

Silver

★36 5 LIRE. 1858............750.00

ITALY

PARTHENOPEAN REPUBLIC.
See Naples and Sicily.

PERGOLA, City

In the Province of Pesaro Urbino, Papal States.

Monetary System:
100 baiocchi = 1 scudo.

Pius VI, Pope 1775-99

Copper

VG-F

1 MEZZO (= ½) BAIOCCO. PIVS SEXT. etc. Arms. Rev. Value/PERGOLA. 1797......27.50

2 BAIOCCHI/DVE E MEZZO. (= 2½ B.). S. P. APOST. etc. St. Peter. Rev. Value/ PERGOLA. 1796-97.................15.00

3 BAIOC(chi)/CINQVE (= 5 B.). PIVS PAPA SEXTVS etc. Value/ PERGO/LA. Rev. SANCTA etc. Madonna. 1797...........17.50

Under the Roman Republic 1798-99

Copper

4 MEZZO (= ½)/BAIOCCO. Like No. 5. N.D..........22.50

*5 VN(= 1)/BAIOCCO. 1798...22.50

6 DVE(= 2)/BAIOCCHI. REPUBLICA ROMANA, fasces. Rev. value/PERGOLA. 1798, ND.................17.50

PERUGIA, City

In the Papal States.

Pius VI, Pope 1775-99

Copper

VG-F

1 MEZZO (= ½)/BAIOCCO. Arms. Rev. Value/PERVGIA. 1797....................15.00

VG-F

2 VN (= 1)/BAIOCCO. Arms. Rev. AVGVSTA PERVSIA, value. 1795....................20.00

2a —. Like No. 1. 1797......25.00

3 DVE (= 2)/BAIOCCHI. Like No. 2. 1795..........25.00

3a —. Like No. 1. 1797......22.50

4 BAIOCCHI/DVE E MEZZO (= 2½ B.). St. Peter. Rev. Value/PERVGIA. 1796-97....25.00

5 BAIOC(chi)/CINQVE (= 5 B.). Value/PERVGIA. Rev. SANCTA etc. Madonna. 1797-98.....25.00

5a —. Rev. SANCTA DEI ROMANA (error), Madonna. 1796.....75.00

Billon

V.G.

7 OTTO (= 8)/BAIOC/CHI. PIVS etc. around, PERV/GIA/ 1797. Rev. Value.........15.00

Under the Roman Republic 1798-99

Copper

VG-F

11 DVE (= 2) /BAIOCCHI. Fasces. Rev. Value/PERVGIA. A(nno) VII, N.D. (var.)....20.00

12 BAIOC(chi)/CINQVE (= 5 B.). No. 4 overstruck with dies of No. 5 and then cmkd. fasces. N.D. 45.00

See Roman Republic No. 6 for 2 baiocchi from Perugia with "P" mint mark.

Silver

F-VF

13 SCUDO. Eagle/PERUGIA. Rev. Value. A(nno) VII ..2000.00

PIACENZA (PLACENTIA), Duchy

In North Italy. Mostly united with Parma (q.v.).

Monetary System:
12 denari = 2 sesini = 1 soldo;
20 soldi = 1 lira.

Maria Theresia of Austria 1740-80, Duchess of Piacenza 1740-44

Copper

V.G.

1 (sesino). MAR. THE. REG. BOH. E. VNG. PLA. D. Arms. Rev. SALVS MVNDI. Cross. N.D.........7.50

Carlo Emanuele III, King of Sardinia, Duke of Piacenza 1744-45

Copper

2 (sesino). CA.EM.D.G.R.SAR.D. PLAC. Cwnd knot. Rev. as last. N.D.................4.50

Filippo di Borbone, Duke of Parma and Piacenza 1748-65

Copper

V.G.

*3 (sesino). PHI. HIS. IN. PLAC & DVX. Arms. Rev. as last. N.D......................2.75

3a —. Square planchet........——

Ferdinando di Borbone, Duke of Parma and Piacenza 1765-1802

Copper

4 SESINO. FERD. I. D.G. H.I. PA. PLA. ET VA. DUX. Arms. Rev. SESINO/DI/PIACENZA. 1783-84.................2.25

5 (sesino). FERD. I.H.I.D.G. PLAC. PA. V. DVX. Arms. Rev. SALVS MVNDI. Cross. N.D., 1784... 2.25

Billon

G-VG

6 SOLD(i) V. Arms. Rev. S. IVSTINA. PROT. PLAC. St. Justina. 1784-95.................4.50

*7 SOLD(i) X (=Buttala). St. Anthony 1784-95 ......10.00

Piacenza had no subsequent individual coinages.

PIEDMONT REPUBLIC (REPUBBLICA PIEMONTESE, NAZIONE PIEMONTESE, GAULE SUBALPINE, SUBALPINE REPUBLIC)

Mainland possessions of kingdom of Sardinia. In NW Italy on the French border. Capital and mint: Turin.

I. As Repubblica Piemontese 1798-99.

Republic established by Napoleon. Overthrown by Austro-Russian forces 20 June 1799.

Silver

V.F.

1 QUARTO/DI (= ¼)/SCUDO. Like No. 2. ANNO VII.....350.00

ITALY

PIEDMONT (Cont.)

V.F.

*2 MEZZO (=½)/SCUDO.
ANNO VII 190.00

II. As Nazione Piemontese.
Napoleon returns 1800.

Bronze or Brass

V.G.

*3 Soldi/due (script, =2 S.).
Triangle. Rev. NAZIONE
PIEMONTESE, value.
A(nno) 9 . . . . 3.50

III. As Subalpine Republic 1800-01.
Annexed to France in the year 10
(=1801).

Silver

V.F.

*4 5/FRANCS. France and Italy
stdg. L'AN 9-10 . . . . .95.00

Gold

V.F.

*5 20/FRANCS. L'AN 9-10 . . .1500.00

Regular French coins were struck at Turin (U) during the years 12-14, 1806-13. All exceedingly scarce.

See Sardinia for subsequent coins of this area.

RAVENNA, City

The Papal coinage for this city apparently stopped at 1750, and has been omitted for that reason.

ROMAN REPUBLIC (REPUBBLICA ROMANA)

Short-lived republican government set up in the Papal States 1798-99 (= years 6 and 7).

See also Ancona, Ascoli, Civitavecchia, Clitunno, Fermo, Foligno, Gubbio, Macerata, Pergola and Perugia.

Monetary System:
100 baiocchi = 1 scudo.

Mints:
A(ncona), C(ivitavecchia), P(erugia) and R(ome).

Copper

VG-F

1 MEZZO (=½)/BAIOCCO.
Like No. 6. N.D 8.00

F-VF

*2 VN (=1)/BAIOCCO. 2 fasces.
Rev. Value. ANNO SESTO (= yr. 6) 75.00

3 VN (=1) /BAIOC/CO. Like
No. 6. N.D 15.00

4 DVE (=2) /BA/IOCCHI.
Eagle. Rev. Value. ANNO
SESTO 50.00

5 DVE (=2) /BA/IOCCHI.
2 flags, fasces. Rev. Value,
ANNO SESTO 75.00

*6 DVE (=2) /BAIOC/CHI.
Fasces *. Rev. Value. N.D.,
1798 . . . . 5.00

6a —. Wreath in lieu of
obverse legend. N.D 10.00

6b DVE/BAIOCCHI.
Rev. Value/A(nno) VII 7.50

6c —. Rev. Value/ROMANI.
N.D. 5.00

7 DVE (=2) /BAIOCCHI.
Fasces. Rev. Value. A(nno)
VII 25.00

8 2/baiocchi. Sim. An(no) 7 . . .25.00

9 BAIOC/CHI/CINQVE (=5 B.).
SANCTA DEI GENETRIX. Madonna.
Rev. Value. N.D 30.00

Silver

V.F.

10 (scudo). Eagle, etc. Rev. ALLE/
SPERANZE/etc. A(nno) 6 . .1000.00

ITALY

ROMAN REPUBLIC (Cont.)

V.F.

10a —. Rev. LIBERTA/ROMANA/etc.
AN(no) VII.............850.00

10b —. Rev. LIBERTA/ROMANA/
27/PIOVOSO. N.D. 1000.00

*11 SCVDO. Liberty *. Rev. Value/
ROMANO. N.D...........275.00

ROMAN REPUBLIC (REPUBBLICA ROMANA)

Government established in the Papal
States during the 1848-49 Revolution.

Mints:
B(ologna) and R(ome).
See Ancona for A(ncona).

Copper

Fine

21 ½/BAIOCCO. Like No. 23.
1849R................. 4.00

22 1/BAIOCCO. Sim. 1849R... 8.00

*23 3/BAIOCCHI. Eagle *.
Rev. REPUBBLICA ROMANA.
Value. 1849B, R (2 var.)....15.00

Billon

24 4/BAIOCCHI. Sim.
1849B, R.................10.00

25 8/BAIOCCHI. Sim.
1849R...................10.00

26 16/BAIOCCHI. Sim.
1849R...................20.00

27 40/BAIOCCHI. Sim.
1849R...................50.00

RONCIGLIONE, Town

In the Papal States.

Pius VI, Pope 1775-99

Copper

VG-F

1 (3 baiocchi). L'INCENDIO DI
RONCIGLIONE. Burning city.
Rev. Madonna. 1799.....100.00

2 BAIOCCHI/TRE (=3 B.).
Madonna. Rev. Value/
RONCIGLIONE/1799........50.00

SAN GIORGIO, Princes

In the Province of Reggio Calabria.
Giovanni Domenico, Marchese di
San Giorgio e Polestrina, was made a prince
of the Empire and given the mint right
in 1731.

Giacomo Francesco, 2nd Prince

Silver

E.F.

1 (½ scudo). JACOBUS/FRANCISCUS/
MILANO/MARCHIO/etc. Rev.
Arms. 1753..............750.00

2 (scudo). JAC. FR. etc. Bust.
Rev. Arms. 1753........1500.00

SAN SEVERINO, City

In the Province of Macerata, Papal
States.

Monetary System:

5 quattrini =1 baiocco;
100 baiocchi =1 scudo.

Pius VI, Pope 1775-99

Copper

Fine

1 VN (=1)/QVATRINO. PIVS
SEXT etc. Arms. Rev. Value/
S. SEVERI/NO. A(nno) XXIII
(=1797).................17.50

2 MEZZO (=½)/BAIOCCO.
Sim. A.XXII, 1797 (var.)... 5.00

3 BAIOCCHI/DVE E MEZZO
(=2½ B.). S.P. APOST. etc.
St. Peter. Rev. Value/S. SEVERI/
NO. 1796-97 (var.)........ 4.00

3a —. 1769 (error)...........20.00

4 BAIOC(chi)/CINQVE (=5 B.).
PIVS PAPA SEXTVS etc. Value/
S. SEVERI/NO. Rev. SANCTA etc.
Madonna. 1797...........5.00

SARDINIA (SARDEGNA), Kingdom

The nucleus around which the modern
Italian state was constructed. Ruled by
the House of Savoy, descended from
the counts and later dukes of Savoy
on the French-Italian-Swiss border.
Consisted of Piedmont-Savoy-Montfer-
rat in NW Italy, and the island of
Sardinia. Sardinia and the royal title
were acquired in 1720.

Monetary Systems:

1. On the Mainland until 1816:
12 denari =1 soldo; 20 soldi =1 lira;
6 lire =1 scudo; 2 scudi =1 doppia.

2. On the Island of Sardinia until 1816:
12 denari =6 cagliarese =1 soldo;
50 soldi =10 reales =2½ lire =
1 scudo Sardo;
2 scudi Sardo =1 doppietta.

3. Throughout the Kingdom from 1816 on:
100 centesimi =1 lira.

Carlo Emanuele 1730-73

I. Coins for the Mainland.

Copper

VG-F

1 (2 denari). CAR. EM etc. Cross.
Rev. Cwn./figure-8 knot.
1732-72............... 2.50

Billon

G-VG

2 S(oldi) 1. CAR. EM. etc. Cross.
Rev. cwnd. CE mon. 1732-
72..................... 1.00

*3 (2½ soldi). 3.5 gr. 1732-40.. 1.75

4 (2½ soldi). Sim. but head l.
1744, 47................. 2.00

5 SOL(di) 2.6 (=2½ S.). Head r.
Rev. Eagle, cross on breast.
1755-58................. 2.00

6 (5 soldi). Like No. 3. 4.3 gr.
1732-41................. 3.00

7 (5 soldi). Like No. 4. 1742-
47..................... 4.00

8 SOL(di) 7•6 (=7½ S.). Like
No. 5. 1755-58............. 2.00

Silver

F-VF

9 S(oldi) 10. Like No. 11.
1732-33................. 12.00

10 S(oldi) 10. Sim. but head l.
1742..................... 12.00

*11 S(oldi) 20. 1732............30.00

ITALY

SARDINIA (Cont.)

F-VF

12 S(oldi) 20. Like No. 10.
1742-48.................20.00

13 (⅛ scudo). Like No. 15.
3.7 gr. 1733............30.00

14 (⅛ scudo). Like No. 20.
4.2 gr. 1755-58..........10.00

V.F.

★15 (¼ scudo). 7.4 gr. 1733....50.00

16 (¼ scudo). Like No. 20.
8.5 gr. 1755-72...........35.00

17 (½ scudo). Like No. 15.
14.8 gr. 1733............125.00

18 (½ scudo). Like No. 20.
17.3 gr. 1755-72..........50.00

19 (scudo). Like No. 15. 1733-
35....................500.00

★20 (scudo). 1755-69.........220.00

Gold

21 (½ doppia). Bust r. Rev. Arms.
3.5 gr. 1733-34............——

22 (½ doppia). Bust l. Rev. Arms.
1741-42.................——

23 (doppia). Like No. 21.
1733....................——

24 (doppia). Like No. 22.

V.F.

7.2 gr. 1741.............——

25 ⅙ (zecchino). Virgin kneeling.
Rev. Angel. No legend. N.D.
(1743-46)...............——

26 (½ zecchino). Like No. 28.
1.7 gr. 1744-46.........1350.00

27 (zecchino). Sim. 3.4 gr. 1743-
46....................1750.00

★28 (4 zecchini). The Annunciation.
1745-46.................——

29 (¼ doppia). Like No. 31.
2.4 gr. 1755-58..........——

30 (½ doppia). Sim. 4.8 gr.
1755-71................1750.00

★31 (doppia). 1755-72.........——

32 D(oppie) 2½. Sim. 1755-
57.....................——

33 D(oppie) 5. Sim. 1755-68...——

II. Coins for the Island of Sardinia.
(Often crude)

Arms of the Island: Cross with 4
small heads in angles.

Copper

VG-F

34 (denari). Like No. 35. 1.2 gr.
1736-45.................1.25

★35 (cagliarese). 2.2 gr. 1732-41..1.75

36 (cagliarese). Cross and 4 heads.
Rev. Knot. 1763-68.......1.50

37 3 C(agliarese). Like No. 35.
1732, 41................2.00

Billon

G-VG

38 S(oldo) 1. Cross and 4 heads.
Rev. cwnd. sceptre and baton.
1768-72.................2.25

39 (½ reale). Head r. Rev. island
arms in round shield. 2.6 gr.
1768-72.................3.00

40 (reale). Sim. but arms in cartouche. 3 gr. 1768-72.......3.75

Silver

VG-F

41 (½ reale). Bust. Rev. CRVCIS
VICTORIA. Cross, island arms
in center. 1.1 gr. 1732......10.00

42 (reale). Sim. 2.3 gr. 1732....12.00

43 (¼ scudo). Bust r. Rev. 2
shields (Savoy, Sardinia) cwnd.
1732...................65.00

F-VF

★44 (¼ scudo). 1768-72........70.00

45 (½ scudo). Sim. 11.5 gr.
1768-72.................90.00

46 (scudo). Sim. 23.4 gr. 1768-
69....................275.00

Gold

V.F.

47 (doppieta). Sim. but bust l.
3.2 gr. 1768-72..........2000.00

48 (2½ dopp.). Sim. 8 gr. 1768-
71.....................——

49 (5 dopp.). Sim. 16 gr. 1768-
69.....................——

Vittorio Amadeo III
1773-96

I. Coins for the Mainland.

Copper

VG-F

50 (2 denari). VIC. AM. D.G.R.SAR.
etc. Cross. Rev. Knot. 1773-
96.....................1.25

51 SOL(di) 5. Bust r. Rev. St.
Maurice. 1794-96.........1.50

Billon

G-VG

52 M(ezzo = ½) S(oldo). Cross.
Rev. cwnd. VA mon. 1780-
90.....................1.75

ITALY

SARDINIA (Cont.)

G-VG

53 S(oldo) 1. Sim. 1773-89..... 1.50

54 SOL(di) 2.6 (=2½ S.). Head. Rev. Eagle, Savoy cross on breast. 1781-85...... 1.75

55 SOL(di) 7.6 (=7½ S.). Sim. but eagle in shield. 1781-94...... 3.00

56 SOL(di) 10. Like No. 58. 1794-96...... 4.00

57 SOL(di) 15. Head. Rev. Value. 1794...... 12.00

★58 SOL(di) 20. 1794-96....... 4.00

Nos. 51 and 56-58 were products of inflation.

Silver

V.F.

★59 (¼ scudo). 1773-93....... 35.00

60 (½ scudo). Sim. 17.6 gr. 1773-93...... 45.00

61 (scudo). Sim. 35 gr. 1773..1500.00

Gold

62 (¼ doppia). Head. Rev. Round arms. 2.4 gr. 1773-82....... —

63 (¼ doppia). Like No. 69. 1786...... 1350.00

64 (½ doppia). Like No. 62. 4.8 gr. 1773-78........... —

65 (½ doppia). Like No. 69. 1786-96...... 700.00

66 (doppia). Like No. 62. 9 gr. 1773-78........... —

67 (doppia). Like No. 69. 1786-96...... 1350.00

68 (2½ doppie). Sim. 23 gr. 1786...... —

V.F.

★69 (5 doppie). 1786.......... —

II. Coins for the Island of Sardinia.

Copper

VG-F

70 (cagliarese). Cross, 4 heads. Rev. Knot. 1789, 92........ 3.00

Billon

G-VG

71 S(oldo) 1. Cross, 4 heads. Rev. Cwnd. sceptre and baton. 1773-92................ 2.50

72 (½ reale). Head. Rev. Island arms in round shield, Savoy centershield. 2.4 gr. 1773-96. 5.00

73 (reale). Sim. but arms in cartouche. 3 gr. 1773-95...... 6.00

74 (reale). Head. Rev. INIM EI/ IND CONF/date. 1793-96.....10.00

Silver

F-VF

75 (¼ scudo). Like No. 76. 1773-92.................35.00

★76 (½ scudo). 1773-93....... 100.00

77 (scudo). Sim. 1773.......275.00

Gold

V.F.

77.5 (doppieta). Like No. 78. 3.2 gr. 1773-86........... —

77.7 (2½ dopp.). 1773-84....... —

V.F.

★78 (5 dopp.). 1773-84......... —

Carlo Emanuele IV 1796-1802, In the Island of Sardinia only, 1800-02

(Ousted from the mainland by Napoleon.)

I. Coins for the Mainland.

Copper

VG-F

79 (2 denari). CAROLUS EM. IV D. G. REX SAR. etc. Cross. Rev. Knot. 1798-1800.......... 2.50

Billon

★80 S(oldi) 1. 1797-98......... 3.00

81 SOL(di) 2.6 (=2½ S.). Head. Rev. Eagle. 1798-99........ 4.00

★82 SOL(di) 7.6 (=7½ S.). Head. Rev. Eagle shield. 1798-1800 5.00

Silver

V.F.

83 (¼ scudo). Bust. Rev. Arms. 8.7 gr. 1797-99............50.00

84 (½ scudo). Sim. 17.6 gr. 1797-1800................75.00

Gold

85 (½ doppia). Like No. 86. 1797-98.................2750.00

★86 (doppia). 1797-1800....... —

SARDINIA (Cont.)

II. Coin for the Island of Sardinia.

Billon

V.G.

87 (reale). CAR. EM. etc. Head.
Rev. INIM EI/IND CONF/date.
1797-99...............12.00

Vittorio Emanuele I, 1802-21

On the Island of Sardinia only until
the defeat of Napoleon 1814.

I. Coins for the Island.

Copper

88 CAGLIARESI/TRE (=3 C.).
Savoy cross on island arms.
Rev. Value. N.D. (1813)....40.00

Billon

G-VG

89 (reale). VIC. EM. D. G. REX.
SARD. etc. Head. Rev. Arms.
1812...................35.00

II. Coins for the Mainland.

Billon

V.G.

90 SOL(di) 2.6 (=2½ S.). Head.
Rev. Eagle. 1814-15.......10.00

Silver

V.F.

91 (½ scudo). Bust l. Rev. Arms.
1814-15................150.00

★92 L(ire) 5. 1816-20.........150.00

V.F.

93 L(ire) 5. Sim. but Rev. Savoy
cross in pointed shield.
1821...................750.00

Gold

VF-EF

★94 (doppia). 1814-15.........
95 L(ire) 20. Like No. 92 but
head l. 1816-20..........700.00
96 L(ire) 20. Like No. 93 but
head l. 1821.............. ——
97 L(ire) 80. Sim. 1821....... ——

Carlo Felice 1821-31

Mints:

Turin – Eagle's head; Genoa – Anchor.

Copper

VG-F

98 1/CENTESIMO. Like
No. 99. 1826.............. 1.25

★99 3/CENTESIMI. 1826..... 2.00
100 5/CENTESIMI. Sim. 1826. 3.00

**Nos. 98-100 w/out MM were struck
at Birmingham in 1860.**

Silver

F-VF

101 C(entesimi) 25. Like No. 105
but Rev. Savoy cross in shield.
1829-30.................25.00
102 C(entesimi) 50. Sim. 1823-
31.....................15.00
103 L(ira) 1. Like No. 105.
1823-30................17.50
104 L(ire) 2. Sim. 1823-31.....30.00

F-VF

★105 L(ire) 5. 1821-31.........25.00

Gold

V.F.

106 L(ire) 20. Sim. but head l.
1821-31................250.00
107 L(ire) 40. Sim. 1822-31..1000.00
108 L(ire) 80. Sim. 1823-31..1100.00

Carlo Alberto 1831-49

I. Coins for the Mainland.

Silver

F-VF

109 C(entesimi) 25. Like No. 113.
1832-37.................25.00
110 C(entesimi) 50. Sim. 1832-
47.....................25.00
111 L(ira) 1. Sim. 1831-47.....30.00
112 L(ire) 2. Sim. 1832-49.....60.00

★113 L(ire) 5. 1831-49.........30.00

Gold

V.F.

114 L(ire) 10. Sim. but head l.
1832-47...............1250.00
115 L(ire) 20. Sim. 1831-49...150.00
116 L(ire) 50. Sim. 1832-43..2450.00
117 L(ire) 100. Sim. 1832-45 .1200.00

ITALY

SARDINIA (Cont.)

II. Coins for the Island of Sardinia.

Copper

F-VF

★118 1/CENTESIMO. REGNO DI SARDEGNA. Island arms. Rev. Value. 1842 . . . . 15.00

119 3/CENTESIMI. Sim. 1842 . . . . 10.00

120 5/CENTESIMI. Sim. 1842 . . . . 10.00

Vittorio Emanuele II, King of Sardinia 1849-61, King of Italy 1861-78

As King of Sardinia.

Mints: Turin – Eagle's head; Genoa – Anchor; Milan (1860) – M.

Silver

121 C(entesimi) 50. Like No. 124. 1850-61 . . . . 7.00

122 L(ira) 1. Sim. 1850-60 . . . . . 7.00

123 L(ire) 2. Sim. 1850-60 . . . . . 17.50

V.F.

★124 L(ire) 5. 1850-61 . . . . 55.00

Gold

125 L(ire) 10. Sim. but head l. 1850-60 . . . . 1200.00

V.F.

126 L(ire) 20. Sim. 1850-61 . . . 150.00

For other similar coins of Vittorio Emanuele II, see Emilia and Tuscany. See Yeoman's MWC for his later coins as King of Italy 1861-78.

SICILY, Island

Part of the Kingdom of Naples and Sicily (Two Sicilies). The two districts used the same money of account, but the Sicilian grani, carlini and tari were only worth half as much as the Neapolitan ones. Coins for Sicily alone are listed here, while those for Naples alone or for the entire kingdom are listed under Naples and Sicily.

Monetary System of Sicily:

6 cavalli = 1 grano;
20 grani = 2 carlini = 1 taro;
12 tari = 1 piastri;
15 tari = 1 scudo;
2 scudi = 1 oncia (onza).

Carlo III (IV in Naples) 1734-59

Copper

VG-F

1 3 (cavalli). CAR. D. G. SIC. REX. Sicilian eagle. Rev. HISP. etc. 3. 1737-55 . . . . 10.00

★3 *(grano)*. Eagle. Rev. VT/COMMO/ DIVS. 1737-55 . . . . 12.00

4 (2 grani). Sim. but 28-29mm. 1737-55 . . . . Rare

Silver

F-VF

★6 (2 tari). 1735-51 . . . . 10.00

8 (3 tari). CAROLUS D. G. SIC. etc. Bust. Rev. FAVSTO CORONATIONIS. Cross. 1735-38 . . . . 15.00

9 (3 tari). Sim. but Rev. FAUSTO etc. Eagle. 1737 . . . . 20.00

F-VF

★10 *(3 tari)* . . . .

11 (6 tari). Like No. 8. 1735 . . . 40.00

12 (6 tari). Like No. 10. 1754-55 . . . . 100.00

13 (piastra). Like No. 8. 40mm. 1735 . . . . 150.00

Gold

V.F.

★14 (oncia). Bust. Rev. Phoenix. 1734-35 . . . . 90.00

14a —. CAROLVS D.G. SIC. etc. Bust with long hair. *1736-58* 90.00

15 (2 oncia). Bust. Rev. Eagle. 1752-58 . . . . 150.00

Ferdinando III (IV in Naples) 1759-1825

In Sicily only 1799, 1805-15, adopted title Ferdinando I, King of Two Sicilies, 1816.

I. First period, 1759-99.

Copper

VG-F

16 3 (cavalli). Eagle. Rev. 3. 1776-93 . . . . 4.00

18 (grano). Like No. 20. 1776-84 . . . . 7.00

★18a G(rano) 1. 1795 . . . . 7.00

★20 (2 grani). 1776-95 . . . . 6.00

ITALY

SICILY (Cont.)

Silver

	Fine
23 *G(rani) 10*. Bust. Rev. Eagle. 1796	7.00
25 *G(rani) 20*. Bust. Rev. Eagle. 1795-98	8.00
27 *T(ari) 2*. Bust. Rev. Eagle. 1795	8.00
29 *T(ari) 3*. Bust. *Rev. Eagle*. 1796	10.00

	F-VF
31 (6 tari). 1785-89 G.L.C.	50.00
★**31a** —. 1793, 95 N.d'o.v.	50.00
31b T(ari) 6. 1794 N.d'o.v.	50.00
33 T(ari) 6. Like No. 36 but FERDINANDUS D.G. etc. 1796-98	60.00
35 (piastra). Like No. 36 but w/out arms on eagle's breast. 1785-93	55.00
35a T(ari) 12. 1794-95	55.00

★**36** T(ari) 12. 1796-98	65.00

	V.F.
37 (oncia). Bust. Rev. EX AVRO etc. Phoenix. 1785	550.00
37a —. Large bust. 57mm. 1791	600.00
38 T(ari) 30. Sim. 49mm. 1793 (VF-EF)	500.00

II. Second period, 1799-1816.

Copper

	Fine
41 1/GRANO. Eagle. Rev. Value. 1801-03	3.00

★**42** G(rano) 1. 1814-15	5.00
43 2/GRANI. Like No. 41. 1801-04	3.00

★**44** G(rani) 2. 1814-15	5.00
45 5/GRANI. Like No. 41. 1801-04	15.00
46 G(rani) 5. Cwnd. head. Rev. SECVRITAS etc. Security std. 1814-16	5.00
47 10/GRANI. Like No. 41. 1801-04	15.00
48 G(rani) 10. Cwnd. head. Rev. FELICITAS etc. Cornucopiae. 1814-15	7.50

Silver

	F-VF
48.5 T(ari) 6. Like No. 33. 1799-1801	12.00
48.5a —. Value not shown. 1799	12.00
48.5b —. FERDINAN. III etc. 1799-1801	12.00
49 T(ari) 12. Like No. 36. 1799-1803	20.00
49a —. FERDINAN. III D. G. etc. 1799-1804	20.00

	V.F.
★**50** TARI 12. 1805-10	75.00

Gold

51 O(ncia) 2. Cwnd. head. Rev. Triquetra. 1814	—

Ferdinando II 1830-59

Copper

	VF-EF
52 MEZZO (=½)/GRANO. Head. Rev. Value/SICILIANO/ 1836	250.00
53 UN (=1)/GRANO. Sim. 1836	250.00
54 DUE (=2)/GRANI. Sim. but SICILIANI. 1836	250.00
55 CINQUE (=5) GRANI. Sim. 1836	250.00
56 DIECI (=10) GRANI. Sim. 1836	250.00

See Naples and Sicily for the common coinage of the dual realm.

SPOLETO (SPOLETVM), Town

In Umbria, Papal States.

Monetary System:
100 baiocchi = 1 scudo.

Pius VI, Pope 1775-99

Copper

	VG-F
1 *BAIOCCHI/DVE E MEZZO* (= 2½ B.). St. Peter. Rev. Value. *1796-97*	37.50
2 BAIOC(chi)/CINQVE (= 5 B.). Madonna. Rev. Value/ SPOLETVM/UMB. CAP. 1797	40.00

SUBALPINE REPUBLIC (SUBALPINE GAULE).

See Piedmont Republic.

TERNI

Town in the Papal States lying 50 miles N. of Rome.

Monetary System: See Papal States.

ITALY

TERNI (Cont.)

Pius VI, Pope 1775-99

Copper

VG-F

2 BAIOC(chi)/CINQVE (=5 B.).
Madonna. Rev. value/TERNI.
1797....................50.00

Billon

4 QVAT/TRO (=4)/BAIOC/
CHI. Like No. 8. 1797......*15.00*
6 SEI (=6)/BAIOC/CHI.
Sim: 1797....................*35.00*
8 OTTO (=8)/BAIOC/CHI.
TER/NI/ 1797, PIVS etc.
around. Rev. value........*40.00*

TIVOLI

Town in the Papal States lying 15
miles NE. of Rome.

Pius VI, Pope 1775-99

Copper

2 BAIOC(chi)/CINQVE (=5 B.).
Like TERNI No. 2 but TIVOLI.
1797....................10.00

TRENT
(TRIENT, TRENTO, TRIDENT),
Bishopric

56 miles N. of Verona, Italy. Obtained
mint right 12th century. Secularized
and annexed to Austria 1803. Part of
the Napoleonic kingdom of Italy 1810-
14. Back to Austria 1814-1918.

Peter Vigilius von
Thun-Hohnstein,
Bishop 1776-1800

Gold

E.F.

*11 (ducat). On his election.
1776..................1000.00

TUSCANY
(ETRURIA, TOSCANA),
Grand Duchy

In N.W. Italy. Belonged to the Medici
family until extinction of the ruling line
in 1737. Given then to Franz, duke of
Lorraine (later Emperor Franz I) as
compensation for Lorraine which he
ceded to France.

Monetary Systems:

1. Until 1826:

12 denari =3 quattrini =1 soldo;
20 soldi =1 lira;
10 lire =1 dena (in Florence, weight
39.1 gr.);
40 quattrini =8 crazie =1 Paolo
(in Pisa);
1½ Paoli =1 lira;
10 Paoli =1 Francescone
(scudo, tallero);
1 Unghero =13 lire;
3 zecchini (florins) =1 Ruspone =
40 lire.

2. 1826-59:

100 quattrini =1 fiorino;
4 fiorini =10 Paoli.

Arms: Lorraine: 3 eaglets on a bend;
Medici: 6 pills; Austria: Red, a white
fesse.

Mints: Florence; Pisa (Pisis).

Francesco (Franz) II, 1737-65

Copper

V.G.

1 QVATTRINI TRE (=3 Q.).
Arms of Lorraine-Medici.
Rev. Patriarch's cross. 1741. 3.50

Silver

F-VF

2 QVATT(rini) DIECI (=10 Q.).
FRANC. D. G. R.I.S.A.M.D. ETR. D.
Bust. Rev. Arms. 1759, 64.. 5.00
3 (½ Paolo). SVP. OMNES SPECIOSA.
Madonna. Rev. IN TE etc. Arms
of L-M. 1738.............10.00

*4 (Paolo). 1738.............15.00
5 (2 Paoli). Sim. but Rev. Arms
with L-M centershield. 1738 .25.00

V.F.

6 (5 Paoli). FRANC. II etc. Bust.
Rev. Arms. 1738-45........40.00
7 (5 Paoli). FRANCISCUS D. G. R.I.
etc. Bust. Rev. Imp. eagle,
arms of L-M on breast. PISIS.
13.4 gr. 1746, 64..........35.00
7a —. 1757-58.............40.00
8 (Francescone =10 Paoli). Like
No. 8a but sword does not
touch eagle wing. 1747.....150.00

V.F.

*8a —. 1747, 58-65..........100.00
8b —. PISIS divides date. 1748-
58.....................100.00
8c —. 1748 R.N...........250.00

"Francescone" or "Big Francis" —
big silver coin of Francesco. See
also Nos. 21-26, 37 and 59.

Gold (zecchino =3.4 gr.)

9 (Unghero). Like No. 5. (2 var.).
1738, 41................. —
10 (zecchino). FRANC. III etc. . . .
M.D. ETR. Lily. Rev. S. IOANNES
BAPTISTA, St. John. 1737-
43.....................450.00
11 (Ruspone). Sim. 1743-45. .1250.00
11a —. FRANCISCVS D. G. ROM. IMP.
1746-64................1250.00

Pietro Leopoldo 1765-90,
Emperor as Leopold II 1790-92

Copper

VG-F

*12 UN (=1) /QVATTRINO.
1771-90................. 5.00
13 DVETTO (=2 quattrini). Sim.
1778-85................. 5.00
14 SOLDO. Sim. 1778-90...... 6.00

Billon

G-VG

15 QUATTRINI DIECI (=10 Q.).
Bust. Rev. Arms. 1778-88... 4.00

ITALY

TUSCANY (Cont.)

Silver

F-VF

16 (½ Paolo). Bust. Rev. Arms.
1.3 gr. 1784 . . . . .12.00

17 (Paolo). Sim. 2.7 gr. 1783 . . .15.00

17a —. 1788-90 . . . . .15.00

*18 (2 Paoli). 1770-87 . . . . .25.00

V.F.

19 (5 Paoli). Sim. Unbound hair.
13.4 gr. 1777-79 . . . . .150.00

19a —. Bound hair. 1778-87 . . . . .75.00

20 (5 Paoli). Bust. Rev. square
arms. 1790 . . . . .75.00

21 (10 Paoli). Bust r. Rev. thin
oval arms. 1765-66 . . . . . . .120.00

21a —. Bound hair. Wide irregular
arms. 1766 . . . . .95.00

21b —. Like No. 21a but unbound
hair. 1766-71 . . . . .60.00

22 (10 Paoli). Like No. 21b but
bust l. 1767-68 . . . . .120.00

*23 (Levant thaler). 1769, 73-
74 . . . . .200.00

24 (10 Paoli). Bust. Rev. Arms
in order chain. (5 var.).
1771-90 . . . . .60.00

25 (10 Paoli). Bust. Rev. Arms
supported. PISIS. 1790 . . . . .350.00

26 (10 Paoli). Bust. Rev. Imp.
eagle. PISIS. 1790 . . . . .250.00

Gold (zecchino = 3.4 gr.)

V.F.

27 (zecchino). P. LEOPOLDVS D. G.
etc. . . . M.D. ETR. Lily. Rev.
St. John. 1779-89 . . . . .125.00

28 (Ruspone). Sim. 1765-90 . . .300.00

28a —. LEOPOLDUS II D. G. H. etc.
1790 . . . . .350.00

28b —. LEOPOLDUS II D.G.R.I. etc.
1790 . . . . .150.00

Ferdinando III,
In Tuscany 1791-1801,
In Salzburg 1803-05,
In Würzburg 1806-14

Copper

VG-F

29 QVAT/TRINO. FERD. III
A.A.M.D.ETR. Ptd. arms.
Rev. Value. 1791-1800 . . . . . . 3.00

30 UN (=1)/QUATTRINO. Sim.
Square arms. 1801 . . . . 3.00

*31 SOLDO. 1791 . . . . 5.00

Billon

32 QUATTRINI DIECI (=10 Q.).
LEX TUA etc. Cross. Rev. Value.
1800-01 . . . . 5.00

Silver

V.F.

*33 (½ Paolo). 1792 . . . . .20.00

34 (Paolo). Sim. 2.6 gr. 1791 . . .50.00

35 (2 Paoli). Sim. 1791 . . . . . . .75.00

36 (5 Paoli). Head. Rev. oval
arms/PISIS. 1791 . . . . .75.00

37 (10 Paoli). Head. Rev. sq.
arms in order chain. 1791-
1801 .100.00

Gold (zecchino = 3.4 gr.)

38 (zecchino). FERDINANDUS III
etc. Lily. Rev. St. John. 1791-
92 . . . . .600.00

39 (Ruspone). Sim. 1791
1801 . . . . .1100.00

Lodovico (Louis) I di Borbone,
Infante of Spain,
Ex Duke of Parma,
Installed by Napoleon in Tuscany
As King of Etruria,
1801-03

Copper

VG-F

40 UN (=1)/QUATTRINO.
LUD. D. G. HISP. I. REX. ETR.
Arms. Rev. Value. 1802-03,
05 (error) 3.00

Billon

41 QUATTRINI/DIECI (=10 Q.).
VIDEANT etc. Arms. Rev. Value
on sarcophagus. 1801-02 . . . . 7.00

41a —. Value in field. 1802 . . . . .10.00

41b DIECI/QUATTRINI.
1802 . . . . 4.00

Silver

V.F.

*42 (10 Paoli). 1801-03 . . . . . . .75.00

Gold

43 (Ruspone). LUDOVICUS I etc.
Lily. Rev. St. John. 1801,
03 .1650.00

Carlo Lodovico
(Infant Son of Lodovico I),
Under Regency of his Mother,
Maria Louisa (Aloysia),
1803-07

Copper

VG-F

44 UN (=1)/QUATTRINO.
C. LUD. R. ETR. etc. Arms.
Rev. Value. 1803-07 . . . . 7.00

45 MEZZO (=½)/SOLDO. C. LUD.
etc. 3 lilies. Rev. Value. N.D. 3.00

46 2/SOLDI. Arms. Rev. Value.
1804-05 . . . . 5.00

ITALY

TUSCANY (Cont.)

Silver

V.F.

47 UNA (=1)/LIRA. CAROLVS
LVD. etc. Arms. Rev. Value.
1803, 06 . . . . .40.00

*48 CINQUE (=5) LIRE (on edge).
2 busts. Rev. Arms. 1803-
04 . . . . .175.00

49 DIECI (=10) LIRE (on edge).
Sim. 1803-07 . . . . .175.00

*50 (10 Paoli). 2 busts. Rev. Arms.
1803-07 . . . . .110.00

Gold

51 (zecchino for Levant). S. JOAN.
BATT–F. ZACHAR. St. John. Rev.
St. Zenobio kneeling before
Christ. N.D. (1805) . . . . ——

52 (Ruspone). CAROLUS. L. etc.
Lily. Rev. St. John.
1803-07 . . . . .2250.00

Tuscany was annexed to France
1807-14, and from 1809 on was ruled
by Napoleon's sister Elisa Baciocchi
(see Lucca).

Ferdinando III of
Austria-Lorraine,
Restored 1814-24

Copper

Fine

53 UN (=1)/QUATTRINO. FERD.
III A.D.A.G.D. DI TOSC. Arms.
Rev. Value. 1819-24 . . . . 5.00

Fine

54 SOLDO. Sim. 1822-23 . . . . . . 5.00

55 2/SOLDI. FERDINANDUS III
D. G. A.A.M.D. ETR. Arms. Rev.
Value. 1818, 22 . . . . 5.00

Silver

V.F.

56 10/SOLDI. Sim. 1821, 23 . . .25.00

57 LIRA. Head (short hair).
Rev. Value. 1821-23 . . . . . .25.00

58 (5 Paoli). Head (short hair).
Rev. Arms. 1819-20 . . . . . . .80.00

58a —. 1823 . . . . .200.00

*59 (10 Paoli). Head. Rev. Arms.
1814-24 . . . . .60.00

Gold (zecchino = 3.4 gr.)

60 (zecchino). FERDINANDUS III etc.
Lily. Rev. St. John. 1816,
21 . . . . .550.00

61 (Ruspone). Sim. 1815-23 . .1750.00

Leopoldo II 1824-48, 49-59
New Monetary System.

Copper

Fine

62 1/QUATTRINO. LEOP. II
A.D.A. GRAND. DI TOSC. Arms.
Rev. Value. 1827-43 . . . . 3.00

*62a —. LEOP.II.A.D'A. G-D. etc.
1841-57 . . . . 3.00

63 SOLDO. Sim. but round arms.
1824 . . . . .40.00

*64 3/QUATTRINI.
1826-54 . . . . 6.00

65 5/QUATTRINI. Sim. 1826-
30 . . . . 6.00

Billon

Fine

66 10/QUATTRINI. Like No. 63.
1826-27, 53-54 . . . . 9.00

*67 QUATTRINI DIECI (=10 Q.).
1858 .20.00

Silver

V.F.

68 (½ Paolo = 20 Q.). LEOP. II
etc. . . . . M.D. ETR. Young head.
Rev Arms. 1.3 gr. 1832, 39 . .12.00

*68a —. Older head. 1839-59 . . . .20.00

69 ¼/DI/FIORINO (=25 Q.).
Spade arms. Rev. Value.
1827 . . . . .40.00

70 (Paolo). Like No. 68. 2.6 gr.
1831-38 . . . . .25.00

70a —. Like No. 68a. 1842-58 . .15.00

71 ½/FIORINO. Like No. 69.
1827 . . . . .45.00

*72 FIORINO. 1826-42 . . . . .30.00

72a —. Older head. 1843-58 . . . .30.00

*73 DUE (=2) FIORINI (on edge).
1827-29 . . . . .150.00

73a —. Older head. Rev. sq. arms.
1834 . . . . .275.00

74 QUATTRO (=4) FIORINI
(on edge). Head. Rev. Arms,
flags. 1826 . . . . .250.00

75 QUATTRO FIORINI (on edge).
Big head. Rev. Arms. 1830 . 250.00

75a —. Small head. 1833-41 . . . .125.00

ITALY

TUSCANY (Cont.)

V.F.

★75b —. Older head. 1845-59.... 60.00

Gold (zecchino = 3.4 gr.)
VF-EF

76 (zecchino). LEOPOLDUS II etc.
Lily. Rev. St. John
1824-53................. 600.00

77 (Ruspone). Sim. 1824-36.. 1100.00

78 OTTANTA (=80) FIORINI
(on edge). Lily. Rev. Arms.
1827-28................. ——

Provisional Government 1859
Silver

★79 FIORINO. 1859........... 30.00

Gold

80 (Ruspone). GOVERNO DELLA
TOSCANA. Lily. Rev. St. John.
1859................... ——

Tuscany United to Italy
Provisional Government 1859-61
Vittorio Emanuele
(of Sardinia), King-Elect

FIRENZE (Florence) Mint.

Monetary System:
100 centesimi = 1 lira.

Copper
V.F.

81 I/CENTESIMO. Like No. 82.
1859................... 5.00

V.F.

★82 2/CENTESIMI 1859...... 5.00
83 5/CENTESIMI. Sim. 1859.. 5.00

Silver

★84 CINQUANTA (=50)
CENTESIMI. 1860-61..... 10.00

85 UNA (=1) LIRA. Sim.
1859-60................. 25.00

86 DUE (=2) LIRE. Sim.
1860................... 35.00

For coinage of Vittorio Emanuele II as King of Italy 1861-78 see Yeoman's M.W.C.

VENICE (VENEZIA), Republic

During the period covered by this catalog the city of Venice, at the head of the Adriatic, was an oligarchy with extensive possessions, ruled by an elected doge (=duke). In 1797 the last doge was ousted and a provisional government established 1797-98. Absorbed by Austria 1798. To France 1806-14. Returned to Austria 1814-60. To Italy thereafter.

Arms: Winged lion of St. Mark (references to "lion" are to this animal).

Monetary System:
6 denari = 1 bezzo; 12 denari = 1 soldo;
20 soldi = 1 lira; 30 soldi = 1 lirazza;
124 soldi = 1 ducatone; 140 soldi =
1 scudo.

I. Doges of Venice to 1797.

Francesco Loredano, Doge 1752-62

Billon
V.G.

1 6 (denari). S.M.V. FRANC. LAVRED.
Lion, doge. Rev. DEFENS.
NOSTER. Christ stdg. N.D... 2.00

2 12 (denari). Sim. N.D.
(See No. 26).............. 2.00

Silver
F-VF

3 (5 soldi). S.M.V. FRANC.
LAVREDANO. Lion. Rev.
IVDICIVM etc. Justice std.
1752.................. 8.00

4 (10 soldi). FRANC. LAVREDANO.
Doge. Rev. SANCT. MARCVS VEN.
Lion. 2.2 gr. 1752........ 8.00

5 (15 soldi). Sim. 3.4 gr.
(See No. 121). 1752....... 10.00

6 17½ (soldi = ⅛ scudo). FRANC
etc. Cross. Rev. SANCT MARCVS
etc. Lion. N.D............ 15.00

7 35 (soldi = ¼ scudo). Sim.
N.D................... 25.00

8 70 (soldi = ½ scudo). Sim.
N.D................... 30.00

9 140 (soldi = scudo). Sim.
N.D................... 50.00

10 15½ (soldi = ⅛ ducatone).
S.M.V. FRANC etc. Lion, doge.
Rev. MEMOR ERO etc. St.
Justine. N.D............. 20.00

11 31 (soldi = ¼ ducatone).
Sim. N.D............... 35.00

12 62 (soldi = ½ ducatone). Sim.
N.D................... 55.00

13 124 (soldi = ducatone). Sim.
N.D................... 175.00

14 QVAR (= ¼) DVCAT(o).
S.M.V. FRANC. etc. St. Mark,
doge. Rev. Value, lion. N.D. 12.00

15 MEDI (= ½) DVCAT(o).
Sim. N.D................ 25.00

16 DVCATVS (= ducato). Sim.
22.4 gr. N.D. (See No. 100). 45.00

16a Double thick (= 2 ducati).
44.5 gr. N.D............ 450.00

17 (½ tallero). Like No. 18.
1756................... 50.00

★18 (tallero). 1756, 60-61..... 100.00

ITALY

VENICE (Cont.)

Gold

(zecchino = 3.4 gr.; doppia = 6.8 gr.)

V.F.

19 (¼ zecchino). FRANC. LAVRED. etc. St. Mark, doge. Rev. EGO SVM etc. Christ. N.D.....425.00

20 (½ zecchino). Sim. N.D...450.00

21 (zecchino). Sim. but Rev. SIT. T. XPE etc. Christ. N.D. (See No. 71).............200.00

22 (2 zecchini). Sim. N.D...... ——

23 (¼ doppia). FRANC. etc. Cross. Rev. SANCTVS MARCVS etc. Lion. N.D................ ——

24 (½ doppia). Sim. N.D...... ——

25 (doppia). Sim. N.D....... ——

Venice struck numerous gold coins with the dies for silver or billon coins. Nearly all are rare.

The annual osellas, or presentation pieces (= 9.8 gr. silver), were also struck in gold. These ornate dated objects, with the doge's name and PRINC(IPIS) MUNUS etc. are omitted as being more medal than coin. All are scarce or rare.

Marco Foscarini, Doge 1762-63

Billon

VG-F

★26 12 (denari). N.D..........5.00

Silver

V.F.

27 (5 soldi). Like No. 3 but S.M.V. FOSCARENVS. 1762..........40.00

28 (10 soldi). Like No. 4 but MARC FOSCARENVS. 1762.....30.00

29 (15 soldi). Sim. 3.6 gr. 1762..30.00

30 (30 soldi). Like No. 53. 1762...................35.00

31 17½ (soldi). Like No. 6 but MARC. etc. N.D.............30.00

32 35 (soldi). Sim. N.D.......45.00

33 70 (soldi). Sim. N.D..:...40.00

34 140 (soldi). Sim. N.D......75.00

34a Double thick (= 2 scudi). 63 gr. N.D.............400.00

35 15½ (soldi). Like No. 10 but S.M.V.M. FOSCARENVS D. N.D....................50.00

V.F.

36 31 (soldi). Sim. N.D......100.00

37 124 (soldi). Sim. N.D....450.00

38 QVAR (=¼) DVCAT(o). Like No. 14 but S.M.V. MARC. FOSCAREN. N.D.........65.00

39 MEDI (=½) DVCAT(o). Sim. N.D...............125.00

40 DVCATVS (=ducato). Sim. N.D...................250.00

41 (½ tallero). Like No. 17 but MARCO etc. 14 gr. 1762.....100.00

42 (tallero). Sim. 28.4 gr. 1762.350.00

Gold

(zecchino = 3.4 gr.; doppia = 6.8 gr.)

43 (¼ zecchino). Like No. 19 but M. FOSCARENVS etc. N.D...1200.00

44 (½ zecchino). Sim. N.D...650.00

45 (zecchino). Like No. 21 but M. FOSCARENVS etc. N.D...250.00

46 (¼ doppia). Like No. 23 but M. FOSCARENVS etc. N.D.... ——

47 (½ doppia). Sim. N.D...... ——

48 (doppia). Sim. N.D....... ——

Alvise (Aloysius) Mocenigo IV, Doge 1763-78

Coins with mint marks not shown here belong to Alvise Mocenigo II 1700-09 or A.M. III 1722-32.

Billon
V.G.

49 12 (denari). Like No. 26 but S.M.V. ALOY. MOCENI. N.D... 2.50

Types of No. 49 with ALOY-MOC. were struck 1700-09 or 1722-32.

Silver
V.F.

50 (5 soldi). Like No. 3 but S.M.V. ALOY etc. 1763, 77-78. 5.00

51 (10 soldi). Like No. 4 but ALOY etc. 1763, 77-78....... 4.00

52 (15 soldi). Sim. but 3.4 gr. 1763, 77-78............... 7.50

★53 (30 soldi). 1767-78........12.00

54 17½ (soldi). Like No. 6 but ALOY etc. ND. mmk. D.G...15.00

55 35 (soldi). Sim. ND. mmk. D.G., M.A.T.............30.00

56 70 (soldi). Sim. ND. mmk. D.G., M.A.T.............50.00

57 140 (soldi). Sim. ND. mmk. D.G., B.C., M.A.T........75.00

V.F.

58 15½ (soldi). Like No. 10 but ALOY:MOCENI. ND. mmk. D.G..............20.00

59 31 (soldi). Sim. ND. mmk. D.G...............35.00

60 62 (soldi). Sim. ND. mmk. D.G., B.C..........:...60.00

61 124 (soldi). Sim. ND. mmk. D.G., B.C.........150.00

61a Double thick (= 2 ducatone). ND...................750.00

62 QVAR (=¼) DVCAT(o). Like No. 14 but S.M.V. ALOY: MOCENI. ND. mmk. D.G., G.A.F., V.V..............15.00

63 MEDI (=½) DVCAT(o). Sim. ND. mmk. D.G., G.A.F., G.P.............30.00

64 DVCATVS (=ducato). Sim. ND. mmk. D.G., R.B.P., B.C., G.A.F., G.P., G.M.B., L.B., V.V., A.M.P., P.D., V.S....50.00

64a Double thick (= 2 ducati). 44.5 gr. ND. mmk. D.G., R.B.P., V.V., A.M.P.....450.00

65 (¼ tallero). Like No. 17 but ALOYSII etc. 7.1 gr. 1766....75.00

66 (½ tallero). Sim. 14.2 gr. 1764, 66................100.00

67 (tallero). Sim. 28.4 gr. 1764, 66.................175.00

68 (tallero). Like No. 102. 1768-69.................125.00

Gold

(zecchino = 3.4 gr.; doppia = 6.8 gr.)

69 (¼ zecchino). Like No. 19 but ALOY. MOCEN. N.D.......400.00

70 (½ zecchino). Sim. N.D...425.00

Types of Nos. 69 and 70 with ALOY. MOC. or MOCE. struck 1700-09 or 1722-32.

★71 (zecchino). N.D.........170.00

No. 71 with MOCENI struck 1700-09 or 1722-32.

72 (8 zecchini). Sim. but ALOY. MOCENICO. N.D............ ——

73 (10 zecchini). Sim. N.D..... ——

74 (12 zecchini). Sim. N.D..... ——

75 (18 zecchini). Sim. N.D..... ——

76 (20 zecchini). Sim. N.D..... ——

77 (25 zecchini). Sim. N.D..... ——

78 (30 zecchini). Sim. N.D..... ——

79 (50 zecchini). Sim. N.D..... ——

ITALY

VENICE (Cont.)

Types of Nos. 72-79 with ALOY or
ALOYS. MOCENI were struck 1700-09
or 1722-32.   *V.F.*

79.5 (60 zecchini). Sim. ND...... ——
  80 (100 zecchini). Sim. ND .... ——
  81 (¼ doppia). Like No. 23
but ALOY MOCENICO. ND.
mmk. G.P................. ——
  82 (½ doppia). Sim. ND.
mmk. G.P................. ——
  83 (doppia). Sim. ND.
mmk. G.P................. ——

Paulo (Paul) Renier (Rainero),
Doge 1779-89

Billon   *V.G.*

  84 6 (denari). Like No. 26 but
S.M.V. PAVL. RAINER. N.D... 1.75
  85 12 (denari). Sim. N.D...... 2.00

Silver   *V.F.*

  87 (10 soldi). Like No. 4 but
PAVL etc. 1781............ 6.00
  88 (15 soldi). Sim. 3.4 gr. 1781 .10.00
  89 (30 soldi). Like No. 53. 1781-
84...................... 15.00
  90 17½ (soldi). Like No. 6 but
PAVL etc. N.D............ 12.00
  91 35 (soldi). Sim. N.D........ 20.00
  92 70 (soldi). Sim. N.D........ 35.00
  93 140 (soldi). Sim. N.D....... 50.00
  94 15½ (soldi). Like No. 10 but
S.M.V. PAVL etc. N.D...... 25.00
  95 31 (soldi). Sim. N.D........ 35.00
  96 62 (soldi). Sim. N.D........ 75.00
  97 124 (soldi). Sim. N.D..... 150.00
  98 QVAR (=¼) DVCAT(o).
Like No. 100. N.D......... 15.00
  99 MEDI (=½) DVCAT(o).
Sim. N.D................. 25.00

  ★100 DVCATVS (=ducato).
N.D.................... 35.00

100a —. Double thick (=2 ducati).
44.3 gr. ND............ 350.00
  101 (⅛ tallero). Like No. 102.
3.5 gr. 1780-86.......... 20.00

★102 (¼ tallero). 1780-86....... 25.00
  103 (½ tallero). Sim. 13.9 gr.
1780-87................. 50.00
  104 (tallero). Sim. 28.2 gr.
1781-88................. 70.00

Gold
(zecchino = 3.4 gr.; doppia = 6.8 gr.)

  105 (¼ zecchino). Like No. 19 but
PAVL RAINE. N.D........ 250.00
  106 (½ zecchino). Sim. N.D.. 250.00
  107 (zecchino). Like No. 71 but
PAVL etc. N.D........... 170.00
  108 (4 zecchini). Sim. N.D..... ——
  109 (8 zecchini). Sim. N.D..... ——
  110 (10 zecchini). Sim. N.D..... ——
  111 (18 zecchini). Sim. N.D..... ——
  112 (24 zecchini). Sim. N.D..... ——
112.5 *(30 zecchini). Sim. ND* ....
  113 (40 zecchini). Sim. N.D.... ——
  114 (50 zecchini). Sim. N.D.... ——
114.5 (55 zecchini). Sim. N.D.... ——
  115 (¼ doppia). Like No. 23 but
PAVL RAINE etc. N.D...... ——
  116 (½ doppia). Sim. N.D...... ——
  117 (doppia). Sim. N.D....... ——

Lodovico Manin, Doge
1789-97

Billon   *VG-F*

  118 12 (denari). Like No. 26 but
S.M.V. LVDO.MANIN. N.D... 3.00

Silver   *V.F.*

  119 (5 soldi). Like No. 3 but
LVDO etc. 1789, 97......... 7.00
  120 (10 soldi). Like No. 121.
1789-97................. 6.00

★121 (15 soldi). 1789-97....... 8.00
  122 (30 soldi). Like No. 53.
1789-96................. 12.00

  123 17½ (soldi). Like No. 6 but
LUDOVIC etc. N.D........ 15.00
  124 35 (soldi). Sim. N.D...... 25.00
  125 70 (soldi). Sim. N.D...... 35.00
  126 140 (soldi). Sim. N.D..... 60.00
126a —. Double thick (=2 scudi).
63 gr. N.D............. 750.00
  127 15½ (soldi). Like No. 10 but
S.M.V. LVDOVI etc. N.D 30.00
  128 31 (soldi). Sim. N.D...... 65.00
  129 62 (soldi). Sim. N.D...... 90.00
  130 124 (soldi). Sim. N.D..... 150.00
130a —. Double thick (=2 ducatoni).
55.6 gr. N.D........... 800.00
  131 QVAR (=¼) DUCAT(o).
Like No. 100 but S.M.V.
LVDOV. etc. N.D......... 17.50
  132 MEDI (=½) DVCAT(o).
Sim. N.D............... 25.00
  133 DVCATVS (=ducato).
Sim. N.D............... 35.00
133a —. Double thick (=2 ducati).
45 gr. N.D............. 425.00
  134 (⅛ tallero). Like No. 136.
3.4 gr. 1790-96........... 18.00
  135 (¼ tallero). Sim. 7.1 gr.
1790-94................. 30.00

★136 (½ tallero). 1789-97....... 50.00
  137 (tallero). Sim. 1789-97..... 75.00

Gold
(zecchino = 3.4 gr.; doppia = 6.8 gr.)

  138 (¼ zecchino). Like No. 19 but
LVD. MANIN. N.D........ 225.00
  139 (½ zecchino). Sim. N.D.. 225.00
  140 (zecchino). Like No. 71 but
LVDO. MANIN. N.D...... 170.00
  141 (2 zecchini). N.D....... 3000.00
  142 (5 zecchini). N.D........ ——
  143 (6 zecchini). N.D........ ——
  144 (8 zecchini). N.D........ ——
  145 (9 zecchini). N.D........ ——
  146 (10 zecchini). N.D........ ——
  147 (50 zecchini). N.D........ ——
  148 (105 zecchini). N.D........ ——
  149 (¼ doppia). Like No. 23 but
LVD.MANIN. N.D........ 1250.00
  150 (½ doppia). Sim. N.D...1400.00
  151 (doppia). Sim. N.D..... 2250.00

....

VENICE (Cont.)

II. Provisional Government 1797-98.

Silver

V.F.

★155 LIRE/DIECI (=10L.).
1797 (vars.)............100.00

III. Under Austria 1798-1806.

Franz II 1792-1835, In Venice 1798-1806

Billon

VG-F

160 MEZZA (=½)/LIRA. Like
No. 162. 1800.........15.00

161 UNA (=1)/LIRA. Sim.
1800................15.00

★162 DUE (=2)/LIRE. 1801....20.00

163 ½/LIRA. FRANC. II etc.
Imp. eagle. Rev. Value/
VENETA. 1802............15.00

164 1/LIRA. Sim. 1802.......15.00

165 1½/LIRA. Sim. 1802.....20.00

Gold

V.F.

166 (zecchino). S.M. VENEI. FRANC.
II. Like No. 71. ND.....850.00

166a —. Improved dies. Christ
holds orb. N.D.........750.00

IV. Under Napoleon 1806-14.

A. See Italy, Kingdom, for Napoleonic coinage with mmk. V.

B. The 1813 series of 4 denominations with rev. BLOCCO/DI/VENEZIA, are rare patterns for coinage to have been struck by the French defenders, but are known only as patterns. See Pagani, **Prove e Progetti** (Milan 1957), Nos. 531-536.

V. Under Austria 1814-66.

In 1814 Venice was returned to Austria. See Lombardy-Venetia for Austrian and other types with mmk. V. Except for the revolutionary period 1848-49, Venice remained in Austrian hands until 1877.

VI. Provisional Government 1848-49.

Monetary System:
100 centesimi = 1 lira.

Copper

V.F.

★181 1 CENTESIMO. GOVERNO PROVVISORIO DI VENEZIA. Lion. Rev. Value. 1849.... 3.00

182 3 CENTESIMI. Sim.
1849................. 4.00

183 5 CENTESIMI. Sim.
1849................. 4.00

Billon

Fine

★184 15 CENTESIMI. Sim. but lion passant guardant. 1848. 7.50

Silver

V.F.

★185 5/LIRE. 1848..........90.00

★186 5/LIRE. 1848..........90.00

Gold

VF-EF

187 20/LIRE. Like No. 185.
1848.................2000.00

Venice was annexed to Italy in 1866.

VITERBO

City in the Papal States lying about 40 miles NNW of Rome.
Monetary System:
See Papal States.

Pius VI, Pope 1775-99

Copper

Fine

1 MEZZO (=½) /BAIOCCO.
Arms. Rev. Value/VITERBO.
1797, N.D..............10.00

2 BAIOCCHI/DVE E MEZZO (=2½ B.). St. Peter. Rev. Value/VITERBO. (var.) 30mm. 1796-98................19.50

2a —. 25mm. 1797..........19.50

3 BAIOC(chi)/CINQVE. (=5 B.). Madonna. Rev. Value/VITERBO. 1797....................19.50

JAMAICA. See CARIBBEAN ISLANDS AND TERRITORIES.

JAPAN, Empire

Island empire off the east coast of Asia. First coins issued 708AD. During the period covered by this catalog the emperors were figureheads and the actual rulers of Japan were the Shoguns of the Tokugawa family. Further confusion arises from reference of coins to the "era" in which first issued, not to a reign. A new era was commenced each time it was thought necessary to commemorate an auspicious event or ward off an evil one.

None of the listed coins carry dates and the dates shown are those of the periods during which the coins were minted.

The following eras are mentioned in this catalog:

Kanei or Kwanei 1624-44AD
Kioho or Kyoho 1716-36AD
Gembun or Genbun 1736-41AD
Meiwa 1764-72AD
Bunsei 1818-30AD
Tenpo or Tempo 1830-44AD
Kaei 1848-54AD
Ansei 1854-60AD
Manen 1860-61AD
Bunkiu or Bunkyu 1861-64AD
Meiji 1868AD-

Monetary System until 1867:
4000 mon = 16 shu = 4 bu = 1 ryo (tael).

In practice the relative values of the coins varied widely. The Cho gin and Mameita gin passed by weight. Most gold and silver coins were badly debased.

Counterfeits exist of all Japanese gold and silver coins.

I. Base Metal Coinage.

Nos. 1 through 7 bear the names of the eras in which they were first struck. Unlike Chinese and Annamese coins of similar style, their minting continued through later eras without changing the titles on the coins.

On round coins the era name consists of the 2 characters at top and bottom. Characters at right and left on Nos. 1 and 4 are "tsu-ho" (=current coin). The obverse legend on No. 7 is similar but reads vertically from top to bottom. No. 6 has "ei-ho" (everlasting coin) at right and left.

There seems to be little agreement between specialists on the exact dates of most base metal varieties. Authoritative information on dating is invited.

Note: For other cast coins with square center hole, of the general style listed here, see ANNAM, CHINA, KOREA.

Mint Marks: The following characters appear on varieties of coin Nos. 1 and 4. Mark No. 2 is said to denote coins

---

cast from a giant statue of Buddha melted in 1668; all others distinguish various provincial mints. Except where noted in the listings, these mmks. appear on the reverse above the hole.

1	(no mmk.)	11	長
2	文	12	千
3a	佐	13	久
3b	佐	14a	㇠
4	仙	14b	㇀
5	十	15	ノ
6	小	16	イ
7	川	17	盛
8	元	18	ア
9	足	19	山
10	一		

Cast Copper Alloy
(except where otherwise noted)

Fine

★1.1 (mon). Kanei tsuho (top-bottom, right-left). Rev. blank. (1626-1828).... .50
1.1a —. Iron. *(1736-1867)*...... 5.00

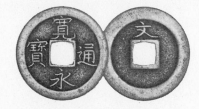

★1.2 —. Rev. mmk. No. 2..... .50
1.3a —. Rev. mmk. No. 3a.... 2.00
1.3b —. Rev. mmk. No. 3b.... 2.00
1.4 —. Rev. mmk. No. 4.....10.00
1.5 —. Rev. mmk. No. 5..... 7.50
1.5a —. Mmk. No. 5 stamped on obv. rim. Rev. blank... ——
1.6 —. Rev. mmk. No. 6..... 3.50
1.7 —. Rev. mmk. No. 7..... 5.00
1.7a —. Mmk. No. 7 stamped on obv. rim. Rev. blank... ——
1.8 —. Rev. mmk. No. 8..... 2.00
1.9 —. Rev. mmk. No. 9..... 3.00
1.10 —. Rev. mmk. No. 10....15.00
1.10a —. Mmk. No. 10 stamped on obv. rim. Rev. blank... ——
1.11 —. Rev. mmk. No. 11..... 2.50
1.12 —. Rev. mmk. No. 12. Iron................... 5.00

Fine
1.13 —. Rev. mmk. No. 13.... 3.00
1.14 —. Rev. mmk. No. 14a... ——

Cast Brass or Iron

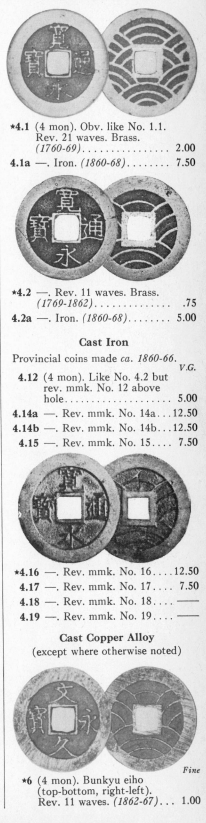

★4.1 (4 mon). Obv. like No. 1.1. Rev. 21 waves. Brass. *(1760-69)*.............. 2.00
4.1a —. Iron. *(1860-68)*....... 7.50

★4.2 —. Rev. 11 waves. Brass. *(1769-1862)*.............. .75
4.2a —. Iron. *(1860-68)*....... 5.00

Cast Iron
Provincial coins made *ca. 1860-66.*
V.G.
4.12 (4 mon). Like No. 4.2 but rev. mmk. No. 12 above hole.................. 5.00
4.14a —. Rev. mmk. No. 14a..12.50
4.14b —. Rev. mmk. No. 14b...12.50
4.15 —. Rev. mmk. No. 15.... 7.50

★4.16 —. Rev. mmk. No. 16....12.50
4.17 —. Rev. mmk. No. 17.... 7.50
4.18 —. Rev. mmk. No. 18.... ——
4.19 —. Rev. mmk. No. 19.... ——

Cast Copper Alloy
(except where otherwise noted)

Fine
★6 (4 mon). Bunkyu eiho (top-bottom, right-left). Rev. 11 waves. *(1862-67)*... 1.00

JAPAN

6a —. Sim. Top character like No. 6b .... *Fine* .75

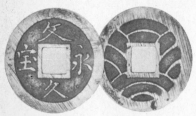

★6b —. Sim. Top character in diff. script, left char. abbreviated 1.75

6c —. No. 6a in iron 25.00

★7 100 (mon). Tempo tsuho (top to bottom). Rev. "value/ 100"/hole/official signature. *(1835-70)* .... 2.00 *VF-EF*

II. Billon and Silver Coinage.

A. Bullion Issues.

Nos. 8 through 9c circulated by weight, with no fixed relationship to copper or gold. Theoretical weight of a cho gin piece was 161.3 gr., but in practice most were ca. 120-150 gr. due to imprecise casting. The "bean" pieces were used to make up the deficiency when weighed on a scale, thus they have no fixed size or weight.

The stamp used at sides of Nos. 9-9c consists of a stylized God of Plenty with legend at left. Only a small part of the design appears on any given specimen.

Era characters (stylized) are as follows:

1a Genbun 1736-41 –"bun"

1b Bunsei 1818-30 –"bun"

2 Tempo 1830-44 –"ho"

3 Ansei 1854-60 –"sei"

 V.F.

★8 (Mameita gin = bean-shaped silver). Characters and designator. Rev. blank (except for occasional chop marks). (1601-1865) 10.00

8a —. God of Plenty both sides. (1695-1865) 30.00

★8b —. God of Plenty with era character between legs. (1695-1844) 30.00

No. 9b

9 ("cho gin" = long silver). Official stamp punched 3 *or* 6 times along each edge; era char. No. 1a at each end. Rev. blank. Genbun era (1736-41) 150.00

9a —. Sim. but era char. No. 1b at each end. Bunsei era (1818-30) 125.00

★9b —. Sim. but era char. No. 2 at each end. Tempo era (1830-44) 100.00

9c —. Sim. but era char. No. 3 at each end. Ansei era (1854-60) 100.00

B. Coin Issues.

Nos. 10-16 all circulated with fixed denominations.

 *V.F.*

★10 (1/12 ryo = Meiwa go momme gin). "Fixed weight silver 5 momme" (= 18.75 gr.). Rev. mintmaster's name. (1765-72) .. 375.00

★11 1/16 ryo (= shu = Bunsei isshu gin). Legend "16 (pieces) = 1 ryo." Rev. mint and mintmaster's names, official cmk. 2.6 gr. (1829-37) 30.00

★12 1 shu (= Kaei isshu gin). Value/"gin" (= silver). Rev. sim. to No. 11. 1.9 gr. (1854) 4.00

12a —. (= Meiji isshu gin). Sim. but diff. style "jyo" (see below). 1.9 gr. (1868) .. 6.00

No. 12 常   No. 12a 常

To distinguish between Nos. 12 and 12a, compare the tops of the upper left character on the reverse.

★13 1/8 ryo (= 2 shu = Meiwa nishu gin). Like No. 11 but "8 (pieces) = 1 ryo." 10 gr. 15 x 26mm. (1772-1824) 60.00

13a (ex 14) —. (= Bunsei nishu gin). Sim. but smaller. 7.5 gr. 13 x 22mm. (1824-30) 35.00

JAPAN

V.F.

★15 2 shu (=Ansei nishu gin).
Obv. like No. 12. Rev. like
No. 11. 13.6 gr. (1859) 400.00
No. 15 has been much counterfeited.

16 1 bu (=Tempo ichibu gin).
Like No. 12 but rosette
borders. 8.66 gr. (1837-54) . 7.50

16a —. (=Ansei ichibu gin).
Sim. but diff. style rev.
chars. (see below). 8.66 gr.
(1859-68) 7.50

★16b —. (=Meiji ichibu gin).
Sim. but diff. style rev.
chars. (see below). 8.3 gr.
(1868-69) 100.00

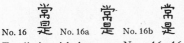

No. 16   No. 16a   No. 16b

To distinguish between Nos. 16, 16a
and 16b, compare the two characters
at left on the reverse.

III. Gold Coinage.

Era characters on Nos. 20-23:

1a Genbun 1736-41,
   Bunsei 1818-30 –"bun"   文

1b Bunsei 1818-30 –"bun"   ぶ

2 Tempo 1830-44 –"ho"   保

3 Ansei 1854-60 –"sho"   正

★17 1 shu (=Bunsei isshu kin).
Kiri flower/value. Rev. mintmaster's signature. 1.4 gr.
10 x 10mm. (1824-32) 75.00

V.F.

18 2 shu (=Tempo nishu kin).
Obv. sim. Rev. mintmaster's
name/signature. 1.65 gr.
7 x 13mm. (1832-58) 15.00

★18a (ex 19) —. (=Manen nisku kin).
Sim. but smaller. 0.7 gr.
6 x 12mm. (1860-69) 20.00

★20 1 bu (=Bunsei ichibu kin).
2 kiri flowers, value at sides.
Rev. like No. 18, with era char.
No. 1b in top r. corner. 3.0 gr.
9 x 15mm. (1819) 75.00

20a —. (=Tempo ichibu kin).
Sim., with era char. No. 2.
2.8 gr. (1837) 100.00

20b —. (=Ansei ichibu kin).
Sim., with era char. No. 3.
2.3 gr. (1859) 1000.00

20c (ex 20a) —. (=Manen ichibu
kin). Sim., but smaller, no
era char. *0.8 gr.* 7 x 12mm.
(1860-67) 300.00

No. 21c

21 2 bu (=Shinbun nibu kin).
Like No. 20. Rev. with era
char. No. 1a in top r. corner.
6.5 gr. 13 x 22mm. (1818) .250.00

21a —. (=Sobun nibu kin).
Sim. with era char. No. 1b.
6.5 gr. (1828) 225.00

21b (ex 21a) —. (=Ansei nibu kin).
Sim. but no era char.
5.6 gr. (1856-60) 65.00

★21c (ex 21b) —. (=Manen nibu kin).
Sim. but smaller, no era char.
3.3 gr. 12 x 19mm. (1860) . 100.00

21d (ex 21c) —. (=Meiji nibu kin).
Sim. but diff. style "bu"
(see below). *3.0 gr.* 12 x 19mm.
(1868) 17.50

No. 21c 分   No. 21d 分

To distinguish between Nos. 21c and
21d, compare the tops of the character
"bu," at left center of obverse.

V.F.

22 1 ryo (=Genbun koban kin).
Value in panel/mintmaster's
name and signature in panel.
Rev. era char. No. 1a (top r.)/
official signature (center)/2
hallmarks (lower l.). 13.1 gr.
36 x 65mm. (1736-1818) . .600.00

22a —. (=Bunsei koban kin).
Sim., with era char. No. 1b.
13.1 gr. 33 x 62mm.
(1819-28) 600.00

★22b —. (=Tempo koban kin).
Sim., with era char. No. 2.
11.3 gr. 32 x 61mm.
(1837-58) 500.00

22c —. (=Ansei koban kin).
Sim., with era char. No. 3.
9.0 gr. 31 x 56mm.
(1859) 2000.00

22d —. (=Manen koban kin).
Sim. but much smaller.
Rev. no era char. 3.3 gr.
20 x 36mm. (1860-67) 350.00

23 5 ryo (=Tempo goryoban kin).
Sim. Rev. era char. No. 2 at
top r. 33.8 gr. 51 x 89mm.
(1837-54) 2800.00

24 10 ryo (=Kyoho oban kin
1725-1838, Tempo oban kin
1838-60). Sim. but 4 round
kiri flower cmks. (top, bottom,
right, left); value/name/
signature written in india ink.
Rev. cmks do not include
era char. 165.4 gr.
95 x 156mm 10,000.00

24a (ex 25) —. (=Manen oban kin).
Sim. but smaller. 112.9 gr.
79 x 133mm. (1860-62 . . . .4000.00

**Note: Coins similar to Nos. 22-24
but of other sizes and weights are
of earlier vintage. Novak considers
that 90% of all koban and oban
type gold currently available is not
legitimate.**

IV. Ryukyu (Liu-Kiu) Islands.

Chain of islands extending S.W. from
Japan toward Formosa.

<table>
<tr><td>

JAPAN

....

RYUKYU ISLANDS (Cont.)

**King Sho-Tai 1848-79
Under Domination of
Satsamo Diamyo**

Cast Bronze

V.F.

★100 100 (mon). Ryukyu tsuho (top to bottom). Rev. "value (hole) 100." *(1862)*.......25.00

★115 ½ shu. Ryukyu tsuho (top-bottom, right-left). Rev. value. Characters in archaic style. *(1862)*.......40.00

</td><td>

JERSEY

....

Island off the west coast of France belonging to Great Britain.

Monetary System:

26 sous = 13 pence (Jersey) = 12 pence (English) = 1 shilling (English).

George III 1760-1820

Silver

F-VF

★1 EIGHTEEN/PENCE. 1813...................27.50
2 THREE/SHILLINGS. Sim. 1813................65.00

UNVERIFIED DATA

Note: Throughout this catalog, any uncertain, indefinite or unconfirmed information is shown in *italic type*. Such material may be, for example, coin descriptions, dates and prices, names of rulers, or supplementary notes. Further information to confirm or correct *material in italics* should be sent to the author at the following address:

William D. Craig
c/o Whitman Coin Supply Division
1220 Mound Avenue
Racine, Wisconsin 53404, U.S.A.

</td></tr>
</table>

KOREA (COREA)

Peninsula in N.E. Asia extending south from Manchuria. Kingdom until 1896, Empire 1896-1910. Became a pawn between China, Russia and Japan and was finally annexed to Japan in 1910.

Monetary System:

400-700 copper mun (yopchon = "leaf coin," cash, wen) =
10 silver chon (ch'ien, mace) =
1 yang (liang, ounce, tael).

Most of these relationships were changed in the period subsequent to that covered by this catalog.

Copper Alloy

Legends: Obverses of Korean copper-alloy issues from 1633 bear the legend "sang p'yong t'ong bo" (=always even current coin). See listing Nos. 1 through 4 for this obverse. For coins with other legends made during the period covered by this catalog see ANNAM, CHINA and JAPAN.

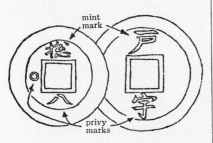

Typical reverses of 1 and 2 mun

Reverse legends are quite varied on the 1 and 2 mun (coins with blank reverses predate this catalog). The top character is the mint mark, sometimes in conjunction with another character at side or bottom. Usually present are one or more additional characters, numerals or special symbols (e.g., dots, circles, crescents). These other markings can be part of the mmk. (or the value on 2 mun), but are most often privy marks denoting a specific emission or casting furnace of a mint. Numerals used as privy marks may run from 1 to 20 or more, and it is emphasized that numerals may be construed as denominations only in some cases where a 2 appears on a 2 mun (usually at bottom).

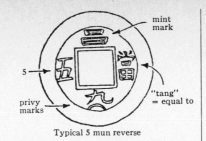

Typical 5 mun reverse

Reverses of the 5 and 100 mun are more consistent, with mint mark at top, value at sides and privy mark(s) at bottom.

Nearly fifty mints issued a total of several thousand varieties of the 1, 2 and 5 mun, and a full treatment is beyond the scope of this catalog. For a complete listing see Whitman's *Cast Coinage of Korea* by Edgar J. Mandel (1972).

Fine

★**1** (mun). "Sang p'yong t'ong bo." Rev. mmk. (top) and usually 1 or more privy marks. 3.3-4.5 gr. 23-27mm. (1678-ca. 1900)............75

★**1.5** (2 mun). Sim. 6.7-9.0 gr. 27-33mm. (1679-1753)..... 2.00

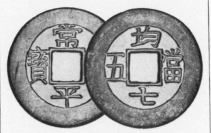

★**2** 5 (mun). Obv. sim. Rev. mmk./ privy mark (top-bottom), value (right-left). 27-33mm. (1883).................... 2.00

3 —. Sim. but struck in brass, not cast. Round hole. 6 gr. 31mm. With mmk. No. 21 only. (1890).............(V.F.) 75.00

Fine

★**4** 100 (mun). Like No. 2. With mmk. No. 13 only. 39-40mm. (1866)..........15.00

Silver

Nos. 5-7 bear the obverse legend "tae dong" (=great east[ern kingdom]) at top and bottom, with the value at right and left. Reverses bear mint mark No. 13 in a disc of dark blue-green cloisonné enamel. Prices are for specimens with substantially intact enamel.

V.F.

5 1 chon. Like No. 7. 20mm. (1883)....................30.00

6 2 chon. Sim. 28mm. (1883)..45.00

★**7** 3 chon. (1883).............60.00

Korean Mint Marks

The following chart shows all mint marks used on Korean coins during the period covered by this catalog. All mint marks appear on the reverse, and single-character mint marks are located at the top. As a general rule, 2-character mint marks (Nos. 45, 48, 50, 51, 54-56, 58-60) have the first character at the top and the second at the bottom or right side.

Other characters, numerals or special symbols on the reverses of Korean coins are privy marks (see text on previous page).

Dots to the right of each mint name indicate the coin varieties issued by that mint. The columns headed "Plain" indicate reverses bearing mint marks (1 or 2 characters) only; those headed "Series No." refer to varieties bearing numerals or characters as privy marks.

Mint marks are numbered according to the catalog numbers in *Cast Coinage of Korea*, from which the following chart is taken.*

Mint Mark Number	Mint Mark	Romanization and Issuing Agency	Value 100	Value 5	Value 2 Series No.	Value 2 Plain	Value 1 Series No.	Value 1 Plain
13	戶 or 戶 or 戶	戶曹 *Hojo* — Treasury Department	•	•				
14	工	工曹 *Kongjo* — Ministry of Industry					•	•
15	均	均役廳 *Kyunyŏkch'ŏng* — Government Tithe Office				•		
16	司僕寺	司僕寺 (*Kyŏng*) *Saboksi* — Bureau of Royal Transportation				•	•	
17	賑	賑恤廳 *Chinhyulch'ŏng* — Charity Office in Seoul				•	•	
18	向	根餉廳 *Yanghyangch'ŏng* — Food Supply Office				•	•	
19	宣	宣惠廳 *Sŏnhyech'ŏng* — Rice & Cloth Department				•	•	
20	惠	宣惠廳 *Sŏnhyech'ŏng* — Rice & Cloth Department					•	
21	典	典圜局 *Chŏnhwan'guk* — Central Government Mint			•			
22	兵	兵曹 *Pyŏngjo* — Ministry of Defense				•	•	
23	備 or 俻	備邊司 *Pibyŏnsa* — National Defense Bureau				•	•	
24	捴	摠戎廳 *Ch'ongyungch'ŏng* — General Military Office				•	•	
25	營 or 营	御營廳 *Ŏyŏngch'ŏng* — Special Army Unit				•	•	
26	武 / 武	武備司 *Mubisa* — Armaments Bureau and / 武衛營 *Muwiyŏng* — Guard Office at the Palace				•	•	
27	禁	禁衛營 *Kŭmwiyŏng* — Court Guard Military Unit				•	•	
28	訓 or 訓	訓練都監 *Hullyŏndogam* — Military Training Command				•	•	•
29	抄	精抄廳 *Chŏngch'och'ŏng* — Commando Military Unit				•	•	
30	統 or 統	統營 *T'ongyŏng* — T'ongyŏng Naval Office and				•	•	
	統	統衛營 *T'ongwiyŏng* — Military Office in Seoul		•				
31	経	經理廳 *Kyŏngnich'ŏng* — Government Office of Pukhan Mountain Fortress						•
32	守	守禦廳 *Suŏch'ŏng* — Seoul Defense Fort				•		
33	沁	江華管理營 (*Sim*) *Kanghwa Kwalliyŏng* — Kanghwa Township Military Office. Simyŏng 沁營 is another name for Kanghwa.		• V.5		•	•	
34	開	開城管理營 *Kaesŏng Kwalliyŏng* — Kaesŏng Township Military Office				•	•	•
35	松	開城管理營 (*Song*) *Kaesŏng Kwalliyŏng* — Kaesŏng Township Military Office. Songdo 松都 is another name for Kaesŏng.					•	
36	利	利原管理營 *Iwŏn Kwalliyŏng* — Iwŏn Township Military Office					•	•
37	水	水原管理營 *Suwŏn Kwalliyŏng* — Suwŏn Township Military Office				•	•	

Mint Mark Number	Mint Mark	Romanization and Issuing Agency	Value 5	Value 2 Series No.	Value 2 Plain	Value 1 Series No.	Value 1 Plain
38	原	原州管理營 *Wŏnju Kwalliyŏng* — Wŏnju Township Military Office				•	•
39	海	海州管理營 *Haeju Kwalliyŏng* — Haeju Township Military Office				•	•
40	春 or 睿	春川管理營 *Ch'unch'ŏn Kwalliyŏng* — Ch'unch'ŏn Township Military Office	•				
41	川	端川管理營 *Tanch'ŏn Kwalliyŏng* — Tanch'ŏn Township Military Office	•				
42	昌 / 昌	昌德宮 *Ch'angdŏk Kung* — Ch'angdŏk Palace Mint and / 昌原管理營 *Ch'angwŏn Kwalliyŏng* — Ch'angwŏn Township Military Office					
43	圻	廣州管理營 (*Ki*) *Kwangju Kwalliyŏng* — Kwangju Township Military Office in Kyŏnggi Province			•		•
44	京	京畿監營 *Kyŏnggi Kamyŏng* — Kyŏnggi Provincial Office				•	•
45	京水	京畿水營 *Kyŏnggi Suyŏng* — Kyŏnggi Naval Station			•		
46	黄	黃海監營 *Hwanghae Kamyŏng* — Hwanghae Provincial Office				•	•
47	平	平安監營 *P'yŏngan Kamyŏng* — P'yŏngan Provincial Office	•			•	•
48	平兵	平安兵營 *P'yŏngan Pyŏngyŏng* — P'yŏngan Military Fort			•		
49	咸	咸鏡監營 *Hamgyŏng Kamyŏng* — Hamgyŏng Provincial Office				•	•
50	咸北	咸鏡北營 *Hamgyŏng Pugyŏng* — North Hamgyŏng Provincial Office			•		
51	咸南	咸鏡南營 *Hamgyŏng Namyŏng* — South Hamgyŏng Provincial Office			•		
52	江	江原監營 *Kangwŏn Kamyŏng* — Kangwŏn Provincial Office				•	•
53	尙	慶尙監營 *Kyŏngsang Kamyŏng* — Kyŏngsang Provincial Office	•			•	•
54	尙水	慶尙水營 *Kyŏngsang Suyŏng* — Kyŏngsang Naval Station			•		
55	尙右	慶尙右營 *Kyŏngsang Uyŏng* — Kyŏngsang Right Naval Base			•		
56	尙左	慶尙左營 *Kyŏngsang Chwayŏng* — Kyŏngsang Left Naval Base			•		
57	全	全羅監營 *Chŏlla Kamyŏng* — Chŏlla Provincial Office	•			•	•
58	全兵	全羅兵營 *Chŏlla Pyŏngyŏng* — Chŏlla Military Fort			•		
59	全右	全羅右營 *Chŏlla Uyŏng* — Chŏlla Right Naval Base				•	•
60	全左	全羅左營 *Chŏlla Chwayŏng* — Chŏlla Left Naval Base				•	•
61	忠	忠清監營 *Ch'ungch'ŏng Kamyŏng* — Ch'ungch'ŏng Provincial Office	•			•	•

NOTES

KRIM (CRIMEA), Khans

Ruled the Crimean Peninsula and neighboring areas in South Russia. Vassals of Turkey after 1475. Subject to Russian protectorate 1777, annexed to Russia 1783. See RUSSIA for later coins.

Mints: Bagchih-Serai, Kaffa.

Monetary System:

3 manghir (aqcheh, asper) = 1 para;
40 para = 20 ikilik = 8 beshlik = 4 onlik = 2 yirmilik = 1 piastre (gurush);
60 para = 1 altmishlik.
4 polushka = 2 denga = 1 kopek;
10 kopek = 2 kyrmis = *1 ishal (tschal).*

Coin types:

Most coins of Krim show a tamgha (tribal or dynastic emblem) resembling a 3-legged stool. Some show a toughra, mostly with the upper strokes resembling three flagpoles with drooping pennants.

Krim Giray bin Daulat
1171-77AH (=1758-64AD)

Silver
VG-F

50 (ikilik). Khan's name. Rev. Tamgha/Mint. 17-20mm. 1 gr. 1172AH, N.D *20.00*

Sahib Giray II bin Ahmad Giray
1185-89AH (=1772-75AD)

Copper

125 (manghir). Legends each side. 15mm. 1185AH *10.00*

Shahin Giray bin Ahmad Giray
1191-97AH (=1777-83AD)

Copper
Fine

135 (denga). Like No. 136. 21mm. Yrs. 4-6 . . . .*20.00*

★136 (kopeck). Khan's name. Rev. tamgha/DURIBA/FI/(yr.) BAGCHIH-SERAI/1191. 27-29mm. Yrs. 4-6 . . . .*10.00*

Fine

138 (kyrmis). Sim. 44-45mm. Yrs. 4-6 . . . .*25.00*

★140 (ischal). Toughra. Rev. (Yr.) 5/ Mint (KAFFA)/Tamgha/ 1191. 51-52mm *30.00*

Billon

150 (manghir). Khan's name. Rev. Mint. 11mm. .2 gr. Yr. 2 . . . .*15.00*

152 (para). Like No. 150. 16mm. .6 gr. Yr. 2 . . . .*15.00*

156 (ikilik). Toughra. Rev. Tamgha, Mint. 17mm. 1.3 gr. Yrs. 4-5 . . . .*15.00*

160 (beshlik). Khan's name. Rev. Tamgha/Mint. 16-19mm. Yrs. 3-4 . . . .*20.00*

Silver
F-VF

165 (yirmilik). Like No. 170a. 29mm. 7.3 gr. Yr. 4 . . . .*25.00*

F-VF

170 (piastre). Sim. 35mm. 16 gr. Yr. 4 . . . .*65.00*

★170a —. 34mm. 14.4 gr. Yr. 5 . .*65.00*

175 (altmishlik). Sim. 38-40mm. 19.8-22.8 gr. Yrs. 2, 4-6 . . . . .*RR*

LOW COUNTRIES (PAYS BAS)

Area occupied by present-day Netherlands, Belgium and Luxemburg. Intermingled to such an extent, during the period covered by this catalog, that logic requires it be treated as a whole.

ANVERS (ANTWERP)

City, now in Belgium.

French, Under General Carnot, Besieged by Allies, 1814-15

Monetary System:

100 centimes = 1 franc.

Bronze

I. In Name of Napoleon.

Fine

1 5/CENT(imes). Like No. 2. 1814, 15 . . . .*10.00*

LOW COUNTRIES

Fine
★2 10/CENT(imes). 1814......12.50

II. In Name of Louis XVIII.

★3 5/CENT(imes). 1814.......12.50
4 10/CENT(imes). Sim. 1814..15.00

AUSTRIAN NETHERLANDS

The Burgundian legacy, including Brabant and Flanders, constituting much of present-day Belgium. To Austria 1700 at the extinction of the Spanish Hapsburg line. Revolted 1790. The revolt was quelled, but in 1793 the Austrian Netherlands were taken by France. Part of the Kingdom of Netherlands 1815-30. To Belgium 1830.

Monetary System:

4 liards = 1 sol (patard);
14 liards = 1 plaquette;
6 sols = 1 escalin; 20 sols = 1 florin;
54 sols = 1 Kronenthaler;
60 sols = 1 ducaton;
7 florins, 13 sols = 1 Sovereign (Souverain) d'or.

Mints:

Antwerp – Hand; Bruges – Lion;
Brussels – Head; Vienna – W.

Maria Theresia 1740-80

Copper

Fine

1 (liard). MAR. TH. D. G. etc. Young unveiled bust. Rev. AD/USUM/BELGII/AUSTR./date. 22mm. 1744-45................. 6.50

1a —. Bust with pearl necklaces. 1749-52................. 6.50

1b —. Veiled bust. 1776-80..... 6.50

2 (2 liards). Obv. like No. 1a. Rev. like No. 2a. 1749-53.... 8.50

★2a —. 1777-80................ 8.50

Billon or Silver

3 (10 liards). Like No. 21 but MAR. TH. etc. 1750-53....... 16.50

4 XIV (liards). Like No. 37 but MAR. TH. etc. 1755-78....... 22.50

5 (20 liards). Like No. 3. 4.78 gr. 1750-53................. 18.00

★6 (escalin). 1749-54, 63-68....14.00

7 (2 escalins). Sim. 10 gr. 1751-53................. 18.00

Silver

V.F.
9 (⅛ ducaton). Bust. Rev. Arms. 4.15 gr. 1749-53......30.00

10 (¼ ducaton). Sim. 8.31 gr. 1749-53................. 95.00

11 (½ ducaton). Sim. 16.6 gr. 1749-54................. 140.00

12 (ducaton). Sim. 33.2 gr. 1749-54................. 225.00

13 (½ Kronenthaler). Like No. 14. 14.7 gr. 1755-79..........37.50

V.F.
14 (Kronenthaler). MARIA THERESIA etc. Burgundian cross, 4 crowns in angles. Rev. Imp. eagle, arms on breast. 1755-80........37.50

Gold (Souv. d'or = 5.5 gr.)

15 (Souverain d'or). Like No. 15b but Rev. squarish arms. 25mm. 1749.........500.00

15a —. Sim. 22mm. 1750-52..450.00

★15b —. 1751-65............450.00

15c —. Veiled bust. 1770-77..450.00

16 (2 Souv. d'or). Like No. 15. 28mm. 1749...........1150.00

16a —. Sim. 27mm. 1750-51..1000.00

16b —. Like No. 15b. 1757-63................. 850.00

16c —. Veiled bust. 1766-79...850.00

Franz I,
Holy Roman Emperor 1745-65

Silver

17 (½ Kronenthaler). FRANCIS D. GRATIA etc. Imp. eagle, arms on breast. Rev. Burgundian cross, 3 crowns in angles. 14.7 gr. 1755-65..................50.00

18 (Kronenthaler). Sim. 1755-65.....................100.00

Joseph II 1780-90

Copper

VG-F
★19 (liard). 1781-89........... 7.50

20 (2 liards). Sim. AD/USUM etc. in wreath. 27mm. 1781-89... 8.00

Billon

Fine
★21 (10 liards). 1788-89........22.50

AUSTRIAN NETHERL'DS (Cont.)

Fine

22 XIV (liards). Like No. 37 but
IOS. II etc. 1788-89........22.50

Silver

V.F.

*23 (¼ Kronenthaler). 1788-90A, B, 88H..............15.00

24 (½ Kronenthaler). Sim. 1786-89 (Brussels), 88-90A, 88B..25.00

25 (Kronenthaler). Sim. 29.44 gr. 1781-89 (Brussels), 83-90A, 84, 88B..............60.00

Gold (Souv. d'or = 5.5 gr.)

26 (Souverain d'or). Head. Rev. oval arms. 1786, 88 (Brussels), 86-90A, F..............400.00

27 (2 Souv. d'or). Sim. 1781-89 (Brussels), 83-87A, 86F.650.00

Note: Nos. 23-27, 38-42, and 46-50, especially those struck after 1793 outside the Austrian Netherlands at Vienna (A), Kremnitz (B), Prague (C), Karlsburg (E), Hall (F), Nagybanya (G), Günzburg (H), and Milan (M), are by way of being trade coins and have no real home. The Italian issues are listed under Milan, but the rest are listed here because the types are clearly those of the Austrian Netherlands.

Insurrection 1790

Copper

28 (liard). Lion holds liberty hat on lance. Rev. AD/USUM/FOEDERATI/BELGII/1790..............12.50

29 (2 liards). Sim. but AD/USUM etc. in wreath. 1790........16.00

Silver

30 X SOLS. MON. NOV. ARG. PROV. FOED. BELG. Lion. Rev. IN VNIONE SALVS. 2 hands hold arrows. 1790..............60.00

30a —. Diff. legends. Obv. DOMINI etc. 1790..............90.00

31 I FLOR(in). Like No. 30. 1790..............175.00

31a —. Like No. 30a. 1790.....200.00

32 (3 florins). Like No. 33. 1790..............235.00

Gold

V.F.

*33 (lion d'or). 1790........400.00

Leopold II 1790-92

Copper

Fine

34 (liard). Bust. Rev. AD/USUM/BELGII/AUSTR./date. 1791-92..............20.00

35 (2 liards). Sim. but AD/USUM etc. in wreath. 27mm. 1791-92..............20.00

Billon

36 (10 liards). Like No. 21 but LEOP. II etc. 1791........37.50

*37 XIV (liards). 1790-92......40.00

Silver

V.F.

38 (¼ Kronenthaler). Head. Rev. Like No. 23. 1790-92A, 91-92B, H..............35.00

39 (½ Kronenthaler). Sim. 1790A, 91-92H..............45.00

40 (Kronenthaler). Sim. 29.4 gr. 1790A, 91-92H..........75.00

Gold (Souv. d'or = 5.5 gr.)

41 (Souverain d'or). Head. Rev. Oval arms. 1791-92A, 92B, E..............400.00

42 (2 Souv. d'or). Sim. 1790-91A, 92B, E, F..............2000.00

See note following No. 27 regarding Nos. 38-42.

Franz II 1792-1835, In Austrian Netherlands 1792-93/94

Copper

Fine

43 (liard). Like No. 44 but no wreath around AD/USUM etc. 1792-94..............7.50

Fine

*44 (2 liards). 1793-94.......8.50

Billon

44.5 (10 liards). Like No. 21 but FRANC. II etc. 1792....... RR

45 XIV (liards). Like No. 37 but FRANC. II etc. 1792-94.....85.00

Silver

V.F.

46 (¼ Kronenthaler). Head. Rev. Like No. 23. 1792-97A-C, E, G..............20.00

47 (½ Kronenthaler). Sim. 1792-97A-C, E-G..........30.00

48 (Kronenthaler). Sim. 29.4 gr. 1792-98A-C, E-H..........40.00

48a —. 1794 (Brussels)........175.00

Gold (Souv. d'or = 5.5 gr.)

49 (Souverain d'or). Head. Rev. Oval arms. 1792-98A, B, F, H..............450.00

50 (2 Souv. d'or). 1792-98A, B, F, H..............400.00

50a —. 1793 (Brussels)......1450.00

See note following No. 27 regarding Nos. 46-50.

BELGIUM, Kingdom

The former Austrian Netherlands, together with the Bishopric of Liege, and certain other territory. United with the Kingdom of the Netherlands 1815-30. Revolted and became independent in the latter year.

Monetary System:
100 centimes = 1 franc.

Leopold I 1831-65

Copper

A number of Netherlands cents were cmkd. in 1830-31 with B(elgique) or L(eopold).

VG-F

1 1 CENT(ime). Like No. 4. 1833-62..............   .75

2 2 CENT(ime)S. Sim. 1833-65..............   .50

3 5 CENT(ime)S. Sim. 1833-60.............. 1.25

LOW COUNTRIES

BELGIUM (Cont.)

		VG-F
*4	10 CENT(ime)S. 1832-56	15.00

The 1853 copper, silver and gold pieces on the marriage of the Duke of Brabant, and the 1856 25th anniversary pieces with Belgia crowning the king are medals.

Copper-Nickel

		F-VF
6	5/CENTIMES. Value. Rev. lion. 1861-64	.40
7	10/CENTIMES. Sim. 1861-64	.40

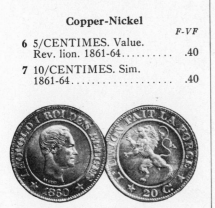

*8	20 C(entime)s. 1860-61	2.50

Silver

		Fine
9	¼/FRANC. Like No. 13. 1834-44	15.00
10	½/FRANC. Sim. 1833-44	20.00
11	1/FRANC. Sim. 1833-44	30.00
12	2/FRANCS. Sim. 1834-44	75.00

		V.F.
*13	5/FRANCS. 1832-49	15.00
14	20 C(entim)ES. Like No. 20. 1852-53, 58	6.00
15	¼ F(ranc). Sim. 1850	200.00
16	½ F(ranc). Sim. 1850	250.00
17	1 F(ranc). Sim. 1849-50	150.00

The 1849 ¼, ½ and 2 francs are patterns.

19	2½ F(rancs). Sim. 1848-50	95.00

*20	5 F(rancs). 1849-65	10.00

Gold

		E.F.
22	20/FRANCS. Laureate head. Rev. value. 1835-41	——
23	40/FRANCS. Sim. 1835-41	——

Nos. 22-23 were not circulated.

		V.F.
24	10 F(rancs). Bare head. Rev. arms. 1849-50	300.00
25	25 F(rancs). Sim. 1848-50	275.00
26	20/FRANCS. Bare head. Rev. value. 1865	75.00

GELDERS, Province.
See Netherlands to 1806.

HOLLAND, Kingdom.
See Netherlands 1806-10.

HOLLAND, Province.
See Netherlands to 1806.

LIEGE
(LÜTTICH, LEODICUM),
Bishopric

In Belgium. First coins 11th century. Liege was annexed to France in 1794 and completely secularized in 1802. Most of the territories of the former bishopric went to the new kingdom of the Netherlands in 1815 (and thence to Belgium in 1830).

Monetary System:
Same as Austrian Netherlands.

Johann Theodor von Bayern, Bishop 1744-63

Copper

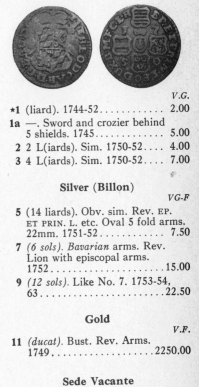

		V.G.
*1	(liard). 1744-52	2.00
1a	—. Sword and crozier behind 5 shields. 1745	5.00
2	2 L(iards). Sim. 1750-52	4.00
3	4 L(iards). Sim. 1750-52	7.00

Silver (Billon)

		VG-F
5	(14 liards). Obv. sim. Rev. EP. ET PRIN. L. etc. Oval 5 fold arms. 22mm. 1751-52	7.50
7	(6 sols). Bavarian arms. Rev. Lion with episcopal arms. 1752	15.00
9	(12 sols). Like No. 7. 1753-54, 63	22.50

Gold

		V.F.
11	(ducat). Bust. Rev. Arms. 1749	2250.00

Sede Vacante
1763, 71, 84 and 92

Silver

13	(6 sols). S. LAMBERTUS PATRONUS LEOD. Bust of St. Lambert. Rev. Lion with arms. 1763, 71, 84, 92	35.00

LOW COUNTRIES

LIEGE (Cont.)

14 (patagon = 48 sols). Obv. sim. Rev. Arms on mantle. 1763, 71, 84, 92 ....300.00 *V.F.*

Gold

15 (ducat). Sim. 1763, 71, 84, 92 ....700.00

LUXEMBURG (LUXEMBOURG), Duchy

On the French-Belgian-German frontier. First coins 11th century. County of Luxemburg raised to duchy 1354. To Burgundy 1444. To Austria 1713-95 as part of the Burgundian inheritance at the extinction of the Spanish Hapsburgs. To France 1795-1813. To the kingdom of the Netherlands as a grand duchy 1815.

Monetary System:
8 gigot = 4 liards = 1 sol;
6 sols = 1 escalin; see Austrian Netherlands.

Arms: On a field barry of blue and silver, a red lion.

Maria Theresia 1740-80

Copper

VG-F

1 ⅛/SOL. Cwnd. arms, no legend. Rev. value. 1775 ....10.00
2 (liard). Bust. Rev. AD/USUM/DUCATUS/LUXEM./1757 ......14.00
3 (2 liards). Sim. but AD/USUM etc. in wreath. 6.9 gr. 1757..16.00
4 (liard). Like No. 5. 3.8 gr. 1759-60 ....17.50

*5 (2 liards). 6.9 gr. 1759-60...17.50

Billon

6 I/SOL. Like No. 7. 1775....20.00

*7 III/SOLS. 1775...........20.00

Silver

Fine

8 VI/SOLS. Sim. 1775, 77....37.50
9 XII SOLS. MAR. TH. etc. ... DUX. LUXEMB. Bust. Rev. Arms. 1775-77 ....65.00

Joseph II 1780-90

Copper

*11 DEMI (= ½)/LIARD. 1783-89 ....7.50

*12 (2 liards). 1789 ....47.50

*13 I/SOL. 1786 ....30.00

Silver (billon)

14 VI/SOLS. Sim. 1786 ....17.50
14a —. 1789 ....35.00
15 XII/SOLS. Bust. Rev. Arms. 1786, 89 ....45.00

Leopold II 1790-92

Copper

16 I/SOL. Like No. 18. 1790...22.50

Silver (billon)

17 III/SOLS. Sim. 1790 ......22.50

*18 VI/SOLS. Sim. 1790 ....35.00

Franz II 1792-1835, In Luxemburg 1792-95

Coined by Austrian defenders during siege of Luxemburg City 1794-95.

Copper

V.G.

*19 1/SOL. Cast. 13.25 gr. 1795 ....35.00
19a —. Struck. 15 gr. 1795....*Exists?*

Silver

F-VF

20 LXXII/ASSES (= 72 sols = Kronenthaler). AD/USUM/LUXEMBURG/etc. Rev. Value. 1795 ....1000.00

MAESTRICHT (TRAIECTUM AD MOSAM), City

In Netherlands. Besieged 1794 by French. Emergency coinage of the Austrian defenders under the Prince of Hesse.

Bronze

Fine

1 5 St(übers). Like No. 3. Uniface. 1794 ....120.00
2 100 St(übers). TRAIECTUM AD MOSAM. Star. Rev. Like No. 3. 1794 ....45.00

Silver

F-VF

*3 50 St(übers). Uniface. 1794.250.00
3a —. Struck over French 3 livre coin 125.00
5 100 St(übers). Like No. 2. 1794 ....475.00
6 100 ST(ube)RS. Obv. Sim. Rev. URBE OBSESSA 100 STRS. 1794 ....475.00
7 100 St(übers). Like No. 3. Uniface. 1794 ....125.00
7a —. Struck over French 6 livre coin 140.00

LOW COUNTRIES

NETHERLANDS (NEDERLAND)

Northern portion of the Burgundian inheritance, which revolted and became independent from Spain in the 16th century. Passed through several governmental stages before becoming the present-day kingdom of the Netherlands.

Monetary System to 1816:

4 duiten = 1 stuiver (stiver);
6 stuivers = 1 schelling;
20 stuivers = 1 gulden (guilder, florin);
50 stuivers = 1 Rijksdaalder (silver ducat);
60 stuivers = 1 ducaton (silver rider);
14 gulden = 1 golden rider.

I. United Netherlands. (United Provinces)

Union of seven provinces, Gelders, Groningen, Holland, Overyssel, Utrecht, Friesland, and Zeeland, occupying the site of the present-day kingdom. Governed by the Estates General and a stadholder of the House of Orange.

Friesland (Frisia), with a mint at Leeuwarden, seems not to have struck coins dated after 1738. West Friesland (also called North Holland) was part of the County of Holland, but nevertheless had its own coinage struck at Hoorn, Enkhuizen and Medemblik until 1796.

In 1794 France invaded the United Netherlands, ousted the stadholder, and set up the Batavian Republic 1795-1806.

Arms of the Estates General:
Lion with sword and bundle of seven arrows.

The provinces used the same monetary system and coin types, but struck separate series to 1806.

For similar coins with the United East India Company's VOC bale mark, see NETHERLANDS EAST INDIES.

A. Gelderland (Ducatus Gelriae), Duchy.

(Combined with the county of Zutphen.)

Arms: 2 lions combattant.

Copper

The ½ duits of 1753-57 (former No. A1) are presentation pieces struck in silver.

Fine

A2 (duit). Like No. A2a but rev. D/GEL/etc. in plain field. 1703-52 . . . . 4.00

Fine

★A2a —. Rev. with wreath. 1753-57 . . . . 4.00

★A2b —. Legend not abbreviated. Rev. D/GEL/etc. in cartouche. 1758-68 . . . . 3.00

A2c —. Rev. legend in plain field. 1783-88 . . . . 3.00

A2d —. Rev. legend in floral border. 1788-94 (var.) 3.00

Silver

F-VF

★A4 I S(tuiver). 1738-66 . . . . . . 14.00

★A4a —. No wreath either side. 1785 . . . . 12.50

★A6 I S(tuiver). 1757 . . . . 25.00

A7 2 S(tuivers). Sim. 1785 . . . 8.00

★A8 2 S(tuivers). 1786-92 . . . . . 6.00

V.F.

A10 (¼ gulden). Like No. A13 but shield divides date. 1756, 59 . . . . 40.00

A12 10 ST(uiver). Like No. A13a. 1751 . . . . 200.00

A12a X ST(uiver). Sim. 1759-65 . . . . *500.00*

A13 I G(ulden). Like No. A13a. 1694-1738 . . . . 40.00

V.F.

★A13a I G(u)L(den). 1760-86 . . . 40.00

A14 3 G(u)L(den). Sim. 1694-1786 . . . . 175.00

A17 (½ Rijsdaalder). Like No. A18. 1762-65 . . . . . 225.00

A18 (Rijksdaalder). Like No. H18 but obv. legend ends D. GEL. & C.Z., knight holds Gelderland arms. 1693-1785 . . . . 185.00

A21 (½ ducaton). Like No. F21 but obv. legend ends D: GEL: & C:Z., rider over Gelderland arms. 1761-90 . . . . 185.00

A22 (ducaton). Sim. 42mm. 1704-92 . . . . 160.00

Gold (ducat = 3.5 gr.)

A25 (ducat). CONCORDIA etc. . . . . D. G(EL) & C.Z. Knight stdg. Rev. MO:ORD/PROVIN/FOEDER/ BELG. AD/LEG. IMP. on tablet. 1586-1792 . . . . 275.00

A26 (2 ducats). Sim. 1656-1761 . . . . 800.00

A27 7 G(u)L(den). MO:AUR etc. . . . . GELRIA (or D:G:&:C:Z:). Rev. CONCORDIA etc. Union arms. 1750-62 . . . . 500.00

A28 14 G(u)L(den). Sim. 1750-62 . . . . 750.00

B. Groningen (and Ommeland), Town and Province.

Copper

VG-F

★B2 (duit). Arms. Rev. GRON/EN/ OMMEL. 1770-72 . . . . 7.00

Silver

F-VF

★B4 I S(tuiver). 1738, 65-66 . . . 25.00

LOW COUNTRIES

NETHERLANDS (Cont.)

Gold

V.F.

B27 7 G(u)L(den). Like No. A27 but obv. legend ends *GRON* and rider over Groningen arms. 1761 . . . . 500.00

B28 14 G(u)L(den). Sim. 1761 . . . . 750.00

C. Holland (Hollandia), County.
Arms: Lion rampant.

Copper

VG-F

★C2 (duit). 1702-80 . . . . 2.75

Silver

F-VF

★C4 I S(tuiver). 1738-64 . . . . . . 8.00

C6 I S(tuiver). Like No. C8. 1724-37 . . . . 9.50

★C8 2 S(tuiver). 1672-1793 . . . . 3.50

Note: No. C8 dated 1791 w/out large dot after/DIA is a Singapore merchants' token struck 1834-44.

★C10 (¼ gulden). Rev. legend ends HOLL. 1759 . . . . 17.50

★C11 6 S(tuiver). Obv. legend ends HOLL. ET WESTFRI. 1670-1767 . . . . 12.50

F-VF

C12 X ST(uiver). Like No. C10. 1748-62 . . . . 40.00

C13 I G(ulden). Sim. 1694-1794 . . . . 25.00

C14 3 G(ulden). Sim. 1694-1794 . . . . 140.00

C18 (Rijksdaalder). Like No. H18 but obv. legend ends HOL: and knight holds Holland arms. 1672-1772 (var.) . . 120.00

C21 (½ ducaton). Like No. F21 but obv. legend ends HOL: and rider over Holland arms. 1765-92 . . . . *120.00*

C22 (ducaton). Sim. 1672-1793 . . . . 120.00

C23 (2 ducaton). Sim. 1719-54 . . . . *pattern?*

C24 (3 ducaton). Sim. 1754 . . . . *pattern?*

Gold (ducat = 3.5 gr.)

C25 (ducat). Like No. A25 but obv. legend ends HOL. 1586-1791 . . . . 250.00

C26 (2 ducats). Sim. 1645-1793 . . . . 500.00

C27 7 G(u)L(den). Like No. C28. 1749-63 . . . . 400.00

C28 14 G(u)L(den). Like No. A28 but obv. legend ends HOLLAND and rider over Holland arms. 1749-63 . . . . 600.00

D. Holland and Westfriesland.

For former No. D11 see C11.

E. Overyssel (Overijsel, Transisulania), Province.

Arms: Lion rampant in front or behind a fesse.

Copper

VG-F

★E2 (duit). 1741-69 . . . . 3.50

E2a —. Rev. legend in wreath. 1753-54 . . . . 5.00

Silver

V.F.

E4 I S(tuiver). Obv. like No. A4. Rev. TRANS/ISALA/NIA. 1738-69 . . . . 17.50

E13 I G(ulden). Like No. A13 but obv. legend ends TRANSI. 1698-1765 . . . . 40.00

E14 3 G(u)L(den). Sim. 1694-1727 . . . . 185.00

V.F.

★E15 (⅛ Rijksdaalder). 1770 . . . *pattern*

E18 (Rijksdaalder). Like No. H18 but obv. legend ends TRANSI and knight holds Overyssel arms. 1695-1767 . . . . 150.00

E22 (ducaton). Like No. A22 but obv. legend ends TRANSI(SULANIA) and rider over Overyssel arms. 1720-64 (var.) 200.00

Gold

E25 (ducat). Like No. A25 but obv. legend ends TRANSI. 1593-1773 . . . . 350.00

E27 7 G(u)L(den). Like No. E28. 1760-63 . . . . 500.00

E28 14 G(u)L(den). Like No. A28 but obv. legend ends TRANSI and rider over Overyssel arms. 1760-63 . . . . 750.00

F. Utrecht (Trajectum), City and Province.

Arms:
City – Per bend, white and red.
Province – Cross and lion quartered.

Copper

Fine

★F2 (duit). 1739-93 . . . . 3.00

Silver

F-VF

F4 I S(tuiver). Obv. like No. A4. Rev. TRA/JEC/TUM/date. 1738-65 . . . . 10.00

★F8 2 S(tuiver). 1757-94 . . . . . . 4.50

Note: F8 dated 1786 with TRA/I.F.C./TUM was privately struck in England for the Singapore Malay trade circa 1834-44.

F10 (¼ gulden). Like No. F14. 24mm. 1758-59 . . . . 22.50

NETHERLANDS (Cont.)

F-VF

★F11 6 S(tuiver). Rev. legend ends TRAIECT. 1742-94 .... 15.00

V.F.

F12 X ST(uiver). Like No. F14. 1750-94 .... 27.50

F13 I G(ulden). Sim. 1697-1794 .... 30.00

★F14 3 G(u)L(den). Rev. legend ends TRAI. 1694-1794 .... 100.00

F17 (½ Rijksdaalder). Like No. F18. 1761-83 .... 175.00

★F18 (Rijksdaalder). Obv. legend ends TRAI, knight holds Utrecht arms. 1739-94 ... 140.00

F-VF

F19 (2 Rijksdaalder). Sim. 1772-76 .... *pattern?*

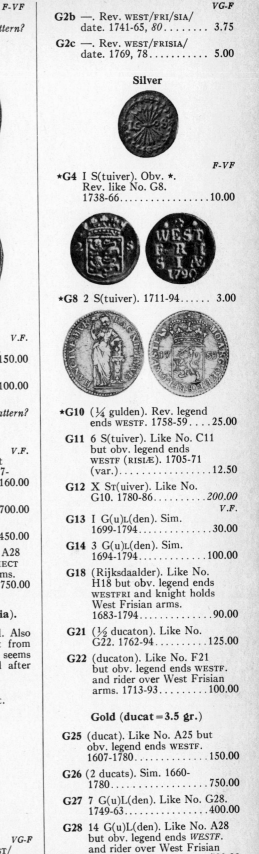

V.F.

★F21 (½ ducaton). Obv. legend ends TRAI. 1761-94 ..... 150.00

F22 (ducaton). Sim. 1679-1794 .... 100.00

F23 (2 ducaton). Sim. 1715-76 .... *pattern?*

Gold (ducat = 3.5 gr.)

V.F.

F25 (ducat). Like No. A25 but obv. legend ends TRA. 1587-1794 .... 160.00

F26 (2 ducats). Sim. 1652-1794 .... 700.00

F27 7 G(u)L(den). Like No. F28. 1749-63 .... 450.00

F28 14 G(u)L(den). Like No. A28 but obv. legend ends TRAIECT and rider over Utrecht arms. 1749-63 .... 750.00

G. West Friesland (West Frisia).

Part of the County of Holland. Also called North Holland. Distinct from the province of Friesland, which seems to have struck no coins dated after 1738.

Arms:
Billety, 2 lions passant guardant.

Copper

VG-F

★G2 (duit). Arms ★. Rev. WEST/FRISIÆ/date. 1702-39 .... 3.75

VG-F

G2b —. Rev. WEST/FRI/SIA/date. 1741-65, *80* 3.75

G2c —. Rev. WEST/FRISIA/date. 1769, 78 .... 5.00

Silver

F-VF

★G4 I S(tuiver). Obv. ★. Rev. like No. G8. 1738-66 .... 10.00

★G8 2 S(tuiver). 1711-94 ...... 3.00

★G10 (¼ gulden). Rev. legend ends WESTF. 1758-59 .... 25.00

G11 6 S(tuiver). Like No. C11 but obv. legend ends WESTF (RISIÆ). 1705-71 (var.) 12.50

G12 X ST(uiver). Like No. G10. 1780-86 .... *200.00*

V.F.

G13 I G(u)L(den). Sim. 1699-1794 .... 30.00

G14 3 G(u)L(den). Sim. 1694-1794 .... 100.00

G18 (Rijksdaalder). Like No. H18 but obv. legend ends WESTFRI and knight holds West Frisian arms. 1683-1794 .... 90.00

G21 (½ ducaton). Like No. G22. 1762-94 .... 125.00

G22 (ducaton). Like No. F21 but obv. legend ends WESTF. and rider over West Frisian arms. 1713-93 .... 100.00

Gold (ducat = 3.5 gr.)

G25 (ducat). Like No. A25 but obv. legend ends WESTF. 1607-1780 .... 150.00

G26 (2 ducats). Sim. 1660-1780 .... 750.00

G27 7 G(u)L(den). Like No. G28. 1749-63 .... 400.00

G28 14 G(u)L(den). Like No. A28 but obv. legend ends *WESTF.* and rider over West Frisian arms. 1749-63 .... 700.00

LOW COUNTRIES

NETHERLANDS (Cont.)

H. Zeeland (Zelandia), County.
Arms: Lion arising from sea.

Copper

The ½ duit 1753 (former No. H1) is a
presentation piece struck in gold.

VG-F

★H2 (duit). LUCTOR ET EMERGO,
arms in cwnd. shield. Rev.
ZEE/LAN/DIA. 1724-66. 21mm. ... 2.75

The 1754 with LUCTOR ET EMENTOR is
a scarce fantasy piece.

H2a —. Arms in cartouche.
Rev. ZELAN/DIA/date in cartouche. 1766-92 .... 3.00

H2b —. Like No. 2 but rev. ZEE/
etc. in wreath. 1792-94 .... 3.00

Silver

F-VF

H4 I S(tuiver). Obv. like No.
A4. Rev. ZEE/LAN/DIA/
1738-91 .... 12.50

H7 2 S(tuiver). Zeeland arms.
Rev. ZEE/LAN/DIA/date.
1681-1765 .... 5.00

★H11 6 ST(uiver). 1750-93 ..... 14.00

H12 ½ G(u)L(den). Like No.
H13. 1719 .... —

H12a X ST(uiver). Like No. H13.
1788 .... —

V.F.

H13 I G(u)L(den). Like No.
A13a but obv. legend ends
ZELANDIA. 1763-64 ..... 225.00

★H15 (⅛ Rijksdaalder). 1762-
93 .... 25.00

H16 (¼ Rijksdaalder). Sim.
1762-93 .... 70.00

V.F.

H17 (½ Rijksdaalder). Sim.
1672-1793 .... 125.00

★H18 (Rijksdaalder).
1672-1794 .... 90.00

H19 (2 Rijksdaalder). Sim.
1747-48, 77 .... *pattern?*

H21 (½ ducaton). Like No. F21
but obv. legend ends COM.
ZEL. and rider over Zeeland
arms. 1766-93 .... 140.00

H22 (ducaton). Sim.
1680-1794 .... 120.00

H23 (2 ducaton). Sim.
1741, 48, 54 .... *pattern?*

Gold (ducat = 3.5 gr.)

H25 (ducat). Like No. A25 but
obv. legend ends COM. ZEL.
1586-1763 .... 275.00

H27 7 G(u)L(den). Like No. H28.
1760-64 .... 400.00

H28 14 G(u)L(den). Like No. A28
but obv. legend ends ZELAND.
and rider over Zeeland arms.
1760-64 .... 700.00

II. Batavian Republic.

The United Netherlands under French
domination 1795-1806.

A. Gelders.

Silver

A35 I G(u)L(den). Like No. A13.
1795-96 .... 95.00

A35a —. 1798 AN7. *Pattern?* ... —

A36 3 G(u)L(den). Sim. 1795-
96 .... 275.00

A37 (Rijksdaalder). Like No. A18.
1795-1802 .... 600.00

Gold

V.F.

A40 (ducat). Like No. A25.
1795-1803 .... 275.00

C. Holland.

Silver

C35 I G(ulden). Like No. C13.
1795, 1800 .... 35.00

C35a I G(u)L(den). 1797 ..... 100.00

C36 3 G(ulden). Sim. 1795-
1801 .... 125.00

C37 (Rijksdaalder). Like No. C18.
1796-1806 .... 275.00

Gold (ducat = 3.5 gr.)

C40 (ducat). Like No. C25.
1795-1805 .... 180.00

C41 (2 ducats). Sim. 1795,
1802 .... 1500.00

E. Overyssel.

Silver

E35 I G(ulden). Like No. E13.
1795-96 .... 55.00

E37 (Rijksdaalder). Like No. E18.
1795-96 .... 600.00

F. Utrecht.

Silver

F33 2 S(tuivers). Lion shield divides 2-S. Rev. TRA/IEC/TUM/
date. 1796-99 .... 90.00

F34 X ST(uiver). Like No. F12.
1795-96 .... 90.00

F35 I G(ulden). Sim. 1795-99 .. 90.00

F36 3 G(u)L(den). Sim. 1795-
96 .... 125.00

★F37 (Rijksdaalder).
1795-1805 .... 110.00

F38 (½ ducaton). Like No. F39.
1796, 98 .... 700.00

LOW COUNTRIES

NETHERLANDS (Cont.)

V.F.

★**F39** (ducaton). 1796, 98....1350.00

Gold (ducat = 3.5 gr.)

F40 (ducat). Like No. F41.
1795-1805.............225.00

★**F41** (2 ducats). 1796-1805....650.00

G. Westfriesland.

Silver

G34 ½ G(u)L(den). Like No. G12.
1796................150.00

G35 I G(u)L(den). Sim. 1795-
96................165.00

G36 3 G(u)L(den). Sim. 1795-
96................90.00

G37 (Rijksdaalder). Like No. G18.
1795-96...............550.00

H. Zeeland.

Copper

Fine

★**H31** (duit). 1795-97..........4.50

V.F.

H32 2½ STUIVER (⅛ French
Livre). Obv. sim. Rev. ⅛/
LIVRE etc. 1795......1250.00

Silver

H37 (Rijksdaalder). Like No. H18.
1795-98...............110.00

III. Holland, Kingdom.
Napoleonic protectorate.

Lodewyk (Louis) Napoleon, King 1806-10

Silver

51 10 S(tuiver). Like No. 53.
1808-09................360.00

52 1 G(ulde)N. Sim. 1808-10..275.00

VF-EF

★**53** 2½ G(ulde)N. 1808......2500.00

VF-EF

★**54** 50 S(tuiver)S. 1808......500.00

55 (Rijksdaalder). Like Nos.
F18, F37. 1806-08.........300.00

56 R-DR (= Rijksdaalder).
Like No. 54. 1809........2500.00

57 (Rijksdaalder). Head r.
Rev. Knight stdg. 1809...2500.00

Gold (ducat = 3.5 gr.)

58 (ducat). Like Nos. F25, F40.
1806-08..................225.00

59 (2 ducats). Sim. 1806-08...600.00

60 (ducat). Head l. Rev. Knight
stdg. 1808-09..............750.00

61 (ducat). Head l. Rev. Arms.
1809-10..................500.00

62 10 G(ulde)N. Sim. 1808,
10.................._____

63 20 G(ulde)N. Sim. 1808,
10.................._____

There exist many rare patterns of this reign, mostly dated 1807.

The Kingdom of Holland was annexed to France 1810-14.

Emperor Napoleon struck a scarce series of coins in regular French denominations at Utrecht (MM: Fish) 1812-13.

IV. Netherlands, Kingdom.
Created 1815. Included present-day Belgium until 1830 when the latter revolted and became independent.

Monetary System:
100 cents = 1 gulden;
2½ gulden = 1 Rijksdaalder.

Mints:
Utrecht (Caduceus); Brussels (B).

Willem I, Sovereign Prince 1813-15, King 1815-40

Copper

Fine

71 ½ C(ent). Like No. 72.
1819-37...................7.50

★**72** 1 C(ent). 1817-37..........9.00

Silver

V.F.

73 5 C(ents). Like No. 75.
1818-28..................50.00

74 10 C(ents). Sim. 1818-28....45.00

LOW COUNTRIES

NETHERLANDS (Cont.)

V.F.

*75 25 C(ents). 1817-30 . . . . . . .45.00
76 ½ G(ulden). Like No. 79.
1818-22, 29-30 . . . . .300.00
77 1 G(ulden). Sim. 1818-37 . .300.00
78 (Rijksdaalder). Like Nos. F18,
F37. 1816 . . . . .800.00

*79 3 G(ulden). 1818-32 . . . . . . .650.00
80 1 G(ulden). Like No. 81.
1840 . . . . .175.00

V.F.

*81 2½ G(ulden). Head.
Rev. Arms. 1840 . . . . .300.00

Gold

82 5 G(ulden). Head l. Rev. Arms.
1826-27 . . . . .350.00
83 10 G(ulden). Sim. 1819-40 .375.00
84 (ducat). Like Nos. F25, F40.
1814-16 . . . . .200.00
85 (ducat). Sim. but w/out TRA
and rev. MO. AUR/REG BELGII/
etc. on tablet. 1817-40 . . . . .150.00
85a —. 1831. Eagle mint mark.
See POLAND.

Willem II 1840-49

Copper

Fine

86 ½ C(ent). Like No. 71. 1841-
47 . . . . .10.00

Silver

F-VF

87 5 CENTS. Head l. Rev. value.
1848 . . . . .1500.00
88 10 CENTS. Sim. 1848-49 . . .45.00
89 25 CENTS. Sim. 1848-49 . . .25.00
90 ½ G(ulden). Like No. 92.
1846-48 . . . . .55.00
91 1 G(ulden). Sim. 1840-49 . . .30.00

F-VF

*92 2½ G(ulden). 1841-49 . . . . .30.00

Gold

V.F.

93 5 G(ulden). Head r.
Rev. Arms. 1843 . . . . .1400.00
94 10 G(ulden). Sim. 1842 . . .2000.00
**The 1848 head r. rev. arms gold
pieces are extremely rare patterns.**
95 (ducat). Like No. 85. 1841 .175.00

UNVERIFIED DATA

Note: Throughout this catalog, any uncertain, indefinite or unconfirmed information is shown in *italic type*. Such material may be, for example, coin descriptions, dates and prices, names of rulers, or supplementary notes. Further information to confirm or correct *material in italics* should be sent to the author at the following address:

William D. Craig
c/o Whitman Coin Supply Division
1220 Mound Avenue
Racine, Wisconsin 53404, U.S.A.

MALAY PENINSULA

In S.E. Asia. The British established trading settlements here in the 18th century and acquired political control piecemeal from the Netherlands, Siam, and the local Malay rulers, chiefly in the 19th century.

Monetary Systems:
Until 1826 —
  100 pice or cents = 4 suku = 1 ringgit (Spanish dollar).
1826-45 —
  48 pice = 1 rupee.

The token coinage, copper 1 and 2 keping, tin pitjis, and the like, had no fixed relation to silver, and depending on the time and place, passed for as much as 80 keping to the dollar, and as little as 1600.

The merchants' tokens, of which several hundred million were circulated throughout Malaya and the Netherlands East Indies circa 1828-53, are mentioned under Singapore, but have been removed. See II Pridmore.

1. Kedah (Quedah).

Malay sultanate controlled by Siam 1821-1909.

Mohammed Dschiwa Zeinal Aladin Ma Alem Shah, Sultan 1154-92AH (= 1741-78AD)

Silver
Good

110 (real = ⅛ peso). Arabic legends both sides. 1154AH *12.50*

Tadsch ed-din Alem Shah 1219-37AH (= 1804-21AD)

Tin
Fair-G

120 (trah). Arabic legends both sides. 22.5mm. Holed. 1224AH . . 5.00

Tunku Anum, Siamese Governor After 1821

Tin

130 (trah). Arabic legend. Rev. 12 ptd. star. 18mm. N.D. Holed 3.50

135 (trah). Arabic legend. Rev. 6 ptd. star. 22mm. N.D. Holed 5.00

140 (trah). Arabic legend. Rev. Lotus blossom. 24mm. Holed. 1262AH 3.00

143 (timma). Rooster on 2 rings. 43mm. N.D 10.00

2. Ligor (Lachon).

Malay state controlled by Siam.

Tin
Fair-G

175 (pitjis). Arabic legends both sides. Holed. 28.5mm. 1256AH 6.00

4. Patani.

Malay state ruled by rajah subject to Siam.

Tin

231 (pitjis). Arabic legends both sides. 30mm. Holed. 1261AH 3.75

Pewter

★241 (pitjis) (1284AH) 5.00

6. Penang (Pulu Penang = Prince of Wales Island).

Ceded to the British East India Company in 1786 by Captain Light, who had acquired it through marriage to the daughter of the Sultan of Kedah. Off the west coast of the peninsula.

A. First Series

Copper
VG-F

271 (cent). Bale mark in circle. Rev. blank. N.D. (1786) . . . 10.00

272 (1/10 cent). Like No. 277. 12-14mm. 1787 . . . . 17.50

273 (½ cent). Sim. 18-20mm. 1787 . . . . 9.00

274 (cent). Sim. 25-28mm. 1787 . . . . 10.00

Silver
V.F.

275 (1/10 dollar). Sim. 17mm. 1788 . . . . 150.00

276 (¼ dollar). Sim. 24mm. 1788 . . . . 150.00

VG-F

★277 (½ dollar). Bale mark. Rev. Legend. 1788 . . . . . . 275.00

B. Second Series

Cast Tin
Good

281 (cent). G(overnor) F(arquhar). Script in circle. Rev. blank. 44mm. N.D. (1805) *100.00*

282 (cent). A(nderson) & C(lubley)/ 1809. Rev. blank. 42-44mm *100.00*

C. Third Series

Copper
VG-F

291 (½ cent = ½ pice). Like No. 292. 24.5mm. 1810, 25, 28 . . . . 5.00

★292 (cent = pice). 1810, 25, 28 . . . . 6.50

293 (2 pice). Sim. 31.5mm. 1825, 28 . . . . 12.00

8. Singapore

Entrepôt at the southern tip of the Malay Peninsula, founded by Sir Stamford Raffles in 1819. Joined with Penang and Malacca in 1826 to form a single government. Controlled by the British East India Company until 1858.

During the period 1828-53 the merchants of Singapore caused hundreds of millions of tokens, mostly copper, to be struck in England and shipped to Singapore. These were then used in trade with the Malays on the peninsula and in the East Indies. There were many diverse types, the earliest being copies of the V.E.I.C. Sumatra coinage of 1804. Some had English legends such as ISLAND OF SUMATRA, ISLAND OF SULTANA and C.R. READ. Others were copies of Netherlands and Netherlands East Indies coins. Some bore the names (in Arabic) of Malay Kingdoms and localities, such as Atcheh, Celebes, Deli, Menangkabau, Perak, Percha (Sumatra), Selangor, Siak, Tarumon and

MALAY PENINSULA

SINGAPORE (Cont.)

Trengganu. A popular obverse showed a fighting cock. Fictitious dates appear from 1786 (copies of Netherlands coins) to 1835AD (western numerals) and 1197-1411AH (mostly in Arabic numerals).

All of these tokens were used indiscriminately, without limitation to any particular locality. The series is interesting, and a number of varieties are rare today. But as private tokens without fixed official value, they were not coins and have been omitted from this second edition.

Representative examples of Singapore merchants' tokens:

See II Pridmore 147-172 for a complete listing.

MARTINIQUE. See CARIBBEAN ISLANDS AND TERRITORIES.

MAURITIUS AND REUNION

Islands in the Indian Ocean. Mauritius was discovered by the Portuguese in 1505. Taken by the Dutch in 1598 and renamed for Prince Maurice of Orange. Thereafter, both places were acquired by France and named Isles de France (Mauritius) et de Bourbon (Reunion). Isle de France was taken by the British in 1810 and renamed Mauritius. Isle

de Bourbon remained in French possession and was successively called Reunion (1792-1801), Isle de Bonaparte (1801-14), Isle de Bourbon (1814-48), and Reunion (1848 on).

Monetary System:
20 sols (sous) = 1 livre;
100 centimes = 1 franc.

1. Isles de France et de Bourbon.

Louis XV 1715-74

Copper

0.1 (sol). Like No. 0.2. 4 gr. 23mm. ND (1723)........20.00 *V.G.*

★0.2 (2 sols). 8 gr. ND (1723)...15.00

Louis XVI 1774-93

Billon

1 2/SOLS. Like No. 2. 1780...............*pattern?* *VF-EF*

★2 3/SOLS. 1779-80...........15.00 *VG-F*
2a 3/SOUS. Sim. 1781........15.00

2. Iles de France et Bonaparte.

Napoleon I 1804-14

Silver

★11 DIX (= 10) LIVRES (= piastre de Caen). Eagle ★. Rev. Value. 1810....................200.00 *V.F.*

3. Isle de Bourbon.

Louis XVIII 1814-24

Billon

★21 10/CENT(imes). 1816......15.00 *Fine*

---

4. Mauritius.

George IV 1820-30

Billon

★31 25/SOUS. REÇU/AU/TRESOR. Rev. Value. (1822)........25.00

★32 50/SOUS. (1822)..........35.00

Silver

35 XVI (=1/16 dollar). Like No. 36. 1820..............20.00

★36 VIII (= 1/8 dollar). 1820....25.00
37 IV (= 1/4 dollar). Sim. 1820..40.00
38 II (= 1/2 dollar). Sim. 1820....................*exist?*

Note: For similar coinage dated 1822 see CARIBBEAN ISLANDS and TERRITORIES (British West Indies).

MESOPOTAMIA
(Now IRAQ)

Area in the Middle East governed by Turkey, lying between the Tigris and Euphrates Rivers. Coins struck at Baghdad (name appears on all coins).

In AH1209 the area of present-day Iraq was divided into the pashaliks of Baghdad, Schehrsor, Basrah and Mosul. In AH1249 the first three were united into one pashalik. It is doubtful that the Baghdad coinage circulated to any extent outside Baghdad.

Monetary System:

Same as TURKEY.

Mahmud I
AH1143-68 (=AD1730-54)

Billon or Silver

                                           V.G.

8 (5 para). Toughra. Rev.
DURIBA/FI/BAGHDAD/1143.
2.6 gr. 19mm............... —

Mustafa III
AH1171-87 (=AD1757-73)

Copper

                                           Good

*21 *(para).* Toughra. Rev. DURIBA/
FI/BAGHDAD. ND............*RR*

Abdul Hamid I
AH1187-1203 (=AD1773-89)

Billon or Silver

                                           V.G.

73 (5 para). Like No. 74. 2.1 gr.
21mm. Yr. 9............. —

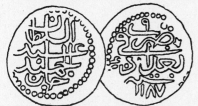

*74 (10 para). SULTAN/'ABD/AL-
HAMID/KHAN. Rev. yr. 9/
BAGHDAD etc./1187. 4.4 gr... —

Mahmud II
AH1223-55 (=AD1808-39)

Copper

Note: No. 111 was struck by Sa'id Pasha, wali (governor) of Baghdad and Basrah, in his own name.

                                           G-VG

*101 (2 para). Lion. Rev. yr. 8/
BAGHDAD etc./1230.
15-18mm.................*10.00*

*111 (5 para). SA'ID/PASHA in
octogram. Rev. BAGHDAD etc./
date. 24-27mm. AH1231.....*RR*

111a —. Tamgha in octogram.
23-27mm. 1231..........*7.50*

117 *(2 para).* Like No. 118.
16-*19*mm. AH1241 *yr. 16,*
1244...................

*118 (5 para). Toughra. Rev. like
No. 111. 20-23mm. 1238...*10.00*

118a —. Sim. but narrow floral
borders both sides. 20-21mm.
1240....................*10.00*

118b (ex 123) —. Rev. yr. 18/
BAGHDAD etc./1223. 22mm. —

*125 *(5 para).* Crescent and star
in hexagram. Rev. *Yr. 22/*
BAGHDAD etc. 19-20mm......*RR*

125a —. Rev. yr. 25/BAGHDAD
etc./1223. 25mm.......... —

128 *(5 para).* Hexagram. Rev. like
No. 125a. 25mm. Yr. 25...

*128a (ex 141) —. Rev. like No. 111.
25-*29*mm. AH1248........*10.00*

                                           G-VG

*131 (ex 127, 139) *(5 para).*
Star/crescent. Rev. yr./
BAGHDAD etc./1223. 21-
25mm. Yrs. 25-26........ *7.50*

*134 (ex 157) *(5 para).* Toughra.
Rev. like No. 131. Wavy
octagon border both sides.
22-23mm. Yrs. 28-29..... *6.00*

137 *(5 para). Legend like rev. of
No. 134 both sides (mule?).*
20mm. Yr. 28...........

Billon

152 (10 para). Toughra. Rev. yr./
BAGHDAD etc./1223. Pearl
borders both sides. 2.1 gr.
24mm. Yr. 13...........*15.00*

154 (ex 159) (20 para). Sim.
3.5 gr. 28mm. Yr. 13......*15.00*

155 (piastre). Sim. 9.5 gr.
31mm. Yr. 13............*RR*

158 (10 para). Toughra/BAGHDAD
etc./1223. Rev. 4-line legend.
1.8 gr. 26mm. Yr. 15......*12.50*

158a —. Ornate borders both sides.
1.55 gr. 26mm. Yr. 17.....*17.50*

160 (ex 165) (20 para). Like
No. 158. 3.2 gr. 27mm.
Yr. 15..................*15.00*

161 (ex 170) (zolota). 4-line
legends both sides. 4.5 gr.
31mm. Yr. 15............*RR*

163 (ex 150) (5 para). Like
No. 152 but ornate borders
both sides. 0.8 gr. 18mm.
Yr. 17..................*10.00*

164 (10 para). Sim. 1.4 gr.
22mm. Yr. 17...........*12.50*

166 (20 para). Sim. 2.97 gr.
28mm. Yr. 17...........*20.00*

169 *(20 para).* Sim. but vine and
rosette borders both sides.
1.2 gr. 22mm. Yr. 21......*12.50*

171 (ex 168) *(piastre).* Sim.
3.2 gr. 29mm. Yr. 21......*20.00*

174 (20 para). Sim. but legend
borders both sides. 1.8 gr.
22mm. Yr. 21...........*15.00*

176 (piastre). Sim. 3.97 gr.
29mm. Yr. 21...........*25.00*

MESOPOTAMIA

G-VG

178 (20 para). *Like No. 158.*
2.05 gr. 26mm. Yr. 22 . . . . *20.00*

180 *(20 para). Generally like
No. 163. 22-24mm.
Yrs. 26, 28, 29* *15.00*

182 (100 para). Like No. 152 but
double ornate borders both
sides. 3.2 gr. 31mm.
Yr. 26 . . . . *RR*

183 (ex 175) (5 piastres). Sim.
5.3-6.2 gr. 36mm. Yrs.
26-27 . . . . *RR*

Note: The authorities are not consistent regarding the denominations of Nos. 152-183. The foregoing (which generally follow Ölçer) are therefore all tentative pending further original study by someone, which will probably have to be done in Iraq.

Gold

Fine

185 (altun). Like TURKEY
No. 233a but BAGHDAD.
20-21mm. 1.2-1.4 gr.
Yr. 25 . . . . *RRR*

Abdul Mejid
AH1255-77 (=AD1839-61)

Billon

G-VG

★201 (5 para). Toughra. Rev.
Yr. 1/BAGHDAD etc./1255.
18-21mm *15.00*

UNVERIFIED DATA

Note: Throughout this catalog, any uncertain, indefinite or unconfirmed information is shown in *italic type*. Such material may be, for example, coin descriptions, dates and prices, names of rulers, or supplementary notes. Further information to confirm or correct *material in italics* should be sent to the author at the following address:

William D. Craig
c/o Whitman Coin Supply Division
1220 Mound Avenue
Racine, Wisconsin 53404, U.S.A.

MEXICO (NEW SPAIN)

Country to the south of the United States. The Spanish Viceroyalty of New Spain, including the Captaincy-General of Guatemala, covered present-day Mexico and Central America. After an unsuccessful revolt in 1811-15 under Hidalgo and Morelos, Mexico became independent in 1821. Its first government, an empire under Agustin Iturbide, was succeeded by the republic, which, in various forms, has endured to this day.

Monetary System:
8 octavos = 4 cuartillos = 1 real; 16 reales = 2 pesos = 1 escudo (scudo).

Mint: M̊ – Mexico City.

Felipe V 1700-24-46

Milled Silver 1732-47

		Fine
1	(½ real). Like No. 8. Flat crown on arms. Assayer's initials shown. 1732-41	5.00
2	—. Sim. but legend PHS. V. D. G. HISP. ET IND. R. Taller crown, and no assayer's initials. 1742-47	5.00
3	I (real). Like No. 1 but value shown. 1732-41	6.50
4	R(eal) I. Like No. 2 but value shown. 1742-47	6.00
5	2 (reales). Like No. 3. 1732-41	14.00
6	R(eales) 2. Like No. 4. 1742-47	12.50

		F-VF
7	4 (reales). Like No. 3. 1732-47	100.00

		F-VF
*8	8 (reales). Sim. 1732-47	40.00

Sim. coins but MX mint mark

1a	(½ real). 1733	375.00
3a	1 (real). 1733	350.00
5a	2 (reales). 1733	900.00
7a	4 (reales). 1733	2000.00
8a	8 (reales). 1733	2000.00

Gold

*9	I (escudo). Head. Rev. 4 fold arms. 1732-47	450.00
10	2 (escudos). Sim. but bust like No. 12. 1732-47	600.00
11	4 (escudos). Sim. 1732-47	—

*12	8 (escudos). Armored bust. Rev. manifold arms in order chain. 1732-47	—

Fernando VI 1746-59

Silver

		Fine
13	(½ real). Like No. 14. 1747-60	4.00

*14	R(eal) I. 1747-60	5.50

		Fine
15	R(eales) 2. Sim. 1747-60	12.50

		F-VF
16	4 (reales). Sim. 1747-60	110.00
17	8 (reales). Sim. 1747-60	40.00

Gold

A. Bust with large head.

18	I (escudo). Obv. like No. 21. Rev. like No. 9. 1747	1250.00
19	2 (escudos). Sim. 1747	1500.00
20	4 (escudos). Sim. 1747	—

*21	8 (escudos). Sim. but rev. like No. 12. 1747	—

B. Small High-relief Bust.

22	I S(cudo). Bust. Rev. NOMINA etc., arms like No. 9. 1748-51	400.00
22a	(escudo). Sim. but no value expressed. 17mm. 1752-56	400.00
23	2 S(cudos). Like No. 22. 1748-51	600.00
23a	(2 escudos). Like No. 22a. 22mm. 1752-56	550.00
24	4 S(cudos). Like No. 22. 1748-51	1950.00
24a	(4 escudos). Like No. 22a. 30mm. 1752-56	2250.00

MEXICO

F-VF

★25 8 S(cudos). Sim. but rev.
manifold arms in order chain.
1748-51 . . . . 2250.00

25a (8 escudos). Sim. but no value
expressed. 1752-56 . . . . . . 2250.00

C. Medium Low-relief Bust.

26 (escudo). Bust. Rev. like
No. 22a. 1757-59 . . . . 450.00

27 (2 escudos). Sim. 1757-59 . . 650.00

28 (4 escudos). Sim. 1757-59 . 2250.00

29 (8 escudos). Sim. but arms
like No. 25. 1757-59 . . . . . 2250.00

Carlos III 1759-88

Silver

A. Pillar Type.

Fine

31 (½ real). Like No. 13 but
CAR(OLVS)III etc. 1760-71 . . . 3.00

32 R(eal) I. Sim. 1760-71 . . . . . . 5.00

33 R(eales) 2. Sim. 1760-71 . . . . 10.00

F-VF

34 4 (reales). Sim. 1760-71 . . . . 100.00

35 8 (reales). Sim. 1760-72 . . . . . 35.00

B. Bust Type.

36 (½ real). Like No. 38.
1772-89 . . . . 2.50

37 1 R(eal). Sim. 1772-89 . . . . . . 3.00

★38 2 R(eales). Rev. mmk. follows
REX. 1772-89 . . . . 4.75

39 4 R(eales). Sim. 1772-89 . . . . 35.00

40 8 R(eales). Sim. 1772-89 . . . . 15.00

Gold (escudo=3.4 gr.)

A. Young Local Bust.

F-VF

51 (escudo). Obv. like No. 54.
Rev. like No. 22a. 1760-61 . 750.00

52 (2 escudos). Sim. 1760-61 . . . 950.00

53 (4 escudos). Sim. 1760-61 . . 1650.00

★54 (8 escudos). Small bust
with short wig. Rev. like
No. 25a. 1760-61 . . . . 1650.00

B. Young Standard Bust.

55 (escudo). CAR. III etc., large
bust (like Peru No. 58). Rev.
IN UTROQ. FELIX, 4 fold arms.
1762-71 . . . . 750.00

56 (2 escudos). Sim. but CAROLUS
III etc., rev. IN UTROQ . . .
DEO. 1762-71 . . . . 1100.00

57 (4 escudos). Sim. but rev.
manifold arms in order chain.
1763-69 . . . . 1750.00

58 (8 escudos). Sim.
1762-71 . . . . 1500.00

C. Older Standard Bust.

59 1 S(cudo). CAROL. III etc., bust.
Rev. IN UTROQ . . . A.D., arms
like No. 88. 1772-88 . . . . . . 225.00

60 2 S(cudos). Sim. but rev.
IN UTROQ . . . DEO.
1772-87 . . . . 400.00

61 4 S(cudos). Sim. 1772-88 . . . 900.00

62 8 S(cudos). Sim. 1772-88 . . . 750.00

Carlos IV 1788-1808

Silver

A. Bust of Carlos III,
Legend CAROLUS IV.

Fine

69 (½ real). Like No. 38 but
CAROLUS IV etc. 1789-90 . . . . 5.00

70 1 R(eal). Sim. 1789 . . . . 15.00

71 2 R(eales). Sim. 1789-90 . . . . 10.00

F-VF

72 4 R(eales). Sim. 1790 . . . . . . 55.00

★73 8 R(eales). Sim. 1789-90 . . . . 35.00

B. Bust of Carlos III,
Legend CAROLUS IIII.

Fine

73.5 (½ real). Like No. 38 but
CAROLUS IIII etc. 1790 . . . . 5.00

73.6 1 R(eal). Sim. 1790 . . . . . . 15.00

73.7 2 R(eales). Sim. 1789-90 . . 10.00

F-VF

74 4 R(eales). Sim. 1789-90 . . . 50.00

75 8 R(eales). Sim. 1790 . . . . 32.50

C. Castle/Lion.

★76 ¼ (real). 1796-1808 . . . . 10.00

D. Standard Bust of Carlos IV.

77 (½ real). Like No. 78.
1792-1808 . . . . 2.50

★78 1 R(eal). Rev. mmk. follows
REX. 1792-1808 . . . . 3.00

79 2 R(eales). Sim. 1792-1808 . . 4.50

F-VF

80 4 R(eales). Sim. 1792-1808 . . 30.00

MEXICO

*81 8 R(eales). Sim. 1791-1808..12.50   *F-VF*

Gold

A. Bust of Carlos III.

82 1 S(cudo). Like No. 59 but
     CAROL. IV. etc. 1789-90....250.00

83 2 S(cudos). Sim. but rev.
     like No. 88. 1789-90.........RR

84 4 S(cudos). Sim. 1790.......RR

84a —. Legend CAROL IIII.
     1789-90..................RR

85 8 S(cudos). Like No. 82.
     1789-90...............650.00

85a —. Legend CAROL IIII.
     1790..................650.00

B. Standard Bust of Carlos IV.

86 1 S(cudo). Obv. like No. 88.
     Rev. like No. 59. 1792-
     1808...................165.00

87 2 S(cudos). Like No. 88.
     1791-1808..............250.00

*88 4 S(cudos). 1792-1808.....750.00

89 8 S(cudos). 1791-1808.....600.00

Fernando VII of Spain, In Mexico 1808-21

Mints: Cᴬ – Chihuahua; D or Dᵒ –
Durango; Gᴬ – Guadalajara; Ḡ or Gᵒ –
Guanajuato; Ṁ – Mexico City; Z or
Zˢ – Zacatecas. **Except as otherwise
shown, prices are for coins from Ṁ
Mint. Coins from the smaller mints
are generally worth more.**

Copper

90 ⅛ (real). Like No. 93.   *VG-F*
     1814-15................. 6.00

91 OCTAVO/DE (= ⅛)/REAL.
     Double F7ᵒ mon. Rev.
     DURANGO, value. 1812-13....Rare

91a —. 1814-18..............15.00

*93 ¼ (real). 1814-16......... 5.00

95 2/4 (real). Like No. 93. 1814-
     16, 21................. 8.00

Former Nos. 92 and 94 have been ten-
tatively reassigned to Santo Domingo.
See CARIBBEAN ISLANDS AND
TERRITORIES.

Silver

A. Castle/Lion.

106 ¼ (real). Like No. 76.   *Fine*
     1809-16................. 7.50

B. Local Uniformed Bust.

Mints: Ṁ, CA, D, Z.

107 (½ real). Like No. 108.
     1808-19................. 2.50

*108 1 R(eal). 1808-18......... 3.50

109 2 R(eales). Sim. 1808-19... 4.75

                                    F-VF
110 4 R(eales). Sim. 1808-12...40.00

                                    Fine
*116 —. Cast, with cmk. each side
     of head. *1810*-13CA......65.00

C. Standard Draped Bust.

Mints: Ṁ, Cᴬ, D, Gᴬ, Ḡ, Z or Zˢ.

117 (½ real). Like No. 119.
     1812-21................. 2.50

118 1 R(eal). Sim. 1811-21..... 3.50

*119 2 R(eales). 1812-21....... 4.00

119a —. 1822.............,.12.50

                                    F-VF
120 4 R(eales). Sim. 1812-21...50.00

121 8 R(eales). Sim. 1811-21...12.50

121a —. 1822...........25.00-60.00

121b (ex 116a) —. Struck over
     No. 116. *1813*-22Cᴬ.......60.00

Gold

A. Local Uniformed Busts.

Mints: Ṁ, Gᴬ.

131 1 S(cudo). Obv. like No. 133.
     Rev. like No. 59.
     1808-12 Ṁ.............300.00

131.5 2 S(cudos). Like No. 133.
     1808-11 Ṁ..............RR

132 4 S(cudos). Sim.
     1808-12 Ṁ.............750.00

*111 8 R(eales). Sim. 1808-11...15.00

MEXICO

F-VF

★133 8 S(cudos). Uniformed bust
in wig. Rev. arms. 1808-
12 Ṁ 650.00

134 4 S(cudos). Like No. 135.
1812 Gᴬ .... RR

★135 8 S(cudos). Uniformed bust
with short hair. Rev. arms.
1812-13 Gᴬ *3500.00*

C. Standard Undraped Bust.

136 (½ scudo). Obv. like No. 137
but FERD. VII etc. Rev. oval
4 fold arms. 1814-20 Ṁ ... 125.00

F-VF

★137 1 S(cudo). 1814-20 ...... 175.00
138 2 S(cudos). Sim. 1814-21 .... RR
139 4 S(cudos). Sim. 1814-20 .. 750.00
140 8 S(cudos). Sim. 1814-21 .. 600.00
140a —. 1821 Gᴬ 1500.00
141 8 S(cudos). Sim. but draped
bust. 1821 Gᴬ 1850.00

Coins of Various Congresses
Ostensibly Governing Mexico
In the Name of
Fernando VII 1811-14

I. Suprema Junta
(=Supreme National Council of
America).

Copper
V.G.

151 (½ real). Like No. 160.
1811 .... 45.00
155 8 R(eales). Like No. 160.
1812 .... 150.00

Silver

157 1 R(eal). Like No. 160.
1811 .... *75.00*
160 8 R(eales). FERDIN. VII DEI
GRATIA. Eagle on bridge.
Rev. PROVICIONAL POR LA
SUPREMA JUNTA DE AMERICA.
Bow, quiver, etc. 1811-12.
Cast 275.00
160a —. Struck. 1811-12 .... Rare

II. National Congress.

Copper

161 (½ real). Like No. 167.
1811-13 .... ———
163 2 R(eales). Like No. 167.
1812-14 .... 50.00

Silver

166 (½ real). Like No. 167.
1812-13 .... *40.00*

★167 1 R(eal), VICE FERD. VII DEI
GRATIA ET. Eagle on bridge.
Rev. S. P. CONG. NAT. IND.
GUV. T. etc. Bow, quiver, etc.
1812-13 .... 65.00
168 2 R(eales). Sim. 1813 ..... *250.00*
169 4 R(eales). Sim. 1813 .... RR
170 *8 R(eales).* Sim. 1812-13 ..... RR

III. Congreso Americano
(=American Congress).

Silver

V.G.

★172 1 R(eal). (1813) 60.00

During the War for Independence, a
variety of validation counterstamps
were employed by both Royalists and
insurgents. See Utberg, *The Coins of
Colonial Mexico* (1966).

Agustín I Iturbide,
Emperor 1822-23

Silver

181 (½ real). Like No. 182.
1822-23 .... 7.50

★182 1 R(eal). 1822 .... 65.00
183 2 R(eales). Sim. 1822-23 .. 10.00

Fine
184 8 R(eales). Sim. but small
head, small eagle. 1822 .... 40.00
185 8 R(eales). Like No. 182.
1822-23 .... 40.00

Gold
V.F.

186 4 S(cudos). Head. Rev.
Eagle in oval. 1823 ..... 1850.00
187 8 S(cudos). Sim. 1823 ... 2000.00
188 8 S(cudos). Head. Rev. Eagle
on cactus. 1822 .... 2000.00

MEXICAN LOCAL
AND STATE COINS

From 1810 onward the almost continuous warfare and confusion produced
much local coinage.

MEXICO

Catorce (Real del Catorce)

City in the state of San Luis Potosi.

Silver

VF (crude)

★**L5** 8 R(eales). EL R. D. CATORC.
POR FERNA. VII. Rev. MONEDA
etc. 1811................RRR

Chihuahua, State

Copper

                V.G.

L21 ⅛ (real). Like No. L22.
1833-34................12.50

★**L22** ¼ (real). ESTADO SOBERANO
1833-35.................. 6.00

L24 ¼ (real). Sim. but ESTADO
LIBRE. 1846............. 4.50

★**L25** ⅛ (real). ESTADO DE.
1855................... 8.00

L26 ¼ (real). Sim. 1854-56.... 4.00

L28 ¼ (real). Sim. but
DEPARTAMENTO. 1855..... 7.00

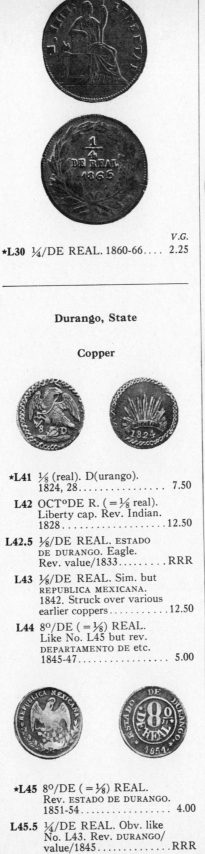

               V.G.

★**L30** ¼/DE REAL. 1860-66.... 2.25

Durango, State

Copper

★**L41** ⅛ (real). D(urango).
1824, 28............... 7.50

L42 OCTᵒDE R. (= ⅛ real).
Liberty cap. Rev. Indian.
1828...................12.50

L42.5 ⅛/DE REAL. ESTADO
DE DURANGO. Eagle.
Rev. value/1833........RRR

L43 ⅛/DE REAL. Sim. but
REPUBLICA MEXICANA.
1842. Struck over various
earlier coppers...........12.50

L44 8ᵒ/DE (= ⅛) REAL.
Like No. L45 but rev.
DEPARTAMENTO DE etc.
1845-47................ 5.00

★**L45** 8ᵒ/DE (= ⅛) REAL.
Rev. ESTADO DE DURANGO.
1851-54................ 4.00

L45.5 ¼/DE REAL. Obv. like
No. L43. Rev. DURANGO/
value/1845..............RRR

                     V.G.

★**L46** ¼ (real). 1858.
(also Brass)............. 6.00

★**L47** ¼ (real). 1860, 66........ 3.00

L48 ¼ (real). Sim. but rev. motto
INDEPENDENCIA Y LIBERTAD.
1866.................. 6.50

                   Fine

★**L49** ¼ (real). 1872.......... 5.00

Guanaxuato (Guanajuato), State

Brass

                 V.G.

L51 UN OCTAVO (= ⅛ real).
Like No. L52. 1829-30.... 6.00

★**L52** UNA CUARTILLA
(= ¼ real). 1828-29...... 6.00

L53 OCTAVO (= ⅛ real).
Like No. L54. 29mm.
1856...................10.00

L53a —. 25mm. 1856-57....... 5.00

MEXICO

★L54 CUARTILLA (= ¼ real).
V.G.
1856-57 . . . . 5.50

Hermosillo. See Sonora.

Jalisco, State

Copper

★L61 UN OCTAVO (= ⅛ real).
ESTADO LIBRE. 1828-34 . . . . 5.00

L62 UN QUARTO (= ¼ real).
Sim. 28mm. 1828-35 . . . . 5.00

L64 —. Sim. but DEPARTAMENTO.
1836 . . . . 12.50

L65 MEDIO OCTAVO
(= 1/16 real). Sim. 21mm.
1860 . . . . 6.00

L66 UN OCTAVO (= ⅛ real).
Sim. 28mm. 1858-60 . . . . . . 4.00

L67 UNA CUARTILLA
(= ¼ real). Sim. 32mm.
1858-60 . . . . 5.50

L68 MEDIO OCTAVO. Like
No. L70. 1861. ESTADO LIBRE.
1861 . . . . 6.00

L69 UN OCTAVO (= ⅛ real).
1856-62 . . . . 3.75

★L70 UNA CUARTILLA
V.G.
(= ¼ real). 1858-62 . . . . . . 6.00

Nueva Galicia

Later became state of Jalisco.

Silver

Crude

L72 2 R(eales). PROVYCIONAL
etc., N.G. in center.
1813 . . . . *RR*

Nueva Vizcaya, Province

Later became state of Durango.

Fernando VII 1808-22

Silver

Good

L74 8 R(eales). MUN. PROV. DE
NUEV. VYZCA. Arms of
Durango. Rev. Royal arms.
1811 . . . . *RRR*

Agustín I Iturbide 1822-23

Copper

V.G.

★L77 ⅛ (real). 1821-23 . . . . 10.00

L78 ¼ (real). Sim. 1822 . . . . *RR*

Oaxaca

I. The Province.

Fernando VII 1808-22

Silver

L86 R(eal) M(edio = ½ R.).
Like No. L87. 1812 . . . . . 100.00

V.G.

★L87 1 R(eal). 1812 . . . . 200.00

L90 8 R(eales). Like No. L87.
1812 . . . . 1200.00

II. The District.

Under Rebel General José María Morelos 1812-14

Copper

Crude

L93 2 R(eales). Like No. L94.
1813-14 . . . . 40.00

L93a —. OAXACA. 1814 . . . . 40.00

★L94 4 R(eales). 1814 . . . . *200.00*

L95 8 R(eales). Sim. 1814 . . . . . Rare

L95a —. OAXACA. 1814 . . . . 50.00

Note: The authenticity of No. L94 has
been questioned.

Silver

★L96 (½ real). 1813 . . . . 85.00

L97 (1 real). Sim. but only rev.
legend SUD under bow.
1813 . . . . Rare

L100 8 R(eales). PROV. D.
OAXACA, M(orelos) mon.
Rev. Lion shield with or
w/out bow above. 1812 . . *RRR*

L100a —. w/out obv. legend.
1813 . . . . *RRR*

L101 (8 reales). Bow/M/SUD.
Rev. PROV. DE etc., arms.
1813 . . . . *RRR*

Cast Silver

L105 4 R(eales). Like No. L94.
1813 . . . . *75.00*

L106 8 R(eales). Sim. 1814 . . . ——

Occidente, State

Later divided into states of Sinaloa and
Sonora.

Copper

Good

L107 (⅛ real). Cap and rays.
Rev. Eagle. 1828-29 . . . . . *40.00*

MEXICO

San Luis Potosí, State

Copper

V.G.

L108 ⅛ (real). Like No. 110 but obv. MEXICO LIBRE. 1829-59 . . . . 6.00

L109 ¼ (real). Sim. 1828-60 . . 3.50

★L110 ¼ (real). 1862 . . . . 8.00

★L111 ¼ (real). 1867 . . . . 3.00

Sinaloa, State

Copper

★L123 ¼/DE REAL. 1847-66 . . 3.50

Sombrerete
Royalist General Vargas

Silver

Good

L131 ½ R(eal). FERDIN VII SOMBRETE. Cwnd. globes. Rev. Lys in oval btwn. ½–R. 1811-12 . . . . 75.00

Good

★L132 1 R(eal). Sim. 1811-12 . . . . 60.00

L133 2 (reales). Like No. L135. 1811 . . . . Rare

★L134 4 (reales). R. CAXA DE SOMBRETE. Royal arms. Rev. VARGAS. 1812 . . . . . 200.00

★L135 8 (reales). Obv. like No. L134. Rev. ★. 1810, 11 . . 250.00

★L136 8 (reales). Like No. L134. (Rev. ★). 1811, 12 . . . . . . 125.00

Sonora, State

Copper

Good

★L143 UNA CUART (= ¼ real). EST. D. SONORA, arrow btwn. 2 quivers. Rev. HERMOSILLO etc., Liberty cap. 1832-36 . . . . 6.50

L145 OCTAVO DE (= ⅛) REAL. Like No. L146. 1859 . . . . RRR

V.G.

★L146 UNA CUARTILLA (= ¼ real). 1859-63 . . . . . 5.00

Sud (= Southern Mexico)
Under Rebel General
José María Morelos 1811-14

There are many varieties of each coin.

Mint: Guadalupe de Técpan.

Copper

Crude

★L151 M(edio = ½ real). Bow/SUD. Rev. Morelos mon./M/ date. 1811-13 . . . . 20.00

MEXICO

*L152 I R(eal). 1811-13......*17.50* *Crude*
L153 2 R(eales). Sim. 1811-13.10.00
L155 8 R(eales). Sim. 1811-14.10.00

Silver (Struck)

*L161 M(edio = ½) R(eal).
        1813-14...............*60.00*

*L162 1 R(eal). 1813.........*45.00*

*L163 2 R(eales). 1812.......*45.00*

*L164 4 R(eales). 1811-12....*250.00*
L165 8 R(eales). Sim.
        1811-14..............*175.00*

Notes:

1. The authenticity of Nos. L161-165 has been questioned.
2. A number of earlier coins, especially 8 reales, as well as various of the foregoing, appear cmkd. with Morelos' monogram between 2 stars in a circular indent.
3. Other cmks. with the Morelos' monogram between rosettes, dots or w/out flanking ornaments, or in oval or rectangular indents may be spurious. See Pradeau article in *The Numismatist*, February 1968.

Tierra Caliente (=Hot Country) Under General Morelos

Copper
Crude

L171 M(edio = ½) R(eal). Like
        No. L175. 1813........*45.00*
L172 1 R(eal). Sim. 1813......*35.00*
L173 2 R(eales). 1813........*30.00*

*L175 8 R(eales). 1813.......*25.00*

Nos. L161-L175 are said to exist in cast silver, but the difficulties of authenticating genuine specimens, if any, would be enormous.

Valladolid

Now the city of Morelia.

Silver

L178 8 R(eales). Royal arms in wreath, value at sides. Rev. PROVISIONAL/DE/ VALLADOLID/1813........RRR

Zacatlán

These coins were struck by insurgent General Osorno.

Copper

L179 *Medio* (=½ real). Like No. L179.3. 1813.......Rare
L179.3 Real. OSORNO mon./ Zacatlan/1813. Rev. crossed arrows in wreath/value..*85.00*

Silver

L179.5 2 R(eales). Sim. 1813....Rare

Note: Nos. 179, 179.3, and 179.5 have been liberally counterfeited in copper.

Zacatecas

I. Royal Mint.

Fernando VII 1808-22

Silver

(a) Arms/Mountain.

Good

*L181 (½ *real*). Royal arms. Rev. MONEDA PROVISIONAL DE ZACATECAS. Mountain. 1811..............50.00
L181a —. Like No. L183a (Local arms: Flowers 1 and 4, Castles 2 and 3). 1810-11...................Rare
L182 (1 real). Like No. L181. 20mm. 1811...........40.00
L182a —. Like No. L183a 1810-11..............100.00
L183 2 R(eales). Like No. L181. 1811.................60.00

*L183a —. 1810-11...........100.00
L184 8 R(eales). Like No. L181. 1811................150.00
L184a —. Like No. L183a. 1810-11..............200.00

(b) Provisional Bust/Arms.
Fair

L185 (½ *real*). Like No. L189. 1811-12................RR
L186 1 R(eal). Sim. 1812.......RR
L187 2 R(eales). Sim. 1811-12................Rare
L189 8 R(eales). FERDIN. VII 8R DE GRATIA. Bust. Rev. MONEDA PROVISIONAL DE ZACATECAS. Cwnd. arms btwn. pillars. 1811-12...100.00
L189a —. Draped bust. 1812-13..............125.00

II. State.

Brass
V.G.

L191 OCTAVO (=⅛ real). Like No. L192. 1825-63.. 3.50

MEXICO

		V.G.
★**L192**	QUARTILLA (= ¼ real). 1824-63	2.25
L193	UN OCTAVO (= ⅛ real). Sim. but DEPARTAMENTO. 1836, 45, 46	6.00
L194	QUARTILLA (= ¼ real). Sim. 1836, 46	6.00

Zongolica

Town in state of Veracruz.

Silver

L197	*2 R(eales).* VIVA FERNANDO VII Y AMERICA, bow and arrow. Rev. SONGOLICA/ value/crossed palm branch and sword/1812	——
L198	*4 R(eales). Sim. 1812*	——
L199	*8 R(eales). Sim. 1812*	——

MONACO.
  See **ITALY (Monaco).**

MONTSERRAT. See CARIBBEAN ISLANDS and TERRITORIES.

UNVERIFIED DATA

Note: Throughout this catalog, any uncertain, indefinite or unconfirmed information is shown in *italic type.* Such material may be, for example, coin descriptions, dates and prices, names of rulers, or supplementary notes. Further information to confirm or correct *material in italics* should be sent to the author at the following address:

William D. Craig
c/o Whitman Coin Supply Division
1220 Mound Avenue
Racine, Wisconsin 53404, U.S.A.

MOROCCO (MAROC)

A monarchy on the NW coast of Africa. European penetration culminated in the creation 1904-12 of French and Spanish protectorates in Morocco. The Moroccan rulers during the period covered by this catalog styled themselves Sultans. They are also referred to as Sharifs (descendants of Muhammed) of Morocco and Fez.

Monetary System:

2 to 5 zelagh = 4 kirat = 1 falus;
24 falus (fels, fulus, fluce) = 1 muzuna (= blanquil, blanquillo = Udja);
4 muzuna = 1 dirhem (= Ukiya = Uqijeh, plural Awak);
7 (originally), 10 (later), and finally 13½ dirhem (circa 1850) = 1 Mitkal (= metsqal = dollar = 28.5 gr.).

Mints:

(Style used on coins often deviates highly from the forms shown here.)

العرايش al-'Araish	
العرايشة al-'Araishah }	(Larache)
فاس Fas	(Fès, Fez)
مراكش Marakush	(Marrakech)
مكناس Miknas	
مكناسة Miknasah }	(Meknès)
رباط الفتح Rabat al-Fath	(Rabat)
الصوير al-Suwair	(Essaouira,
الصويرة al-Suwairah }	Mogador)
طنجة Tanjah	(Tangier)
تطوان Tatwan	(Tétouan)

Dates:

The chief peculiarity of Moroccan coinage is that the AH dates almost always appear in European numerals.

Coin types:

Except where otherwise indicated, the silver and gold have a legend (many varieties) on obverse with the mint name and date on the reverse; most copper after AH1207 has a seal of Solomon (hexagram) obverse, with the mint name and date on the reverse.

Muhammed
(Abd-Allah ben Ismail) XVI
1171-1205AH (=1757-90AD)

Cast Copper

                       Good

2 (zelagh). Mint name. Rev. Date. 16mm. 1200AH...... *3.00*

6 (falus). *Like No. 2* or mint name/date each side. 19-20mm. 1184, 90AH.............. 2.00

Silver

                       V.G.

15 (muzuna). 14-18mm. .7-.8 gr. 1186-1201AH............. 7.50

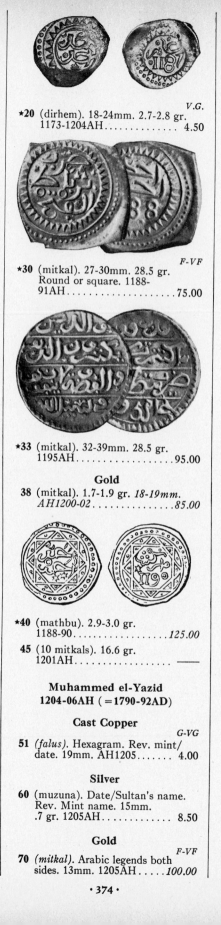

                       V.G.

*20 (dirhem). 18-24mm. 2.7-2.8 gr. 1173-1204AH............. 4.50

                       F-VF

*30 (mitkal). 27-30mm. 28.5 gr. Round or square. 1188-91AH................... 75.00

*33 (mitkal). 32-39mm. 28.5 gr. 1195AH.................95.00

Gold

38 (mitkal). 1.7-1.9 gr. *18-19mm. AH1200-02*..............*85.00*

*40 (mathbu). 2.9-3.0 gr. 1188-90..................*125.00*

45 (10 mitkals). 16.6 gr. 1201AH.................. ———

Muhammed el-Yazid
1204-06AH (=1790-92AD)

Cast Copper

                       G-VG

51 *(falus).* Hexagram. Rev. mint/date. 19mm. AH1205....... 4.00

Silver

60 (muzuna). Date/Sultan's name. Rev. Mint name. 15mm. .7 gr. 1205AH............. 8.50

Gold

                       F-VF

70 *(mitkal).* Arabic legends both sides. 13mm. 1205AH.....*100.00*

El Hisham
1206-09AH (=1792-95AD)

Cast Copper

                       Good

75 (falus). 17-18mm. *1207AH* .. 4.00

76 (2 falus). 21-25mm. *1207-09*................. 3.00

Silver

                       V.G.

80 (½ *dirhem*). 15mm. 1209... 8.00

82 (dirhem). 18-21mm. 2.7 gr. 1207-09............. 6.50

Gold

                       F-VF

88 (½ *mitkal*). Mint name in octogram. Rev. date. 0.9 gr. 13mm. 1207..............*70.00*

89 (mitkal). 1.5-1.7 gr. 16-18mm. 1209..........*100.00*

(Muley = Mulai)
Soliman (Sulaiman) II
1209-38AH (=1795-1822AD)

Cast Copper

                       Good

*95 (falus). 17-20mm. *1209-38AH*.................. 2.00

96 (2 falus). 22-25mm. *1209-38AH*.................. 1.50

98 (4 falus). 31-34mm. N.D.... 3.00

Silver

105 (½ dirhem). *15-20mm.* 1.3-1.5 gr. 1211-15AH..... 5.00

108 (dirhem). Generally like No. 140a. 2.4-2.9 gr. 17-23mm. 1211-37............. 3.50

Gold

                       F-VF

115 *(mathbu).* Arab legend in star each side. *3 gr. 20mm.* 1209-38.................*125.00*

(Muley) Abd-er-Rahman II
1238-76AH (=1822-59AD)

Cast Copper

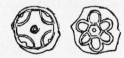

                       Good

*120 (zelagh). 12-13mm. ND.................... 3.00

121 —. Like No. 128. 15mm. AH1245.......... 2.50

122 (falus). 17-21mm. 1240-76AH (many var., incl. w/out mint name).............. 1.00

MOROCCO

126 (2 falus). 22-25mm. *1239-76AH* (many var., as No. 122).................... 1.50 *(Good)*

★128 (3 falus). 27-29mm. 1267-68AH................... 2.50

Silver
V.G.

135 (½ dirhem). 13-18mm. 1.4-1.8 gr. 1241-64AH..... 2.00

140 (dirhem). 19-22mm. 2.7 gr. 1240-52AH............... 6.00

★140a —. 15-19mm. 2 gr. 1266-75AH................... 3.00

Gold
F-VF

145 (½ Benduqi). Mint name and date each side. 1.7 gr. 1248-49AH................... *100.00*

150 (Benduqi). Like No. 145. 3.3 gr. 1243-73AH........ *125.00*

(Sidi) Muhammed XVII
1276-90AH (=1859-73AD)

Cast Copper
Good

160 (falus). 17-18mm. 1277-89AH.................... 2.50

163 (2 falus). 22-25mm. 1277-89AH.................... 2.00

★166 (3 falus). 27-29mm. 1280-90AH................... 1.00

Silver
V.G.

170 (muzuna). 13mm. .75 gr. 1284-88AH............... 3.00

V.G.

175 (½ dirhem). 15mm. 1.5 gr. 1283-88AH.............. 3.50

★176 (dirhem). 2.7 gr. 1284-86AH.............. 3.00

Mulai Hassan (El Hasan) III
1290-1312AH (=1873-94AD)

Cast Copper
Good

181 (falus). *17-20mm. 1291-95*.. 6.00
182 (2 falus). *22-25mm. 1291-95*.................... 6.00
183 (3 falus). *27-29mm. 1291-95*.................... 6.00

Silver
E.F.

190 (½ mitkal). 3 lines ea. side. 30.5mm. 1298AH........ *pattern*
191 (mitkal). Sim. 38mm. 1298AH............... *pattern*

The gold 4 mitkal piece of 1297AH did not circulate.

For modern style coins of this reign dated 1299AH onward, see Yeoman.

MOZAMBIQUE

Portuguese colony in SE Africa.

Monetary System:

Same as PORTUGAL.

José I 1750-77

Silver
G-VG

6 100 (réis). Like No. 8. 19mm. 1755....................20.00
7 200 (réis). Sim. 23mm. 1755....................20.00

★8 400 (réis). IOSEPHUS I ... AF(rica) OR(iental), arms. Rev. globe. 1755..........50.00
9 800 (réis). Sim. 34mm. 1755....................100.00

Gold
F-VF

11 1000 (réis). IOSEPHUS I D.G. PORTUG. REX. Arms. Rev. ET DOMINUS AF(rica) OR(iental), Cross. 1755...................1500.00

★12 2000 (réis). Sim. 1755.....1750.00
13 4000 (réis). Sim. 1755.....1750.00

João, Prince Regent 1799-1816

Copper
Fine

51 20 (réis). Like No. 52. 1813, 15...................30.00

★52 40 (réis). 1813, 15..........30.00
53 80 (réis). Sim. 1813........25.00

João, as King João VI 1816-26

Copper

54 20 (réis). Like No. 56. 1819-25...................25.00
55 40 (réis). Sim. 1819-25......15.00
55a —. Cmkd. 10 (réis)........20.00

MOZAMBIQUE

Fine

*56 80 (réis). 1819-25 . . . . 25.00
56a — . Cmkd. 20 (réis) 25.00

Nos. 51-56 were also used on St. Thomas and Prince Islands. For similar coins with values in Roman numerals, see BRAZIL.

Maria II 1834-53

Copper

57 I (réis). MARIA II DEI GRATIA.
Arms. Rev. PORTUGALIAE etc.
I in wreath. 1853 . . . . 8.00

Fine

58 II (réis). Sim. 1853 . . . . 12.00
59 20 (réis). Like No. 60.
1840 . . . . 15.00

*60 40 (réis). 1840 . . . . 15.00
61 80 (réis). Sim. 1840 . . . . 20.00

Silver

Fine

*62 ONCA (= 6 cruzados = 2880
réis). 1843, 45 . . . . 85.00

Gold

VG-F

65 1¼ (Maticaes). "M" in pearl
oval. Rev. 1¼. 11x17mm.
N.D. (1835) 750.00
66 2½ (Maticaes). Sim. 11x25mm.
N.D. (1835) 1000.00

NEPAL

Kingdom on the N.E. frontier of India, lying between the Indian plain and the Himalayas.

Modern Nepal resulted from Gurkha (Gorkhali) conquest in 1768 of the Nepalese principalities of the former Malla rajas.

Monetary System:

The copper mostly consisted of "dumpy pice" manufactured by private persons.

The silver and gold coins were all expressed in terms of the mohar (=5.5 grams). The silver mohar was therefore about half the Indian rupee and the gold mohar about half the Indian mohur.

Dates on coins are in the Saka Era which began AD 78.

Prithvi Narayana, Raja of Gorkha
1742AD-, In Nepal Saka 1690-96
(=1768-74AD)

Silver

		V.G.
★1 ($^1/_{128}$ mohar). Uniface. .043 gr. N.D.		2.50
4 (⅛ mohar). N.D.		Unique
6 (½ mohar). Saka 1693		RRR

		V.G.
★7 (mohar). Saka 1676-96		8.00
8 (2 mohars). Saka 1693		Unique

Gold

		V.F.
9 ($^1/_{64}$ mohar). N.D.		RRR
10 ($^1/_{32}$ mohar). N.D.		RRR
11 ($^1/_{16}$ mohar). N.D.		RRR
12 (⅛ mohar). N.D.		RRR
14 (½ mohar). Saka 1693		RRR
15 (mohar). Saka 1693-95		RR
16 (2 mohars). Saka 1693, 95		RR
17 (4 mohars). Saka 1693		RRR

Queen Narindra Laksmi Devi
(Wife of Prithvi Narayana)

Silver

		Fine
22 (¼ mohar). N.D.		RR

		Fine
★23 (¼ mohar). Saka 1690-93		7.50

Gold

		V.F.
26 (¼ mohar). Saka 1693		Unique

Pratapa Simha
Saka 1696-99 (=1774-77AD)

Silver

		VG-F
28 ($^1/_{128}$ mohar). N.D.		2.00
29 ($^1/_{16}$ mohar). N.D.		10.00
30 (⅛ mohar). N.D.		10.00
32 (½ mohar). Saka 1697-98		12.50

★33 (mohar). Two vars. Saka 1696-99		9.00
34 (2 mohars). Saka 1696		RRR

Gold

		V.F.
35 ($^1/_{128}$ mohar). N.D.		Unique
36 ($^1/_{16}$ mohar). N.D.		Unique
37 (⅛ mohar). N.D.		Unique
38 (½ mohar). Saka 1697		Unique
39 (mohar)		—
40 (2 mohars). Saka 1696		Unique
41 (4 mohars). Saka 1698		Unique

Queen Rajendra Laksmi Devi
(Wife of Pratapa Simha)

Silver

		Fine
★42 (¼ mohar). Saka 1696-1700		7.50

Gold

		V.F.
46 (¼ mohar). Saka 1698, 1700		RRR

Rana Bahadur
Saka 1699-1721 (=1777-99AD)

Bronze

		Good
47 (¼ paisa). Legend in Arabic script. For the Terai (border area S. of Nepal) 10-12mm		2.00
48 (½ paisa). Sim. 20mm		2.00

★49 (paisa)		2.00

Silver

		Fine
51 ($^1/_{128}$ mohar). N.D.		2.00
53 ($^1/_{32}$ mohar). N.D.		5.00
54 ($^1/_{16}$ mohar). N.D.		5.00
55 (⅛ mohar). N.D.		2.00
56 (¼ mohar). Trident, legend, date. Rev. Vase with wreath. Saka 1705-12		4.00
59 ½ (mohar). Saka 1701, 12		7.50

★61 (mohar). Saka 1699-1720. Large flan until 1711, small flan thereafter		7.50
63 (2 mohars). Same, double thick. Saka 1703-19		17.50

Gold

		V.F.
64 ($^1/_{128}$ mohar). N.D.		35.00
66 ($^1/_{16}$ mohar). N.D.		Unique
67 (⅛ mohar). N.D.		55.00
68 (¼ mohar). Saka 1712-16		45.00
69 (½ mohar). Saka 1700-12		RRR
70 (mohar). Saka 1700-20		125.00
71 (4 mohars). Saka 1718		—

Queen Raja Rajeshvari Devi
(Wife of Rana Bahadur)

Silver

		Fine
72 (¼ mohar). Saka 1711-24		10.00

Gold

		V.F.
72.5 (¼ mohar). Saka 1716-24		55.00

NEPAL

Queen Amara Raja Rajesvari Devi
(Wife of Rana Bahadur)

Gold
V.F.
73.5 (¼ mohar). Saka 1724 ...RRR

Queen Suvarna Prabha Devi
(Wife of Rana Bahadur)

Silver
Fine
74 (¼ mohar). Saka 1723 ..... 7.50

Gold
V.F.
74.5 (¼ muhar). Saka 1723 ..125.00

Queen Lalita Tripura
Sundari Devi
(Wife of Rana Bahadur,
Regent for her son,
Girvan Yuddha, and
grandson, Rajendra)

Silver

Fine
★75 (ex 116) (¼ mohar).
Saka 1728-44.............10.00

Gold
V.F.
75.5 (¼ mohar). Saka 1728-41...55.00

Girvan Yuddha Vikrama
Saka 1721-38 (=1799-1816AD)

Silver
V.G.
76 (¹/₁₂₈ mohar). N.D. 4.00
76.2 (¹/₃₂ mohar). N.D. ....RRR
76.3 (¹/₁₆ mohar). N.D. 2.50
76.4 (⅛ mohar). (vars.) N.D. ... 3.00
77 (¼ mohar). Saka 1723-30....RR
77.2 (½ mohar). Saka 1721-38...10.00
77.5 (¾ mohar). Saka 1727......RR
78 (mohar). Like No. 86.
Saka 1720-38............. 7.50
79 (1½ mohar). Saka 1725-27...10.00
79.5 (3 mohars). Saka 1725-26...25.00
79.7 (4 mohars). Saka 1725......RR

Gold
Fine
80 (¹/₁₂₈ mohar). N.D. 35.00
81 (¹/₃₂ mohar). N.D. ....RR
82 (¹/₁₆ mohar). N.D. 60.00
83 (⅛ mohar). N.D. (vars.) ...45.00
84 (¼ mohar). Saka 1730......RR

Fine
85 (½ mohar). Saka 1721-36...60.00

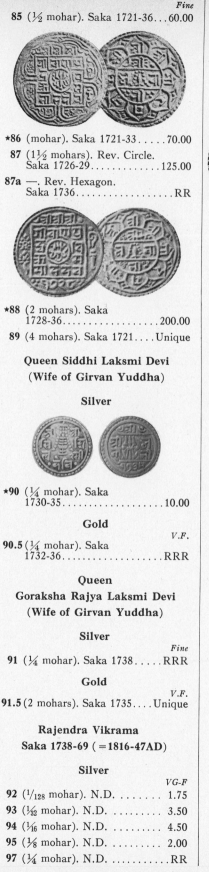

★86 (mohar). Saka 1721-33.....70.00
87 (1½ mohars). Rev. Circle.
Saka 1726-29............125.00
87a —. Rev. Hexagon.
Saka 1736.................RR

★88 (2 mohars). Saka
1728-36.................200.00
89 (4 mohars). Saka 1721....Unique

Queen Siddhi Laksmi Devi
(Wife of Girvan Yuddha)

Silver

★90 (¼ mohar). Saka
1730-35.................10.00

Gold
V.F.
90.5 (¼ mohar). Saka
1732-36.................RRR

Queen
Goraksha Rajya Laksmi Devi
(Wife of Girvan Yuddha)

Silver
Fine
91 (¼ mohar). Saka 1738.....RRR

Gold
V.F.
91.5 (2 mohars). Saka 1735....Unique

Rajendra Vikrama
Saka 1738-69 (=1816-47AD)

Silver
VG-F
92 (¹/₁₂₈ mohar). N.D. 1.75
93 (¹/₃₂ mohar). N.D. 3.50
94 (¹/₁₆ mohar). N.D. 4.50
95 (⅛ mohar). N.D. 2.00
97 (¼ mohar). N.D. ....RR

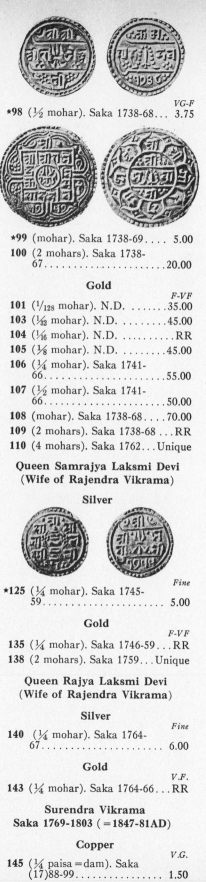

VG-F
★98 (½ mohar). Saka 1738-68... 3.75

★99 (mohar). Saka 1738-69.... 5.00
100 (2 mohars). Saka 1738-
67.....................20.00

Gold
F-VF
101 (¹/₁₂₈ mohar). N.D. 35.00
103 (¹/₃₂ mohar). N.D. 45.00
104 (¹/₁₆ mohar). N.D. ....RR
105 (⅛ mohar). N.D. 45.00
106 (¼ mohar). Saka 1741-
66.....................55.00
107 (½ mohar). Saka 1741-
66.....................50.00
108 (mohar). Saka 1738-68....70.00
109 (2 mohars). Saka 1738-68 ...RR
110 (4 mohars). Saka 1762...Unique

Queen Samrajya Laksmi Devi
(Wife of Rajendra Vikrama)

Silver

★125 (¼ mohar). Saka 1745-
59..................... 5.00

Gold
F-VF
135 (¼ mohar). Saka 1746-59...RR
138 (2 mohars). Saka 1759...Unique

Queen Rajya Laksmi Devi
(Wife of Rajendra Vikrama)

Silver
Fine
140 (¼ mohar). Saka 1764-
67..................... 6.00

Gold
V.F.
143 (¼ mohar). Saka 1764-66...RR

Surendra Vikrama
Saka 1769-1803 (=1847-81AD)

Copper
V.G.
145 (¼ paisa =dam). Saka
(17)88-99............... 1.50

NEPAL

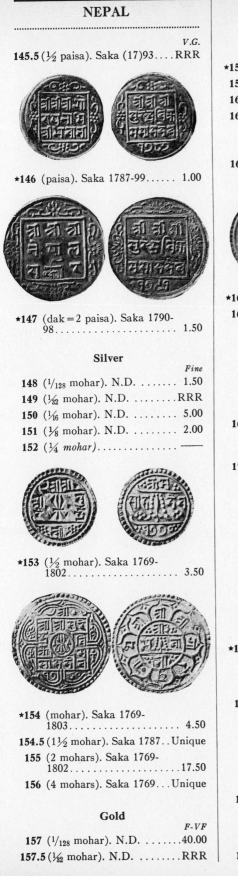

V.G.

145.5 (½ paisa). Saka (17)93....RRR

★146 (paisa). Saka 1787-99...... 1.00

★147 (dak = 2 paisa). Saka 1790-98...................... 1.50

Silver

Fine

148 (1/128 mohar). N.D. 1.50
149 (1/32 mohar). N.D. ....RRR
150 (1/16 mohar). N.D. 5.00
151 (⅛ mohar). N.D. 2.00
152 (¼ *mohar*)............... —

★153 (½ mohar). Saka 1769-1802.................. 3.50

★154 (mohar). Saka 1769-1803.................. 4.50
154.5 (1½ mohar). Saka 1787..Unique
155 (2 mohars). Saka 1769-1802...................17.50
156 (4 mohars). Saka 1769...Unique

Gold

F-VF

157 (1/128 mohar). N.D. 40.00
157.5 (1/32 mohar). N.D. ....RRR

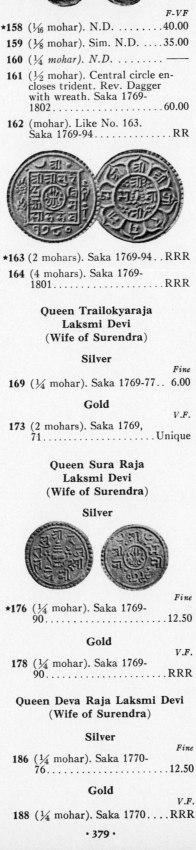

F-VF

★158 (1/16 mohar). N.D. 40.00
159 (⅛ mohar). Sim. N.D. 35.00
160 (¼ *mohar*). N.D. .... —
161 (½ mohar). Central circle encloses trident. Rev. Dagger with wreath. Saka 1769-1802.....................60.00
162 (mohar). Like No. 163. Saka 1769-94..............RR

★163 (2 mohars). Saka 1769-94..RRR
164 (4 mohars). Saka 1769-1801....................RRR

Queen Trailokyaraja Laksmi Devi
(Wife of Surendra)

Silver

Fine

169 (¼ mohar). Saka 1769-77.. 6.00

Gold

V.F.

173 (2 mohars). Saka 1769, 71....................Unique

Queen Sura Raja Laksmi Devi
(Wife of Surendra)

Silver

★176 (¼ mohar). Saka 1769-90....................12.50

Gold

V.F.

178 (¼ mohar). Saka 1769-90....................RRR

Queen Deva Raja Laksmi Devi
(Wife of Surendra)

Silver

Fine

186 (¼ mohar). Saka 1770-76....................12.50

Gold

V.F.

188 (¼ mohar). Saka 1770....RRR

Queen Purayakumari Raja Laksmi Devi
(Wife of Surendra?)

Silver

Fine

★193 (¼ mohar). Saka 1802....RRR

Note: The 4 mohar size silver and gold pieces of Trailokya Vira Vikrama (Surendra's son) dated Saka 1771 are deemed to be medals, not coins.

NETHERLANDS EAST INDIES

Numerous group of islands between SE Asia and Australia. Trade controlled by the Netherlands United East India Company (Vereenigde Oostindische Compagnie), commencing at the end of the 16th century when the Dutch ousted the Portuguese. Sporadic strife with the British Company, which held various settlements in the islands, persisted until 1824 when the British exchanged their Sumatra holdings for a free hand in Malacca. The Netherlands Company was abolished in 1798-99 and its interests taken over by the Netherlands Government (Batavian Republic). Beginning about 1808 the Dutch established full political control over the islands. This process, which required several generations, was interrupted by various British occupations 1811-24.

Monetary System:

120 duits = 30 stuivers = 1 gulden = 1 Java rupee; 16 silver rupees = 1 gold rupee.

I. United East India Company.

Coins struck in Netherlands at various provincial mints.

A. Gelderland.

Arms: 2 lions combattant.

Copper

VG-F

A1 (½ duit). Like No. A2. 18mm. 1788-90.................... 1.25

★A2 (duit). 1731-94............ .75

Silver

		V.F.
A4 X ST(uiver = ½ gulden). Like No. H5 but rev. legend ends D:GEL: & C:Z. 1786....50.00

A5 1 G(u)L(den). Sim. 1786, 90......100.00

A6 3 G(u)L(den). Sim. 1786..475.00

C. Holland.

Arms: Lion rampant.

Copper

C1 (½ duit). Like No. C2. 17mm. 1749-54, 69-70...... 3.50   *V.G.*

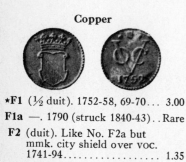

★**C2** (duit). 1726-93........... 1.50

F. Utrecht.

City Arms: Per bend, white and red.

Copper

★**F1** (½ duit). 1752-58, 69-70... 3.00

F1a —. 1790 (struck 1840-43)..Rare

F2 (duit). Like No. F2a but mmk. city shield over VOC. 1741-94................. 1.35

★**F2a** —. 1790. Mmk. child or star ★. (Struck 1827-43)......... .40

F3 (2 duits). Like No. F2a. 26mm. 1790 (struck 1840-43)................. .75

Silver

	V.F.
F4 X ST(uiver = ½ gulden). Like No. H5 but rev. legend ends TRAI. 1786.........50.00

F5 I G(ulden). Sim. 1786, 90.110.00

F6 3 G(u)L(den). Sim. 1786..350.00

G. Westfriesland.

Arms: Billety, 2 lions passant guardant.

Copper

G1 (½ duit). Like No. G2. 17mm. 1765-70.......... 3.50   *V.G.*

★**G2** (duit). 1729-94........... 1.50

Silver

	V.F.
G4 X ST(uiver = ½ gulden). Like No. H5 but rev. legend ends WESTF. 1786-87......40.00

G5 I G(u)L(den). Sim. 1786, 87, 90................90.00

G6 3 G(u)L(den). Sim. 1786..300.00

H. Zeeland.

Arms: Lion rising from sea.

Copper

H1 (½ duit). Like No. H2a. 17mm. 1770-72, 89...... 5.00   *V.G.*

H2 (duit). Like No. H2a but obv. legend LUCTOR etc. 1726-29................. 3.50

★**H2a** —. No obverse legend. 1729-94................. 1.50

Silver

H4 X ST(uiver = ½ gulden). Like No. H5. 1791.......70.00   *V.F.*

★**H5** I G(u)L(den). Rev. legend ends ZEL. 1791..........110.00

H6 3 G(u)L(den). Sim. 1789...................375.00

II. United East India Company.
Coins struck in the islands.

Copper

10 DUyT (duit) /IAVAS/date. Rev. same in Arabic. 1764-65...................... 9.50   *V.G.*

10a —. Obv. wreath. 1783...... 9.50   *V.G.*

Tin

11 DUIT. B(atavia) over VOC mon. Rev. value. Holed. N.D. (1796)..........*unknown today*   *G-VG*

★**12** I/DUIT. N(ederlandsche) over VOC mon. 1796-97.....RRR

Rectangular Copper
(**Cuttings from copper bars = "BONKS."**)

13 I:S:(tuiver). Like No. 32a. 23.16 gr. 1796-99..........20.00   *V.G.*

14 2:S:(tuiver). Sim. 46.32 gr. 1796-99..................30.00

Silver

★**15** (Java rupee). 11.8-13.15 gr. 1747-50..................85.00   *Fine*

16 (rupee). Various rupees, including No. 15, Surat, Persia, etc. Cmkd. like No. 20. (1750-60)..............V. Rare

17 (Java rupee). Like No. 15. 1764-67, 82-99 (var.)......37.50

Gold

★**18** (Dirhem Djawi = Java ducat). 4.3 gr. 1744-46 (var.)........RR

19 (2 Java ducats). Sim. 8.6 gr. 1746-48..................RR

★**20** (ducat). Regular Netherlands provincial ducats (Holland ★ 1750-58, Utrecht 1758-59, Westfriesland 1754-59, Zeeland 1758-59). Cmkd. (Djawa = Java) in circle. (1753-61).......400.00

NETHERLANDS EAST INDIES

Fine

22 (½ gold rupee). Like No. 23.
8 gr. 1783-99 . . . . 450.00

⋆23 (gold rupee). 16 gr.
1783-97 . . . . 1000.00

III. Coinage Struck Under the Batavian Republic 1799-1806

Copper

V.G.

⋆24 (duit). Like No. A2. Gelders
arms. 1802-06 . . . . 3.50

25 (duit). Like No. C2. Holland
arms. 1802-04 . . . . 3.50

26 5–¹⁄₃₂/G (=1/160 gulden =
½ duit). Like No. 62. 1802-06 1.75

27 5–¹⁄₁₆/G (=1/80 gulden =
duit). Sim. 1802-06 . . . . 1.75

⋆28 5–¹⁄₁₆/G (=duit). Overysel
arms. 1803-06 . . . . 1.75

29 (duit). Like No. 42. 1806 . . . . 8.50

30 ½:S:(tuiver). Bonk. *Like No.
32a.* 7.7 gr. 1804-05 . . . . 60.00

31 1:S:(tuiver). Sim. 23.16 gr.
1800-02 . . . . 25.00

31a —. 19.3 gr. 1803-06 . . . . 22.50

32 2:S:(tuiver). Sim. 46.32 gr.
1800-02 . . . . 40.00

⋆32a —. 38.6 gr. 1803-06 . . . . 30.00

V.G.

33 8/ST(ui)V(er). Date in pearl
circles. Bonk. 1803 . . . . 200.00

Lead-Bronze

⋆34 I: S\underline{t}(uiver). 1799, 1800 . . . . . 20.00

Silver

Fine

35 (½ Java rupee). Like No. 36.
6.6 gr. 1805-06 . . . . 50.00

⋆36 (Java rupee). 13.15 gr.
1800-03 . . . . 40.00

37 (Java rupee). Like No. 52.
31.5mm. 1804-06 . . . . 40.00

V.F.

38 ¹⁄₁₆–G(ulden). Like No. 40.2.
1802 . . . . 20.00

39 ⅛–G(ulden). Sim. 1802 . . . . 35.00

40 ¼–G(ulden). Sim. 1802 . . . . . 35.00

40.1 ½–G(ulden). Sim. 1802 . . . . . 50.00

⋆40.2 I G(ulden). 1802 . . . . 80.00

Gold

⋆41 (½ gold rupee). 1800-03 . . . 750.00

IV. Coinage Struck 1806-11 Under Louis Napoleon, King of Holland.

Copper

V.G.

⋆42 (duit). 1807-10 . . . . 1.75

43 (duit). L.N. Rev. JAVA/date.
1808-10 . . . . 1.75

44 (duit). Like No. 46. 1810-11. 1.75

45 ½ St(uiver). Sim. but value/
LN script mon. 1810 . . . . . . 50.00

45a —. Like No. 46. 1810-11 . . . . 2.50

⋆46 I St(uiver). 1810 . . . . 75.00

47 1:S:(tuiver). Bonk. Like No.
48. 1807-10 . . . . 25.00

⋆48 2:S:(tuiver). 1807-10 . . . . . . 30.00

49 5–¹⁄₃₂/G (=1/160 gulden =
½ duit). Like No. 62. 1807-
09 . . . . 1.75

50 5–¹⁄₁₆/G (=1/80 gulden =
duit). Sim. 1807-09 . . . . 1.25

51 5–¹⁄₁₆/G (=duit). Like No.
28. 1807 . . . . 2.50

NETHERLANDS EAST INDIES

Silver

Fine

*52 (Java rupee). 1808........50.00

Gold

53 (½ gold rupee). Like No. 41.
1807....................900.00

V. British East India Company Occupation of Java 1811-16.

Monetary System:

4 doit = 1 stiver;
30 stivers = 1 rupee;
66 stivers = 1 dollar.

Copper

V.G.

54 (doit). Like No. 55. 1811-13. 3.50

*55 ½ St(iver). B/VEIC. Bale mark.
Rev. JAVA/date. 1811-15.... 3.50

56 1 St(iver). Sim. 1812-15.....10.00

Tin

*57 1/DOIT. VEIC mon. Rev. value/
JAVA. 1813-14............25.00

Genuine specimens of No. 57 have a
broad and squat 8 in the date.

Silver

Fine

58 (½ rupee). Like No. 59.
6.65 gr. 1668 (error = 1228),
1229AH................90.00

*59 (rupee). 1668 (error = 1228),
1229-32AH..............45.00

Gold

*60 (½ gold rupee). 1813-16..1200.00

F-VF

VI. Under Kingdom of the Netherlands.

Willem I 1815-40

Copper

VG-F

61 5-1/32/G (= 1/160 gulden =
½ dui cript H(eus, Amsterdam) mmk. 1814-16........ .75

61a —. S(uermond, Utrecht) mmk.
1816 (coined 1820-22)..... 1.25

61b —. No mmk. (Surabaya).
1816 (coined 1821), 18-22... .75

*62 5-1/16/G (= duit). Like No. 61.
Script H. 1814-16.......... .75

62a —. Like No. 61a. S. 1816
(coined 1820-22)........... .75

62b —. Like No. 61b. No mmk.
1816 (coined 1820), 18-26... .75

63 ½ St(uiver). Sim. 1818-
20G.................... 2.25

63a —. W/out G. 1821-26...... 1.50

64 ⅛ St(uiver). Obv. sim. Rev.
NEDERL./INDIE/date. 1822-
26...................... .75

65 ¼ St(uiver). Sim. 1822-26,
36...................... .40

66 ½ St(uiver). Sim. 1821-26.. .75

V.G.

67 ½ St(uiver). Bonk. Value/1818,
each in rectangle..........20.00

68 1 St(uiver). Sim. 1818.....10.00

69 2 St(uiver). Sim. 1818-19...14.00

70 1 C(en)t. Like No. 64.
1833-40.................. .35

71 2 C(en)t. Sim. 1833-40..... .75

Nos. 70 and 71 passed for 1 and 2
duit, respectively.

Silver

F-VF

72 KWART (= ¼)/GULDEN.
Head. Rev. value. 1826-27,
34, 40..................25.00

73 HALVE (= ½)/GULDEN.
Sim. 1826-27, 34..........35.00

*74 1 G(ulden). 1821, 39-40.....40.00

Willem II 1840-49

Copper

75 2 C(en)t. Like No. 71.
1841.................... 5.00

See also Nos. F1a, F2a and F3 dated
1790 but mostly struck 1840-43.

VII. British Settlements in what later became the Netherlands East Indies.

Monetary System:

400 kepings = 100 cents = 4 suku = 1
dollar — or as in Netherlands Settlements.

**A. Fort Marlborough (Marlbro).
See Sumatra.**

B. Maluka (in Bandarmassin).
District on Borneo ruled 1812-18 by
an English adventurer, Alexander Hare.

Copper

G-VG

11 (duit). "Maluka" in Arabic
in hexagon. Rev. value (Arabic)
in 2 lines. N.D. .... V. Rare

NETHERLANDS EAST INDIES

BRITISH SETTLEMENTS (Cont.)

G-VG

12 I (duit). 9 pointed fan/1227AH.
Rev. I/duit in Arabic...... 2.00

13 I (duit). 1813/1228 (Arabic)
in shield. Rev. Value (Arabic)
in shield............... 1.50

14 (duit). 4/heart shield containing value (Arabic)/1228AH.
Rev. Flower, 4 branches.....RR

15 1 (duit). 1228AH in wreath.
Rev. 1/duit (Arabic).......RR

C. Sumatra.
Settlements of the British East India
Company on the west coast of Sumatra 1685-1824 (including occupation
of Netherlands settlements 1781-88, 95-
1824). All ceded to Netherlands 1824.

Copper

V.G.

★20 2/keping. 20-22mm. 1783... 6.00

★21 1/keping. 1786-87......... 5.00

21a 3 (error, =1)/keping.
21mm. 1798.............. 5.00

22 2/keping. Sim. 25mm.
1786-87................. 4.00

22a 3 (error, =2)/keping.
25mm. 1798............. 5.00

23 3/keping. Sim. 28mm.
1786-87, 98............ 8.00

25 1/keping. Like No. 27.
3.4 gr. 21mm. 1804.......

25a —. 2 gr. 1804............ 2.00

26 2/keping. Sim. 6.4 gr.
26mm. 1804.............

26a —. 4.4 gr. 1804........... 2.00

V.G.

★27 4/keping. 12.8 gr. 1804.....

27a —. 8.5 gr. 1804........... — 3.00

Note: Pieces similar to No. 25 but in-
scribed ISLAND OF SUMATRA (or SUL-
TANA) are tokens. See MALAY PEN-
INSULA (Singapore).

★30 ½/DOLLAR. (1797)...Very Rare

Silver

VG-F

★35 2 (suku). 1783-84........200.00

VIII. Native States in the Nether-
lands East Indies.

Monetary System:

pitjis (pitis) = 1/400 to 1/20,000 peso,
depending on size.

A. Atcheh (Atschi, Negri Atcheh).
Kingdom in Northwest Sumatra.

Ala-ed-dim Dschohor Alam Shah
1209-39AH (=1795-1824AD)

Tin
Good

10 (keping). Arab legends.
21mm. 1220AH............ 5.00

B. Bandarmassin (=Banjarmasin,
Bandschermasin).
Kingdom in South Borneo.

Copper
Good

23 (keping). BANJAR/MASIN
(in Arabic) in shield. Rev. VOC
mon./blundered and partial
dates circa 1789-90. 21mm. 5.00

23a —. Rev. Arabic numerals/
1221AH................ 6.00

Silver

28 BANJAR (Arabic). Cmkd.
on various silver coins.
(Ca. 1800)............... ——

Gold

33 (gold rupee). Spanish 2 escudos.
Cmkd. BANJAR (Arabic)..... ——

C. Bantam.
Former Kingdom in West Java.

Abu-'l-Nasr Mohammed
Arif Zeinal-Aschiqin
1166-91AH (=1753-77AD)

Tin

40 (pitjis). Arab legends both sides.
19½mm. Holed. 1181AH... 4.00

D. Cheribon.
Residency in West Java.

Tin

50 (pitjis). CHERIBON. 19-21mm.
Holed. N.D. (var.)........ 2.50

F. Dschambi.
Sultanate on Sumatra.

Anum Ingalaga Abd-er-rahman
1156AH- (=1743AD-)

Tin (Uniface)

70 (pitjis). Sultan's name (Malay).
Octagonal. 19mm. *Holed.*
N.D..................... 3.00

71 (pitjis). Sim. 22mm....... 4.00

73 (pitjis). Sim. Round. 25mm.. 6.00

Anonymous Tin (Uniface)

80 (pitjis). Malayan legend.
17mm. Holed.(end 18th cent.) 2.50

82 (pitjis). Javanese legend.
22mm. Holed............ 4.00

83 (pitjis). Sim. 24 mm....... 6.00

H. Palembang.
State on Sumatra.

Najm-ed-din

Tin

100 (pitjis). 1183AH
(=1769AD)............. 7.50

NETHERLANDS EAST INDIES

Mohammed Bahu-ed-din
1189-1218AH (= 1775-1803AD)

Tin (Uniface)
Good

107 (pitjis). Arabic legend. 15mm.
(= 1/8000 peso). 1193AH . . 3.00

108 (pitjis). Arab legend. 19mm.
Holed. *(1/4000 peso).* N.D. 5.00

108a —. Diff. legend. 1203AH . . . 4.00

Copper (Uniface)

112 (duit). Like No. 108a. 21mm.
(1/2000 peso). 1198AH 7.50

Mahmud Bedr-ed-din
1218-36AH (= 1803-21AD)

Tin (Octagonal Uniface)

120 (pitjis = 1/20,000 peso).
Arab legend. 14mm.
1219AH 4.00

123 (pitjis = 1/4000 peso). Like
No. 120. 18mm. Holed
1219AH 5.00

I. Pontianaq.
Small principality in West Borneo.

Abd-er-rahman
1185-1222AH (= 1772-1808AD)

Copper

130 (keping). Copy of Bombay
coinage of British East India
Co. VEIC Bale Mark. Rev.
Scales. 20-22mm. Blundered
date. 1791 . . . . 6.00

Moquette attributes No. 130 to Bandarmassin (II Pridmore 172).

Abdul Qasim
1223-34AH (= 1808-19AD)

Copper
Good

135 (keping). Arms supported by
2 lions. Rev. Scales. 21mm.
1810 . . . . 7.50

138 (keping). Arab legend. Rev.
Scales. 22mm. 1226AH 7.50

139 (2 kepings). Sim. 26mm.
1226AH 8.50

K. Siak (Negri Siak).
Sultanate on Sumatra.

Tin (Uniface)
Good

151 (pitjis). Malay legend.
22mm. Holed. N.D.
(18th century) 5.00

L. Sumenep.
Sultanate on the Island of Madura.

Paku Nata Ningrat
d 1270AH (= 1854AD)

Cmkd. Silver

170 (rupee). Java rupees of 1765-
1805. Cmkd. 5 petalled flower
in pointed shield 25.00

173 (real batu). Cob 8 reales with
SUMENEP (Arabic) in square
cmk. (1)235AH, N.D 75.00

Gold

178 (gold rupee). Spanish 2 escudos.
Cmkd. like No. 173 . . . . ——

NETHERLANDS WEST INDIES.
NEVIS.

See CARIBBEAN ISLANDS
and TERRITORIES.

NICARAGUA

Until 1821 Nicaragua formed part of
the Spanish Captaincy-General of
Guatemala. Part of Mexico 1822-23.
State in the Republic of Central America 1823-47. An independent republic
thereafter.

Monetary System:
16 reales = 1 escudo.

As a State
in the Republic of
Central America 1823-47

No coinage was made specifically for
Nicaragua under the confederation.
The first independent coinage took
place in 1878. The 2 Reales of 1825,
usually cataloged as an issue of Nicaragua, is listed in this book under
HONDURAS.

NORWAY, KINGDOM

In Northern Europe, occupying the western portion of the Scandinavian peninsula. United with Denmark until 1814, with Sweden 1814-1905, independent thereafter.

Monetary System:
120 skilling (Dansk) = 1 Speciedaler (Rigsdaler Species) = 6 marks.

Mint:
Kongsberg – MM: Crossed hammers.

Arms:
Until 1845 — Red, cwnd. golden lion holding (and standing on) axe with rocker handle.

From 1845 — Lion holds axe with short, straight handle.

Frederik V,
King of Denmark, 1746-66

Billon
V.G.

2 I/SKILLING. Cwnd. double F5 mon. Rev. value. 1761-65 . . . . 3.50

4 II SKILLING. Like No. 6. 1747-64 . . . . 2.50

Silver

V.F.

★6 24 SKILLING. Cwnd. double F5 mon. Rev. lion. 1746-63 . . . . 30.00

6a —. Obv. legend extends below mon. 1763-65 . . . . 35.00

9 6 M(arks). Armored bust. Rev. TROE LOVE etc. Lion in double legend. 1749. So-called "Reisedaler." Struck to pay for King's Norwegian travels 300.00
VF-EF

10 (Speciedaler). Head. Rev. PRUDENTIA etc. Lion shield. 1765 . . . . 600.00

See DENMARK for other coins of this reign.

Christian VII,
King of Denmark, 1766-1808

Billon
G-VG

12 I/SKILLING. Cwnd. double c7 mon. Rev. value. 1768-70 . . . . 8.00

G-VG

14 I/SKILLING. Cwnd. c7 mon. Rev. value. 1779-80 . . . . 5.00

16 2 SKILLING. Cwnd. c7 mon. Rev. oval Danish arms. 1778-88 . . . . 1.50

★18 2/SKILLING. 1800-07 . . . . . 1.25

Silver
Fine

20 4 SKILLING. Like No. 16 but rev. oval 3-fold arms. 1778, 88 . . . . 5.00

22 VIII/SKILLING. Cwnd. c7 mon. Rev. value. 1773-75 . . . 10.00

24 8 SKILLING. Like No. 20. 1778-95 . . . . 7.50

★26 15 STYKKER. I. RIGSDALER SPECIES (= 1/15 Rigsdaler Sp.). 1795-1802 . . . 7.50

28 24 SKILLING. Cwnd. double c7 mon. Rev. lion. 1767 . . . . 100.00

★30 24 SKILLING. Cwnd. double c7 mon. Rev. cwnd. oval lion arms. 1772-88 . . . . 20.00

32 5 STYKKER etc. (= 1/5 Rigsdaler Sp.). Cwnd. CR VII mon. Rev. value. 1796-1803 . . . . 10.00

V.F.

★34 1/3 RIGSDALER SPECIES. 1795-1803 . . . . 35.00

V.F.

★36 ½ SP(eciesdaler). Cwnd. double c7 mon. Rev. cwnd. 3 fold arms. 1776-79 . . . . 65.00

38 2/3 RIGSDALER SPECIES. Like No. 34. 1795-96 . . . . . . 85.00

40 (Speciedaler). Cwnd. double c7 mon. Rev. lion shield. 1767-69 . . . . 300.00

41 (Speciedaler). Like No. 36. 1776-85 . . . . 125.00

42 (Albertus thaler). Wild man stdg. with Danish shield. Rev. Norwegian lion shield. 1781-86, 96. For Baltic trade 600.00

43 1 RIGSDALER. Armored bust. Rev. UROKKELD etc. Lion in double legend. "Reisedaler." 1788 . . . . (E.F.) 750.00

44 1 RIGSDALER SPECIES. Like No. 34. 1791-95 . . . . . . 150.00

See DENMARK for other coins of this and the following reign.

Frederik VI of Denmark,
In Norway 1808-14

Copper
VG-F

51 1/SKILLING/COURANT. Like No. 59. 1809 . . . . 3.00

52 1/SKILLING/DANSK. Sim. 1812 . . . . 1.75

53 2/SKILLING/COURANT. Like No. 59. 1810-11 . . . . 1.00

54 4/SKILLING/COURANT. Sim. 1809, 10 (unique) 3.00

Billon
V.G.

58 4/SKILLING/SKILLE/MYNT. Like No. 59. 1809 . . . . 1.25

NORWAY

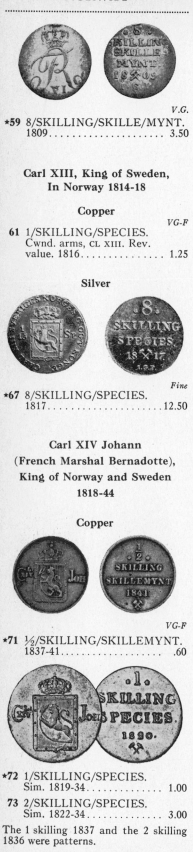

V.G.

★59 8/SKILLING/SKILLE/MYNT.
1809.................... 3.50

Carl XIII, King of Sweden, In Norway 1814-18

Copper

VG-F

61 1/SKILLING/SPECIES.
Cwnd. arms, CL XIII. Rev.
value. 1816.............. 1.25

Silver

★67 8/SKILLING/SPECIES.
Fine
1817.................... 12.50

Carl XIV Johann (French Marshal Bernadotte), King of Norway and Sweden 1818-44

Copper

VG-F

★71 ½/SKILLING/SKILLEMYNT.
1837-41.................. .60

★72 1/SKILLING/SPECIES.
Sim. 1819-34............. 1.00

73 2/SKILLING/SPECIES.
Sim. 1822-34............. 3.00

The 1 skilling 1837 and the 2 skilling
1836 were patterns.

Billon (Silver)

Fine

78 2/SKILLING. Arms.
Rev. value. 1825......... 10.00

79 4/SKILLING. Sim. 1825... 8.00

80 8/SKILLING. Sim. 1819... 12.50

81 24/SKILLING. Sim. 27mm.
1819................... 35.00

81a —. 23mm. 1823-24........ 30.00

Silver

V.F.

83 ½ SP(ecie)S(daler). Like
No. 84. 1819-24........... 75.00

★84 1 SP(ecie)S(daler). 1819-
24..................... 200.00

Billon (Silver)

Fine

87 8 SK(illing). Like No. 90.
1825, 27................ 15.00

88 24 SK(illing). Sim. 1825-36.. 50.00

Silver

V.F.

89 ½ SP(ecie)s(daler). Sim.
1827-36................ 85.00

V.F.

★90 1 SP(ecie)S(daler). 1826-
36..................... 200.00

For other coins of this and the adjacent reigns, see SWEDEN.

Billon

★93 2/SKILLING. Cwnd. CJ XIV
mon. Rev. value. 1842-43... 3.00

94 4/SKILLING. Bust. Rev.
value. 1842.............. 6.00

95 ½ SP(ecie)S(daler). Like
No. 96. 1844............. 75.00

★96 1 SP(ecie)S(daler). 1844... 175.00

Oscar I, King of Norway and Sweden 1844-59

Silver

101 12 SK(illing). Like No. 104.
1845-56................. 15.00

NORWAY

V.F.

102 24 SK(illing). Sim. 1845-
55 . . . . 22.50

Note: Two varieties of Nos. 101-102
exist, with smooth rims 1845-48, and
beaded rims 1850 onward.

103 ½ SP(ecie)S(daler). Sim.
1846-55 . . . . 75.00

⋆104 1 SP(ecie)S(daler). 1846-
57 . . . . 175.00

NUEVA GRANADA.
See COLOMBIA.

OTTOMAN EMPIRE.
See TURKEY.

PERSIA (Now IRAN)

A monarchy in the Near East.

The coinage of Persia during the
period covered by this catalog was in
such confusion that no complete listing
is possible within the space which can
appropriately be allocated for that purpose here. Between 1500AD and the
monetary reformation of 1877-78, a-
bout 120 provincial mints operated at
various times, many of them until well
into the 19th century. The central government had little control over the coinage issued by most of these mints, and
such control as it had was exercised
arbitrarily. Enforced recoinages for the
purpose of taxation were frequent. The
local copper coins (all with the name

of the mint town, mostly dated, but
virtually all without the ruler's name)
were in fact devalued and recoined
every year in many cities. Rabino di
Borgomale lists 123 different obverse
designs for these anonymous copper
coins.

Silver and gold coins were frequently
reminted on the accession of a new
Shah.

When one considers the facts set
forth above, together with the further
information that all Persian coins were
struck by the hammer method until
1877, causing dies to be short-lived, it
may be seen that literally tens of thou-
sands of different Persian coins were
struck between 1750 and 1877. As a
result of recoinage, many of these are
probably no longer in existence. Any
attempt to create in a few pages a com-
prehensive catalog of what remains is
fruitless. What has been provided a-
mounts to a survey of Persian coinage
during the period, with a general indication of the price range within which
such material can be obtained.

Monetary system:

fulus = ½ dinar;
20 dinar = 4 qaz (qazbak, kazbeg) =
   2 tanga = 1 bisti;
50 dinar = 4 jandak = 2 pul =
   2 nim shahi = 1 shahi (yah shahi);
100 dinar = 1 sannar = 1 mahmudi
   (muhammadi);
200 dinar = 1 abbasi;
500 dinar = 1 panahabad (panabat)
   = 1 rupi (circa 1150-93AH);
750 dinar = 1 rupi (circa 1193-1212);
1000 dinar = 1 kran (qiran) or
   hazardinar (1242AH onward);
1250 dinar = 1 riyal (1212-41AH);
10,000 dinar = 1 toman.

During the entire period covered by
this catalog Persia suffered from galloping inflation. In the period from
1502 to 1878 the toman shrank to 1/40
of its original value in silver.

In addition, each town had its own
toman and established its own relation
between the toman (money of account)
and the actual currency. In the early
19th century local tomans ranged in
value between 142 and 500 shahis. The
values of the copper coins varied with
the local toman.

Gold coins were not used in ordinary
trade. Large gold and silver were used
by the sovereign as presentation pieces
and also by the treasury to facilitate
transfers.

I. Anonymous Copper Coinage.

Abushahr (Bushire) Mint. 1270AH.

Ardabil Mint. 1123AH.

Bandar-Abbas Mint. N.D.

Behbehan Mint. N.D.

Borujird Mint. N.D.

Demawand Mint. N.D.

Hamadan Mint. 1054AH.

PERSIA

Isfahan Mint. N.D.

Kashan Mint. N.D.

Khui (Khoi) Mint. 1189AH.

Kirmanshahan Mint. 1172AH.

Mashhad Mint. N.D.

Mazandaran Mint. 1138AH.

Qazvin (Kazwin) Mint.

Resht Mint. 1233AH.

Sauj Bulagh Mint. N.D.

Tabriz Mint. 1235AH.

Teheran Mint. 1222AH.

Tui Mint. N.D.

Urumi Mint. 122xAH.

Yazd Mint. N.D.

Note: The designs shown are typical but many others occur, and most types were produced at many mints (see text on previous page). Definite attribution must be made from the mint name on the reverse.

Persian mints not illustrated above, but which also struck copper coins, include the following:

> Abarquh
> Astarabad
> Dizful
> Farahabad
> Gilan
> Kirman
> Lahijan
> Maragha
> Nihavand
> Sari
> Shiraz
> Shushtar
> Sultanabad
> Tabaristan
> Zanjan

For other similar copper coins see AFGHANISTAN and CAUCASIA.

VG (Crude)

★1 Anonymous copper. Denominations from ½ to 100 dinars depending on the date and place of issue and use. each . . . 2.00-6.00

II. Zand Dynasty, AH1172-1209 (=1759-94AD).

Karim Khan
AH1172-93 (=1759-79AD)

Silver

	VG-F
101 (shahi). 1.2 gr	5.00
102 (mahmudi). 2.3 gr	4.00

PERSIA

Shiraz. 1176AH.

Yazd. 1181AH.

Shiraz. 1176AH.

Fine

**110 (muhr ashrafi). 11 gr....120.00
111 (ashrafi). 4.7 gr.........90.00

VG-F

**103 (abbasi). 4.7 gr......... 2.50
104 (300 dinars). 7.0 gr...... 4.00

Abul Fath Khan
1193AH (=1779AD)

Gold

145 (rupi =750 dinars). 11.7 gr.
    *Isfahan. 1198AH........ 8.50

Gold

Fine

146 (¼ muhr ashrafi). 2.8 gr...50.00

148 (muhr ashrafi). 11 gr.
    *Shiraz. 1197AH........120.00

Jafar Khan
1199-1203AH (=1785-89AD)

Silver

VG-F

149.3 (300 dinars). 4.7 gr...... 5.00

105 (rupi =500 dinars).
    *Mazandaran. 1173AH.... 5.00

Gold

117 (¼ muhr ashrafi). 2.8 gr.
    *Yazd. 1193AH.........200.00

Ali Murad Khan, 1st Reign
1193AH (=1779AD)

Sadik Khan
1193-96AH (=1779-82AD)

Silver

Fine

108 (¼ muhr ashrafi). 2.8 gr.
    *Khui. 1192AH..........40.00

VG-F

131 (75 dinars). 1.2 gr......... 7.50
134 (600 dinars). 9.3 gr.......10.00

149.5 (rupi =750 dinars). 11.7 gr.
    *Isfahan. 1199AH....... 8.50

Gold

Fine

149.8 (muhr ashrafi). 11 gr.
    Shiraz. 1201AH.......120.00

Luftf Ali Khan
1203-09AH (=1789-94AD)

Silver

VG-F

151 (75 dinars). 1.2 gr......... 6.00

135 (rupi =750 dinars). 11.7 gr.
    *Tabriz. 1195AH........ 8.50

Gold

Gold

Fine

136 (¼ muhr ashrafi). 2.8 gr...50.00

Fine

109 (½ muhr ashrafi). 5.5 gr.
    *Resht. 1190AH.........65.00

138 (muhr ashrafi). 11 gr.
    *Shiraz. 1195AH........120.00

Fine

157 (½ ashrafi). 2.3 gr.
    *Kerman. 1208AH........50.00

III. Qajar Dynasty,
AH1163-1344 (=1750-1925AD).

Aka Muhammad Khan
AH1193-1211 (=1779-97AD)

Silver

VG-F

161 (75 dinars). 1.2 gr........ 5.00
162 (300 dinars). 4.7 gr........ 4.00
163 (600 dinars). 7.4 gr........ 6.00

Jalu (Army) Mint. 1172AH.

Ali Murad Khan, 2nd Reign
1196-99AH (=1782-85AD)

Silver

VG-F

141 (75 dinars). 1.2 gr......... 6.50

PERSIA

Isfahan. 1199AH.

Shiraz. 1209AH.

VG-F

**165 (rupi = *750* dinars). 11 gr.. 7.50

166 (1250 dinar). 12.6 gr. 1210-
11AH. *Khui. 1210AH.... 9.00

Gold (toman = 8.2 gr.)

Fine

167 (¼ muhr ashrafi). 2.8 gr.
1193-1206AH..............50.00
168 (¼ toman). *1206-12AH*.... ——

169 (½ toman). *1206-12AH.*
*Kashan. 1209AH......125.00
170 (toman). *1206-12AH*.....125.00
171 (2 tomans). *1206-12AH*.... ——
173 (8 tomans). *1206-12AH*.... ——
174 (20 tomans). *1206-12AH*... ——
175 (50 tomans). *1206-12AH*... ——
176 (60 tomans). *1206-12AH*... ——

Baba Khan (=Fath Ali Shah)
1211-12AH (=1797AD)

Silver

VG-F

180 (300 dinar). 4.61 gr.
Shiraz. AH1212..........10.00

VG-F

181 (rupee=*750* dinar). 11.53 gr.
*Shiraz. 1212...........15.00

Fath Ali Shah
1211-50AH (=1797-1834AD)

Silver

188 (rupee). 11.53 gr. Teheran.
AH1212................17.50
191b (⅛ riyal). 1.30 gr.
1222-32, ND............. 5.00
191c —. 1.15 gr. 1232-41, ND... 6.00
192b (¼ riyal). 2.59 gr.
1222-32................ 2.00
192c —. 2.31 gr. 1232-41...... 2.00
193 (½ riyal). 5.19 gr.
1213-17................ 4.00
193a —. 1217-22............. 4.50
193b —. 1222-32............. 4.00
193c —. 4.61 gr. 1232-41...... 3.50

Isfahan, AH1213.

Tabriz, AH1221.

*194 (riyal =*1250* dinar).
10.37 gr. 1212-17........ 4.75
*194a —. 1217-22............. 5.50
194b —. 1222-32............. 4.75
194c —. 9.22 gr. 1232-41..... 4.75
195 (1500 dinars). 12.6 gr.
1212-32AH............10.00
196 (1½ riyals). 15.8 gr.
1212-32AH............10.00
200 (⅛ qiran). 0.86 gr.
AH1241-50............. 5.00
201 (¼ qiran). 1.73 gr.
1241-45................ 6.00
202 (½ qiran). 3.46 gr.
1241-45................ 5.00

Hamadan, AH1240.

*203 (qiran =1000 dinar). 6.92 gr.
1241-50................ 5.00

Gold

Fine

204a (¼ toman). 1.44 gr.
AH1220-24.............25.00
204d —. 1.15 gr. 1230-45.....20.00
205 (½ toman). 3.07 gr.
1213-17...............40.00
205a —. 2.88 gr. 1220-24....40.00
205b —. 2.69 gr. 1224-27.....45.00
205d —. 2.31 gr. 1230-45....35.00
205e —. 1.73 gr. 1246-50.....45.00

Isfahan, AH1213.

*206 (toman). 6.15 gr.
1213-17...............65.00
206a —. 5.76 gr. 1220-24......60.00
206b —. 5.38 gr. 1224-27......60.00
206c —. 4.80 gr. 1227-29......60.00

Tabriz, AH1244.

*206d —. 4.61 gr. 1230-45......50.00

Teheran, AH1249.

*206e —. 3.46 gr. 1246-50......50.00

V.F.

*207 (toman). 4.6 gr. Zanjan.
1236AH................125.00

Isfahan, AH1249.

*208 (toman). 3.46 gr. 1245,
49 (var.)...............100.00
209 (3 tomans). 17.5 gr.
1220-24AH............. ——
210 (3 tomans). Like No. 207 but
Shah mtd. r. 13.9 gr.
1239AH................400.00
211 (4 tomans). 19.4 gr. *1227-
29AH*.................. ——

PERSIA

V.F.

212 (5 tomans). 29.2 gr. *1220-24AH*. . . . . ——
212a —. 27.2 gr. *1224-27AH*. . . . ——
212b —. 23-24 gr. *1222-44AH*. .150.00
213 (50 tomans). 233.3 gr. *1239-44AH*. . . . . ——
214 (100 tomans). 467 gr. *1239-44AH*. . . . . ——

Sultan Ali Shah
AH1250 (=1834)

Silver and gold coins were struck at Teheran.

Muhammad Shah
1250-64AH (=1834-48AD)

Copper
Good

221 —. Persian legend IRAN.
(See No. 250). 1.50

Silver
VG-F

224a (⅛ qiran). 0.72 gr.
AH1252-55. . . . . 3.50
224b —. 0.67 gr. 1255-64. . . . . . 3.50

Teheran, AH1250.

★225 (¼ qiran). 1.73 gr.
1250-51. . . . . 4.00
225a —. 1.44 gr. 1252-55. . . . . . 4.00
225b —. 1.34 gr. 1255-64. . . . . . 3.00
226 (½ qiran). 3.46 gr.
1250-51. . . . . 3.75
226a —. 2.88 gr. 1252-54. . . . . . 3.75
226b —. 2.69 gr. 1254-64. . . . . . 2.50
227 (qiran = 1000 dinar).
6.91 gr. 1250-51. . . . . 3.50
227a —. 5.76 gr. 1252-55. . . . . . 3.00

Resht, AH1255.

★227b —. 5.38 gr. 1254-64. . . . . . 2.25

★228 (qiran). Lion and sun type.
Teheran. 1258-63. . . . . 5.00
229 (2 qiran). Sim. 10.76 gr.
Teheran. 1263. . . . . .15.00

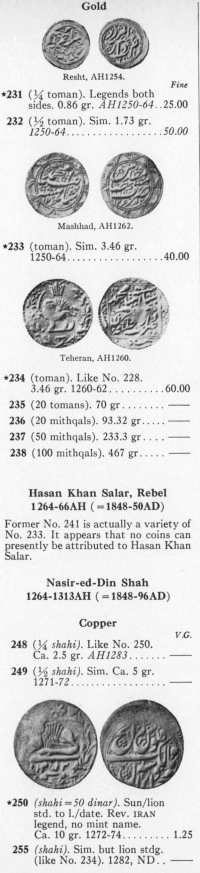

Gold

Resht, AH1254.

Fine

★231 (¼ toman). Legends both
sides. 0.86 gr. *AH1250-64*. .25.00
232 (½ toman). Sim. 1.73 gr.
1250-64. . . . . .50.00

Mashhad, AH1262.

★233 (toman). Sim. 3.46 gr.
1250-64. . . . . .40.00

Teheran, AH1260.

★234 (toman). Like No. 228.
3.46 gr. 1260-62. . . . . .60.00
235 (20 tomans). 70 gr. . . . . ——
236 (20 mithqals). 93.32 gr. . . . . ——
237 (50 mithqals). 233.3 gr. . . . . ——
238 (100 mithqals). 467 gr . . . . . ——

Hasan Khan Salar, Rebel
1264-66AH (=1848-50AD)

Former No. 241 is actually a variety of No. 233. It appears that no coins can presently be attributed to Hasan Khan Salar.

Nasir-ed-Din Shah
1264-1313AH (=1848-96AD)

Copper
V.G.

248 (¼ *shahi*). Like No. 250.
Ca. 2.5 gr. *AH1283*. . . . . . . ——
249 (½ *shahi*). Sim. Ca. 5 gr.
1271-72. . . . . ——

★250 (*shahi = 50 dinar*). Sun/lion
std. to l./date. Rev. IRAN
legend, no mint name.
Ca. 10 gr. 1272-74. . . . . 1.25
255 (*shahi*). Sim. but lion stdg.
(like No. 234). 1282, ND. . ——

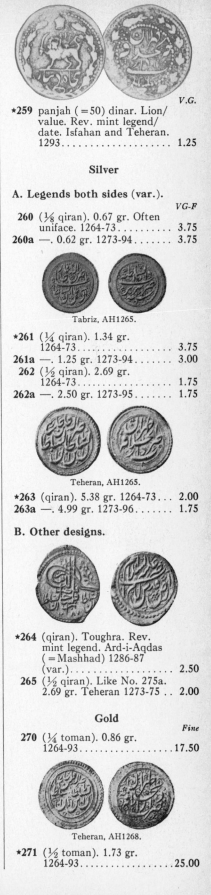

V.G.

★259 panjah (=50) dinar. Lion/
value. Rev. mint legend/
date. Isfahan and Teheran.
1293. . . . . 1.25

Silver

A. Legends both sides (var.).
VG-F

260 (⅛ qiran). 0.67 gr. Often
uniface. 1264-73. . . . . 3.75
260a —. 0.62 gr. 1273-94. . . . . . 3.75

Tabriz, AH1265.

★261 (¼ qiran). 1.34 gr.
1264-73. . . . . 3.75
261a —. 1.25 gr. 1273-94. . . . . . 3.00
262 (½ qiran). 2.69 gr.
1264-73. . . . . 1.75
262a —. 2.50 gr. 1273-95. . . . . . 1.75

Teheran, AH1265.

★263 (qiran). 5.38 gr. 1264-73. . . 2.00
263a —. 4.99 gr. 1273-96. . . . . . 1.75

B. Other designs.

★264 (qiran). Toughra. Rev.
mint legend. Ard-i-Aqdas
(=Mashhad) 1286-87
(var.). 2.50
265 (½ qiran). Like No. 275a.
2.69 gr. Teheran 1273-75 . . 2.00

Gold
Fine

270 (¼ toman). 0.86 gr.
1264-93. . . . . .17.50

Teheran, AH1268.

★271 (½ toman). 1.73 gr.
1264-93. . . . . .25.00

PERSIA

Ard-i-Aqdas (Mashhad), AH1268.

Tabaristan, AH1273.

Fine

272 (toman). 3.46 gr.
1264-93................40.00

*273** (2 toman). 6.92 gr.
Mashhad. 1281.........150.00

275 (toman). Bust facing.
Rev. mint legend. 3.46 gr.
1271...................55.00

Teheran, AH1272.

*275a** —. Sim. but bust turned
slightly l. 1272-75........50.00

276 (2 toman). Like No. 275.
6.92 gr. 1271..........100.00

For the modern coinage of Nasired-Din
Shah, commencing about 1877-78, see
Yeoman, *Modern World Coins*.

PERU

Presently a republic on the west coast of South America. Formerly a Spanish Viceroyalty, liberated by San Martín and Bolívar after strenuous campaigns in the period 1821-25. Peru and neighboring Bolivia (q.v.) had rich silver and gold mines and an extensive coinage.

Monetary System:
16 reales = 1 escudo (scudo) = 2 pesos.

I. Under Spain.

Mint marks:
Lima – LIMA mon. (see No. 22),
  LIMAE mon. (see No. 69),
  L (see No. 91).
Cuzco – C° or CUZ°.

Fernando VI 1746-59

Note: Coins of the old cob type with fictitious mint marks LM or ML and later or fictitious 3 digit dates were struck in Venezuela in the second decade of the 19th century.

Milled Silver

8 (½ real). Like No. 9.   *F-VF*
  1752-60...................17.50

★9 R(eal) I. FRD. VI etc.
  Rev. mmk. at left of date.
  1752-60...................20.00
10 R(eales) 2. Sim. 1752-59....25.00
11 4 (reales). Sim. but FERDND
  VI etc. Rev. mmk. each side
  of date. 1753-60...........175.00
12 8 (reales). Sim. 1752-60.....70.00

Gold (escudo = 3.38 gr.)

A. Large local bust.
                              V.F.
19 I (escudo). Like No. 22 but
  rev. arms not in order chain.
  1751-53....................325.00
20 2 (escudos). Sim.
  1751-53....................425.00
21 4 (escudos). Sim.
  1751-53...................2000.00

                              V.F.
★22 8 (escudos). 1751-53......950.00

B. Medium high-relief bust.

23 (escudo). Like No. 24.
  1754-59....................300.00

★24 (2 escudos). 1758, 59.....400.00
25 (4 escudos). Sim.
  1754-59...................2100.00
26 (8 escudos). Sim. but rev.
  like No. 54. 1754-60......1300.00

Carlos III 1759-88

Silver

A. Pillar Type.

31 (½ real). Like No. 32.   *F-VF*
  1761-72....................12.50

★32 R(eal) I. Like No. 9 but
  CAR. III etc. 1760-72........17.50
33 R(eales) 2. Sim. 1760-72....27.50
34 4 (reales). Sim. but CAROLUS
  III etc. Rev. mmk. each side
  of date. 1760-72...........135.00

                              F-VF
★35 8 (reales). Sim. 1760-72.....65.00

B. Bust Type.
                              Fine
41 (½ real). Like No. 43.
  1772-88.....................2.50
42 1 R(eal). Sim. 1772-89......3.00

★43 2 R(eales). Rev. mmk.
  LIMAE mon. follows REX.
  1772-89.....................5.00
                              F-VF
44 4 R(eales). Sim. 1773-88....60.00
45 8 R(eales). Sim. 1772-89....25.00

Gold (escudo = 3.4 gr.)

A. Small Bust.
                              V.F.
51 (escudo). Obv. like No. 54.
  Rev. like No. 24. 1761-62.....RR
52 (2 escudos). Sim. 1761-62.....RR
53 (4 escudos). Sim. 1761-62.....RR

★54 (8 escudos). Sim. but rev.
  manifold arms in order chain.
  1761-62...................950.00

PERU

B. Young Standard Bust.

V.F.

55 (escudo). CAR. III etc. Rev. IN UTROQ. FELIX, 4 fold arms. 1765-72........RR

56 (2 escudos). Sim. but CAROLUS III etc., rev. IN UTROQ... DEO. 1765-72..............RR

57 (4 escudos). Sim. 1764-70.....RR

★58 (8 escudos). Sim. but rev. manifold arms in order chain. 1763-72................1000.00

C. Older Standard Bust.

59 1 S(cudo). Like No. 62. 1772-89.................200.00

60 2 S(cudos). Sim. 1772-89....400.00

61 4 S(cudos). Sim. 1777-88...950.00

★62 8 S(cudos). Sim. 1771-89...700.00

Carlos IV 1788-1808

Silver

A. Bust of Carlos III.

F-VF

65 (½ real). Like No. 69. 1789-91.................. 7.50

66 1 R(eal). Sim. 1789-91.....12.50

67 2 R(eales). Sim. 1789-91....10.00

68 4 R(eales). Sim. 1789-91....75.00

★69 8 R(eales). Like No. 43 but CAROLUS IV etc. 1789-91.................35.00

B. Bust of Carlos IV.

70 (¼ real). CAROLUS IIII DEI G., head. Rev. HISPAN. ET IND. REX, mmk., arms like No. 24. 1792-95........50.00

72 (½ real). Like No. 76. 1791-1808................. 3.50

73 1 R(eal). Sim. 1791-1806.... 4.00

74 2 R(eales). Sim. 1791-1808.. 5.00

75 4 R(eales). Sim. 1791-1807..25.00

★76 8 R(eales). Bust ★. Rev. like No. 69. 1791-1808......12.50

C. Castle/Lion.

78 ¼ (real). Like No. 91. 1796-1808................. 7.50

Gold

A. Bust of Carlos III.

V.F.

81 1 S(cudo). Like No. 62 but CAROL. IV etc. 1789-91.....250.00

82 2 S(cudos). Sim. 1790-91..400.00

83 4 S(cudos). Sim. 1789, 91..950.00

84 8 S(cudos). Sim. 1789-91...600.00

B. Bust of Carlos IV.

85 1 S(cudo). Sim. but CAROL IIII and his bust. 1792-1808....150.00

86 2 S(cudos). Sim. 1792-1808.350.00

87 4 S(cudos). Sim. 1792-1807.700.00

88 8 S(cudos). Sim. 1792-1807.500.00

Fernando VII 1808-33, In Peru 1808-24, 26

Silver

A. Castle/Lion.

F-VF

★91 ¼ (real). L–castle–¼. Rev. lion. 1809-23......... 7.50

B. Local Draped Bust.

92 (½ real). Like No. 96. 1810-11......................12.50

93 1 R(eal). Sim. 1810-11......17.50

94 2 R(eales). Sim. 1809-12....10.00

95 4 R(eales). Sim. 1808-11....37.50

★96 8 R(eales). Bust. Rev. Arms. 1808-11..................17.50

PERU

C. Standard Draped Bust.

F-VF

97 (½ real). Like No. 101. 1812-21 . . . . 3.50

98 1 R(eal). Sim. 1812-23 . . . . . . 4.00

98a —. Cuzco Mint. 1824 . . . . . 100.00

99 2 R(eales). Sim. 1812-21 . . . . 5.00

99a —. Cuzco Mint. 1824 . . . . . 150.00

99b —. 1826 . . . . 400.00

No. 99b was struck in Callao by Royalists prior to final capitulation on Jan. 22, 1826.

100 4 R(eales). Sim. 1812-21 . . . 15.00

F-VF

★101 8 R(eales). Bust ★. Rev. like No. 69. 1810-24 . . . . 15.00

101a —. 1824. Cuzco Mint 85.00

Gold

A. Local Uniformed Bust.

V.F.

105 1 S(cudo). Like No. 108. 1809-12 . . . . 250.00

106 2 S(cudos). Sim. 1809-11 . . . . RR

107 4 S(cudos). Sim. *1809-11* . . . . RR

★108 8 S(cudos). 1808-12 . . . . . 900.00

B. Laureate Draped Bust.

Nos. 110-113a use the standard bust intended for silver coins.

V.F.

110 1 S(cudo). Obv. like No. 101. Rev. like No. 108. 1812-14 . . . . 200.00

111 2 S(cudos). Sim. 1812-13 . . 400.00

112 4 S(cudos). Sim. Large bust. 1812 . . . . 850.00

112a —. Small bust (ca. 19mm. tall). 1812-13 . . . . 750.00

★113 8 S(cudos). Sim. Large bust (ca. 29mm. tall). 1812 . . . . 650.00

113a —. Small bust (ca. 25mm. tall). 1812-13 . . . . 550.00

C. Laureate Undraped Bust.

★115 (½ scudo). 1815-21 . . . . . . 125.00

116 1 S(cudo). Like No. 119a. 1814-12. LIMAE mon. 150.00

117 2 S(cudos). Sim. 1814-21 . . 250.00

118 4 S(cudos). Sim. 1814-21 . . 600.00

119 8 S(cudos). Sim. 1814-21. LIMAE mon 600.00

V.F.

★119a —. 1824. C(uzc)° 1500.00

Silver

Fine

★120 (ex 125a) 8 R(eales). No. 125 (republican issue) cmkd. crown/1824 by royalists . . . 100.00

II. Republic 1822-35, 39 onward.

Mints:
Lima, Arequipa, Cuzco, Pasco.

A. Provisional Issues.

Copper

★121 ¼ (real). 1822-23 . . . . 8.50

★122 OCTAVO/DE (= ⅛) PESO. 1823 . . . . 4.00

123 QUARTO/DE (= ¼) PESO. Sim. 1823 . . . . 4.00

Silver

PERU

F-VF

★125 8 R(eales). POR LA VIRTUD Y LA JUSTICIA. Virtue and Justice stdg. Rev. PERU LIBRE, arms. 1822-23 . . . . 45.00

See No. 120 for this coin cmkd. crown/ 1824 by royalists.

B. Regular Issues.

Note: In this section, suffix numbers 1 through 4 have been added to the original type numbers, to distinguish more clearly the four mints, and to provide for the listing of more varieties.

1. Lima Mint.

Silver

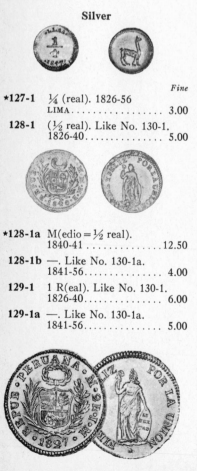

Fine

★127-1 ¼ (real). 1826-56 LIMA 3.00

128-1 (½ real). Like No. 130-1. 1826-40 . . . . 5.00

★128-1a M(edio = ½ real). 1840-41 . . . . 12.50

128-1b —. Like No. 130-1a. 1841-56 . . . . 4.00

129-1 1 R(eal). Like No. 130-1. 1826-40 . . . . 6.00

129-1a —. Like No. 130-1a. 1841-56 . . . . 5.00

Fine

★130-1 2 R(eales). Obv. mmk. LIMA mon. follows PERUANA. 1825-40 . . . . 3.00

★130-1a —. Obv. with fineness 10DS 20GS added. 1840-56 . . . . 6.00

V.F.

131-1a 4 R(eales). Sim. 1842-56 . . . . 10.00

132-1 8 R(eales). Like No. 130-1. Rev. small Liberty stdg. 1825-28 . . . . 32.50

132-1a —. Large Liberty stdg. 1828-40 . . . . 27.50

132-1b —. Like No. 130-1a. 1840-41 . . . . 45.00

132-1c (ex 139) —. Sim. but modified dies. 1841-55 . . 27.50

Gold

141-1 (½ escudo). Like No. 141-3 (Cuzco) but LIMA. 1826-33, 39-56 . . . . 95.00

The above type dated 1838 was struck under North Peru. See No. 151.5.

142-1 1 E(scudo). Like No. 145-1. 1826-29 . . . . 150.00

142-1a —. *Obv. with fineness 21Qs. 1850, 55* 200.00

143-1 2 E(scudos). Like No. 145-1. 1826-29 . . . . 275.00

143-1a —. Like No. 145-1b but LIMA in monogram. *1850-55* 200.00

144-1 4 E(scudos). Like No. 145-1. 1828 . . . . Rare

144-1a —. Like No. 145-1a but LIMA in monogram. *1850-54* 450.00

144-1b —. Like No. 145-1b. 1855 . . . . 400.00

V.F.

★145-1 8 E(scudos). REPUBLICA PERUANA. LIMA mon. Arms divide value. 1826-33 . . . . 650.00

145-1a —. REPUBLICA PERUANA. LIMA. 8E. 21 QS. 1853-54 . . . . 500.00

145-1b —. REPUB. PERUANA. LIMA etc. 1855 . . . . 500.00

2. Arequipa Mint.

Silver

VG-F

127-2 (ex 127b) ¼ (real). Like No. 127-1. 1839 AREQUIPA 40.00

128-2 (ex 128b) (½ real). Like No. 130-1. 1836 AREQ. 10.00

131-2 (ex 131b) 4 R(eales). Sim. 1836-40 AREQ 17.50

V.F.

132-2 (ex 132b) 8 R(eales). Sim. 1839-40 AREQ . . . 1000.00

132-2a —. Obv. with fineness added (like No. 130-1a). 1841 AREQ 2250.00

3. Cuzco Mint.

Mint marks:
CUZCO, CUZo (Zo in monogram).

Silver

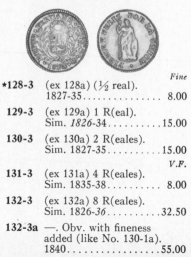

Fine

★128-3 (ex 128a) (½ real). 1827-35 . . . . 8.00

129-3 (ex 129a) 1 R(eal). Sim. *1826*-34 . . . . 15.00

130-3 (ex 130a) 2 R(eales). Sim. 1827-35 . . . . 15.00

V.F.

131-3 (ex 131a) 4 R(eales). Sim. 1835-38 . . . . 8.00

132-3 (ex 132a) 8 R(eales). Sim. 1826-*36* 32.50

132-3a —. Obv. with fineness added (like No. 130-1a). 1840 . . . . 55.00

PERU

Gold

V.F.

*★141-3** (ex 141a) (½ escudo).
1826, *33* 100.00

142-3 (ex 142a) 1 E(scudo).
Like No. 145-1 (Lima).
1826, 30, *38* 175.00

142-3a —. Obv. with fineness
21Q^S. 1840, 45, *46* 150.00

145-3 (ex 145a) 8 E(scudos).
Like No. 145-1 (Lima).
1826-39 . . . . .600.00

145-3a —. Like No. 145-1a.
1840-*53* 550.00

4. Pasco Mint.

Mint marks:
PASCO, P^O, PAZu (Zo in monogram).

Silver
Fine

130-4 (ex 130c) 2 R(eales).
Like No. 131-4a.
1843 P^O 350.00

131-4 (ex 131c) 4 R(eales).
Like No. 130-1 (Lima)
but REPUBLICA etc.
1844-*45* PASCO 27.50

131-4a —. Like No. 131-4c
but REPUB. etc.
1843-44, *55* 20.00

*★131-4c** —. REP. PERUANA etc.,
with fineness 10D^S. 20G^S.
1844, 55, *56*, 57 PASCO . .15.00

132-4 (ex 132c) 8 R(eales).
Like No. 130-1 (Lima).
1836 PASCO . . . . .RRR

132-4a —. Like No. 131-4a.
1857 PASCO 1750.00

III. Divided Peru.

During the period 1835-39 Peru was
divided into two republics. North
Peru remained independent and
South Peru entered into a confederation with Bolivia.

A. North Peru (Estado Nor-
Peruano).

Mint: Lima.

Silver
Fine

147 (½ real). Like No. 130 but
obv. EST. NOR-PERUANO.
1836-38 . . . . .25.00

147a —. REP. NOR-PERUANA.
1839 . . . . .200.00

148 1 R(eal). Like No. 147.
1838 . . . . .RRR

149 2 R(eales). Sim. 1837 . . . . . .RRR

151 8 R(eales). Sim. 1836-39 . . .27.50

151a —. REP. NOR-PERUANA.
1839 . . . . .550.00

Gold
V.F.

151.5 (½ escudo). Like No.
141-1. 1838 LIMA *500.00*

152 1 E(scudo). Like No. 145 but
obv. ESTADO NOR-PERUANO.
Arms. 1838 . . . . .1000.00

153 2 E(scudos). Sim. 1838 . .1500.00

154 4 E(scudos). Sim. 1838 . .4000.00

*★155** 8 E(scudos). Sim. 1838 . .3000.00

B. South Peru (Estado Sud Peru-
ano, Republica Sud Peruana).

Mints: AREQ(uipa); CUZCO.

Arequipa Silver

V.F.

*★171** ½/REAL. 1837. AREQ 40.00

173 2/REALES. Like No. 171.
1838. AREQ 25.00

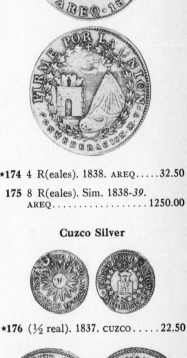

*★174** 4 R(eales). 1838. AREQ 32.50

175 8 R(eales). Sim. 1838-*39*.
AREQ 1250.00

Cuzco Silver

*★176** (½ real). 1837. CUZCO 22.50

*★178** 2/REALES. 1837. CUZCO . . .15.00

180 8 R(eales). Like No. 174
but FEDERACION. CUZCO.
1837 . . . . .85.00

180a —. CONFEDERACION. 1837-
39 .65.00

Gold

181 ½/ESCUDO. REPUB. SUD
PERUANA. Sun. Rev. value.
1838 . . . . .175.00

PERU

V.F.

★182 1/ESCUDO. Sim. 1838...250.00

183 8 E(scudos). Like No. 184
but ESTADO SUD PERUANO etc.
1837. CUZCO...........1000.00

★184 8 E(scudos). 1837-39....1000.00

UNVERIFIED DATA

Note: Throughout this catalog, any uncertain, indefinite or unconfirmed information is shown in *italic type*. Such material may be, for example, coin descriptions, dates and prices, names of rulers, or supplementary notes. Further information to confirm or correct *material in italics* should be sent to the author at the following address:

William D. Craig
c/o Whitman Coin Supply Division
1220 Mound Avenue
Racine, Wisconsin 53404, U.S.A.

NOTES

PHILIPPINE ISLANDS (FILIPINAS)

Group of islands lying north of Indonesia. Spanish colony until 1898.

Monetary System:
8 octavos = 4 quartos = 1 real;
8 reales = 1 peso.

Carlos III 1759-88

Copper

V.F.

*1 B(arilla) I. CIUDAD D MAN(ila), cwnd. castle. Rev. lion with dolphin tail. 1766 ....500.00

G-VG

2 (octavo). Like No. 3. (circa 1782-83) 175.00

3 (quarto). Like No. 12 but CAR. III. 22mm. 1771-83....70.00

Carlos IV 1788-1808

Silver

Fine

6 (¼ real). Castle. Rev. lion. No inscription, date or mint mark. (circa 1788-90)......20.00

Vicenti assigns this type to Venezuela in the reign of Fernando VII.

Copper

G-VG

11 *(octavo). Like No. 12. 1805-06*...................25.00

*12 (quarto). 1798-1807.......17.50

Fernando VII 1808-33

Copper

Fine

21 (octavo). Like No. 12, but 19mm. 1820-30...........40.00

G-VG

22 (quarto). Sim. but 22mm. 1817-30..................15.00

*24 1 Q(uarto). 1822-23.......30.00

G-VG

*27 1 Q(uarto). 1834..........20.00

28 2 Q(uartos). Sim. 1834....125.00

29 4 Q(uartos). Sim. 1834....150.00

Silver

VG-F (cmk.)

*39 (peso). HABILITADO etc. Arms. Rev. MANILA/1828. Struck over foreign dollars............150.00

39a —. Same, but defective cmk. w/out legends around Spanish arms.....................90.00

VG-F (cmk.)

*41 (peso). Foreign dollars cmkd. like No. 39. but MANILA/ 1830.......................RRR

*42 (peso). F7° cmk. on foreign dollars, usually from Peru. Cmk. applied 1832-34......25.00

Notes regarding Nos. 42 and 54.

1. Values vary according to the coin itself, plus the counterstamp.

2. These cmks. are also found on both gold and minor silver coins. Such specimens are very rare.

3. Both cmks. have been extensively counterfeited.

Isabel II 1833-68

Copper

V.G.

51 1 Q(uarto). Like No. 52. 1835...................150.00

*52 2 Q(uartos). 1835..........85.00

53 4 Q(uartos). Sim. 1835....150.00

PHILIPPINE ISLANDS

Silver

VG-F (cmk.)

*54 (peso). Y-II cmk. on foreign dollars, usually from Peru. Cmk. applied 1834-37......20.00

POLAND

An elective monarchy in Eastern Europe. First attributable coins struck under Miseco I 963-92.

The Polish state was paralyzed by the *liberum veto*, or constitutional requirement of unanimity for passage of legislation in the Diet (legislature). As a result of this paralysis, Poland was swallowed up by Russia, Prussia and Austria in three partitions, 1772, 1793 and 1795.

During the Napoleonic era considerable shuffling of Polish territory occurred. Most of the Russian portion was given independence as the Grand Duchy of Warsaw 1807-14 (enlarged at Austrian expense 1809).

In 1815 much of the Grand Duchy was converted into the so-called "Congress Kingdom" of Poland, under Russian suzerainty. This area was reduced to the status of a Russian province after the unsuccessful revolt of 1830-31.

Subsequently, coins were struck showing both Polish and Russian denominations. These were supplanted by Russian coins struck at the Warsaw Mint. After the 1863 revolt, Poland disappeared from numismatic view until the First World War. Warsaw Mint closed 1867.

Before the first partition the Polish kingdom occupied about 284,000 square miles and contained over 12 million inhabitants. Russian Poland covered 49,000 square miles, and during the first half of the 19th century, had a population of about 6 million.

Monetary System:

Before 1815:

solidus = schilling;

3 solidi = 2 poltura = 1 grosz (grossus or copper groschen);

3 poltura = 1½ grosze = 1 polturak (drei polker);

6 groszy = 1 szostak;

18 groszy = 1 tympf;

30 groszy = 4 silbergroschen = 1 zloty (Polish gulden);

6 zlotych = 1 Reichsthaler (talar);

8 zlotych = 1 Speciesthaler;

5 Speciesthaler = 1 August d'or;

9⅔ (1733-63) to 18 (1787-94) zlotych = 1 ducat;

3 ducats = 1 Stanislaus d'or.

1815 onward:

30 groszy = 15 Russian kopecks = 1 zloty;

10 zlotych = 1½ rubles.

Arms:

Poland: Eagle; Lithuania: Horseman.

Augustus III
(= Elector Friedrich August II of Saxony) 1733-63

His Polish coins call him Augustus III. See GERMANY (Saxony) for those with Fridericus Augustus.

Copper

		V.G-F
1 (solidus). Like No. 2a. 15-16mm. 1749-55		2.25
2 3 (solidi). Sim. 22mm. 1752-55, 58		2.50

*2a (3 solidi). H in lieu of 3. 19-20mm. 1754-55......... 1.50

Billon

		V.G.
3 PUL/TO/RAK. Arms. Rev. value. 1753		4.50
4 *PULTORAK.* Cwnd. bust. Rev. eagle. 1755-56		6.00
5 ½ Sz(ostak = 3 grosze). Like No. 12. 1753		5.00
6 3 (grosze). Sim. 1753-54, 56		2.25

V.G.

7 SZ(ostak = 6 groszy). Sim. 1753..................... 9.00

8 VI (groszy). Sim. 1753-56... 3.25

8a —. 1754-55 with error IV... 6.50

*9 T(ympf = 18 groszy). 1752-53, 55.............. 10.00

10 18 (groszy). Sim. 1753-56... 6.50

Silver

F-VF

11 XXX GROS(zy). Cwnd. bust. Rev. value in wreath. 1762.....................Rare

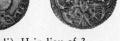

*12 8 (silber) GR(oschen = 2 zlote). 1753, 56, 61-62.....(VF-EF) 9.00

12a —. 1753. W/out 8 GR......Rare

13 LX GROS(zy). Cwnd. bust. Rev. cwnd. arms in 3 shields. 1762.................Very Rare

14 III EINEN THALER (= 2 zlote). Sim. 1762......Very Rare

15 (4 zlotych). Like No. 12. 35mm. 1753-55...........25.00

16 (8 zlotych). Sim. 42mm. 1753-56..................60.00

The 1762 is a pattern.

Gold (ducat = 3.49 gr.)

21 ½ *(ducat).* Bust. Rev. Arms. 1750 FWoF..............950.00

22 (ducat). Like No. 26. 1752-54, 56-57...........750.00

23 (2 ducats). Sim. 1753-54..1500.00

24 2½ TH(aler). Sim. 1753...600.00

25 5 TH(aler). Sim. 1753-56..700.00

25a "Ephraimiten" (Prussian copy in base gold). 1755-56, 58. (Struck 1758-61)........... ——

POLAND

F-VF

*26 10 TH(aler). 1753-54, 56..1200.00

26a —."Ephraimiten" 1755.
(Struck 1758-)............ ——

Stanislaus Augustus
(Poniatowski) 1764-95

Copper

VG-F

33 1/SOLID(us). Like No. 34.
1766-68, 76, 92........... 2.25

33a —. N.D.............Very Rare

*34 ½/GROSSUS (=½ grosz).
SAR mon. Rev. value. 1766-
82.................... 2.25

35 POL/GROSZA (=½ grosz).
Sim. but with Z MIEDZI KRAIOW
(="of native copper," i.e.,
mining coin). 1786, 92...... 7.50

36 GROSSVS POLONICVS
(=grosz). STA:/NISLAUS. . . .
Rev. Arms. 1765......Very Rare

37 I GROSSVS (=grosz). SAR mon.
Rev. cwnd. arms. 1765..Very Rare

38 I GROSSVS (=grosz).
Sim. but arms in wreath.
1765-95................. 2.00

39 I GROSSVS. Sim. but with
MIEDZI KRAIOWEY (=mining
grosz). 1786-88........... 6.00

40 GROS III (=3 grosze). Like
No. 41. 1765.............Rare

41 GROSSVS POLON:TRIPLEX
(=3 grosze). Bust. Rev. Arms.
1765-66................. 4.50

VG-F

*41a —. Head. 1766-95........ 2.25

The 3 grosze size pieces of 1767 with
head, rev. legend, are rare presentation
jetons.

43 TROIAK etc. (=3 grosze).
Head. Rev. TROIAK MIEDZI etc.
Arms (=mining coin). 1786-
95..................... 7.50

Billon (Silver)

Note: The 6 and 18 (groszy) silver of
1766 with bust, rev. arms, are rare patterns.

V.G.

46 6/GROSZY. Arms. Rev. value.
**Struck by Kosciuszko from
"Krakow Saints."** 1794-
95..................... 3.50

47 1 (silber) GR(oschen =7½
groszy). SAR in square. Rev.
320/EX/etc. on tablet.
1766-82................. 3.00

*48 10/GR(oszy). 1787-95...... 3 00

49 2 (silber) GR(oschen =15
groszy). Arms. Rev. 2. GR./
CLX. EX/etc. 1766-86........ 2.50

Silver

F-VF

*50 4 (silber) GR(oschen =
1 zloty). 1766-86........... 4.50

51 4 GR (=1 zloty). Sim. but
ptd. shield and 83½ EX etc.
1787-94................. 5.00

52 4 GR (=1 zloty). Sim. but
84½ EX etc. 1793-95...... 6.00

53 8 GR (=2 zlote). Like No. 50
but XL EX etc. 1766-85...... 6.50

54 8 GR (=2 zlote). Like No. 51
but 41¾ EX etc. 1787-94.... 7.50

55 8 GR (=2 zlote). Sim. but
42½ EX etc. 1794-95......10.00

56 XX EX etc. (=4 zlotych).
Like No. 50. 1767-84......17.50

F-VF

57 20⅞ EX (=4 zlotych). Like
No. 51. 1788, 92...........20.00

58 6 ZL(otych). Like No. 52.
1794-95..................32.50

59 (8 zlotych). By Morikofer.
1765.................Very Rare

60 TALERVS POLONICVS
(=8 zlotych). 1766....Very Rare

61 (8 zlotych). Rev. 2 allegorical
figures. 1766..........Very Rare

Nos. 59-61 are probably patterns or
medals.

62 X EX etc. (=8 zlotych). Bust.
Rev. Arms. 1766..........60.00

63 X EX etc. (=8 zlotych).
Like No. 50. 1768-85
(2 var.)..................40.00

64 10⁷⁄₁₆ EX etc. (=8 zlotych).
Like No. 51. 1788, 92......40.00

V.F.

65 10⁷⁄₁₆ EX etc. (=8 zlotych).
GRATITUDO etc. 9 lines in wreath.
Rev. value, DECRETO/etc. 1793.
Convention of Targowitz...100.00

Gold (ducat =3.49 gr.)

F-VF

66 DVCAT. Bust. Rev. Arms.
1765...................950.00

67 (ducat). SAR mon. in star.
Rev. MON AUR POLONIC. Arms.
1766...................900.00

68 (ducat). Head. Rev. MON.
AUR. POLON etc. on tablet.
1766...................900.00

69 (ducat). King stdg. Rev. as
last. 1766-72.............550.00

70 (ducat). Head. Rev. tablet.
1772-79.................450.00

71 (ducat). Head. Rev. NUMMUS/
etc. in wreath. 1779-95.....400.00

72 1½ (ducats). Like No. 73.
1794...................800.00

*73 3 (ducats). 1794........1750.00

In addition to the regular coinage
of this reign, there exists a series of
patterns with Latin mottos, dated
1771, and a pattern ducat of 1791.

POLAND

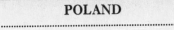

GRAND DUCHY OF WARSAW

Friedrich August I, King of Saxony, As Grand Duke 1807-14

Copper
                                     VG-F

81 1/GROSZ. Like No. 82. 1810-14................. 3.50

*82 3/GROSZE. 1810-14...... 3.50

Billon

83 5/GROSZY. Sim. 1811-12... 3.50

84 10/GROSZY. Sim. 1810-15.. 5.00

Silver
                                     F-VF

85 ⅙ TALARA (=zloty). Like No. 87. 1811-14.......... 15.00

86 ⅓ TALARA (=2 zlote). Sim. 1810-14.................20.00

*87 TALAR (=6 zlotych). 1811-15.................50.00

Gold

*88 DUCAT. 1812-13.......1150.00
                                     V.F.

CONGRESS KINGDOM OF POLAND

Alexander I, Czar of Russia, as King 1815-25

Copper
                                     VG-F

*93 1/GROSZ. 1815-22, 24...... 3.00

94 1/GROSZ. Like No. 108. 1822-25................. 5.00

95 3/GROSZE. Like No. 93. 1815-20, 24.............. 4.00

The 1815 and 1824 dates of Nos. 93 and 95 are novodels.

Billon
                                     V.G.

96 5/GROSZY. Like No. 97. 1816-25................. 4.50

*97 10/GROSZY. 1816-25...... 5.00

Silver
                                     F-VF

*98 1 ZLOTY. 1818.......... 12.50

98a —. Struck in collar. 1822-25.................. 7.50

                                     F-VF

99 2 ZLOTE. Sim. 1816-20....10.00

99a —. Struck in collar. 1819-25.................10.00

100 5 ZLOTYCH. Sim. 1816-18..................30.00

*101 10 ZLOTYCH. Obv. sim. Rev. ★. 1820-25.........100.00

Gold
                                     V.F.

102 25 ZLOT(ych). Like No. 98. 1817-19..............1000.00

102a —. Struck in collar. 1822-25..............1000.00

103 50 ZLOT(ych). Sim. 1817-19................500.00

103a —. Struck in collar. 1819-23................500.00

Nicholas (Mikolay) I, Czar of Russia, as King 1825-55

A. With Polish Denominations Only.

Copper
                                     VG-F

104 1/GROSZ. Like No. 108. Mining coin. 1826 (novodel). RR

105 1/GROSZ. Like No. 93. 1828-35................. 2.25

*106 1/GROSZ. Rev. value in wreath. 1835-41... 3.75

106a —. No wreath. 1840.....pattern

107 JEDEN (=1) /GROSZ. Sim. 1840-41..........pattern

107a 1/GROSZ/JEDEN. 1841................pattern

*108 3/GROSZE. Rev. Z MIEDZI KRAIOWEY (=mining coin). 1826-27... 5.00

POLAND

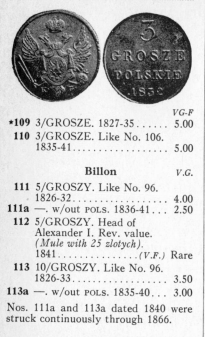

*109 3/GROSZE. 1827-35 . . . . . . 5.00 VG-F
110 3/GROSZE. Like No. 106.
1835-41 . . . . 5.00

Billon   V.G.

111 5/GROSZY. Like No. 96.
1826-32 . . . . 4.00
111a —. w/out POLS. 1836-41 . . . 2.50
112 5/GROSZY. Head of
Alexander I. Rev. value.
(Mule with 25 zlotych).
1841 . . . .(V.F.) Rare
113 10/GROSZY. Like No. 96.
1826-33 . . . . 3.50
113a —. w/out POLS. 1835-40 . . . 3.00

Nos. 111a and 113a dated 1840 were
struck continuously through 1866.

Silver   F-VF

114 1/ZLO(ty). Like No. 119.
1827-34 . . . . 8.00
115 2/ZLO(te). Sim. 1826,
28, 30 . . . . 10.00

*116 5 ZLOTYCH. 1829-34 . . . . . 20.00   V.F.
117 10 ZLOTYCH. Sim.
1827 . . . . 1000.00

Gold

118 25/ZLO(tych). Like No. 119.
1828-33 . . . . 1000.00

---

*119 50/ZLO(tych). 1827, 29 . .1000.00   V.F.

Insurrection of 1830-31 Revolutionary Coinage

Copper   Fine

120 3/GROSZE. Like No. 123.
1831 . . . . 4.00

Billon   VG-F

121 10/GROSZY. Sim. 1831 . . . 3.00

See Zamosc for somewhat similar 10
groszy 26mm. 1831.

Silver   V.F.

122 1/ZLOTY. Sim. 1831 . . . . . 12.50

*123 2/ZLOTE. 1831 . . . . 17.50
124 5/ZLOT(ych). Sim. 1831 . . .40.00

Gold

125 (ducat). Knight. Rev. MO AUR/
REG BELGII/etc. on tablet.
(Type of Netherlands No. 85.)
Polish eagle beside knight's
head. 1831 . . . . .300.00

Reign of Nicholas I (continued)

B. Series with both Polish and Russian Denominations.

Silver

The 10 groszy/5 kopecks and 20 groszy
/10 kopecks pieces of 1842 are patterns.

129 1/ZLOTY = 15 kopecks.   Fine
Like No. 132. 1832-41 . . . . . 8.00
130 40/GROSZY = 20/kopecks.
Sim. but values in wreath.
1842-50 . . . . 10.00
131 50/GROSZY = 25/kopecks.
Sim. but Russian legend on
obv. 1842-50 . . . . 15.00

*132 2/ZLOTE = 30/kopecks.
1834-41 . . . . .13.50

---

133 5/ZLOT(ych) = ¾ ruble.   F-VF
Like No. 131. 1833-41 . . . .20.00
134 10/ZLOT(ych) = 1½ rubles.
Sim. 1833-41 . . . . .35.00

For the 1½ ruble/10 zlotych of 1835-
36 with Nicholas' head, rev. heads of
Czarina and children, see RUSSIA No.
172.

Gold   V.F.

136 20/ZLOTYCH = 3 rubles.
Like No. 132. 1834-41 . . .1000.00

**For Russian coins struck at War-
saw Mint (mint marks B.M. and
M.W.), see RUSSIA.**

POLAND — CITIES AND STATES

COINS OF CITIES AND STATES IN POLAND

Monetary System: Same as Poland
except where otherwise indicated.

CRACOW. See Krakow.

CURLAND (COURLAND, KURLAND), Duchy

The duchies of Curland and Semgallia
were situated on the Baltic between
Memel and Riga. They were carved
out of lands belonging to the Livonian
Order of Knights, for the benefit of
Gotthard Kettler, the Order's last Land
Master, who placed himself under Polish suzerainty in 1561. He became first
hereditary duke of Curland 1563-87.

In 1741 Ernst Johann Biron, duke
of Curland, was exiled to Siberia and
his duchy annexed to Russia 1741-59.
Russian coinage for Livonia-Esthonia
(see RUSSIA) circulated in Curland
during this period.

Carl of Saxony-Poland, Duke of Curland 1759-62

Copper   V.G.

1 SOLID(us). Bust. Rev. 2
oval shields. 1762 . . . . .12.50

Billon   G-VG

3 *GROSSUS (= grosz).* Like
No. 5 but Rev. MONET. ARGENT
under the arms H/C–1762-s . .15.00
5 VI (groszy). D. G. CAROL. P.R.P.
ET. S. IN. L. CVR. ET. S. DVX.
Bust. Rev. MON: ARG: DVC.
CVRLAND. 1762. Cwnd. double
arms/c–H–s 22.50

Ernst Johann Biron, Restored 1762-69

Copper   V.G.

9 (solidus). cwnd. mon.
Rev. cwnd. double arms.
1763 . . . . 7.50
10 *(solidus).* Bust. Rev. cwnd.
double arms. 1764 . . . . .12.50

POLAND —
CITIES and STATES

....
CURLAND (Cont.)

Billon
V.G.

13 *GROSSUS (=grosz)*. Cwnd.
EJ mon. Rev. double arms.
1763-65....................13.50

15 3 (grosze). Bust. Rev. double
arms. 1763-64.............17.50

17 VI (groszy). Like No. 15.
1763-65..................22.50

Gold
F-VF

20 *(ducat)*. Bust. Rev. double
arms. 1764.............1250.00

Peter Biron 1769-95

Silver

V.F.

*23 TAL(er) ALB(ertus). 1780.120.00

Gold

25 (ducat). Like No. 23.
1780...................1000.00

**Curland was absorbed by Russia in
1795.**

_____

DANZIG (DANTZIC, GDANSK, GEDANENSIS), City

On the Baltic at the mouth of the
Vistula. Free city under Polish overlordship 1466-1772. City coinage commenced 1455. Overlordship transferred
to Prussia 1772. City formally absorbed into Prussia 1793-1807, 1814-
1919. French Marshal Lefebvre, duke
of Danzig 1807-14.

Arms:
Red, 2 white crosses under crown.

Augustus III of Poland
1733-63

Copper

Fine

*1 SOLID(us). 1753-63....... 4.00

Billon
G-VG

2 GROSSUS TRIPLEX
(=3 grosze). Cwnd. A3R mon.
Rev. Arms supported by lions.
1755-63.................. 3.50

*3 VI (groszy). 1760-63....... 6.50

Silver
VG-F

4 18 (groszy). Sim. 1758-60,
63.....................12.50

5 30 GR(oszy). Sim. 1762-63..15.00

6 2 PR. GULDEN (=2 zlote).
Sim. 1760.........*(Fine)* 100.00

7 Polish 8 GR (=2 zlote).
No. 12 1753 cmkd. with Danzig arms.................27.50

**Examples of Nos. 1-5 in fine silver,
gold, or on non-circular planchets,
are rare patterns.**

Gold

V.F.

*8 (ducat). 1734...........950.00

Stanislaus Augustus of Poland
1764-72

Copper
VG-F

9 SOLID(us). Like No. 1 but
SAR mon. 1765-66..........4.00

Billon
G-VG

10 GROSSUS TRIPLEX
(=3 grosze). Like No. 2 but
SAR mon. 1765-66......... 5.00

*11 VI (groszy). 1764-65...... 7.50

Silver
F-VF

12 60 GR(oszy). Bust. Rev. Arms
supported. 1764, 67......150.00

Gold
VF-EF

13 (ducat). Bust. Rev. as No. 8.
1765.................... ——

Friedrich Wilhelm II of
Prussia 1786-97

Copper
VG-F

14 SOLID(us). Type of No. 9
with SAR mon. 1793........Rare

Friedrich Wilhelm III of
Prussia 1797-1840

Copper

15 I/SCHILLING. FW mon.
Rev. I/DANZIG/SCHILLING/
1801/A.................. 4.00

Marshal Lefebvre,
Duke of Danzig 1807-14

Copper

*16 I/SCHILLING. 1808, 12... 5.00
16a — Date on rev. 1808....... 7.50

*17 EIN/GROSCHEN (=grosz).
1809, 12................. 6.00

**The 5 Einen Danziger Gulden of
1809 is a pattern. Nos. 16-17 in fine
silver are presentation pieces.**

POLAND —
CITIES and STATES

EAST PRUSSIA
(OST PREUSSEN), Duchy

Substantial territory along the Baltic east of Danzig. Formed in 1525 out of remnants of the dominion of the Teutonic Knights. Fell to Brandenburg in 1618. Remained an integral part of Brandenburg and (after 1701) the kingdom of Prussia until 1918. Taken from Germany by Russia after World War II.

Mint marks:
C.S. – Königsberg 1718-43;
A – Berlin 1750-1811;
E – Königsberg 1750-98.

See GERMAN STATES (Prussia) for other similar coins.

Friedrich II the Great, King of Prussia, 1740-86

Billon

V.G.

2 SOLID(us). Like No. 6 but *flowery FR mon.* 1741-43 C.S., 53E................ 3.00

*6 SOLID(us). 1764-86E, 76A................ 2.50

8 I/GROSSUS (=grosz). FRIDERIC BOR.REX, eagle. Rev. value/REGNI/PRUSS/date. 1752-70E................ 3.50

*10 I/GROSSUS (=grosz). 1771-86E............ 3.50

11 DUPLEX (=2)/(GROSSUS). Like No. 8 but FRIDERICUS etc. 1752E.................... *6.00*

12 II/GROSSUS. Sim. 1752-68E............... 4.00

12a —. FRIDERICUS. 1752E...... ——

14 2 (grose). 1773E.......... 4.50

Fine

16 3 (grose = 1 Dütchen). Armored bust. Rev. MON ARG REG PRUS., 2 eagle shields. 1751-54E............... 5.00

17 3 (grose). Bare head. Rev. eagle. 1765E.......... 7.50

18 3 (grose). Cwnd. head. Rev. eagle. 1765-67E....... 5.00

Fine

*21 3 gr(osze). *1771*, 77-86E.... 4.00

Note: Former No. 23 struck at A (Berlin) mint passed in East Prussia for 3 grosze and in Silesia for 3 kreuzer. It is now listed as Silesia No. 24.

23 (ex 25) VI (groszy). Like No. 16. 1752-57, 63E (var.)..... 5.00

24 VI (groszy). Cwnd. armored bust with sword. Rev. like No. 16. 1755E............10.00

Note: Former No. 25a dated 1756-57C is now listed as Silesia No. 28.

26 VI (groszy). FRIDERICUS etc. but cwnd. bust of August III of Poland. Rev. round arms. 1755-56E................ 7.50

28 VI (groszy). Cwnd. head. Rev. MONETA ARGENTEA, eagle. *1764*, 73-77, *84*E.......... 5.00

30 18 (groszy = tympf). Armored bust. Rev. MONETA ARGENT REG PRUSS, eagle. 1751-63E. 8.50

30a —. 1753G.................25.00

32 18 (groszy). Like No. 28. 1764-65E................ 7.00

Russian Occupation of East Prussia 1759-62
Elizabeth, Empress

Silver (lower values billon)

*41 SOLID(us). 1759-61........20.00

42 I/GROSSUS (=grosz). Like No. 43. 1759-61............20.00

*43 II/GROSSUS. 1759-61.....20.00

44 3 (grose). Like No. 46. 1759-61.................20.00

45 VI (groszy). Sim. (var.). 1759-62................25.00

Fine

*46 18 (groszy). 1759-61.......55.00

47 6. EIN. R.TH./COUR. (=1 zloty). Sim. 1761.....50.00

*48 3 EIN R. TH./COUR. (=2 zlote). 1761..........90.00

Friedrich Wilhelm II of Prussia
1786-97

Copper

VG-F

*50 I/SCHILLING. 1787-97E.. 4.00

Billon

51 I/SCHILLING. FWR mon. Rev. value. 1788E......... 5.00

*52 1 GR(osz). Bust. Rev. eagle shield. 1787-98E........... 4.00
The 1798 may not exist.

Friedrich Wilhelm III of Prussia
1797-1840

Copper

53 I/SCHILLING. Like No. 50. 1804-06A................. 2.00

54 I/SCHILLING. Cwnd. F.W. Rev. value/PREUSS. 1810A.................... 2.00

The 1810A schilling with eagle shield is a pattern.

56 ½/GROSCHEN (= ½ grosz). Like No. 58. 1811A........ 3.00

58 1/GROSCHEN (=grosz). Cwnd. oval eagle shield. Rev. value/PREUSS. 1810-11A..................... 3.75

POLAND — CITIES and STATES

EAST PRUSSIA (Cont.)

Billon

		V.G.
60	III (grosze). Bust. Rev. MON. ARGENT., eagle. 1800-07A	3.00
60a	—. 1807-08G	6.00

Nos. 60 and 60a passed for 3 kreuzer in Silesia.

ELBING (ELBLAG), City

Near the Baltic, about 50 miles E.S.E. of Danzig. Free, under Polish overlordship 1454-1772. Had its own coinage 1454-1763. Absorbed by Prussia 1772.

Arms: Parted per fesse silver and black, a cross of the opposite color in each canton.

Augustus III of Poland 1733-63

Copper

		Fine
1	SOLID(us). Cwnd. A3R mon. Rev. SOLID./CIVITAT/ELBING/ arms. 1760-63	7.50

Silver (lower values billon)

		VG-F
*2	GROS(S)US TRIPLEX (=3 grosze). 1761, 63	15.00
3	VI (groszy). Cwnd. bust. Rev. Arms supported by angels. 1762	Very Rare
4	VI (groszy). Sim. but no angels. 1762-63	15.00

		V.F.
5	18 GR(oszy). Sim. 1763	17.50
6	1 T(ympf = 18 groszy). Sim. 1763	20.00

Gold

7	2 DUC(ats). Sim. 1763	V. Rare

GALICIA and LODOMERIA, Kingdom

Portion of South Poland annexed by Austria in 1772.

Monetary System:
6 schillinge (solidi) = 2 grosze = 1 kreuzer.

Maria Theresia of Austria, In Galicia 1772-80

Copper

		Fine
1	1/SCHILLING. Arms of kingdom (see No. 3 rev). Rev. value/1774/S	5.00

Silver

2	15 KR(euzer). Like No. 3. 1775-77	7.50

*3	30 KR(euzer). 1775-77	10.00

Franz II of Austria 1792-1835

Coins for use by the Austrian army fighting Kosciuszko.

Copper

4	I/GROSSUS (=grosz). Like No. 5. 1794	5.00

*5	III/GROSSI (=3 grosze). 1794	5.00

Billon

6	VI/GROSSI (=6 groszy). Sim. 1794	Rare

KRAKOW (KRAKAU, CRACOVIA, CRACOW)

Important city in south Poland.

I. Bishopric.

Cajetan Soltyk, Bishop 1759-82

Gold

		V.F.
5	(ducat). CAI.SO. . . . EPI:CRAC: DVX SEVERIAE. Bust. Rev. MONETA/AUREA/DUCATUS/ SEVERIAE/A. 1762	1000.00

II. Republic.

Small free city established at the Congress of Vienna 1815 as a sop to Polish nationalism. Annexed by Austria 1846.

Billon

11	5/GROSZY Like No. 13 1835	10.00
12	10/GROSZY. Sim. 1835	10.00

Silver

*13	1/ZLOTY. 1835	22.50

Note: The copper 3 grosze and silver 2 zlote of this series are rare patterns.

POSEN, Grand Duchy (= Grosherzogthum)

Western portion of South Prussia, returned to Prussia by the Congress of Vienna in 1815.

Friedrich Wilhelm III of Prussia 1797-1840

Copper

		VG-F
*1	1/GROSCHEN (=grosz). 1816-17A, 16B	3.00
2	3/GROSCHEN (=3 grosze). Sim. 1816-17A, 16B	5.00

SOUTH PRUSSIA (BORUSSIA MERIDIONALIS)

Portion of Poland lying in the angle between West Prussia and Silesia. Annexed by Prussia 1793. Taken by Napoleon for the Grand Duchy of Warsaw 1807.

Copper

1	1/SOLID(us). FWR mon. in cwnd. oval. Rev. value/BOR. MER. 1796-97	3.50

POLAND — CITIES and STATES

SOUTH PRUSSIA (Cont.)

VG-F

2 ½/GROSSUS. Like No. 2a but rev. value/REGNI/ BORUSS/1796 .... 7.50

★2a —. 1796-97 .... 3.50

★3 I GROSSUS. 1796-98 ..... 5.00

4 GROSSUS . . . TRIPLEX (=3 grosze). Sim. BORUSSLÆ TRIPLEX. 1796 .... 8.00

4a —. BORUSS. MERID. TRIPLEX. 1796-97 .... 6.00

Note: Examples of the above in silver are rare presentation pieces.

THORN (THORUN, TORUN), City

Town on the Vistula 92 miles S. of Danzig. Under Polish overlordship 1466-1793, absorbed by Prussia in the latter year. Had its own coinage circa 1466-1766.

Arms: Wall with 3 towers.

Augustus III of Poland 1733-63

Copper

Fine

★1 SOLID(us). 1760-63 .... 7.50

Billon   *VG-F*

2 GROSSUS TRIPLEX (=3 grosze). Cwnd. A3R mon. Rev. angel above arms. 1763 .... 7.50

3 VI (groszy). Cwnd. bust. Rev. angel above arms. 1761-63 .... 20.00

Stanislaus Augustus of Poland 1764-93

Copper

4 SOLID(us). Like No. 1 but SAR mon. 1765 .... 6.00

Billon

VG-F

5 GROSSUS TRIPLEX (=3 grosze). Like No. 2 but SAR mon. 1764-65 .... 7.50

6 VI (groszy). Cwnd. head. Rev. angel above arms. 1765 .... 20.00

ZAMOSC (ZAMOSCIA)

Fortress in S.E. Poland twice besieged by Russians.

I. Siege of 1813.

Coinage of the Saxon-Polish garrison under General Hauke.

Bronze

V.F. (crude)

★1 6/GROSZY. 1813 .... 600.00

Silver

★2 2/ZLOTE. 1813 .... 200.00

2a —. Obv. legend in 4 lines. 1813 .... *500.00*

II. Siege of 1831.

Coinage of the Polish garrison.

Billon   *V.F. (crude)*

6 10 GROSZY. BOZE DOPOMOZ etc. Arms. Rev. W OBLEZENJU ZAMOSCIA. Value. 1831 ...... *RRR*

PORTUGAL, KINGDOM

On the Iberian Peninsula, between Spain and the Atlantic.

Monetary System:
Until 1822:
20 réis =1 vintem;
100 réis =1 Tostão;
480 réis =1 cruzado;
1600 réis =1 escudo;
6400 réis =1 peça or dobra.

After 1822:
7500 réis =1 peça or dobra.
Owing to inflation many Portuguese coins were officially current at more than their face values.

Mint: Lisbon (no mmk.).

For gold coins of Portuguese types with mmks. B(ahia) and R(io), see BRAZIL. See also BRAZIL, MOZAMBIQUE and PORTUGUESE ISLANDS for similar (though not identical) coins in other metals.

José (Josephus) I 1750-77

Copper

VG-F

★1 III (réis). 1751-76 .... 4.00

2 V (réis). Sim. 1751-76 ...... 3.00

2b —. Like No. 3b. 1752 ...... ——

3 X (réis). Sim. 1751-76 ...... 3.00

3a —. 1738, 49 (mules) 15.00

3b —. IOANNES V etc. 1751-52 (mule) 15.00

Silver

Fine

4 (20 réis). Globe. Rev. cross with rosettes in angles. .61 gr. N.D. (1747-1800) 4.00

5 XXXX (=50 réis!) IOSEPHUS I. D. G. PORT etc. Cwnd. value. Rev. IN HOC etc. Cross. N.D. .. 6.00

6 (60 réis). Like No. 8. 1.83 gr. N.D. 5.00

7 LXXX (=100 réis!) Like No. 5. N.D. 10.00

PORTUGAL

F-VF

*8 (120 réis). 3.67 gr. N.D..... 8.00

9 200 (=240 réis!). Sim.
1752-78................20.00

10 400 (=480 réis!). Sim.
1762-75................40.00

Gold

V.F.

(escudo =1600 réis =3.6 gr.)

11 400 (=480 réis!) IOSE/I in
branches, cwnd. Rev. IN HOC
etc. Cross. 1752-76........55.00

12 (½ scudo). IOSEPHUS I D.G.
PORT etc. Bust. Rev. Arms.
1751-76................95.00

13 1000 (=1200 réis!). Like
No. 8. 1752, 68-69........110.00

13a —. 1749 (mule)..........200.00

14 (escudo). Like No. 12.
1751-76................175.00

15 (2 escudos). Sim. 1751-76..400.00

16 (4 escudos). Sim. 1751-76..500.00

Maria I and Pedro (Petrus) III
1777-86
Copper

VG-F

17 III (réis). MARIA I ET PETRUS
III DEI GRATIA. Arms. Rev.
PORTUGAL etc. Value in wreath.
1777-78................5.00

18 V (réis). Sim. 1777-85......4.00

19 X (réis). Sim. 1777-85......2.50

Silver

F-VF

*20 XXXX (=50 réis!). N.D... 4.00

21 (60 réis). MARIA I ET PETRUS
III etc. Arms. Rev. IN HOC etc.
Cross. 1.83 gr. N.D.......5.00

22 LXXX (=100 réis!). Like No.
20. N.D.................7.50

23 (120 réis). Like No. 21.
3.67 gr. N.D.............6.00

24 200 (=240 réis!). Sim.
1779-85................15.00

25 400 (=480 réis!). Sim.
1778-85................30.00

Gold

(escudo =1600 réis =3.6 gr.)

V.F.

26 400 (=480 réis!). MARIA I/ET
P. III in wreath, cwnd. Rev.
IN HOC etc. Cross. 1777-85..100.00

27 (½ escudo). MARIA I ET PETRUS
III. Their busts. Rev. Arms.
1777-84................125.00

28 1000 (=1200 réis!). Like No.
21 but ornate arms. 1777-
84......................150.00

29 (escudo). Like No. 27.
1777-84................200.00

30 (2 escudos). Sim. 1778, 84.400.00

31 (4 escudos). Sim. 1778-85..500.00

Maria I, Alone 1786-99
Copper

VG-F

32 III (réis). Like No. 33.
1797, 99................4.50

*33 V (réis). 1791-99..........3.00

34 X (réis). Sim. 1791-99......3.00

See AZORES for copper 5, 10 and 20
réis of this reign with value in Arabic
numerals, and for silver 75, 150 and
300 réis coins.

Silver

F-VF

35 XXXX (=50 réis!). Like No.
37. N.D.................5.00

36 (60 réis). Like No. 21 but
w/out PETRUS III. 1.83 gr.
N.D.....................5.00

*37 LXXX (=100 réis!). N.D...7.50

38 (120 réis). Like No. 36.
3.67 gr. N.D.............6.00

39 200 (=240 réis!). Sim.
1786-99................22.50

40 400 (=480 réis!). Sim.
1786-99................35.00

Gold

(escudo =1600 réis =3.6 gr.)

V.F.

41 400 (=480 réis!). Like No. 26
but w/out ET P. III.
1787-96................100.00

V.F.

42 (½ escudo). MARIA I D.G. PORT
etc. Bust with widow's veil.
Rev. Arms. 1787-88......350.00

42a —. Jeweled hair dress.
1789-96................200.00

43 1000 (=1200 réis!). Like No.
28 but w/out PETRUS III.
1787-92................150.00

44 (escudo). Like No. 42. 1787.400.00

44a —. Like No. 42a. 1789-96..200.00

45 (2 escudos). Like No. 42a.
1789...................500.00

46 (4 escudos). Like No. 42.
1786-87................600.00

46a —. Like No. 42a. 1789-99..500.00

João (Joannes),
Prince Regent for Maria I
1799-1816

(The Portuguese court was in exile in
Brazil 1807-22.)

Copper

VG-F

48 III (réis). Like No. 50a.
1804...................4.00

49 V (réis). Sim. but legend ends
PRINCEPS. 1800-01.........25.00

49a —. 1799. Rev. legend ends
REGINA. (Mule)...........25.00

49c —. Like No. 50a.
1812-14................5.00

49d —. Obv. No. 33. Rev. No. 49c.
(Mule). 1812.............25.00

50 X (réis). Like No. 49. 1800..30.00

*50a —. 1803-13.............5.00

PORTUGAL

VG-F

51 XX (réis). Like No. 49.
1800 . . . . .25.00

Bronze

★52 40 (réis). 1811-15 . . . . 7.50

Silver

F-VF

53 (20 réis). N.D. See No. 4.

54 XXXX (=50 réis!). JOANNES
D.G.P. PORTUGAL etc. Cwnd.
value. Rev. IN HOC etc. Cross.
N.D 10.00

54a —. JOANNES etc. P. REGENS.
N.D 5.00

55 (60 réis). Like No. 59.
1.83 gr. N.D 7.50

55a —. JOANNES etc. P. REGENS.
N.D 4.00

56 LXXX (=100 réis!). Like No.
54. N.D 15.00

56a —. Like No. 54a. N.D 7.50

57 (120 réis). Like No. 59.
3.67 gr. N.D 15.00

57a —. Like No. 55a. N.D 5.00

58 200 (=240 réis!). Like No.
55a. 1806-16 . . . . .30.00

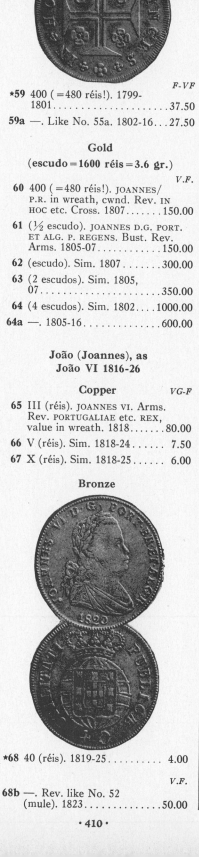

★59 400 (=480 réis!). 1799-
1801 . . . . .37.50

F-VF

59a —. Like No. 55a. 1802-16 . . .27.50

Gold
(escudo = 1600 réis = 3.6 gr.)

V.F.

60 400 (=480 réis!). JOANNES/
P.R. in wreath, cwnd. Rev. IN
HOC etc. Cross. 1807 . . . . . .150.00

61 (½ escudo). JOANNES D.G. PORT.
ET ALG. P. REGENS. Bust. Rev.
Arms. 1805-07 . . . . .150.00

62 (escudo). Sim. 1807 . . . . . . .300.00

63 (2 escudos). Sim. 1805,
07 . . . . .350.00

64 (4 escudos). Sim. 1802 . . . .1000.00

64a —. 1805-16 . . . . .600.00

João (Joannes), as João VI 1816-26

Copper

VG-F

65 III (réis). JOANNES VI. Arms.
Rev. PORTUGALIAE etc. REX,
value in wreath. 1818 . . . . . .80.00

66 V (réis). Sim. 1818-24 . . . . . . 7.50

67 X (réis). Sim. 1818-25 . . . . . . 6.00

Bronze

★68 40 (réis). 1819-25 . . . . 4.00

V.F.

68b —. Rev. like No. 52
(mule). 1823 . . . . .50.00

Silver

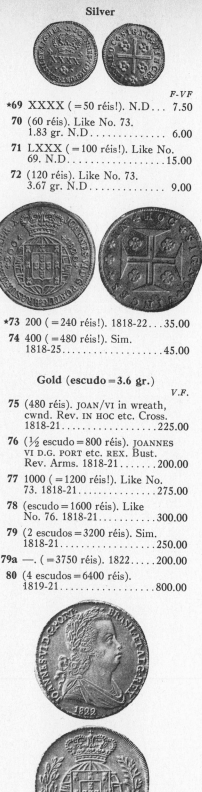

F-VF

★69 XXXX (=50 réis!). N.D . . . 7.50

70 (60 réis). Like No. 73.
1.83 gr. N.D 6.00

71 LXXX (=100 réis!). Like No.
69. N.D 15.00

72 (120 réis). Like No. 73.
3.67 gr. N.D 9.00

★73 200 (=240 réis!). 1818-22 . . .35.00

74 400 (=480 réis!). Sim.
1818-25 . . . . .45.00

Gold (escudo = 3.6 gr.)

V.F.

75 (480 réis). JOAN/VI in wreath,
cwnd. Rev. IN HOC etc. Cross.
1818-21 . . . . .225.00

76 (½ escudo = 800 réis). JOANNES
VI D.G. PORT etc. REX. Bust.
Rev. Arms. 1818-21 . . . . . . .200.00

77 1000 (=1200 réis!). Like No.
73. 1818-21 . . . . .275.00

78 (escudo = 1600 réis). Like
No. 76. 1818-21 . . . . .300.00

79 (2 escudos = 3200 réis). Sim.
1818-21 . . . . .250.00

79a —. (=3750 réis). 1822 . . . . .200.00

80 (4 escudos = 6400 réis).
1819-21 . . . . .800.00

★80a —. (=7500 réis).
1822-24 . . . . .500.00

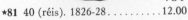

Pedro (Petrus) IV 1826-28

Bronze

VG-F

★81 40 (réis). 1826-28.........12.00

Silver

F-VF

82 (60 réis). PETRUS IV etc. REX. Arms. Rev. IN HOC etc. Cross. 1.83 gr. N.D.............75.00

83 LXXX (=100 réis!). PETRUS IV etc. REX. Cwnd. value. Rev. IN HOC etc. Cross. N.D....125.00

84 (120 réis). Like No. 82. 3.67 gr. N.D...........100.00

85 400 (=480 réis!). Sim. 1826....................100.00

Gold

(escudo = 1875 réis = 3.6 gr.)

V.F.

86 (2 escudos). Like No. 81 but w/out rev. legend. 1827...1000.00

★87 (4 escudos). Sim. 1826, 28..................1250.00

Miguel (Michael) I 1828-34

Copper

VG-F

88 V (réis). Like No. 89. 1829..10.00

★89 X (réis). 1829-33..........12.00

Bronze

★90 40 (réis). 1828-33.........25.00

Silver

V.F.

91 XXXX (=50 réis!). MICHAEL I etc. REX. Cwnd. value. Rev. IN HOC etc. Cross. N.D....15.00

92 (60 réis). Like No. 94. 1.83 gr. ND.............15.00

93 LXXX (=100 réis!). Like No. 91. N.D.............25.00

★94 (120 réis). 3.67 gr. ND.....20.00

95 200 (=240 réis!). Sim. 1829-30...................50.00

96 400 (=480 réis!). Sim. 1828-33................100.00

Gold

(escudo = 1875 réis = 3.6 gr.)

V.F.

97 (2 escudos). Bust. Rev. Arms. 1828.................1250.00

97a —. Diff. dies. Like No. 98a. 1830-31.............800.00

98 (4 escudos). Like No. 97. 1828.................1500.00

★98a —. 1830-31............900.00

Maria II,
Pretender 1828-34, Queen 1834-53

Copper

A. Struck in England.

Fine

99 V (réis). Like No. 100. 1830....................4.00

★100 X (réis). Irregular shield 1830....................4.00

Nos. 99-100 were used in the Azores.

PORTUGAL

B. Struck at Porto.

Fine

99a V (réis). Like No. 99b but shield like No. 102. 1833...75.00

100a X (réis). Sim. 1833.......55.00

Bronze

V.F.

102 20 (réis). Shield pointed at upper corners. Rev. cwn. in wreath/value. 1833.......50.00

103 40 (réis). Sim. but rev. value in wreath/1833.......25.00

C. Struck at Lisbon and Porto.

Fine

★99b V (réis). Shield with square upper corners. 1836.................10.00

100b X (réis). Sim. 1835-37.....10.00

100c —. Struck in collar. 1837-39.................6.00

103a 40 (réis). Sim. 1833-34 (Lisbon), 47 (Porto).......6.00

Fine

★99c V (réis). Ornate shield. 1840-53.................1.50

100d X (réis). Sim. 1840-53.....1.50

101 XX (réis). Sim. 1847-53...2.00

VG-F (cmk. F)

★103b 40 (réis). No. 68, 81, 103 or 103a cmkd. G(overno) C(ivil do) P(orto) in 1847.................15.00

Silver

V.F.

104 100/REIS. Head. Rev. value in wreath. 1836.........100.00

104a —. 1838-53...............15.00

105 200/REIS. Sim. 1836.....100.00

105a —. 1838-48...............25.00

106 400 (=480 réis!). MARIA II etc. REGINA. Arms. Rev. IN HOC etc. Cross. 1833-37....45.00

★107 500 REIS. 1836.........200.00

107a —. 1837-53..............20.00

108 1000 REIS. Sim. 1836...1000.00

108a —. 1837-45..............75.00

Note: Silver coins dated 1836 with plain edges are patterns.

Gold

V.F.

109 1000 REIS. Sim. 1851.....75.00

110 2500 REIS. Sim. 1838....200.00

110a —. 1851, 53............100.00

111 5000 REIS. Sim. 1836....1000.00

111a —. 1838-51............300.00

112 (7500 réis). Bare head. Rev. Arms. 1833........2000.00

★112a —. Diademed head. 1833-35.................800.00

Countermarks

Cmk: cwnd. arms incuse (see No. 99b for style of arms).

Silver

F-VF

113 (870 réis). Spanish and Spanish-American 8 reales of the 18th and early 19th centuries. (cmked. in 1834).........80.00

Gold

Fine

115 20,000 (=30,000 réis). Dobrão of Joannes V. 1724-27 (cmkd. 1847).......2000.00

Pedro (Petrus) V 1853-61

Coins of this reign appear with 4 different heads, juvenile through adult.

Silver

F-VF

116 50/REIS. Cwnd. date. Rev. value. 1855, 61 ......4.00

117 100 REIS. Like No. 118. 1854...................5.00

117a —. 1857-61...............5.00

PORTUGAL

F-VF

*118 200 REIS. 1854-55....... 6.00

118a —. 1858-61............. 6.00

V.F.

*119 500 REIS. 1854......... 12.50

119a —. 1855-56............. 10.00

119b —. 1857-59............. 10.00

Gold

120 1000 REIS. Like No. 119a.
1855.................55.00

121 2000 REIS. Sim. 1856-57..85.00

121a —. 1858-60.............85.00

122 5000 REIS. Like No. 119b.
1860-61................180.00

PORTUGUESE ISLANDS IN THE ATLANTIC

AZORES

Group of islands lying about 1000 miles west of Lisbon.

José I 1750-77

Copper

The III (réis) 1750 like No. 3 is a pattern.....................RRR

F-VF

2 V (réis). Like No. 3.
1750-51.................20.00

3 X (réis). IOSEPHUS I D.G. etc.,
cwnd. pillars/x. Rev. PECUNIA
INSULANA, Portuguese arms.
1750...................15.00

Maria I, Alone 1786-99

Copper

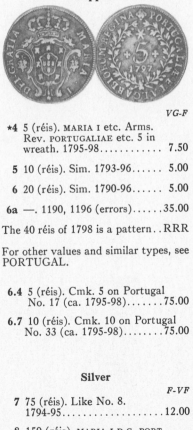

VG-F

*4 5 (réis). MARIA I etc. Arms.
Rev. PORTUGALIAE etc. 5 in
wreath. 1795-98........... 7.50

5 10 (réis). Sim. 1793-96...... 5.00

6 20 (réis). Sim. 1790-96...... 5.00

6a —. 1190, 1196 (errors)......35.00

The 40 réis of 1798 is a pattern..RRR

For other values and similar types, see PORTUGAL.

6.4 5 (réis). Cmk. 5 on Portugal
No. 17 (ca. 1795-98).......75.00

6.7 10 (réis). Cmk. 10 on Portugal
No. 33 (ca. 1795-98)........75.00

Silver

F-VF

7 75 (réis). Like No. 8.
1794-95.................12.00

8 150 (réis). MARIA I D.G. PORT.
ET ALG. REGINA. Arms. Rev. IN
HOC etc. Cross. 1794-98.....15.00

9 300 (réis). Sim. 1794-97.....35.00

João (Joannes), Prince Regent for Maria I 1799-1816

For copper V, X and XX (réis) 1800-01 with rev. legend ending PRINCEPS, see PORTUGAL Nos. 49, 50 and 51.

Insurrection on Terceira Island

Copper

V.G.

9.5 LXXX (réis). AZORES
INDEPEDEN. ILHA TERCEIRA.
Eagle. Rev. fasces/value.
1826....................RRR

Maria II, 1828-53

I. As an Exile on Terceira Island 1828-33.

Cast Gun or Bell Metal

Fine (crude)

*12 80 (réis). MARIA II etc.
Rev. UTILITATE . . . TERCEIRA.
1829...................40.00

See also PORTUGAL Nos. 99 and 100. Other coins of Maria II dated 1829 are patterns.

II. As Reigning Queen of Portugal 1834-53.

Copper

Fine

13 5 (réis). Like No. 14. 1843.. 7.50

PORTUGUESE ISLANDS

....

AZORES (Cont.)

		Fine
★**14**	10 (réis). 1843.............	6.00
15	20 (réis). Sim. 1843.........	6.00

MADEIRA
Group of islands off Morocco.

Maria II 1834-53

Copper

1 V (réis). Like No. 2.
1850...................*pattern*

★**2** X (réis). MARIA·II·D·G·etc.,
Arms. Rev. PECUNIA
MADEIRENSIS, X in
wreath. 1842-52..........10.00

3 XX (réis). Sim. 1842,52.....10.00

UNVERIFIED DATA

Note: Throughout this catalog, any uncertain, indefinite or unconfirmed information is shown in *italic type*. Such material may be, for example, coin descriptions, dates and prices, names of rulers, or supplementary notes. Further information to confirm or correct *material in italics* should be sent to the author at the following address:

William D. Craig
c/o Whitman Coin Supply Division
1220 Mound Avenue
Racine, Wisconsin 53404, U.S.A.

RUSSIA

Empire in Eastern Europe which expanded, during the 18th and 19th centuries, to encompass Siberia and Transcaucasia. Earliest Russian coinage was struck at the beginning of the 11th century.

Monetary System:

¼ kopeck = 1 polushka;
½ kopeck = 1 denezhka (denga);
10 kopecks = 1 grivna (grivennik);
25 kopecks = 1 polupoltina (polupoltinnik);
50 kopecks = 1 poltina (poltinnik);
100 kopecks = 1 ruble;
10 roubles = 1 Imperial.

Legends are in the Cyrillic alphabet. Numbers and denominations appearing on coins, together with their translations, are as follows:

POLUSHKA (= ¼ KOPECK)... ПОЛУШКА
DENGA, DENEZHKA (= ½ K).. ДЕНГА, ДЕНЕЖКА
KOPECK .... КОПѢИКА, (2, 3 or 4) КОПѢИКИ, (5 and up) КОПѢЕКЪ
GRIVNA, GRIVENNIK (= 10K). ГРИВНА, ГРИВЕННИКЪ
POLUPOLTINA POLUPOL-
-TINNIK (= 25K)......... ПОЛУПОЛТИНА, ПОЛУПОЛ-
-ТИННИКЪ
POLTINA POLTINNIK (= 50K). ПОЛТИНА, ПОЛТИННИКЪ
RUBLE (= 100K)........... РУБЛЬ, РУБЛЬ, РУБЛЬ, etc.
ONE .... ОДИН, ОДНА (feminine)
TWO .... ДВА, ДВѢ (feminine)
THREE .... ТРИ
FOUR .... ЧЕТЫРЕ
FIVE .... ПЯТЬ
TEN .... ДЕСЯТЬ
TWENTY .... ДВАДЦАТЬ
FIFTY .... ПЯТЬДЕСЯТ

NOTE: Λ and ȣ are early versions of Л and У, respectively.

Official restrikes and copies were made of many Russian coins – particularly copper – of the 18th and early 19th centuries. These are known as NOVODELS. They are usually found in EF-Unc. condition, and in most cases bring higher prices than the originals. Sometimes *no* original exists.

Elizabeth I 1741-62

Mint marks:

MM or MM△ (Moscow);
СПБ or СПМ (St. Petersburg);
and w/out mint mark.

Copper

Fine

1 polu/shka. Like No. 2.
1743-54 .... 6.00

*2 de/nga. 1743-54 .... 3.00

F-VF

*3 1/kop/eck. Eagle on clouds,
both sides. 1755-57 .... 15.00

Fine

4 polushka. Like No. 6.
1757-59 .... 9.00

5 denga. Sim. 1757-60 .... 6.50

*6 kopeck. 1757-61 .... 5.00
The illustration shows a novodel.

7 two kopecks. Sim. 1757-62 .. 3.00

*8 two kopecks. Sim. but value
above St. George. 1757-60 .. 9.00

9 five kopecks. EP monogram.
Rev. Imp. eagle. 1757-62 ...12.50

Silver

F-VF

*15 5/KOP(ecks). Eagle, cwnd. mon.
Rev. eagle, value in cartouche.
1755-61 .... 7.50

*16 griven/nik. Bust. Rev. cwn./
value. 1742-57 .... 9.00

16.2 15 (kopecks). Bust. Rev.
like No. 62a. 1760 ....RRR

16.5 20 (kopecks). Sim. but 20
in shield on eagle's breast.
1760 ....RRR

Note: Severin calls Nos. 16.2 and 16.5 patterns, but a few are said to have circulated. No. 16.2 of 1761 is a restrike.

*17 polupoltinnik. 1743-58 ......15.00

18 poltina. Sim. 1741-61 ....65.00

19 ruble. Sim. 1741-61.
(4 bust var.) 70.00

Gold Coinage for Russia

V.F.

*21 poltina. Bust. Rev. EP script
mon. 1756 ....100.00

22 ruble. 1756-58 ....150.00

23 two rubles. Sim. 1756, 58 ...185.00

27 five rubles. Like No. 28.
1755-59 ....275.00

RUSSIA

V.F.

★28 ten rubles. 1755-59.......600.00

Gold Trade Coins
(ducat = 3.47 gr.)

30 (ducat). Like No. 22.
1742-53, 57..............185.00

★31 (ducat). 1749-53.........225.00

33 (2 ducats). Like No. 22.
1749, 51................325.00

34 (2 ducats). Like No. 31.
1749, 51................475.00

Other dates, types, and denominations of gold from this reign are patterns, mostly quite rare.

See POLAND (East Prussia) for Russian occupation coins for that area 1759-62.

Peter III 1762

Mint marks:
CIIБ; MM△; and w/out mint mark.

Copper   F-VF

40 denga. Like No. 41.
1762.....................RRR

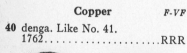

★41 1/–/kopeck. 1762........275.00

42 2/–/kopecks. Sim. 1762.....50.00

43 4/–/kopecks. Sim. 1762.....50.00

44 10/–/kopecks. Imp. eagle.
Rev. value over trophies.
1762....................70.00

Nos. 40-44 are almost always struck over earlier issues. Similar large-scale copper recoinages occurred frequently during the 18th century. Nos. 40-44 of 1760-61 are patterns or restrikes.

Silver   F-VF

46 poltina. Bust (like No. 50).
Rev. Imp. eagle. 1762.....150.00

47 ruble. Sim. 1762.........150.00

The 5, 15 and 20 kopecks silver of this reign, and the rouble with Rev. cwnd. PIIIs cruciform, are all rare patterns.

Gold   V.F.

49 five rubles. Like No. 50.
1762....................475.00

★50 ten rubles. 1762..........800.00

51 (ducat). Bust. Rev. Imp.
eagle. 1762..............450.00

Catherine II (the Great) 1762-96

Mint marks:
AM (Annensk);
EM (Ekaterinenburg);
KM (Kolyvan);
MM or MM△;
CM (Sestroretsk);
CII or CIIБ;
TM (Feodosia, Crimea);
and w/out mint mark.

Copper

Fine

★55 polushka. 1766-96
(★1765 = novodel)..........4.00

56 denga. Sim. 1763-96.......5.00

57 kopeck. Sim. 1763-96......5.50

58 two kopecks. Sim. 1763-96..5.00

59 five kopecks. Obv. sim.
Rev. Imp. eagle. 1763-96...10.00

★59a —. Royal (not Imperial) crowns. Struck by Swedish gov't.
1787............(V.F.) 300.00

Fine

60 10/–/kopecks. Crowned cipher E. Rev. value and date.
1796...................60.00

The 1796 series (polushka, denga, and 1, 2, 4 and 5 kopecks) types of No. 60 were not circulated.

Portrait Issues

Dates, denominations and types of silver and gold not listed below are patterns or novodels. The pattern silver 5 kopecks 1763 is said to have circulated.

A. Young bust, ruff around neck 1762-66.

Silver   F-VF

61 griven/nik. Rev. like No. 61a.
1764-66...................16.00

62 15 (kopecks). Rev. like No. 62a.
1764-66...................20.00

63 20 (kopecks). Sim.
1764-66...................25.00

65 polupoltinnik. Rev. like No. 65b. 1764-66.........32.50

66 poltina. Sim. 1762-65......60.00

67 ruble. Sim. 1762-65........60.00

Gold

V.F.

★78 five rubles. 1762-65.......175.00

79 ten rubles. Sim. 1762-65...425.00

80 (ducat). Rev. like No. 65b.
1763...................240.00

RUSSIA

B. Mature bust, no ruff 1766-76.

Silver

F-VF

⋆61a griven/nik. 1766-76.......16.00

⋆62a 15 (kopecks). 1767-75.....18.00

63a 20 (kopecks). Sim.
1766-76.................20.00

65a polupoltinnik. Rev. like
No. 65b. 1767-75........32.50

66a poltina. Sim. 1766-76.....50.00

67a ruble. Sim. 1766-76.......60.00

Gold

V.F.

77 two rubles. Sim. 1766....150.00

78a five rubles. Rev. like
No. 78. 1766-76........200.00

79a ten rubles. Sim. 1766-76..450.00

80a (ducat). Rev. like No. 65b.
1766.................240.00

C. Older bust, wreath around crown 1777-82.

Silver

F-VF

61b griven/nik. Rev. like No. 61a.
1777-81................14.00

62b 15 (kopecks). Rev. like
No. 62a. 1778-82........18.00

63b 20 (kopecks). Sim.
1778-81................18.00

⋆65b polupoltinnik. 1779, 81....27.50

66b poltina. Sim. 1777-79......35.00

67b ruble. Sim. 1777-82.......60.00

Gold

V.F.

⋆75 poltina. 1777-78........95.00

76 ruble. Rev. like No. 65b.
1779..................110.00

78b five rubles. Rev. like No. 78.
1777-82................185.00

79b ten rubles. Sim. 1777-82..425.00

D. Aged bust 1783-96.

Silver

F-VF

61c griven/nik. Rev. like
No. 61a. 1783-96.........14.00

62c 15 (kopecks). Rev. like
No. 62a. 1783-94.........14.00

63c 20 (kopecks). Sim.
1783-93.................18.00

65c polupoltinnik. Rev. like
No. 65b. 1783-96........27.50

66c poltina. Sim. 1785-96.....35.00

67c ruble. Sim. 1783-96.......60.00

Gold

V.F.

77c two rubles. Sim. 1785....150.00

78c five rubles. Rev. like
No. 78. 1783-96..........185.00

79c ten rubles. Sim. 1783-96..425.00

80c (ducat). Rev. like No. 65b.
1796..................240.00

Paul I 1796-1801

Mint marks: AM, EM; KM; CII,
СПБ, БМ or CM (all St. Petersburg);
and w/out mint mark.

Copper

Fine

92 1/polushka. Like No. 93.
1797-1800................6.50

⋆93 1/denga. 1797-1801........6.50

94 1/kopeck. Sim. 1797-1801...5.00

95 2/kopecks. Sim. 1797-1801..5.00

Silver

F-VF

96 5/kopecks. Sim. 1797-1801..12.00

97 10/kopecks. Sim. 1797-1801.14.00

98 polupoltinnik. Like No. 101a.
1797-1801................27.50

99 poltina. Sim. 1797-1801.....40.00

Nos. 96-99 dated 1797 are heavier than
later dates.

V.F.

100 (Albertus ruble). Imp. eagle.
Rev. like No. 101a. 28 gr.
1796.................265.00

101 Heavy ruble. Like No. 101a
but 28 gr. 1797.........135.00

⋆101a ruble. 1798-1801........47.50

Gold

102 (ducat). Like No. 100.
1796.................265.00

103 (ducat). Like No. 101a.
1797.................240.00

104 5 rubles. Sim. 1798-1801..240.00

Alexander I 1801-25

Mint marks: ИМ (Izhorsk); EM;
KM; СПБ; and w/out mint mark.

Copper

Fine

111 1/polushka. Like No. 112.
1802-10.................27.50

⋆112 1/denga. 1802-10.........27.50

113 1/kopeck. Sim. 1802-10....20.00

Nos. 111-113 dated 1802 are novodels.

114 2/kopecks. Sim. 1802-10...12.50

115 5/kopecks. Sim. 1802-10...12.50

RUSSIA

116 denga. Like No. 118. *Fine*
1810-25 . . . . 5.00

117 1/kopeck. Sim. 1810-25 . . . . 3.50

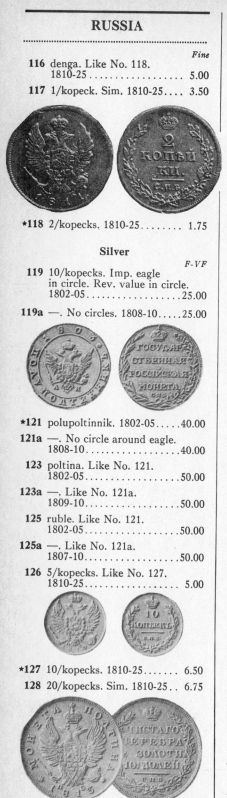

*118 2/kopecks. 1810-25 . . . . 1.75

Silver

F-VF

119 10/kopecks. Imp. eagle
in circle. Rev. value in circle.
1802-05 . . . . 25.00

119a —. No circles. 1808-10 . . . . . 25.00

*121 polupoltinnik. 1802-05 . . . . . 40.00

121a —. No circle around eagle.
1808-10 . . . . 40.00

123 poltina. Like No. 121.
1802-05 . . . . 50.00

123a —. Like No. 121a.
1809-10 . . . . 50.00

125 ruble. Like No. 121.
1802-05 . . . . 50.00

125a —. Like No. 121a.
1807-10 . . . . 50.00

126 5/kopecks. Like No. 127.
1810-25 . . . . 5.00

*127 10/kopecks. 1810-25 . . . . 6.50

128 20/kopecks. Sim. 1810-25 . . 6.75

*129 poltina. 1810-25 . . . . 15.00

130 ruble. Sim. 1810-25 . . . . 17.50

Other dates, types and denominations
of silver coins of this reign are patterns
or restrikes.

Gold

V.F.

131 five rubles. Like No. 133.
1802-05 . . . . 200.00

*132 five rubles. 1817-25 . . . . . . 185.00

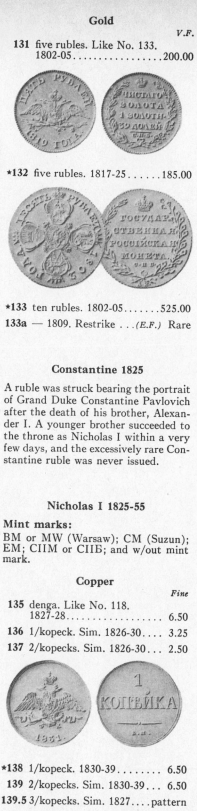

*133 ten rubles. 1802-05 . . . . . . 525.00

133a — 1809. Restrike . . . *(E.F.)* Rare

Constantine 1825

A ruble was struck bearing the portrait
of Grand Duke Constantine Pavlovich
after the death of his brother, Alexander I. A younger brother succeeded to
the throne as Nicholas I within a very
few days, and the excessively rare Constantine ruble was never issued.

Nicholas I 1825-55

Mint marks:
BM or MW (Warsaw); CM (Suzun);
EM; CIIM or CIIБ; and w/out mint
mark.

Copper

Fine

135 denga. Like No. 118.
1827-28 . . . . 6.50

136 1/kopeck. Sim. 1826-30 . . . . 3.25

137 2/kopecks. Sim. 1826-30 . . . 2.50

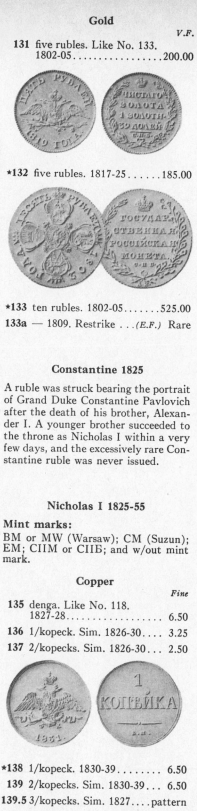

*138 1/kopeck. 1830-39 . . . . 6.50

139 2/kopecks. Sim. 1830-39 . . . 6.50

139.5 3/kopecks. Sim. 1827 . . . . pattern

140 5/kopecks. Sim. 1830-39 . . . 6.50

141 10/kopecks. Sim. 1830-39 . . 12.50

142 ¼/kopeck. Like No. 144.
1839-46 . . . . 3.50

143 ½/kopeck. Sim. 1839-48 . . . 3.50

Fine

*144 1/kopeck. 1839-47 . . . . 5.00

145 2/kopecks. Sim. 1839-48 . . . 6.50

146 3/kopecks. Sim. 1839-48 . . . 8.00

147 polushka. Like No. 148.
1849-55 . . . . 1.75

*148 denezhka. 1849-55 . . . . 1.75

149 kopeck. Sim. 1849-56 . . . . . . 1.75

*150 2/kopecks. 1849-55 . . . . 3.50

151 3/kopecks. Sim. 1849-55 . . . 3.50

152 5/kopecks. Sim. 1849-55 . . . 5.00

Silver

F-VF

152.3 5/kopecks. Like No. 127.
1826 . . . . 7.50

152.7 10/kopecks. Sim. 1826 . . . . 7.50

153 20/kopecks. Sim. 1826 . . . . . 10.00

154 poltina. Like No. 129.
1826 . . . . 30.00

155 ruble. Sim. 1826 . . . . 20.00

156 5/kopecks. Like No. 158.
1826-31 . . . . 6.50

157 10/kopecks. Sim. 1826-31 . . 6.50

*158 20/kopecks. 1826-31 . . . . . . 12.50

159 25/kopecks. Sim. 1827-31 . . 8.00

RUSSIA

E.F.

F-VF

*160 poltina. 1826-31........15.00

161 ruble. Sim. 1826-31......25.00

163 5/kopecks. Like No. 164. V.F.
    1832-55................ 3.50

*164 10/kopecks. Sim. 1832-55 .. 4.50

165 20/kopecks. Sim. 1832-55 .. 4.50

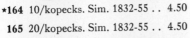

*166 25/kopecks. 1832-55......10.00

167 poltina. Sim. 1832-55.....15.00

168 ruble. Sim. 1832-55......22.50

See POLAND for other coins of this reign.

E.F.

*170 1 ruble. Battle of Borodino
    Memorial. 1839.........100.00

*171 (ruble). Heads of Czarovitch
    and bride l. Rev. cwnd.
    initials, supporters. 21 gr.
    1841..................500.00

Types of No. 171 weighing 23.5-27.5
grams are medals.

*172 1½ rubles. Head of Nicholas.
    Rev. Heads of Czarina and
    7 children. 1836 (vars.). .2000.00

No. 172 dated 1835 is a pattern.

173 1½ rubles. Like No. 170.
    1839.................1300.00

Dates, types and denominations of silver of this reign not listed are patterns.

Gold

V.F.

174 five rubles. Imp. eagle/date.
    Rev. legend. 1826-31.....200.00

175 5 rubles. Like No. 178.
    1832-55.................160.00

*176 5 rubles. Sim. but with
    additional legend above 5 on
    rev. Kolyvan Mines.
    1832..................475.00

The 1836 10 ruble pieces are rare patterns.

Platinum

177 3 rubles. Like No. 178.
    1828-45................185.00

*178 6 rubles. 1829-45........950.00

179 12 rubles. Sim. 1830-45 ..2400.00

E.F.

*169 1 ruble. Czar Alexander
    Memorial. 1834.........100.00

RUSSIAN PROVINCES IN EUROPE

Crimea
(Krim, Tauric Khersonese)

The Crimean Peninsula and other neighboring areas in South Russia were governed until 1783 by the Khans of Krim, vassals of Turkey (see KRIM). Annexed to Russia in that year.

Catherine II, in Crimea
1783-96

See RUSSIA Nos. 55-59, mint mark TM, for copper from Feodosia Mint.

Silver

VF-EF

7 2 (kopeck). Cwnd. EII mon./ date. Rev. 2, two dots/т.м. 1787.....................RRR

8 5 (kopeck). Sim., but 5, five dots. 1787..................RR

*9 10 (kopeck). Sim., but 10, ten dots. 1787.............Rare

10 20 (kopeck). Sim., but 20, twenty dots. 1787..........75.00

No. 10 with inward curl on upper stem of 2 is a restrike.

Livonia and Esthonia

Baltic provinces acquired by Russia from Sweden 1721. Known as Latvia and Estonia in our day.

Monetary System:
96 kopeck = 1 thaler.

Arms:
Those of Riga and Reval (see No. 3).

Elizabeth of Russia 1741-61
Silver (lower values billon)

F-VF

*1 2 (kopeck). Imp. eagle. Rev. Arms of L–E. 1756-57......35.00

2 4 (kopeck). Sim. LIVO ESTHONICA added to rev. 1756-57......15.00

F-VF

*3 24 (kopeck). 1756-57......37.50

4 48 (kopeck). Sim. 1756-57...80.00

5 96 (kopeck). 1756-57.....275.00

Originals of Nos. 1-5 dated 1756 are excessively rare. Restrikes of all of these coins exist. These are also rather rare.

Moldavia-Wallachia

For copper coinage 1771-74 of the Russian occupation of these States, see BALKANS.

RYUKYU ISLANDS.
See JAPAN.

UNVERIFIED DATA

Note: Throughout this catalog, any uncertain, indefinite or unconfirmed information is shown in *italic type*. Such material may be, for example, coin descriptions, dates and prices, names of rulers, or supplementary notes. Further information to confirm or correct *material in italics* should be sent to the author at the following address:

William D. Craig
c/o Whitman Coin Supply Division
1220 Mound Avenue
Racine, Wisconsin 53404, U.S.A.

NOTES

NOTES

ST. BARTHOLOMEW.

ST. CHRISTOPHER.

SAINT-DOMINGUE.

SAINT EUSTATIUS.

ST. KITTS.

ST. LUCIA.

ST. MARTIN.

ST. VINCENT.

See CARIBBEAN ISLANDS
AND TERRITORIES.

ST. HELENA

Island in the south Atlantic, 1100 miles
off SW Africa. Discovered 1502. Held
alternately by English and Netherlands
until 1673, by the British East India
Company thereafter. Prison and death-
place of Napoleon.

Monetary System:
12 pence = 1 shilling.

Copper

VG-F

★1 HALF PENNY. 1821...... 7.50

ST. THOMAS
AND PRINCE ISLANDS

Portuguese possessions in the Gulf of
Guinea off the west coast of Africa.
MOZAMBIQUE Nos. 51-56, 1813-
25 were also used here and are often attributed to St. Thomas & Prince in lieu
of Mozambique.

SALVADOR
(EL SALVADOR)

A republic in Central America. Until
1821 Salvador was part of the Spanish Captaincy-General of Guatemala.
Thereafter, it was united to Mexico
1822-23. Salvador was a state in the
Republic of Central America 1823-
47. Independent republic 1847 onward.

Monetary System:
16 reales = 1 escudo.

As a State in
Central America

Silver

Note: Nos. 11-18 are general types
only. There are many varieties in style
of designs, ornamentation, spelling of
legends, etc.

VG-F

11 (½ real). POR LA LIVERTAD DEL
SAL. Mountain in wreath.
Rev. MONEDA PROVISIONAL.
Column. 1833-35..........150.00

14 1 R(eal). Like No. 11.
1833-35.................70.00

15 1 R(eal). ESTADO L. DEL
SALVADOR. Mountain. Rev.
MONEDA PROVISIONAL.
Column. 1834...........125.00

★**16** 2 R(eales). 1828-29........50.00

17 2 R(eales). Like No. 11.
1832-34..................70.00

18 4 R(eales). Sim. 1828.....1000.00

Countermarked Silver

**A. Cmk. mountain/1839 in incuse
square.**

*This cmk. also has been reported with
s—s at sides of mountain.*

21 (½ real). 1839............ ——

22 (real). 1839.............. ——

23 (2 reales). 1839........... ——

25 (8 reales). 1839........... ——

B. Cmk. Salvador arms in circle.

There are many minor varieties of this
cmk.

Fine (cmk.)

41 (½ real). Cmkd. flag-draped
arms in 10-12mm circle.....35.00

42 (1 real). Sim. 15.00

Fine (cmk.)

★**43** (2 reales). Sim. 20.00

44 (4 reales). Sim. ....Rare

45 (8 reales). Sim. ....RRR

SANTO DOMINGO. See
CARIBBEAN ISLANDS AND
TERRITORIES.

SIAM, (THAILAND)

Kingdom in southeast Asia which arose
ca. AD1250-1350. Vied with Cambodia,
Burma and Vietnam for regional control until 19th century.

Monetary System:

8 fuang = 4 saleung = 1 baht (bat) =
1 tical (obsolete term) = 15.4 grams;
other values proportional.
12 to 16 silver baht = 1 gold baht.

Certain odd denominations, such as ¾
baht, are known from some reigns, but
being both extremely rare and presum-
ably not for general circulation, are not
listed.

"Bullet" money:

**Side view with   Bottom view
side cmk. shown**

The silver and (rarely) gold coins used
from the 13th through 19th centuries
are often called "bullet money" because
of their shape. They consist of small in-
gots folded double by hammering, and
validated with one or more countermarks.

Countermarks:

Coins before 1767 tend to have only
one cmk.; those after 1767 have one
cmk. on the side just above the crease,
and often another on the top surface of
the coin. The side cmks. served as symbols of the reigning monarch, changing
not only with each reign but frequently

SIAM

within a reign to denote special occasions. Some side cmks. appear alone (coin Nos. 39, 51-74, 121-127, 153-155) but all others occur in conjunction with the top cmks. illustrated below.

Top countermark:
The "chakra" or sharp-edged discus (symbol of Hindu god Vishnu) appears on the top surface of bullet coins after 1767 except as noted above. This mark became the dynastic symbol of the Bangkok dynasty. The style varies, and 6, 8 or 9 blades are found.

Copies and counterfeits:
Contemporary counterfeits of bullet coins are usually cast, and are rare. More recent copies have been made for jewelry purposes in silver or silver-plated copper. They are generally more crude than genuine pieces, and always have a button loop or drilled hole for stringing. Such replicas of the 1/8 and 1/4 baht are common, as are copies of Nos. 135-137. Some genuine bullet coins are also found holed or looped.

Presentation coins:
It is contended by at least one modern expert that prior to Rama IV only the 1/8, 1/4 and 1 baht silver bullet coins (and only certain of these) were for commercial use, all other denominations being for ceremonial and presentation purposes. Rama IV unsuccessfully tried to introduce other denominations for circulation. All bullet coins of Rama V were for presentation.

I. Thonburi Period.

King Taksin 1767-82

First side mark:
"Hang-hong" or stylized conch shell; occurs without top cmk. Attributed by le May to the Ayudhaya Dynasty before 1767, but now contended to be Taksin's mark on 1/8 and 1/4 baht coins intended for circulation.

Silver

		F-VF
0.4 (1/8 baht). Hang-hong		4.00
0.5 (1/4 baht). Sim		4.00
Other values with hang-hong		RRR

Second side mark:
"Tri" or trident, symbol of god Siva; occurs with chakra as top cmk. Le May attributed the tri to Rama I, but others now believe it was produced by Taksin.

		F-VF
1 (1/32 baht). Chakra and tri		RRR
2 (1/16 baht). Sim		RRR
3 (1/8 baht). Sim		RRR
4 (1/4 baht). Sim		RRR
5 (1/2 baht). Sim		RRR
6 (baht). Sim		12.50

II. Bangkok Dynasty, 1782 on.

Rama I (P'ra Buddha Yot Fa or Chao P'ya Chakri) 1782-1809

Side mark:
"Unalom" or ornamented conch shell; occurs with chakra as top cmk.

Silver

8 (1/32 baht). Chakra and Unalom		25.00
9 (1/16 baht). Sim		25.00
10 (1/8 baht). Sim		15.00
11 (1/4 baht). Sim		15.00
12 (1/2 baht). Sim		25.00
13 (baht). Sim		10.00
14 (2 baht). Sim		Unique?

See note following No. 74 regarding additional possible coinage of Rama I.

Rama II (P'ra Buddha Lot La) 1809-24

Side mark:
"Krut" = Garuda bird or vehicle of Vishnu; occurs with chakra as top cmk.

Silver

17 (1/8 baht). Chakra and Krut		RRR
18 (1/4 baht). Sim		RRR
19 (1/2 baht). Sim		RRR
20 (baht). Sim		12.50

See note following No. 60 regarding additional possible coinage of Rama II.

Rama III (P'ra Nang Klao) 1824-51

A. Silver Presentation Coins.

1. First side mark:
"Krut sio" or Garuda bird in profile; occurs with chakra as top cmk.

---

31 (2½ baht). Chakra and Krut Sio		300.00

F-VF

2. Second side mark:
"Chaleo," a lucky symbol. Appears twice, as both side and top cmks.

39 (baht). Chaleo		RR

B. Silver for Circulation.

3. Third side mark:
"Prasat" = palace, occurs with chakra as top cmk.

42 (1/32 baht). Chakra and Prasat		30.00
43 (1/16 baht). Sim		30.00
44 (1/8 baht). Sim		7.50
45 (1/4 baht). Sim		7.50
46 (1/2 baht). Sim		20.00
47 (baht). Sim		5.00

4. Fourth side mark:
"Dok mai" = flower; occurs without top cmk.

51 (1/32 baht). Dok Mai		Rare
52 (1/16 baht). Sim		Rare
53 (1/8 baht). Sim		7.50
54 (1/4 baht). Sim		4.00
55 (1/2 baht). Sim		RR
56 (baht). Dok Mai repeated 4 times within frame		RR

5. Fifth side mark:
"Bai matum" or bale-fruit tree; occurs without top cmk.

61 (1/32 baht). Bai Matum		25.00
62 (1/16 baht). Sim		25.00
63 (1/8 baht). Sim		3.00
64 (1/4 baht). Sim		4.00
65 (1/2 baht). Sim		RR
66 (baht). Sim		RR

Note: It is now contended that Nos. 61-66 were coined under Rama II (and possibly continued into the reign of Rama III), with Nos. 63-64 being for general circulation and the others for presentation only.

SIAM

6. Sixth side mark:

"Ruang pu'ng" = beehive; occurs without top cmk.

F-VF

71 (1/32 baht). Ruang Pu'ng 25.00

72 (1/16 baht). Sim 25.00

73 (1/8 baht). Sim 4.00

74 (1/4 baht). Sim 7.50

Note: It is now contended that Nos. 71-74 were coined by Rama I, with the 1/8 and 1/4 baht being for general circulation and the others for presentation.

7. Seventh side mark:

Arrow head (considered a variant of "dok mai"); occurs with chakra as top cmk.

81 (1/32 baht). Chakra and
arrow head 25.00

82 (1/16 baht). Sim 25.00

83 (1/8 baht). Sim 4.50

84 (1/4 baht). Sim 10.00

Gold Presentation Coins

92 (1/16 baht). Chakra and
3rd mark . . . . Rare

93 (1/8 baht). Sim . . . . Rare

96 (baht). Sim . . . . Rare

103 (1/8 baht). 4th mark . . . . . . Rare

113 (1/8 baht). 5th mark . . . . . . Rare

Rama IV (Mongkut)
1851-68

Silver

1. First side mark:

"P'ra tao" or Royal water pot; occurs without top cmk.

121 (1/64 baht). P'ra tao . . . . . . Rare

122 (1/32 baht). Sim 20.00

123 (1/16 baht). Sim 15.00

124 (1/8 baht). Sim 3.00

125 (1/4 baht). Sim 4.00

127 (baht). Sim . . . . ——

2. Second side mark:

"Mongkut" or Siamese crown; occurs with chakra as top cmk.

F-VF

133 (1/16 baht). Chakra and
Mongkut 20.00

134 (1/8 baht). Sim 4.00

135 (1/4 baht). Sim 4.00

136 (1/2 baht). Sim 10.00

137 (baht). Sim 5.00

138 (2 baht). Sim 100.00

139 (4 baht). Sim 200.00

Cmkd. Coins

141 Mexican dollar cmkd. Chakra
and Mongkut (1858-60). Many
counterfeits. Originals . . . . . RRR

Gold

1. First mark:

153 (1/16 baht). Like No. 121 . . . . 40.00

154 (1/8 baht). Sim 60.00

155 (1/4 baht). Sim 80.00

2. Second mark:

165 (1/4 baht). Like No. 133 . . . . 80.00

166 (1/2 baht). Sim 100.00

167 (baht). Sim 200.00

168 (2 baht). Sim 300.00

169 (4 baht). Sim 500.00

Rama V (Chulalongkorn)
1868-1910

Silver Presentation Coins

1. First issue:

Side mark = "P'ra kieo" or Royal coronet; occurs with chakra as top cmk. Issued in 1874.

177 (baht). Chakra and
p'ra kieo . . . . RRR

2. Second issue:

Coins have 2 side marks, **(a)** rampeui flower/Siamese date 1242 (=AD1880) and **(b)** Royal crown/urn flanked by ceremonial umbrellas. Elaborate chakra as top cmk. On death of Queen Mother.

188 (2 baht). Chakra, flower
and crown . . . . RR

189 (4 baht). Sim . . . . RR

190 (10 baht). Sim . . . . RRR

191 (20 baht). Sim . . . . RRR

192 (40 baht). Sim . . . . RRR

193 (80 baht). Sim . . . . RRR

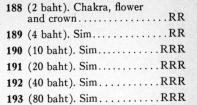

SIBERIA

Russian possessions east of the Ural Mountains.

Monetary System: See RUSSIA.

Mint: K(olyvan) M(int).

Catherine II (the Great)
1762-96

Copper

		Fine
*1	polushka. 16-18mm. 1767-79	30.00
2	denga. Like No. 3. 19-22mm. 1766-79	20.00

*3	kopek. 23-25mm. 1766-79	15.00
4	two kopek. Sim. 27-30mm. 1766-80	20.00
5	five kopek. Sim. 35-38mm. 1766-80	20.00
6	ten kopek. Sim. 44-47mm. 1766-81	45.00

Copper coins not listed above with dates 1763, 64, 66 and 80 exist only as novodels (official restrikes). Silver 10, 15 and 20 kopeks of 1764 were likewise struck later from unused original dies.

SIERRA LEONE COMPANY

Sierra Leone, on the west coast of Africa north of Liberia, belonged to Portugal until 1787. A number of freed slaves and lewd women were sent there as colonists from London in 1776. The area was acquired from Portugal and in 1791 the Sierra Leone Company was incorporated in England to govern it.

Monetary System:
100 cents = 50 pence = 1 dollar.

George III 1760-1820,
In Sierra Leone 1787-1820

Bronze

		VF-EF
1	ONE CENT. Like No. 2. 1791, 96	25.00

*2	ONE PENNY. 1791 (2 var.)	25.00

Silver

		F-VF
3	TEN CENTS. Sim. 1791, 96, 1805	35.00
4	TWENTY CENTS. Sim. 1791	65.00
5	HALF DOLLAR. Sim. 1791	110.00
6	ONE DOLLAR. Sim. 1791	250.00
6a	—. 100 (cents). 1791	500.00

William IV 1830-37

Silver

		Fine (cmk.)
11	(¼ dollar). Cwnd. WR on cut fourth of 8 reales. (1831-35)	*100.00*
12	(½ dollar). Sim. cmk. on ½ dollar size coin	80.00

SPAIN (HISPANIA), KINGDOM

A monarchy occupying most of the Iberian Peninsula in southwestern Europe. The Spanish colonies, which covered most of Latin America, became independent during the first quarter of the 19th century, making Spain a second-class power.

Monetary Systems:

Until 1810:

8 octavos = 4 quartos =
  34 maravedi = 1 real (de plata);
2 reales = 1 peseta;
16 reales = 2 duros = 1 escudo;
8 escudos = 1 onza.

The "S" abbreviation of escudo represents "Scutum" (Latin for "escudo").

1810-64:

20 reales de vellon (billon) =
  8 reales de plata;
4 reales de v. = 1 peseta.

Mint Marks:

The regular Spanish mints were Madrid – Cwnd. M; Segovia (copper only) – aqueduct; Sevilla – S. Other mints were added during the Napoleonic era and are mentioned as they appear. Additional letters are the initials of mint officials.

Coins of the Spanish-American colonies are generally distinguishable by type, but always by mint mark. See BOLIVIA (MM: PTS mon.); CHILE (MM: Š); COLOMBIA (MMs: NR, P or Pᴺ); GUATEMALA (MMs: G or N.G.); MEXICO (MMs: Cᴬ, D or Dᴼ, Gᴬ, Gᴼ, M̃, Z or Zˢ); and PERU (MMs: LM or LIMAE mon., CUZO mon.).

Fernando VI 1746-59

Copper

		Fine
⋆1	I (maravedi). 1746-47	7.50

Note the aqueduct MM in the illustration.)

2 2 (maravedi). Sim. 1750 . . . . —

Silver

		F-VF
5	(½ real). Arms. Rev. Cross with arms of Castile (castle) and Leon (lion) in corners. 1746-59	10.00
6	R(eal) I. Arms. Rev. 4 fold arms of Castile-Leon. 1746-59	10.00
7	R(eales) II. Sim. 1754-59	7.50

Gold (escudo = 3.4 gr.)

		V.F.
⋆10	(½ escudo). 1746-59	50.00
11	(2 escudos). Like No. 14 but head like No. 10. 1749S	450.00
12	(2 escudos). Like No. 14. 1749 cwnd. M	850.00

⋆14	(4 escudos). 1747-49	1100.00
15	(8 escudos). Sim. 1747-50	3000.00

Carlos III 1759-88

Copper

		Fine
26	1 (maravedi). Like No. 28. 1770-75	25.00
27	2 (maravedi). Sim. 1770-88	5.00

⋆28	4 (maravedi). 1770-88	6.00
29	8 (maravedi). Sim. 1770-88	5.00

Silver

		F-VF
31	(½ real). Like No. 5. 1760-71	10.00
32	R(eal) I. Like No. 6. 1759-71	15.00
33	R(eales) II. Sim. 1759-71	8.50
34	R(eales) 4. Sim. 1760-61	85.00
35	R(eales) 8. Sim. 1762	125.00
36	(½ real). Like No. 40. 1772-88	7.50
37	R(eal) I. Sim. 1772-88	12.50
38	R(eales) 2. Sim. 1772-88	10.00

		V.F.
⋆39	R(eales) 4. Sim. 1772-88	40.00
40	R(eales) 8. CAROLUS III DEI G. Bust. Rev. HISPANIARUM REX. Arms. 1772-88	350.00

Gold (escudo = 3.4 gr.)

41	(½ escudo). Head. Rev. like No. 10. 1759-71	65.00
45	(4 escudos). Young bust. Rev. arms in order chain. 1761 cwnd. M	750.00
47	(8 escudos). Sim. 1760 cwnd. M	3500.00
51	(ex 42) (½ escudo). Old bust. Rev. 4 fold arms in order chain, no legend. 1772-85	55.00
51a	—. Sim. but arms are oval. 1786-88	45.00
52	(ex 43) 1 S(cudo). Obv. sim. Rev. like No. 143. 1772-88	70.00
53	(ex 44) 2 S(cudos). Sim. 1772-88	100.00
54	(ex 46) 4 S(cudos). Sim. 1772-88	200.00
55	(ex 48) 8 S(cudos). Sim. 1772-88	600.00

Carlos IV 1788-1808

Copper

		Fine
59	1 (maravedi). Like No. 62. 1791-1802	17.50
60	2 (maravedi). Sim. 1788-1808	4.75
61	4 (maravedi). Sim. 1788-1808	3.00

SPAIN

Fine

*62 8 (maravedi). 1788-1808.... 5.50

Silver
F-VF

66 (½ real). Like No. 68.
1789-1808................ 8.00

*68 R(eales) 1. 1788-1808......15.00

69 R(eales) 2. Sim. 1788-1808.. 7.50

70 R(eales) 4. Sim. 1788-1808..45.00

71 R(eales) 8. Sim. 1788-1808.125.00

Gold (escudo = 3.4 gr.)
V.F.

72 (½ escudo). CAROL IIII D.G.
HISP. R., bust. Rev. like
No. 51a. 1788-96.........350.00

73 1 S(cudo). Obv. sim. but
... HISP. ET IND. R. Rev. like
No. 143. 1788-1807........55.00

74 2 S(cudos). Sim. 1788-1808.125.00

75 4 S(cudos). Sim. 1788-1808.225.00

76 8 S(cudos). Sim. 1788-1805.400.00

Fernando VII 1808-33

See his coins following those of José
Napoleon.

José Napoleon
(Ex King of Naples),
King of Spain 1808-14

Copper

G-VG

*82 8 M(aravedi). 1809-13...... 9.00

Silver
F-VF

88 1 R(eal de vellon). Like
No. 91. 1812-13..........45.00

89 2 R(eales de v.). Sim.
1811-12.................80.00

90 4 R(eales de v.). Sim.
1808-13.................17.50

*91 10 R(eales de v.). 1809-13...95.00

92 20 (reales de v.). Sim.
1808-13.................80.00

*93 R(eales de plata) 8.
1809-10................200.00

Gold
V.F.

94 80 R(eales de v.). Obv. sim.
Rev. like No. 143.
1809-10.................300.00

94a —. Laureate head.
1811-13.................300.00

95 320 R(eales de v.). Like No.
94a. 1810-12...........3500.00

Fernando VII 1808-33

Exiled in France 1808-14. Coins struck
during his exile were those of his ad-
herents in arms against Joseph Napoleon.

Copper

Mints: Jubia – J; Segovia – Aqueduct

A. Bare Head. Jubia.
VG-F

106 2 (maravedi). Like No. 108.
1812-17................. 6.00

107 4 (maravedi). Sim. 1812-17. 5.00

*108 8 (maravedi). 1811-17..... 7.50

B. Small Laureate Head. Jubia.

109 2 (maravedi). Sim. but
laureate head. 1817-21..... 6.00

110 4 (maravedi). Sim. 1817-20. 5.00

111 8 (maravedi). Sim. 1817-21. 3.00

**C. Large Bare Head.
Jubia and Segovia.**

112 1 (maravedi). Like No.
108 but head like No. 115.
1824J...................15.00

113 2 (maravedi). Sim. 1824-27. 4.50

114 4 (maravedi). Sim.
1824-27J................ 4.50

114.5 8 (maravedi). Sim.
1823-27J................ 7.50

114.7 —. 1823-24 aqueduct...... 6.50

SPAIN

D. Constitutional Type. Jubia and Segovia.

VG-F

★115 8 (maravedi). 1822-23..... 8.50

E. Big Laureate Head. Segovia.

116 2 (maravedi). Like No. 109.
1816-33................ 2.50

117 4 (maravedi). Sim. 1816-33. 2.50

118 8 (maravedi). Sim. 1815-33. 2.50

118a —. 1823. P(amplona)......20.00

Silver

Mint marks:
Madrid – Cwnd. M; Cadiz – Cwnd. C;
Reus, in Catalonia – C; Valencia – V;
Barcelona – B; Sevilla – S.

F-VF

132 (½ real de plata). Like No.
136. 1812-33............10.00

132a —. Like No. 136a. 1813-14. 22.50

133 R(eal de p.) 1. Like No.
136. 1811-33............15.00

133a —. Like No. 136a.
1811, 14................35.00

134 R(eales de p.) 2. Like No.
136. 1810-33............15.00

134a —. Like No. 136a. 1810-14. 20.00

135 R(eales de p.) 4. Like No.
136. 1811-33............25.00

135a —. Like No. 136a. 1809-14. 70.00

135b —. Like No. 136b.
1813-14................150.00

V.F.

★136 R(eales de p.) 8. Laureate
bust ★. Rev. like No. 68.
1809-30................50.00

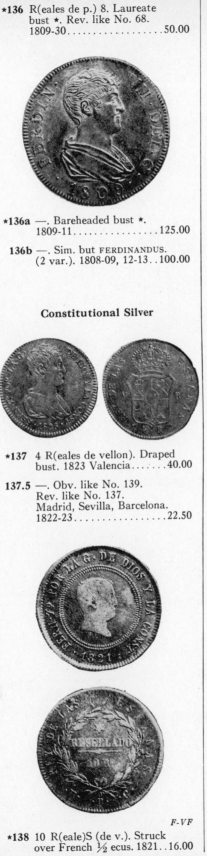

★136a —. Bareheaded bust ★.
1809-11...............125.00

136b —. Sim. but FERDINANDUS.
(2 var.). 1808-09, 12-13..100.00

Constitutional Silver

★137 4 R(eales de vellon). Draped
bust. 1823 Valencia.......40.00

137.5 —. Obv. like No. 139.
Rev. like No. 137.
Madrid, Sevilla, Barcelona.
1822-23................22.50

F-VF

★138 10 R(eale)S (de v.). Struck
over French ½ ecus. 1821..16.00

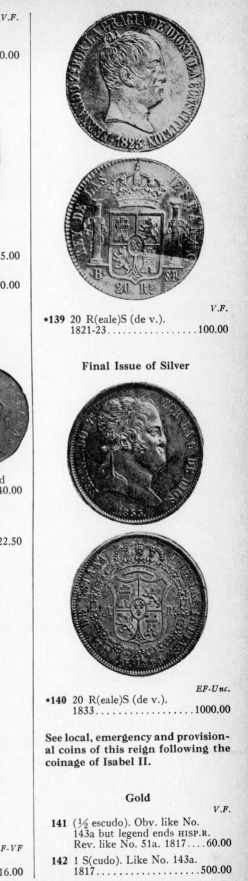

V.F.

★139 20 R(eale)S (de v.).
1821-23................100.00

Final Issue of Silver

EF-Unc.

★140 20 R(eale)S (de v.).
1833................1000.00

See local, emergency and provisional coins of this reign following the coinage of Isabel II.

Gold

V.F.

141 (½ escudo). Obv. like No.
143a but legend ends HISP.R.
Rev. like No. 51a. 1817....60.00

142 1 S(cudo). Like No. 143a.
1817................500.00

SPAIN

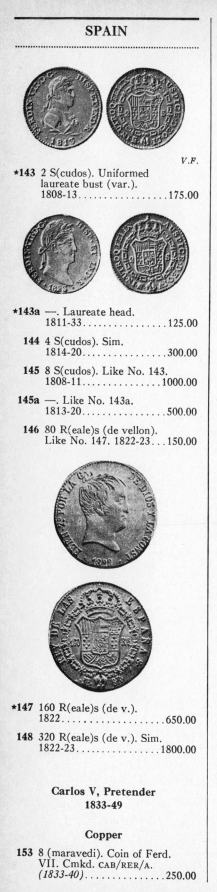

V.F.

*143 2 S(cudos). Uniformed laureate bust (var.). 1808-13 .... 175.00

*143a —. Laureate head. 1811-33 .... 125.00

144 4 S(cudos). Sim. 1814-20 .... 300.00

145 8 S(cudos). Like No. 143. 1808-11 .... 1000.00

145a —. Like No. 143a. 1813-20 .... 500.00

146 80 R(eale)s (de vellon). Like No. 147. 1822-23 ... 150.00

*147 160 R(eale)s (de v.). 1822 .... 650.00

148 320 R(eale)s (de v.). Sim. 1822-23 .... 1800.00

Carlos V, Pretender 1833-49

Copper

153 8 (maravedi). Coin of Ferd. VII. Cmkd. CAB/RER/A. *(1833-40)* 250.00

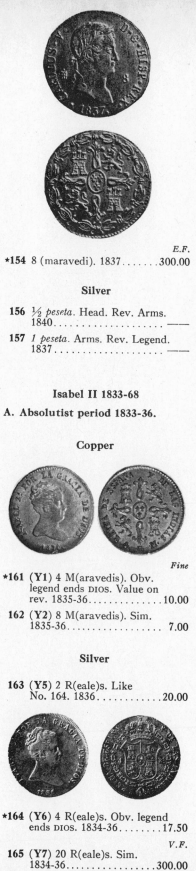

E.F.

*154 8 (maravedi). 1837 ...... 300.00

Silver

156 ½ *peseta.* Head. Rev. Arms. 1840 .... ——

157 *1 peseta.* Arms. Rev. Legend. 1837 .... ——

Isabel II 1833-68

A. Absolutist period 1833-36.

Copper

Fine

*161 (Y1) 4 M(aravedis). Obv. legend ends DIOS. Value on rev. 1835-36 .... 10.00

162 (Y2) 8 M(aravedis). Sim. 1835-36 .... 7.00

Silver

163 (Y5) 2 R(eale)s. Like No. 164. 1836 .... 20.00

*164 (Y6) 4 R(eale)s. Obv. legend ends DIOS. 1834-36 .... 17.50

V.F.

165 (Y7) 20 R(eale)s. Sim. 1834-36 .... 300.00

Gold

V.F.

166 (YA7) 80 R(eale)s. Sim. 1834-37 .... 120.00

B. Constitutional period 1836 on.

Copper

Fine

167 (Y3) 1 M(aravedi). Like No. 169. 1842-43 .... 12.50

168 (Y4) 2 M(aravedis). Sim. 1836-58 .... 3.50

*169 (YA4) 4 M(aravedis). Obv. legend ends CONST. Value on obv. 1837-55 ..... 2.50

170 (YB4) 8 M(aravedis). Sim. 1837-58 .... 3.00

Cast Bell Metal

*170a (YB4a) 8 M(aravedis). Obv. like No. 170 but w/out value. Rev. like No. 162. 1837PP (Pamplona) 80.00

Silver

171 (Y8) 1 R(ea)L. Like No. 173. 1837-52 .... 7.50

172 (Y9) 2 R(eale)s. Sim. 1837-51 .... 6.00

*173 (Y10a) 4 R(eale)s. Obv. legend ends CONST. 1837-49 .... 8.50

173a (Y10) —. CONSTITUCION. 1837-38B 15.00

SPAIN

Fine

174 (Y11) 10 R(eale)s. Like
No. 173. 1840-45.........40.00

V.F.

175 (Y12) 20 R(eale)s. Sim.
1837-49................75.00

Gold

176 (Y14a) 80 R(eale)s. Sim.
1837-49..............115.00

176a (Y14) —. CONSTITUCION.
1837-38B.............140.00

See Yeoman, *Modern World Coins*, for
decimal issues of Isabel II starting
1848.

Local, Emergency and Provisional Coins

BALEARIC ISLANDS (YSLAS BALEARES)

In the Mediterranean off the Spanish
coast. See also Majorca.

Monetary System:

12 dineros = 6 doblers = ½ real =
  1 sueldo (sou); *6 sueldos = 1 peseta.*

Fernando VII 1808-33
Silver

Fine

⋆L7 30 S(ueldos). Cwnd. 4 fold
arms. Rev. ⋆. (2 var.).
1808.................50.00

**For similar coins see Majorca 1808
and Tarragona 1809.**

L9 5 P(esetas). FERN. 7º etc.
Arms. Rev. YSLAS/BALEARES/
1823 (2 vars.)..........60.00

BARCELONA

Province and large port city in N.E.
Spain.

Monetary System:
4 quartos = *1 sueldo;* 6 *sueldos* = 1 peseta.

José Napoleon 1808-14

Copper

Fine

L11 ½/QUARTO. Arms of
Barcelona in lozenge (see No.
L14). Rev. value. N.D...35.00

L12 1/QUARTO. Like No. L14.
1808-13................17.50

L13 2/QUARTOS. Sim.
1808-14................10.00

⋆L14 4/QUARTOS. 1808-14.... 5.00

Silver

F-VF

L15 PESETA. Like No. L16.
1808-14................12.50

⋆L16 2½/PESETAS. 1808-14..95.00

L17 5/PESETAS. Sim.
1808-14...............150.00

Gold

V.F.

L18 20/PESETAS. Sim.
1812-14...............300.00

Fernando VII, Restored
1814-33

Copper

Fine

L21 3/QUAR(tos). Like No.
L22. 1823..............9.00

⋆L22 6/QUAR(tos). 1823......15.00

CATALONIA
(CATHALUÑA, CATALUÑA),
Principality

N.E. corner of Spain, comprising the
provinces of Barcelona, Gerona, Lérida
and Tarragona.

Monetary System:

*12 ardites (dineros) = 8 ochavos =
  4 quartos = 1 sueldo;
6 sueldos = 1 peseta;
5 pesetas = 1 duro.*

Fernando VI 1746-59

Copper

VG-F

L31 (ardite). FERDINANDUS VI
D.G. Arms of Castile and
Leon. Rev. CATALON
PRINCEPS, 4 fold Cat. arms.
1754-55................7.50

L31a —. Rev. unitary Cat. arms.
1756.................10.00

Fernando VII 1808-33

Fine

L34 OCHAVO. Generally like
No. 38. 1812-13.........25.00

L35 QUARTO. Sim. 1813.....17.50

L36 QUARTO/Y MEDIO
(= 1½ quartos). Sim.
1811, 13................10.00

L37 II/QUAR(tos). Sim.
1813-14................12.50

SPAIN

CATALONIA (Cont.)

*L38 III/QUAR(tos). 1810-14... 7.50

L39 VI/QUAR(tos). Sim.
  1810-14................17.50

Isabel II 1833-68

Copper

L40 *III/QUAR(tos).* Like
  No. L40a. 1836..........20.00

*L40a (Y48) 3/CUAR(tos).
  1836-46............... 5.00

L40.3 (Y49) 6/CUAR(tos).
  Sim. 1836-48...........7.50

Silver

L40.7 (Y50) 1/PESETA. ISABEL
  2A etc., Cat. arms. Rev.
  value. 1836-37..........17.50

GERONA

Province and city in Catalonia.

Fernando VII 1808-33

Silver

---

*L41 UN (=1) DURO (=5
  pesetas). FER/VII. Rev. ★.
  1808..................40.00

L41a —. Same in copper.......RR

*L42 5 P(esetas). Bust. Rev.
  Arms ★. 1809.....(crude) 1000.00

LÉRIDA

Province and city in Catalonia.

Fernando VII 1808-33

Silver

Fine (V.Crude)

L45 5 P(eseta)S/FER–VII/1809.
  Rev. Arms/ILD........1250.00

L46 5 P(esetas). Head. Rev.
  LERIDA. Arms. 1809....1000.00

MAJORCA (MALLORCA)

One of the Balearic Islands in the Mediterranean, south of Spain. Capital: Palma.

Monetary System:

12 dineros = 6 doblers = 1 sueldo (sou);
30 sueldos = 1 duro.

Fernando VII 1808-33

Copper

VG-F

*L51 12 (dineros). Laureate bust.
  Rev. Arms. P(alma).
  1811-12................12.50

Silver

Fine

*L52 30 S(ueldos). Uncwnd.
  lozenge-shaped arms.
  Rev. ★ (2 var.). 1808....125.00

For similar coins see Balearic Islands 1808 and Tarragona 1809.

F-VF

*L53 30 SOUS. Arms/SALUS
  POPULI. Rev. ★. 1821.....35.00

NAVARRE (NAVARRA),

Kingdom

Formerly independent kingdom on the Spanish-French border, divided between those two countries in the early 16th century. The following coins were issued at Pamplona for Spanish Navarre.

Arms: Escarbuncle (shield stiffener) = chain rectangle with 8 spokes.

Fernando II (=VI in Spain) 1746-59

Copper

VG-F

L61 *(2 maravedi).* Like
  No. L64. Square. ND..... 5.00

L63 (4 maravedi). Like No. L64
  but FD/VI. 1749..........5.00

*L64 (4 maravedi). F(ernand)O/II.
  Rev. P(amplon)A, Navarre
  arms. 1749-58..........5.00

SPAN

NAVARRA (Cont.)

Carlos VI (=III in Spain)
1759-88

Copper

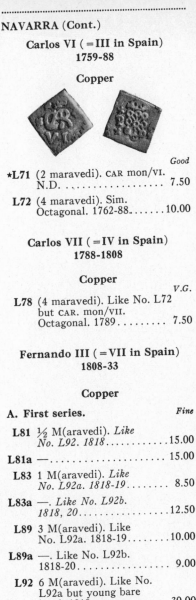

Good

*L71 (2 maravedi). CAR mon/VI.
N.D. 7.50

L72 (4 maravedi). Sim.
Octagonal. 1762-88....... 10.00

Carlos VII (=IV in Spain)
1788-1808

Copper

V.G.

L78 (4 maravedi). Like No. L72
but CAR. mon/VII.
Octagonal. 1789........ 7.50

Fernando III (=VII in Spain)
1808-33

Copper

A. First series. *Fine*

L81 ½ M(aravedi). *Like
No. L92*. 1818........... 15.00

L81a —..................... 15.00

L83 1 M(aravedi). *Like
No. L92a. 1818-19* 8.50

L83a —. *Like No. L92b.
1818, 20*............... 12.50

L89 3 M(aravedi). *Like
No. L92a. 1818-19*....... 10.00

L89a —. *Like No. L92b.
1818-20*. 9.00

L92 6 M(aravedi). *Like No.
L92a but young bare
head.* 1818............. 30.00

Fine

*L92a —. FERDINANDUS III etc.,
laureate head. 1818-19...25.00

L92b —. FERDIN. III etc.
1819-20............... 20.00

B. Second series.

L83b 1 M(aravedi). Sim. but
older bare head. 1825-26.. 9.00

L89b 3 M(aravedi). Sim.
1825-26. .... 9.00

C. Third series.

L82 (½ *maravedi*). F. III. D.G.N.R.
Rev. Navarre arms. Square.
1831-32, 1381(!) .... (V.F.) 60.00

L84 1 M(aravedi). Head r.
Rev. NAVARRAE−REX,
arms not on cross.
1829-33. .... 9.00

L90 3 M(aravedi). Sim.
1829-33. .... 8.00

TARRAGONA
Province and city in Catalonia.

Struck by General Palafox
for Fernando VII

Silver

Fine

*L96 5 P(eseta)s. Cwnd. Aragon
arms (5 pales). Rev. ⋆.
1809. .... 45.00

**See Balearic Islands and Majorca
for similar coins of 1808.**

TORTOSA

Fernando VII 1808-33

Silver

Fine

L100 I DURO (=5 pesetas).
4 stamps: tower, I, DURO,
and TOR·SA. Rev. Blank.
(1808-09)............... *RRR*

VALENCIA
City in S.E. Spain.

Fernando VII 1808-33

Silver

Fine

L103 2 R(eales). Bust. Rev. Arms
in lozenge-shield. 1809...35.00

V.F.

*L106 4 R(eales de vellon).
Siege of 1823.......... 20.00

SURINAM
(DUTCH GUIANA)

On the N.E. coast of South America.
Netherlands colony from 1667 except
for English occupations 1781-84, 1796-
1802 and 1802-14.

Copper

F-VF

*1 (duit). Cocoa tree btwn.
17-64. Rev. SOCIETEIT/VAN/
SURINAME................. 75.00

SWEDEN, KINGDOM

In Scandinavia between Norway and
Finland. In addition to Sweden proper,
the Swedish kings ruled over (i) part
of Pomerania (GERMAN STATES)
until 1815, and (ii) NORWAY 1814-
1905.

The financial difficulties attendant
upon several glorious but unsuccessful
wars caused Sweden to employ much
copper coinage, some of it of extraordinary size, and to have, in the 18th
century, a three level monetary system,
also extraordinary.

Monetary Systems:

Circa 1704-98:

8 öre = 1 mark;
32 öre = 1 daler;
96 öre S(ilver) M(oney) =
  1 Riksdaler = 3 daler S(ilver)
  M(oney) = 9 daler K(opper)
  M(oney).

SWEDEN

1798-1855:
48 skilling = 1 Riksdaler Species (Speciedaler).

1855-73:
100 öre = 1 Riksdaler Riksmont;
4 Riksdaler Riksmont = 1 Speciedaler.

Arms; Blue, 3 gold crowns.

Adolf Frederik of Holstein-Gottorp, King of Sweden 1751-71

Copper

VG-F

1 I ÖR K.M. Like No. 51 but
A.F.R.S. above cwns. 1768... 4.00

*3 I ÖR S.M. 1751-68....... 2.00

*5 2 ÖR S.M. A.F-S.G-V-R.
Cwnd. lion shield, 3 cwns.
Rev. as No. 3. 1751-68..... 2.50

Copper Plate Money
(Photo ½ actual size.)

F-VF

*8 ½ DALER S.M. 1751-68..100.00

9 1/DALER S.M. Sim. 1751-
59...................150.00

10 2/DALER S.M. Sim. 1751-
59...................200.00

11 4/DALER S.M. Sim. 1753-
58...................375.00

12 8/DALER S.M. Sim. ......RRR

Silver (lower values billon)

*15 1 Ö(r S.M.). Cwnd. AF.
Rev. 3 cwns. 1753-61...... 7.50

17 5 Ö(r) S.M. Like No. 15.
1751-67.................12.50

19 10 Ö(r) S.M. Like No. 15.
1751-64.................25.00

21 2 M(ark). Like No. 25.
1752, 54...............100.00

23 4 M(ark). Like No. 25.
1752-55.................75.00

*25 ⅛ R(iks)D(aler). 1767-68...15.00

27 (¼ Riksdaler). Like No. 25.
1752-65.................75.00

28 ¼ R(iks)D(aler). Sim.
1767-68.................60.00

29 (½ Riksdaler). Sim.
1752-66................100.00

30 ½ R(iks)D(aler). Sim.
1767-68................100.00

31 (Riksdaler). Sim. 1751-66..100.00

32 1 R(iks)D(aler). Sim.
1767-69................100.00

35 4 Ö(r) S.M. Like No. 37.
1771....................10.00

*37 8 Ö(r) S.M. 1771.........20.00

F-VF

38 16 Ö(r) S.M. Sim. 1770.....27.50

40 1 D(aler) S.M. Like No. 25.
1770....................50.00

41 2 D(aler) S.M. Sim. 1770...65.00

42 3 D(aler) S.M. Sim. 1770-
71......................90.00

Gold (ducat = 3.5 gr.)

V.F.

45 ¼ (ducat). Like No. 25.
1754-55.................300.00

46 ½ (ducat). Sim. 1754-55...750.00

*47 (ducat). 1751-71.........1500.00

48 (ducat). Sim. but rev. ÖSTRA
etc. Arms. From Dalarna Mines.
1751, 54................——

*49 (ducat). Rev. star
over cwn., Smaland arms
(lion with crossbow) in
exergue. From Adelförs mines.
1752-70.................——

Gustaf III 1771-92

Copper

VG-F

*51 I ÖR K.M. G.R.S./3 cwns.
Rev. arrow shield. 1772, 78.. 1.50

*53 1 ÖR S.M. 1778..........10.00

55 2 ÖR S.M. Like No. 5 but
G.III-S.G-V-R. 1777.......... 6.00

SWEDEN

Silver (lower values billon)

F-VF

61 1/24 R(iksdaler)/4 Ö(r) S.M. Like No. 61a. 1777......... 8.00

★61a —. W/out 4 Ö(r) S.M. 1778-83..................... 6.00

62 1/12 R(iksdaler)/8 Ö(r) S.M. Sim. 1777...............15.00

62a —. W/out 8 Ö(r) S.M. 1778-79..................... 9.00

64 16 ÖRE SILF-MYNT. Like No. 61a. 1773-74.........17.50

66 1/6 R(iks)D(aler)/16 ÖR S.M. Head. Rev. FADERNESLANDET/ arms. 1776-77.............15.00

★66a —. W/out 16 ÖR S.M. 1778-90......................10.00

67 1/3 R(iks)D(aler)/1 D(aler) S.M. Sim. 1776-77.............15.00

67a —. W/out 1 D(aler) S.M. 1778-89.................12.50

68 2/3 R(iks)D(aler)/2 D(aler) S.M. Sim. 1776-77.............37.50

68a —. W/out 2 D(aler) S.M. 1778-80..................40.00

69 3 D(aler) S.M. Sim. 1771-75...................120.00

69a —. I R(iks)D(aler)/3 D(aler) S.M. 1775-77...............60.00

69b —. W/out 3 D(aler) S.M. 1779-92.................55.00

Gold

V.F.

71 (ducat). Like No. 66a. 1771-92.................850.00

72 —. Obv. sim. Rev. like No. 49 but FADERNESLANDET. From Adelförs mines. 1771-86...2250.00

Gustaf IV Adolph 1792-1809

Copper

VG-F

75 1/4/SKILLING. Like No. 76. 1799-1800................ 1.75

★76 1/2/SKILLING. 1799-1802.. 1.75

78 1/12/SKILLING. Like No. 79. 1802-08................ .75

★79 1/4/SKILLING. 1802-08.... 1.00

80 1/2/SKILLING. Sim. but D:9–IULI beneath rev. arrows. Royal visit to Avesta and Dalarna copper mines. 1794.40.00

81 1/2/SKILLING. Like No. 79. 1802-09................... 1.50

82 I/SKILLING. Sim. 1802-05................... 2.00

Silver

F-VF

★85 1/6 R(iks)D(aler). Head. Rev. arms. 1799...........75.00

★86 —. Uniformed bust. 1800-09...................10.00

87 1/3 R(iks)D(aler). Like No. 85. 1798.................225.00

88 —. Like No. 86. 1799-1800...............125.00

F-VF

★89 I R(iks)D(aler). Hair combed back. 1792-95.................100.00

89a —. Like No. 85. 1796-97...110.00

90 —. Like No. 86. 1801-07...110.00

Gold

V.F.

91 (ducat). Like No. 89. 1793-95.................750.00

91a —. Like No. 85. 1796-98...750.00

92 --. Obv. sim. Rev. like No. 49 but GUD OCH FOLKET. From Adelförs mines. 1796..................... ——

93 (ducat). Like No. 86. 1799-1809..............650.00

94 —. Obv. sim. Rev. like No. 92. Adelförs mines. 1801................... ——

95 —. Rev. like No. 92 but Dalarna arms (crossed arrows) in exergue. From Dalarna mines. 1804............2250.00

Carl XIII 1809-18, Also King of Norway 1814-18

Copper

Fine

★100 1/12/SKILLING. 1812...... .75

★101 1/4/SKILLING. 1817...... 8.00

102 1/2/SKILLING. Sim. 1815-17................. 4.00

103 I/SKILLING. Sim. 1812-17................. 5.00

SWEDEN

Silver

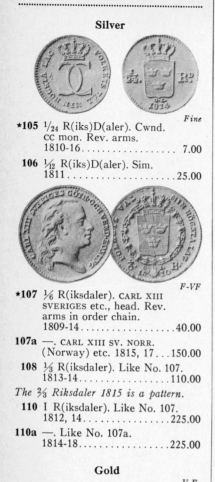

			Fine
*105	1/24 R(iks)D(aler). Cwnd. CC mon. Rev. arms. 1810-16		7.00
106	1/12 R(iks)D(aler). Sim. 1811		25.00

			F-VF
*107	1/6 R(iksdaler). CARL XIII SVERIGES etc., head. Rev. arms in order chain. 1809-14		40.00
107a	—. CARL XIII SV. NORR. (Norway) etc. 1815, 17		150.00
108	1/3 R(iksdaler). Like No. 107. 1813-14		110.00

The 2/3 Riksdaler 1815 is a pattern.

110	I R(iksdaler). Like No. 107. 1812, 14	225.00
110a	—. Like No. 107a. 1814-18	225.00

Gold

			V.F.
111	(ducat). Like No. 107. 1810-14		700.00
111a	—. Like No. 107a. 1815-17		500.00

*112	(ducat). Sim. Dalarna arms in rev. exergue. Dalarna mines. 1810	2000.00

Carl XIV Johan
(French Marshal Bernadotte)
1818-44

Copper

			Fine
*120	1/12/SKILLING. 1825		2.00

121	1/6/SKILLING. Sim. 1830-31	*Fine* 1.50

*122	1/4/SKILLING. 1819-30	1.50
123	1/2/SKILLING. Sim. 1819-30	2.00
124	I/SKILLING. Sim. 1819-30	4.00
125	1/6/SKILLING. Like No. 128. 1832	2.00
125a	—. Naked bust. 1832	20.00
126	1/4/SKILLING. Like No. 128. 1832-33	10.00
127	1/2/SKILLING. Sim. 1832-33	15.00

*128	1/SKILLING. 1832	65.00
129	1/6/SKILLING. Obv. like No. 122. Rev. like No. 132. 1835-44	2.00
130	1/3/SKILLING. Sim. 1835-43	1.50
131	2/3/SKILLING. Like No. 133. 1835-43	3.50

*132	1/SKILLING. 1835-43	5.00
133	2/SKILLING. Sim. 1835-43	10.00

Silver

		F-VF
*135	1/6 R(iksdaler). Young head. Rev. Swedish arms. 1819, 26	125.00
138	I R(iksdaler). Sim. 1818-27	150.00

		E.F.
*139	(Riksdaler). 1821	300.00

		F-VF
140	1/6 R(iksdaler). Like No. 141. 1828-29	37.50

*141	1/3 R(iksdaler). Older head. Rev. 3 fold arms. 1827-29	75.00
143	I R(iksdaler). Sim. 1827, 29	1000.00
144	1/16 R(iksdaler) SP(ecies). Sim. but rev. like No. 135. 1835-36	10.00
145	1/12 R(iksdaler) SP. Sim. 1831-33	15.00
146	1/8 R(iksdaler) SP. Sim. 1830-37	9.00

SWEDEN

F-VF

147 ¼ R(iksdaler) SP. Sim.
1830-36.............35.00

148 ½ R(iksdaler) SP. Sim.
1831-36.............50.00

149 1 R(iksdaler) SP. Sim.
1831-42.............100.00

Gold (ducat = 3.5 gr.)

150 (ducat). Like No. 135. 21-23mm.
1818-29.............650.00

151 (ducat). Like No. 153.
19mm. 1830-43.........450.00

152 (2 ducats). Sim. 21mm.
1836-43.............1750.00

★153 (4 ducats). Older head.
Rev. draped arms.
1837-43.............2250.00

Oscar I 1844-59

A. Skilling System.

Copper

Fine

160 ⅙/SKILLING. Like
No. 161. 1844-55.........1.50

★161 ⅓/SKILLING. Cwnd. o.
Rev. value in wreath.
1844-55.............2.00

★162 ⅔/SKILLING. Large
head. 1844-45.............7.50

163 1/SKILLING. Sim.
1844-45.............7.50

164 2/SKILLING. Sim.
1844-45.............15.00

Fine

★165 ⅔/SKILLING. Small
head. 1845-55.............3.00

166 1/SKILLING. Sim. 1845-
55.............4.00

★167 2/SKILLING. Sim. 1845-
55.............7.50

168 4/SKILLING. Sim. 1849-
55.............10.00

Silver

F-VF

★171 1/32 RDR (=riksdaler) SP(ecies).
1852-53.............5.00

173 1/16 R(iksdaler) SP. Like
No. 177. 1845-55.........6.00

175 ⅛ R(iksdaler) SP. Sim.
1852.............150.00

★177 ¼ R(iksdaler) SP. Small head.
Rev. arms. 1846-52.......40.00

V.F.

★179 ½ R(iksdaler) SP. Small
head. Rev. arms supported.
1845-52.............85.00

180 1 R(iksdaler) SP. Sim. but
large head (like No. 162).
1844-45.............100.00

181 —. Small head. 1845-55....85.00

B. Öre System.

Bronze

F-VF

★185 ½ ÖRE. Cwnd. o.
Rev. value. 1856-58.......1.50

★186 1/Öre. 1856-58.........1.25

187 2/ÖRE. Sim. 1856-58......2.50

188 5/ÖRE. Sim. 1857-58......4.00

Silver

192 10/ÖRE. Like No. 193
but rev. w/out cwn.
1855-59.............3.50

★193 25/ÖRE. 1855-59.........3.50

194 50/ÖRE. Sim. 1857.......25.00

195 1 R(iks)D(aler) RIKSM(ynt).
Like No. 196. 1857........30.00

★196 2 R(iks)D(aler) RIKSM.
1857.............125.00

197 4 R(iks)D(aler) RIKSM.
Sim. 1855-59.............85.00

Gold (ducat = 3.5 gr.) V.F.

198 (ducat). Head. Rev. Draped
arms. 1844-45.............400.00

198a —. Smaller head.
1845-59.............325.00

199 (2 ducats). Sim.
1850-57.............2000.00

200 (4 ducats). Sim.
1846, 50.............2500.00

NOTES

NOTES

SWITZERLAND
(HELVETIA, SCHWEIZ, SUISSE)

A small country in Western Europe which, except for the Napoleonic era, consisted until 1848 of a loose confederation of virtually independent states (cantons).

AARGAU
(ARGAU, ARGOVIE), Canton

Small district in north Switzerland, formed by the union in 1803 of Bernese Aargau and the short-lived Canton of Baden. Admitted to the Swiss Confederation at that time.

Arms: Per pale.
Dexter: Black, a white wavy fesse.
Sinister: Blue, 3 white stars.

Monetary System:
10 rappen = 4 kreuzer = 1 batzen;
10 batzen = 1 frank.

Billon
VG-F

1 I/RAPPEN. Like No. 6.
1809-16 .... 5.00

2 2/RAPPEN. Sim. 1808-16.. 4.00

3 ½/BATZEN. Sim. 1807-15.. 6.00

4 1/BATZEN. Sim. but AARGAU and oval arms. 1805 .... 25.00

4a —. ARGAU. Oval arms.
1806, 08 .... 10.00

4b —. Pointed arms. 1806 ...... 8.00

5 1/BATZEN. Like No. 6.
1807-16 .... 7.00

Silver

F-VF

*6 5/BATZEN. 1807-13 ...... 17.50

8 10/BATZEN. Sim.
1808-09, 18 .... 75.00

Note: The 1809 20 BATZEN like No. 6 is a rare pattern.

9 20 BATZ(en). Arms. Rev. seated Swiss. 1809 .... 120.00

VF-EF

10 4 FRANK. Arms. Rev. stdg. Swiss. 1812 .... 600.00

Billon
Fine

11 EIN (=1) KREUZER. Like No. 14 but w/out DIE CONCORDIER etc. 1831 .... 4.50

12 5 RAP(pen). Like No. 14. 1829, 31 .... 7.00

13 1 BATZ(en). Sim. 1826 ..... 8.00

Silver

F-VF

*14 5 BATZ(en). 1826 .... 12.50

APPENZEL, Canton

In N.E. Switzerland, entirely surrounded by the Canton of St. Gall. Achieved independence from the abbots of St. Gall in the period 1377/1411. Divided by religious differences into two half cantons, Ausser-Rhoden (Protestant) and Inner-Rhoden (Catholic). Both were joined to the Canton of Säntis 1797-1803, but regained their independent status in 1803.

Monetary System:
4 pfenning = 1 kreuzer;
10 rappen = 4 kreuzer = 1 batzen;
10 batzen = 1 franken.

I. Ausser-Rhoden.

Copper
VG-F

1 1/PFENNING. Obv. Like No. 8. Rev. value. 1816 .... 40.00

Billon
V.G.

2 1/KREUZER. Generally similar. 1813 .... 12.00

3 ½/BATZEN. Generally similar. 1808-09, 16 .... 12.00

4 1/BATZEN. Sim. but pointed shield. 1808, 16 .... 10.00

Silver
F-VF

5 ½/SCHWEIZ/FRANKEN. Sim. 1809 .... 100.00

VF-EF

*6 2 FRANK(e)N. 1812 ...... 125.00

*7 4 FRANK(e)N. 1812 ...... 500.00

SWITZERLAND

APPENZEL (cont.)

		VF-EF
*8	4 FRANK(e)N. 1816	600.00

II. Inner-Rhoden.

Gold

		V.F.
21	DUCATUS (=ducat). St. Martin stdg. Rev. DUCATUS/REIP/APPENZEL/ etc. 1739, 79	RR

ARGAU. See Aargau.

BASEL, Bishopric

In N.W. Switzerland. Founded in the 5th century. First coins circa 1000 A.D. Bishops resided at Porrentruy 1525-1792. Bishopric secularized and divided between France and Baden in 1801.

Arms: Silver, a red crozier head.

Monetary System:
4 kreuzer = 1 batzen.

Joseph, Freiherr von Roggenbach, Bishop 1783-94

Billon

		G-VG
22	½/BATZEN. Arms. Rev. value. 1787	12.00
23	1/BATZEN. Sim. 1787	12.00

Silver

		Fine
*26	12 (kreuzer). 1786-88	25.00
28	24 (kreuzer). Sim. 1788	35.00

BASEL (BASILEA), City and Canton

In N.W. Switzerland. City obtained the mint right 1373. Joined the Swiss confederation 1501. Drove the bishops out 1525. Absorbed into the Helvetian Republic 1798-1803. Independent status reestablished 1803.

Arms: Silver, a black crozier head (= "Baselstab," see No. 53).

Monetary System:
Until 1798: 8 rappen = 1 batzen;
30 batzen = 2 gulden = 1 thaler.

After 1803: 10 rappen = 1 batzen;
10 batzen = 1 frank.

I. Coinage before 1798.

Billon

		V.G
50	(rappen). Obv. like No. 53 but no legend. Rev. MON./BASIL in wreath. ND (after 1750)	3.00
51	½/BATZEN. Obv. sim. Rev. like No. 53. 1762-94	7.00
52	1/BATZEN. Sim. 1762	RRR

*53	1/BATZEN. 1763-65	8.00
56	III/BATZEN. Sim. 1764-65	12.00

Silver

		V.F.
58	⅙ (thaler). Basilisk holding arms. Rev. value. 1764, 66	40.00
60	⅓ (thaler). Sim. 1764, 66	65.00
62	(½ thaler). City view. Rev. Basilisk holding arms. 13 gr. 1757 (2 var.)	110.00
64	½/THALER. Like No. 58. 1765	85.00
66	(½ thaler). Like No. 62, shields over city. 12.7 gr. 1785-86	100.00
68	(½ thaler). Oval arms. Rev. Motto: DOMINE etc. 1797	150.00
70	(thaler). Like No. 62. 1756 (2 var.)	135.00
71	I/THALER. Like No. 58. 1765	110.00
72	(thaler). Like No. 66. 1785	135.00
73	(thaler). Like No. 62. 1793 (2 var.)	120.00

		V.F.
74	(thaler). Like No. 68. 1795-96 R.N	160.00

The 2 thaler 1762 R.N. is a pattern.

Gold

		VF-EF
86	¼/DUCAT. Like No. 87. ND (1750-80, 3 var.)	550.00

*87	½/DUCAT. ND (1770-80)	600.00
87.5	DUCAT. Sim. but rev. DUCAT/REIPUBL./BASILIEN/SIS. ND (1775-80, 2 var.)	700.00

*88	DUCATUS DUPLEX (=2 ducats). ND (1795)	1500.00
89	DVCAT/DVPLEX (=2 d.). Obv. like No. 92 obv. Rev. DOMINE etc., value. 1795	RR

*90	FLORENVS AVREVS (=gold gulden). ND (1790)	800.00
91	FLOREN. AVR DVPL (=2 gold gulden). Sim. ND (1790)	1500.00

*92	(duplone). 1795	1500.00

*93	(duplone). 1795, 96	600.00

SWITZERLAND

BASEL (Cont.)

II. Coinage after 1803.

Silver (lower values billon)

Fine

101 1/RAPPEN. Arms. Rev. value. 1810, 18...... 3.00

102 2/RAPPEN. Sim. 1810, 18. 3.00

103 ½/BATZEN. Sim. 1809... 9.00

104 I/BATZEN. Obv. like No. 53. Rev. value in wreath. 1805............20.00

104a —. CANTON BASEL. Pointed arms. 1805-11.....10.00

105 3/BATZ(en). DOMINE etc. Arms. Rev. value. 1809, 10....................8.50

*106 5/BATZ(en). 1809, 10.....17.50

*108 5 RAP(pen). 1826.......10.00

108a —. Oval arms. 1826......20.00

109 1 BATZ. Like No. 108. 1826....................10.00

109a —. Oval arms. 1826......20.00

110 5 BATZ^N or BATZEN. Sim. 1826................15.00

BELLINZONA, Territory

The three forest cantons, Uri, Schwyz and Unterwalden, conquered the district of Bellinzona in Lombardy at an early date and thereafter ruled it as subject territory. In 1803 Bellinzona was admitted to the Swiss confederation as a full member under the name Canton of Ticino (q.v.).

Monetary System:

12 denari = 3 quattrini = 1 soldo;
20 soldi = 1 lira.

Copper Patterns

V.F.

1 UN (=1) QUATTRINO. Shields of the 3 cantons (Bull's head, key, cross). Rev. value. 1788....................RR

V.F.

2 MEZZO (=½) SOLDO. Sim. 1788.............250.00

3 UN (=1) SOLDO. Sim. but obv. legend URANIEN. SUITEN. etc. added. 1788............RR

BERN, City and Canton

The city of Bern, founded in 1191, became a free city and obtained the mint right in 1218. It thereafter became the most important of the Swiss cantons.

Arms: Red, a black bear on a gold bend.

Monetary System:

Until 1798: 8 vierer = 4 kreuzer = 1 batzen;
40 batzen = 1 thaler.

1803 onward: 10 rappen = 1 batzen;
10 batzen = 1 frank.

I. Coinage Prior to Foundation of the Helvetian Republic 1798.

Billon

V.G.

*2 (vierer). MONETA BERNENSIS. 1731-32................. 2.75

2a —. 1762-97.............. 2.00

4 (kreuzer). Sim. but MONETA REIPUB. BERNENS. 18mm. 1718.............. 2.75

4a —. 1755-97............. 2.00

The 1792 (kreuzer) with RESPUBLICA BERNENSIS (former No. 5) is a pattern....................RR

*8 (½ batzen). 1718-98....... 3.00

9 (ex 6) 2/CREÜ/ZER. Sim. but rev. value in center of cross. 1770.............15.00

11 CR.4 (=batzen). Like No. 8 but MONETA REIPUB. etc., value in exergue. Rev. no decorations in field. 1717-98.................. 4.50

Notes: No. 11 dated 1799 is counterfeit. Nos. 8 and 11 dated 1798 were restruck for circulation after 1803-04.

Silver

F-VF

14 10/KREUT/ZER. Arms. Rev. value in cartouche. 1755-56.................20.00

F-VF

16 (10 kreuzer). MONETA REIPUB. BERNENS., Arms. Rev. 8 cwnd. B's cruciform. 2.2 gr. 1759-90...........15.00

16a —. RESPUBLICA BERNENSIS. 1797....................12.00

18 20/KREUT/ZER. Like No. 14. 1755-56............15.00

20 (20 kreuzer). Like No. 16. 4.5 gr. 1758-87............15.00

20a —. Like No. 16a. 1797-98...17.50

30 (¼ thaler). Like No. 16. 31mm. 7.8 gr. 1757-74....30.00

31a —. Like No. 16a. 1797.....30.00

V.F.

32 (½ thaler). Arms. Rev. Swiss stands on ground 13mm. wide. 1796-97..................70.00

32a —. Swiss stands on ground 20mm wide. 1797-98.......80.00

F-VF

*34 40/BZ (batzen). Cmkd. 1816-19 on French ecus....100.00

V.F.

36 (thaler). Like No. 32. 1795-96......................125.00

36a —. Arms and Swiss in ovals. 1798....................150.00

Gold

(ducat = 3.5 gr; 2 ducats = 1 duplone)

Nos. 2 and 2a were struck in gold with weights of ¼ and ½ ducat (former Nos. 41-42).

E.F.

*43 1 DUC(at). ND (1772)....500.00

43a —. 1788.................800.00

43b —. 1789.................700.00

SWITZERLAND

BERN (Cont.)

E.F.

45 2 DUC(ats). Sim. but 2 lions hold cap over arms. 1703-71 . . . . 1500.00

46 2 DUC(ats). 1788 . . . . RR

*46a —. 1789 . . . . 1200.00

47 (ex 48) 3 DUCAT. Like No. 43. 1772 . . . . 4000.00

48 DUC(ats). 4. Sim. but kidney-shaped arms. ND (ca. 1750) 4000.00

48a 4 (ducats). ND (ca. 1750). RRR

49 4 (ducats). Arms. Rev. man and woman clasp hands over altar. ND (ca. 1750) . . . . RR

49a (4 ducats). Sim. ND . . . . RRR

49.5 5 (ducats). Sim. ND (ca. 1750) . . . . RRR

49.5a (5 ducats). Sim. ND . . . . RRR

50 (4 ducats). Like No. 48, MK below arms. 32mm. ND (ca. 1750) 4000.00

50.1 (5 ducats). From dies of No. 50 . . . . RRR

50.2 (6 ducats). Ditto . . . . RRR

50.3 (7 ducats). Ditto . . . . RRR

51 (4 ducats). Sim. but no initials. 34mm. ND (ca. 1775) . . . . RR

51.2 (6 ducats). From dies of No. 51 . . . . 5000.00

51.4 (8 ducats). Ditto . . . . RR

51.6 (10 ducats). Ditto . . . . RRR

52 (7 ducats). Sim. but 40mm. ND (ca. 1775) . . . . RRR

52.1 (8 ducats). From dies of No. 52 . . . . RRR

52.3 (10 ducats). Ditto 6000.00

52.5 (12 ducats). Ditto . . . . RRR

53 1/DUCAT. Oval arms. 1793 . . . . RRR

*53a —. Pointed arms. 1794 . . . 400.00

E.F.

54 II/DUCAT. Sim. 1796 . . 1250.00

55 IV/DUCAT. Sim. 1796, 98, 1825 . . . . 4000.00

56 VI/DUCAT. Sim. 1796 . . . . RRR

57 VIII/DUCAT. Sim. 1796, 98 . . . . 6000.00

*58 (duplone). 1793-95 . . . . 600.00

58a —. 1796 . . . . 600.00

59 (2 duplones). Sim. 1793-95 . . . . 900.00

59a —. 1796 . . . . 900.00

60 (½ duplone). Like No. 61. 1797 . . . . 600.00

*61 (duplone). 1793, 97, 1819, 29 . . . . 750.00

62 (2 duplones). Sim. 1794, 96-98 . . . . 1250.00

Nos. 32-32a were struck in gold with weights of 6 and 8 ducats (former Nos. 63-64).

II. Coinage After Dissolution of the Helvetian Republic 1803.

Billon

V.G.

71 1/RAPPEN. CANTON BERN. Arms. Rev. value. 1811, 29 . . . . 2.50

71a —. REPUBL. BERN 1818, 19, 36 . . . . 2.50

73 2/RAPPEN. Like No. 71. 1809 . . . . 3.00

75 2½/RAPPEN. Sim. 1811 . . . 3.00

77 (½ batzen). Like No. 8. 1818, 24 . . . . 6.00

The 1/BATZEN 1804 is a pattern.

79 CR.4 (=batzen). Like No. 11. 1818, 24 . . . . 6.00

Silver

V.F.

81 5/BATZ. CANTON BERN, Arms. Rev. DOMINUS etc., value. 1808-18 . . . . 15.00

VF-EF

*82 1 FRANK. 1811 . . . . 100.00

83 (2 franken). Arms. Rev. stdg. Swiss (like No. 32). 1835 . . . 150.00

85 (4 franken). Like No. 83. 1823, 35 . . . . 600.00

Billon

Fine

87 5 RAP(pen). Like No. 88, with or w/out quatrefoil on rev. 1826 . . . . 4.00

*88 1 BATZ (or BAZ). 1826 . . . . 5.00

89 2½ BATZ. (or BAZ). Sim. but arms cwnd. 1826 . . . . 8.00

Silver

V.F.

*90 5 BATZ. (or BAZ). 1826 . . . . 18.00

91 4 FR(an)K(e)N. Sim. 1826 . . . . (E.F.)RR

The 1825 Concordat coins are patterns. No. 91 is probably also a pattern.

For gold after 1803 see Nos. 55 and 61. For 18th century French ecus cmkd. in 1816-19 see No. 34.

SWITZERLAND

CHUR
(CURIAE RHETHICAE),
Bishopric

In present-day Canton Graubünden. First mentioned 452 A.D. Bishops obtained the mint right 959. *Secularized circa 1798.*

Monetary System:
See GERMANY, and:
12 pfennig = 4 bluzger = 1 schilling;
60 kreuzer = 70 bluzger = 1 gulden.

Arms:
Silver, a black goat rampant.

Johann Anton,
Freiherr von Federspiel,
Bishop 1755-77

Billon

V.G.

★11 (bluzger). 1764-66........ 4.00
12 1/KREU/ZER. I.A.D.G.E.S.C. R.I.P., bust. Rev. value. 1759.....................RR
12.5 1 K(reuzer). Arms. Rev. JAEC mon. 1761.........50.00
13 6/KREU/ZER. Bust. Rev. value in cartouche. 1758.....RR

Silver
V.F.

14 VI/EINEN (= ⅙)/REICHS/ THALER. Bust. Rev. value. 1758.....................RRR
15 (Convention thaler). IOANNES ANTONIUS D.G. EP. CUR. etc. Arms. Rev. AD/NORMAM/ CONVENT/1766, in wreath...............1500.00
15.5 (ex 15a) —. Obv. sim. Rev. IOSEPHUS II etc., Imp. eagle. 1766................RR
16 (2 Conv. thaler). No. 15 double thick. 1766.......RRR
16.5 —. No. 15.5 double thick. 1766.....................RRR

Gold
VF-EF

17 (ducat). Madonna. Rev. Arms. 1767.............2000.00

CHUR, City

The city of Chur, capital of Graubünden, was originally ruled by the

---

bishops of Chur, but became completely independent by 1526.

Monetary System:
70 bluzger = 1 gulden.

Arms. Goat rampant in city gate.

Billon
V.G.

5 (bluzger). MON(ETA) NOVA CURIAE RET(H)ICAE. City arms. Rev. DOMINI etc., cross. 1705-66.................. 5.00

EINSIEDELN, Abbey

In Canton Schwyz 25 miles S.E. of Zürich. Abbey founded 934.

Beatus Kuttel, Abbot 1780-1808

Gold
VF-EF

3 (ducat). Arms. Rev. Madonna. 1783.........1250.00

FREYBURG
(FRIBURG, FRIBOURG),
Canton

In western Switzerland. Joined Swiss Confederation 1481. Renamed Canton de Sarine et de Broye 1798-1803.

Arms: Per fesse, black and silver.

Until 1798:
16 denier = 8 vierer = 4 kreuzer = 1 batzen; 56 kreuzer = 8 piecette = 1 gulden; 24 piecette = 1 thaler (ecu).

After 1798: 10 rappen = 1 batzen; 10 batzen = 1 frank.

I. Coinage Before Formation of the Helvetian Republic.

Billon
V.G.

1 (denier). FRIBVRG, cross. Rev. blank. 1735-63....... 5.00
2 (vierer). Like No. 6 but MONETA FRIBURGENSIS. 15mm. 1736-51........... 3.00
2a —. MONETA REIP. FRIBURGENS. 1769-90.................. 3.00
4 (kreuzer). Like No. 6. 19mm. 1732-89........... 3.00

★6 (½ batzen). 1741-98........ 3.50

Silver
F-VF

10 7 (kreuzer). Like No. 12. 1786-97.................. 7.00

★12 14 (kreuzer). 1787-98......16.50
14 28 (kreuzer). Sim. 1793, 98..25.00
16 56 (kreuzer). Sim. 1796-97..85.00

II. Canton de Sarine et de Broye.
Name given to Freyburg 1798-1803.

Silver

V.F.

★21 42 CR(euzer). 1798......175.00

III. Coinage After 1803.

Billon
V.G.

31 5/RAP(pen). Arms. Rev. value. 1806......... 7.00
32 ½/BATZEN. Arms. Rev. value. 1810-11........ 5.00
33 I BATZ(en). Arms. Rev. cross. 1806.......... 7.00
34 1/BATZ(en). Arms. Rev. value. 1810......... 8.00
34a 1/BATZEN. 1811......... 5.00

Silver
V.F.

35 5/BATZ(en). Arms. Rev. value. 1811, 14......27.50

SWITZERLAND

FREYBURG (Cont.)

V.F.

*37 10 BATZ(en). 1811-12.....90.00

39 4 FRANK(e)N. Sim.
1813............(*VF-EF*) 600.00

Billon
Fine

41 2½ RAP(pen). Like No. 42.
1827...................3.00

41.5 2½/RAP(pen). Arms.
Rev. value. 1846.........3.00

42 5 RAP(pen). Like No. 42a
but date on obv. 1827-28...6.00

*42a —. 1830-31.............3.00

43 1 BAZ(en). Variety of No. 42.
1827-29..................5.00

43a 1 BATZ(en). 1830.........5.00

Silver
V.F.

44 5 BAZ(en). Sim. 1827-29...25.00

44a 5 BATZEN. 1830.........35.00

GENEVA
(GENEVE, GENF),
City and Canton

In S.W. Switzerland. The town of Geneva was first mentioned by Caesar. Achieved freedom from Savoy in 1530. Annexed to France in 1798. Regained independence 1813. Became a canton in the Swiss Confederation in 1815.

Arms: Per pale.
Dexter: Gold, ½ black eagle.
Sinister: Red, a gold key.

Monetary Systems:

Until 1794:
12 deniers = 4 quarts = 1 sol;
12 sols = 1 florin;
12 florins, 9 sols = 1 thaler;
35 florins = 1 pistole.

1794-95:
10 decimes = 1 Genevoise.

1795-98, 1813-38:
Same as pre 1794.

1838 onward:
100 centimes = 1 franc.

I. Coinage Before the Constitutional Changes of 1794.

Billon

V.G.

*2 (6 deniers). 1709-88 (var.)... 2.50

4 (9 deniers). Arms. Rev.
Imp. eagle. 17-18mm.
1730-85..................3.50

6 UN (=1)/SOL. 1785-88 .... 3.50

8 (6 Quarts). Like No. 10.
19mm. 1722-76...........5.00

10 (3 sols). Date at top.
1722-76.................6.00

*10a —. Date at bottom. 1791.. 5.00

12 SIX/SOLS. Obv. sim.
Rev. like No. 6. 1765-91... 7.00

Gold

V.F.

*21 (pistole). 1752-70........500.00

22 (pistole). Arms. Rev. Imp.
eagle. 1772..............800.00

23 (3 pistoles). Like No. 21.
1771..................1500.00

II. Coinage of the Revolutionary Era 1794-98.

Billon
VG-F

31 SIX/D(eniers). Arms,
L'AN etc. Rev. motto, value.
1795...................5.00

VG-F

32 I SOL/SIX D(eniers).
Sim. 1795...............7.00

33 UN (=1)/SOL/6 D(eniers).
Sim. 1795...............8.00

35 TROIS (=3)/SOLS.
Sim. 1795, 98............9.50

37 SIX/SOLS. Sim. 1795-97... 9.50

Silver

CINQ CENTIMES and DECIME of 1794 are patterns.
F-VF

39 15/SOLS. Eagle. Rev. value
in sun. 1794.............12.50

V.F.

41 VI/FLORINS/IV S(ols)
VI D(eniers). Round arms.
Rev. sun, value. 1795.....85.00

43 (10 decimes). REPUBLIQUE
GENEVOISE, Head. Rev. PRIX/
DU/TRAVAIL etc. 1794......125.00

44 XII/FLORINS/IX/SOLS.
Like No. 41. 1795-96.....110.00

III. Canton of Geneva.
Old Monetary System.

Billon
VG-F

51 6 D(eniers). Like No. 53a
but round arms. 1817......2.50

51a SIX/D(eniers). 1819-33..... 2.50

52 UN(=1)/SOL. Like No. 53a.
1817, 19.................2.50

*52a—. 1825, 33..............2.00

53 UN SOL/6 D(eniers). Sim.
1817...................3.00

*53a 1/SOL/6 D(eniers). 1825... 5.00

IV. New Monetary System.

Copper
F-VF

61 I/CENTIME. Like No. 68.
1840, 44, 46.............2.50

62 1/CENTIME. Sim. but arms
in shield. 1847.............3.00

Billon

63 I/CENTIME. Like No. 68.
1839...................2.50

64 2/CENTIMES. Sim. 1839.. 5.00

SWITZERLAND

GENEVA (Cont.)

F-VF

65 4/CENTIMES. Sim. 1839.. 4.00

66 5/CENTIMES. Sim. 1840.. 4.00

67 10/CENTIMES. Sim.
1839, 44................. 5.00

★68 25/CENTIMES. 1839, 44... 6.00

69 5/CENTIMES. Sim. but arms
in shield. 1847............ 4.50

70 10/CENTIMES. Sim. 1847.. 4.50

71 25/CENTIMES. Sim. 1847.. 6.50

**Nos. 61-71 in fine silver are rare
presentation pieces.**

Silver

E.F.

★72 5/FRANCS. 1848........400.00

73 10/FRANCS. Sim. 1848,
51...................700.00

Gold

74 10/FRANCS. Like No. 68.
1848...................3000.00

75 20/FRANCS. Sim. 1848..2200.00

GLARUS, Canton

In N.E. Switzerland. Became independent 1388/98. Absorbed into the Can-

ton of Linth 1798-1803. Regained its independent status within the confederation 1803.

Monetary System:

3 rappen = 1 schilling;
100 rappen = 1 frank.

Silver (Billon)

Fine

1 1/SCHIL(ling). Like No. 2.
1806-13.................. 9.00

★2 III/SCHILLING. 1806-14...20.00

3 XV/SCHILLING. Sim.
1806-14...................65.00

GRAUBÜNDEN
(GRISONS, = "Grey Leagues"),
Canton

Largest and most easterly Swiss canton. Until the advent of the Helvetian Republic in 1798 this area was parceled among various independent rulers, chief amongst whom were the bishop of Chur, the abbots of Disentis and Pfaefers, the free barons of Haldenstein, and the city of Chur. From 1799 to 1803 Graubünden was renamed Raetia. In 1803 it became a Canton of the Confederation.

Arms: 3 shields, containing arms of the three leagues into which the various rulers of the area were formerly divided.

Monetary System:

15 rappen = 6 bluzger = 1 Schweizer
batzen;
10 Schweizer batzen = 1 frank;
16 franken = 1 duplone.

Billon

V.G.

1 ⅙/-/BATZEN. Like No. 7.
1807, 20.................. 8.00

1a ⅙/-/BAZEN. 1842....... 6.50

2 ½/-/BATZEN. Sim.
1807-20.................. 8.00

3 ½/-/BAZEN. Like No. 8.
1836, 42.................. 9.00

4 1/-/BATZEN. Like No. 7.
1807, 20, 26..............10.00

5 1/-/BAZEN. Like No. 8.
1836, 42.................. 8.00

Silver

Fine

6 V/-/BATZEN. Like No. 7.
1807, 20, 26.............45.00

V.F.

★7 X/-/BATZEN. 1825......150.00

Gold

★8 16/-/FRANKEN. 1813 ..4000.00

HALDENSTEIN, Lordship

In Graubünden. Received the mint right in 1612. Mediatized in 1798-99 during the French invasion. Much of the Haldenstein coinage was produced for export.

Arms:

Haldenstein: Steinbok's horn.

Reichenau: 3 fishes. (The Reichenau coinage predates this catalog.)

Baron Thomas III von Salis,
In Schauenstein 1737-83

Copper

Fine

1 (pfennig). Count's crown over Salis arms (tree/3 pales). Rev. Prince's crown over Liechtenstein-Grottenstein arms. 11.5mm. ND.........RR

Billon

Former No. 2 was struck for Reichenstein prior to 1750.

3 I/KREVT/ZER. T.D.S.D.-
IN. H.L.B., bust. Rev. value.
1758...................120.00

SWITZERLAND

....

HALDENSTEIN (cont.)

Fine

4 2/KREVT/ZER. H(errschaft) H(aldenstein)/arms (2 steinbok horns). Rev. value. 1749...200.00

5 I/ALBUS. D. IN HAL etc., TDS mon. Rev. value. 1752.................150.00

6 3 (kreuzer). T.D.S. etc., arms. Rev. SI. DEVS etc., Imp. eagle. 1748.......................RR

7 V/SOLDI. Like No. 3 but IN. H. L. & G. 1748..........RR

8 6 (kreutzer). T.D.S. etc., arms. Rev. F. ST. I. etc., Imp. eagle/IC–M. 1747..........RRR

Gold

V.F.

11 (ducat). Bust. Rev. eagle. 1767-70..................RRR

HELVETIAN REPUBLIC

Centralized government for all Switzerland, created by the French and existing 1798-1803. The Swiss Confederation was reestablished in 1803.

Monetary System:

10 rappen = 1 batzen;
10 batzen = 1 frank;
16 franken = 1 duplone.

Mints: B(ern); S(olothurn).

Billon

VG-F

1 1/RAPPEN. HELVET. REPUBL. Liberty hat on fasces. Rev. value. 1800-02............ 6.00

2 ½/BATZEN. HELVET/REPUBL. in wreath. Rev. value. 1799.................40.00

2a —. HELVET/REPUBL./5. 1799-1803.................10.00

3 I/BATZEN. Like No. 2. 1799....................20.00

3a —. 1/BATZEN. HELVET./ REPUBL./IO. 1799-1803......8.00

Silver

V.F.

4 5/BATZEN. Like No. 8. 1799-1802.................85.00

5 10/BATZEN. Sim. 1798- 99, 1801...............135.00

6 20/BATZEN. Sim. 1798...200.00

V.F.

★7 40/BATZEN. Obv.★. Rev. value. 1798.............400.00

8 4/FRANKEN. 1799.......500.00
★8a —. 1801................500.00

Gold

★9 16/FRANKEN. 1800.....1800.00
10 32/FRANKEN. Sim. 1800..................5000.00

LUZERN (LUCERN), City and Canton

In central Switzerland. Became the fourth member of the Swiss Confederation, and in 1386 obtained its freedom from the Hapsburgs.

Arms: Per pale, blue and silver.

Monetary Systems:

Until 1798:

240 angster = 120 rapen =
40 schillinge = 1 gulden;
4 kreuzer = 1 batzen;
40 batzen = 3 gulden = 1 thaler;
12 gulden = 1 duplone.

1803 Onward:

2 angster = 1 rapen;
10 rapen = 1 rapen;
10 batzen = 1 frank;
4 franken = 1 thaler.

Copper

VG-F

★1 I/ANGSTER. 1773....... 3.00

2 I/RAPEN. Sim. N.D. (=1773)................. 2.75

3 I/ANGSTER. Like No. 4. 1773-1834................ 2.50

★4 I/RAPEN. 1774-1804...... 2.00

5 I/RAPPEN. Arms in pointed shield. Rev. value. 1831.... 2.75

5a —. Smaller. 1834.......... 4.00

6 I/ANGSTER. Like No. 7. 1839, 43................. 2.50

★7 1/RAPPEN. 1839-46....... 2.25

Billon and Silver

I. Until 1798.

Billon

V.G.

11 (schilling). Arms. Rev. SANCT LEODEGARIUS. 1794-95...... 4.00

★13 (½ batzen). 1795-96....... 2.50

14 1 BAZ (batzen). Sim. 1796-97.................. 2.50

LUZERN (cont.)

Silver

V.F.

16 ⅛ (gulden). Like No. 21.
1793.................12.50

17 ¼ (gulden). Sim. 1793, 96...20.00

19 (40 Kreuzer). Arms.
Rev. double L mon. 8 gr.
29-30mm. ND. 1782.......70.00

20 20 (kreuzer). Like No. 21.
1793.................20.00

20a —. Like No. 21a. 1795-96...20.00

★21 40 (kreuzer). 1793........50.00

21a —. No garland across top
of arms. 1795-96.........35.00

23 20 BAZ (=20 batzen). Sim.
1795.................80.00

24 40 BAZ (=40 batzen). Sim.
1796.................175.00

II. 1803 Onward.

Billon

VG-F

28 ½ BATZEN/5 RAP. Arms.
Rev. value. 1813......... 6.00

30 1 BAZ (batzen). Arms/1 BAZ.
Rev. X/RAPPEN/1803.......10.00

30a —. Oval arms. 1804, 06..... 7.50

30b —. Rev. 1/BATZEN/1805.. 8.00

31 I/BATZEN/X/RAPPEN.
Like No. 28. 1807-11....... 5.00

31b –/–/10/RAPPEN. 1813 .... 5.00

Silver

V.F.

33 2½/BATZ(en). Like No. 34a.
1815.................15.00

33a —. RESPUBLICA LUCERNENSIS.
1815.................15.00

34 V/BATZEN. Arms.
Rev. value. 1806.........20.00

V.F.

★34a 5/BATZ(en), 1810-14
(var.)..................15.00

34b —. Obv. Arms/date.
1815-16..................15.00

35 10 BATZ(en). Like No. 36.
1811, 12..................50.00

★36 4 FRANKEN. 1813, 14...175.00

37 40/BATZEN. Obv. Sim.
Rev. value. 1816, 17......300.00

Gold

★41 12/MZ:GL (=12 gulden).
1794, 96..............1000.00

42 24/MZ:GL (=24 g). Sim.
1794, 96..............1500.00

★43 10 FR(anken). 1804.......600.00

44 20 FR(anken). Sim. 1807.1500.00

NEUCHATEL
(NEUENBURG, NOVICASTRI),
Principality

On the French border. Acquired by
Prussia in 1707 at the extinction of the
Longuevilles (ruling family). To Prussia
1707-1806. To French Marshal Alexandre Berthier 1806-14. Back to Prussia
1814-48. Republic proclaimed 1848.
Prussia renounced all rights in 1857
and the canton became a full fledged
member of the Swiss Confederation.

Arms: Gold, 3 silver chevrons on red
pale.

Monetary System:
4 kreuzer = 1 batzen;
7 kreuzer = 1 piecette;
168 kreuzer = 42 batzen = 2 gulden =
1 thaler.

Friedrich Wilhelm II of
Prussia 1786-97

Billon

G-VG

10 (½ kreuzer). Like No. 13 but
no circle around arms or cross.
14mm. 1789-96........... 4.50

11 (kreuzer). Sim. 18.5mm.
1789-94.................. 5.00

12 (2 kreuzer). Sim. 22mm.
1789-94.................. 5.00

The 2 kreuzer 1788 is a RR pattern.

★13 CR. 4 (=batzen). 1790-93 .. 7.50

Silver

F-VF

15 28 (kreuzer). Like No. 19.
1793, 96................50.00

17 10½ BZ (=42 kreuzer).
Like No. 21. 1796.........80.00

★19 56 (kreuzer). 1795.......135.00

SWITZERLAND

NEUCHATEL (cont.)

21 21 BZ (=21 batzen). Pointed arms, value. Rev. cross, sun in center. 1796 . . . . 135.00 *(F-VF)*

Friedrich Wilhelm III of Prussia, In Neuchatel 1797-1806

Billon

V.G.

25 (½ kreuzer). Like No. 29. 16mm. 1802, 03 . . . . 15.00

27 CR(euzer) 1. Sim. 19mm. 1800-03 . . . . 7.50

28 (2 kreuzer). Sim. 23mm. 1798-1800 . . . . 6.00

28a CR. 2. 1800, 03 . . . . 6.00

★29 CR. 4 (=batzen). 1798-1800 . . . . 6.00

Silver

★32 21 BZ (=21 batzen). 1799 . . . . 100.00 *(V.F.)*

(Marshal) Alexandre (Berthier), Prince 1806-14

Billon

V.G.

35 1/CREUT(zer). Like No. 36. 1807-08 . . . . 4.00

V.G.

★36 ½/BATZ. 1807-09 . . . . 3.00

36a DEMI (=½)/BATZ. 1807 . . . . 5.00

37 1 BATZ. Sim. 1806-10 . . . . . 3.00

37a UN (=1)/BATZ. 1807-08 . . 4.50

Note: Other Marshal Berthier values are patterns.

Friedrich Wilhelm III, Restored 1814-40

Billon

★40 CR. 1 (=1 kreuzer). 1817-18 . . . . 4.00

NIDWALDEN. See Unterwalden.
OBWALDEN. See Unterwalden.

ST. GALL (ST. GALLEN), Princely Abbey

In N.E. Switzerland. Established about 720 A.D. Obtained the mint right 947 A.D. Lost control of Canton Appenzell in 1411, and of the city of St. Gall in 1457. Secularized and incorporated into the Canton of Saentis (quickly renamed St. Gall) in 1798.

Arms: Gold, black bear with gold collar, often carrying club.

Monetary System:
4 pfennig =1 kreuzer;
4 kreuzer =1 batzen;
120 kreuzer =1 Convention thaler.

Beda Angehrn von Hagenwyl, Abbot 1767-96

Billon

Fine

1 1/PFEN(nig). Bear l. Rev. value in cartouche. ND 35.00

2 1/KREUT/ZER. Sim. ND 20.00

2a —. Bear r. ND 15.00

3 2/KREU/ZER. Bear r. Rev. value in wreath. 1780 . . 15.00

4 4/KREU/ZER. Sim. 1780, 82 . . . . 20.00

5 5 (kreuzer). Like No. 15. 1774-75 . . . . 12.50

Fine

★6 6 (kreuzer). N.D 150.00

6a —. 1773 . . . . 20.00

Silver

F-VF

7 10 (kreuzer). Like No. 15. 1774-75 . . . . 27.50

8 12 (kreuzer) Like No. 6. ND . . RR

8a —. 1773 . . . . 50.00

9 15 (kreuzer). Bear in branches. Rev. MON PRINCIP. TERRIT. GALLI. 1781 . . . . 45.00

10 20 (kreuzer). Like No. 15. 1774 . . . . 30.00

★11 20 (kreuzer). 1777, 79 . . . . . 40.00

11a —. Diff. arms. 1780, 83 . . . . 30.00

12 30 (kreuzer). Like No. 9. 1781, 96 . . . . 55.00

13 (½ thaler). Like No. 11. 1776-77 . . . . 120.00

13a —. Diff. arms. 1780, 82 . . . . 80.00

13.5 I (gulden). Like No. 9. 1781 . . . . RR

14 (thaler). Like No. 11. 39mm. 1776-79 . . . . 125.00

14a —. Diff. arms. 1780 . . . . . . 125.00

Gold

V.F.

14.5 (½ ducat). Like No. 6. 1773 . . . . RRR

★15 (ducat). 1773-74 . . . . 1250.00

★16 (ducat). 1781 . . . . 1000.00

SWITZERLAND

ST. GALL, City

Nine miles S.W. of Lake Constance. Obtained the mint right 1415. Freed itself from the abbots in 1457. Absorbed into the Canton of Saentis 1798.

Arms:
Silver, black bear with gold collar.

Monetary System: See Abbey.

Billon

V.G.

31 (pfennig). Bear l. Rev. blank.
N.D...................... 6.00

32 2 D(enar = 2 pfennig). Sim.
N.D...................... 5.50

*33 1 K(reuzer). N.D.......... 5.00

33a 1 Kr(euzer). Sim. ND...... 5.00

34 2 K(reuzer). Bear l.
Rev. SOLI/DEO/GLORIA/date.
1714-68 (var.)........... 6.50

35 3 (kreuzer). Bear l. Rev. 3 in
floral cross. 1721-90 (var.) .. 7.00

37 4 KR(euzer). Like No. 33.
1721-25................. 15.00

38 VI KREUZER. Bear l.
Rev. value in branches.
1725-90 (var.)...........10.00

Silver

F-VF

*39 15 (kreuzer). 1724-89
(var.)...................15.00

40 30 (kreuzer). Bear l. Rev.
LIBERTAS/CARIOR/AURO/
1738....................55.00

ST. GALL (ST. GALLEN), Canton

During the Helvetian Republic 1798-1803, the city and abbey of St. Gall and the Canton of Appenzell were joined together to form the Canton of Saentis. In 1803 Appenzell regained its independence and the remainder of Saentis became the Canton of St. Gall.

Arms: Green, a fasces.

Monetary System:
4 pfennig = 1 kreuzer;
4 kreuzer = 1 batzen;
10 batzen = 1 frank.

Billon

V.G.

51 1 PF(ennig). Arms. Uniface.
Dish shaped. N.D......... 5.00

52 2/PFENNING. CANTON ST. GALLEN. Arms. Rev. value/
date. 1808...............65.00

53 ½/KREUZER. Sim. 1808-
17.....................10.00

54 ¼/SCHWEIZ./BAZEN
(= 1 kreuzer). Sim. 1807-
08...................... 8.00

*55 1/KREUZER. 1807-16..... 4.00

56 ½/SCHWEIZER/BAZEN.
Sim. 1807-10............. 6.00

57 ½/BAZEN. Sim. 1807-17... 5.00

58 1/BAZEN. Sim. 1807...... 8.00

59 1/SCHWEIZER/BAZEN.
Sim. 1807-09............. 6.00

*60 1/BAZEN. Arms/date.
Rev. value. 1810-17....... 5.00

61 VI/KREUZER. Like No. 52.
1807...................35.00

Silver

Fine

62 ½/SCHWEIZ./FRANKEN.
Like No. 63. 1810........250.00

*63 5/BAZEN. 1810-17.......25.00

SCHAFFHAUSEN (SCAPHUSIA, SCAFUSENSIS), City and Canton

In N.W. Switzerland. Became a free city of the Empire about 1190/1208. First local coins issued in 13th century. Member of the Swiss Confederation 1501.

Arms: Ram (leaping from tower).

Monetary System:
4 kreuzer = 1 batzen.

Billon

VG-F

1 1/KREUZER. Like No. 2.
1808...................25.00

*2 ½/BATZEN. 1808-09.....15.00

3 1/BATZEN. Sim. 1808-09 ..20.00

Note: Nos. 2 and 3 of 1808 have SCHWEIZ(ER) in the denomination.

SCHWYZ (SCHWYTZ, SUITENSIS), Canton

In central Switzerland. Member of the "Everlasting League" with Uri and Unterwalden in 1291. Obtained the mint right in 1424. So important was Schwyz's part in the formation of the Swiss Confederation that its name, slightly altered, became that of the whole country.

Arms: Red, silver cross in upper sinister corner.

Monetary System: Same as Luzern.

I. Coinage Before Formation of the Helvetian Republic 1798.

Copper

V.G.

1 EIN (=1)/ANGSTER. Like
No. 32 but rev. w/out wreath.
1773-80................. 2.50

2 I/ANGSTER. Sim.
1781-97................. 3.00

2a —. Rev. value in wreath.
1797-98................. 3.00

3 I/RAPEN. Sim. but
rev. value in cartouche.
1777-82................. 2.00

3a —. Wreath forms top of
cartouche. 1782-98........ 2.00

Billon

6 I/RAPEN. Arms. Rev. value.
1776...................12.00

8 EIN (=1)/GROSCHEN
(=2½ schillinge). MONETA
REIP. SUITENSIS. Arms.
Rev. value. 1791..........20.00

8a —. 1793.................20.00

Silver

F-VF

12 5/SCHIL/LING. Like
No. 15. 1785.............20.00

12a V/SCHIL/LING. Sim.
1787...................20.00

SWITZERLAND

SCHWYZ (cont.)

F-VF

*15 X/SCHIL/LING. 1786..... 20.00

18 ½ G(u)L(den). Arms.
Rev. PAX/OPTIMA/etc.
1785.................... 65.00

19 20 S(chilling). Arms. Rev.
motto, S on cross. 1797..... 65.00

23 1 G(u)L(den). Oval arms
and lion. Rev. PAX/OPTIMA/
RERUM/1785............. 120.00

25 1 G(u)L(den). Like No. 19.
1797.................... 150.00

Gold

V.F.

*29 DUCATUS (=ducat.)
1781, 88, 90 N.D. 1000.00

II. Coinage After 1803.

Copper

VG-F

31 I/ANGSTER. Like No. 32.
1810-46.................. 3.00

*32 1/RAPEN. 1812-15........ 2.00

33 1/RAPPEN. Sim.
1811, 15-46.............. 2.00

Silver (or Billon)

Fine

35 2/RAPPEN. Like No. 36.
1811-13.................. 4.00

35a —. Pointed shield. 1811-
46........................ 2.75

*36 ⅔/BATZ. 1810-11........ 20.00

36a ⅔/BATZEN. 1812........ 30.00

Fine

38 2/BATZ. Sim. 1810....... 40.00

38a 2/BATZEN. 1810......... 40.00

40 4/BATZEN. Sim.
1810-11.................. 90.00

Gold

E.F.

45 (ducat). Lion and arms.
Rev. CONSERVA/NOS IN/PACE/
1844 .... RR

SITTEN
(SION, SEDUNENSIS),
Bishopric

Generally equivalent to Canton Valais.
Bishopric located at Sitten in 580 A.D.
The bishops first obtained temporal
power over Valais in 999. Their titles
read: EPISCOPUS SEDUNENSIS, PRAEFEC-
TUS ET COMES REIPUBLICA VALLESY.

In 1798 Sitten was occupied by
French troops and forcibly united to
the Helvetian Republic.

Arms of Valais:

Per pale silver and red, 7 stars.

Monetary System:

4 kreuzer = 1 batzen.

Franz Friedrich am Buel
1760-80

Silver (lower values billon)

V.G.

*11 (kreuzer). (17)76........... 7.00

12 (½ batzen). Sim. but
obv. arms 4 fold. 20mm.
(17)76-77................. 8.00

13 (batzen). Sim. but rev. legend
ends PRÆF. UTR. VALLE.
23mm. 1776.............. 30.00

13a —. Rev. legend ends PRÆF.
REIP. VALLES. (17)76,
1776-78 (var.).......... 6.00

14 CR(euzer) 6. Sim. 1777..... 15.00

*15 CR(euzer) 12. 1777....... 20.00

17 CR(euzer) 20. Four fold
family arms. Rev. SUB TUUM
etc., Madonna and Valais
arms. 1777.............. 35.00

SOLOTHURN
(SOLODORNENSIS, SOLEURE),
City and Canton

In N.W. Switzerland. Became a free
city of the Empire in 1218. First coins
13th century. Joined Swiss Confederation 1411.

Arms: Per fesse red and silver.

Monetary Systems:

Until 1798:

2 vierer = 1 kreuzer;
4 kreuzer = 1 batzen;
40 batzen = 2 gulden = 1 thaler.

After 1803:

10 rappen = 4 kreuzer = 1 batzen;
10 batzen = 1 frank.

I. Coinage Before Formation of
the Helvetian Republic 1798.

Billon

V.G.

*5 (vierer). 1761-98.......... 2.50

6 (kreuzer). MONETA REIP.
SOLOD. Arms. Rev. CUNCTA*
PER*DEUM, cross. 18mm.
1760-98.................. 3.50

8 (½ batzen). Sim. 23mm.
1760-96.................. 3.50

10 CR(euzer) 4. Sim. but S
twines around cross. 1760... 60.00

11 CR.4. Like No. 6 but ornaments in angles of cross.
1760-62.................. 8.00

12 CR.4. (=batzen). Like No. 6.
1766-97.................. 4.50

Silver

F-VF

16 CR(euzer) 10. Like No. 22.
1760, 62 (var.)............ 25.00

16a —. Like No. 22a. 1785..... 20.00

17 (10 kreuzer). Like No. 22b.
21mm. 1787-95............ 12.50

19 CR(euzer) 20. Like No. 22.
1760, 63 (var.)............ 45.00

19a —. Like No. 22a. 1785..... 40.00

20 (20 kreuzer). Like No. 22b.
26mm. 1787-95............ 30.00

V.F.

22 (10 batzen). Arms. Rev.
CUNCTA etc., flowery s on
cwnd. cross in wreath. 30mm.
1761-67 (var.)............ 90.00

SWITZERLAND

SOLOTHURN (Cont.)

		V.F.
★22a	—. Rev. so on cross, w/out cwn. or wreath. 1773-85	90.00
22b	(ex 23) —. Sim. but RES- PUBLICA etc. Rev. s on cross in circle. 1787-94	75.00
25	20 BA(t)Z(en). Sim. 1795, 98	100.00

Gold

(ducat = 3.5 gr; duplone = 7.64 gr.)

31	(¼ duplone). Like No. 33. 1789, 96	275.00
32	DUCATUS. Sim. 1768	RR

★33	(½ duplone). 1787, 96	600.00
34	(duplone). Sim. 1787, 96-98	800.00
35	(2 duplones). Sim. 1787, 96-98	1400.00

II. First Cantonal Coinage After 1803.

Billon

		VG-F
41	1/RAPPEN. Arms. Rev. value. 1813	12.00
42	1/KREUZER. Sim. 1813	6.00
44	1/BATZEN. Arms in pointed shield on s of laurel. Rev. I/BATZEN/X/RAPPEN in wreath. 1805	10.00
45	1/BATZEN. Like No. 45a but rev. 10 (rappen) in lower field. 1807-09	8.00

		VG-F
★45a	—. 1810-11	4.00

Silver

		F-VF
46	5/BATZEN. Arms. Rev. value. 1809, 11	30.00
		V.F.
47	1 FRANK. Like No. 48. 1812	150.00

		VF-EF
★48	4 FRANKEN. 1813	700.00

Gold

		V.F.
49	8 FRANKᴺ. Obv. sim. Rev. stdg. Swiss. 1813	2000.00
50	16 FRANKᴺ. Sim. 1813	2500.00

III. Concordat Coinage.

Silver (lower values billon)

		F-VF
52	2½ RAP(pen) = 1 KREUZER. Arms. Rev. cross. 1830	5.00
53	5 RAP(pen). Like No. 54. 1826	8.00

★54	1 BAZ (or BATZ). 1826	6.00

		F-VF
55	2½ BAZ. Sim. but oval arms. 1826	15.00
56	5 BAZ. or BATZ. Sim. 1826	20.00

TESSIN. See Ticino.

THURGAU (THURGOVIE), Canton

In N.E. Switzerland. Formerly subject territory of the Swiss Confederation. Admitted in 1803 to the confederation as a member canton.

Arms: Parted per bend, white above, green below. In each canton is gold lion passant.

Monetary System:
4 kreuzer = 1 Schweizer (Swiss) batzen; 10 batzen = 1 frank.

Silver (lower values billon)

		Fine
1	½/KREUZER. Like No. 4. 1808	60.00
2	1/KREUZER. Sim. 1808	12.00
3	½/SCHWEIZ/BATZEN. Sim. 1808	20.00

★4	1/SCHWEIZ/BATZEN. 1808-09	20.00
		V.F.
5	5/SCHWEIZ/BATZEN. Sim. 1808	200.00

TICINO (TESSIN), Canton

The former subject territory of Bellin- zona in Lombardy, admitted as a full member of the Swiss Confederation in 1803.

Arms: Per pale, red and blue.

Monetary System:
12 denari = 1 soldo; 20 soldi = 1 franco.

Copper

		VG-F
★1	DENARI/TRE (= 3 d.). Like No. 5 but round arms. 1814, 35	9.00
1a	—. Pointed arms. 1841	8.00
2	DENARI/SEI (= 6 d.). Sim. 1813, 35, 41	12.00

SWITZERLAND

TICINO (Cont.)

Billon
V.G.

3 SOLDI/TRE (= 3 s.).
Sim. 1813-41 . . . . 8.00

Silver
F-VF

4 1/QUARTO (= ¼)/FRANCO.
Sim. 1835 . . . . 30.00

*5 1/MEZZO (= ½)/FRANCO.
1835 . . . . 60.00

V.F.

*6 1 FRANCO. 1813 . . . . 200.00
7 2 FRANCHI. Sim. 1813 . . . 450.00

VF-EF

8 4 FRANCHI. Sim. 1814 . . . 500.00

UNTERWALDEN (SUBSILVANIA), Canton

In central Switzerland. Member, with Schwyz and Uri, of the "Everlasting League" (progenitor of the Swiss confederation) in 1291. Composed of two half cantons, Obwalden and Nidwalden.

Monetary System:
4 kreuzer = 1 batzen;
10 batzen = 1 frank.

I. Nidwalden (Unterwalden Nid Dem Wald).

Silver (lower values billon)
F-VF

11 ½/BATZEN. Like No. 13.
1811 . . . . 30.00

12 1/BATZEN. Sim. 1811 . . . . . 25.00

*13 5/BATZEN. 1811 . . . . 135.00

II. Obwalden (Subsilvania Superioris, Unterwalden Ob Dem Wald).

Silver (lower values billon)
Fine

21 ½/BATZEN. Like No. 22.
1812 . . . . 30.00

*22 1/BATZEN. 1812 . . . . 30.00
23 5/BATZEN. Sim. 1812 . . . . 125.00

Gold
V.F.

31 (ducat). Arms. Rev.
St. Nicholas v. der Flue,
kneeling. 1774 . . . . RR

*32 DUCAT. 1787 . . . . 1000.00
32a —. Restruck (1887) . . (Unc.) 600.00

URI (URANIE), Canton

On Lake Luzern. Member of the Everlasting League 1291.

Arms: Gold, a black bull's head.

Monetary System:
10 rappen = 1 batzen;
10 batzen = 1 frank.

Billon
Fine

11 1/RAPPEN. Like No. 14
but w/out motto. 1811 . . . . . 70.00

12 ½/BATZEN. Sim. 1811 . . . . 50.00

13 1/BATZEN. Sim. 1811 . . . . . 50.00

Silver

*14 2/BATZ. 1811 . . . . 75.00
15 4/BATZ. Sim. 1811 . . . . . . 100.00

For joint coinage patterns with Schwyz and Unterwalden, see Bellinzona.

VAUD (WAADT), Canton

In S.W. Switzerland. Subject to Bern 1536-1798. Admitted to the Swiss Confederation 1803.

Arms: Per fesse, white over green. LIBERTE ET PATRIE in chief.

Monetary System:
10 rappes = 1 batz; 10 batz = 1 franc;
4 francs = 1 thaler.

Billon
VG-F

1 1/Rappe. CANTON DE VAUD.
Arms. Rev. value. 1804 . . . . . 15.00

1a 1/RAPPE. 1807 . . . . 10.00

2 2½/RAPPES. Sim. 1809 . . . . 6.00

2a 2½/Rap(pes). 1816 . . . . 6.00

*3 ½/Batz. 1804-19 (var.) 4.00
4 1/Batz. Sim. 1804-20 . . . . . . 5.00

Silver
F-VF

5 5/Batz. Sim. 1804 . . . . 125.00
5a 5/BATZ. 1805-14 . . . . 20.00
6 10/Batz. Sim. 1804 . . . . . . 175.00
7 10 BATZ. Like No. 7a but
rev. XIX/CANT. on shield.
1810-11 . . . . 100.00

*7a —. Rev. XXII/CANT. on shield.
1823 . . . . 100.00

8 20 BATZ. Like No. 7.
1810-11 . . . . 135.00

9 39 BZ (batz) and Vaud
arms cmkd. on French ecu
(1830) 1000.00

VF-EF

10 40 BATZ. Like No. 7.
1812 . . . . 500.00

Concordat Coinage
Billon

SWITZERLAND

VAUD (Cont.)

Fine

★11 1 BATZ. 1826-34 . . . . 6.00

Silver

F-VF

12 5 BATZ. Sim. 1826-31 . . . . . . 20.00

E.F.

13 1 FRANC. Like No. 10 but
10 Aout 1845. Shooting fest . 80.00

ZUG
(TUGIUM, TUGIENSIS),
City and Canton

Between Zürich and Luzern. Admitted to the Swiss Confederation in 1352.

Arms: White, a blue fesse.

Monetary System:
6 angster = 3 rappen =
1 schilling (assis).

Copper

VG-F

1 I/ANGSTER. Like No. 2.
1778-96, 1804 . . . . 15.00

★2 I/RAPEN. 1781-94, 1805 . . . 6.00

Billon

3 ⅙/ASSIS. Arms. Rev. value/
TV/GIENSIS. 1747-67 . . . . 15.00

The undated billon angsters with rev. ⅙ or eagle were struck before 1747.

4 (rappen). Arms. Rev.
MONETA/TVGIENS/IS. ND
(var.), 1756 . . . . 15.00

5 (schilling). Arms. Rev.
St. Wolfgang. 1783-84 . . . . . . 15.00

ZÜRICH
(THIGURINAE, THURICENSIS,
TIGURINAE, TURICENSIS),
City and Canton

In north-central Switzerland. Became a free city of the Empire *13th century*. Obtained the mint right in 1238. Joined the Swiss Confederation in 1351 and thereafter became the most populous canton.

Arms: Per bend, white over black.

Monetary Systems:
Until 1798:
12 haller = 4 rappen = 1 schilling;
72 (later 80) schillinge = 2 gulden =
1 thaler.
1803 Onward:
10 schilling = 4 batzen;
10 batzen = 1 frank.

I. Coinage Prior to Formation of the Helvetian Republic in 1798.

Billon

V.G.

★4 3/HALLER. N.D. (18th
cent. and 1827-41) 2.00

4a 3/HALER. N.D. 4.00

★8 I/SCHIL/LING. 1725-54 . . . 3.00

Silver

F-VF

12 V/SCHIL/LING. Lion
with sword, arms. Rev.
value. 1783-84 . . . . 10.00

15 10 (schillinge). MONETA
REIPUB. TIGURINAE, Arms.
Rev. PRO/DEO/etc. 1718-
53 . . . . 12.50

19 20 (schillinge). Arms. Rev.
DOMINE/etc. in cartouche.
1718-68 . . . . 40.00

20 (20 schillinge). Arms.
Rev. IUSTITIA/etc. 30mm.
1773 . . . . 100.00

20a 20 SCHIL(linge). 1774-80 . . 45.00

21 XX/SCHIL/LING. Arms.
Rev. value. 1783-98 . . . . 40.00

V.F.

25 ½ (thaler). MONETA
REIPUBLICAE TIGURINAE.
Lion with sword, arms.
Rev. DOMINE/etc. in cartouche,
36 (schillinge) below.
1723-61 . . . . 100.00

25a —. w/out 36. 1730-68 . . . . . 100.00

25b —. Rev. IUSTITIA/etc.
1773 (mule) 175.00

V.F.

★26 ½ (thaler). Obv. sim. Rev.
★ city view. 1720-68 . . . . 90.00

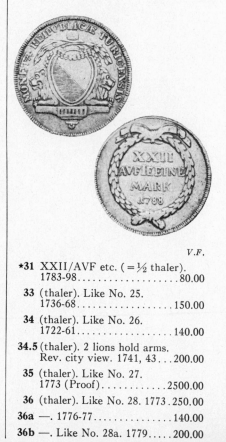

E.F.

★27 (½ thaler). 1773 . . . . 750.00

28 (½ thaler). Obv. sim. Rev.
IUSTITIA/ET/CONCORDIA.
1773, 76 (var.) 95.00

28a —. Sim. but liberty cap
on arms. 1779 . . . . 110.00

29 (½ thaler). 2 lions hold arms.
Rev. IUSTITIA/etc. 1780 . . . . . 95.00

V.F.

★31 XXII/AVF etc. (= ½ thaler).
1783-98 . . . . 80.00

33 (thaler). Like No. 25.
1736-68 . . . . 150.00

34 (thaler). Like No. 26.
1722-61 . . . . 140.00

34.5 (thaler). 2 lions hold arms.
Rev. city view. 1741, 43 . . . 200.00

35 (thaler). Like No. 27.
1773 (Proof) 2500.00

36 (thaler). Like No. 28. 1773 . 250.00

36a —. 1776-77 . . . . 140.00

36b —. Like No. 28a. 1779 . . . . . 200.00

SWITZERLAND

ZÜRICH (Cont.)

V.F.

37 (thaler). Arms supported by 2 lions. Rev. IUSTITIA/etc. 1780 . . . . 200.00

38 XI/AUF etc. (=thaler). Like No. 31. 1783, 94, 96 . . . . . . 160.00

39 (thaler). Obv. sim. Rev. city view. 1790 . . . . 160.00

Gold (ducat=3.5 gr.)

★41 ¼ (ducat). 1718-67 . . . . . . 125.00

42 ½ (ducat). Lion with sword, arms. Rev. DOMINE/ etc. 1718-67 . . . . 200.00

42.3 ½ (ducat). Like No. 28. 1776 . . . . 225.00

42.7 DUCATUS (=ducat). Like No. 42. 1718-67 . . . . . . 400.00

★43 DUCATUS (=ducat). 1775 . . . . 400.00

V.F.

★44 (2 ducats). 1718-67 . . . . 800.00

45 (2 ducats). Obv. sim. but . . . TURICENSIS. Rev. IUSTITIA/ etc. 1776 . . . . 750.00

46 (5 ducats). No. 26 in gold. 1720-53 . . . . RR

II. Coinage from 1803 Onward.

Billon

Note: 3 heller No. 4 (=1 rappen) was also struck 1827-41.

Fine

51 1/RAPPEN. Like No. 56. 1842-48 . . . . 3.00

52 2/RAPPEN. Sim. 1842 . . . . . 3.00

The ½ kreuzer 1811 and kreuzer 1842 are patterns.

Silver

V.F.

55 10 (schilling). Like No. 15. N.D., 1807-11 . . . . 12.50

★56 8/BATZEN. 1810, 14 . . . . . . 20.00

57 10 BATZ. Like No. 59. 1812 . . . . 50.00

58 20 BATZ. 1813, 26 . . . . . . 100.00

★59 40 BATZ. Obv. ★. Rev. DOMINE/etc. 1813 . . . . 135.00

Gold

VF-EF

60 DUCATUS (=ducat). Like No. 43. 1810 . . . . 700.00

The 1819 ducat-size Zwingli commemorative is a medal.

SYRIA

Present-day Syria, Lebanon, Jordan and Israel were at AH1209 generally included within the Turkish pashaliks of Syria (Damascus), Haleb (Aleppo), Raqqa, Saïda and Tripolis. The following coin struck at Haleb is thought to be an emergency issue.

Mustafa III 1171-87AH (=1757-73AD)

Copper

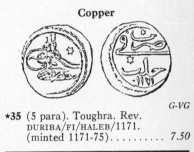

G-VG

★35 (5 para). Toughra. Rev. DURIBA/FI/HALEB/1171. (minted 1171-75) 7.50

UNVERIFIED DATA

Note: Throughout this catalog, any uncertain, indefinite or unconfirmed information is shown in *italic type.* Such material may be, for example, coin descriptions, dates and prices, names of rulers, or supplementary notes. Further information to confirm or correct *material in italics* should be sent to the author at the following address:

William D. Craig
c/o Whitman Coin Supply Division
1220 Mound Avenue
Racine, Wisconsin 53404, U.S.A.

TIBET

A mountainous theocracy in Central Asia under nominal Chinese suzerainty from 1792 to 1911. It is bounded by China on the north and east, and by India, Nepal, Sikkim and Bhutan on the south and west.

Monetary System:
1½ sho = 1 tangka.

Silver

I. Autonomous Tibetan Coinage.

V.F.

★27 (tangka). Debased copy of Nepalese mohar of Pratap Simha (AD1774-77). Dated 13th cycle 31st yr. (=AD1777)..............12.00

Note: Similar coins are dated yrs. 28-46 of the 15th cycle (=AD1894-1912). Controversy exists as to when No. 27 was actually issued.

50 (tangka). ND. (ca 1840-1925). See Y-13.

★60 (kong-par tangka). Yrs. 44-48 of 13th cycle (=AD1790-94). Giamda and Lhasa Mints................. 4.50

Note: Similar coins are dated yrs. 24-25 of the 15th cycle (=AD1890-91).

II. Tibetan Coinage Under Chinese Suzerainty.

Silver

Emperor Kao Tsung (Ch'ien Lung Era) 1736-96

71 (½ sho). Like No. 72. *F-VF* 21mm. Yr. 58.............40.00

F-VF

★72 (sho). Yrs. 58-61..........25.00
73 (tangka). Sim. 28-31mm. Yr. 58..................60.00

Coins of the yr. 57 are patterns.

Emperor Jen Tsung (Chia Ching Era) 1796-1820

82 (½ sho). Like No. 83. Yr. 3....................35.00

★83 (sho). Yrs. 1-25..........25.00

Emperor Hsuan Tsung (Tao Kuang Era) 1821-50

★93 (sho). Yrs. 1-16..........25.00

TOBAGO.
TORTOLA.
TRINIDAD.
See CARIBBEAN ISLANDS AND TERRITORIES.

TRIPOLI (TARABALUS GHARB)

North African seaport and adjacent territory between Egypt and Tunis. Nominally under Ottoman (Turkish) rule 1551-1911, governed by hereditary local pashas of the Karamanli family 1711-1835. One of the "Barbary pirate" states, its attacks on Mediterranean shipping led to conflicts with other maritime nations (including the United States 1801-1805). Captured by Italy 1911-1912.

Mint: Name in Arabic on all coins is TARABALUS GHARB, "Tripoli West" (as distinguished from Tripoli in Lebanon).

Monetary System:
Copper and Silver: 52 asper (aqcheh) =13 grimellini =40 para =1 piastre. See TURKEY for alternative denominations and names of multiples.
Gold: zeri mahbub=2.4-2.5 gr.; sultani (altun)=3.3-3.4 gr.

Sultan Mahmud I AH1143-68 (=AD1730-54)

Copper

Former No. 2 (=Valentine 21) appears to be a worn specimen of No. 93 under Mahmud II.

Gold

Fine

8 (sultani). Legends each side. 22-24mm. 3.3 gr. AH1143..125.00

Sultan Osman III AH1168-71 (=AD1754-57)

Copper

Good

★10 (asper). SULTAN/KHAN. Rev. TARABALUS/1168......10.00

Gold

Fine

18 (sultani). Like No. 8 but OSMAN in obv. legend. 3.4 gr. 23mm. 1168..............175.00

Sultan Mustafa III AH1171-87 (=AD1757-74)

Copper

Good

★20 (asper). SULTAN/MUSTAFI/KHAN. Rev. date/TARABALUS/GHARB. (11)77....................10.00
22 (asper). Obv. sim. Rev. TARA/BALUS in hexagram. 15mm. ND......................10.00

Gold

Fine

28 (sultani). Like No. 8 but MUSTAFA in obv. legend. 3.3 gr. 25mm. 1171.......125.00

TRIPOLI

Sultan Abdul Hamid I
AH1187-1203 (=AD1774-89)

Copper

G-VG

30 (para). Toughra. Rev. mint
name. 19-20mm. 1187......*10.00*

★**33** (para). Sultan's name. Rev.
mint name, date around.
19-22mm. 1188........... 7.50

Silver (Billon)

VG-F

★**38** (5 para). Sultan's name.
Rev. mint name/date.
1.6-2.6 gr. 19-24mm.
1188....................*10.00*

40 (10 para). *Sim.* 4.5 gr.
25mm. 1187..............*15.00*

44 (piastre). Toughra/mint
name/1187. Rev. 4-line
legend. 18.4 gr. 38mm.
Yr. 7....................*40.00*

47 (piastre). 4-line legend
each side. 15.7 gr. 35mm.
1187/yr. 1...............*25.00*

Gold

F-VF

52 (zeri mahbub). Like No. 44.
2.5 gr. 20mm. 1187, 91
(both with yr. 7).........*100.00*

Sultan Selim III
AH1203-22 (=AD1789-1807)

Copper coins of this reign exist.

Billon

VG-F

56 *(5 para).* Like No. 58.
1.1-1.9 gr. 21-25mm.
1203, 10................*10.00*

★**58** *(10 para).* Sultan's name.
Rev. mint name/date.
2.1-3.3 gr. 27-28mm. 1210...*10.00*

VG-F

63 *(20 para).* Sim. 5.3 gr.
30mm. 1205.............*20.00*

66 *(30 para).* 4-line legend.
Rev. yr./mint name/1203.
7.5 gr. 31mm. Yr. 14......*20.00*

67 (piastre). Toughra. Rev. like
No. 66. 12.5 gr. 37mm.
Yr. 1 *(10?)*..............*40.00*

68 (2 piastres). Sim. 24.3 gr.
44mm. Yrs. 16-*17*.........*60.00*

70 (100 para = 2½ piastres).
Toughra/mint name/date.
Rev. 4-line legend. 30.5 gr.
43-45mm. 1203-10........*60.00*

Gold

F-VF

73 (sultani). 4-line legend each
side. 3.4 gr. 24-26mm.
1203/yrs. 15, 17.........*100.00*

Sultan Mahmud II
AH1223-55 (=AD1803-39)

Copper

A. Types with Sultan's name or toughra.

Fine (Crude)

★**92** (para). SULTAN/MAHMUD/KHAN.
Rev. DURIBA/FI/TARABALUS/
GHARB. ND, 1223, and yrs.
13, 20 (var.)............. 7.50

93 (para). MAHMUD/(yr.) 24.
Rev. SULTAN/1223. No mint
name. 17-18mm...........*12.50*

★**94** (para). Toughra. Rev. like
No. 92. 1223 (var.)........ 7.50

94a —. Sim. with various ornate
borders (wreath, square,
lozenge, etc.).............*12.50*

★**96** (ex 108) (para). Arabesque,
SULTAN MAHMUD KHAN 1223.
Rev. like No. 92. Yrs. 25-29,
62(!)....................*10.00*

B. Types with mint name only.

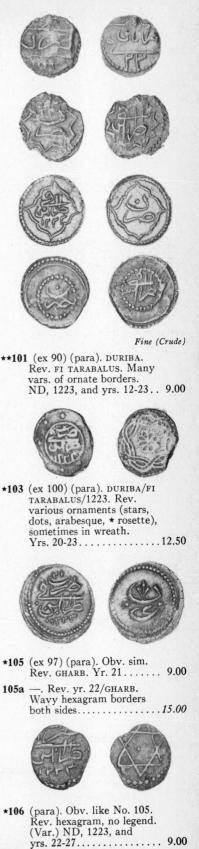

Fine (Crude)

★★**101** (ex 90) (para). DURIBA.
Rev. FI TARABALUS. Many
vars. of ornate borders.
ND, 1223, and yrs. 12-23.. 9.00

★**103** (ex 100) (para). DURIBA/FI
TARABALUS/1223. Rev.
various ornaments (stars,
dots, arabesque, ★ rosette),
sometimes in wreath.
Yrs. 20-23...............*12.50*

★**105** (ex 97) (para). Obv. sim.
Rev. GHARB. Yr. 21....... 9.00

105a —. Rev. yr. 22/GHARB.
Wavy hexagram borders
both sides................*15.00*

★**106** (para). Obv. like No. 105.
Rev. hexagram, no legend.
(Var.) ND, 1223, and
yrs. 22-27................ 9.00

TRIPOLI

Low Grade Billon

All dated 1223, most with regnal years.

Note: Much new material on coins of this reign was published by Ölçer in 1970. He correctly (it is submitted) relisted some of Valentine's "copper" coins as billon. While the numismatic world is indebted to him for his research, many of his denomination listings for Tripoli are controversial and some appear to be quite wrong. The list which follows does not, therefore, correspond with Ölçer in all respects. Perhaps further research will verify the true denominations of these coins.

Type I. Toughra. Rev. year/mint legend/1223.

Fine (Crude)

112 *(10 para).* 3.09 gr. 26mm. Yr. 19 . . . .*30.00*

117 (ex 142) *(40 para).* 9.53 gr. 32mm. Yr. 20 . . . .*40.00*

117a —. Dated 1243, no regnal yr. 15.3 gr. 37mm *50.00*

Type II. As Type I but with ornamental borders.

125 (ex 115) *(20 para).* Like No. 126. 4.84 gr. 23mm. Yr. 2 *(21?)* *30.00*

★126 *(30 para).* Lozenges both sides. 7.7-9.2 gr. 28mm. Yr. 20 . . . .*20.00*

127 (ex 137) *(40 para).* Sim. 12.2 gr., 35mm. Yr. 21 . . . . .*45.00*

★129 *(40 para).* Space between inner circle and floral border. 2.5-3.1 gr. 22-24mm. ND, yr. 4 . . . .*20.00*

131 *(80 para).* Sim. 6.3-7.8 gr. 31-33mm. Yrs. 7-8 . . . .*30.00*

131a —. 3.2-4.5 gr. 29-31mm. No regnal yr *20.00*

132 (ex 144, 146) *(120 para).* Sim. 12.2 gr. 36-39mm. Yrs. 19, 21 . . . .*45.00*

Fine (Crude)

★140 (ex 145) *(200 para).* Sim. but space btwn. pearl circle and floral border eliminated. 12.9-18.3 gr. 36-39mm. Yr. 20 . . . .*25.00*

141 (ex 147) *(100 para).* Crescents both sides (like Turkey No. 197 but no wreaths). 7.62 gr. 35mm. Yr. 24 . . . . . ——

143 *(20 para).* Double vine borders both sides. 1.7 gr. 21mm. Yr. 28 (on obv.) *15.00*

148 *(200 para).* Sim. 14.5-17 gr. 37-38mm. Yr. 28 . . . .*65.00*

Type III. Toughra/mint/1223. Rev. 4-line legend.

162 (ex 110) *(5 para).* Like No. 166. 1.2 gr. 22-23mm. Yrs. 7, 18 . . . .*30.00*

163 (ex 114) *(10 para).* Sim. 1.7-2.5 gr. 24-27mm. Yrs. 16-25 . . . .*15.00*

164 (ex 133) *(20 para).* Sim. 4.0-6.35 gr. 28-30mm. Yrs. 13-24, 25 . . . .*15.00*

Fine (Crude)

★166 (ex 138) *(40 para).* 9.1-12.2 gr. 35-37mm. Yrs. 14-25 . . . .*40.00*

Type IV. Obv. 4-line legend. Rev. as indicated below.

172 (ex 113) *(½ zolota = 15 para).* Rev. 4-line legend. 2.85 gr., 25mm. Yr. 14 *(bogus?)* . . . . . ——

174 (ex 116) *(30 para).* Sim. but both sides in floral border. 6.43 gr., 29mm. Yr. 20 . . . . .*30.00*

★175 *(40 para).* Sim. 8.9-11.0 gr. 34mm. Yr. 20 . . . .*35.00*

176 (ex 118) *(60 para).* Like No. 172. 12.65 gr. 36mm. Yr. 19 . . . .*50.00*

183 (ex 121) *(20 para).* Rev. mint legend/1223 in hexagon. 3.86 gr. 29mm. Yr. 17 . . . . .*35.00*

185 (ex 122) *(40 para).* Sim. 7.7 gr. 33-34mm. Yrs. 17-18 . . . .*35.00*

187 (ex 123) *(80 para).* Sim. but rev. legend in lozenge (like No. 126). 11.75 gr. 33mm. 1243 . . . .*45.00*

Type V. Legends generally like No. 92.

191 (ex 133) *(10 para).* Like No. 192. 2.9 gr. 19mm. Yr. 12 . . . .*30.00*

TRIPOLI

192 (ex 134, 135) *(20 para)*.
Like No. 92 (1223 some-
times replaces KHAN). Both
sides in double rope border.
4.4-5.3 gr. 23mm.
Yrs. 12-13 . . . .*30.00*

193 (ex 136) *(20 para)*. Sim.
Obv. legend/yr. Rev. legend/
1223. 6.0 gr. 32mm. Yr. 22 . .*30.00*

194 *(30 para)*. Sim. Rev. yr./
legend/1223. 9-12.4 gr.
34mm. Yr. 20 . . . .*35.00*

Type VI. Circular legends around border, both sides.

198 (ex 124) *(10 para)*. Toughra.
Rev. yr./mint legend/1223.
Circular legends around.
(= No. 214 struck in billon?)
2.4 gr. 22mm. Yr. 20 . . . . . . —

199 (ex 139) *(200 para)*. Both
sides legend in field, circular
legend around. 7.0 gr.
34mm. Yr. 23 . . . . —

Gold

V.F.

210 (ex 150) (zeri mahbub). Like
No. 166. 2.1-2.4 gr. 21-23mm.
Yrs. 12-13 . . . .*75.00*

212 (ex 152) (zeri mahbub).
4-line legend. Rev. like
No. 129. 2.3 gr. 24mm.
Yr. 18 . . . .*75.00*

214 (ex 154) (zeri mahbub). Like
No. 198. 2.5 gr. 22mm.
Yr. 20 . . . .*90.00*

218 (ex 158) (sultani). 4-line
legends both sides.
3.1-3.4 gr. 24-26mm.
ND, yr. 6 . . . .*125.00*

218a —. 28mm. Yr. 19 . . . .*140.00*

TUNIS

North African territory nominally un-
der Turkish suzerainty until 1881.
Coastal areas governed by the Bey of
Tunis while the interior was controlled
by tribal rulers. To France 1881 as a
Protectorate. All coins show the name
Tunis in Arabic.

Monetary System:

6 burben (bourbines, fels rakik) =
  1 burbe (bourbe, fels);
104 burbe = 52 asper (aqceh, nasri) =
  16 kharub (karub) =
  1 piastre (sebili, riyal sebili,
  buriyal, ghurush).
Gold: sultani (sequin = 3 to 6 piastres).

Sultan Mahmud I
AH1143-68 (=AD1730-54)

Copper

G-VG

1a (burben). Sultan/Mahmud.
Rev. Tunis etc./*1167*.
13mm 7.50

2 (2 burben). Legends each
side. 14-15mm. 1157-58 . . . . . 3.00

Silver (Billon)

V.G.

★4 (kharub). 2 lines. Rev. date/
Tunis etc. 14-15mm. 1.3 gr.
1152-66 . . . . 3.00

4a —. TUNIS etc./1167 . . . . 5.00

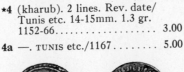

★5 (2 kharub). 19-21mm.
2.3-2.9 gr. 1151-56 . . . . 7.50

6 (¼ piastre). 4 lines. Rev.
3 lines/date/line. 23-24mm.
5-6 gr. 1147-50 . . . . 9.00

Gold

V.F.

10 (½ sultani). 2 to 3 lines
each side. 16mm. 1.7 gr.
1144, 66 . . . .*75.00*

11 (sultani). 4 lines each side.
24mm. 3.4 gr. 1151 . . . . . .*125.00*

Sultan Mustafa III
AH1171-87 (=AD1757-75)

Copper (Crude)

G-VG

21 (burben). "Dharb." Rev.
date/Tunis. 11-13mm.
1172-78 . . . . 3.00

22 (2 burben). Sim. 15mm.
1173-82 . . . . 5.00

23 (burbe). Sultan/Mustafa/
Khan. Rev. date/Tunis.
18-22mm. 1171-88 . . . . 2.00

G-VG

★23a —. Tunis/date. 19-22mm.
1171-87 . . . . 1.50

Billon

V.G.

★27 (kharub). Sultan/Mustafa.
Rev. legend/date. 13-14mm.
0.9-1.3 gr. 1171-78 . . . . 3.00

30 (½ piastre). Sultan's name
(4 lines). Rev. Tunis/date.
28mm. 7.6 gr. 1187 . . . .*15.00*

31 (piastre). Sim. 35mm.
15.2 gr. 1180-88 . . . .*20.00*

Gold

V.F.

34 (½ sultani). Like No. 30.
14-15mm. 1.2-1.3 gr.
1185-87 . . . .*65.00*

35 (sultani). Sim. 22mm.
3 gr. 1171 . . . .*125.00*

35a —. 19-20mm. 2.6 gr.
1181-86 . . . .*100.00*

Sultan Abdul Hamid I
AH1187-1203 (=AD1774-89)

Copper (Crude)

G-VG

39 (burben). Sultan's name.
(3 lines). Rev. date/Tunis.
8-10mm. 1188-95 . . . . 5.00

40 (2 burben). Dharb. Rev.
date/Tunis. 13mm.
1195-98 . . . . 5.00

43 (burbe). Like No. 39.
19-22mm. 1188-98 . . . . 2.00

Billon

V.G.

50 (½ piastre). Sultan's name.
Rev. Tunis/date. 28mm.
6.2-8.0 gr. 1187-1202 . . . .*10.00*

52 (piastre). Sim. 34-35mm.
11.3-16 gr. 1188-1202 . . . .*15.00*

Gold

V.F.

55 (½ sultani). Sultan's name
(4 lines). Rev. date/Tunis.
14-15mm. 1.2-1.3 gr.
1188-89 . . . .*75.00*

Sultan Selim III
AH1203-22 (=AD1789-1807)

Billon

VG-F

60 (½ piastre). Like No. 62.
27-28mm. 7.1-7.7 gr.
1206-22 . . . . 9.00

TUNIS

*62 (piastre). Sultan's name. VG-F
Rev. Tunis/date. 34-36mm.
14.9-16 gr. 1203-22.........12.50

Sultan Mustafa IV
AH1222-23 (=AD1807-08)

Billon

63 (4 kharub). Like No. 62 but
MUSTAFA. 21mm. 3.5 gr.
1223.....................20.00

64 (½ piastre). Sim. 27mm.
7.5 gr. 1223..............20.00

65 (piastre). Sim. 35mm.
16 gr. 1222...............35.00

Sultan Mahmud II
AH1223-55 (=AD1808-39)

The copper 1, 2 and 4 kharubs AH1255
are patterns.

Billon

A. First Standard 1225-32.

66 (4 kharub). Like No. 62
but MAHMUD. 21mm. 3.5 gr.
1228, 31..................20.00

67 (½ piastre). Sim. 27mm.
7.5 gr. 1228-32...........20.00

*68 (piastre). Sim. 35mm.
16 gr. 1225-32............20.00

69 (2 piastres). Like No. 80.
39mm. 27.4 gr. 1232.......75.00

B. Second Standard 1240-55.

*70 (kharub). Sultan's name. Fine
Rev. date/Tunis. 14mm.
0.7 gr. 1241-55...........4.00

72 (2 kharub). Sim. 17mm.
1.3 gr. 1242-43..........15.00

74 (4 kharbu). Like No. 76.
20-21mm. 2.5 gr. 1240-55...15.00

*76 (½ piastre). Sim. 5.3-5.7 gr.
26-27mm. 1240-55.........12.50

78 (piastre). Sim. 11 gr.
31-32mm. 1240-55.........10.00

*80 (2 piastres). 23 gr. 1244-48..50.00

Gold
V.F.

82 (sultani). Sultan's name
(3 lines). Rev. Tunis/date.
13mm. 1.3 gr. 1255.......75.00

Sultan Abdul Mejid
AH1255-77 (=AD1839-61)

A. First Standard 1255-56.

Billon
VG-F

86 (4 kharub). Sultan's name
(4 lines). Rev. Tunis/date.
20mm. 2.5 gr. 1256.......20.00

88 (½ piastre). Sim. 26mm.
5 gr. 1256...............20.00

90 (piastre). Sim. 32mm.
11 gr. 1255..............35.00

B. Second Standard 1263-71.

Copper

*95 (burbe). Sultan's name V.G.
(4 lines). Rev. Tunis/date.
Wreaths both sides. 20mm.
1263-67..................2.50

96 (asper). Sim. 22-23mm.
1263-67..................2.00

97 (3 asper). Sim. 24mm.
5.8 gr. 1263-69..........2.00

98 (6 asper). Sim. 29-30mm.
1263-71..................1.50

*98a —. Cmkd. "1" (kharub) in
5mm circle. (1275).......2.50

Silver

The silver ¼, ½ and 1 piastre (.8, 1.7
and 3.4 gr) 1270 are patterns.
Fine

101 (2 piastres). Generally like
No. 101a. 6.5 gr. 1263-
64......................10.00

*101a —. 1267.............12.50

102 (5 piastres). Like No. 101.
33.5mm. 15.5-16 gr.
1263-64.................25.00

102a —. Like No. 101a. 15.5-
16 gr. 1265-71..........22.50

C. With Name of Muhammed
Bey AH1271-76 (=AD1855-59).

Copper
V.G.

112 3 (asper). Like No. 113.
25mm. 1272-74...........2.50

TUNIS

113 6 (asper). Sultan's name
around value. Rev. Bey's
name/TUNIS/date.
1272-74.................. 2.00 *V.G.*

113a —. Cmkd. "1" (kharub)
in 5mm. circle. (1275)..... 2.00

114 13 (asper). Like No. 113.
33-34mm. 1272-75.......... 2.50

114a —. Cmkd. "2" (kharubs)
in 6.5mm. circle. (1275).... 2.50

115 2 (kharub). Sim. 33-35mm.
1274-76.................. 3.00

Silver

120 2 (kharub). Sultan's name. *Fine*
Rev. Bey's name and TUNIS
around value and date.
0.35 gr. 12.5mm. 1273-76... 5.00

121 4 (kharub). Like No. 125
but no wreaths. 0.7 gr.
14.5mm. 1274-75.......... 5.00

122 8 (kharub). Sim. but
wreaths both sides. 1.5 gr.
18mm. 1274-75.......... 10.00

123 1 (piastre). Sim. 3.0-3.2 gr.
24mm. 1272-73.......... 7.50

124 2 (piastres). Sim. 6.2-6.4 gr.
28.5mm. 1272.......... 10.00

125 3 (piastres). Sultan's name.
Rev. Bey's name/TUNIS/
value/date. 9.3-9.6 gr.
1272.................. 20.00

126 4 (piastres). Sim. 31mm.
12.4-12.8 gr. 1272........ 20.00

127 5 (piastres). Sim. 16 gr.
1272-73................ 30.00

Gold

First Standard

128 10 (piastres). Like No. 125. *V.F.*
1.77 gr. 1272............ 100.00

129 20 (piastres). Sim. 3.55 gr.
21mm. 1272............ 150.00

130 40 (piastres). Sim. 7.1 gr.
26mm. 1272............ 225.00

131 80 (piastres). Sim. 14.21 gr.
31mm. 1272............ 350.00

132 100 (piastres). Sim.
17.71 gr. 1272.......... 400.00

Second Standard

133 5 (piastres). Like No. 121.
0.98 gr. 1272-74.......... 50.00

134 10 (piastres). Like No. 122.
1.97 gr. 18mm. 1272-75.... 65.00

135 25 (piastres). Sim. 4.92 gr.
20mm. 1273-75.......... 95.00

136 50 (piastres). Sim. 9.84 gr.
27mm. 1272-75.......... 150.00

137 100 (piastres). Sim.
19.68 gr. 1272-75....... 275.00

D. Coinage of Abdul Mejid with Muhammed es Sadik Bey AH1276-99 (=AD1859-82).

Copper

140 2 (kharub). Like No. 113 *V.G.*
but rev. MUHAMMED ES
SADIK instead of MUHAMMED.
34mm. 1276............. 7.50

Silver

147 1 (piastre). Like No. 125 but *Fine*
rev. MUHAMMED ES SADIK
etc. 3.2 gr. 1278.......... 20.00

148 2 (piastres). Sim. 6.4 gr.
28mm. 1276............. ——

Gold

155 25 (piastres). Sim. *V.F.*
4.8 gr. 1276............ 175.00

156 50 (piastres). Sim.
9.8 gr. 1276............ 275.00

157 100 (piastres). Sim.
19.7 gr. 1276........... 500.00

Sultan Abdul Aziz AH1277-93 (=AD1861-76) with Muhammed es Sadik Bey AH1276-99 (=AD1859-82)

Copper

161 ¼ (kharub). Like No. 163. *F-VF*
14mm. 1281............. 2.50

162 ½ (kharub). Sim. 18mm.
1281.................. 1.50

163 1 (kharub). Sultan's name.
Rev. value/Bey's name/
TUNIS/1281............. 1.50

164 2 (kharub). Sim. 28mm.
1281.................. 2.00

165 4 (kharub). Sim. 31mm.
1281, 83.............. 3.00

166 8 (kharub). Sim. 34mm.
1281.................. 4.00

169 (2 kharub). Sim. but no *VG-F*
value or inner circles.
31mm. 1283-84.......... 3.50

170 (¼ kharub). Like No. 113 but
ABDUL AZIZ and MUHAMMED
ES SADIK. 17.5mm. 1289... 5.00

171 2 (sideways = ½ kharub).
Sim. 25mm. 1289........ 3.00

172 1 (kharub). Sim. 29mm.
1289-90................ 2.00

173 2 (kharub). Sim. 31-32mm.
1289.................. 2.00

Silver

176 8 (kharub). Sultan's name *F-VF*
(3 lines). Rev. Bey's name/
Tunis/date. Wreaths both
sides. 1.5-1.8 gr. 1283-
93.................... 5.00

177 1 (piastre). Sim. 3-3.2 gr.
1284-93............... 5.00

177a —. Cmkd. star in circle.
(1295)................ 5.00

178 2 (piastres). Like No. 176
but rev. TUNIS/date
(no Bey's name). 6.4 gr.
1281................. 35.00

178.5 2 (piastres). Like No. 176.
6.4 gr. 1287-93.......... 7.50

178.5a —. Cmkd. star in circle.
(1295)................ 7.50

179 3 (piastres). Like No. 176.
9.6 gr. 1288........... 35.00

TUNIS

F-VF

179.5 4 (piastres). Sim.
12.8 gr. 1288-93 .... 12.50

★179.5a —. Cmkd. star in circle.
(1295) 10.00

180 5 (piastres). Like No. 176.
16 gr. 1288-93 .... 40.00

Note: The 1, 2, 3 and 4 piastres silver
and 5 and 10 piastres gold of this reign
were cmkd. with a star in a circle in
AH1295 to reduce their value.

Gold

This series was struck at both Tunis
and Paris. Minor varieties exist.

VF-EF

181 5 (piastres). Sultan's name
(3 lines). Rev. Bey's name/
Tunis/5/date. 0.98 gr. 1281-
91 .... 50.00

181a —. Cmkd. star in circle.
(1295) 60.00

182 10 (piastres). Like No. 176.
1.97 gr. 1280-88 .... 85.00

182a —. Cmkd. star in circle.
(1295) 100.00

183 25 (piastres). Like No. 176.
4.92 gr. 1279-91 .... 85.00

184 50 (piastres). Sim. 9.84 gr.
1280-88 .... 200.00

185 100 (piastres). Sim.
19.68 gr. 1279-85 .... 350.00

Sultan Murad V
AH1293 (=AD1876) with
Muhammed es Sadik Bey

Gold

190 25 (piastres). Sim. but
MURAD legend. 4.92 gr.
1293 .... 600.00

Sultan Abdul Hamid II
AH1293-1327 (=AD1876-1909) with
Muhammed es Sadik Bey

Copper

Fine

192 2 (kharub). Like No. 113
but ABDUL HAMID and
MUHAMMED ES SADIK.
31mm. 1293 .... 8.00

Silver

F-VF

193 8 (kharub). Like No. 176
but ABDUL HAMID. 18.5mm.
1.6 gr. 1296-98 .... 7.50

194 1 (piastre). Sim. 22.5mm.
3.2 gr. 1293-94 .... 15.00

194a —. Same with "el Ghazi"
("The Victorious") 1294-
98 .... 10.00

194b —. Cmkd. star in circle.
(1295) 10.00

195 2 (piastres). Like No. 193.
26.5mm. 6.4 gr. 1293-
94 .... 15.00

195a —. "el Ghazi." 1294 ...... 15.00

195b —. Cmkd. star in circle.
(1295) 15.00

196 4 (piastres). Like No. 193.
31mm. 12.8 gr. 1293-
94 .... 25.00

196a —. "el Ghazi." 1294 ...... 25.00

196b —. Cmkd. star in circle.
(1295) 25.00

Gold

VF-EF

197 5 (piastres). Sultan's names.
Rev. Bey's name, Tunis,
date. 0.98 gr. 1294 .... 85.00

200 25 (piastres). Sim. 20mm.
4.9 gr. 1294-97 .... 100.00

For coins of Muhammed es Sadik AH
1298-1300 under the French Protectorate, see Yeoman, *Modern World Coins.*

TURKESTAN

Extensive area in central Asia, lying
east of the Caspian Sea, north of Afghanistan, west of China and south of
Siberia. The Muhammedan states into
which Turkestan was then divided
were annexed piecemeal to China and
Russia in the 18th and 19th centuries.

Monetary System:

44 puls = 1 tanga;
21 tangas = 1 tilla (dinar);
tanga (silver) = *1.7-3.1 gr.;*
tilla (gold) = *3.7-5 gr.*

BUKHARA
(BOKHARA, SOGDIANA),
Emirate

In Russian Central Asia. Had Uzbeg
rulers from about AH900. At times the
Emirs of Bukhara exercised suzerainty
over the Khans of Khokand (q.v.).
Capitals: Bukhara and Samarkand.
Bukhara became a Russian tributary
in AH1284 (=AD1867).

Abu'l-Ghazi
AH1171-1200 (=AD1758-85)

Gold

Fine

★20 (tilla). 1181-1201, ND 120.00

Shah Murad
AH1200-15 (=AD1785-1800)

Haidar Tora
(Amir Said Mir Haidar)
AH1215-42 (=AD1800-26)

Copper

G-VG

48 (pul). Legends both sides.
15mm. 1232 ..... 4.00

51 *(pul).* Legends both sides
in Greek border. 19mm.
1241 .... 4.00

Silver

Crude

55 (tanga). Legends both sides.
3 gr. 1226-36 .... 7.00

Gold

V.F.

★61 (tilla). HAIDAR TORA.
1215-25 .... 85.00

65 (tilla). Sim. but with the
name of deceased Amir
Danial Maasoom (d. 1185).
1230-34 .... 85.00

65a —. Obv. legend in circular
(not teardrop) border.
1235-40 .... 85.00

Nasr Allah
AH1242-77 (=AD1826-60)

Silver

Crude

72 (tanga). HAIDAR TORA legend.
1244-45 .... 10.00

75 (tanga). 3.2 gr. 1273 ...... 7.00

Gold

TURKESTAN

BUKHARA (Cont.)

V.F.

★85 (tilla). DANIAL MAASOOM
legend. 1243-75..........100.00

Muzaffar ad-Din
AH1277-84 (=AD1860-67)
Russian Vassal
AH1284-1303 (=AD1867-85)

Silver

91 (tanga). 1293.............7.50

Gold

★95 (tilla). 1278-96...........85.00

KHIVA (=KWAREZM),
Khanate

In Russian Turkestan, Central Asia,
lying east of the Caspian Sea and south
of Lake Aral. Ancient Chorasmia. Became a monarchy called Kwarezm under the Seljuks in AD1092. Occupied
by Russia 1873, annexed 1875.

Allah Kuli
AH1241-58 (=AD1825-42)

Silver

Crude

50 (tanga). Legends both sides.
2.2 gr. 1247-48 (var.).......10.00

KHOKAND (=FARGHANA),
Khanate

In Russian Turkestan, Central Asia.
Established about 1700. Controlled by
Russia from 1866, annexed 1875-76.

Shah Rukh II AH1184 (=AD1770)

Copper

G-VG

30 (pul). Legends both sides.
17mm. 1184.............5.00

Alim AH1222-33 (=AD1807-17)
Omar AH1233-38 (=AD1817-22)
Muhammad Ali
AH1238-56 (=AD1822-40)

Copper

60 (pul). Legends both sides in
ornamental borders. 20mm.
Khokand. 1249...........5.00

G-VG

63 (pul). Legends both sides.
13x13mm. Farghana.
1252..................7.50

Silver

Crude

65 (tanga). Legends both sides.
Khokand. 1241...........10.00

Gold

V.F.

67 (tilla). Legends both sides.
Farghana. 1247........... ———
68 (tilla). Sim. Khokand.
1252-57................100.00

Sher Ali
AH1258-61 (=AD1842-45)

Gold

78 (tilla). Legends both sides.
1259-60................140.00

Muhammad Khudayar
(=Khudayar Khan),
First Reign AH1261-75
(=AD1845-58)

Copper

Good

87 (pul). 19mm. 1265........4.00

Silver

Crude

95 (tanga). 3 gr. 1266-75......6.00

Gold

V.F.

★100 (tilla). 1260-75 (var.).....85.00

Muhammad Fulad, Rebel
AH1275-90 (=AD1858-73)

Gold

★110 (tilla). 1275-90...........85.00

Malla AH1275-78 (=AD1858-62)

Copper

G-VG

112 —. Legend in tear drop.
Rev. Legend. 1277........5.00

Silver

115 (tanga). Like No. 118.
1275-76.................7.50

Gold

V.F.

★118 (tilla). 1275-78..........125.00

Shah Murad
AH1278-79 (=AD1862)

Gold

★128 (tilla). 1278...........Unique ?

Muhammad Khudayar, 2nd Reign
AH1279-80 (=AD1862-63)

Gold

135 (tilla). Like No. 100....Unique ?

Sayyid Sultan
AH1280-82 (=AD1863-65)

Gold

145 (tilla). Type of previous.
1280..................125.00

Muhammad Khudayar, 3rd Reign
AH1282-92 (=AD1865-75)

Copper

V.G.

148 (pul). 1287.............5.00

Silver

151 (tanga). Like No. 155.
2.5 gr. 1282-84...........6.00

Gold

V.F.

★155 (tilla). 1282-85..........100.00

Nasiraddin
AH1292-93 (=AD1875-76)

No coins.

TURKESTAN
(EASTERN OR CHINESE
TURKESTAN =SIN-KIANG)

In Central Asia, east of Russian Turkestan. The Muhammedan Kalmuk population was conquered by China in
1758, but was in a constant state of
revolt thereafter. Chief cities: Kashgar,
Yarkand, Aksu, Kuja and Ushi. See
CHINA for coins.

TURKEY

The former "Ottoman Empire" covering present-day Turkey, most of the Balkans, the Near East excluding Persia, and North Africa excluding Morocco. The local coinages for ALGERIA, CAUCASIA (Armenia, Ganjah, Georgia), EGYPT, MESOPOTAMIA, SYRIA, TRIPOLI and TUNIS are listed under those places. Here follow Turkish coins for the rest of the Empire, mostly struck at Constantinople (Qustantiniah, Islambul).

Monetary Systems:

(a) to 1844:

Silver

3 aspers (akçe or akcheh) = 1 para;
40 para = 8 beshlik = 4 onlik =
  2 yirmilik = 1 piastre (kuruç or gurush);
60 para = 2 zolota = 1 altmishlik;
2 piastres = 1 ikilik;
100 para = 1 yuzluk;
5 piastres = 1 beshlik.

Gold

zeri mahbub = 2.6 gr.;
altun (altin, altun fundukly, findik) = Sequin (from Venetian ducat or *zecchino*, originally 3.4 gr. but gradually debased in the 19th century).

(b) after 1844:

40 para = 1 piastre;
100 piastres = 1 lira (pound).

Copies (and fantasies) of Turkish coins:

Many silver and gold coins of Turkey (and Algeria) prior to the introduction of machine-struck coinage were holed and used as ornaments on clothing. Brass copies or fantasy coins, usually with silver or gold plating, were made for persons who could not afford the real thing. The most common Turkish copies seem to be Mahmud II types, often bearing fictitious regnal year 78. These jewelry "coins" are usually not deceptive when actually seen because plating is generally worn off the high spots and legends are altered or often blundered.

Condition:

Because they were frequently used as ornaments, many genuine Turkish coins (in particular the gold) are found holed. These pierced coins are commonly priced one grade downward (e.g., VF holed coin treated as Fine).

Mahmud I
AH1143-68 (= AD1730-54)

All dated AH1143, no regnal years are shown.

Silver (lowest values billon)

VG-F
1 (asper). Like No. 2.
0.17 gr. 11.5mm *6.00*

VG-F
*2 (para). Toughra. Rev.
DURIBA/FI/QUSTANTINIAH/
1143. 0.57 gr. 15-17mm 1.50

*3 (5 para). Toughra/QUSTANTIN-
IAH/1143. Rev. 4-line legend.
2.4-3.2 gr. 19-20mm 8.50

4 (10 para). Sim. 23.5-25mm
(3 var.) 5.00

5 (20 para). Sim. 30-33mm
(2 var.) 10.00

6 (piastre). Sim. 38-41mm.
22-25 gr. (var.) 20.00

Note: *Davenport's No. 324 (1807) "zolota" of 18.8 gr. is a clipped piastre.*

Gold

V.F.
7 (½ zeri mahbub). Like No. 3
but ISLAMBUL. 1.3 gr.
17mm 30.00

8 (zeri mahbub). Sim. 2.6 gr.
18-24mm 50.00

9 (½ altun). Like No. 2 but
ISLAMBUL. 1.7 gr. 14-15mm . . 35.00

10 (altun). Sim. 3.4 gr.
19-20mm 50.00

11 (1½ altun). Sim. 5.2 gr.
26-28 mm *90.00*

11a —. Sim. but broad ornate
borders. 4.9-5.2 gr. 29-
32mm *100.00*

12 (2 altun). Like No. 11a.
6.9 gr. 29-30mm *150.00*

13 (3 altun). Sim. 9.8-10.4 gr.
36-37mm *250.00*

13a —. Plain borders. 10 gr.
36mm *250.00*

14 (5 altun). Like No. 11a.
17 gr. 48mm *350.00*

Osman III
AH1168-71 (= AD1754-57)

All dated AH1168, no regnal years are shown.

Silver (lowest values billon)

VG-F
15 (asper). Like No. 2 but
dated 1168. 12mm 10.00

VG-F
*16 (para). Sim. 15-16mm 2.50

17 (5 para). Like No. 3 but dated
1168. 2.4 gr. 20mm . . . . *Rare*

*18 (10 para). Sim. 5.7 gr.
25mm 15.00

19 (20 para). Sim. 31mm.
11.6 gr. . . . . *RR*

21 (piastre). Sim. 38-41mm.
23.7 gr. . . . . *RRR*

Gold

V.F.
24 (½ zeri mahbub). Like No. 18
but ISLAMBUL. 1.3 gr.
17mm *40.00*

25 (zeri mahbub). Sim.
2.6 gr. 21mm *65.00*

27 (1½ altun). Like No. 16 but
ISLAMBUL. Narrow ornamented
borders. 4.85 gr. 28mm *150.00*

27a —. Wide vine borders.
5.20 gr. 31mm *150.00*

27b (ex 27a) —. 38mm. *200.00*

28 (3 altun). Sim. 9.3-10.4 gr.
37-38mm *300.00*

29 (5 altun). Sim. 17.3 gr.
44mm *400.00*

29a —. 49mm *500.00*

Mustafa III
AH1171-87 (= AD1757-74)

All dated AH1171, actual years shown by final digits.

Silver (lowest values billon)

VG-F
32 (asper). 3 lines/date. Rev.
3 lines/1171. 12.5mm.
(117)7, 80 . . . . 5.00

35 (10 para). Like No. 3 but
dated 1171. 5.8 gr. 25mm . . . . *RR*

36 (15 para). Like No. 45.
6-6.7 gr. 27-28mm.
(117)2 . . . . .15.00

40 (asper). Like No. 41. 0.15 gr.
12mm. (11)80-81 . . . . 5.00

*41 (para). Toughra. Rev. actual
yr./DURIBA/FI/ISLAMBUL/1171.
0.3-0.7 gr. (117)1-9, 80-87 . . . 1.50

42 (5 para). Sim. 19.5-20mm.
(117)1-9, 81-85 . . . . 5.00

· 464 ·

TURKEY

VG-F

43 (10 para). Sim. 24-26mm.
(117)1-9, 80-87 . . . . 5.00

44 (20 para). Sim. 30-33mm.
(117)3-6, 82-87 . . . . 8.50

45 (zolota). 4 line legends
each side. 35-37mm. 13.8-
14.7 gr. (117)1-9, 82-87 . . . . . 13.50

46 (piastre). Like No. 41.
36-40mm. 18-19.7 gr.
(117)2-9, 80-87 . . . . 15.00

47 (2 zolota). Like No. 45.
42-44mm. 27.7-30.1 gr.
(117)1-9, 80-82 . . . . 17.50

Gold
V.F.

48 (½ zeri mahbub). Like No. 3
but ISLAMBUL/1171. 1.3 gr.
14-15mm. (117)1-7, 81-86 . . . 25.00

49 (zeri mahbub). Sim. 2.5 gr.
18-19.5mm. (117)7-8,
80-87 . . . . 45.00

51 (½ altun). Like No. 41.
1.7 gr. 12mm. (117)1-7 . . . . . 37.50

52 (altun). Sim. 3.4 gr.
18-20mm. (117)3-7, 81 . . . . . . 60.00

53 (altun). Toughra in ornate
border. Rev. ISLAMBUL etc.,
1171 in cartouche. 3.7 gr.
30mm 100.00

54 (1½ altun). Like No. 41 but
double pearl border each side.
4.6-4.9 gr. 30mm. (117)7-
9, 80-81 . . . . 100.00

55 (2 altun). Sim. 6.9 gr.
31mm. (117)2-9 . . . . 150.00

56 (3 altun). Like No. 41.
10.45 gr. 22mm. (117)5 . . . . 400.00

57 (3 altun). Like No. 54.
9.6 gr. 36mm. (117)9 . . . . . . 300.00

Abdul Hamid I
AH1187-1203 (=AD1774-89)

All dated AH1187. Regnal years shown.

Silver (lowest values billon)

VG-F

★60 (asper). Toughra. Rev. regnal
yr./DURIBA/FI/QUSTANTINIAH/
1187. 0.13-0.20 gr. 11-14mm.
Yrs. 1-14 . . . . 5.00

61 (para). Sim. .4-.5 gr.
15mm. Yrs. 1-16 . . . . 1.50

62 (5 para). Like No. 64.
20mm. Yrs. 1-15 . . . . 10.00

63 (10 para). Sim. 24-25mm.
Yrs. 1-16 . . . . 7.50

VG-F

★64 (20 para). Toughra/DURIBA/
FI/QUSTANTINIAH/1187. Rev.
4-line legend, yr. in 3rd line.
31-32mm. Yrs. 1-13 . . . . 10.00

65 (zolota). 4-line legends
each side. QUSTANTINIAH.
13.3-14.7 gr. 35-37mm.
Yrs. 1-15 . . . . 15.00

F-VF

66 (piastre). Like No. 64.
37-39mm. 16.4-19.2 gr.
Yrs. 1-8 . . . . 12.50

66a —. Flower at 2 o'clock
over Toughra. Yrs. 8-16 . . . . 12.50

67 (2 zolota). Like No. 65.
41.5-45mm. 25.3-29.6 gr.
Yrs. 1-16 . . . . 15.00

68 (2 piastres). Like No. 60
but yr. and 1187 in frames.
30-31 gr. 43-45mm. Yr. 16 . . . 37.50

Gold
V.F.

69 (½ zeri mahbub). Like No. 64
but ISLAMBUL. 1.3 gr. 19mm.
Yrs. 1-14 . . . . 30.00

70 (zeri mahbub). Sim. 2.6 gr.
22mm. Yrs. 2-10 . . . . 45.00

71 (¼ altun). Like No. 60 but
ISLAMBUL. 0.85 gr. 14-15mm.
Yrs. 2-16 . . . . 30.00

72 (½ altun). Sim. 1.7 gr.
16mm. Yr. 15 . . . . 50.00

73 (altun). Sim. 3.5 gr. 20mm.
Yr. 16 . . . . 90.00

73a (zeri mahbub). Sim. 2.3 gr.
20mm. Yr. 15 . . . . 90.00

74 (1½ altun). Sim. but ornate
borders. 4.4-5.2 gr. 29-31mm.
Yrs. 1-16 . . . . 100.00

76 (3 altun). Sim. 8.7-10.45 gr.
36-39mm 250.00

78 (5 altun). Sim. 16.25 gr.
47mm. Yr. 1 . . . . 400.00

Selim III
AH1203-22 (=AD1789-1807)

All dated AH1203 plus regnal year.

Base (.465) Silver

Note: Selim III silver of year 1 was
struck in both a heavy and a light
standard (cf. Nos. 92 and 92a).

VG-F

85 (asper). Like No. 88. 0.16 gr.
12mm. Yrs. 1-9 . . . . 5.00

86 (para). Sim. 15mm. 0.3 gr.
Yrs. 1-16 . . . . 1.50

VG-F

87 (5 para). Sim. 20mm.
Yrs. 1-18 . . . . 5.00

Note: Pere No. 711 (22mm 2.2 gr. yr.
10) appears to be No. 95 in silver.

★88 (10 para). Toughra. Rev. yr./
DURIBA/FI/ISLAMBUL/1203.
Yrs. 1-19 . . . . 3.50

89 (20 para). Sim. 30mm.
Yrs. 5-9 . . . . 12.50

F-VF

90 (piastre). Sim. 36-38mm.
11.8-13.15 gr. Yrs. 1-18 . . . . . 15.00

91 (2 zolota). Four line legends
each side. 40mm. 18.3-18.7 gr.
Yrs. 1-3 (Query yrs. 6-12
listed by Davenport) 50.00

92 (2 piastres). Like No. 88.
43-45mm. 29-31.6 gr.
Yr. 1 . . . . 35.00

92a —. 41-43mm. 23.5-26.4 gr.
Yrs. 1-19 . . . . 12.50

★93 (2½ piastres). ISLAMBUL.
29.6-34.5 gr. 43-45mm.
Yrs. 1-17 . . . . 15.00

Gold
V.F.

94 (½ zeri mahbub). Sim. to
No. 93. 1.2 gr. 18mm.
Yrs. 5-17 . . . . 40.00

95 (zeri mahbub). Sim. 2.5 gr.
21-22mm. Yrs. 3-15 . . . . 60.00

TURKEY

96 (¼ altun). Like No. 88.
0.8 gr. 14-15mm. (2 vars.).
Yrs. 1-18 . . . .*V.F.* 25.00

97 (½ altun). Sim. but ornate
borders. 1.65 gr. 16mm.
Yr. 1 . . . . .50.00

98 (altun). Sim. 3.4 gr.
20mm. Yr. 2 . . . . .60.00

98a —. Like No. 88. Yr. 18 . . . . .60.00

99 (1½ altun). Like No. 96.
4.2-4.5 gr. 30-31mm.
Yr. 1 . . . .*125.00*

Mustafa IV
AH1222-23 (=AD1807-08)

All dated AH1222 plus regnal year.

Base (.465) Silver

110 (asper). Like No. 111. *Fine*
0.17 gr. 12mm. Yrs. 1-2 . . . .*12.50*

★**111** (para). Toughra. Rev.
DURIBA/FI/QUSTANTINIAH/
1222. 0.35 gr. 14-15mm.
Yrs. 1-2 . . . . 7.50

112 (5 para). Like No. 113.
1.2-1.5 gr. 19.5mm.
Yrs. 1-2 . . . . .20.00

★**113** (10 para). 2.9-3.35 gr.
Yrs. 1-2 . . . . .20.00

115 (piastre). Sim. 12.5 gr.
33-36mm. Yr. 1 . . . .*60.00*

116 (2 zolota). Four line legends
each side. QUSTANTINIAH.
18-20 gr. 40-41mm. Yr. 1 . .*85.00*

117 (2½ piastres). Like No. 113.
25 gr. 42mm. Yr. 1 . . . . .RR

Gold
V.F.

121 (½ zeri mahbub). Like
No. 113. 1.2 gr. 19mm.
Yr. 1 . . . .*90.00*

122 (zeri mahbub). Sim. 2.4 gr.
21-22mm. Yr. 1 . . . .*125.00*

125 (¼ altun). Like No. 111.
0.77 gr. 15mm. Yrs. 1-2 . . . .50.00

127 (altun). Sim. 3.2 gr.
19-20mm. Yr. 1 . . . .*160.00*

Mahmud II
AH1223-55 (=AD1808-39)

All dated AH1223 plus regnal year.

A. First standard, years 1-2.

0.465 Silver (piastre = 12.83 gr.)

171 (asper). Like No. 172. *Fine*
0.11-0.15 gr. 11-12mm.
Yrs. 1-2 . . . .*10.00*

★**172** (para). Toughra. Rev.
DURIBA/FI/QUSTANTINIAH/
1223. 0.32-0.35 gr. 14-15mm.
Yrs. 1-2 . . . . 6.00

★**173** (5 para). Toughra/
QUSTANTINIAH/1223. Rev.
4-line legend. 1.3-1.75 gr.
19mm. Yrs. 1-2 . . . . .12.50

174 (10 para). Sim. 2.6-3.2 gr.
20-22mm. Yrs. 1-2 . . . . . . .17.50

176 (piastre). Sim. 12.8-13.2 gr.
33-37mm. Yr. 1 . . . . .RR

The 20 para, 1 and 2 zolota yr. 1, and 2
and 2½ piastres yrs. 1-2 *are patterns.*

B. Second standard, years 3-14.

0.465 Silver (piastre = 9.62 gr.)

171a (ex 177) (asper). Like
No. 172. 0.08-0.12 gr. *9-11mm.*
Yrs. 5, 12 . . . . 6.00

★**172a** (ex 178) (para). Sim. 0.19-
0.28 gr. 13-14mm.
Yrs. 3-14 . . . . 1.50

173a (ex 179) (5 para). Like
No. 173. 1.05-1.25 gr.
18-19mm. Yrs. 3-14 . . . . . . 7.50

★**174a** (ex 180) (10 para). Sim.
2.1-2.5 gr. 22mm.
Yrs. 3-14 . . . . 5.00

F-VF

★**176a** (piastre). Sim. but circle
and rope border. 8.3-9.7 gr.
33mm. Yrs. 3-13 . . . . .12.50

C. Third standard, years 3-11.

Nos. 181, 183 and 184 are "Jihadiye"
(coins issued for war expenses).

0.730 Silver

★**181** (*40* para). 4.5-4.9 gr.
Yr. 3 . . . .*30.00*

Controversy exists as to whether No.
181 is a 40 para (piastre) or 50 para
(1¼ piastres).

183 (100 para). Like No. 181
but more ornate borders.
12.4-13.3 gr. 34-37mm.
Yrs. *2,* 3-10 . . . .*20.00*

184 (5 piastres). Sim. 24.15-
26.4 gr. 41mm. Yrs. 3-11 . . .25.00

D. Fourth standard, years 14-15.

0.465 Silver (piastre = 6.41 gr.)

Fine

★**172b** (ex 185) (para). Like
No. 172. 0.14-0.16 gr.
13-14mm. Yrs. 14-15 . . . . . 1.75

173b (ex 179a) (5 para). Like
No. 176a. 0.72-0.88 gr.
18mm. Yr. 14 . . . . .10.00

TURKEY

174b (ex 180a) (10 para). Like
No. 173. 1.4-1.8 gr. 22mm.
Yrs. 14-15 . . . . *15.00*

Fine

176b (ex 189) (piastre). Like
No. 176a. 5.4-*6.4* gr. 32mm.
Yrs. 14-15 . . . . *20.00*

★190 (2 piastres). 11.5-12.6 gr.
Yrs. 14-15 . . . . *25.00*

E. Fifth standard, years 15-*18*.

0.730 **Silver** (piastre = **6.41 gr.**)

★172c (ex 191) (para). Like
No. 172 but flower added
on obv. 0.14-0.16 gr.
12-13mm. Yrs. 15-16 . . . . . 2.50

★186 (5 para). 0.8 gr.
Yrs. 15-18 . . . . 5.00

★174c (ex 187) (10 para). Like
No. 176a. 1.6-1.8 gr.
20-21mm. Yrs. 15-18 . . . . . 5.00

176c (ex 189a) (piastre). Sim.
5.9-*6.9* gr. 32mm.
Yrs. 15-16 . . . . 10.00

190a (2 piastres). Like No. 190
but borders like No. 181.
11.6-12.9 gr. 38mm.
Yrs. 15-16 . . . . 20.00

F. Sixth standard, years 16-21.

0.600 **Silver** (piastre = **4.28 gr.**)

Fine

172d (para). Like No. 172c.
0.11-0.18 gr. 12-13mm.
Yrs. *17-21* 1.75

V.F.

★192 (zolota). 3.25-3.4 gr.
Yrs. 17-21 . . . . 7.00

193 (2 zolota). Sim. 6.1-6.7 gr.
Yrs. 16-21 . . . . 10.00

G. Seventh standard, years 21-22.

0.833 **Silver** (piastre = *1.60* **gr.**)

★194 *(20 para)*. Double vine borders
both sides. 0.70-0.86 gr.
17-19mm. Yrs. 21-22 . . . . . 5.00

195 *(piastre)*. Sim. 1.4-1.6 gr.
22mm. Yrs. 21-22 . . . . 5.00

H. Eighth standard, years 22-25.

0.220 **Silver** (piastre = **3.21 gr.**)

F-VF

★172e (ex 196a) (para). Like
No. 172c. 0.08-0.15 gr.
11-12mm. Yrs. 22-25 . . . . . 1.75

197 (10 para). Like No. 198.
0.8 gr. 17mm. Yrs. 22-25 . . 3.00

★198 (20 para). 1.2-1.9 gr.
21mm. Yrs. 22-25 . . . . 1.75

199 (piastre). Sim. 2.3-3.3 gr.
27-28mm. Yrs. 22-25 . . . . . 3.00

200 (100 para). Sim. 7.4-8 gr.
33-35mm. Yrs. 22-25 . . . . . 4.50

201 (5 piastres). Sim. 14-16.6 gr.
39mm. Yrs. 22-25 . . . . 9.00

Other types of 5 piastres yr. 22 (15.65-
15.75 gr., 40-41mm) are RRR patterns.

I. Ninth standard, years 25-32.
0.170 **Silver** (piastre = 3.21 gr.)

F-VF

★171f (ex 196) *(asper)*. Like
No. 172c. 0.04-0.07 gr.
9-10mm. Yrs. *26-27* 3.50

★172f (ex 202) (para). Sim.
0.08-0.30 gr. 12-13mm.
Yrs. *26-32* 1.00

197a (ex 203) (10 para). Like
No. 198a. 0.55-0.72 gr.
17mm. Yrs. 25-32 . . . . 2.00

★198a (ex 204) (20 para). Like
No. 198 but large dot below
wreath bows both sides
to denote changed standard.
1.2-2.0 gr. 20-21mm.
Yrs. 26-32 . . . . 1.75

199a (ex 205) (piastre). Sim.
2.5-3.3 gr. 27-28mm.
Yrs. 25-26 . . . . 3.00

200a (100 para). Sim. 6.3-8 gr.
34-35mm. Yrs. 25-26 . . . . . 4.50

201a (5 piastres). Sim.
13.5-16.6 gr. 38-39mm.
Yrs. 25-26 . . . . 7.50

J. Tenth standard, years 26-32.
0.435 Silver

★206 (1½ piastres = Altmishlik).
2.5-3.1 gr. Yrs. 26-32 . . . . . 9.00

207 (3 piastres = Uchluk).
Sim. 5.4-6.75 gr. 33mm.
Yrs. 26-32 . . . . 7.50

208 (6 piastres = Altilik).
Sim. 10.9-13 gr. 36-38mm.
Yrs. 26-32 . . . . 12.50

Gold

A. Zerimahbub series.

V.F.

209 (½ zeri mahbub). Like
No. 173. 1.1-1.2 gr. 18-19mm.
Yrs. 1-12 . . . . 45.00

TURKEY

B. Rumi series... (continued)

V.F.

209a —. Reduced standard.
0.76-0.84 gr. 16mm.
Yrs. 15-32 .... *60.00*

210 (zeri mahbub). Sim. 2.2-
2.4 gr. 22mm. Yrs. 1-15 .... 55.00

210a —. 1.46-1.60 gr. 19mm.
Yrs. 15-20 .... *100.00*

B. Rumi series.

212 (½ *rumi altun*). Like
No. 194 but wavy floral
borders both sides. 1.18 gr.
19mm. Yrs. 10-13 .... *50.00*

213 (*rumi altun*). Sim. 2.36 gr.
22mm. *Yr. 10* .... *RRR*

214 (*2 rumi altun*). Sim. 4.7 gr.
27-28mm. Yrs. 8-12 and 22
(*error?*) *100.00*

215 (*new rumi altun*). Sim. but
legend borders in place of
floral borders. 2.38 gr.
23mm. Yrs. 10-15 .... *60.00*

217 (*2 new rumi altun*). Sim.
4.55-4.76 gr. 29mm.
Yrs. 9-12 .... *100.00*

Note: Nos. 212-214 are .956 gold,
while Nos. 215-217 are .800 gold. There
is no agreement regarding the names
of these denominations or the relationships, whether fractional or multiple,
within each series. They were listed as
1, 2, 2½ and 4 rumi altun in the 2nd
edition. However, Olçer lists them as
½, 1 and 2, and this parity has now
been accepted.

C. Miscellaneous issues.

★218 (¼ altun). Like No. 172.
0.68-0.79 gr. 14-15mm.
Yrs. 1-14 .... 25.00

218a —. Reduced standard.
Rev. AZZ NASRAHU added
at top. 0.54-0.59 gr. 14mm.
Yrs. 13-15 .... 25.00

218c —. Further reduction.
0.26-0.35 gr. 13mm. Yr. 21
(*pattern?*) .... RRR

237 (¼ altun). Sim. but border
of zigzag lines each side.
0.26-0.31 gr. 12mm.
Yrs. 24-30 .... 20.00

D. Coins with mint name Darülhilafe.

219 (¼ altun). Toughra, roses
and ADLI in field (like
No. 206), beaded border.
Rev. yr./Darülhilafe/1223/
Esseniye. 0.48 gr. 13mm.
Yr. 15 .... *Rare*

V.F.

219a —. Darülhilafe/1223/
Elaliye. Yrs. 15-16 .... 35.00

220 (½ altun). Like No. 219.
0.78 gr. 17mm. Yr. 15 ..... *Rare*

220a —. Like No. 219a. 0.78 gr.
15-16mm. Yrs. 15-16 ..... 50.00

221 (altun). Like No. 219.
1.50 gr. 21mm. Yr. 15 ..... *Rare*

221a —. Like No. 219a.
1.57 gr. 19-20mm 90.00

E. Cedid (=new) Adli series.

227 (ex 219b) (¼ altun). Toughra,
ornaments and ADLI in field.
Rev. yr./DURIBA/FI/QUSTAN-
TINIAH/1223/AL-MAHRUSA.
0.40-0.45 gr. 12-13mm.
Yrs. 16-17 .... 30.00

228 (¼ altun). Sim. but legend
borders both sides. 0.38-
0.43 gr. 12-13mm. Yrs. 15,
17-24 .... 25.00

229 (½ altun). Sim. 0.78 gr.
16mm. Yrs. 16-20 .... 35.00

230 (altun). Sim. 1.58 gr.
19mm. Yrs. 16-20 .... 47.50

F. Hayriye series.

232 (½ altun). Like No. 233a
but branches in place of
stars, rev. QUSTANTINIAH.
0.78-0.86 gr. 15mm.
Yrs. 15-16 .... 30.00

232a —. Like No. 233a. 0.88 gr.
16.5mm. Yr. 24 .... *50.00*

233 (altun). Like No. 232.
1.73 gr. Yrs. 21-26 .... 55.00

★233a —. Rev. EDIRNE (=Adrian-
ople). 1.80 gr. Yr. 24 ..... *85.00*

234 (2 altun). Like No. 232.
3.55 gr. 27mm. Yr. 21 ... *125.00*

234a —. Like No. 233a. 3.55 gr.
27mm. Yr. 24 .... *150.00*

G. Cedid Mahmudiye series.

239 (5 piastres). Like No. 206
but different floral borders,
no beaded inner circles.
0.38-0.40 gr. 13mm.
Yrs. 26-32 .... 25.00

240 (10 piastres). Sim. 0.76 gr.
15mm. Yrs. 26-32 .... 45.00

241 (20 piastres). Sim. 1.56-
1.60 gr. 20mm. Yrs. 26-32 .. 65.00

Abdul Mejid
AH1255-77 (=AD1839-61)

I. Old Standard Coinage.

AH1255, Yrs. 1-5
0.170 Silver

Fine

265 (para). Like No. 267 but
rope border. 0.12-0.32 gr.
12mm. Yrs. 1-5 .... 2.00

266 (10 para). Like No. 267.
0.6-.85 gr. 17mm. Yrs.
1-5 .... 3.00

★267 (20 para). 1.1-2.0 gr.
Yrs. 1-5 .... 2.00

★269 (1½ piastres). 1.6-3.25 gr.
26mm. Yrs. 1-5 .... 5.50

270 (3 piastres). Sim. 5.9-6.3 gr.
33mm. Yrs. 1-2 .... 15.00

271 (6 piastres). Sim. 12.3-
12.6 gr. 37mm. Yr. 1 ..... 20.00

Gold

V.F.

272 (5 piastres). Like No. 269.
.4 gr. 13mm. Yrs. 1-5 ..... 25.00

273 (10 piastres). Sim. .8 gr.
15mm. Yrs. 1-2 .... 45.00

274 (20 piastres). Sim. 1.6 gr.
19mm. Yrs. 1, 5 .... 65.00

278 (*10 piastres*). 4 lines. Rev.
Toughra/Constantinople/
1255. .85 gr. 15.5 gr.
Yr. 5 .... *60.00*

II. New Standard Coinage.

AH1255, Yrs. 6-23

Copper

Fine

282 1 (para). Like No. 286.
1.05-1.1 gr. 13.5mm.
Yrs. 8-16 .... 1.25

282a —. 0.8-0.9 gr. Yrs. 16-18 ... 1.00

282b —. 0.55 gr. Yrs. 18-21 ..... .50

283 5 (para). Sim. 4.9-6.8 gr.
21-22mm. Yrs. 8-15, *16* .... .75

283a —. 3.7-4.2 gr. Yrs. 15-17 ... 1.25

283b —. 2.5-3.3 gr. Yrs. *17*,
18-21 .... .75

TURKEY

		Fine
284	10 (para). Sim. 9.0-12.75 gr. 27mm. Yrs. *13-15*	2.50
284a	—. 7.5-8.2 gr. Yrs. 16-18	1.50
284b	—. 4.9-5.7 gr. Yrs. 18-21	.75
285	20 (para). Sim. 14.4-16.0 gr. 31mm. Yr. 16	2.50
285a	—. 10.2-11 gr. Yrs. 17-21	1.00

★286	40 (para). 19.8-21.8 gr. Yrs. 17-23	1.75

0.830 Silver. Years 6-23
F-VF

287	(20 para). Like No. 289 but wreaths instead of stars. 0.55 gr. 13mm. Yrs. *9-23*	4.00
288	(piastre). Like No. 289. 1.2 gr. 15mm. Yrs. 9-23	2.25

★289	(2 piastres). 2.2 gr. 18mm. Yrs. 7-20	2.50

★290	(5 piastres). 5.8-6.0 gr. 24mm. Yrs. 6-23	3.00
291	(10 piastres). 11.7-12 gr. 27mm. Yrs. 6-7 (and yrs. 9, 13, *both unique?*)	25.00
292	(20 piastres). 23.6 gr. 37mm. Yrs. 6-23	10.00

Gold. Years 6-19
100 piastres = 7.2 gr.
V.F.

295	(25 piastres). Toughra in wreath, stars above. Rev. Constantinople etc. in wreath. 15mm. Yrs. 20-23	40.00
296	(50 piastres). Sim. 18mm. Yr. 13	50.00
297	(100 piastres). Sim. 22mm. Yrs. 5-23	60.00
298	250 (piastres). Sim. 27mm. *Yr. 18*	200.00
299	500 (piastres). Sim. 34mm. *Yr. 18*	*500.00*
300	(50 piastres). Sim. but Edirne (Adrianople) Mint. 3.5 gr. 18mm. Yr. 8	*150.00*
301	(100 piastres). Sim. 7.12 gr. 22mm. Yr. 8	*150.00*

UNVERIFIED DATA

Note: Throughout this catalog, any uncertain, indefinite or unconfirmed information is shown in *italic type*. Such material may be, for example, coin descriptions, dates and prices, names of rulers, or supplementary notes. Further information to confirm or correct *material in italics* should be sent to the author at the following address:

William D. Craig
c/o Whitman Coin Supply Division
1220 Mound Avenue
Racine, Wisconsin 53404, U.S.A.

UNITED STATES OF AMERICA

I. COLONIAL AND STATE COINAGES.

A. Connecticut, State.

Copper

Good

1 (½ penny). AUCTORI CONNEC.,
bust r. Rev. INDE ET LIB.,
Liberty std. 1785-88........20.00

*1a —. Bust l. 1785-88........12.00
Many varieties of Nos. 1 and 1a exist.

B. Massachusetts, State.

Copper

V.G.

*2 HALF/CENT. 1787-88.....40.00
3 CENT. Sim. 1787-88......30.00

C. New Jersey (Nova Caesarea), State.

Copper

Good

*4 (½ penny). 1786-88........17.50
4a Horse head l. 1788........75.00
Many varieties of Nos. 4 and 4a exist.

D. New York, State.

Copper

Good

8 (½ penny). NOVA EBORAC,
bust l. Rev. VIRT. ET LIB.,
Liberty std. r. 1787.......60.00
8a —. Rev. Liberty std. l.
1787..................50.00

E. Vermont, State.

Copper

*5 (½ penny). 1785-86.......60.00
6 (½ penny). VERMON: AUCTORI:,
bust r. Rev. INDE: ET LIB.,
Liberty std. 1786-88........40.00
6a —. Bust l. 1786-87.......65.00
Many varieties of Nos. 5-6a exist.

F. Virginia, Colony.

George III of England

Copper

*7 (½ penny). GEORGIVS III REX,
his bust. Rev. VIRGI—NIA,
arms. 1773...............25.00

II. FEDERAL COINAGE.

Monetary System:
100 cents = 10 dimes = 1 dollar.

Copper

V.G.

*10 (cent). FUGIO. Sun dial.
Rev. UNITED STATES etc.
13 links. 1787 (var.).......45.00

Good

*11 HALF/CENT. 1793.....300.00
11.5 HALF/CENT. Like No. 16.
1794-97.................55.00

*12 HALF/CENT. 1800-08.....15.00

V.G.

*13 HALF/CENT. 1809-37.....19.00

Fine

14 HALF/CENT. Like No. 19.
1840-57..................18.00

Good

*15 ONE/CENT. 1793........375.00
15a —. Rev. value in wreath.
1793...................300.00

*16 ONE/CENT. 1793-96......40.00
17 ONE/CENT. Like No. 12.
1796-1807................11.00
18 ONE/CENT. Like No. 13.
1808-14..................14.00

FEDERAL COINAGE (Cont.)

V.G.

19 ONE/CENT. 1816-57 . . . . . . 6.50

Silver

21 (½ dime). 1794-95 . . . . 260.00

22 (½ dime). 1796-97 . . . . 300.00

22a —. Obv. sim. Rev. like No. 35.
1800-05 . . . . 250.00

23 5 C(ents). 1829-37 . . . . 18.50

25 (dime). 1796-97 . . . . 500.00

25a —. Obv. sim. Rev. like No. 35.
1798-1807 . . . . 175.00

26 10 C(ents). Like No. 23.
1809-37 . . . . 18.00

V.G.

28 (25 cents). 1796 . . . . 1600.00

28a 25 C(ents). Obv. sim. Rev.
like No. 35. 1804-07 . . . . 100.00

29 25 C(ents). Like No. 23.
1815-28 . . . . 40.00

29a —. Reduced size. 1831-38 . . . 32.50

30 (½ dollar). 1794-95 . . . . 200.00

31 ½ (dollar). Like No. 28.
1796-97 . . . . 3200.00

31a (½ dollar). Obv. sim. Rev.
like No. 35. 1801-07 . . . . 50.00

32 50 C(ents). Like No. 23.
1807-36 . . . . 20.00

32a 50 CENTS. 1836-37 . . . . 30.00

32b HALF DOL(lar). 1838-39 . . . 30.00

33 (dollar). Like No. 30.
1794-95 . . . . 400.00

34 (dollar). Like No. 28.
1795-98 . . . . 375.00

34a —. Like No. 31a.
1798-1803 . . . . 275.00

34b —. 1804 . . . . 150,000.00

Gold

V.F.

35 (2½ dollars). 1796 . . . . 7500.00

35a —. 13 stars around bust.
1796-1807 . . . . 1475.00

V.F.

36 2½ D(ollars). 1808 . . . . . . 7250.00

36a —. Reduced size.
1821-34 . . . . 1700.00

37 2½ D(ollars). 1834-39 . . . . . 175.00

38 (5 dollars). 1795-96 . . . . . . 3350.00

38a —. Shield on eagle's breast.
1795-1807 . . . . 850.00

39 5 D(ollars). Like No. 36.
1807-12 . . . . 750.00

39a —. Liberty head l. 1813-34 . . 900.00

40 5 D(ollars). Like No. 37.
1834-38 . . . . 200.00

41 (10 dollars). Like No. 38.
1795-97 . . . . 3500.00

41a —. Shield on eagle's breast.
1797-1804 . . . . 1500.00

VENEZUELA

On the north coast of South America. Constituted the Captaincy-General of Caracas under Spain until 1821. Revolutionary confusion 1810-21. Part of the Republic of Gran Colombia 1821-30. Independent as the Republic of Venezuela thereafter.

Monetary System:
16 reales = 1 escudo.

I. Spanish Royalist Coinage.

A. National issues.

Copper

Fine

★1 ⅛ (real). 1802-18........250.00

★2 ¼ (real). 1802-21.........9.00

Silver

5 1 (real). Like No. 6. 1817-
21.................350.00

★6 2 (reales). 1817-21........20.00

7 4 (reales). Sim. 1819-20....275.00

B. *Province of Maracaibo.*

Copper

10 ½ (real). Head of King
Fernando VII. Rev. date/
value. 1813.............500.00

Note: A copper ⅛ real and silver 2 reales have been reported for this series but not confirmed at this time. *(query?)*

II. Royalists, Republicans, or both.

Silver

VG-F

12 I (real). Copy of 18th century
Lima cob (sim. to No. 6 but
on small flan and w/out
CARACAS. Fictitious mmks.
L–M and M–L. Dates 18(1)2
and others.............35.00

13 2 (reales). Sim. Blundered
dates 182-187, 281, 781,
812-817; or actual dates
1816-17................20.00

The blundered dates above are said to represent the years 1812 through 1817. Other blundered or false dates observed include 142, 172, 174, 231, 471, 751 and 931, but Stohr says these cannot be positively attributed to Venezuela. *They may be part of the series mentioned under* ARGENTINA, Tucumán (q.v.).

III. Republican Coinage.

Copper

Fine

21 ⅛/DE (=of) REAL. Like
No. 22. 1812............250.00

★22 ¼/DE (=of) REAL. 1812..65.00

Silver

★25 ½ (real.) AÑO (=year) 2
(1812)..................400.00

Fine

★26 UN (=1)/REAL.
AÑO 2 (1812)...........450.00

The "19" refers to 19 April 1810, date of the Venezuelan declaration of independence.

IV. Venezuela under Colombia.

Silver

★31 ¼ (real). 1821-22........100.00

★34 ¼ (real). Cornucopia.
Rev. c–¼–s. 1829-30.......22.50

V. Province of Guiana (Provincia de Guaiana).

Portion of British Guiana initially part of the Captaincy General of Caracas.

Ferdinand (Fernando) VII of Spain

Copper

V.G. (crude)

40 ¼ (real). Like No. 41.
1815..................200.00

★41 ½ (real). 1813-17.........17.50

VIEQUE. See CARIBBEAN ISLANDS AND TERRITORIES.

NOTES

BIBLIOGRAPHY

In compilation of the first edition of this catalog, reference was made to scores of leading numismatic publications and hundreds of sale catalogs and price lists. In preparing the later editions I relied principally on the following authorities, some new and some old:

Buttrey and Hubbard, *A Guide Book of Mexican Coins* (Racine 1971).

Cermentini and Toderi, *Prezzario Moneta Coniate in Italia dal 1800 al 1966* (Firenze 1966).

Chenoy, P.B., *Rare Coins of Hyderabad State* (The Numismatist, July 1970).

Coole, Rev. A. B., *Coins in China's History* (4th ed., Kansas 1965).

Davenport, J. S., *German Talers 1700-1800* (2nd ed., Spink 1965).

——, *European Crowns 1700-1800* (3rd ed., Galesburg 1971).

——, *European Crowns and Rhalers Since 1800* (2nd ed., Spink 1964).

Dietzel, H., *Die Münzen des Königreichs Preussen ab 1701* (1974).

Divo and Tobler, *Die Münzen der Schweiz im 19. und 20. Jahrhundert* (Zürich & Luzern 1967).

——, *Die Münzen der Schweiz im 18. Jahrhundert* (Zürich 1974).

Eklund, O. P., *Copper Coins of Italy (excluding Papal)* (Reprint from the Numismatist, 1963).

——, *Copper Coins of Russia and Poland* (Reprint from the Numismatist, 1962).

——, *The Copper Coins of the Papal States* (Reprint from the Numismatist, 1962).

Ferrari, J. N., *Amonedación de La Rioja* (2 Vols., Buenos Aires 1962-64).

Ferrari and Pardo, *Amonedación de Cordoba* (Buenos Aires 1951).

Ferraro Vaz, J., *Livro das Moedas de Portugal* (Braga 1969).

Friedberg, R., *Coins of the British World* (New York 1962).

——, *Gold Coins of the World* (2nd ed., New York 1965).

Glück and Hesselblad, *Svenska Mynt* (Stockholm 1964).

Guilloteau, V., *Monnaies Francaises – Colonies 1670-1942 – Metropole 1774-1942* (Versailles 1942).

Gumowski, M., *Handbuch der Polnischen Numismatik* (Revised German ed., Graz 1960).

Hahn, W. R. O., *Typenkatalog der Münzen der bayerischen Herzöge und Kurfürsten 1506-1805* (Braunschweig 1971).

Haxby and Willey, *Coins of Canada* (2nd ed., Racine 1972).

Hede, H., *Danmarks og Norges Mønter 1541-1963* (København 1964).

Hürlimann, H., *Zürcher Münzgeschichte* (Zürich 1966).

Interphilatelie, *Catalogue des Monnaies Luxembourgeoises 1740-1967* (Luxembourg 1967).

Jaeckel, P., *Die Münzprägungen des Hauses Habsburg 1780-1918, etc.* (3rd ed., Basel 1967).

Jaeger, K., *Die neueren Münzprägungen der deutschen Staaten vor Einführung der Reichswährung* (Vols. 1-2, 5-11 — 1951-70).

Jacobs and Vermeule, *Japanese Coinage* (New York 1953).

Kann, E., *Illustrated Catalog of Chinese Coins* (2nd ed., New York 1966).

Kocaer, R., *Osmanlı Altınları* (Istanbul 1967).

Lane-Poole, S., *Catalogue of Oriental Coins in the British Museum* (Vols. VII, VIII and X, London 1882-90).

Mandel, E. J., *Cast Coinage of Korea* (Racine 1972).

Morin, F., *Catalogue des Monnaies Belges de 1832 a 1964* (Boom).

Neumann, J., *Beschreibung der Bekanntesten Kupfermünzen* (Facsimile reprint of First ed. 1858).

Ölçer, C., *Sultan Mahmud II Zamanında Darp Edilen Osmanlı Madeni Paraları* (Istanbul 1970).

Pagani, A., *Monete Italiane (1796-1963)* (2nd ed., Milan 1965).

——, *Prove e Progetti di Monete Italiane 1796-1955* (Milan 1957).

Pere, N., *Osmanlılarda Madenî Paralar* (Istanbul 1968)

Pridmore, F., *The Coins of the British Commonwealth of Nations* (Parts 1-4, European, Asian Territories, West Indies, India, Spink 1960-75).

Prober, K., *Catálogo das Moedas Brasileiras* (2nd ed. São Paolo 1966).

Probszt, G., *Die Münzen Salzburgs* (Graz 1959).

Remick, James et al., *The Guide Book and Catalogue of British Commonwealth Coins* (3rd ed., Winnipeg 1971).

(Romanov), Georgii Mikhailovich, *Monnaies de l'Empire de Russie 1725-1894* (French ed., Paris 1916, reprinted Boston 1973).

Scholten, G., *The Coins of the Dutch Overseas Territories 1601-1948* (Schulman, Amsterdam 1953).

Schulman, J., *Nederlandse Munten van 1795-1945* (Amsterdam 1946).

Seaby, *Standard Catalogue of British Coins* (London 1967).

Severin, H. M., *Gold and Platinum Coinage of Imperial Russia* (New York 1958).

——, *The Silver Coinage of Imperial Russia* (Basel 1963).

Smith, R. B., *Notes on the Anglo-Hanoverian Coinage* (Seaby's Bulletin, Jan. 1971).

Utberg, N.S., *The Coins of Colonial Mexico 1536-1821* (1966).

Vicenti, J. A., *Catálogo General de la Moneda Española* (5th ed., Madrid 1973).

Wallace, H., *Central American Coinage Since 1821* (Weslaco 1965).

Welter, G., *Die Münzen der Welfen seit Heinrich dem Löwen* (Braunschweig 1971).

Weyl, A., Catalog of his sale of the Australian, Asiatic and African Coins in the Fonrobert collection, 1878-79 (Annotated reprint, Münich 1962).

Wielandt, F., *Schaffhauser Münz und Geldgeschichte* (Schaffhausen 1959).

——, *Münz und Geldgeschichte des Standes Schwyz* (Schwyz 1964).

——, *Badische Münz und Geld-Geschichte* (2nd ed., 1973).

INDEX AND FINDING LIST

In using this list, do not forget the frequent substitution on older coins of "V" for "U" and "I" for "J." Here, all "U"s are shown as "U", and all "J"s as "J".

INDEX

INDEX

INDEX